FEDERAL AVIATION REGULATIONS FOR
AVIATION MAINTENANCE TECHNICIANS

FAR AMT 2023

Includes parts:
   1, 3, 13, 21, 23, 26, 27, 33, 34, 35, 39, 43, 45,
   47, 65, 91, 110, 119, 121 (J, L, and AA), 125,
   135, 145, 147, 183 and 193
Advisory Circulars:
   00-46F, 20-62E, 20-109A, 21-12C,
   39-7D, 43-9C, 43.9-1G

and Aviation Safety Reporting System

U.S. DEPARTMENT OF TRANSPORTATION
FEDERAL AVIATION ADMINISTRATION

REPRINTED BY

International Standard Book Number: 1-933189-94-0
ISBN 13: 978-1-933189-94-9
Order # T-FARTECH-2301

For Sale by: Avotek
A Select Aerospace Industries, Inc., company

Mail to:
P.O. Box 219
Weyers Cave, VA 24486
USA

Ship to:
200 Packaging Drive
Weyers Cave, VA 24486

Toll Free: 800-828-6835
Telephone: 540-234-9090
Fax: 540-234-9399

Printed in the USA

www.avotek.com

See our online courses at
Avotek-Online.com.

FAR-AMT CONTENTS

INTRODUCTION

The *Federal Aviation Regulations for Aviation Maintenance Technicians* (FAR AMT) reference guide is one of numerous information resources made available to the student AMT and the certificated AMT. Please see the listing of additional reference materials available from Avotek at the end of this introduction.

Reading and Citing the Regulations

The *Code of Federal Regulations* (CFR) is a published set of about 200 volumes and is organized into 50 titles according to broad subject matter categories. Examples include Environment, Defense, Public Health and Transportation. Title 14, Aeronautics and Space, contains the regulations that pertain to the aviation industry.

The CFR has a uniform numbering system. Most of the 50 titles conform to this system, with the exceptions of Title 3, Title 41, and Title 48 having significant variations. Title 14 consists of five volumes and five chapters and numerous parts. Table 1 gives an overview of Title 14.

Table 2 provides a description of the various levels of the CFR numbering system.

As noted in Table 2, sections are one provision of a program or function of the rules. Sections are further divided and can contain up to six levels. Table 3 illustrates the various levels.

Citing a Regulation. When formally citing a regulation use the following format: [Title] CFR [Part.Section (Paragraph)] as in 14 CFR 91.413(c)(1)(i).

The entire 14 CFR is commonly referred to as the "Federal Aviation Regulations" (FAR). Informal and everyday reference to these regulations might look like this: FAR 145.3(d)(1).

Organization of this Guide

Each part of 14 CFR and Advisory Circulars in this reference guide has been coded on the page fore-edge for easy location. Section numbers and titles included in each part are provided at the beginning of that part for quick review.

TABLE 1 — TITLE 14 OF THE CFR BREAKDOWN

Title	Volume	Chapter	Browse Part	Regulatory Entity
Title 14 Aeronautics and Space	1	I	1-59	Federal Aviation Administration, Department of Transportation
	2		60-109	
	3		110-199	
	4	II	200-399	Office of the Secretary, Department of Transportation (Aviation Proceedings)
		III	400-1199	Commercial Space Transportation, Federal Aviation Administration, Department of Transportation
	5	V	1200-1299	National Aeronautics and Space Administration
		VI	1300-1399	Air Transportation System Stabilization

TABLE 2 — EXPLANATION OF THE CFR NUMBERING SYSTEM

Title	14	Broad subject area of regulations
Chapter	I	Rules of individual agency
Part	65	Rules on a single program or function
Section	65,83	One provision of program or function rules
Paragraph	65.83(a)	Detailed, specific requirement of rule

TABLE 3 — LEVELS OF PARAGRAPHS FOR SECTIONS OF THE CFR

PARAGRAPH	DESIGNATIONS	PARAGRAPH CITATION
Level 1	(a), (b), (c), etc.	303.1(a)
Level 2	(1), (2), (3), etc.	303.1(a) (1)
Level 3	(i), (ii), (iii), etc.	303.1(a) (1) (i)
Level 4	(A), (B), (C), etc.	303.1(a) (1) (i) (A)
Level 5	*(1), (2), (3),* etc.	303.1(a) (1) (i) (A) *(1)*
Level 6	*(i), (ii), (iii),* etc.	303.1(a) (1) (i) (A) *(1) (i)*

Changes to Regulations

This reference guide is published each year to bring you the updated FAR. The regulations presented in this guide were effective as of September 30, 2022.

Federal regulations are ever changing and therefore it is the responsibility of the AMT to always make sure he or she has the most up-to-date regulations. Each title is completely revised and reissued once each year on a staggered scheduled (Table 4).

TABLE 4 — TITLE REISSUE DATES	
TITLE	REISSUE DATE
1-16	January 1
17-27	April 1
28-41	July 1
42-50	October 1

In today's world of electronic technology, the printed word is not always the most current. To view the most current regulations in effect please visit the Federal Aviation Administration's website at faa.gov, click on the Regulations and Policies tab, then click on the link for Current Federal Aviation Regulations. If you prefer, you may go directly to the electronic regulations at ecfr.gov.

Changes made to regulations since this guide's last printing are denoted by a bold, vertical line placed in the margin next to the text. Lines are also placed next to that section number and title listed at the beginning of each part.

21.1   Applicability and definitions

(a) This part prescribes—
   (1) Procedural requirements for issuing and changing—
      (i)   Design approvals;
      (ii)   Production approvals;
      (iii) Airworthiness certificates; and
      (iv)   Airworthiness approvals;
   (2) Rules governing applicants for, and holders of, any approval or certificate specified in paragraph (a)(1) of this section; and
   (3) Procedural requirements for the approval of articles

Intended Use

This reference guide is intended primarily for general training and familiarization, and as reference if the Internet is not available. ALWAYS follow the current Federal Aviation Regulations and other FAA approved documents.

The regulations listed in this guide have been chosen because they are among the most pertinent for the average AMT, however, they are not the only regulations with which an AMT should be familiar. Remember, it is the responsibility of the AMT to follow all applicable regulations, even if not listed in this reference guide.

Comments

This reference guide is as faithful a duplication of these regulations as is humanly possible. However, as with all human endeavors, errors and omissions can occur in the most unexpected places. If any exist, they are unintentional and we ask that you please bring them to our attention. You can email us at comments@avotek.com.

ADDITIONAL TITLES AVAILABLE FROM AVOTEK®

Avotek® Aircraft Maintenance Series

Introduction to Aircraft Maintenance

Aircraft Structural Maintenance

Aircraft System Maintenance

Aircraft Powerplant Maintenance

Avotek Avionics Series

Avionics: Fundamentals of Aircraft Electronics

Avionics: Beyond the AET

Avionics: Instruments and Auxiliary Systems

Avionics: Systems and Troubleshooting

Other Books by Avotek

Advanced Composites

Aircraft Corrosion Control Guide

Aircraft Hydraulics

Aircraft Nondestructive Testing

Aircraft Structural Technician

Aircraft Turbine Engines

Aircraft Wiring and Electrical Installation

AMT Reference Handbook

Aviation Mechanic Instructor's Handbook

Avotek Aeronautical Dictionary

Fundamentals of Modern Aviation

Helicopter Maintenance

Introduction to Aircraft Structures, Systems, and Powerplants

Light Sport Aircraft Inspection Procedures

Structural Composites: Advanced Composites in Aviation

Transport Category Aircraft Systems

PART 1 — DEFINITIONS AND ABBREVIATIONS

1.1 General Definitions
1.2 Abbreviations and Symbols
1.3 Rules of Construction

Authority: 49 U.S.C. 106(f), 106(g), 40113, 44701.

1.1 General Definitions

As used in Subchapters A through K of this chapter, unless the context requires otherwise:

Administrator means the Federal Aviation Administrator or any person to whom he has delegated his authority in the matter concerned.

Aerodynamic coefficients means non-dimensional coefficients for aerodynamic forces and moments.

Air carrier means a person who undertakes directly by lease, or other arrangement, to engage in air transportation.

Air commerce means interstate, overseas, or foreign air commerce or the transportation of mail by aircraft or any operation or navigation of aircraft within the limits of any Federal airway or any operation or navigation of aircraft which directly affects, or which may endanger safety in, interstate, overseas, or foreign air commerce.

Aircraft means a device that is used or intended to be used for flight in the air.

Aircraft engine means an engine that is used or intended to be used for propelling aircraft. It includes turbosuperchargers, appurtenances, and accessories necessary for its functioning, but does not include propellers.

Airframe means the fuselage, booms, nacelles, cowlings, fairings, airfoil surfaces (including rotors but excluding propellers and rotating airfoils of engines), and landing gear of an aircraft and their accessories and controls.

Airplane means an engine-driven fixed-wing aircraft heavier than air, that is supported in flight by the dynamic reaction of the air against its wings.

Airport means an area of land or water that is used or intended to be used for the landing and takeoff of aircraft, and includes its buildings and facilities, if any.

Airship means an engine-driven lighter-than-air aircraft that can be steered.

Air traffic means aircraft operating in the air or on an airport surface, exclusive of loading ramps and parking areas.

Air traffic clearance means an authorization by air traffic control, for the purpose of preventing collision between known aircraft, for an aircraft to proceed under specified traffic conditions within controlled airspace.

Air traffic control means a service operated by appropriate authority to promote the safe, orderly, and expeditious flow of air traffic.

Air Traffic Service (ATS) route is a specified route designated for channeling the flow of traffic as necessary for the provision of air traffic services. The term "ATS route" refers to a variety of airways, including jet routes, area navigation (RNAV) routes, and arrival and departure routes. An ATS route is defined by route specifications, which may include:

(1) An ATS route designator;

(2) The path to or from significant points;

(3) Distance between significant points;

(4) Reporting requirements; and

(5) The lowest safe altitude determined by the appropriate authority.

Air transportation means interstate, overseas, or foreign air transportation or the transportation of mail by aircraft.

Alert Area. An alert area is established to inform pilots of a specific area wherein a high volume of pilot training or an unusual type of aeronautical activity is conducted.

Alternate airport means an airport at which an aircraft may land if a landing at the intended airport becomes inadvisable.

Altitude engine means a reciprocating aircraft engine having a rated takeoff power that is producible from sea level to an established higher altitude.

Amateur rocket means an unmanned rocket that:

(1) Is propelled by a motor or motors having a combined total impulse of 889,600 Newton-seconds (200,000 pound-seconds) or less; and

(2) Cannot reach an altitude greater than 150 kilometers (93.2 statute miles) above the earth's surface.

Appliance means any instrument, mechanism, equipment, part, apparatus, appurtenance, or accessory, including communications equipment, that is used or intended to be used in operating or controlling an aircraft in flight, is installed in or attached to the aircraft, and is not part of an airframe, engine, or propeller.

Approved, unless used with reference to another person, means approved by the FAA or any person to whom the FAA has delegated its authority in the matter concerned, or approved under the provisions of a bilateral agreement between the United States and a foreign country or jurisdiction.

Area navigation (RNAV) is a method of navigation that permits aircraft operations on any desired flight path.

Area navigation (RNAV) route is an ATS route based on RNAV that can be used by suitably equipped aircraft.

Armed Forces means the Army, Navy, Air Force, Marine Corps, and Coast Guard, including their regular and reserve components and members serving without component status.

Autorotation means a rotorcraft flight condition in which the lifting rotor is driven entirely by action of the air when the rotorcraft is in motion.

Auxiliary rotor means a rotor that serves either to counteract the effect of the main rotor torque on a rotorcraft or to maneuver the rotorcraft about one or more of its three principal axes.

Balloon means a lighter-than-air aircraft that is not engine driven, and that sustains flight through the use of either gas buoyancy or an airborne heater.

Brake horsepower means the power delivered at the propeller shaft (main drive or main output) of an aircraft engine.

Calibrated airspeed means the indicated airspeed of an aircraft, corrected for position and instrument error. Calibrated airspeed is equal to true airspeed in standard atmosphere at sea level.

Canard means the forward wing of a canard configuration and may be a fixed, movable, or variable geometry surface, with or without control surfaces.

Canard configuration means a configuration in which the span of the forward wing is substantially less than that of the main wing.

Category:

(1) As used with respect to the certification, ratings, privileges, and limitations of airmen, means a broad classification of aircraft. Examples include: airplane; rotorcraft; glider; and lighter-than-air; and

(2) As used with respect to the certification of aircraft, means a grouping of aircraft based upon intended use or operating limitations. Examples include: transport, normal, utility, acrobatic, limited, restricted, and provisional.

Category A, with respect to transport category rotorcraft, means multiengine rotorcraft designed with engine and system isolation features specified in Part 29 and utilizing scheduled takeoff and landing operations under a critical engine failure concept which assures adequate designated surface area and adequate performance capability for continued safe flight in the event of engine failure.

Category B, with respect to transport category rotorcraft, means single-engine or multiengine rotorcraft which do not fully meet all Category A standards. Category B rotorcraft have no guaranteed stay-up ability in the event of engine failure and unscheduled landing is assumed.

Category II operations, with respect to the operation of aircraft, means a straight-in ILS approach to the runway of an airport under a Category II ILS instrument approach procedure issued by the Administrator or other appropriate authority.

Category III operations, with respect to the operation of aircraft, means an ILS approach to, and landing on, the runway of an airport using a Category III ILS instrument approach procedure issued by the Administrator or other appropriate authority.

Ceiling means the height above the earth's surface of the lowest layer of clouds or obscuring phenomena that is reported as "broken", "overcast", or "obscuration", and not classified as "thin" or "partial".

Civil aircraft means aircraft other than public aircraft.

Class:

(1) As used with respect to the certification, ratings, privileges, and limitations of airmen, means a classification of aircraft within a category having similar operating characteristics. Examples include: single engine; multiengine; land; water; gyroplane; helicopter; airship; and free balloon; and

(2) As used with respect to the certification of aircraft, means a broad grouping of aircraft having similar characteristics of propulsion, flight, or landing. Examples include: airplane; rotorcraft; glider; balloon; landplane; and seaplane.

Clearway means:

(1) For turbine engine powered airplanes certificated after August 29, 1959, an area beyond the runway, not less than 500 feet wide, centrally located about the extended centerline of the runway, and under the control of the airport authorities. The clearway is expressed in terms of a clearway plane, extending from the end of the runway with an upward slope not exceeding 1.25 percent, above which no object nor any terrain protrudes. However, threshold lights may protrude above the plane if their height above the end of the runway is 26 inches or less and if they are located to each side of the runway.

(2) For turbine engine powered airplanes certificated after September 30, 1958, but before August 30, 1959, an area beyond the takeoff runway extending no less than 300 feet on either side of the extended centerline of the runway, at an elevation no higher than the elevation of the end of the runway, clear of all fixed obstacles, and under the control of the airport authorities.

Climbout speed, with respect to rotorcraft, means a referenced airspeed which results in a flight path clear of the height-velocity envelope during initial climbout.

Commercial operator means a person who, for compensation or hire, engages in the carriage by aircraft in air commerce of persons or property, other than as an air carrier or foreign air carrier or under the authority of Part 375 of this title. Where it is doubtful that an operation is for "compensation or hire", the test applied is whether the carriage by air is merely incidental to the person's other business or is, in itself, a major enterprise for profit.

Configuration, Maintenance, and Procedures (CMP) document means a document approved by the FAA that contains minimum configuration, operating, and maintenance requirements, hardware life-limits, and Master Minimum Equipment List (MMEL) constraints necessary for an airplane-engine combination to meet ETOPS type design approval requirements.

Consensus standard means, for the purpose of certificating light-sport aircraft, an industry-developed consensus standard that applies to aircraft design, production, and airworthiness. It includes, but is not limited to, standards for aircraft design and performance, required equipment, manufacturer quality assurance systems, production acceptance test procedures, operating instructions, maintenance and inspection procedures, identification and recording of major repairs and major alterations, and continued airworthiness.

Controlled airspace means an airspace of defined dimensions within which air traffic control service is provided to IFR flights and to VFR flights in accordance with the airspace classification.

> **NOTE:** *Controlled airspace is a generic term that covers Class A, Class B, Class C, Class D, and Class E airspace.*

Controlled Firing Area. A controlled firing area is established to contain activities, which if not conducted in a controlled environment, would be hazardous to nonparticipating aircraft.

Crewmember means a person assigned to perform duty in an aircraft during flight time.

Critical altitude means the maximum altitude at which, in standard atmosphere, it is possible to maintain, at a specified rotational speed, a specified power or a specified manifold pressure. Unless otherwise stated, the critical altitude is the maximum altitude at which it is possible to maintain, at the maximum continuous rotational speed, one of the following:

(1) The maximum continuous power, in the case of engines for which this power rating is the same at sea level and at the rated altitude.

(2) The maximum continuous rated manifold pressure, in the case of engines, the maximum continuous power of which is governed by a constant manifold pressure.

Critical engine means the engine whose failure would most adversely affect the performance or handling qualities of an aircraft.

Decision altitude (DA) is a specified altitude in an instrument approach procedure at which the pilot must decide whether to initiate an immediate missed approach if the pilot does not see the required visual reference, or to continue the approach. Decision altitude is expressed in feet above mean sea level.

Decision height (DH) is a specified height above the ground in an instrument approach procedure at which the pilot must decide whether to initiate an immediate missed approach if the pilot does not see the required visual reference, or to continue the approach. Decision height is expressed in feet above ground level.

Early ETOPS means ETOPS type design approval obtained without gaining non-ETOPS service experience on the candidate airplane-engine combination certified for ETOPS.

EFVS operation means an operation in which visibility conditions require an EFVS to be used in lieu of natural vision to perform an approach or landing, determine enhanced flight visibility, identify required visual references, or conduct a rollout.

Enhanced flight visibility (EFV) means the average forward horizontal distance, from the cockpit of an aircraft in flight, at which prominent topographical objects may be clearly distinguished and identified by day or night by a pilot using an enhanced flight vision system.

Enhanced flight vision system (EFVS) means an installed aircraft system which uses an electronic means to provide a display of the forward external scene topography (the natural or manmade features of a place or region especially in a way to show their relative positions and elevation) through the use of imaging sensors, including but not limited to forward-looking infrared, millimeter wave radiometry, millimeter wave radar, or low-light level image intensification. An EFVS includes the display element, sensors, computers and power supplies, indications, and controls.

Equivalent airspeed means the calibrated airspeed of an aircraft corrected for adiabatic compressible flow for the particular altitude. Equivalent airspeed is equal to calibrated airspeed in standard atmosphere at sea level.

ETOPS Significant System means an airplane system, including the propulsion system, the failure or malfunctioning of which could adversely affect the safety of an ETOPS flight, or the continued safe flight and landing of an airplane during an ETOPS diversion. Each ETOPS significant system is either an ETOPS group 1 significant system or an ETOPS group 2 significant system.

(1) An ETOPS group 1 Significant System—

(i) Has fail-safe characteristics directly linked to the degree of redundancy provided by the number of engines on the airplane.

(ii) Is a system, the failure or malfunction of which could result in an IFSD, loss of thrust control, or other power loss.

(iii) Contributes significantly to the safety of an ETOPS diversion by providing additional redundancy for any system power source lost as a result of an inoperative engine.

(iv) Is essential for prolonged operation of an airplane at engine inoperative altitudes.

(2) An ETOPS group 2 significant system is an ETOPS significant system that is not an ETOPS group 1 significant system.

Extended Operations (ETOPS) means an airplane flight operation, other than an all-cargo operation in an airplane with more than two engines, during which a portion of the flight is conducted beyond a time threshold identified in part 121 or part 135 of this chapter that is determined using an approved one-engine-inoperative cruise speed under standard atmospheric conditions in still air.

Extended over-water operation means—

(1) With respect to aircraft other than helicopters, an operation over water at a horizontal distance of more than 50 nautical miles from the nearest shoreline; and

(2) With respect to helicopters, an operation over water at a horizontal distance of more than 50 nautical miles from the nearest shoreline and more than 50 nautical miles from an off-shore heliport structure.

External load means a load that is carried, or extends, outside of the aircraft fuselage.

External-load attaching means the structural components used to attach an external load to an aircraft, including external-load containers, the backup structure at the attachment points, and any quick-release device used to jettison the external load.

Final approach fix (FAF) defines the beginning of the final approach segment and the point where final segment descent may begin.

Final takeoff speed means the speed of the airplane that exists at the end of the takeoff path in the en route configuration with one engine inoperative.

Fireproof —

(1) With respect to materials and parts used to confine fire in a designated fire zone, means the capacity to withstand at least as well as steel in dimensions appropriate for the purpose for which they are used, the heat produced when there is a severe fire of extended duration in that zone; and

(2) With respect to other materials and parts, means the capacity to withstand the heat associated with fire at least as well as steel in dimensions appropriate for the purpose for which they are used.

Fire resistant —

(1) With respect to sheet or structural members means the capacity to withstand the heat associated with fire at least as well as aluminum alloy in dimensions appropriate for the purpose for which they are used; and

(2) With respect to fluid-carrying lines, fluid system parts, wiring, air ducts, fittings, and powerplant controls, means the capacity to perform the intended functions under the heat and other conditions likely to occur when there is a fire at the place concerned.

Flame resistant means not susceptible to combustion to the point of propagating a flame, beyond safe limits, after the ignition source is removed.

Flammable, with respect to a fluid or gas, means susceptible to igniting readily or to exploding.

Flap extended speed means the highest speed permissible with wing flaps in a prescribed extended position.

Flash resistant means not susceptible to burning violently when ignited.

Flightcrew member means a pilot, flight engineer, or flight navigator assigned to duty in an aircraft during flight time.

Flight level means a level of constant atmospheric pressure related to a reference datum of 29.92 inches of mercury. Each is stated in three digits that represent hundreds of feet. For example, flight level 250 represents a barometric altimeter indication of 25,000 feet; flight level 255, an indication of 25,500 feet.

Flight plan means specified information, relating to the intended flight of an aircraft, that is filed orally or in writing with air traffic control.

Flight simulation training device (FSTD) means a full flight simulator or a flight training device.

Flight time means:

(1) Pilot time that commences when an aircraft moves under its own power for the purpose of flight and ends when the aircraft comes to rest after landing; or

(2) For a glider without self-launch capability, pilot time that commences when the glider is towed for the purpose of flight and ends when the glider comes to rest after landing.

Flight training device (FTD) means a replica of aircraft instruments, equipment, panels, and controls in an open flight deck area or an enclosed aircraft cockpit replica. It includes the equipment and computer programs necessary to represent aircraft (or set of aircraft) operations in ground and flight conditions having the full range of capabilities of the systems installed in the device as described in part 60 of this chapter and the qualification performance standard (QPS) for a specific FTD qualification level.

Flight visibility means the average forward horizontal distance, from the cockpit of an aircraft in flight, at which prominent unlighted objects may be seen and identified by day and prominent lighted objects may be seen and identified by night.

Foreign air carrier means any person other than a citizen of the United States, who undertakes directly, by lease or other arrangement, to engage in air transportation.

Foreign air commerce means the carriage by aircraft of persons or property for compensation or hire, or the carriage of mail by aircraft, or the operation or navigation of aircraft in the conduct or furtherance of a business or vocation, in commerce between a place in the United States and any place outside thereof; whether such commerce moves wholly by aircraft or partly by aircraft and partly by other forms of transportation.

Foreign air transportation means the carriage by aircraft of persons or property as a common carrier for compensation or hire, or the carriage of mail by aircraft, in commerce between a place in the United States and any place outside of the United States, whether that commerce moves wholly by aircraft or partly by aircraft and partly by other forms of transportation.

Forward wing means a forward lifting surface of a canard configuration or tandem-wing configuration airplane. The surface may be a fixed, movable, or variable geometry surface, with or without control surfaces.

Full flight simulator (FFS) means a replica of a specific type; or make, model, and series aircraft cockpit. It includes the assemblage of equipment and computer programs necessary to represent aircraft operations in ground and flight conditions, a visual system providing an out-of-the-cockpit view, a system that provides cues at least equivalent to those of a three-degree-of-freedom motion system, and has the full range of capabilities of the systems installed in the device as described in part 60 of this chapter and the qualification performance standards (QPS) for a specific FFS qualification level.

Glider means a heavier-than-air aircraft, that is supported in flight by the dynamic reaction of the air against its lifting surfaces and whose free flight does not depend principally on an engine.

Ground visibility means prevailing horizontal visibility near the earth's surface as reported by the United States National Weather Service or an accredited observer.

Go-around power or thrust setting means the maximum allowable in-flight power or thrust setting identified in the performance data.

Gyrodyne means a rotorcraft whose rotors are normally engine-driven for takeoff, hovering, and landing, and for forward flight through part of its speed range, and whose means of propulsion, consisting usually of conventional propellers, is independent of the rotor system.

Gyroplane means a rotorcraft whose rotors are not engine-driven, except for initial starting, but are made to rotate by action of the air when the rotorcraft is moving; and whose means of propulsion, consisting usually of conventional propellers, is independent of the rotor system.

Helicopter means a rotorcraft that, for its horizontal motion, depends principally on its engine-driven rotors.

Heliport means an area of land, water, or structure used or intended to be used for the landing and takeoff of helicopters.

Idle thrust means the jet thrust obtained with the engine power control level set at the stop for the least thrust position at which it can be placed.

IFR conditions means weather conditions below the minimum for flight under visual flight rules.

IFR over-the-top, with respect to the operation of aircraft, means the operation of an aircraft over-the-top on an IFR flight plan when cleared by air traffic control to maintain "VFR conditions" or "VFR conditions on top".

Indicated airspeed means the speed of an aircraft as shown on its pitot static airspeed indicator calibrated to reflect standard atmosphere adiabatic compressible flow at sea level uncorrected for airspeed system errors.

In-flight shutdown (IFSD) means, for ETOPS only, when an engine ceases to function (when the airplane is airborne) and is shutdown, whether self induced, flightcrew initiated or caused by an external influence. The FAA considers IFSD for all causes: for example, flameout, internal failure, flightcrew initiated shutdown, foreign object ingestion, icing, inability to obtain or control desired thrust or power, and cycling of the start control, however briefly, even if the engine operates normally for the remainder of the flight. This definition excludes the airborne cessation of the functioning of an engine when immediately followed by an automatic engine relight and when an engine does not achieve desired thrust or power but is not shutdown.

Instrument means a device using an internal mechanism to show visually or aurally the attitude, altitude, or operation of an aircraft or aircraft part. It includes electronic devices for automatically controlling an aircraft in flight.

Instrument approach procedure (IAP) is a series of predetermined maneuvers by reference to flight instruments with specified protection from obstacles and assurance of navigation signal reception capability. It begins from the initial approach fix, or where applicable, from the beginning of a defined arrival route to a point:

(1) From which a landing can be completed; or

(2) If a landing is not completed, to a position at which holding or en route obstacle clearance criteria apply.

Interstate air commerce means the carriage by aircraft of persons or property for compensation or hire, or the carriage of mail by aircraft, or the operation or navigation of aircraft in the conduct or furtherance of a business or vocation, in commerce between a place in any State of the United States, or the District of Columbia, and a place in any other State of the United States, or the District of Columbia; or between places in the same State of the United States through the airspace over any place outside thereof; or between places in the same territory or possession of the United States, or the District of Columbia.

Interstate air transportation means the carriage by aircraft of persons or property as a common carrier for compensation or hire, or the carriage of mail by aircraft in commerce:

(1) Between a place in a State or the District of Columbia and another place in another State or the District of Columbia;

(2) Between places in the same State through the airspace over any place outside that State; or

(3) Between places in the same possession of the United States;

Whether that commerce moves wholly by aircraft of partly by aircraft and partly by other forms of transportation.

Intrastate air transportation means the carriage of persons or property as a common carrier for compensation or hire, by turbojet-powered aircraft capable of carrying thirty or more persons, wholly within the same State of the United States.

Kite means a framework, covered with paper, cloth, metal, or other material, intended to be flown at the end of a rope or cable, and having as its only support the force of the wind moving past its surfaces.

Landing gear extended speed means the maximum speed at which an aircraft can be safely flown with the landing gear extended.

Landing gear operating speed means the maximum speed at which the landing gear can be safely extended or retracted.

Large aircraft means aircraft of more than 12,500 pounds, maximum certificated takeoff weight.

Light-sport aircraft means an aircraft, other than a helicopter or powered-lift that, since its original certification, has continued to meet the following:

(1) A maximum takeoff weight of not more than—

    (i) 1,320 pounds (600 kilograms) for aircraft not intended for operation on water; or

    (ii) 1,430 pounds (650 kilograms) for an aircraft intended for operation on water.

(2) A maximum airspeed in level flight with maximum continuous power (V_H) of not more than 120 knots CAS under standard atmospheric conditions at sea level.

(3) A maximum never-exceed speed (V_{NE}) of not more than 120 knots CAS for a glider.

(4) A maximum stalling speed or minimum steady flight speed without the use of lift-enhancing devices (V_{S1}) of not more than 45 knots CAS at the aircraft's maximum certificated takeoff weight and most critical center of gravity.

(5) A maximum seating capacity of no more than two persons, including the pilot.

(6) A single, reciprocating engine, if powered.

(7) A fixed or ground-adjustable propeller if a powered aircraft other than a powered glider.

(8) A fixed or feathering propeller system if a powered glider.

(9) A fixed-pitch, semi-rigid, teetering, two-blade rotor system, if a gyroplane.

(10) A nonpressurized cabin, if equipped with a cabin.

(11) Fixed landing gear, except for an aircraft intended for operation on water or a glider.

(12) Fixed or retractable landing gear, or a hull, for an aircraft intended for operation on water.

(13) Fixed or retractable landing gear for a glider.

Lighter-than-air aircraft means aircraft that can rise and remain suspended by using contained gas weighing less than the air that is displaced by the gas.

Load factor means the ratio of a specified load to the total weight of the aircraft. The specified load is expressed in terms of any of the following: aerodynamic forces, inertia forces, or ground or water reactions.

Long-range communication system (LRCS). A system that uses satellite relay, data link, high frequency, or another approved communication system which extends beyond line of sight.

Long-range navigation system (LRNS). An electronic navigation unit that is approved for use under instrument flight rules as a primary means of navigation, and has at least one source of navigational input, such as inertial navigation system or global positioning system.

Mach number means the ratio of true airspeed to the speed of sound.

Main rotor means the rotor that supplies the principal lift to a rotorcraft.

Maintenance means inspection, overhaul, repair, preservation, and the replacement of parts, but excludes preventive maintenance.

Major alteration means an alteration not listed in the aircraft, aircraft engine, or propeller specifications—

(1) That might appreciably affect weight, balance, structural strength, performance, powerplant operation, flight characteristics, or other qualities affecting airworthiness; or

(2) That is not done according to accepted practices or cannot be done by elementary operations.

Major repair means a repair:

(1) That, if improperly done, might appreciably affect weight, balance, structural strength, performance, powerplant operation, flight characteristics, or other qualities affecting airworthiness; or

(2) That is not done according to accepted practices or cannot be done by elementary operations.

Manifold pressure means absolute pressure as measured at the appropriate point in the induction system and usually expressed in inches of mercury.

Maximum engine overtorque, as it applies to turbopropeller and turboshaft engines incorporating free power turbines for all ratings except one engine inoperative (OEI) ratings of two minutes or less, means the maximum torque of the free power turbine rotor assembly, the inadvertent occurrence of which, for periods of up to 20 seconds, will not require rejection of the engine from service, or any maintenance action other than to correct the cause.

Maximum speed for stability characteristics, V_{FC}/M_{FC} means a speed that may not be less than a speed midway between maximum operating limit speed (V_{MO}/M_{MO}) and demonstrated flight diving speed (V_{DF}/M_{DF}), except that, for altitudes where the Mach number is the limiting factor, M_{FC} need not exceed the Mach number at which effective speed warning occurs.

Medical certificate means acceptable evidence of physical fitness on a form prescribed by the Administrator.

Military operations area. A military operations area (MOA) is airspace established outside Class A airspace to separate or segregate certain nonhazardous military activities from IFR Traffic and to identify for VFR traffic where theses activities are conducted.

Minimum descent altitude (MDA) is the lowest altitude specified in an instrument approach procedure, expressed in feet above mean sea level, to which descent is authorized on final approach or during circle-to-land maneuvering until the pilot sees the required visual references for the heliport or runway of intended landing.

Minor alteration means an alteration other than a major alteration.

Minor repair means a repair other than a major repair.

National defense airspace means airspace established by a regulation prescribed, or an order issued under, 49 U.S.C. 40103(b)(3).

Navigable airspace means airspace at and above the minimum flight altitudes prescribed by or under this chapter, including airspace needed for safe takeoff and landing.

Night means the time between the end of evening civil twilight and the beginning of morning civil twilight, as published in the American Air Almanac, converted to local time.

Nonprecision approach procedure means a standard instrument approach procedure in which no electronic glide slope is provided.

Operate, with respect to aircraft, means use, cause to use or authorize to use aircraft, for the purpose (except as provided in 91.13 of this chapter) of air navigation including the piloting of aircraft, with or without the right of legal control (as owner, lessee, or otherwise).

Operational control, with respect to a flight, means the exercise of authority over initiating, conducting or terminating a flight.

Overseas air commerce means the carriage by aircraft of persons or property for compensation or hire, or the carriage of mail by aircraft, or the operation or navigation of aircraft in the conduct or furtherance of a business or vocation, in commerce between a place in any State of the United States, or the District of Columbia, and any place in a territory or possession of the United States; or between a place in a territory or possession of the United States, and a place in any other territory or possession of the United States.

Overseas air transportation means the carriage by aircraft of persons or property as a common carrier for compensation or hire, or the carriage of mail by aircraft, in commerce:

(1) Between a place in a State or the District of Columbia and a place in a possession of the United States; or

(2) Between a place in a possession of the United States and a place in another possession of the United States; whether that commerce moves wholly by aircraft or partly by aircraft and partly by other forms of transportation.

Over-the-top means above the layer of clouds or other obscuring phenomena forming the ceiling.

Parachute means a device used or intended to be used to retard the fall of a body or object through the air.

Person means an individual, firm, partnership, corporation, company, association, joint-stock association, or governmental entity. It includes a trustee, receiver, assignee, or similar representative of any of them.

Pilotage means navigation by visual reference to landmarks.

Pilot in command means the person who:

(1) Has final authority and responsibility for the operation and safety of the flight;

(2) Has been designated as pilot in command before or during the flight; and

(3) Holds the appropriate category, class, and type rating, if appropriate, for the conduct of the flight.

Pitch setting means the propeller blade setting as determined by the blade angle measured in a manner, and at a radius, specified by the instruction manual for the propeller.

Portable oxygen concentrator means a medical device that separates oxygen from other gasses in ambient air and dispenses this concentrated oxygen to the user.

Positive control means control of all air traffic, within designated airspace, by air traffic control.

Powered parachute means a powered aircraft comprised of a flexible or semi-rigid wing connected to a fuselage so that the wing is not in position for flight until the aircraft is in motion. The fuselage of a powered parachute contains the aircraft engine, a seat for each occupant and is attached to the aircraft's landing gear.

Powered-lift means a heavier-than-air aircraft capable of vertical takeoff, vertical landing, and low speed flight that depends principally on engine-driven lift devices or engine thrust for lift during these flight regimes and on nonrotating airfoil(s) for lift during horizontal flight.

Precision approach procedure means a standard instrument approach procedure in which an electronic glide slope is provided, such as ILS and PAR.

Preventive maintenance means simple or minor preservation operations and the replacement of small standard parts not involving complex assembly operations.

Prohibited area. A prohibited area is airspace designated under part 73 within which no person may operate an aircraft without the permission of the using agency.

Propeller means a device for propelling an aircraft that has blades on an engine-driven shaft and that, when rotated, produces by its action on the air, a thrust approximately perpendicular to its plane of rotation. It includes control components normally supplied by its manufacturer, but does not include main and auxiliary rotors or rotating airfoils of engines.

Public aircraft means any of the following aircraft when not being used for a commercial purpose or to carry an individual other than a crewmember or qualified non-crewmenber:

(1) An aircraft used only for the United States Government; an aircraft owned by the Government and operated by any person for purposes related to crew training, equipment development, or demonstration; an aircraft owned and operated by the government of a State, the District of Columbia, or a territory or possession of the United States or a political subdivision of one of these governments; or an aircraft exclusively leased for at least 90 continuous days by the government of a State, the District of Columbia, or a territory or possession of the United States or a political subdivision of one of these governments.

(i) For the sole purpose of determining public aircraft status, commercial purposes means the transportation of persons or property for compensation or hire, but does not include the operation of an aircraft by the armed forces for reimbursement when that reimbursement is required by any Federal statute, regulation, or directive, in effect on November 1, 1999, or by one government on behalf of another government under a cost reimbursement agreement if the government on whose behalf the operation is conducted certifies to the Administrator of the Federal Aviation Administration that the operation is necessary to respond to a significant and imminent threat to life or property (including natural resources) and that no service by a private operator is reasonably available to meet the threat.

(ii) For the sole purpose of determining public aircraft status, governmental function means an activity undertaken by a government, such as national defense, intelligence missions, firefighting, search and rescue, law enforcement (including transport of prisoners, detainees, and illegal aliens), aeronautical research, or biological or geological resource management.

(iii) For the sole purpose of determining public aircraft status, qualified non-crewmember means an individual, other than a member of the crew, aboard an aircraft operated by the armed forces or an intelligence agency of the United States Government, or whose presence is required to perform, or is associated with the performance of, a governmental function.

(2) An aircraft owned or operated by the armed forces or chartered to provide transportation to the armed forces if—

(i) The aircraft is operated in accordance with title 10 of the United States Code;

(ii) The aircraft is operated in the performance of a governmental function under title 14, 31, 32, or 50 of the United States Code and the aircraft is not used for commercial purposes; or

(iii) The aircraft is chartered to provide transportation to the armed forces and the Secretary of Defense (or the Secretary of the department in which the Coast Guard is operating) designates the operation of the aircraft as being required in the national interest.

(3) An aircraft owned or operated by the National Guard of a State, the District of Columbia, or any territory or possession of the United States, and that meets the criteria of paragraph (2) of this

definition, qualifies as a public aircraft only to the extent that it is operated under the direct control of the Department of Defense.

Rated 30-second OEI power, with respect to rotorcraft turbine engines, means the approved brake horsepower developed under static conditions at specified altitudes and temperatures within the operating limitations established for the engine under part 33 of this chapter, for continued one-flight operation after the failure of one engine in multiengine rotorcraft, limited to three periods of use no longer than 30 seconds each in any one flight, and followed by mandatory inspection and prescribed maintenance action.

Rated 2-minute OEI power, with respect to rotorcraft turbine engines, means the approved brake horsepower developed under static conditions at specified altitudes and temperatures within the operating limitations established for the engine under part 33 of this chapter, for continued one-flight operation after the failure of one engine in multiengine rotorcraft, limited to three periods of use no longer than 2 minutes each in any one flight, and followed by mandatory inspection and prescribed maintenance action.

Rated continuous OEI power, with respect to rotorcraft turbine engines, means the approved brake horsepower developed under static conditions at specified altitudes and temperatures within the operating limitations established for the engine under Part 33 of this chapter, and limited in use to the time required to complete the flight after the failure of one engine of a multiengine rotorcraft.

Rated maximum continuous augmented thrust, with respect to turbojet engine type certification, means the approved jet thrust that is developed statically or in flight, in standard atmosphere at a specified altitude, with fluid injection or with the burning of fuel in a separate combustion chamber, within the engine operating limitations established under Part 33 of this chapter, and approved for unrestricted periods of use.

Rated maximum continuous power, with respect to reciprocating, turbopropeller, and turboshaft engines, means the approved brake horsepower that is developed statically or in flight, in standard atmosphere at a specified altitude, within the engine operating limitations established under Part 33, and approved for unrestricted periods of use.

Rated maximum continuous thrust, with respect to turbojet engine type certification, means the approved jet thrust that is developed statically or in flight, in standard atmosphere at a specified altitude, without fluid injection and without the burning of fuel in a separate combustion chamber, within the engine operating limitations established under Part 33 of this chapter, and approved for unrestricted periods of use.

Rated takeoff augmented thrust, with respect to turbojet engine type certification, means the approved jet thrust that is developed statically under standard sea level conditions, with fluid injection or with the burning of fuel in a separate combustion chamber, within the engine operating limitations established under Part 33 of this chapter, and limited in use to periods of not over 5 minutes for takeoff operation.

Rated takeoff power, with respect to reciprocating, turbopropeller, and turboshaft engine type certification, means the approved brake horsepower that is developed statically under standard sea level conditions, within the engine operating limitations established under Part 33, and limited in use to periods of not over 5 minutes for takeoff operation.

Rated takeoff thrust, with respect to turbojet engine type certification, means the approved jet thrust that is developed statically under standard sea level conditions, without fluid injection and without the burning of fuel in a separate combustion chamber, within the engine operating limitations established under Part 33 of this chapter, and limited in use to periods of not over 5 minutes for takeoff operation.

Rated 30-minute OEI power, with respect to rotorcraft turbine engines, means the approved brake horsepower developed under static conditions at specified altitudes and temperatures within the operating limitations established for the engine under Part 33 of this chapter, and limited in use to a period of not more than 30 minutes after the failure of one engine of a multiengine rotorcraft.

Rated 2 1/2-minute OEI power, with respect to rotorcraft turbine engines, means the approved brake horsepower developed under static conditions at specified altitudes and temperatures within the operating limitations established for the engine under Part 33 of this chapter, and limited in use to a period of not more than 2 1/2 minutes after the failure of one engine of a multiengine rotorcraft.

Rating means a statement that, as a part of a certificate, sets forth special conditions, privileges, or limitations.

Reference landing speed means the speed of the airplane, in a specified landing configuration, at the point where it descends through the 50 foot height in the determination of the landing distance.

Reporting point means a geographical location in relation to which the position of an aircraft is reported.

Restricted area. A restricted area is airspace designated under Part 73 within which the flight of aircraft, while not wholly prohibited, is subject to restriction.

Rocket means an aircraft propelled by ejected expanding gases generated in the engine from self-contained propellants and not dependent on the intake of outside substances. It includes any part which becomes separated during the operation.

Rotorcraft means a heavier-than-air aircraft that depends principally for its support in flight on the lift generated by one or more rotors.

Rotorcraft-load combination means the combination of a rotorcraft and an external-load, including the external-load attaching means. Rotorcraft-load combinations are designated as Class A, Class B, Class C, and Class D, as follows:

(1) Class A rotorcraft-load combination means one in which the external load cannot move freely, cannot be jettisoned, and does not extend below the landing gear.

(2) Class B rotorcraft-load combination means one in which the external load is jettisonable and is lifted free of land or water during the rotorcraft operation.

(3) Class C rotorcraft-load combination means one in which the external load is jettisonable and remains in contact with land or water during the rotorcraft operation.

(4) Class D rotorcraft-load combination means one in which the external-load is other than a Class A, B, or C and has been specifically approved by the Administrator for that operation.

Route segment is a portion of a route bounded on each end by a fix or navigation aid (NAVAID).

Sea level engine means a reciprocating aircraft engine having a rated takeoff power that is producible only at sea level.

Second in command means a pilot who is designated to be second in command of an aircraft during flight time.

Show, unless the context otherwise requires, means to show to the satisfaction of the Administrator.

Small aircraft means aircraft of 12,500 pounds or less, maximum certificated takeoff weight.

Small unmanned aircraft means an unmanned aircraft weighing less than 55 pounds on takeoff, including everything that is on board or otherwise attached to the aircraft.

Small unmanned aircraft system (small UAS) means a small unmanned aircraft and its associated elements (including communication links and the components that control the small unmanned aircraft) that are required for the safe and efficient operation of the small unmanned aircraft in the national airspace system.

Special VFR conditions mean meteorological conditions that are less than those required for basic VFR flight in controlled airspace and in which some aircraft are permitted flight under visual flight rules.

Special VFR operations means aircraft operating in accordance with clearances within controlled airspace in meteorological conditions less than the basic VFR weather minima. Such operations must be requested by the pilot and approved by ATC.

Standard atmosphere means the atmosphere defined in U.S. Standard Atmosphere, 1962 (Geopotential altitude tables).

Stopway means an area beyond the takeoff runway, no less wide than the runway and centered upon the extended centerline of the runway, able to support the airplane during an aborted takeoff, without causing structural damage to the airplane, and designated by the airport authorities for use in decelerating the airplane during an aborted takeoff.

Suitable RNAV system is an RNAV system that meets the required performance established for a type of operation, e.g. IFR; and is suitable for operation over the route to be flown in terms of any performance criteria (including accuracy) established by the air navigation service provider for certain routes (e.g. oceanic, ATS routes, and IAPs). An RNAV system's suitability is dependent upon the availability of ground and/or satellite navigation aids that are needed to meet any route performance criteria that may be prescribed in route specifications to navigate the aircraft along the route to be flown. Information on suitable RNAV systems is published in FAA guidance material.

Synthetic vision means a computer-generated image of the external scene topography from the perspective of the flight deck that is derived from aircraft attitude, high-precision navigation solution, and database of terrain, obstacles and relevant cultural features.

Synthetic vision system means an electronic means to display a synthetic vision image of the external scene topography to the flight crew.

Takeoff power:

(1) With respect to reciprocating engines, means the brake horsepower that is developed under standard sea level conditions, and under the maximum conditions of crankshaft rotational speed and engine manifold pressure approved for the normal takeoff, and limited in continuous use to the period of time shown in the approved engine specification; and

(2) With respect to turbine engines, means the brake horsepower that is developed under static conditions at a specified altitude and atmospheric temperature, and under the maximum conditions of rotor shaft rotational speed and gas temperature approved for the normal takeoff, and limited in continuous use to the period of time shown in the approved engine specification.

Takeoff safety speed means a referenced airspeed obtained after lift-off at which the required one-engine-inoperative climb performance can be achieved.

Takeoff thrust, with respect to turbine engines, means the jet thrust that is developed under static conditions at a specific altitude and atmospheric temperature under the maximum conditions of rotorshaft rotational speed and gas temperature approved for the normal takeoff, and limited in continuous use to the period of time shown in the approved engine specification.

Tandem wing configuration means a configuration having two wings of similar span, mounted in tandem.

TCAS I means a TCAS that utilizes interrogations of, and replies from, airborne radar beacon transponders and provides traffic advisories to the pilot.

TCAS II means a TCAS that utilizes interrogations of, and replies from airborne radar beacon transponders and provides traffic advisories and resolution advisories in the vertical plane.

TCAS III means a TCAS that utilizes interrogation of, and replies from, airborne radar beacon transponders and provides traffic advisories and resolution advisories in the vertical and horizontal planes to the pilot.

Time in service, with respect to maintenance time records, means the time from the moment an aircraft leaves the surface of the earth until it touches it at the next point of landing.

Traffic pattern means the traffic flow that is prescribed for aircraft landing at, taxiing on, or taking off from, an airport.

True airspeed means the airspeed of an aircraft relative to undisturbed air. True airspeed is equal to equivalent airspeed multiplied by $(\rho 0/\rho)^{1/2}$.

Type:

(1) As used with respect to the certification, ratings, privileges, and limitations of airmen, means a specific make and basic model of aircraft, including modifications thereto that do not change its handling or flight characteristics. Examples include: DC–7, 1049, and F–27; and

(2) As used with respect to the certification of aircraft, means those aircraft which are similar in design. Examples include: DC–7 and DC–7C; 1049G and 1049H; and F–27 and F–27F.

(3) As used with respect to the certification of aircraft engines means those engines which are similar in design. For example, JT8D and JT8D–7 are engines of the same type, and JT9D–3A and JT9D–7 are engines of the same type.

United States, in a geographical sense, means (1) the States, the District of Columbia, Puerto Rico, and the possessions, including the territorial waters, and (2) the airspace of those areas.

United States air carrier means a citizen of the United States who undertakes directly by lease, or other arrangement, to engage in air transportation.

Unmanned aircraft means an aircraft operated without the possibility of direct human intervention from within or on the aircraft.

Unmanned aircraft system means an unmanned aircraft and its associated elements (including communication links and the components that control the unmanned aircraft) that are required for the safe and efficient operation of the unmanned aircraft in the airspace of the United States.

VFR over-the-top, with respect to the operation of aircraft, means the operation of an aircraft over-the-top under VFR when it is not being operated on an IFR flight plan.

Warning area. A warning area is airspace of defined dimensions, extending from 3 nautical miles outward from the coast of the United States, that contains activity that may be hazardous to nonparticipating aircraft. The purpose of such warning areas is to warn nonparticipating pilots of the potential danger. A warning area may be located over domestic or international waters or both.

Weight-shift-control aircraft means a powered aircraft with a framed pivoting wing and a fuselage controllable only in pitch and roll by the pilot's ability to change the aircraft's center of gravity with respect to the wing. Flight control of the aircraft depends on the wing's ability to flexibly deform rather than the use of control surfaces.

Winglet or tip fin means an out-of-plane surface extending from a lifting surface. The surface may or may not have control surfaces.

[Doc. No. 1150, 27 FR 4588, May 15, 1962]

1.2 Abbreviations and Symbols

In Subchapters A through K of this chapter:

AFM means airplane flight manual.

AGL means above ground level.

ALS means approach light system.

APU means auxiliary power unit.

ASR means airport surveillance radar.

ATC means air traffic control.

ATS means Air Traffic Service.

CAMP means continuous airworthiness maintenance program.

CAS means calibrated airspeed.

CAT II means Category II.

CMP means configuration, maintenance, and procedures.

DH means decision height.

DME means distance measuring equipment compatible with TACAN.

EAS means equivalent airspeed.

EFVS means enhanced flight vision system.

Equi-Time Point means a point on the route of flight where the flight time, considering wind, to each of two selected airports is equal.

ETOPS means extended operations.

EWIS, as defined by 25.1701 of this chapter, means electrical wiring interconnection system.

FAA means Federal Aviation Administration.

FFS means full flight simulator.

FM means fan marker.

FSTD means flight simulation training device.

FTD means flight training device.

GS means glide slope.

HIRL means high-intensity runway light system.

IAS means indicated airspeed.

ICAO means International Civil Aviation Organization.

IFR means instrument flight rules.

IFSD means in-flight shutdown.

ILS means instrument landing system.

IM means ILS inner marker.

INT means intersection.

LDA means localizer-type directional aid.

LFR means low-frequency radio range.

LMM means compass locator at middle marker.

LOC means ILS localizer.

LOM means compass locator at outer marker.

M means mach number.

MAA means maximum authorized IFR altitude.

MALS means medium intensity approach light system.

MALSR means medium intensity approach light system with runway alignment indicator lights.

MCA means minimum crossing altitude.

MDA means minimum descent altitude.

MEA means minimum en route IFR altitude.

MEL means minimum equipment list.

MM means ILS middle marker.

MOCA means minimum obstruction clearance altitude.

MRA means minimum reception altitude.

MSL means mean sea level.

NDB (ADF) means nondirectional beacon (automatic direction finder).

NM means nautical mile.

NOPAC means North Pacific area of operation.

NOPT means no procedure turn required.

OEI means one engine inoperative.

OM means ILS outer marker.

OPSPECS means operations specifications.

PACOTS means Pacific Organized Track System.

PAR means precision approach radar.

PMA means parts manufacturer approval.

POC means portable oxygen concentrator.

PTRS means Performance Tracking and Reporting System.

RAIL means runway alignment indicator light system.

RBN means radio beacon.

RCLM means runway centerline marking.

RCLS means runway centerline light system.

REIL means runway end identification lights.

RFFS means rescue and firefighting services.

RNAV means area navigation.

RR means low or medium frequency radio range station.

RVR means runway visual range as measured in the touchdown zone area.

SALS means short approach light system.

SATCOM means satellite communications.

SSALS means simplified short approach light system.

SSALSR means simplified short approach light system with runway alignment indicator lights.

TACAN means ultra-high frequency tactical air navigational aid.

TAS means true airspeed.

TCAS means a traffic alert and collision avoidance system.

TDZL means touchdown zone lights.

TSO means technical standard order.

TVOR means very high frequency terminal omnirange station.

V_A means design maneuvering speed.

V_B means design speed for maximum gust intensity.

V_C means design cruising speed.

V_D means design diving speed.

V_{DF}/M_{DF} means demonstrated flight diving speed.

V_{EF} means the speed at which the critical engine is assumed to fail during takeoff.

V_F means design flap speed.

V_{FC}/M_{FC} means maximum speed for stability characteristics.

V_{FE} means maximum flap extended speed.

V_{FTO} means final takeoff speed.

V_H means maximum speed in level flight with maximum continuous power.

V_{LE} means maximum landing gear extended speed.

V_{LO} means maximum landing gear operating speed.

V_{LOF} means lift-off speed.

V_{MC} means minimum control speed with the critical engine inoperative.

V_{MO}/M_{MO} means maximum operating limit speed.

V_{MU} means minimum unstick speed.

V_{NE} means never-exceed speed.

V_{NO} means maximum structural cruising speed.

V_R means rotation speed.

V_{REF} means reference landing speed.

V_S means the stalling speed or the minimum steady flight speed at which the airplane is controllable.

V_{S0} means the stalling speed or the minimum steady flight speed in the landing configuration.

V_{S1} means the stalling speed or the minimum steady flight speed obtained in a specific configuration.

V_{SR} means reference stall speed.

V_{SR0} means reference stall speed in the landing configuration.

V_{SR1} means reference stall speed in a specific configuration.

V_{SW} means speed at which onset of natural or artificial stall warning occurs.

V_{TOSS} means takeoff safety speed for Category A rotorcraft.

V_X means speed for best angle of climb.

V_Y means speed for best rate of climb.

V_1 means the maximum speed in the takeoff at which the pilot must take the first action (e.g., apply brakes, reduce thrust, deploy speed brakes) to stop the airplane within the accelerate-stop distance. V1 also means the minimum speed in the takeoff, following a failure of the critical engine at VEF, at which the pilot can continue the takeoff and achieve the required height above the takeoff surface within the takeoff distance.

V_2 means takeoff safety speed.

V_{2min} means minimum takeoff safety speed.

VFR means visual flight rules.

VGSI means visual glide slope indicator.

VHF means very high frequency.

VOR means very high frequency omnirange station.

VORTAC means collocated VOR and TACAN.

[Doc. No. 1150, 27 FR 4590, May 15, 1962]

1.3   Rules of Construction

(a) In Subchapters A through K of this chapter, unless the context requires otherwise:

> (1) Words importing the singular include the plural;
>
> (2) Words importing the plural include the singular; and
>
> (3) Words importing the masculine gender include the feminine.

(b) In Subchapters A through K of this chapter, the word:

> (1) Shall is used in an imperative sense;
>
> (2) May is used in a permissive sense to state authority or permission to do the act prescribed, and the words "no person may * * *" or "a person may not * * *" mean that no person is required, authorized, or permitted to do the act prescribed; and
>
> (3) Includes means "includes but is not limited to".

[Doc. No. 1150, 27 FR 4590, May 15, 1962]

PART 3 — GENERAL REQUIREMENTS

Subpart A — General Requirements Concerning Type Certificated Products or Products, Parts, Appliances, or Materials That May Be Used on Type Certificated Products

Subpart B — Security Threat Disqualification

Authority: 49 U.S.C. 106(g), 40113, 44701, 44704, and 46111.

Source: 70 FR 54832, Sept. 16, 2005, unless otherwise noted.

Subpart A — General Requirements Concerning Type Certificated Products or Products, Parts, Appliances, or Materials That May Be Used on Type Certificated Products

3.1   Applicability

(a) This part applies to any person who makes a record regarding:

(1) A type-certificated product, or

(2) A product, part, appliance or material that may be used on a type-certificated product.

(b) Section 3.5(b) does not apply to records made under part 43 of this chapter.

3.5   Statements about products, parts, appliances and materials

(a) Definitions. The following terms will have the stated meanings when used in this section:

Airworthy means the aircraft conforms to its type design and is in a condition for safe operation.

Product means an aircraft, aircraft engine, or aircraft propeller.

Record means any writing, drawing, map, recording, tape, film, photograph or other documentary material by which information is preserved or conveyed in any format, including, but not limited to, paper, microfilm, identification plates, stamped marks, bar codes or electronic format, and can either be separate from, attached to or inscribed on any product, part, appliance or material.

(b) Prohibition against fraudulent and intentionally false statements. When conveying information related to an advertisement or sales transaction, no person may make or cause to be made:

(1) Any fraudulent or intentionally false statement in any record about the airworthiness of a type-certificated product, or the acceptability of any product, part, appliance, or material for installation on a type-certificated product.

(2) Any fraudulent or intentionally false reproduction or alteration of any record about the airworthiness of any type-certificated product, or the acceptability of any product, part, appliance, or material for installation on a type-certificated product.

(c) Prohibition against intentionally misleading statements.

(1) When conveying information related to an advertisement or sales transaction, no person may make, or cause to be made, a material representation that a type-certificated product is airworthy, or that a product, part, appliance, or material is acceptable for installation on a type-certificated product in any record if that representation is likely to mislead a consumer acting reasonably under the circumstances.

(2) When conveying information related to an advertisement or sales transaction, no person may make, or cause to be made, through the omission of material information, a representation that a type-certificated product is airworthy, or that a product, part, appliance, or material is acceptable for installation on a type-certificated product in any record if that representation is likely to mislead a consumer acting reasonably under the circumstances.

(d) The provisions of 3.5(b) and 3.5(c) shall not apply if a person can show that the product is airworthy or that the product, part, appliance or material is acceptable for installation on a type-certificated product.

Subpart B—Security Threat Disqualification

Source: 84 FR 42803, Aug. 19, 2019, FAA-2018-0656; Amendment No. 3-2, unless otherwise noted.

3.200   Effect of Transportation Security Administration notification on a certificate or any part of a certificate held by an individual

When the Transportation Security Administration (TSA) notifies the FAA that an individual holding a certificate or part of a certificate issued by the FAA poses, or is suspected of posing, a risk of air piracy or terrorism or a threat to airline or passenger safety, the FAA will issue an order amending, modifying, suspending, or revoking any certificate or part of a certificate issued by the FAA.

3.205   Effect of Transportation Security Administration notification on applications by individuals for a certificate or any part of a certificate

(a) When the TSA notifies the FAA that an individual who has applied for a certificate or any part of a certificate issued by the FAA poses, or is suspected of posing, a risk of air piracy or terrorism or a threat to airline or passenger safety, the FAA will hold the individual's certificate applications in abeyance pending further notification from the TSA.

(b) When the TSA notifies the FAA that the TSA has made a final security threat determination regarding an individual, the FAA will deny all the individual's certificate applications. Alternatively, if the TSA notifies the FAA that it has withdrawn its security threat determination, the FAA will continue processing the individual's applications.

PART 13 — INVESTIGATIVE AND ENFORCEMENT PROCEDURES

FAR 13

Subpart I — Flight Operational Quality Assurance Programs

13.401   Flight Operational Quality Assurance Program: Prohibition against use of data for enforcement purposes

Authority: 18 U.S.C. 6002; 28 U.S.C. 2461 (note); 49 U.S.C. 106(g), 5121-5124, 40113-40114, 44103-44106, 44701-44704, 44709-44710, 44713, 44725, 44742, 44802 (note), 46101-46111, 46301, 46302 (for a violation of 49 U.S.C. 46504), 46304-46316, 46318-46320, 46501-46502, 46504, 46507, 47106, 47107, 47111, 47122, 47306, 47531-47532; 49 CFR 1.83.

Source: Docket No. 18884, 44 FR 63723, Nov. 5, 1979, unless otherwise noted.

Subpart A — General Authority to Re-Delegate and Investigative Procedures

Source: Docket No. FAA-2018-1051; Amdt. No. 13-40, 86 FR 54526, Oct. 1, 2021, unless otherwise noted.

13.1 Re-delegation

Unless otherwise specified, the Chief Counsel, each Deputy Chief Counsel, and the Assistant Chief Counsel for Enforcement may re-delegate the authority delegated to them under this part.

13.2 Reports of violations.

(a) Any person who knows of any violation of 49 U.S.C. subtitle VII, 49 U.S.C. chapter 51, or any rule, regulation, or order issued under those statutes, should report the violation to FAA personnel.

(b) FAA personnel will review each report made under this section to determine whether any additional investigation or action is warranted.

13.3—Investigations (general).

(a) The Administrator may conduct investigations; hold hearings; issue subpoenas; require the production of relevant documents, records, and property; and take evidence and depositions.

(b) The Administrator has delegated the authority to conduct investigations to the various services and offices for matters within their respective areas.

(c) The Administrator delegates to the Chief Counsel, each Deputy Chief Counsel, and the Assistant Chief Counsel for Enforcement the authority to:

   (1) Issue orders;

   (2) Conduct formal investigations;

   (3) Subpoena witnesses and records in conducting a hearing or investigation;

   (4) Order depositions and production of records in a proceeding or investigation; and

   (5) Petition a court of the United States to enforce a subpoena or order described in paragraphs (c)(3) and (4) of this section.

(d) A complaint against the sponsor, proprietor, or operator of a federally assisted airport involving violations of the legal authorities listed in 16.1 of this chapter must be filed in accordance with the provisions of part 16 of this chapter.

13.5 Formal complaints

(a) Any person may file a complaint with the Administrator with respect to a violation by a person of any requirement under 49 U.S.C. subtitle VII, 49 U.S.C. chapter 51, or any rule, regulation, or order issued under those statutes, as to matters within the jurisdiction of the Administrator. This section does not apply to complaints against the Administrator or employees of the FAA acting within the scope of their employment.

(b) Complaints filed under this section must -

   (1) Be submitted in writing and identified as a complaint seeking an appropriate order or other enforcement action;

   (2) Be submitted to the Federal Aviation Administration, Office of the Chief Counsel, Attention: Formal Complaint Clerk (AGC-300), 800 Independence Avenue SW, Washington, DC 20591;

   (3) Set forth the name and address, if known, of each person who is the subject of the complaint and, with respect to each person, the specific provisions of the statute, rule, regulation, or order that the complainant believes were violated;

   (4) Contain a concise but complete statement of the facts relied upon to substantiate each allegation;

   (5) State the name, address, telephone number, and email of the person filing the complaint; and

   (6) Be signed by the person filing the complaint or an authorized representative.

(c) A complaint that does not meet the requirements of paragraph (b) of this section will be considered a report under 13.2.

(d) The FAA will send a copy of a complaint that meets the requirements of paragraph (b) of this section to the subject(s) of the complaint by certified mail.

(e) A subject of the complaint may serve a written answer to the complaint to the Formal Complaint Clerk at the address specified in paragraph (b)(2) of this section no later than 20 days after service of a copy of the complaint. For purposes of this paragraph (e), the date of service is the date on which the FAA mailed a copy of the complaint to the subject of the complaint.

(f) After the subject(s) of the complaint have served a written answer or after the allotted time to serve an answer has expired, the Administrator will determine if there are reasonable grounds for investigating the complaint, and -

   (1 If the Administrator determines that a complaint does not state facts that warrant an investigation or action, the complaint may be dismissed without a hearing and the reason for the dismissal will be given, in writing, to the person who filed the complaint and the subject(s) of the complaint; or

   (2) If the Administrator determines that reasonable grounds exist, an informal investigation may be initiated or an order of investigation may be issued in accordance with subpart F of this part, or both. The subject(s) of a complaint will be advised which official has been delegated the responsibility under 13.3(b) or (c), as applicable, for conducting the investigation.

(g) If the investigation substantiates the allegations set forth in the complaint, the Administrator may take action in accordance with applicable law and FAA policy.

(h) The complaint and other records relating to the disposition of the complaint are maintained in the Formal Complaint Docket (AGC-300), Office of the Chief Counsel, Federal Aviation Administration, 800 Independence Avenue SW, Washington, DC 20591. Any interested person may examine any docketed material at that office at any time after the docket is established, except material that is required to be withheld from the public under applicable law, and may obtain a copy upon paying the cost of the copy.

13.7 Records, documents, and reports

Each record, document, and report that FAA regulations require to be maintained, exhibited, or submitted to the Administrator may be used in any investigation conducted by the Administrator; and, except to the extent the use may be specifically limited or prohibited by the section which imposes the requirement, the records, documents, and reports may be used in any civil penalty action, certificate action, or other legal proceeding.

Subpart B - Administrative Actions

Source: Docket No. FAA-2018-1051; Amdt. No. 13-40, 86 FR 54527, Oct. 1, 2021, unless otherwise noted.

13.11   Administrative disposition of certain violations

(a) If, after an investigation, FAA personnel determine that an apparent violation of 49 U.S.C. subtitle VII, 49 U.S.C. chapter 51, or any rule, regulation, or order issued under those statutes, does not require legal enforcement action, an appropriate FAA official may take administrative action to address the apparent violation.

(b) An administrative action under this section does not constitute a formal adjudication of the matter, and may take the form of -

   (1) A Warning Notice that recites available facts and information about the incident or condition and indicates that it may have been a violation; or

   (2) A Letter of Correction that states the corrective action the apparent violator has taken or agrees to take. If the apparent violator does not complete the agreed corrective action, the FAA may take legal enforcement action.

Subpart C — Legal Enforcement Actions

Source: Docket No. FAA-2018-1051; Amdt. No. 13-40, 86 FR 54527, Oct. 1, 2021, unless otherwise noted.

13.13   Consent orders

(a) The Chief Counsel, each Deputy Chief Counsel, and the Assistant Chief Counsel for Enforcement may issue a consent order to resolve any matter with a person that may be subject to legal enforcement action.

(b) A person that may be subject to legal enforcement action may propose a consent order. The proposed consent order must include -

   (1) An admission of all jurisdictional facts;

   (2) An express waiver of the right to further procedural steps and of all rights to legal review in any forum;

   (3) An express waiver of attorney's fees and costs;

   (4) If a notice or order has been issued prior to the proposed consent order, an incorporation by reference of the notice or order and an acknowledgment that the notice or order may be used to construe the terms of the consent order; and

   (5) If a request for hearing or appeal is pending in any forum, a provision that the person will withdraw the request for hearing or notice of appeal.

13.14   [Reserved]

13.15   Civil penalties: other than by administrative assessment

(a) The FAA uses the procedures in this section when it seeks a civil penalty other than by the administrative assessment procedures in 13.16 or 13.18.

(b) The authority of the Administrator to seek a civil penalty, and the ability to refer cases to the United States Attorney General, or the delegate of the Attorney General, for prosecution of civil penalty actions sought by the Administrator is delegated to the Chief Counsel, each Deputy Chief Counsel, and the Assistant Chief Counsel for Enforcement. This delegation applies to cases involving one or more of the following:

   (1) An amount in controversy in excess of:

      (i) $400,000, if the violation was committed by a person other than an individual or small business concern; or

      (ii) $50,000, if the violation was committed by an individual or small business concern.

   (2) An in rem action, seizure of aircraft subject to lien, suit for injunctive relief, or for collection of an assessed civil penalty.

(c) The Administrator may compromise any civil penalty proposed under this section, before referral to the United States Attorney General, or the delegate of the Attorney General, for prosecution.

   (1) The Administrator, through the Chief Counsel, a Deputy Chief Counsel, or the Assistant Chief Counsel for Enforce-

ment sends a civil penalty letter to the person charged with a violation. The civil penalty letter contains a statement of the charges; the applicable law, rule, regulation, or order; and the amount of civil penalty that the Administrator will accept in full settlement of the action or an offer to compromise the civil penalty.

   (2) Not later than 30 days after receipt of the civil penalty letter, the person cited with an alleged violation may respond to the civil penalty letter by -

      (i) Submitting electronic payment, a certified check, or money order in the amount offered by the Administrator in the civil penalty letter. The agency attorney will send a letter to the person charged with the violation stating that payment is accepted in full settlement of the civil penalty action; or

      (ii) Submitting one of the following to the agency attorney:

         (A) Written material or information that may explain, mitigate, or deny the violation or that may show extenuating circumstances; or

         (B) A written request for an informal conference to discuss the matter with the agency attorney and to submit any relevant information or documents that may explain, mitigate, or deny the violation; or that may show extenuating circumstances.

   (3) The documents, material, or information submitted under paragraph (c)(2)(ii) of this section may include support for any claim of inability to pay the civil penalty in whole or in part, or for any claim of small business status as defined in 49 U.S.C. 46301(i).

   (4) The Administrator will consider any material or information submitted under paragraph (c)(2)(ii) of this section to determine whether the person is subject to a civil penalty or to determine the amount for which the Administrator will compromise the action.

   (5) If the parties cannot agree to compromise the civil penalty, the Administrator may refer the civil penalty action to the United States Attorney General, or the delegate of the Attorney General, to begin proceedings in a U.S. district court to prosecute and collect a civil penalty.

13.16   Civil penalties: Administrative assessment against a person other than an individual acting as a pilot, flight engineer, mechanic, or repairman; administrative assessment against all persons for hazardous materials violations.

(a) General. The FAA uses the procedures in this section when it assesses a civil penalty against a person other than an individual acting as a pilot, flight engineer, mechanic, or repairman for a violation cited in the first sentence of 49 U.S.C. 46301(d)(2), or in 49 U.S.C. 47531, or any implementing rule, regulation, or order, except when the U.S. district courts have exclusive jurisdiction.

(b) District court jurisdiction. The U.S. district courts have exclusive jurisdiction of any civil penalty action initiated by the FAA for violations described in paragraph (a) of this section if -

   (1) The amount in controversy is more than $400,000 for a violation committed by a person other than an individual or small business concern;

   (2) The amount in controversy is more than $50,000 for a violation committed by an individual or a small business concern;

   (3) The action is in rem or another action in rem based on the same violation has been brought;

   (4) The action involves an aircraft subject to a lien that has been seized by the Government; or

   (5) Another action has been brought for an injunction based on the same violation.

(c) Hazardous materials violations. An order assessing a civil penalty for a violation under 49 U.S.C. chapter 51, or a rule, regulation, or order issued under 49 U.S.C. chapter 51, is issued only after the following factors have been considered:

(1) The nature, circumstances, extent, and gravity of the violation;

(2) With respect to the violator, the degree of culpability, any history of prior violations, the ability to pay, and any effect on the ability to continue to do business; and

(3) Other matters that justice requires.

(d) Delegation of authority. The authority of the Administrator is delegated to each Deputy Chief Counsel and the Assistant Chief Counsel for Enforcement, as follows:

(1) Under 49 U.S.C. 46301(d), 47531, and 5123, and 49 CFR 1.83, to initiate and assess civil penalties for a violation of those statutes or a rule, regulation, or order issued under those provisions;

(2) Under 49 U.S.C. 5123, 49 CFR 1.83, 49 U.S.C. 46301(d), and 49 U.S.C. 46305, to refer cases to the Attorney General of the United States or a delegate of the Attorney General for collection of civil penalties;

(3) Under 49 U.S.C. 46301(f), to compromise the amount of a civil penalty imposed; and

(4) Under 49 U.S.C. 5123(e) and (f) and 49 CFR 1.83, to compromise the amount of a civil penalty imposed.

(e) Order assessing civil penalty.

(1) An order assessing civil penalty may be issued for a violation described in paragraph (a) or (c) of this section, or as otherwise provided by statute, after notice and opportunity for a hearing, when:

(i) A person charged with a violation agrees to pay a civil penalty for a violation; or

(ii) A person charged with a violation does not request a hearing under paragraph (g)(2)(ii) of this section within 15 days after receipt of a final notice of proposed civil penalty.

(2) The following also serve as an order assessing civil penalty:

(i) An initial decision or order issued by an administrative law judge as described in 13.232(e).

(ii) A decision or order issued by the FAA decisionmaker as described in 13.233(j).

(f) Notice of proposed civil penalty. A civil penalty action is initiated by sending a notice of proposed civil penalty to the person charged with a violation, the designated agent for the person, or if there is no such designated agent, the president of the company charged with a violation. In response to a notice of proposed civil penalty, a company may designate in writing another person to receive documents in that civil penalty action. The notice of proposed civil penalty contains a statement of the charges and the amount of the proposed civil penalty. Not later than 30 days after receipt of the notice of proposed civil penalty, the person charged with a violation may -

(1) Submit the amount of the proposed civil penalty or an agreed-upon amount, in which case either an order assessing civil penalty or compromise order under paragraph (n) of this section may be issued in that amount;

(2) Submit to the agency attorney one of the following:

(i) Written information, including documents and witness statements, demonstrating that a violation of the regulations did not occur or that a penalty or the amount of the penalty is not warranted by the circumstances.

(ii) A written request to reduce the proposed civil penalty, stating the amount of reduction and the reasons and providing any documents supporting a reduction of the proposed civil penalty, including records indicating a financial inability to pay or records showing that payment of the proposed civil penalty would prevent the person from continuing in business.

(iii) A written request for an informal conference to discuss the matter with the agency attorney and to submit relevant information or documents; or

(3) Request a hearing conducted in accordance with subpart G of this part.

(g) Final notice of proposed civil penalty. A final notice of proposed civil penalty will be sent to the person charged with a violation, the designated agent for the person, the designated agent named in accordance with paragraph (f) of this section, or the president of the company charged with a violation. The final notice of proposed civil penalty contains a statement of the charges and the amount of the proposed civil penalty and, as a result of information submitted to the agency attorney during informal procedures, may modify an allegation or a proposed civil penalty contained in a notice of proposed civil penalty.

(1) A final notice of proposed civil penalty may be issued -

(i) If the person charged with a violation fails to respond to the notice of proposed civil penalty within 30 days after receipt of that notice; or

(ii) If the parties participated in any procedures under paragraph (f)(2) of this section and the parties have not agreed to compromise the action or the agency attorney has not agreed to withdraw the notice of proposed civil penalty.

(2) Not later than 15 days after receipt of the final notice of proposed civil penalty, the person charged with a violation may do one of the following:

(i) Submit the amount of the proposed civil penalty or an agreed-upon amount, in which case either an order assessing civil penalty or a compromise order under paragraph (n) of this section may be issued in that amount; or

(ii) Request a hearing conducted in accordance with subpart G of this part.

(h) Request for a hearing. Any person requesting a hearing, under paragraph (f)(3) or (g)(2)(ii) of this section must file the request with the FAA Hearing Docket Clerk and serve the request on the agency attorney in accordance with the requirements in subpart G of this part.

(i) Hearing. The procedural rules in subpart G of this part apply to the hearing.

(j) Appeal. Either party may appeal the administrative law judge's initial decision to the FAA decisionmaker under the procedures in subpart G of this part. The procedural rules in subpart G of this part apply to the appeal.

(k) Judicial review. A person may seek judicial review only of a final decision and order of the FAA decisionmaker in accordance with 13.235.

(l) Payment.

(1) A person must pay a civil penalty by:

(i) Sending a certified check or money order, payable to the Federal Aviation Administration, to the FAA office identified in the notice of proposed civil penalty, the final notice of proposed civil penalty, or the order assessing civil penalty; or

(ii) Making an electronic payment according to the directions specified in the notice of proposed civil penalty, the final notice of proposed civil penalty, or the order assessing civil penalty.

(2) The civil penalty must be paid within 30 days after service of the order assessing civil penalty, unless otherwise agreed to by the parties. In cases where a hearing is requested, an appeal to the FAA decisionmaker is filed, or a petition for

review of the FAA decisionmaker's decision is filed in a U.S. court of appeals, the civil penalty must be paid within 30 days after all litigation in the matter is completed and the civil penalty is affirmed in whole or in part.

(m) Collection of civil penalties. If an individual does not pay a civil penalty imposed by an order assessing civil penalty or other final order, the Administrator may take action to collect the penalty.

(n) Compromise. The FAA may compromise the amount of any civil penalty imposed under this section under 49 U.S.C. 5123(e), 46301(f), or 46318 at any time before referring the action to the United States Attorney General, or the delegate of the Attorney General, for collection.

(1) When a civil penalty is compromised with a finding of violation, an agency attorney issues an order assessing civil penalty.

(2) When a civil penalty is compromised without a finding of violation, the agency attorney issues a compromise order that states the following:

   (i) The person has paid a civil penalty or has signed a promissory note providing for installment payments.

   (ii) The FAA makes no finding of a violation.

   (iii) The compromise order will not be used as evidence of a prior violation in any subsequent civil penalty proceeding or certificate action proceeding.

13.17   Seizure of aircraft

(a) The Chief Counsel, or a Regional Administrator for an aircraft within the region, may issue an order authorizing a State or Federal law enforcement officer or a Federal Aviation Administration safety inspector to seize an aircraft that is involved in a violation for which a civil penalty may be imposed on its owner or the individual commanding the aircraft.

(b) Each person seizing an aircraft under this section places it in the nearest available and adequate public storage facility in the judicial district in which it was seized.

(c) The Regional Administrator or Chief Counsel, without delay, sends a written notice and a copy of this section to the registered owner of the seized aircraft and to each other person shown by FAA records to have an interest in it, stating the -

(1) Time, date, and place of seizure;

(2) Name and address of the custodian of the aircraft;

(3) Reasons for the seizure, including the violations alleged or proven to have been committed; and

(4) Amount that may be tendered as -

   (i) A compromise of a civil penalty for the alleged violation; or

   (ii) Payment for a civil penalty imposed for a proven violation.

(d) The Chief Counsel or Assistant Chief Counsel for Enforcement immediately sends a report to the United States Attorney for the judicial district in which it was seized, requesting the United States Attorney to institute proceedings to enforce a lien against the aircraft.

(e) The Regional Administrator or Chief Counsel directs the release of a seized aircraft when -

(1) The alleged violator pays a civil penalty or an amount agreed upon in compromise, and the costs of seizing, storing, and maintaining the aircraft;

(2) The aircraft is seized under an order of a court of the United States in proceedings in rem initiated under 49 U.S.C. 46305 to enforce a lien against the aircraft;

(3) The United States Attorney General, or the delegate of the Attorney General, notifies the FAA that the United States Attorney General, or the delegate of the Attorney General, refuses to institute proceedings in rem under 49 U.S.C. 46305 to enforce a lien against the aircraft; or

(4) A bond in the amount and with the sureties prescribed by the Chief Counsel or the Assistant Chief Counsel for Enforcement is deposited, conditioned on payment of the penalty or the compromise amount, and the costs of seizing, storing, and maintaining the aircraft.

13.18   Civil penalties: administrative assessment against an individual acting as a pilot, flight engineer, mechanic, or repairman

(a) General.

(1) This section applies to each action in which the FAA seeks to assess a civil penalty by administrative procedures against an individual acting as a pilot, flight engineer, mechanic, or repairman under 49 U.S.C. 46301(d)(5) for a violation listed in 49 U.S.C. 46301(d)(2). This section does not apply to a civil penalty assessed for a violation of 49 U.S.C. chapter 51, or a rule, regulation, or order issued thereunder.

(2) Notwithstanding the provisions of paragraph (a)(1) of this section, the U.S. district courts have exclusive jurisdiction of any civil penalty action involving an individual acting as a pilot, flight engineer, mechanic, or repairman for violations described in paragraph (a)(1), or under 49 U.S.C. 46301(d)(4), if:

   (i) The amount in controversy is more than $50,000;

   (ii) The action involves an aircraft subject to a lien that has been seized by the government; or

   (iii) Another action has been brought for an injunction based on the same violation.

(b) Definitions. As used in this part, the following definitions apply:

(1) Flight engineer means an individual who holds a flight engineer certificate issued under part 63 of this chapter.

(2) Individual acting as a pilot, flight engineer, mechanic, or repairman means an individual acting in such capacity, whether or not that individual holds the respective airman certificate issued by the FAA.

(3) Mechanic means an individual who holds a mechanic certificate issued under part 65 of this chapter.

(4) Pilot means an individual who holds a pilot certificate issued under part 61 of this chapter.

(5) Repairman means an individual who holds a repairman certificate issued under part 65 of this chapter.

(c) Delegation of authority. The authority of the Administrator is delegated to the Chief Counsel and each Deputy Chief Counsel, and the Assistant Chief Counsel for Enforcement, as follows:

(1) To initiate and assess civil penalties under 49 U.S.C. 46301(d)(5);

(2) To refer cases to the Attorney General of the United States, or the delegate of the Attorney General, for collection of civil penalties; and

(3) To compromise the amount of a civil penalty under 49 U.S.C. 46301(f).

(d) Notice of proposed assessment. A civil penalty action is initiated by sending a notice of proposed assessment to the individual charged with a violation specified in paragraph (a) of this section. The notice of proposed assessment contains a statement of the charges and the amount of the proposed civil penalty. The individual charged with a violation may do the following:

(1) Submit the amount of the proposed civil penalty or an agreed-upon amount, in which case either an order of assessment or a compromise order will be issued in that amount.

(2) Answer the charges in writing by submitting information, including documents and witness statements, demonstrating that a violation of the regulations did not occur or that a penalty, or the amount of the penalty, is not warranted by the circumstances.

(3) Submit a written request to reduce the proposed civil penalty, stating the amount of reduction and the reasons, and providing any documents supporting a reduction of the proposed civil penalty, including records indicating a financial inability to pay.

(4) Submit a written request for an informal conference to discuss the matter with an agency attorney and submit relevant information or documents.

(5) Request that an order of assessment be issued so that the individual charged may appeal to the National Transportation Safety Board.

(e) Failure to respond to notice of proposed assessment. An order of assessment may be issued if the individual charged with a violation fails to respond to the notice of proposed assessment within 15 days after receipt of that notice.

(f) Order of assessment. An order of assessment, which imposes a civil penalty, may be issued for a violation described in paragraph (a) of this section after notice and an opportunity to answer any charges and be heard as to why such order should not be issued.

(g) Appeal. Any individual who receives an order of assessment issued under this section may appeal the order to the National Transportation Safety Board. The appeal stays the effectiveness of the Administrator's order.

(h) Judicial review. A party may seek judicial review only of a final decision and order of the National Transportation Safety Board under 49 U.S.C. 46301(d)(6) and 46110. Neither an initial decision, nor an order issued by an administrative law judge that has not been appealed to the National Transportation Safety Board, nor an order compromising a civil penalty action, may be appealed under any of those sections.

(i) Compromise. The FAA may compromise any civil penalty imposed under this section at any time before referring the action to the United States Attorney General, or the delegate of the Attorney General, for collection.

(1) When a civil penalty is compromised with a finding of violation, an agency attorney issues an order of assessment.

(2) When a civil penalty is compromised without a finding of violation, the agency attorney issues a compromise order of assessment that states the following:

    (i) The individual has paid a civil penalty or has signed a promissory note providing for installment payments;

    (ii) The FAA makes no finding of violation; and

    (iii) The compromise order will not be used as evidence of a prior violation in any subsequent civil penalty proceeding or certificate action proceeding.

(j) Payment.

(1) An individual must pay a civil penalty by:

    (i) Sending a certified check or money order, payable to the Federal Aviation Administration, to the FAA office identified in the order of assessment; or

    (ii) Making an electronic payment according to the directions specified in the order of assessment.

(2) The civil penalty must be paid within 30 days after service of the order of assessment, unless an appeal is filed with the National Transportation Safety Board. In cases where an appeal is filed with the National Transportation Safety Board, or a petition for review is filed with a U.S. court of appeals, the civil penalty must be paid within 30 days after all litigation in the matter is completed and the civil penalty is affirmed in whole or in part.

(k) Collection of civil penalties. If an individual does not pay a civil penalty imposed by an order of assessment or other final order, the Administrator may take action provided under the law to collect the penalty.

13.19   Certificate actions appealable to the National Transportation Safety Board.

(a) The Administrator may issue an order amending, modifying, suspending, or revoking all or part of any type certificate, production certificate, airworthiness certificate, airman certificate, air carrier operating certificate, air navigation facility certificate, or air agency certificate if as a result of a reinspection, reexamination, or other investigation, the Administrator determines that the public interest and safety in air commerce requires it, if a certificate holder has violated an aircraft noise or sonic boom standard or regulation prescribed under 49 U.S.C. 44715(a), or if the holder of the certificate is convicted of violating 16 U.S.C. 742j-1(a).

(b) The agency attorney will issue a notice before issuing a non-immediately effective order to amend, modify, suspend, or revoke a type certificate, production certificate, airworthiness certificate, airman certificate, air carrier operating certificate, air navigation facility certificate, air agency certificate, or to revoke an aircraft certificate of registration because the aircraft was used to carry out or facilitate an activity punishable under a law of the United States or a State related to a controlled substance (except a law related to simple possession of a controlled substance), by death or imprisonment for more than one year, and the owner of the aircraft permitted the use of the aircraft knowing that the aircraft was to be used for the activity.

(1) A notice of proposed certificate action will advise the certificate holder or aircraft owner of the charges or other reasons upon which the Administrator bases the proposed action, and allows the holder to answer any charges and to be heard as to why the certificate should not be amended, suspended, modified, or revoked.

(2) In response to a notice of proposed certificate action described in paragraph (b)(1) of this section, the certificate holder or aircraft owner, within 15 days of the date of receipt of the notice, may -

    (i) Surrender the certificate and waive any right to contest or appeal the charged violations and sanction, in which case the Administrator will issue an order;

    (ii) Answer the charges in writing by submitting information, including documents and witness statements, demonstrating that a violation of the regulations did not occur or that the proposed sanction is not warranted by the circumstances;

    (iii) Submit a written request for an informal conference to discuss the matter with an agency attorney and submit relevant information or documents; or

    (iv) Request that an order be issued in accordance with the notice of proposed certificate action so that the certificate holder or aircraft owner may appeal to the National Transportation Safety Board.

(c) In the case of an emergency order amending, modifying, suspending, or revoking a type certificate, production certificate, airworthiness certificate, airman certificate, air carrier operating certificate, air navigation facility certificate, or air agency certificate, a person affected by the immediate effectiveness of the Administrator's order may petition the National Transportation Safety Board for a review of the Administrator's determination that an emergency exists.

(d) A person may not petition the National Transportation Safety Board for a review of the Administrator's determination that safety in air transportation or air commerce requires the immediate effectiveness of an order where the action is based on the circumstances described in paragraph (d)(1), (2), or (3) of this section.

(1) The revocation of an individual's airman certificates for the reasons stated in paragraph (d)(1)(i) or (ii) of this section:

    (i) A conviction under a law of the United States or a State related to a controlled substance (except a law related to simple possession of a controlled substance), of an offense punishable by death or imprisonment for more than one year if the Administrator finds that -

(A) An aircraft was used to commit, or facilitate the commission of the offense; and

(B) The individual served as an airman, or was on the aircraft, in connection with committing, or facilitating the commission of, the offense.

   (ii) Knowingly carrying out an activity punishable, under a law of the United States or a State related to a controlled substance (except a law related to simple possession of a controlled substance), by death or imprisonment for more than one year; and -

(A) An aircraft was used to carry out or facilitate the activity; and

(B) The individual served as an airman, or was on the aircraft, in connection with carrying out, or facilitating the carrying out of, the activity.

(2) The revocation of a certificate of registration for an aircraft, and any other aircraft the owner of that aircraft holds, if the Administrator finds that -

   (i) The aircraft was used to carry out or facilitate an activity punishable, under a law of the United States or a State related to a controlled substance (except a law related to simple possession of a controlled substance), by death or imprisonment for more than one year; and

   (ii) The owner of the aircraft permitted the use of the aircraft knowing that the aircraft was to be used for the activity described in paragraph (d)(2)(i) of this section.

(3) The revocation of an airman certificate, design organization certificate, type certificate, production certificate, airworthiness certificate, air carrier operating certificate, airport operating certificate, air agency certificate, or air navigation facility certificate if the Administrator finds that the holder of the certificate or an individual who has a controlling or ownership interest in the holder -

   (i) Was convicted in a court of law of a violation of a law of the United States relating to the installation, production, repair, or sale of a counterfeit or fraudulently-represented aviation part or material; or

   (ii) Knowingly, and with the intent to defraud, carried out or facilitated an activity described in paragraph (d)(3)(i) of this section.

13.20   Orders of compliance, cease and desist orders, orders of denial, and other orders

(a) General. This section applies to all of the following:

(1) Orders of compliance;

(2) Cease and desist orders;

(3) Orders of denial;

(4) Orders suspending or revoking a certificate of registration (but not revocation of a certificate of registration because the aircraft was used to carry out or facilitate an activity punishable, under a law of the United States or a State related to a controlled substance (except a law related to simple possession of a controlled substance), by death or imprisonment for more than one year and the owner of the aircraft permitted the use of the aircraft knowing that the aircraft was to be used for the activity); and

(5) Other orders issued by the Administrator to carry out the provisions of the Federal aviation statute codified at 49 U.S.C. subtitle VII that apply this section by statute, rule, regulation, or order, or for which there is no specific administrative process provided by statute, rule, regulation, or order.

(b) Applicability of procedures.

(1) Prior to the issuance of a non-immediately effective order covered by this section, the Administrator will provide the person who would be subject to the order with notice, advising the person of the charges or other reasons upon which the proposed action is based, and the provisions in paragraph (c) of this section apply.

(2) If the Administrator is of the opinion that an emergency exists related to safety in air commerce and requires immediate action and issues an order covered by this section that is immediately effective, the provisions of paragraph (d) of this section apply.

(c) Non-emergency procedures.

(1) Within 30 days after service of the notice, the person subject to the notice may:

   (i) Submit a written reply;

   (ii) Agree to the issuance of the order as proposed in the notice of proposed action, waiving any right to contest or appeal the agreed-upon order issued under this option in any administrative or judicial forum;

   (iii) Submit a written request for an informal conference to discuss the matter with an agency attorney; or

   (iv) Request a hearing in accordance with the non-emergency procedures of subpart D of this part.

(2) After an informal conference is held or a reply is filed, if the agency attorney notifies the person that some or all of the proposed agency action will not be withdrawn, the person may, within 10 days after receiving the agency attorney's notification, request a hearing on the parts of the proposed agency action not withdrawn, in accordance with the non-emergency procedures of subpart D of this part.

(3) If a hearing is requested in accordance with paragraph (c)(1)(iv) or (c)(2) of this section, the non-emergency procedures of subpart D of this part apply.

(4) Failure to request a hearing within the periods provided in paragraph (c)(1)(iv) or (c)(2) of this section:

   (i) Constitutes a waiver of the right to a hearing and appeal; and

   (ii) Authorizes the agency to make appropriate findings of fact and to issue an appropriate order without further notice or proceedings.

(d) Emergency procedures.

(1) If the Administrator is of the opinion that an emergency exists related to safety in air commerce and requires immediate action, the Administrator issues simultaneously:

   (i) An immediately effective order that expires 80 days after the date of issuance and sets forth the charges or other reasons upon which the order is based; and

   (ii) A notice of proposed action that:

(A) Sets forth the charges or other reasons upon which the notice of proposed action is based; and

(B) Advises that within 10 days after service of the notice, the person may appeal the notice by requesting an expedited hearing in accordance with the emergency procedures of subpart D of this part.

(2) The Administrator will serve the immediately effective order and the notice of proposed action together by personal or overnight delivery and by certified or registered mail to the person subject to the order and notice of proposed action.

(3) Failure to request a hearing challenging the notice of proposed action under the expedited procedures in subpart D of this part within 10 days after service of the notice:

   (i) Constitutes a waiver of the right to a hearing and appeal under subpart D of this part; and

FAR 13

    (ii) Authorizes the Administrator, without further notice or proceedings, to make appropriate findings of fact, issue an immediately effective order without expiration, and withdraw the 80-day immediately effective order.

  (4) The filing of a request for hearing under subpart D of this part does not stay the effectiveness of the 80-day immediately effective order issued under this section.

(e) Delegation of authority. The authority of the Administrator under this section is delegated to the Chief Counsel, each Deputy Chief Counsel, and the Assistant Chief Counsel for Enforcement.

13.21-13.29 [Reserved]

Subpart D — Rules of Practice for FAA Hearings

Source: Docket No. FAA-2018-1051; Amdt. No. 13-40, 86 FR 54532, Oct. 1, 2021, unless otherwise noted.

13.31   Applicability

This subpart applies to proceedings in which a hearing has been requested in accordance with 13.20 or 13.75. Hearings under this subpart are considered informal and are provided through the Office of Adjudication.

13.33   Parties, representatives, and notice of appearance

(a) Parties. Parties to proceedings under this subpart include the following: Complainant, respondent, and where applicable, intervenor.

  (1) Complainant is the FAA Office that issued the notice of proposed action under the authorities listed in 13.31.

  (2) Respondent is the party filing a request for hearing.

  (3) Intervenor is a person permitted to participate as a party under 13.51.

(b) Representatives. Any party to a proceeding under this subpart may appear and be heard in person or by a representative. A representative is an attorney, or another representative designated by the party.

(c) Notice of appearance -

  (1) Content. The representative of a party must file a notice of appearance that includes the representative's name, address, telephone number, and, if available, fax number, and email address.

  (2) Filing. A notice of appearance may be incorporated into an initial filing in a proceeding. A notice of appearance by additional representatives or substitutes after an initial filing in a proceeding must be filed independently.

13.35   Request for hearing, complaint, and answer

(a) Initial filing and service. A request for hearing must be filed with the FAA Hearing Docket, and a copy must be served on the official who issued the notice of proposed action, in accordance with the requirements in 13.43 for filing and service of documents. The request for hearing must be in writing and describe the action proposed by the FAA, and must contain a statement that a hearing is requested under this subpart.

(b) Complaint. Within 20 days after service of the copy of the request for hearing, the official who issued the notice of proposed action must forward a copy of that notice, which serves as the complaint, to the FAA Hearing Docket.

(c) Answer. Within 30 days after service of the copy of the complaint, the Respondent must file an answer to the complaint. All allegations in the complaint not specifically denied in the answer are deemed admitted.

13.37   Hearing officer: Assignment and powers

As soon as practicable after the filing of the complaint, the Director of the Office of Adjudication will assign a hearing officer to preside over the matter. The hearing officer may -

(a) Give notice concerning, and hold, prehearing conferences and hearings;

(b) Administer oaths and affirmations;

(c) Examine witnesses;

(d) Adopt procedures for the submission of evidence in written form;

(e) Issue subpoenas;

(f) Rule on offers of proof;

(g) Receive evidence;

(h) Regulate the course of proceedings, including but not limited to discovery, motions practice, imposition of sanctions, and the hearing;

(i) Hold conferences, before and during the hearing, to settle and simplify issues by consent of the parties;

(j) Dispose of procedural requests and similar matters;

(k) Issue protective orders governing the exchange and safekeeping of information otherwise protected by law, except that national security information may not be disclosed under such an order;

(l) Issue orders and decisions, and make findings of fact, as appropriate; and

(m) Take any other action authorized by this subpart.

13.39   Disqualification of hearing officer

(a) Motion and supporting affidavit. Any party may file a motion for disqualification under 13.49(g). A party must state the grounds for disqualification, including, but not limited to, a financial or other personal interest that would be affected by the outcome of the enforcement action, personal animus against a party to the action or against a group to which a party belongs, prejudgment of the adjudicative facts at issue in the proceeding, or any other prohibited conflict of interest. A party must submit an affidavit with the motion for disqualification that sets forth, in detail, the matters alleged to constitute grounds for disqualification.

(b) Timing. A motion for disqualification must be filed prior to the issuance of the hearing officer's decision under 13.63(b). Any party may file a response to a motion for disqualification, but must do so no later than 5 days after service of the motion for disqualification.

(c) Decision on motion for disqualification. The hearing officer must render a decision on the motion for disqualification no later than 15 days after the motion has been filed. If the hearing officer finds that the motion for disqualification and supporting affidavit show a basis for disqualification, the hearing officer must withdraw from the proceedings immediately. If the hearing officer finds that disqualification is not warranted, the hearing officer must deny the motion and state the grounds for the denial on the record. If the hearing officer fails to rule on a party's motion for disqualification within 15 days after the motion has been filed, the motion is deemed granted.

(d) Self-disqualification. A hearing officer may disqualify himself or herself at any time.

13.41   Separation of functions and prohibition on ex parte communications

(a) Separation of powers. The hearing officer independently exercises the powers under this subpart in a manner conducive to justice and the proper dispatch of business. The hearing officer must not participate in any appeal to the Administrator.

(b) Ex parte communications.

  (1) No substantive ex parte communications between the hearing officer and any party are permitted.

  (2) A hearing, conference, or other event scheduled with prior notice will not constitute ex parte communication prohibited by this section. A hearing, conference, or other event scheduled with prior notice, may proceed in the hearing officer's sole discretion if a party fails to appear, respond, or otherwise participate, and will not constitute an ex parte communication prohibited by this section.

(3) For an appeal to the Administrator under this subpart, FAA attorneys representing the complainant must not advise the Administrator or engage in any ex parte communications with the Administrator or his advisors.

13.43 Service and filing of pleadings, motions, and documents

(a) General rule. A party must file all requests for hearing, pleadings, motions, and documents with the FAA Hearing Docket, and must serve a copy upon all parties to the proceedings.

(b) Methods of filing. Filing must be by email, personal delivery, expedited or overnight courier express service, mail, or fax.

(c) Address for filing. A person filing a document with the FAA Hearing Docket must use the address identified for the method of filing as follows:

(1) If delivery is in person, or by expedited or overnight express courier service. Federal Aviation Administration, 600 Independence Avenue SW, Wilbur Wright Building - Suite 2W100, Washington, DC 20597; Attention: FAA Hearing Docket, AGC-70.

(2) If delivery is via U.S. mail, or U.S. certified or registered mail. Federal Aviation Administration, 800 Independence Avenue SW, Washington, DC 20591; Attention: FAA Hearing Docket, AGC-70, Wilbur Wright Building - Suite 2W100.

(3) Contact information. The FAA Office of Adjudication will make available on its website an email address and fax number for the FAA Hearing Docket, as well as other contact information.

(d) Requirement to file an original document and number of copies. A party must file an original document and one copy when filing by personal delivery or by mail. Only one copy must be filed if filing is accomplished by email or fax.

(e) Filing by email. A document that is filed by email must be attached as a Portable Document Format (PDF) file to an email. The document must be signed in accordance with 13.207. The email message does not constitute a submission, but serves only to deliver the attached PDF file to the FAA Hearing Docket.

(f) Methods of service -

(1) General. A person may serve any document by email, personal delivery, expedited or overnight courier express service, mail, or fax.

(2) Service by email. Service of documents by email is voluntary and requires the prior consent of the person to be served by email. A person may retract consent to be served by email by filing and serving a written retraction. A document that is served by email must be attached as a PDF file to an email message.

(g) Certificate of service. A certificate of service must accompany all documents filed with the FAA Hearing Docket. The certificate of service must be signed, describe the method of service, and state the date of service.

(h) Date of filing and service. If a document is sent by fax or email, the date of filing and service is the date the email or fax is sent. If a document is sent by personal delivery or by expedited or overnight express courier service, the date of filing and service is the date that delivery is accomplished. If a document is mailed, the date of filing and service is the date shown on the certificate of service, the date shown on the postmark if there is no certificate of service, or the mailing date shown by other evidence if there is no certificate of service or postmark.

13.44 [Reserved]

13.45 Computation of time and extension of time

(a) In computing any period of time prescribed or allowed by this subpart, the date of the act, event, default, notice, or order is not to be included in the computation. The last day of the period so computed is to be included unless it is a Saturday, Sunday, or Federal holiday, in which event the period runs until the end of the next day that is not a Saturday, Sunday, or a Federal holiday.

(b) Whenever a party must respond within a prescribed period after service by mail, 5 days are added to the prescribed period.

(c) The parties may agree to extend the time for filing any document required by this subpart with the consent of -

(1) The Director of the Office of Adjudication prior to the designation of a hearing officer;

(2) The hearing officer prior to the filing of a notice of appeal; or

(3) The Director of the Office of Adjudication after the filing of a notice of appeal.

(d) If the parties do not agree, a party may make a written request to extend the time for filing to the appropriate official identified in paragraph (c) of this section. The appropriate official may grant the request for good cause shown.

13.47 Withdrawal or amendment of the complaint, answer, or other filings

(a) Withdrawal. At any time before the hearing, the complainant may withdraw the complaint, and the respondent may withdraw the request for hearing.

(b) Amendments. At any time more than 10 days before the date of hearing, any party may amend its complaint, answer, or other pleading, by filing the amendment with the FAA Hearing Docket and serving a copy of it on every other party. After that time, amendment requires approval of the hearing officer. If an initial pleading is amended, the hearing officer must allow the other parties a reasonable opportunity to respond.

13.49 Motions

(a) Motions in lieu of an answer. A respondent may file a motion to dismiss or a motion for a more definite statement in place of an answer. If the hearing officer denies the motion, the respondent must file an answer within 10 days.

(1) Motion to dismiss. The respondent may file a motion asserting that the allegations in the complaint fail to state a violation of Federal aviation statutes, a violation of regulations in this chapter, lack of qualification of the respondent, or other appropriate grounds.

(2) Motion for more definite statement. The respondent may file a motion that the allegations in the notice be made more definite and certain.

(b) Motion to dismiss request for hearing. The FAA may file a motion to dismiss a request for hearing based on jurisdiction, timeliness, or other appropriate grounds.

(c) Motion for decision on the pleadings or for summary decision. After the complaint and answer are filed, either party may move for a decision on the pleadings or for a summary decision, in the manner provided by Rules 12 and 56, respectively, of the Federal Rules of Civil Procedure.

(d) Motion to strike. Upon motion of either party, the hearing officer may order stricken, from any pleadings, any insufficient allegation or defense, or any redundant, immaterial, impertinent, or scandalous matter.

(e) Motion to compel. Any party may file a motion asking the hearing officer to order any other party to produce discovery requested in accordance with 13.53 if -

(1) The other party has failed to timely produce the requested discovery; and

(2) The moving party certifies it has in good faith conferred with the other party in an attempt to obtain the requested discovery prior to filing the motion to compel.

(f) Motion for protective order. The hearing officer may order information contained in anything filed, or in any testimony given pursuant to this subpart withheld from public disclosure when, in the judgment of the hearing officer, disclosure would be detrimental to aviation safety; disclosure would not be in the public interest; or the information is not otherwise required to be made available to the public. Any person may make written objection to the public disclosure of any information, stating the ground for such objection.

(g) Other motions. Any application for an order or ruling not otherwise provided for in this subpart must be made by motion.

(h) Responses to motions. Any party may file a response to any motion under this subpart within 10 days after service of the motion.

13.51 Intervention

Any person may move for leave to intervene in a proceeding and may become a party thereto, if the hearing officer, after the case is sent to the hearing officer for hearing, finds that the person may be bound by the order to be issued in the proceedings or has a property or financial interest that may not be adequately represented by existing parties, and that the intervention will not unduly broaden the issues or delay the proceedings. Except for good cause shown, a motion for leave to intervene may not be considered if it is filed less than 10 days before the hearing.

13.53 Discovery

(a) Filing. Discovery requests and responses are not filed with the FAA Hearing Docket unless in support of a motion, offered for impeachment, or other permissible circumstances as approved by the hearing officer.

(b) Scope of discovery. Any party may discover any matter that is not privileged and is relevant to any party's claim or defense.

(c) Time for response to written discovery requests.

  (1) Written discovery includes interrogatories, requests for admission or stipulations, and requests for production of documents.

  (2) Unless otherwise directed by the hearing officer, a party must serve its response to a discovery request no later than 30 days after service of the discovery request.

(d) Depositions. After the respondent has filed a request for hearing and an answer, either party may take testimony by deposition.

(e) Limits on discovery. The hearing officer may limit the frequency and extent of discovery upon a showing by a party that -

  (1) The discovery requested is cumulative or repetitious;

  (2) The discovery requested can be obtained from another less burdensome and more convenient source;

  (3) The party requesting the information has had ample opportunity to obtain the information through other discovery methods permitted under this section; or

  (4) The method or scope of discovery requested by the party is unduly burdensome or expensive.

13.55 Notice of hearing

The hearing officer must set a reasonable date, time, and location for the hearing, and must give the parties adequate notice thereof, and of the nature of the hearing. Due regard must be given to the convenience of the parties with respect to the location of the hearing.

13.57 Subpoenas and witness fees

(a) Application. The hearing officer, upon application by any party to the proceeding, may issue subpoenas requiring the attendance of witnesses or the production of documents or tangible things at a hearing or for the purpose of taking depositions, as permitted by law. The application for producing evidence must show its general relevance and reasonable scope. Absent good cause shown, a party must file a request for a subpoena at least:

  (1) 15 days before a scheduled deposition under the subpoena; or

  (2) 30 days before a scheduled hearing where attendance at the hearing is sought.

(b) Procedure. A party seeking the production of a document in the custody of an FAA employee must use the discovery procedure

found in 13.53, and if necessary, a motion to compel under 13.49. A party that applies for the attendance of an FAA employee at a hearing must send the application, in writing, to the hearing officer. The application must set forth the need for that employee's attendance.

(c) Fees. Except for an employee of the agency who appears at the direction of the agency, a witness who appears at a deposition or hearing is entitled to the same fees and allowances as provided for under 28 U.S.C. 1821. The party who applies for a subpoena to compel the attendance of a witness at a deposition or hearing, or the party at whose request a witness appears at a deposition or hearing, must pay the witness fees and allowances described in this section.

(d) Service of subpoenas. Any person who is at least 18 years old and not a party may serve a subpoena. Serving a subpoena requires delivering a copy to the named person. Except for the complainant, the party that requested the subpoena must tender at the time of service the fees for 1 day's attendance and the allowances allowed by law if the subpoena requires that person's attendance. Proving service, if necessary, requires the filing with the FAA Hearing Docket of a statement showing the date and manner of service and the names of the persons served. The server must certify the statement.

(e) Motion to quash or modify the subpoena. A party, or any person served with a subpoena, may file a motion to quash or modify the subpoena with the hearing officer at or before the time specified in the subpoena for compliance. The movant must describe, in detail, the basis for the application to quash or modify the subpoena including, but not limited to, a statement that the testimony, document, or tangible thing is not relevant to the proceeding, that the subpoena is not reasonably tailored to the scope of the proceeding, or that the subpoena is unreasonable and oppressive. A motion to quash or modify the subpoena will stay the effect of the subpoena pending a decision by the hearing officer on the motion.

(f) Enforcement of subpoena. If a person disobeys a subpoena, a party may apply to a U.S. district court to seek judicial enforcement of the subpoena.

13.59 Evidence

(a) Each party to a hearing may present the party's case or defense by oral or documentary evidence, submit evidence in rebuttal, and conduct such cross-examination as may be needed for a full disclosure of the facts.

(b) Except with respect to affirmative defenses and notices of proposed denial, the burden of proof is upon the complainant.

13.61 Argument and submittals

The hearing officer must give the parties adequate opportunity to present arguments in support of motions, objections, and the final order. The hearing officer may determine whether arguments are to be oral or written. At the end of the hearing, the hearing officer may allow each party to submit written proposed findings and conclusions and supporting reasons for them.

13.63 Record, decision, and aircraft registration proceedings

(a) The record.

(1) The testimony and exhibits admitted at a hearing, together with all papers, requests, and rulings filed in the proceedings, are the exclusive basis for the issuance of the hearing officer's decision.

(2) On appeal to the Administrator, the record shall include all of the information identified in paragraph (a)(1) of this section and evidence proffered but not admitted at the hearing.

(3) Any party may obtain a transcript of the hearing from the official reporter upon payment of the required fees.

(b) Hearing officer's decision. The decision by the hearing officer must include findings of fact based on the record, conclusions of law, and an appropriate order.

(c) Certain aircraft registration proceedings. If the hearing officer determines that an aircraft is ineligible for a certificate of aircraft registration in proceedings relating to aircraft registration orders suspending or revoking a certificate of registration under 13.20, the hearing officer may suspend or revoke the aircraft registration certificate.

13.65 Appeal to the Administrator, reconsideration, and judicial review

(a) Any party to a hearing may appeal from the order of the hearing officer by filing with the FAA Hearing Docket a notice of appeal to the Administrator within 20 days after the date of issuance of the order. Filing and service of the notice of appeal, and any other papers, are accomplished according to the procedures in 13.43.

(b) If a notice of appeal is not filed from the order issued by a hearing officer, such order is final with respect to the parties. Such order is not binding precedent and is not subject to judicial review.

(c) Any person filing an appeal authorized by paragraph (a) of this section must file an appeal brief with the Administrator within 40 days after the date of issuance of the order, and serve a copy on the other party. A reply brief must be filed within 40 days after service of the appeal brief and a copy served on the appellant.

(d) On appeal, the Administrator reviews the record of the proceeding and issues an order dismissing, reversing, modifying or affirming the order. The Administrator's order includes the reasons for the Administrator's action. The Administrator considers only whether:

  (1) Each finding of fact is supported by a preponderance of the reliable, probative, and substantial evidence;

  (2) Each conclusion is made in accordance with law, precedent, and policy; and

  (3) The hearing officer committed any prejudicial error.

(e) The Director and legal personnel of the Office of Adjudication serve as the advisors to the Administrator for appeals under this section.

  (1) The Director has the authority to:

    (i) Manage all or portions of individual appeals; and to prepare written decisions and proposed final orders in such appeals;

    (ii) Issue procedural and other interlocutory orders aimed at proper and efficient appeal management, including, without limitation, scheduling and sanctions orders;

    (iii) Grant or deny motions to dismiss appeals;

    (iv) Dismiss appeals upon request of the appellant or by agreement of the parties;

    (v) Stay decisions and orders of the Administrator, pending judicial review or reconsideration by the Administrator;

    (vi) Summarily dismiss repetitious or frivolous petitions to reconsider or modify orders;

    (vii) Correct typographical, grammatical, and similar errors in the Administrator's decisions and orders, and to make non-substantive editorial changes; and

    (viii) Take all other reasonable steps deemed necessary and proper for the management of the appeals process, in accordance with this part and applicable law.

  (2) The Director's authority in paragraph (e)(1) of this section may be re-delegated, as necessary, except to hearing officers and others materially involved in the hearing that is the subject of the appeal.

(f) Motions to reconsider the final order of the Administrator must be filed with the FAA Hearing Docket within thirty days of service of the Administrator's order.

(g) Judicial review of the Administrator's final order under this section is provided in accordance with 49 U.S.C. 5127 or 46110, as applicable.

13.67 Procedures for expedited proceedings

(a) When an expedited administrative hearing is requested in accordance with 13.20(d), the procedures in this subpart will apply except as provided in paragraphs (a)(1) through (7) of this section.

  (1) Service and filing of pleadings, motions, and documents must be by overnight delivery, and fax or email. Responses to motions must be filed within 7 days after service of the motion.

  (2) Within 3 days after receipt of the request for hearing, the agency must file a copy of the notice of proposed action, which serves as the complaint, to the FAA Hearing Docket.

  (3) Within 3 days after receipt of the complaint, the person that requested the hearing must file an answer to the complaint. All allegations in the complaint not specifically denied in the answer are deemed admitted. Failure to file a timely answer, absent a showing of good cause, constitutes withdrawal of the request for hearing.

  (4) Within 3 days of the filing of the complaint, the Director of the Office of Adjudication will assign a hearing officer to preside over the matter.

  (5) The parties must serve discovery as soon as possible and set time limits for compliance with discovery requests that accommodate the accelerated adjudication schedule set forth in this subpart. The hearing officer will resolve any failure of the parties to agree to a discovery schedule.

  (6) The expedited hearing must commence within 40 days after the notice of proposed action was issued.

  (7) The hearing officer must issue an oral decision and order dismissing, reversing, modifying, or affirming the notice of proposed action at the close of the hearing. If a notice of appeal is not filed, such order is final with respect to the parties and is not subject to judicial review.

(b) Any party to the expedited hearing may appeal from the initial decision of the hearing officer to the Administrator by filing a notice of appeal within 3 days after the date on which the decision was issued. The time limitations for the filing of documents for appeals under this section will not be extended by reason of the unavailability of the hearing transcript.

  (1) Any appeal to the Administrator under this section must be perfected within 7 days after the date the notice of appeal was filed by filing a brief in support of the appeal. Any reply to the appeal brief must be filed within 7 days after the date the appeal brief was served on that party. The Administrator must issue an order deciding the appeal no later than 80 days after the date the notice of proposed action was issued.

  (2) The Administrator's order is immediately effective and constitutes the final agency decision. The Administrator's order may be appealed pursuant to 49 U.S.C. 46110. The filing of an appeal under 49 U.S.C. 46110 does not stay the effectiveness of the Administrator's order.

(c) At any time after an immediately effective order is issued, the FAA may request the United States Attorney General, or the delegate of the Attorney General, to bring an action for appropriate relief.

13.69 Other matters: Alternative dispute resolution, standing orders, and forms

(a) Parties may use mediation to achieve resolution of issues in controversy addressed by this subpart. Parties seeking alternative dispute resolution services may engage the services of a mutually acceptable mediator. The mediator must not participate in the adjudication under this subpart of any matter in which the mediator has provided mediation services. Mediation discussions and submissions will remain confidential consistent with the provisions of the Administrative Dispute Resolution Act, the principles of Federal Rule of Evidence 408, and other applicable Federal laws.

FAR 13

(b) The Director of the Office of Adjudication may issue standing orders and forms needed for the proper dispatch of business under this subpart.

Subpart E — Orders of Compliance Under the Hazardous

Source: Docket No. FAA-2018-1051; Amdt. No. 13-40, 86 FR 54536, Oct. 1, 2021, unless otherwise noted.

13.71 Applicability

(a) An order of compliance may be issued after notice and an opportunity for a hearing in accordance with 13.73 through 13.77 whenever the Chief Counsel, a Deputy Chief Counsel, or the Assistant Chief Counsel for Enforcement has reason to believe that a person is engaging in the transportation or shipment by air of hazardous materials in violation of the Hazardous Materials Transportation Act, as amended and codified at 49 U.S.C. chapter 51, or any rule, regulation, or order issued under 49 U.S.C. chapter 51, for which the FAA exercises enforcement responsibility, and the circumstances do not require the issuance of an emergency order under 49 U.S.C. 5121(d).

(b) If circumstances require the issuance of an emergency order under 49 U.S.C. 5121(d), the Chief Counsel, a Deputy Chief Counsel, or the Assistant Chief Counsel for Enforcement will issue an emergency order of compliance as described in 13.81.

13.73 Notice of proposed order of compliance

The Chief Counsel, a Deputy Chief Counsel, or the Assistant Chief Counsel for Enforcement may issue to an alleged violator a notice of proposed order of compliance advising the alleged violator of the charges and setting forth the remedial action sought in the form of a proposed order of compliance.

13.75 Reply or request for hearing

(a) Within 30 days after service upon the alleged violator of a notice of proposed order of compliance, the alleged violator may -

  (1) Submit a written reply;

  (2) Submit a written request for an informal conference to discuss the matter with an agency attorney; or

  (3) Request a hearing in accordance with subpart D of this part.

(b) If, after an informal conference is held or a reply is filed, the agency attorney notifies the person named in the notice that some or all of the proposed agency action will not be withdrawn or will not be subject to a consent order of compliance, the alleged violator may, within 10 days after receiving the agency attorney's notification, request a hearing in accordance with subpart D of this part.

(c) Failure of the alleged violator to file a reply or request a hearing within the period provided in paragraph (a) or (b) of this section, as applicable -

  (1) Constitutes a waiver of the right to a hearing under subpart D of this part and the right to petition for judicial review; and

  (2) Authorizes the Administrator to make any appropriate findings of fact and to issue an appropriate order of compliance, without further notice or proceedings.

13.77 Consent order of compliance

(a) At any time before the issuance of an order of compliance, an agency attorney and the alleged violator may agree to dispose of the case by the issuance of a consent order of compliance.

(b) The alleged violator may submit a proposed consent order to an agency attorney. The proposed consent order must include -

  (1) An admission of all jurisdictional facts;

  (2) An express waiver of the right to further procedural steps and of all rights to legal review in any forum;

  (3) An express waiver of attorney's fees and costs;

  (4) If a notice has been issued prior to the proposed consent order of compliance, an incorporation by reference of the notice and an acknowledgement that the notice may be used to construe the terms of the consent order of compliance; and

  (5) If a request for hearing is pending in any forum, a provision that the alleged violator will withdraw the request for a hearing and request that the case be dismissed.

13.79 [Reserved]

13.81 Emergency orders

(a) Notwithstanding 13.73 through 13.77, the Chief Counsel, each Deputy Chief Counsel, or the Assistant Chief Counsel for Enforcement may issue an emergency order of compliance, which is effective upon issuance, in accordance with the procedures in subpart C of 49 CFR part 109, if the person who issues the order finds that there is an "imminent hazard" as defined in 49 CFR 109.1.

(b) The FAA official who issued the emergency order of compliance may rescind or suspend the order if the criteria set forth in paragraph (a) of this section are no longer satisfied, and, when appropriate, may issue a notice of proposed order of compliance under 13.73.

(c) If at any time in the course of a proceeding commenced in accordance with 13.73 the criteria set forth in paragraph (a) of this section are satisfied, the official who issued the notice may issue an emergency order of compliance, even if the period for filing a reply or requesting a hearing specified in 13.75 has not expired.

13.83-13.87 [Reserved]

Subpart F — Formal Fact-Finding Investigation Under an Order of Investigation

Source: Docket No. FAA-2018-1051; Amdt. No. 13-40, 86 FR 54536, Oct. 1, 2021, unless otherwise noted.

13.101 Applicability

(a) This subpart applies to fact-finding investigations in which an investigation has been ordered under 13.3(c) or 13.5(f)(2).

(b) This subpart does not limit the authority of any person to issue subpoenas, administer oaths, examine witnesses, and receive evidence in any informal investigation as otherwise provided by law.

13.103 Order of investigation

The order of investigation -

(a) Defines the scope of the investigation by describing the information sought in terms of its subject matter or its relevancy to specified FAA functions;

(b) Sets forth the form of the investigation which may be either by individual deposition or investigative proceeding or both; and

(c) Names the official who is authorized to conduct the investigation and serve as the presiding officer.

13.105 Notification

Any person under investigation and any person required to testify and produce documentary or physical evidence during the investigation will be advised of the purpose of the investigation, and of the place where the investigative proceeding or deposition will be convened. This may be accomplished by a notice of investigation or by a subpoena. A copy of the order of investigation may be sent to such persons when appropriate.

13.107 Designation of additional parties

(a) The presiding officer may designate additional persons as parties to the investigation, if in the discretion of the presiding officer, it will aid in the conduct of the investigation.

(b) The presiding officer may designate any person as a party to the investigation if -

(1) The person petitions the presiding officer to participate as a party;

(2) The disposition of the investigation may as a practical matter impair the ability to protect the person's interest unless allowed to participate as a party; and

(3) The person's interest is not adequately represented by existing parties.

13.109 Convening the investigation

The presiding officer will conduct the investigation at a location convenient to the parties involved and as expeditious and efficient as handling of the investigation permits.

13.111 Subpoenas

(a) At the discretion of the presiding officer, or at the request of a party to the investigation, the presiding officer may issue a subpoena directing any person to appear at a designated time and place to testify or to produce documentary or physical evidence relating to any matter under investigation.

(b) Subpoenas must be served by personal service on the person or an agent designated in writing for the purpose, or by registered or certified mail addressed to the person or agent. Whenever service is made by registered or certified mail, the date of mailing will be considered the time when service is made.

(c) Subpoenas extend in jurisdiction throughout the United States and any territory or possession thereof.

13.113 Noncompliance with the investigative process

(a) If a person disobeys a subpoena, the Administrator or a party to the investigation may petition a court of the United States to enforce the subpoena in accordance with applicable statutes.

(b) If a party to the investigation fails to comply with the provisions of this subpart or an order issued by the presiding officer, the Administrator may bring a civil action to enforce the requirements of this subpart or any order issued under this subpart in a court of the United States in accordance with applicable statutes.

13.115 Public proceedings

(a) All investigative proceedings and depositions must be public unless the presiding officer determines that the public interest requires otherwise.

(b) The presiding officer may order information contained in any report or document filed or in any testimony given pursuant to this subpart withheld from public disclosure when, in the judgment of the presiding officer, disclosure would adversely affect the interests of any person and is not required in the public interest or is not otherwise required by statute to be made available to the public. Any person may make written objection to the public disclosure of information, stating the grounds for such objection.

13.117 Conduct of investigative proceeding or deposition

(a) The presiding officer may question witnesses.

(b) Any witness may be accompanied by counsel.

(c) Any party may be accompanied by counsel and either the party or counsel may -

(1) Question witnesses, provided the questions are relevant and material to the matters under investigation and would not unduly impede the progress of the investigation; and

(2) Make objections on the record and argue the basis for such objections.

(d) Copies of all notices or written communications sent to a party or witness must, upon request, be sent to that person's attorney of record.

13.119 Immunity and orders requiring testimony or other information

(a) Whenever a person refuses, on the basis of a privilege against self-incrimination, to testify or provide other information during the course of any investigation conducted under this subpart, the presiding officer may, with the approval of the United States Attorney General, or the delegate of the Attorney General, issue an order requiring the person to give testimony or provide other information. However, no testimony or other information so compelled (or any information directly or indirectly derived from such testimony or other information) may be used against the person in any criminal case, except in a prosecution for perjury, giving a false statement, or otherwise failing to comply with the order.

(b) The presiding officer may issue an order under this section if -

(1) The testimony or other information from the witness may be necessary to the public interest; and

(2) The witness has refused or is likely to refuse to testify or provide other information on the basis of a privilege against self-incrimination.

(c) Immunity provided by this section will not become effective until the person has refused to testify or provide other information on the basis of a privilege against self-incrimination, and an order under this section has been issued. An order, however, may be issued prospectively to become effective in the event of a claim of the privilege.

13.121 Witness fees

All witnesses appearing, other than employees of the Federal Aviation Administration, are entitled to the same fees and allowances as provided for under 28 U.S.C. 1821.

13.123 Submission by party to the investigation

(a) During an investigation conducted under this subpart, a party may submit to the presiding officer -

(1) A list of witnesses to be called, specifying the subject matter of the expected testimony of each witness; and

(2) A list of exhibits to be considered for inclusion in the record.

(b) If the presiding officer determines that the testimony of a witness or the receipt of an exhibit in accordance with paragraph (a) of this section will be relevant, competent, and material to the investigation, the presiding officer may subpoena the witness or use the exhibit during the investigation.

13.125 Depositions

Depositions for investigative purposes may be taken at the discretion of the presiding officer with reasonable notice to the party under investigation. Depositions must be taken before the presiding officer or other person authorized to administer oaths and designated by the presiding officer. The testimony must be reduced to writing by the person taking the deposition, or under the direction of that person, and where possible must then be subscribed by the deponent. Any person may be compelled to appear and testify and to produce physical and documentary evidence.

13.127 Reports, decisions, and orders

The presiding officer must issue a written report based on the record developed during the formal investigation, including a summary of principal conclusions. A summary of principal conclusions must be prepared by the official who issued the order of investigation in every case that results in no action, or no action as to a particular party to the investigation. All such reports must be furnished to the parties to the investigation and made available to the public on request.

13.129 Post-investigation action

A decision on whether to initiate subsequent action must be made on the basis of the record developed during the formal investigation and any other information in the possession of the Administrator.

13.131 Other procedures

Any question concerning the scope or conduct of a formal investigation not covered in this subpart may be ruled on by the presiding officer on his or her own initiative, or on the motion of a party or a person testifying or producing evidence.

FAR 13

Subpart G — Rules of Practice In FAA Civil Penalty Actions

Source: Docket No. FAA-2018-1051; Amdt. No. 13-40, 86 FR 54538, Oct. 1, 2021, unless otherwise noted.

13.201   Applicability

This subpart applies to all civil penalty actions initiated under 13.16 in which a hearing has been requested.

13.202   Definitions

For this subpart only, the following definitions apply:

Administrative law judge means an administrative law judge appointed pursuant to the provisions of 5 U.S.C. 3105.

Agency attorney means the Deputy Chief Counsel or the Assistant Chief Counsel responsible for the prosecution of enforcement-related matters under this subpart, or attorneys who are supervised by those officials or are assigned to prosecute a particular enforcement-related matter under this subpart. Agency attorney does not include the Chief Counsel or anyone from the Office of Adjudication.

Complaint means a document issued by an agency attorney alleging a violation of a provision of the Federal aviation statute listed in the first sentence of 49 U.S.C. 46301(d)(2) or in 49 U.S.C. 47531, or of the Federal hazardous materials transportation statute, 49 U.S.C. 5121-5128, or a rule, regulation, or order issued under those statutes, that has been filed with the FAA Hearing Docket after a hearing has been requested under 13.16(f)(3) or (g)(2)(ii).

Complainant means the FAA office that issued the notice of proposed civil penalty under 13.16.

FAA decisionmaker means the Administrator of the Federal Aviation Administration, acting in the capacity of the decisionmaker on appeal, or any person to whom the Administrator has delegated the Administrator's decisionmaking authority in a civil penalty action. As used in this subpart, the FAA decisionmaker is the official authorized to issue a final decision and order of the Administrator in a civil penalty action.

Mail includes U.S. mail, U.S. certified mail, U.S. registered mail, or use of an expedited or overnight express courier service, but does not include email.

Office of Adjudication means the Federal Aviation Administration Office of Adjudication, including the FAA Hearing Docket, the Director of the Office of Adjudication and legal personnel, or any subsequently designated office (including its head and any legal personnel) that advises the FAA decisionmaker regarding appeals of initial decisions and orders to the FAA decisionmaker.

Order assessing civil penalty means a document that contains a finding of a violation of a provision of the Federal aviation statute listed in the first sentence of 49 U.S.C. 46301(d)(2) or in 49 U.S.C. 47531, or of the Federal hazardous materials transportation statute, 49 U.S.C. 5121-5128, or of a rule, regulation, or order issued under those statutes, and may direct payment of a civil penalty. Unless an appeal is filed with the FAA decisionmaker in a timely manner, an initial decision or order of an administrative law judge is considered an order assessing civil penalty if an administrative law judge finds that an alleged violation occurred and determines that a civil penalty, in an amount found appropriate by the administrative law judge, is warranted. Unless a petition for review is filed with a U.S. Court of Appeals in a timely manner, a final decision and order of the Administrator is considered an order assessing civil penalty if the FAA decisionmaker finds that an alleged violation occurred and a civil penalty is warranted.

Party means the Respondent, the complainant and any intervenor.

Personal delivery includes hand-delivery or use of a contract or express messenger service. "Personal delivery" does not include the use of Federal Government interoffice mail service.

Pleading means a complaint, an answer, and any amendment of these documents permitted under this subpart.

Properly addressed means a document that shows an address contained in agency records; a residential, business, or other address submitted by a person on any document provided under this subpart; or any other address shown by other reasonable and available means.

Respondent means a person named in a complaint.

Writing or written includes paper or electronic documents that are filed or served by email, mail, personal delivery, or fax.

13.203   Separation of functions

(a) Civil penalty proceedings, including hearings, are prosecuted by an agency attorney.

(b) An agency employee who has engaged in the performance of investigative or prosecutorial functions in a civil penalty action must not participate in deciding or advising the administrative law judge or the FAA decisionmaker in that case, or a factually-related case, but may participate as counsel for the complainant or as a witness in the public proceedings.

(c) The Chief Counsel and the Director and legal personnel of the Office of Adjudication will advise the FAA decisionmaker regarding any appeal of an initial decision or order in a civil penalty action to the FAA decisionmaker.

13.204   Appearances and rights of parties

(a) Any party may appear and be heard in person.

(b) Any party may be accompanied, represented, or advised by an attorney or representative designated by the party, and may be examined by that attorney or representative in any proceeding governed by this subpart. An attorney or representative who represents a party must file a notice of appearance in the action, in the manner provided in 13.210, and must serve a copy of the notice of appearance on each party, and on the administrative law judge, if assigned, in the manner provided in 13.211, before participating in any proceeding governed by this subpart. The attorney or representative must include the name, address, and telephone number, and, if available, fax number and email address, of the attorney or representative in the notice of appearance.

(c) Any person may request a copy of a document in the record upon payment of reasonable costs. A person may keep an original document, data, or evidence, with the consent of the administrative law judge, by substituting a legible copy of the document for the record.

13.205   Administrative law judges

(a) Powers of an administrative law judge. In accordance with the rules of this subpart, an administrative law judge may:

(1) Give notice of, and hold, prehearing conferences and hearings;

(2) Administer oaths and affirmations;

(3) Issue subpoenas as authorized by law;

(4) Rule on offers of proof;

(5) Receive relevant and material evidence;

(6) Regulate the course of the hearing in accordance with the rules of this subpart;

(7) Hold conferences to settle or to simplify the issues by consent of the parties;

(8) Dispose of procedural motions and requests;

(9) Make findings of fact and conclusions of law, and issue an initial decision;

(10) Bar a person from a specific proceeding based on a finding of obstreperous or disruptive behavior in that specific proceeding; and

(11) Take any other action authorized by this subpart.

(b) Limitations. The administrative law judge must not issue an order of contempt, award costs to any party, or impose any sanction not specified in this subpart. If the administrative law judge imposes any sanction not specified in this subpart, a party may file an interlocutory appeal of right under 13.219(c).

(c) Disqualification. The administrative law judge may disqualify himself or herself at any time. A party may file a motion for disqualification under 13.218.

13.206 Intervention

(a) A person may submit a motion for leave to intervene as a party in a civil penalty action. Except for good cause shown, a motion for leave to intervene must be submitted not later than 10 days before the hearing.

(b) The administrative law judge may grant a motion for leave to intervene if the administrative law judge finds that intervention will not unduly broaden the issues or delay the proceedings and -

   (1) The person seeking to intervene will be bound by any order or decision entered in the action; or

   (2) The person seeking to intervene has a property, financial, or other legitimate interest that may not be addressed adequately by the parties.

(c) The administrative law judge may determine the extent to which an intervenor may participate in the proceedings.

13.207 Certification of documents

(a) Signature required. The attorney of record, the party, or the party's representative must sign, by hand, electronically, or by other method acceptable to the administrative law judge, or, if the matter is on appeal, to the FAA decision maker, each document tendered for filing with the FAA Hearing Docket or served on the administrative law judge and on each other party.

(b) Effect of signing a document. By signing a document, the attorney of record, the party, or the party's representative certifies that the attorney, the party, or the party's representative has read the document and, based on reasonable inquiry and to the best of that person's knowledge, information, and belief, the document is -

   (1) Consistent with the rules in this subpart;

   (2) Warranted by existing law or a good faith argument for extension, modification, or reversal of existing law; and

   (3) Not unreasonable or unduly burdensome or expensive, not made to harass any person, not made to cause unnecessary delay, and not made to cause needless increase in the cost of the proceedings or for any other improper purpose.

(c) Sanctions. If the attorney of record, the party, or the party's representative signs a document in violation of this section, the administrative law judge or the FAA decisionmaker must:

   (1) Strike the pleading signed in violation of this section;

   (2) Strike the request for discovery or the discovery response signed in violation of this section and preclude further discovery by the party;

   (3) Deny the motion or request signed in violation of this section;

   (4) Exclude the document signed in violation of this section from the record;

   (5) Dismiss the interlocutory appeal and preclude further appeal on that issue by the party who filed the appeal until an initial decision has been entered on the record; or

   (6) Dismiss the appeal of the administrative law judge's initial decision to the FAA decision maker.

13.208 Complaint

(a) Filing. The agency attorney must file the complaint with the FAA Hearing Docket, or may file a written motion to dismiss a request for hearing under 13.218 instead of filing a complaint, not later than 20 days after receipt by the agency attorney of a request for hearing. When filing the complaint, the agency attorney must follow the filing instructions in 13.210. The agency attorney may suggest a location for the hearing when filing the complaint.

(b) Service. An agency attorney must serve a copy of the complaint on the respondent, the president of the corporation or company named as a respondent, or a person designated by the respondent to accept service of documents in the civil penalty action. When serving the complaint, the agency attorney must follow the service instructions in 13.211.

(c) Contents. A complaint must set forth the facts alleged, any regulation allegedly violated by the respondent, and the proposed civil penalty in sufficient detail to provide notice of any factual or legal allegation and proposed civil penalty.

(d) Motion to dismiss stale allegations or complaint. Instead of filing an answer to the complaint, a respondent may move to dismiss the complaint, or that part of the complaint, alleging a violation that occurred more than 2 years before an agency attorney issued a notice of proposed civil penalty to the respondent.

   (1) An administrative law judge may not grant the motion and dismiss the complaint or part of the complaint if the administrative law judge finds that the agency has shown good cause for any delay in issuing the notice of proposed civil penalty.

   (2) If the agency fails to show good cause for any delay, an administrative law judge may dismiss the complaint, or that part of the complaint, alleging a violation that occurred more than 2 years before an agency attorney issued the notice of proposed civil penalty to the respondent.

   (3) A party may appeal the administrative law judge's ruling on the motion to dismiss the complaint or any part of the complaint in accordance with 13.219(b).

13.209 Answer

(a) Writing required. A respondent must file in the FAA Hearing Docket a written answer to the complaint, or may file a written motion pursuant to 13.208 or 13.218 instead of filing an answer, not later than 30 days after service of the complaint. The answer must be dated and signed by the person responding to the complaint. An answer must be typewritten or legibly handwritten.

(b) Filing. A person filing an answer or motion under paragraph (a) of this section must follow the filing instructions in 13.210.

(c) Service. A person filing an answer or a motion under paragraph (a) of this section must serve a copy of the answer or motion in accordance with the service instructions in 13.211.

(d) Contents. An answer must specifically state any affirmative defense that the respondent intends to assert at the hearing. A person filing an answer may include a brief statement of any relief requested in the answer. The person filing an answer may recommend a location for the hearing when filing the answer.

(e) Specific denial of allegations required. A person filing an answer must admit, deny, or state that the person is without sufficient knowledge or information to admit or deny, each allegation in the complaint. All allegations in the complaint not specifically denied in the answer are deemed admitted. A general denial of the complaint is deemed a failure to file an answer.

(f) Failure to file answer. A person's failure to file an answer without good cause will be deemed an admission of the truth of each allegation contained in the complaint.

13.210 Filing of documents

(a) General rule. Unless provided otherwise in this subpart, all documents in proceedings under this subpart must be tendered for filing with the FAA Hearing Docket.

(b) Methods of filing. Filing must be by email, personal delivery, mail, or fax.

(c) Address for filing. A person filing a document with the FAA Hearing Docket must use the address identified for the method of filing as follows:

   (1) If delivery is in person, or by expedited or overnight express courier service. Federal Aviation Administration, 600 Independence Avenue SW, Wilbur Wright Building - Suite 2W100, Washington, DC 20597; Attention: FAA Hearing Docket, AGC-70.

FAR 13

(2) If delivery is via U.S. mail, or U.S. certified or registered mail. Federal Aviation Administration, 800 Independence Avenue SW, Washington, DC 20591; Attention: FAA Hearing Docket, AGC-70, Wilbur Wright Building - Suite 2W100.

(3) If delivery is via email or fax. The email address and fax number for the FAA Hearing Docket, made available on the FAA Office of Adjudication website.

(d) Date of filing. If a document is filed by fax or email, the date of filing is the date the email or fax is sent. If a document is filed by personal delivery, the date of filing is the date that personal delivery is accomplished. If a document is filed by mail, the date of filing is the date shown on the certificate of service, the date shown on the postmark if there is no certificate of service, or the mailing date shown by other evidence if there is no certificate of service or postmark.

(e) Form. Each document must be typewritten or legibly handwritten.

(f) Contents. Unless otherwise specified in this subpart, each document must contain a short, plain statement of the facts on which the person's case rests and a brief statement of the action requested.

(g) Requirement to file an original document and number of copies. A party must file an original document and one copy when filing by personal delivery or by mail. Only one copy must be filed if filing is accomplished by email or fax.

(h) Filing by email. A document that is filed by email must be attached as a PDF file to an email. The document must be signed in accordance with 13.207. The email message does not constitute a submission, but serves only to deliver the attached PDF file to the FAA Hearing Docket.

13.211   Service of documents

(a) General. A person must serve a copy of all documents on each party and the administrative law judge, if assigned, at the time of filing with the FAA Hearing Docket except as provided otherwise in this subpart.

(b) Service by the FAA Hearing Docket, the administrative law judge, and the FAA decisionmaker. The FAA Hearing Docket, the administrative law judge, and the FAA decisionmaker must send documents to a party by personal delivery, mail, fax, or email as provided in this section.

(c) Methods of service -

(1) General. A person may serve any document by email, personal delivery, mail, or fax.

(2) Service by email. Service of documents by email is voluntary and requires the prior consent of the person to be served by email. A person may retract consent to be served by email by filing a written retraction with the FAA Hearing Docket and serving it on the other party and the administrative law judge. A document that is served by email must be attached as a PDF file to an email message.

(d) Certificate of service. A certificate of service must accompany all documents filed with the FAA Hearing Docket. The certificate of service must be signed, describe the method of service, and state the date of service.

(e) Date of service. If a document is served by fax or served by email, the date of service is the date the email or fax is sent. If a document is served by personal delivery, the date of service is the date that personal delivery is accomplished. If a document is mailed, the date of service is the date shown on the certificate of service, the date shown on the postmark if there is no certificate of service, or the mailing date shown by other evidence if there is no certificate of service or postmark.

(f) Valid service. A document served by mail or personal delivery that was properly addressed, was sent in accordance with this subpart, and that was returned as unclaimed, or that was refused or not accepted, is deemed to have been served in accordance with this subpart.

(g) Additional time after service by mail. Whenever a party must respond within a prescribed period after service by mail, 5 days are added to the prescribed period.

(h) Presumption of service. There is a presumption of service where a party or a person, who customarily receives mail, or receives it in the ordinary course of business, at either the person's residence or the person's principal place of business, acknowledges receipt of the document.

13.212   Computation of time

(a) This section applies to any period of time prescribed or allowed by this subpart, by notice or order of the administrative law judge, or by any applicable statute.

(b) The date of an act, event, or default is not included in a computation of time under this subpart.

(c) The last day of a time period is included unless it is a Saturday, Sunday, or a Federal holiday. If the last day is a Saturday, Sunday, or Federal holiday, the time period runs until the end of the next day that is not a Saturday, Sunday, or Federal holiday.

13.213   Extension of time

(a) The parties may agree to extend for a reasonable period the time for filing a document under this subpart. The party seeking the extension of time must submit a draft order to the administrative law judge to be signed by the administrative law judge and filed with the FAA Hearing Docket. The administrative law judge must sign and issue the order if the extension agreed to by the parties is reasonable.

(b) A party may file a written motion for an extension of time. A written motion for an extension of time must be filed with the FAA Hearing Docket in accordance with 13.210. The motion must be filed no later than seven days before the document is due unless good cause for the late filing is shown. The party filing the motion must serve a copy of the motion in accordance with 13.211. The administrative law judge may grant the extension of time if good cause for the extension is shown.

(c) If the administrative law judge fails to rule on a motion for an extension of time by the date the document was due, the motion for an extension of time is deemed granted for no more than 20 days after the original date the document was to be filed.

13.214   Amendment of pleadings

(a) Filing and service. A party must file the amendment with the FAA Hearing Docket and must serve a copy of the amendment on the administrative law judge, if assigned, and on all parties to the proceeding.

(b) Time.

(1) Not later than 15 days before the scheduled date of a hearing, a party may amend a complaint or an answer without the consent of the administrative law judge.

(2) Less than 15 days before the scheduled date of a hearing, the administrative law judge may allow amendment of a complaint or an answer only for good cause shown in a motion to amend.

(c) Responses. The administrative law judge must allow a reasonable time, but not more than 20 days from the date of filing, for other parties to respond if an amendment to a complaint, answer, or other pleading has been filed with the FAA Hearing Docket and served on the administrative law judge and other parties.

13.215   Withdrawal of complaint or request for hearing

At any time before or during a hearing, an agency attorney may withdraw a complaint or a party may withdraw a request for a hearing without the consent of the administrative law judge. If an agency attorney withdraws the complaint or a party withdraws the request for a hearing and the answer, the administrative law judge must dismiss the proceedings under this subpart with prejudice.

13.216   Waivers

Waivers of any rights provided by statute or regulation must be in writing or by stipulation made at a hearing and entered into the record. The parties must set forth the precise terms of the waiver and any conditions.

13.217   Joint procedural or discovery schedule

(a) General. The parties may agree to submit a schedule for filing all prehearing motions, conducting discovery in the proceedings, or both.

(b) Form and content of schedule. If the parties agree to a joint procedural or discovery schedule, one of the parties must file the joint schedule setting forth the dates to which the parties have agreed, in accordance with 13.210, and must also serve a copy of the joint schedule in accordance with 13.211. The filing of the joint schedule must include a draft order establishing a joint schedule to be signed by the administrative law judge.

(1) The joint schedule may include, but need not be limited to, requests for discovery, objections to discovery requests, responses to discovery requests to which there are no objections, submission of prehearing motions, responses to prehearing motions, exchange of exhibits to be introduced at the hearing, and a list of witnesses that may be called at the hearing.

(2) Each party must sign the joint schedule.

(c) Time. The parties may agree to submit all prehearing motions and responses and may agree to close discovery in the proceedings under the joint schedule within a reasonable time before the date of the hearing, but not later than 15 days before the hearing.

(d) Joint scheduling order. The joint schedule filed by the parties is a proposed schedule that requires approval of the administrative law judge to become the joint scheduling order.

(e) Disputes. The administrative law judge must resolve disputes regarding discovery or disputes regarding compliance with the joint scheduling order as soon as possible so that the parties may continue to comply with the joint scheduling order.

(f) Sanctions for failure to comply with joint schedule. If a party fails to comply with a joint scheduling order, the administrative law judge may impose any of the following sanctions, proportional to the party's failure to comply with the order:

(1) Strike the relevant portion of a party's pleadings;

(2) Preclude prehearing or discovery motions by that party;

(3) Preclude admission of the relevant portion of a party's evidence at the hearing; or

(4) Preclude the relevant portion of the testimony of that party's witnesses at the hearing.

13.218   Motions

(a) General. A party applying for an order or ruling not specifically provided in this subpart must do so by filing a motion in accordance with 13.210. A party must serve a copy of each motion in accordance with 13.211.

(b) Form and contents. A party must state the relief sought by the motion and the particular grounds supporting that relief. If a party has evidence in support of a motion, the party must attach any supporting evidence, including affidavits, to the motion.

(c) Filing of motions. A motion made prior to the hearing must be in writing. Unless otherwise agreed by the parties or for good cause shown, a party must file any prehearing motion not later than 30 days before the hearing in the FAA Hearing Docket in accordance with 13.210, and must serve a copy on the administrative law judge, if assigned, and on each party in accordance with 13.211. Motions introduced during a hearing may be made orally on the record unless the administrative law judge directs otherwise.

(d) Responses to motions. Any party may file a response, with affidavits or other evidence in support of the response, not later than 10 days after service of a written motion on that party. When a motion is made during a hearing, the response may be made at the hearing on the record, orally or in writing, within a reasonable time determined by the administrative law judge.

(e) Rulings on motions. The administrative law judge must rule on all motions as follows:

(1) Discovery motions. The administrative law judge must resolve all pending discovery motions not later than 10 days before the hearing.

(2) Prehearing motions. The administrative law judge must resolve all pending prehearing motions not later than 7 days before the hearing. If the administrative law judge issues a ruling or order orally, the administrative law judge must serve a written copy of the ruling or order, within 3 days, on each party. In all other cases, the administrative law judge must issue rulings and orders in writing and must serve a copy of the ruling or order on each party.

(3) Motions made during the hearing. The administrative law judge must issue rulings and orders on oral motions. Oral rulings or orders on motions must be made on the record.

(f) Specific motions. The motions that a party may file include but are not limited to the following:

(1) Motion to dismiss for insufficiency. A respondent may file a motion to dismiss the complaint for insufficiency instead of filing an answer. If the administrative law judge denies the motion to dismiss the complaint for insufficiency, the respondent must file an answer not later than 10 days after service of the administrative law judge's denial of the motion. A motion to dismiss the complaint for insufficiency must show that the complaint fails to state a violation of a provision of the Federal aviation statute listed in the first sentence in 49 U.S.C. 46301(d)(2) or in 49 U.S.C. 47531, or any implementing rule, regulation, or order, or a violation of the Federal hazardous materials transportation statute, 49 U.S.C. 5121-5128, or any implementing rule, regulation, or order.

(2) Motion to dismiss. A party may file a motion to dismiss, specifying the grounds for dismissal. If an administrative law judge grants a motion to dismiss in part, a party may appeal the administrative law judge's ruling on the motion to dismiss under 13.219(b).

(i) Motion to dismiss a request for a hearing. An agency attorney may file a motion to dismiss a request for a hearing instead of filing a complaint. If the motion to dismiss is not granted, the agency attorney must file the complaint in the FAA Hearing Docket and must serve a copy of the complaint on the administrative law judge and on each party not later than 10 days after service of the administrative law judge's ruling or order on the motion to dismiss. If the motion to dismiss is granted and the proceedings are terminated without a hearing, the respondent may appeal to the FAA decisionmaker under 13.233. If required by the decision on appeal, the agency attorney must file a complaint in the FAA Hearing Docket and must serve a copy of the complaint on the administrative law judge and each party not later than 10 days after service of the FAA decisionmaker's decision on appeal.

(ii) Motion to dismiss a complaint. A respondent may file a motion to dismiss a complaint instead of filing an answer, including a motion to dismiss a stale complaint or allegations as provided in 13.208. If the motion to dismiss is not granted, the respondent must file an answer in the FAA Hearing Docket and must serve a copy of the answer on the administrative law judge and on each party not later than 10 days after service of the administrative law judge's ruling or order on the motion to dismiss. If the motion to dismiss is granted and the proceedings are terminated without a hearing, the agency attorney may file an appeal in the FAA Hearing Docket under 13.233 and must serve each other party. If required by the FAA decisionmaker's decision on appeal, the respondent must file an answer in the FAA Hearing Docket, and must serve a copy of the answer on the administrative law judge and on each party not later than 10 days after service of the decision on appeal.

(3) Motion for a more definite statement. A party may file a motion for a more definite statement of any pleading which requires a response under this subpart. A party must set forth, in detail, the indefinite or uncertain allegations contained in a complaint or response to any pleading and must submit the details that the party believes would make the allegation or response definite and certain.

(i) Complaint. A respondent may file a motion requesting a more definite statement of the allegations contained in the complaint instead of filing an answer. If the administrative law judge grants the motion, the agency attorney must supply a more definite statement not later than 15 days after service of the ruling granting the motion. If the agency attorney fails to supply a more definite statement, the administrative law judge may strike the allegations in the complaint to which the motion is directed. If the administrative law judge denies the motion, the respondent must file an answer in the FAA Hearing Docket and must serve a copy of the answer on the administrative law judge and on each party not later than 10 days after service of the order of denial.

(ii) Answer. An agency attorney may file a motion requesting a more definite statement if an answer fails to respond clearly to the allegations in the complaint. If the administrative law judge grants the motion, the respondent must supply a more definite statement not later than 15 days after service of the ruling on the motion. If the respondent fails to supply a more definite statement, the administrative law judge may strike those statements in the answer to which the motion is directed. The respondent's failure to supply a more definite statement may be deemed an admission of unanswered allegations in the complaint.

(4) Motion to strike. Any party may make a motion to strike any insufficient allegation or defense, or any redundant, immaterial, impertinent, or scandalous matter in a pleading. A party must file a motion to strike before a response is required under this subpart or, if a response is not required, not later than 10 days after service of the pleading. A motion to strike must be filed in the FAA Hearing Docket and served on the administrative law judge, if assigned, and on each other party.

(5) Motion for decision. A party may make a motion for decision, regarding all or any part of the proceedings, at any time before the administrative law judge has issued an initial decision in the proceedings. The administrative law judge must grant a party's motion for decision if the pleadings, depositions, answers to interrogatories, admissions, matters that the administrative law judge has officially noticed, or evidence introduced during the hearing shows that there is no genuine issue of material fact and that the party making the motion is entitled to a decision as a matter of law. The party making the motion for decision has the burden of showing that there is no genuine issue of material fact disputed by the parties.

(6) Motion for disqualification. A party may file a motion for disqualification in the FAA Hearing Docket and must serve a copy on the administrative law judge and on each party. A party may file the motion at any time after the administrative law judge has been assigned to the proceedings but must make the motion before the administrative law judge files an initial decision in the proceedings.

(i) Motion and supporting affidavit. A party must state the grounds for disqualification in a motion for disqualification, including, but not limited to, a financial or other personal interest that would be affected by the outcome of the enforcement action, personal animus against a party to the action or against a group to which a party belongs, prejudgment of the adjudicative facts at issue in the proceeding, or any other prohibited conflict of interest. A party must submit an affidavit with the motion for disqualification that sets forth, in detail, the matters alleged to constitute grounds for disqualification.

(ii) Response. A party must respond to the motion for disqualification not later than 5 days after service of the motion for disqualification.

(iii) Decision on motion for disqualification. The administrative law judge must render a decision on the motion for disqualification not later than 15 days after the motion has been filed. If the administrative law judge finds that the motion for disqualification and supporting affidavit show a basis for disqualification, the administrative law judge must withdraw from the proceedings immediately. If the administrative law judge finds that disqualification is not warranted, the administrative law judge must deny the motion and state the grounds for the denial on the record. If the administrative law judge fails to rule on a party's motion for disqualification within 15 days after the motion has been filed, the motion is deemed granted.

(iv) Appeal. A party may appeal the administrative law judge's denial of the motion for disqualification in accordance with 13.219(b).

(7) Motions for reconsideration of an initial decision, order dismissing a complaint, order dismissing a request for hearing or order dismissing a request for hearing and answer. The FAA decisionmaker may treat motions for reconsideration of an initial decision, order dismissing a complaint, order dismissing a request for hearing, or order dismissing a request for hearing and answer as a notice of appeal under 13.233, and if the motion was filed within the time allowed for the filing of a notice of appeal, the FAA decisionmaker will issue a briefing schedule.

13.219 Interlocutory appeals

(a) General. Unless otherwise provided in this subpart, a party may not appeal a ruling or decision of the administrative law judge to the FAA decisionmaker until the initial decision has been entered on the record. A decision or order of the FAA decisionmaker on the interlocutory appeal does not constitute a final order of the Administrator for the purposes of judicial appellate review as provided in 13.235.

(b) Interlocutory appeal for cause. If a party orally requests or files a written request for an interlocutory appeal for cause, the proceedings are stayed until the administrative law judge issues a decision on the request. Any written request for interlocutory appeal for cause must be filed in the FAA Hearing Docket and served on each party and on the administrative law judge. If the administrative law judge grants the request, the proceedings are stayed until the FAA decisionmaker issues a decision on the interlocutory appeal. The administrative law judge must grant the request if a party shows that delay of the appeal would be detrimental to the public interest or would result in undue prejudice to any party.

(c) Interlocutory appeals of right. If a party notifies the administrative law judge of an interlocutory appeal of right, the proceedings are stayed until the FAA decisionmaker issues a decision on the interlocutory appeal. A party may file an interlocutory appeal of right, without the consent of the administrative law judge, before an initial decision has been entered in the case of:

(1) A ruling or order by the administrative law judge barring a person from the proceedings;

(2) Failure of the administrative law judge to dismiss the proceedings in accordance with 13.215; or

(3) A ruling or order by the administrative law judge in violation of 13.205(b).

(d) Procedure. A party must file a notice of interlocutory appeal, with supporting documents, with the FAA Hearing Docket, and must serve a copy of the notice and supporting documents on each party and the administrative law judge not later than 10 days after the administrative law judge's decision forming the basis of an interlocutory appeal of right, or not later than 10 days after the administrative law judge's decision granting an interlocutory appeal for cause, as appropriate. A party must file a reply, if any, with the FAA Hearing Docket, and serve a copy on each party and the administrative law judge not later than 10 days after service of the appeal. The FAA decisionmaker must render a decision on the interlocutory appeal on the record and as a part of the decision in the proceedings, within a reasonable time after receipt of the interlocutory appeal.

(e) Summary rejection. The FAA decisionmaker may reject frivolous, repetitive, or dilatory appeals, and may issue an order precluding one or more parties from making further interlocutory appeals in a proceeding in which there have been frivolous, repetitive, or dilatory interlocutory appeals.

13.220 Discovery

(a) Initiation of discovery. Any party may initiate discovery described in this section without the consent or approval of the administrative law judge at any time after a complaint has been filed in the proceedings.

(b) Methods of discovery. The following methods of discovery are permitted under this section: Depositions on oral examination or written questions of any person; written interrogatories directed to a party; requests for production of documents or tangible items to any person; and requests for admission by a party. A party must not file written interrogatories and responses, requests for production of documents or tangible items and responses, and requests for admission and response with the FAA Hearing Docket or serve them on the administrative law judge. In the event of a discovery dispute, a party must attach a copy of the relevant documents in support of a motion made under this section.

(c) Service on the agency. A party must serve each discovery request directed to the agency or any agency employee on the agency attorney of record.

(d) Time for response to discovery requests. Unless otherwise directed by this subpart or agreed by the parties, a party must respond to a request for discovery, including filing objections to a request for discovery, not later than 30 days after service of the request.

(e) Scope of discovery. Subject to the limits on discovery set forth in paragraph (f) of this section, a party may discover any matter that is not privileged and that is relevant to any party's claim or defense, including the existence, description, nature, custody, condition, and location of any document or other tangible item and the identity and location of any person having knowledge of discoverable matter. A party may discover facts known, or opinions held, by an expert who any other party expects to call to testify at the hearing. A party has no ground to object to a discovery request on the basis that the information sought would not be admissible at the hearing.

(f) Limiting discovery. The administrative law judge must limit the frequency and extent of discovery permitted by this section if a party shows that -

(1) The information requested is cumulative or repetitious;

(2) The information requested can be obtained from another less burdensome and more convenient source;

(3) The party requesting the information has had ample opportunity to obtain the information through other discovery methods permitted under this section; or

(4) The method or scope of discovery requested by the party is unduly burdensome or expensive.

(g) Confidential orders. A party or person who has received a discovery request for information that is related to a trade secret, confidential or sensitive material, competitive or commercial information, proprietary data, or information on research and development, may file a motion for a confidential order in the FAA Hearing Docket in accordance with 13.210, and must serve a copy of the motion for a confidential order on each party and on the administrative law judge in accordance with 13.211.

(1) The party or person making the motion must show that the confidential order is necessary to protect the information from disclosure to the public.

(2) If the administrative law judge determines that the requested material is not necessary to decide the case, the administrative law judge must preclude any inquiry into the matter by any party.

(3) If the administrative law judge determines that the requested material may be disclosed during discovery, the administrative law judge may order that the material may be discovered and disclosed under limited conditions or may be used only under certain terms and conditions.

(4) If the administrative law judge determines that the requested material is necessary to decide the case and that a confidential order is warranted, the administrative law judge must provide:

   (i) An opportunity for review of the document by the parties off the record;

   (ii) Procedures for excluding the information from the record; and

   (iii) Order that the parties must not disclose the information in any manner and the parties must not use the information in any other proceeding.

(h) Protective orders. A party or a person who has received a request for discovery may file a motion for protective order in the FAA Hearing Docket and must serve a copy of the motion for protective order on the administrative law judge and each other party. The party or person making the motion must show that the protective order is necessary to protect the party or the person from annoyance, embarrassment, oppression, or undue burden or expense. As part of the protective order, the administrative law judge may:

(1) Deny the discovery request;

(2) Order that discovery be conducted only on specified terms and conditions, including a designation of the time or place for discovery or a determination of the method of discovery; or

(3) Limit the scope of discovery or preclude any inquiry into certain matters during discovery.

(i) Duty to supplement or amend responses. A party who has responded to a discovery request has a duty to supplement or amend the response, as soon as the information is known, as follows:

(1) A party must supplement or amend any response to a question requesting the identity and location of any person having knowledge of discoverable matters.

(2) A party must supplement or amend any response to a question requesting the identity of each person who will be called to testify at the hearing as an expert witness and the subject matter and substance of that witness's testimony.

(3) A party must supplement or amend any response that was incorrect when made or any response that was correct when made but is no longer correct, accurate, or complete.

(j) Depositions -

(1) Form. A deposition must be taken on the record and reduced to writing. The person being deposed must sign the deposition unless the parties agree to waive the requirement of a signature.

(2) Administration of oaths. Within the United States, or a territory or possession subject to the jurisdiction of the United States, a party must take a deposition before a person authorized to administer oaths by the laws of the United States or authorized by the law of the place where the examination is held. In foreign countries, a party must take a deposition in any manner allowed by the Federal Rules of Civil Procedure.

(3) Notice of deposition. A party must serve a notice of deposition, stating the time and place of the deposition and the name and address of each person to be examined, on the person to be deposed, the administrative law judge, and each party not later than 7 days before the deposition. The notice must be filed in the FAA Hearing Docket simultaneously. A party may serve a notice of deposition less than 7 days before the deposition only with consent of the administrative law judge. The party noticing a deposition must attach a copy of any subpoena duces tecum requesting that materials be produced at the deposition to the notice of deposition.

(4) Use of depositions. A party may use any part or all of a deposition at a hearing authorized under this subpart only upon a showing of good cause. The deposition may be used against any party who was present or represented at the deposition or who had reasonable notice of the deposition.

(k) Interrogatories. A party, the party's attorney, or the party's representative may sign the party's responses to interrogatories. A party must answer each interrogatory separately and completely in writing. If a party objects to an interrogatory, the party must state the objection and the reasons for the objection. An opposing party may use any part or all of a party's responses to interrogatories at a hearing authorized under this subpart to the extent that the response is relevant, material, and not repetitious.

(1) A party must not serve more than 30 interrogatories to each other party. Each subpart of an interrogatory must be counted as a separate interrogatory.

(2) A party must file a motion for leave to serve additional interrogatories on a party with the administrative law judge before serving additional interrogatories on a party. The administrative law judge may grant the motion only if the party shows good cause.

(l) Requests for admission. A party may serve a written request for admission of the truth of any matter within the scope of discovery under this section or the authenticity of any document described in the request. A party must set forth each request for admission separately. A party must serve copies of documents referenced in the request for admission unless the documents have been provided or are reasonably available for inspection and copying.

(1) Time. A party's failure to respond to a request for admission, in writing and signed by the attorney or the party, not later than 30 days after service of the request, is deemed an admission of the truth of the statement or statements contained in the request for admission. The administrative law judge may determine that a failure to respond to a request for admission is not deemed an admission of the truth if a party shows that the failure was due to circumstances beyond the control of the party or the party's attorney.

(2) Response. A party may object to a request for admission and must state the reasons for objection. A party may specifically deny the truth of the matter or describe the reasons why the party is unable to truthfully deny or admit the matter. If a party is unable to deny or admit the truth of the matter, the party must show that the party has made reasonable inquiry into the matter or that the information known to, or readily obtainable by, the party is insufficient to enable the party to admit or deny the matter. A party may admit or deny any part of the request for admission. If the administrative law judge determines that a response does not comply with the requirements of this paragraph (l)(2) or that the response is insufficient, the matter is deemed admitted.

(3) Effect of admission. Any matter admitted or deemed admitted under this section is conclusively established for the purpose of the hearing and appeal.

(m) Motion to compel discovery. A party may make a motion to compel discovery if a person refuses to answer a question during a deposition, a party fails or refuses to answer an interrogatory, if a person gives an evasive or incomplete answer during a deposition or when responding to an interrogatory, or a party fails or refuses to produce documents or tangible items. During a deposition, the proponent of a question may complete the deposition or may adjourn the examination before making a motion to compel if a person refuses to answer. Any motion to compel must be filed with the FAA Hearing Docket and served on the administrative law judge and other parties in accordance with 13.210 and 13.211, respectively.

(n) Failure to comply with a discovery order. If a party fails to comply with a discovery order, the administrative law judge may impose any of the following sanctions proportional to the party's failure to comply with the order:

(1) Strike the relevant portion of a party's pleadings;

(2) Preclude prehearing or discovery motions by that party;

(3) Preclude admission of the relevant portion of a party's evidence at the hearing; or

(4) Preclude the relevant portion of the testimony of that party's witnesses at the hearing.

13.221 Notice of hearing

(a) Notice. The administrative law judge must provide each party with notice of the date, time, and location of the hearing at least 60 days before the hearing date.

(b) Date, time, and location of the hearing. The administrative law judge to whom the proceedings have been assigned must set a reasonable date, time, and location for the hearing. The administrative law judge must consider the need for discovery and any joint procedural or discovery schedule submitted by the parties when determining the hearing date. The administrative law judge must give due regard to the convenience of the parties, the location where the majority of the witnesses reside or work, and whether the location is served by a scheduled air carrier.

(c) Earlier hearing. With the consent of the administrative law judge, the parties may agree to hold the hearing on an earlier date than the date specified in the notice of hearing.

13.222 Evidence

(a) General. A party is entitled to present the party's case or defense by oral, documentary, or demonstrative evidence, to submit rebuttal evidence, and to conduct any cross-examination that may be required for a full and true disclosure of the facts.

(b) Admissibility. A party may introduce any oral, documentary, or demonstrative evidence in support of the party's case or defense. The administrative law judge must admit any relevant oral, documentary, or demonstrative evidence introduced by a party, but must exclude irrelevant, immaterial, or unduly repetitious evidence.

(c) Hearsay evidence. Hearsay evidence is admissible in proceedings governed by this subpart. The fact that evidence submitted by a party is hearsay goes only to the weight of the evidence and does not affect its admissibility.

13.223 Standard of proof

The administrative law judge must issue an initial decision or must rule in a party's favor only if the decision or ruling is supported by, and in accordance with, the reliable, probative, and substantial evidence contained in the record. In order to prevail, the party with the burden of proof must prove the party's case or defense by a preponderance of reliable, probative, and substantial evidence.

13.224 Burden of proof

(a) Except in the case of an affirmative defense, the burden of proof is on the agency.

(b) Except as otherwise provided by statute or rule, the proponent of a motion, request, or order has the burden of proof.

(c) A party who has asserted an affirmative defense has the burden of proving the affirmative defense.

13.225 Offer of proof

A party whose evidence has been excluded by a ruling of the administrative law judge may offer the evidence for the record on appeal.

13.226 Public disclosure of information

(a) The administrative law judge may order that any information contained in the record be withheld from public disclosure. Any party or interested person may object to disclosure of information in the record by filing and serving a written motion to withhold specific information in accordance with 13.210 and 13.211 respectively. A party may file a motion seeking to protect from public disclosure information contained in a document that the party is filing at the same time it files the document. The person or party must state the specific grounds for nondisclosure in the motion.

(b) The administrative law judge must grant the motion to withhold if, based on the motion and any response to the motion, the administrative law judge determines that: Disclosure would be detrimental to aviation safety; disclosure would not be in the public interest; or the information is not otherwise required to be made available to the public.

13.227 Expert or opinion witnesses

An employee of the agency may not be called as an expert or opinion witness for any party other than the FAA in any proceeding governed by this subpart. An employee of a respondent may not be called by an agency attorney as an expert or opinion witness for the FAA in any proceeding governed by this subpart to which the respondent is a party.

13.228 Subpoenas

(a) Request for subpoena. The administrative law judge, upon application by any party to the proceeding, may issue subpoenas requiring the attendance of witnesses or the production of documents or tangible things at a hearing or for the purpose of taking depositions, as permitted by law. A request for a subpoena must show its general relevance and reasonable scope. The party must serve the subpoena on the witness or the holder of the documents or tangible items as permitted by applicable statute. A request for a subpoena must be filed and served in accordance with 13.210 and 13.211, respectively. Absent good cause shown, the filing and service must be completed as follows:

(1) Not later than 15 days before a scheduled deposition under the subpoena; or

(2) Not later than 30 days before a scheduled hearing where attendance at the hearing is sought.

(b) Motion to quash or modify the subpoena. A party, or any person upon whom a subpoena has been served, may file in the FAA Hearing Docket a motion to quash or modify the subpoena and must serve a copy on the administrative law judge and each party at or before the time specified in the subpoena for compliance. The movant must describe, in detail, the basis for the motion to quash or modify the subpoena including, but not limited to, a statement that the testimony, document, or tangible evidence is not relevant to the proceeding, that the subpoena is not reasonably tailored to the scope of the proceeding, or that the subpoena is unreasonable and oppressive. A motion to quash or modify the subpoena will stay the effect of the subpoena pending a decision by the administrative law judge on the motion.

(c) Enforcement of subpoena. Upon a showing that a person has failed or refused to comply with a subpoena, a party may apply to the appropriate U.S. district court to seek judicial enforcement of the subpoena.

13.229 Witness fees

(a) General. The party who applies for a subpoena to compel the attendance of a witness at a deposition or hearing, or the party at whose request a witness appears at a deposition or hearing, must pay the witness fees described in this section.

(b) Amount. Except for an employee of the agency who appears at the direction of the agency, a witness who appears at a deposition or hearing is entitled to the same fees and allowances provided for under 28 U.S.C. 1821.

13.230 Record

(a) Exclusive record. The pleadings, transcripts of the hearing and prehearing conferences, exhibits admitted into evidence, rulings, motions, applications, requests, briefs, and responses thereto, constitute the exclusive record for decision of the proceedings and the basis for the issuance of any orders in the proceeding. Any proceedings regarding the disqualification of an administrative law judge must be included in the record. Though only exhibits admitted into evidence are part of the record before an administrative law judge, evidence proffered but not admitted is also part of the record on appeal, as provided by 13.225.

(b) Examination and copying of record. The parties may examine the record at the FAA Hearing Docket and may obtain copies of the record upon payment of applicable fees. Any other person may obtain copies of the releasable portions of the record in accordance with applicable law.

13.231 Argument before the administrative law judge

(a) Arguments during the hearing. During the hearing, the administrative law judge must give the parties a reasonable opportunity to present arguments on the record supporting or opposing motions, objections, and rulings if the parties request an opportunity for argument. The administrative law judge may request written arguments during the hearing if the administrative law judge finds that submission of written arguments would be reasonable.

(b) Final oral argument. At the conclusion of the hearing and before the administrative law judge issues an initial decision in the proceedings, the administrative law judge must allow the parties to submit oral proposed findings of fact and conclusions of law, exceptions to rulings of the administrative law judge, and supporting arguments for the findings, conclusions, or exceptions. At the conclusion of the hearing, a party may waive final oral argument.

(c) Post-hearing briefs. The administrative law judge may request written post-hearing briefs before the administrative law judge issues an initial decision in the proceedings if the administrative law judge finds that submission of written arguments would be reasonable. If a party files a written post-hearing brief, the party must include proposed findings of fact and conclusions of law, exceptions to rulings of the administrative law judge, and supporting arguments for the findings, conclusions, or exceptions. The administrative law judge must give the parties a reasonable opportunity, but not more than 30 days after receipt of the transcript, to prepare and submit the briefs. A party must file and serve any post-hearing brief in in accordance with 13.210 and 13.211, respectively.

13.232 Initial decision

(a) Contents. The administrative law judge must issue an initial decision at the conclusion of the hearing. In each oral or written decision, the administrative law judge must include findings of fact and conclusions of law, as well as the grounds supporting those findings and conclusions, for all material issues of fact, the credibility of witnesses, the applicable law, any exercise of the administrative law judge's discretion, and the amount of any civil penalty found appropriate by the administrative law judge. The administrative law judge must also include a discussion of the basis for any order issued in the proceedings. The administrative law judge is not required to provide a written explanation for rulings on objections, procedural motions, and other matters not directly relevant to the substance of the initial decision. If the administrative law judge refers to any previous unreported or unpublished initial decision, the administrative law judge must make copies of that initial decision available to all parties and the FAA decisionmaker.

(b) Oral decision. Except as provided in paragraph (c) of this section, at the conclusion of the hearing, the administrative law judge's oral initial decision and order must be on the record.

(c) Written decision. The administrative law judge may issue a written initial decision not later than 30 days after the conclusion of the hearing or submission of the last post-hearing brief if the administrative law judge finds that issuing a written initial decision is reasonable. The administrative law judge must serve a copy of any written initial decision on each party.

(d) Reconsideration of an initial decision. The FAA decisionmaker may treat a motion for reconsideration of an initial decision as a notice of appeal under 13.233, and if the motion was filed within the time allowed for the filing of a notice of appeal, the FAA decisionmaker will issue a briefing schedule, as provided in 13.218.

(e) Order assessing civil penalty. Unless appealed pursuant to 13.233, the initial decision issued by the administrative law judge is considered an order assessing civil penalty if the administrative law judge finds that an alleged violation occurred and determines that a civil penalty, in an amount found appropriate by the administrative law judge, is warranted. The administrative law judge may not assess a civil penalty exceeding the amount sought in the complaint.

13.233   Appeal from initial decision

(a) Notice of appeal. A party may appeal the administrative law judge's initial decision, and any decision not previously appealed to the FAA decisionmaker on interlocutory appeal pursuant to 13.219, by filing a notice of appeal in accordance with 13.210 no later than 10 days after entry of the oral initial decision on the record or service of the written initial decision on the parties. The party must serve a copy of the notice of appeal on each party in accordance with 13.211. A party is not required to serve any documents under 13.233 on the administrative law judge.

(b) Issues on appeal. In any appeal from a decision of an administrative law judge, the FAA decisionmaker considers only the following issues:

(1) Whether each finding of fact is supported by a preponderance of reliable, probative, and substantial evidence;

(2) Whether each conclusion of law is made in accordance with applicable law, precedent, and public policy; and

(3) Whether the administrative law judge committed any prejudicial errors.

(c) Perfecting an appeal. Except as follows in paragraphs (c)(1) and (2) of this section, a party must perfect an appeal to the FAA decisionmaker no later than 50 days after entry of the oral initial decision on the record or service of the written initial decision on the parties by filing an appeal brief in accordance with 13.210 and serving a copy on every other party in accordance with 13.211.

(1) Extension of time by agreement of the parties. The parties may agree to extend the time for perfecting the appeal with the consent of the FAA decisionmaker. If the FAA decisionmaker grants an extension of time to perfect the appeal, the FAA decisionmaker must serve a letter confirming the extension of time on each party.

(2) Written motion for extension. If the parties do not agree to an extension of time for perfecting an appeal, a party desiring an extension of time may file a written motion for an extension in accordance with 13.210 and must serve a copy of the motion on each party under 13.211. Any party may file a written response to the motion for extension no later than 10 days after service of the motion. The FAA decisionmaker may grant an extension if good cause for the extension is shown in the motion.

(d) Appeal briefs. A party must file the appeal brief in accordance with 13.210 and must serve a copy of the appeal brief on each party in accordance with 13.211.

(1) A party must set forth, in detail, the party's specific objections to the initial decision or rulings in the appeal brief. A party also must set forth, in detail, the basis for the appeal, the reasons supporting the appeal, and the relief requested in the appeal. If the party relies on evidence contained in the record for the appeal, the party must specifically refer to the pertinent evidence contained in the transcript in the appeal brief.

(2) The FAA decisionmaker may dismiss an appeal, on the FAA decisionmaker's own initiative or upon motion of any other party, where a party has filed a notice of appeal but fails to perfect the appeal by timely filing an appeal brief with the FAA decisionmaker.

(e) Reply brief. Except as follows in paragraphs (e)(1) and (2) of this section, any party may file a reply brief in accordance with 13.210 not later than 35 days after the appeal brief has been served on that party. The party filing the reply brief must serve a copy of the reply brief on each party in accordance with 13.211. If the party relies on evidence contained in the record for the reply, the party must specifically refer to the pertinent evidence contained in the transcript in the reply brief.

(1) Extension of time by agreement of the parties. The parties may agree to extend the time for filing a reply brief with the consent of the FAA decisionmaker. If the FAA decisionmaker grants an extension of time to file the reply brief, the FAA decisionmaker must serve a letter confirming the extension of time on each party.

(2) Written motion for extension. If the parties do not agree to an extension of time for filing a reply brief, a party desiring an extension of time may file a written motion for an extension in accordance with 13.210 and must serve a copy of the motion on each party in accordance with 13.211. Any party choosing to respond to the motion must file and serve a written response to the motion no later than 10 days after service of the motion The FAA decisionmaker may grant an extension if good cause for the extension is shown in the motion.

(f) Other briefs. The FAA decisionmaker may allow any person to submit an amicus curiae brief in an appeal of an initial decision. A party may not file more than one brief unless permitted by the FAA decisionmaker. A party may petition the FAA decisionmaker, in writing, for leave to file an additional brief and must serve a copy of the petition on each party. The party may not file the additional brief with the petition. The FAA decisionmaker may grant leave to file an additional brief if the party demonstrates good cause for allowing additional argument on the appeal. The FAA decisionmaker will allow a reasonable time for the party to file the additional brief.

(g) Number of copies. A party must file the original plus one copy of the appeal brief or reply brief, but only one copy if filing by email or fax, as provided in 13.210.

(h) Oral argument. The FAA decisionmaker may permit oral argument on the appeal. On the FAA decisionmaker's own initiative, or upon written motion by any party, the FAA decisionmaker may find that oral argument will contribute substantially to the development of the issues on appeal and may grant the parties an opportunity for oral argument.

(i) Waiver of objections on appeal. If a party fails to object to any alleged error regarding the proceedings in an appeal or a reply brief, the party waives any objection to the alleged error. The FAA decisionmaker is not required to consider any objection in an appeal brief, or any argument in the reply brief, if a party's objection or argument is based on evidence contained on the record and the party does not specifically refer to the pertinent evidence from the record in the brief.

(j) FAA decisionmaker's decision on appeal. The FAA decisionmaker will review the record, the briefs on appeal, and the oral argument, if any, when considering the issues on appeal. The FAA decisionmaker may affirm, modify, or reverse the initial decision, make any necessary findings, or remand the case for any proceedings that the FAA decisionmaker determines may be necessary. The FAA decisionmaker may assess a civil penalty but must not assess a civil penalty in an amount greater than that sought in the complaint.

(1) The FAA decisionmaker may raise any issue, on the FAA decisionmaker's own initiative, that is required for proper disposition of the proceedings. The FAA decisionmaker will give the parties a reasonable opportunity to submit arguments on the new issues before making a decision on appeal. If an issue raised by the FAA decisionmaker requires the consideration of additional testimony or evidence, the FAA decisionmaker will remand the case to the administrative law judge for further proceedings and an initial decision related to that issue. If an issue raised by the FAA decisionmaker is solely an issue of law, or the issue was addressed at the hearing but was not raised by a party in the briefs on appeal, a remand of the case to the administrative law judge for further proceedings is not required but may be provided in the discretion of the FAA decisionmaker.

(2) The FAA decisionmaker will issue the final decision and order of the Administrator on appeal in writing and will serve a copy of the decision and order on each party. Unless a petition for review is filed pursuant to 13.235, a final decision and order of the Administrator will be considered an order assessing civil penalty if the FAA decisionmaker finds that an alleged violation occurred and a civil penalty is warranted.

(3) A final decision and order of the Administrator after appeal is precedent in any other civil penalty action. Any issue, finding or conclusion, order, ruling, or initial decision of an administrative law judge that has not been appealed to the FAA decisionmaker is not precedent in any other civil penalty action.

13.234 Petition to reconsider or modify a final decision and order of the FAA decisionmaker on appeal

(a) General. Any party may petition the FAA decisionmaker to reconsider or modify a final decision and order issued by the FAA decisionmaker on appeal from an initial decision. A party must file a petition to reconsider or modify in accordance with 13.210 not later than 30 days after service of the FAA decisionmaker's final decision and order on appeal and must serve a copy of the petition on each party in accordance with 13.211. A party is not required to serve any documents under this section on the administrative law judge. The FAA decisionmaker will not reconsider or modify an initial decision and order issued by an administrative law judge that has not been appealed by any party to the FAA decisionmaker.

(b) Number of copies. The parties must file the original plus one copy of the petition or the reply to the petition, but only one copy if filing by email or fax, as provided in 13.210.

(c) Contents. A party must state briefly and specifically the alleged errors in the final decision and order on appeal, the relief sought by the party, and the grounds that support the petition to reconsider or modify.

(1) If the petition is based, in whole or in part, on allegations regarding the consequences of the FAA decisionmaker's decision, the party must describe these allegations and must describe, and support, the basis for the allegations.

(2) If the petition is based, in whole or in part, on new material not previously raised in the proceedings, the party must set forth the new material and include affidavits of prospective witnesses and authenticated documents that would be introduced in support of the new material. The party must explain, in detail, why the new material was not discovered through due diligence prior to the hearing.

(d) Repetitious and frivolous petitions. The FAA decisionmaker will not consider repetitious or frivolous petitions. The FAA decisionmaker may summarily dismiss repetitious or frivolous petitions to reconsider or modify.

(e) Reply petitions. Any party replying to a petition to reconsider or modify must file the reply in accordance with 13.210 no later than 10 days after service of the petition on that party, and must also serve a copy of the reply on each party in accordance with 13.211.

(f) Effect of filing petition. The filing of a timely petition under this section will stay the effective date of the FAA decisionmaker's decision and order on appeal until final disposition of the petition by the FAA decisionmaker.

(g) FAA decisionmaker's decision on petition. The FAA decisionmaker has discretion to grant or deny a petition to reconsider. The FAA decisionmaker will grant or deny a petition to reconsider within a reasonable time after receipt of the petition or receipt of the reply petition, if any. The FAA decisionmaker may affirm, modify, or reverse the final decision and order on appeal, or may remand the case for any proceedings that the FAA decisionmaker determines may be necessary.

13.235 Judicial review of a final decision and order

(a) In cases under the Federal aviation statute, a party may seek judicial review of a final decision and order of the Administrator, as provided in 49 U.S.C. 46110(a), and, as applicable, in 49 U.S.C. 46301(d)(7)(D)(iii), 46301(g), or 47532.

(b) In cases under the Federal hazardous materials transportation statute, a party may seek judicial review of a final decision and order of the Administrator, as provided in 49 U.S.C. 5127.

(c) A party seeking judicial review of a final order issued by the Administrator may file a petition for review in the United States Court of Appeals for the District of Columbia Circuit or in the United States Court of Appeals for the circuit in which the party resides or has its principal place of business.

(d) The party must file the petition for review no later than 60 days after service of the Administrator's final decision and order.

13.236 Alternative dispute resolution

Parties may use mediation to achieve resolution of issues in controversy addressed by this subpart. Parties seeking alternative dispute resolution services may engage the services of a mutually acceptable mediator. The mediator must not participate in the adjudication under this subpart of any matter in which the mediator has provided mediation services. Mediation discussions and submissions will remain confidential consistent with the provisions of the Administrative Dispute Resolution Act and other applicable Federal laws.

Subpart H — Civil Monetary Penalty Inflation Adjustment

Source: Docket No. 28762, 61 FR 67445, Dec. 20, 1996, unless otherwise noted.

13.301 Inflation adjustments of civil monetary penalties

(a) This subpart provides the maximum civil monetary penalties or range of minimum and maximum civil monetary penalties for each statutory civil penalty subject to FAA jurisdiction, as adjusted for inflation.

(b) Each adjustment to a maximum civil monetary penalty or to minimum and maximum civil monetary penalties that establish a civil monetary penalty range applies to actions initiated under this part for violations occurring on or after March 21, 2022, notwithstanding references to specific civil penalty amounts elsewhere in this part.

(c) Minimum and maximum civil monetary penalties are as follows:

FAR 13

TABLE 1 TO 13:301—MINIMUM AND MAXIMUM CIVIL MONETARY PENALTY AMOUNTS FOR CERTAIN VIOLATIONS					
UNITED STATES CODE CITATION	CIVIL MONETARY PENALTY DESCRIPTION	2021 MINIMUM PENALTY AMOUNT	NEW ADJUSTED MINIMUM PENALTY AMOUNT FOR VIOLATIONS OCCURRING ON OR AFTER MARCH 21, 2022	2021 MAXIMUM PENALTY AMOUNT	NEW ADJUSTED MAXIMUM PENALTY AMOUNT FOR VIOLATIONS OCCURRING ON OR AFTER MARCH 22, 2022
49 U.S.C. 5123(a)(1)	Violation of hazardous materials transportation law	N/A	N/A	$84,425	$89,678
49 U.S.C. 5123(a)(2)	Violation of hazardous materials transportation law resulting in death, serious illness, severe injury, or substantial property destruction	N/A	N/A	$196,992	$209,249
49 U.S.C. 5123(a)(3)	Violation of hazardous materials transportation law relating to training	$508	$540	$84,425	$89,678
49 U.S.C. 44704(d)(3)	Knowing presentation of a nonconforming aircraft for issuance of an initial airworthiness certificate by a production certificate holder	N/A	N/A	$1,000,000	$1,062,220
49 U.S.C. 44704(e)(4)	Knowing failure by an applicant for or holder of a type certificate to submit safety critical information or include certain such information in an airplane flight manual or flight crew operating manual	N/A	N/A	$1,000,000	$1,062,220
49 U.S.C. 44704(e)(5)	Knowing false statement by an airline transport pilot (ATP) certificate holder with respect to the submission of certain safety critical information	N/A	N/A	See entries for 49 U.S.C. 46301(a)(1) and (a)(5)	See entries for 49 U.S.C. 46301(a)(1) and (a)(5)
49 U.S.C. 44742	Interference by a supervisory employee of an organization designation authorization (ODA) holder that manufactures a transport category airplane with an ODA unit member's performance of authorized functions	N/A	N/A	See entries for 49 U.S.C. 46301(a)(1)	See entries for 49 U.S.C. 46301(a)(1)
49 U.S.C. 44802 note	Operation of an unmanned aircraft or unmanned aircraft system equipped or armed with a dangerous weapon	N/A	N/A	$25,742	$27,344
49 U.S.C. 46301(a)(1)	Violation by a person other than an individual or small business concern under 49 U.S.C. 46301 (a)(1)(A) or (B)	N/A	N/A	$35,188	$37,377
49 U.S.C. 46301(a)(1)	Violation by an airman serving as an airman under 49 U.S.C. 46301 (a)(1)(A) or (B) (but not covered by 46301 (a)(5)(A) or (B)	N/A	N/A	$1,548	$1,644
49 U.S.C. 46301(a)(1)	Violation by an individual or small business concern under 49 U.S.C. 46301 (a)(1)(A) or (B) (but not covered in 49 U.S.C. 46301 (a)(5))	N/A	N/A	$1,548	$1,644
49 U.S.C. 46301(a)(3)	Violation of 49 U.S.C. 47107(b) (or any assurance made under such section) or 49 U.S.C. 47133	N/A	N/A	Increase above otherwise applicable maximum amount not to exceed 3 times the amount of revenues used in violation of such section	No change

TABLE 1 TO 13:301—MINIMUM AND MAXIMUM CIVIL MONETARY PENALTY AMOUNTS FOR CERTAIN VIOLATIONS					
UNITED STATES CODE CITATION	CIVIL MONETARY PENALTY DESCRIPTION	2021 MINIMUM PENALTY AMOUNT	NEW ADJUSTED MINIMUM PENALTY AMOUNT FOR VIOLATIONS OCCURRING ON OR AFTER MARCH 21, 2022	2021 MAXIMUM PENALTY AMOUNT	NEW ADJUSTED MAXIMUM PENALTY AMOUNT FOR VIOLATIONS OCCURRING ON OR AFTER MARCH 22, 2022
49 U.S.C. 46301(a)(5)(A)	Violation by an individual or small business concern (except an airman serving as an airman) under 49 U.S.C. 46301 (a)(5)(A)(i) or (ii)	N/A	N/A	$14,074	$14,950
49 U.S.C. 46301(a)(5)(B)(i)	Violation by an individual or small business concern related to the transportation of hazardous materials	N/A	N/A	$14,074	$14,950
49 U.S.C. 46301(a)(5)(B)(ii)	Violation by an individual or small business concern related to the registration or recordation under 49 U.S.C. chapter 441, of an aircraft not used to provide air transportation	N/A	N/A	$14,074	$14,950
49 U.S.C. 46301(a)(5)(B)(iii)	Violation by an individual or small business concern of 49 U.S.C. 44718(d), relating to limitation on construction or establishment of landfills	N/A	N/A	$14,074	$14,950
49 U.S.C. 46301(a)(5)(B)(iv)	Violation by an individual or small business concern of 49 U.S.C. 44725, relating to the safe disposal of life-limited aircraft parts	N/A	N/A	$14,074	$14,950
49 U.S.C. 46301 note	Individual who aims the beam of a laser pointer at an aircraft in the airspace jurisdiction of the United States, or at the flight path of such an aircraft	N/A	N/A	$26,929	$28,605
49 U.S.C. 46301 (b)	Tampering with a smoke alarm device	N/A	N/A	$4,518	$4,799
49 U.S.C. 46302	Knowingly providing false information about alleged violation involving the special aircraft jurisdiction of the United States	N/A	N/A	$24,539	$26,066
49 U.S.C. 46318	Physical or sexual assault or threat to physically or sexually assault crewmember or other individual on an aircraft, or action that poses an imminent threat to the safety of the aircraft or individuals on board	N/A	N/A	$36,948	$39,247
49 U.S.C. 46319	Permanent closure of an airport without providing sufficient notice	N/A	N/A	$14,074	$14,950
49 U.S.C. 46320	Operating an unmanned aircraft and in so doing knowingly or recklessly interfering with a wildfire suppression, law enforcement, or emergency response effort	N/A	N/A	$21,544	$22,884
49 U.S.C. 47531	Violation of 49 U.S.C. 47528-47530 or 47534, relating to the prohibition of operating certain aircraft not complying with stage 3 noise levels	N/A	N/A	See entries for 49 U.S.C. 46301(a)(1) and (a)(5)	See entries for 49 U.S.C. 46301(a)(1) and (a)(5)

[84 FR 37068, July 31, 2019, as amended at 86 FR 1753, Jan. 11, 2021; 86 FR 23249, May 3, 2021; 87 FR 15863, Mar. 21, 2022]

FAR 13

Subpart I — Flight Operational Quality Assurance Programs

13.401 Flight Operational Quality Assurance Program: prohibition against use of data for enforcement purposes

(a) Applicability. This section applies to any operator of an aircraft who operates such aircraft under an approved Flight Operational Quality Assurance (FOQA) program.

(b) Definitions. For the purpose of this section, the terms —

(1) Flight Operational Quality Assurance (FOQA) program means an FAA-approved program for the routine collection and analysis of digital flight data gathered during aircraft operations, including data currently collected pursuant to existing regulatory provisions, when such data is included in an approved FOQA program.

(2) FOQA data means any digital flight data that has been collected from an individual aircraft pursuant to an FAA-approved FOQA program, regardless of the electronic format of that data.

(3) Aggregate FOQA data means the summary statistical indices that are associated with FOQA event categories, based on an analysis of FOQA data from multiple aircraft operations.

(c) Requirements. In order for paragraph (e) of this section to apply, the operator must submit, maintain, and adhere to a FOQA Implementation and Operation Plan that is approved by the Administrator and which contains the following elements:

(1) A description of the operator's plan for collecting and analyzing flight recorded data from line operations on a routine basis, including identification of the data to be collected;

(2) Procedures for taking corrective action that analysis of the data indicates is necessary in the interest of safety;

(3) Procedures for providing the FAA with aggregate FOQA data;

(4) Procedures for informing the FAA as to any corrective action being undertaken pursuant to paragraph (c)(2) of this section.

(d) Submission of aggregate data. The operator will provide the FAA with aggregate FOQA data in a form and manner acceptable to the Administrator.

(e) Enforcement. Except for criminal or deliberate acts, the Administrator will not use an operator's FOQA data or aggregate FOQA data in an enforcement action against that operator or its employees when such FOQA data or aggregate FOQA data is obtained from a FOQA program that is approved by the Administrator.

(f) Disclosure. FOQA data and aggregate FOQA data, if submitted in accordance with an order designating the information as protected under part 193 of this chapter, will be afforded the nondisclosure protections of part 193 of this chapter.

(g) Withdrawal of program approval. The Administrator may withdraw approval of a previously approved FOQA program for failure to comply with the requirements of this chapter. Grounds for withdrawal of approval may include, but are not limited to —

(1) Failure to implement corrective action that analysis of available FOQA data indicates is necessary in the interest of safety; or

(2) Failure to correct a continuing pattern of violations following notice by the agency; or also

(3) Willful misconduct or willful violation of the FAA regulations in this chapter.

[Doc. No. FAA–2000–7554, 66 FR 55048, Oct. 31, 2001; Amdt. 13–30, 67 FR 31401, May 9, 2002]

PART 21 — CERTIFICATION PROCEDURES FOR PRODUCTS AND ARTICLES

SFAR No. 88 — Fuel Tank System Fault Tolerance Evaluation Requirements

FAR 21

Subpart I — Provisional Airworthiness Certificates

Subpart J — [Reserved]

Subpart K—Parts Manufacturer Approvals

Subpart L — Export Airworthiness Approvals

Subpart M — [Reserved]

Subpart N — Acceptance of Aircraft Engines, Propellers, and Articles for Import

Subpart O — Technical Standard Order Approvals

Subpart P — Special Federal Aviation Regulations

Authority: 42 U.S.C. 7572; 49 U.S.C. 106(f), 106(g), 40105, 40113, 44701-44702, 44704, 44707, 44709, 44711, 44713, 44715, 45303.

Editorial Notes: 1. For miscellaneous amendments to cross references in this 21 see Amdt. 21-10, 31 FR 9211, July 6, 1966.
2. Nomenclature changes to part 21 appear at 74 FR 53384, Oct. 16, 2009.

SFAR No. 88—Fuel Tank System Fault Tolerance Evaluation Requirements

1. Applicability. This SFAR applies to the holders of type certificates, and supplemental type certificates that may affect the airplane fuel tank system, for turbine-powered transport category airplanes, provided the type certificate was issued after January 1, 1958, and the airplane has either a maximum type certificated passenger capacity of 30 or more, or a maximum type certificated payload capacity of 7,500 pounds or more. This SFAR also applies to applicants for type certificates, amendments to a type certificate, and supplemental type certificates affecting the fuel tank systems for those airplanes identified above, if the application was filed before June 6, 2001, the effective date of this SFAR, and the certificate was not issued before June 6, 2001

2. Compliance: Each type certificate holder, and each supplemental type certificate holder of a modification affecting the airplane fuel tank system, must accomplish the following within the compliance times specified in paragraph (e) of this section:

(a) Conduct a safety review of the airplane fuel tank system to determine that the design meets the requirements of 25.901 and 25.981(a) and (b) of this chapter. If the current design does not meet these requirements, develop all design changes to the fuel tank system that are necessary to meet these requirements. The responsible Aircraft Certification Service office for the affected airplane may grant an extension of the 18-month compliance time for development of design changes if::

(1) The safety review is completed within the compliance time;

(2) Necessary design changes are identified within the compliance time; and

(3) Additional time can be justified, based on the holder's demonstrated aggressiveness in performing the safety review, the complexity of the necessary design changes, the availability of interim actions to provide an acceptable level of safety, and the resulting level of safety

(b) Develop all maintenance and inspection instructions necessary to maintain the design features required to preclude the existence or development of an ignition source within the fuel tank system of the airplane

(c) Submit a report for approval to the responsible Aircraft Certification Service office for the affected airplane, that

(1) Provides substantiation that the airplane fuel tank system design, including all necessary design changes, meets the requirements of 25.901 and 25.981(a) and (b) of this chapter; and

(2) Contains all maintenance and inspection instructions necessary to maintain the design features required to preclude the existence or development of an ignition source within the fuel tank system throughout the operational life of the airplane

(d) The responsible Aircraft Certification Service office for the affected airplane, may approve a report submitted in accordance with paragraph 2(c) if it determines that any provisions of this SFAR not complied with are compensated for by factors that provide an equivalent level of safety.

(e) Each type certificate holder must comply no later than December 6, 2002, or within 18 months after the issuance of a type certificate for which application was filed before June 6, 2001, whichever is later; and each supplemental type certificate holder of a modification affecting the airplane fuel tank system must comply no later than June 6, 2003, or within 18 months after the issuance of a supplemental type certificate for which application was filed before June 6, 2001, whichever is later

[Doc. No. 1999-6411, 66 FR 23129, May 7, 2001, as amended by Amdt. 21-82, 67 FR 57493, Sept. 10, 2002; 67 FR 70809, Nov. 26, 2002; Amdt. 21-83, 67 FR 72833, Dec. 9, 2002; Doc. No. FAA-2018-0119, Amdt. 21-101, 83 FR 9169, Mar. 5, 2018]

Subpart A — General

21.1 Applicability and definitions

(a) This part prescribes—

(1) Procedural requirements for issuing and changing—

    (i) Design approvals;

    (ii) Production approvals;

    (iii) Airworthiness certificates; and

    (iv) Airworthiness approvals;

(2) Rules governing applicants for, and holders of, any approval or certificate specified in paragraph (a)(1) of this section; and

(3) Procedural requirements for the approval of articles

(b) For the purposes of this part—

(1) Airworthiness approval means a document, issued by the FAA for an aircraft, aircraft engine, propeller, or article, which certifies that the aircraft, aircraft engine, propeller, or article conforms to its approved design and is in a condition for safe operation, unless otherwise specified;

(2) Article means a material, part, component, process, or appliance;

(3) Commercial part means an article that is listed on an FAA-approved Commercial Parts List included in a design approval holder's Instructions for Continued Airworthiness required by 21.50;

(4) Design approval means a type certificate (including amended and supplemental type certificates) or the approved design under a PMA, TSO authorization, letter of TSO design approval, or other approved design;

(5) Interface component means an article that serves as a functional interface between an aircraft and an aircraft engine, an aircraft engine and a propeller, or an aircraft and a propeller. An interface component is designated by the holder of the type certificate or the supplemental type certificate who controls the approved design data for that article;

(6) Product means an aircraft, aircraft engine, or propeller;

(7) Production approval means a document issued by the FAA to a person that allows the production of a product or article in accordance with its approved design and approved quality system, and can take the form of a production certificate, a PMA, or a TSO authorization;

(8) State of Design means the country or jurisdiction having regulatory authority over the organization responsible for the design and continued airworthiness of a civil aeronautical product or article;

(9) State of Manufacture means the country or jurisdiction having regulatory authority over the organization responsible for the production and airworthiness of a civil aeronautical product or article.

(10) Supplier means a person at any tier in the supply chain who provides a product, article, or service that is used or consumed in the design or manufacture of, or installed on, a product or article.

[Doc. No. FAA-2006-25877, Amdt. 21-92, 74 FR 53384, Oct. 16, 2009; Doc. No. FAA-2013-0933, Amdt. 21-98, 80 FR 59031, Oct. 1, 2015; Amdt. 21-98A, 80 FR 59031, Dec. 17, 2015; Docket FAA-2015-0150, Amdt. 21-99, 81 FR 42207, June 28, 2016; Docket FAA-2018-1087, Amdt. 21-105, 86 FR 4381, Jan. 15, 2021]

21.2 Falsification of applications, reports, or records

(a) A person may not make or cause to be made—

(1) Any fraudulent, intentionally false, or misleading statement on any application for a certificate or approval under this part;

(2) Any fraudulent, intentionally false, or misleading statement in any record or report that is kept, made, or used to show compliance with any requirement of this part;

(3) Any reproduction for a fraudulent purpose of any certificate or approval issued under this part

(4) Any alteration of any certificate or approval issued under this part

(b) The commission by any person of an act prohibited under paragraph (a) of this section is a basis for—

(1) Denying issuance of any certificate or approval under this part; and

(2) Suspending or revoking any certificate or approval issued under this part and held by that person

[Doc. No. 23345, 57 FR 41367, Sept. 9, 1992, as amended by Amdt. 21–92, 74 FR 53384, Oct. 16, 2009; Amdt. 21–92A, 75FR 9095, Mar. 1, 2010]

21.3 Reporting of failures, malfunctions, and defects

(a) The holder of a type certificate (including amended or supplemental type certificates), a PMA, or a TSO authorization, or the licensee of a type certificate must report any failure, malfunction, or defect in any product or article manufactured by it that it determines has resulted in any of the occurrences listed in paragraph (c) of this section

(b) The holder of a type certificate (including amended or supplemental type certificates), a PMA, or a TSO authorization, or the licensee of a type certificate must report any defect in any product or article manufactured by it that has left its quality system and that it determines could result in any of the occurrences listed in paragraph (c) of this section

(c) The following occurrences must be reported as provided in paragraphs (a) and (b) of this section:

(1) Fires caused by a system or equipment failure, malfunction, or defect

(2) An engine exhaust system failure, malfunction, or defect which causes damage to the engine, adjacent aircraft structure, equipment, or components

(3) The accumulation or circulation of toxic or noxious gases in the crew compartment or passenger cabin

(4) A malfunction, failure, or defect of a propeller control system

(5) A propeller or rotorcraft hub or blade structural failure

(6) Flammable fluid leakage in areas where an ignition source normally exists

(7) A brake system failure caused by structural or material failure during operation

(8) A significant aircraft primary structural defect or failure caused by any autogenous condition (fatigue, understrength, corrosion, etc.)

(9) Any abnormal vibration or buffeting caused by a structural or system malfunction, defect, or failure

(10) An engine failure

(11) Any structural or flight control system malfunction, defect, or failure which causes an interference with normal control of the aircraft for which derogates the flying qualities

(12) A complete loss of more than one electrical power generating system or hydraulic power system during a given operation of the aircraft

(13) A failure or malfunction of more than one attitude, airspeed, or altitude instrument during a given operation of the aircraft

(d) The requirements of paragraph (a) of this section do not apply to—

(1) Failures, malfunctions, or defects that the holder of a type certificate (including amended or supplemental type certificates), PMA, TSO authorization, or the licensee of a type certificate determines—

    (i) Were caused by improper maintenance or use;

    (ii) Were reported to the FAA by another person under this chapter; or

    (iii) Were reported under the accident reporting provisions of 49 CFR part 830 of the regulations of the National Transportation Safety Board

FAR 21

(2) Failures, malfunctions, or defects in products or articles—

    (i) Manufactured by a foreign manufacturer under a U.S. type certificate issued under 21.29 or under an approval issued under 21.621; or

    (ii) Exported to the United States under 21.502

(e) Each report required by this section—

    (1) Must be made to the FAA within 24 hours after it has determined that the failure, malfunction, or defect required to be reported has occurred. However, a report that is due on a Saturday or a Sunday may be delivered on the following Monday and one that is due on a holiday may be delivered on the next workday;

    (2) Must be transmitted in a manner and form acceptable to the FAA and by the most expeditious method available; and

    (3) Must include as much of the following information as is available and applicable:

        (i) The applicable product and article identification information required by part 45 of this chapter;

        (ii) Identification of the system involved; and

        (iii) Nature of the failure, malfunction, or defect

(f) If an accident investigation or service difficulty report shows that a product or article manufactured under this part is unsafe because of a manufacturing or design data defect, the holder of the production approval for that product or article must, upon request of the FAA, report to the FAA the results of its investigation and any action taken or proposed by the holder of that production approval to correct that defect. If action is required to correct the defect in an existing product or article, the holder of that production approval must send the data necessary for issuing an appropriate airworthiness directive to the FAA.

[Amdt. 21-36, 35 FR 18187, Nov. 28, 1970, as amended by Amdt. 21-37, 35 FR 18450, Dec. 4, 1970; Amdt. 21-50, 45 FR 38346, June 9, 1980; Amdt. 21-67, 54 FR 39291, Sept. 25, 1989; Amdt. 21-92, 74 FR 53385, Oct. 16, 2009; Doc. No. FAA-2018-0119, Amdt. 21-101, 83 FR 9169, Mar. 5, 2018]

21.4　ETOPS reporting requirements

(a) Early ETOPS: reporting, tracking, and resolving problems. The holder of a type certificate for an airplane-engine combination approved using the Early ETOPS method specified in part 25, Appendix K, of this chapter must use a system for reporting, tracking, and resolving each problem resulting in one of the occurrences specified in paragraph (a)(6) of this section

    (1) The system must identify how the type certificate holder will promptly identify problems, report them to the responsible Aircraft Certification Service office, and propose a solution to the FAA to resolve each problem. A proposed solution must consist of—

        (i) A change in the airplane or engine type design;

        (ii) A change in a manufacturing process;

        (iii) A change in an operating or maintenance procedure; or

        (iv) Any other solution acceptable to the FAA

    (2) For an airplane with more than two engines, the system must be in place for the first 250,000 world fleet engine-hours for the approved airplane-engine combination

    (3) For two-engine airplanes, the system must be in place for the first 250,000 world fleet engine-hours for the approved airplane-engine combination and after that until—

        (i) The world fleet 12-month rolling average IFSD rate is at or below the rate required by paragraph (b)(2) of this section; and ·

        (ii) The FAA determines that the rate is stable

    (4) For an airplane-engine combination that is a derivative of an airplane-engine combination previously approved for ETOPS, the system need only address those problems specified in the following table, provided the type certificate holder obtains prior authorization from the FAA:

IF THE CHANGE DOES NOT REQUIRE A NEW AIRPLANE TYPE CERTIFICATE AND...	THEN THE PROBLEM TRACKING AND RESOLUTION SYSTEM MUST ADDRESS.
(i) Requires a new engine type certificate	All problems applicable to the new engine installation, and for the remainder of the airplane, problems in changes systems only
(ii) Does not require a new engine type certificate	Problems in changed systems only

    (5) The type certificate holder must identify the sources and content of data that it will use for its system. The data must be adequate to evaluate the specific cause of any in-service problem reportable under this section or 21.3(c) that could affect the safety of ETOPS

    (6) In implementing this system, the type certificate holder must report the following occurrences:

        (i) IFSDs, except planned IFSDs performed for flight training

        (ii) For two-engine airplanes, IFSD rates

        (iii) Inability to control an engine or obtain desired thrust or power

        (iv) Precautionary thrust or power reductions

        (v) Degraded ability to start an engine in flight

        (vi) Inadvertent fuel loss or unavailability, or uncorrectable fuel imbalance in flight

        (vii) Turn backs or diversions for failures, malfunctions, or defects associated with an ETOPS group 1 significant system

        (viii) Loss of any power source for an ETOPS group 1 significant system, including any power source designed to provide backup power for that system

        (ix) Any event that would jeopardize the safe flight and landing of the airplane on an ETOPS flight

        (x) Any unscheduled engine removal for a condition that could result in one of the reportable occurrences listed in this paragraph

(b) Reliability of two-engine airplanes —

    (1) Reporting of two-engine airplane in-service reliability. The holder of a type certificate for an airplane approved for ETOPS and the holder of a type certificate for an engine installed on an airplane approved for ETOPS must report monthly to their respective Aircraft Certification Service office on the reliability of the world fleet of those airplanes and engines. The report provided by both the airplane and engine type certificate holders must address each airplane-engine combination approved for ETOPS. The FAA may approve quarterly reporting if the airplane-engine combination demonstrates an IFSD rate at or below those specified in paragraph (b)(2) of this section for a period acceptable to the FAA. This reporting may be combined with the reporting required by 21.3. The responsible type certificate holder must investigate any cause of an IFSD resulting from an occurrence attributable to the design of its product and report the results of that investigation to its responsible Aircraft Certification Service office. Reporting must include:

        (i) Engine IFSDs, except planned IFSDs performed for flight training

        (ii) The world fleet 12-month rolling average IFSD rates for all causes, except planned IFSDs performed for flight training

        (iii) ETOPS fleet utilization, including a list of operators, their ETOPS diversion time authority, flight hours, and cycles

(2) World fleet IFSD rate for two-engine airplanes. The holder of a type certificate for an airplane approved for ETOPS and the holder of a type certificate for an engine installed on an airplane approved for ETOPS must issue service information to the operators of those airplanes and engines, as appropriate, to maintain the world fleet 12-month rolling average IFSD rate at or below the following levels:

   (i) A rate of 0.05 per 1,000 world-fleet engine-hours for an airplane-engine combination approved for up to and including 120-minute ETOPS. When all ETOPS operators have complied with the corrective actions required in the configuration, maintenance and procedures (CMP)   document as a condition for ETOPS approval, the rate to be maintained is at or below 0.02 per 1,000 world-fleet engine-hours

   (ii) A rate of 0.02 per 1,000 world-fleet engine-hours for an airplane-engine combination approved for up to and including 180-minute ETOPS, including airplane-engine combinations approved for 207-minute ETOPS in the North Pacific operating area under appendix P, section I, paragraph (h), of part 121 of this chapter

   (iii) A rate of 0.01 per 1,000 world-fleet engine-hours for an airplane-engine combination approved for ETOPS beyond 180 minutes, excluding airplane-engine combinations approved for 207-minute ETOPS in the North Pacific operating area under appendix P, section I, paragraph (h), of part 121 of this chapter

[Doc. No. FAA-2002-6717, 72 FR 1872, Jan. 16, 2007, as amended by Doc. No. FAA-2018-0119, Amdt. 21-101, 83 FR 9169, Mar. 5, 2018]

21.5   Airplane or Rotorcraft Flight Manual

(a) With each airplane or rotorcraft not type certificated with an Airplane or Rotorcraft Flight Manual and having no flight time before March 1, 1979, the holder of a type certificate (including amended or supplemental type certificates) or the licensee of a type certificate must make available to the owner at the time of delivery of the aircraft a current approved Airplane or Rotorcraft Flight Manual

(b) The Airplane or Rotorcraft Flight Manual required by paragraph (a) of this section must contain the following information:

   (1) The operating limitations and information required to be furnished in an Airplane or Rotorcraft Flight Manual or in manual material, markings, and placards, by the applicable regulations under which the airplane or rotorcraft was type certificated

   (2) The maximum ambient atmospheric temperature for which engine cooling was demonstrated must be stated in the performance information section of the Flight Manual, if the applicable regulations under which the aircraft was type certificated do not require ambient temperature on engine cooling operating limitations in the Flight Manual

[Amdt. 21-46, 43 FR 2316, Jan. 16, 1978, as amended by Amdt. 21-92, 74 FR 53385, Oct. 16, 2009]

21.6   Manufacture of new aircraft, aircraft engines, and propellers

(a) Except as specified in paragraphs (b) and (c) of this section, no person may manufacture a new aircraft, aircraft engine, or propeller based on a type certificate unless the person—

   (1) Is the holder of the type certificate or has a licensing agreement from the holder of the type certificate to manufacture the product; and

   (2) Meets the requirements of subpart F or G of this part

(b) A person may manufacture one new aircraft based on a type certificate without meeting the requirements of paragraph (a) of this section if that person can provide evidence acceptable to the FAA that the manufacture of the aircraft by that person began before August 5, 2004

(c) The requirements of this section do not apply to—

   (1) New aircraft imported under the provisions of 21.183(c), 21.184(b), or 21.185(c); and

   (2) New aircraft engines or propellers imported under the provisions of 21.500

[Doc. No. FAA-2003-14825, 71 FR 52258, Sept. 1, 2006]

21.7   Continued airworthiness and safety improvements for transport category airplanes

(a) On or after December 10, 2007, the holder of a design approval and an applicant for a design approval must comply with the applicable continued airworthiness and safety improvement requirements of part 26 of this subchapter

(b) For new transport category airplanes manufactured under the authority of the FAA, the holder or licensee of a type certificate must meet the applicable continued airworthiness and safety improvement requirements specified in part 26 of this subchapter for new production airplanes. Those requirements only apply if the FAA has jurisdiction over the organization responsible for final assembly of the airplane

[Doc. No. FAA-2004-18379, Amdt. No. 21-90, 72 FR 63404, Nov. 8, 2007]

21.8   Approval of articles

If an article is required to be approved under this chapter, it may be approved—

(a) Under a PMA;

(b) Under a TSO;

(c) In conjunction with type certification procedures for a product; or

(d) In any other manner approved by the FAA

[Doc. No. FAA-2006-25877, 74 FR 53385, Oct. 16, 2009]

21.9   Replacement and modification articles

(a) If a person knows, or should know, that a replacement or modification article is reasonably likely to be installed on a type-certificated product, the person may not produce that article unless it is—

   (1) Produced under a type certificate;

   (2) Produced under an FAA production approval;

   (3) A standard part (such as a nut or bolt) manufactured in compliance with a government or established industry specification;

   (4) A commercial part as defined in 21.1 of this part;

   (5) Produced by an owner or operator for maintaining or altering that owner or operator's product;

   (6) Fabricated by an appropriately rated certificate holder with a quality system, and consumed in the repair or alteration of a product or article in accordance with part 43 of this chapter; or

   (7) Produced in any other manner approved by the FAA.

(b) Except as provided in paragraphs (a)(1) through (a)(2) of this section, a person who produces a replacement or modification article for sale may not represent that part as suitable for installation on a type-certificated product

(c) Except as provided in paragraphs (a)(1) through (a)(2) of this section, a person may not sell or represent an article as suitable for installation on an aircraft type-certificated under 21.25(a)(2) or 21.27 unless that article—

   (1) Was declared surplus by the U.S. Armed Forces, and

   (2) Was intended for use on that aircraft model by the U.S. Armed Forces

[Doc. No. FAA-2006-25877, Amdt. 21-92, 74 FR 53385, Oct. 16, 2009; Amdt. 21-92A, 75 FR 9095, Mar. 1, 2010; Doc. No. FAA-2015-1621, Amdt. 21-100, 81 FR 96688, Dec. 30, 2016]

Subpart B — Type Certificates

Source: Docket No. 5085, 29 FR 14564, Oct. 24, 1964, unless otherwise noted

21.11   Applicability

This subpart prescribes—

(a) Procedural requirements for the issue of type certificates for aircraft, aircraft engines, and propellers; and

(b) Rules governing the holders of those certificates

21.13　Eligibility

Any interested person may apply for a type certificate

[Amdt. 21–25, 34 FR 14068, Sept. 5, 1969]

21.15　Application for type certificate

(a) An application for a type certificate is made on a form and in a manner prescribed by the FAA.

(b) An application for an aircraft type certificate must be accompanied by a three-view drawing of that aircraft and available preliminary basic data

(c) An application for an aircraft engine type certificate must be accompanied by a description of the engine design features, the engine operating characteristics, and the proposed engine operating limitations

[Doc. No. 5085, 29 FR 14564, Oct. 24, 1964, as amended by Amdt. 21-40, 39 FR 35459, Oct. 1, 1974; Amdt. 21-67, 54 FR 39291, Sept. 25, 1989; Amdt. 21-92, 74 FR 53385, Oct. 16, 2009; Doc. No. FAA-2018-0119, Amdt. 21-101, 83 FR 9169, Mar. 5, 2018]

21.16　Special conditions

If the Administrator finds that the airworthiness regulations of this subchapter do not contain adequate or appropriate safety standards for an aircraft, aircraft engine, or propeller because of a novel or unusual design feature of the aircraft, aircraft engine or propeller, he prescribes special conditions and amendments thereto for the product. The special conditions are issued in accordance with Part 11 of this chapter and contain such safety standards for the aircraft, aircraft engine or propeller as the Administrator finds necessary to establish a level of safety equivalent to that established in the regulations

[Amdt. 21–19, 32 FR 17851, Dec. 13, 1967; as amended by Amdt. 21–51, 45 FR 60170, Sept. 11, 1980]

21.17　Designation of applicable regulations

(a) Except as provided in 25.2, 27.2, 29.2, and in parts 26, 34, and 36 of this subchapter, an applicant for a type certificate must show that the aircraft, aircraft engine, or propeller concerned meets—

　(1) The applicable requirements of this subchapter that are effective on the date of application for that certificate unless—

　　(i)　Otherwise specified by the Administrator; or

　　(ii)　Compliance with later effective amendments is elected or required under this section; and

　(2) Any special conditions prescribed by the Administrator

(b) For special classes of aircraft, including the engines and propellers installed thereon (e.g., gliders, airships, and other nonconventional aircraft), for which airworthiness standards have not been issued under this subchapter, the applicable requirements will be the portions of those other airworthiness requirements contained in Parts 23, 25, 27, 29, 31, 33, and 35 found by the Administrator to be appropriate for the aircraft and applicable to a specific type design, or such airworthiness criteria as the Administrator may find provide an equivalent level of safety to those parts

(c) An application for type certification of a transport category aircraft is effective for 5 years and an application for any other type certificate is effective for 3 years, unless an applicant shows at the time of application that his product requires a longer period of time for design, development, and testing, and the Administrator approves a longer period

(d) In a case where a type certificate has not been issued, or it is clear that a type certificate will not be issued, within the time limit established under paragraph (c) of this section, the applicant may—

　(1) File a new application for a type certificate and comply with all the provisions of paragraph (a) of this section applicable to an original application; or

　(2) File for an extension of the original application and comply with the applicable airworthiness requirements of this subchapter that were effective on a date, to be selected by the applicant, not earlier than the date which precedes the date of issue of the type certificate by the time limit established under paragraph (c) of this section for the original application

(e) If an applicant elects to comply with an amendment to this subchapter that is effective after the filing of the application for a type certificate, he must also comply with any other amendment that the Administrator finds is directly related

(f) For primary category aircraft, the requirements are:

　(1) The applicable airworthiness requirements contained in parts 23, 27, 31, 33, and 35 of this subchapter, or such other airworthiness criteria as the Administrator may find appropriate and applicable to the specific design and intended use and provide a level of safety acceptable to the Administrator

　(2) The noise standards of part 36 applicable to primary category aircraft

[Doc. No. 5085, 29 FR 14564, Oct. 24, 1964, as amended by Amdt. 21–19, 32 FR 17851, Dec. 13, 1967; Amdt. 21–24, 34 FR 364, Jan. 10, 1969; Amdt. 21–42, 40 FR 1033, Jan. 6, 1975; Amdt. 21–58, 50 FR 46877, Nov. 13, 1985; Amdt. 21–60, 52 FR 8042, Mar. 13, 1987; Amdt. 21–68, 55 FR 32860, Aug. 10, 1990; Amdt. 21–69, 56 FR 41051, Aug. 16, 1991; Amdt. 21–70, 57 FR 41367, Sept. 9, 1992; Amdt. No. 21–90, 72 FR 63404, Nov. 8, 2007]

21.19　Changes requiring a new type certificate

Each person who proposes to change a product must apply for a new type certificate if the Administrator finds that the proposed change in design, power, thrust, or weight is so extensive that a substantially complete investigation of compliance with the applicable regulations is required

[Doc. No. 28903, 65 FR 36265, June 7, 2000]

21.20　Compliance with applicable requirements

The applicant for a type certificate, including an amended or supplemental type certificate, must—

(a) Show compliance with all applicable requirements and must provide the FAA the means by which such compliance has been shown; and

(b) Provide a statement certifying that the applicant has complied with the applicable requirements

[Doc. No. 21–92, 74 FR 53385, Oct. 16, 2009]

21.21　Issue of type certificate: normal, utility, acrobatic, commuter, and transport category aircraft; manned free balloons; special classes of aircraft; aircraft engines; propellers

An applicant is entitled to a type certificate for an aircraft in the normal, utility, acrobatic, commuter, or transport category, or for a manned free balloon, special class of aircraft, or an aircraft engine or propeller, if—

(a) The product qualifies under 21.27; or

(b) The applicant submits the type design, test reports, and computations necessary to show that the product to be certificated meets the applicable airworthiness, aircraft noise, fuel venting, and exhaust emission requirements of this subchapter and any special conditions prescribed by the FAA, and the FAA finds—

　(1) Upon examination of the type design, and after completing all tests and inspections, that the type design and the product meet the applicable noise, fuel venting, and emissions requirements of this subchapter, and further finds that they meet the applicable airworthiness requirements of this subchapter or that any airworthiness provisions not complied with are compensated for by factors that provide an equivalent level of safety; and

(2) For an aircraft, that no feature or characteristic makes it unsafe for the category in which certification is requested

[Doc. No. 5085, 29 FR 14564, Oct. 24, 1964, as amended by Amdt. 21–15, 32 FR 3735, Mar. 4, 1967; Amdt. 21–27, 34 FR 18368, Nov. 18, 1969; Amdt. 21–60, 52 FR 8042, Mar. 13, 1987; Amdt. 21–68, 55 FR 32860, Aug. 10, 1990; Amdt. 21–92, 74 FR 53385, Oct. 16, 2009]

21.23   [Reserved]

21.24   Issuance of type certificate: primary category aircraft

(a) The applicant is entitled to a type certificate for an aircraft in the primary category if—

(1) The aircraft—

  (i) Is unpowered; is an airplane powered by a single, (i) Is unpowered; is an airplane powered by a single, naturally aspirated engine with a 61-knot or less V_{so} stall speed as determined under part 23 of this chapter; or is a rotorcraft with a 6-pound per square foot main rotor disc loading limitation, under sea level standard day conditions;

  (ii) Weighs not more than 2,700 pounds; or, for seaplanes, not more than 3,375 pounds;

  (iii) Has a maximum seating capacity of not more than four persons, including the pilot; and

  (iv) Has an unpressurized cabin

(2) The applicant has submitted—

  (i) Except as provided by paragraph (c) of this section, a statement, in a form and manner acceptable to the Administrator, certifying that: the applicant has completed the engineering analysis necessary to demonstrate compliance with the applicable airworthiness requirements; the applicant has conducted appropriate flight, structural, propulsion, and systems tests necessary to show that the aircraft, its components, and its equipment are reliable and function properly; the type design complies with the airworthiness standards and noise requirements established for the aircraft under 21.17(f); and no feature or characteristic makes it unsafe for its intended use;

  (ii) The flight manual required by 21.5(b), including any information required to be furnished by the applicable airworthiness standards;

  (iii) Instructions for continued airworthiness in accordance with 21.50(b); and

  (iv) A report that: summarizes how compliance with each provision of the type certification basis was determined; lists the specific documents in which the type certification data information is provided; lists all necessary drawings and documents used to define the type design; and lists all the engineering reports on tests and computations that the applicant must retain and make available under 21.49 to substantiate compliance with the applicable airworthiness standards

(3) The Administrator finds that—

  (i) The aircraft complies with those applicable airworthiness requirements approved under 21.17(f) of this part; and

  (ii) The aircraft has no feature or characteristic that makes it unsafe for its intended use

(b) An applicant may include a special inspection and preventive maintenance program as part of the aircraft's type design or supplemental type design

(c) For aircraft manufactured outside of the United States in a country with which the United States has a bilateral airworthiness agreement for the acceptance of these aircraft, and from which the aircraft is to be imported into the United States—

(1) The statement required by paragraph (a)(2)(i) of this section must be made by the civil airworthiness authority of the exporting country; and

(2) The required manuals, placards, listings, instrument markings, and documents required by paragraphs (a) and (b) of this section must be submitted in English

[Doc. No. 23345, 57 FR 41367, Sept. 9, 1992, as amended by Amdt. 21–75, 62 FR 62808, Nov. 25, 1997; Doc. No. FAA-2015-1621, Amdt. 21-100, 81 FR 96689, Dec. 30, 2016]

21.25   Issue of type certificate: Restricted category aircraft

(a) An applicant is entitled to a type certificate for an aircraft in the restricted category for special purpose operations if he shows compliance with the applicable noise requirements of Part 36 of this chapter, and if he shows that no feature or characteristic of the aircraft makes it unsafe when it is operated under the limitations prescribed for its intended use, and that the aircraft—

(1) Meets the airworthiness requirements of an aircraft category except those requirements that the Administrator finds inappropriate for the special purpose for which the aircraft is to be used; or

(2) Is of a type that has been manufactured in accordance with the requirements of and accepted for use by, an Armed Force of the United States and has been later modified for a special purpose

(b) For the purposes of this section, "special purpose operations" includes—

(1) Agricultural (spraying, dusting, and seeding, and livestock and predatory animal control);

(2) Forest and wildlife conservation;

(3) Aerial surveying (photography, mapping, and oil and mineral exploration);

(4) Patrolling (pipelines, power lines, and canals);

(5) Weather control (cloud seeding);

(6) Aerial advertising (skywriting, banner towing, airborne signs and public address systems); and

(7) Any other operation specified by the Administrator

[Doc. No. 5085, 29 FR 14564, Oct. 24, 1964, as amended by Amdt. 21–42, 40 FR 1033, Jan. 6, 1975]

21.27   Issue of type certificate: surplus aircraft of the Armed Forces.

(a) Except as provided in paragraph (b) of this section an applicant is entitled to a type certificate for an aircraft in the normal, utility, acrobatic, commuter, or transport category that was designed and constructed in the United States, accepted for operational use, and declared surplus by, an Armed Force of the United States, and that is shown to comply with the applicable certification requirements in paragraph (f) of this section.

(b) An applicant is entitled to a type certificate for a surplus aircraft of the Armed Forces of the United States that is a counterpart of a previously type certificated civil aircraft, if he shows compliance with the regulations governing the original civil aircraft type certificate.

(c) Aircraft engines, propellers, and their related accessories installed in surplus Armed Forces aircraft, for which a type certificate is sought under this section, will be approved for use on those aircraft if the applicant shows that on the basis of the previous military qualifications, acceptance, and service record, the product provides substantially the same level of airworthiness as would be provided if the engines or propellers were type certificated under Part 33 or 35 of this subchapter.

(d) The FAA may relieve an applicant from strict compliance with a specific provision of the applicable requirements in paragraph (f) of this section, if the FAA finds that the method of compliance proposed by the applicant provides substantially the same level of airworthiness and that strict compliance WITH THOSE REGULATIONS would impose a severe burden on the applicant. The FAA may use experience that was satisfactory to an Armed Force of the United States in making such a determination.

(e) The FAA may require an applicant to comply with special conditions and later requirements than those in paragraphs (c) and (f)

of this section, if the FAA finds that compliance with the listed regulations would not ensure an adequate level of airworthiness for the aircraft.

(f) Except as provided in paragraphs (b) through (e) of this section, an applicant for a type certificate under this section must comply with the appropriate regulations listed in the following table:

TYPE OF AIRCRAFT	DATE ACCEPTED FOR OPERATIONAL USE BY THE ARMED FORCES OF THE UNITED STATES	REGULATIONS THAT APPLY[1]
Small reciprocating engine-powered airplanes	Before May 16, 1956 After May 15, 1956	CAR Part 3, as effective May 15, 1956 CAR Part 3, or 14 CFR Part 23
Small turbine engine-powered airplanes	Before Oct. 2, 1959 After Oct. 1, 1959	CAR Part 3, as effective Oct. 1, 1959 CAR Part 3 or 14 CFR Part 23
Commuter category airplanes	After (Feb. 17, 1987) FAR Part 23 as of (Feb. 17, 1987).	
Large reciprocating engine-powered airplanes	Before Aug. 26, 1955 After Aug. 25, 1955	CAR Part 4b, as effective Aug. 25, 1955 CAR Part 4b or 14 CFR Part 25
Large turbine engine-powered airplanes	Before Oct. 2, 1959 After Oct. 1, 1959	CAR Part 4b, as effective Oct. 1, 1959 CAR Part 4b or 14 CFR Part 25
Rotorcraft with maximum certificated takeoff weight of:		
6,000 pounds or less	Before Oct. 2, 1959 After Oct. 1, 1959	CAR Part 6, as effective Oct. 1, 1959 CAR Part 6, or 14 CFR Part 27
Over 6,000 pounds	Before Oct. 2, 1959 After Oct. 1, 1959	CAR Part 7, as effective Oct. 1, 1959 CAR Part 7, or 14 CFR Part 29[1]

[1]Where no specific date is listed, the applicable regulations are those in effect on the date that the first aircraft of the particular model was accepted for operational use by the Armed Forces.

[Doc. No. 5085, 29 FR 14564, Oct. 24, 1964, as amended by Amdt. 21–59, 52 FR 1835, Jan. 15, 1987; 52 FR 7262, Mar. 9, 1987; 70 FR 2325, Jan. 13, 2005; Amdt. 21–92, 74 FR 53386, Oct. 16, 2009]

21.29 Issue of type certificate: import products

(a) The FAA may issue a type certificate for a product that is manufactured in a foreign country or jurisdiction with which the United States has an agreement for the acceptance of these products for export and import and that is to be imported into the United States if—

(1) The applicable State of Design certifies that the product has been examined, tested, and found to meet—

(i) The applicable aircraft noise, fuel venting, and exhaust emissions requirements of this subchapter as designated in 21.17, or the applicable aircraft noise, fuel venting, and exhaust emissions requirements of the State of Design, and any other requirements the FAA may prescribe to provide noise, fuel venting, and exhaust emission levels no greater than those provided by the applicable aircraft noise, fuel venting, and exhaust emission requirements of this subchapter as designated in 21.17; and

(ii) The applicable airworthiness requirements of this subchapter as designated in 21.17, or the applicable airworthiness requirements of the State of Design and any other requirements the FAA may prescribe to provide a level of safety equivalent to that provided by the applicable airworthiness requirements of this subchapter as designated in 21.17;

(2) The applicant has provided technical data to show the product meets the requirements of paragraph (a)(1) of this section; and

(3) The manuals, placards, listings, and instrument markings required by the applicable airworthiness (and noise, where applicable) requirements are presented in the English language

(b) A product type certificated under this section is considered to be type certificated under the noise standards of part 36 of this subchapter and the fuel venting and exhaust emission standards

of part 34 of this subchapter. Compliance with parts 36 and 34 of this subchapter is certified under paragraph (a)(1)(i) of this section, and the applicable airworthiness standards of this subchapter, or an equivalent level of safety, with which compliance is certified under paragraph (a)(1)(ii) of this section

[Amdt. 21–92, 74 FR 53386, Oct. 16, 2009]

21.31 Type design

The type design consists of—

(a) The drawings and specifications, and a listing of those drawings and specifications, necessary to define the configuration and the design features of the product shown to comply with the requirements of that part of this subchapter applicable to the product;

(b) Information on dimensions, materials, and processes necessary to define the structural strength of the product;

(c) The Airworthiness Limitations section of the Instructions for Continued Airworthiness as required by parts 23, 25, 26, 27, 29, 31, 33 and 35 of this subchapter, or as otherwise required by the FAA; and as specified in the applicable airworthiness criteria for special classes of aircraft defined in 21.17(b); and

(d) For primary category aircraft, if desired, a special inspection and preventive maintenance program designed to be accomplished by an appropriately rated and trained pilot-owner

(e) Any other data necessary to allow, by comparison, the determination of the airworthiness, noise characteristics, fuel venting, and exhaust emissions (where applicable) of later products of the same type

[Doc. No. 5085, 29 FR 14564, Oct. 24, 1964, as amended by Amdt. 21–27, 34 FR 18363, Nov. 18, 1969; Amdt. 21–51, 45 FR 60170, Sept. 11, 1980; Amdt. 21–60, 52 FR 8042, Mar. 13, 1987; Amdt. 21–68, 55 FR 32860, Aug. 10, 1990; Amdt. 21–70, 57 FR 41368, Sept. 9, 1992; Amdt. 21–90, 72 FR 63404, Nov. 8, 2007]

21.33 Inspection and tests

(a) Each applicant must allow the FAA to make any inspection and any flight and ground test necessary to determine compliance with the applicable requirements of this subchapter. However, unless otherwise authorized by the FAA—

  (1) No aircraft, aircraft engine, propeller, or part thereof may be presented to the FAA for test unless compliance with paragraphs (b)(2) through (b)(4) of this section has been shown for that aircraft, aircraft engine, propeller, or part thereof; and

  (2) No change may be made to an aircraft, aircraft engine, propeller, or part thereof between the time that compliance with paragraphs (b)(2) through (b)(4) of this section is shown for that aircraft, aircraft engine, propeller, or part thereof and the time that it is presented to the FAA for test

(b) Each applicant must make all inspections and tests necessary to determine—

  (1) Compliance with the applicable airworthiness, aircraft noise, fuel venting, and exhaust emission requirements;

  (2) That materials and products conform to the specifications in the type design;

  (3) That parts of the products conform to the drawings in the type design; and

  (4) That the manufacturing processes, construction and assembly conform to those specified in the type design

[Doc. No. 5085, 29 FR 14564, Oct. 24, 1964, as amended by Amdt. 21–17, 32 FR 14926, Oct. 28, 1967; Amdt. 21–27, 34 FR 18363, Nov. 18, 1969; Amdt. 21–44, 41 FR 55463, Dec. 20, 1976; Amdt. 21–68, 55 FR 32860, Aug. 10, 1990; Amdt. 21–68, 55 FR 32860, Aug. 10, 1990; Amdt. 21 –92, 74 FR 53386, Oct. 16, 2009; Amdt. 21–92A, 75 FR 9095, Mar. 1, 2010]

21.35 Flight tests

(a) Each applicant for an aircraft type certificate (other than under 21.24 through 21.29) must make the tests listed in paragraph (b) of this section. Before making the tests the applicant must show—

  (1) Compliance with the applicable structural requirements of this subchapter;

  (2) Completion of necessary ground inspections and tests;

  (3) That the aircraft conforms with the type design; and

  (4) That the Administrator received a flight test report from the applicant (signed, in the case of aircraft to be certificated under Part 25 [New] of this chapter, by the applicant's test pilot) containing the results of his tests

(b) Upon showing compliance with paragraph (a) of this section, the applicant must make all flight tests that the Administrator finds necessary—

  (1) To determine compliance with the applicable requirements of this subchapter; and

  (2) For aircraft to be certificated under this subchapter, except gliders and low-speed, certification level 1 or 2 airplanes, as defined in part 23 of this chapter, to determine whether there is reasonable assurance that the aircraft, its components, and its equipment are reliable and function properly.

(c) Each applicant must, if practicable, make the tests prescribed in paragraph (b)(2) of this section upon the aircraft that was used to show compliance with—

  (1) Paragraph (b)(1) of this section; and

  (2) For rotorcraft, the rotor drive endurance tests prescribed in 27.923 or 29.923 of this chapter, as applicable

(d) Each applicant must show for each flight test (except in a glider or a manned free balloon) that adequate provision is made for the flight test crew for emergency egress and the use of parachutes

(e) Except in gliders and manned free balloons, an applicant must discontinue flight tests under this section until he shows that corrective action has been taken, whenever—

  (1) The applicant's test pilot is unable or unwilling to make any of the required flight tests; or

  (2) Items of noncompliance with requirements are found that may make additional test data meaningless or that would make further testing unduly hazardous

(f) The flight tests prescribed in paragraph (b)(2) of this section must include—

  (1) For aircraft incorporating turbine engines of a type not previously used in a type certificated aircraft, at least 300 hours of operation with a full complement of engines that conform to a type certificate; and

  (2) For all other aircraft, at least 150 hours of operation

[Doc. No. 5085, 29 FR 14564, Oct. 24, 1964, as amended by Amdt. 21-40, 39 FR 35459, Oct. 1, 1974; Amdt. 21-51, 45 FR 60170, Sept. 11, 1980; Amdt. 21-70, 57 FR 41368, Sept. 9, 1992; Amdt. 21-95, 76 FR 64233, Oct. 18, 2011; Doc. No. FAA-2015-1621, Amdt. 21-100, 81 FR 96689, Dec. 30, 2016]

21.37 Flight test pilot

Each applicant for a normal, utility, acrobatic, commuter, or transport category aircraft type certificate must provide a person holding an appropriate pilot certificate to make the flight tests required by this part

[Doc. No. 5085, 29 FR 14564, Oct. 24, 1964, as amended by Amdt. 21-59, 52 FR 1835, Jan. 15, 1987]

21.39 Flight test instrument calibration and correction report

(a) Each applicant for a normal, utility, acrobatic, commuter, or transport category aircraft type certificate must submit a report to the Administrator showing the computations and tests required in connection with the calibration of instruments used for test purposes and in the correction of test results to standard atmospheric conditions

(b) Each applicant must allow the Administrator to conduct any flight tests that he finds necessary to check the accuracy of the report submitted under paragraph (a) of this section

[Doc. No. 5085, 29 FR 14564, Oct. 24, 1964, as amended by Amdt. 21-59, 52 FR 1835, Jan. 15, 1987]

21.41 Type certificate

Each type certificate is considered to include the type design, the operating limitations, the certificate data sheet, the applicable regulations of this subchapter with which the Administrator records compliance, and any other conditions or limitations prescribed for the product in this subchapter

21.43 Location of manufacturing facilities

Except as provided in 21.29, the Administrator does not issue a type certificate if the manufacturing facilities for the product are located outside of the United States, unless the Administrator finds that the location of the manufacturer's facilities places no undue burden on the FAA in administering applicable airworthiness requirements

21.45 Privileges

The holder or licensee of a type certificate for a product may—

(a) In the case of aircraft, upon compliance with 21.173 through 21.189, obtain airworthiness certificates;

(b) In the case of aircraft engines or propellers, obtain approval for installation on certificated aircraft;

(c) In the case of any product, upon compliance with subpart G of this part, obtain a production certificate for the type certificated product;

(d) Obtain approval of replacement parts for that product

[Doc. No. 5085, 29 FR 14564, Oct. 24, 1964, as amended by Amdt. 21-92, 74 FR 53386, Oct. 16, 2009; Amdt. 21-92A, 75 FR 9095, Mar. 1, 2010]

FAR 21

21.47 Transferability

(a) A holder of a type certificate may transfer it or make it available to other persons by licensing agreements

(b) For a type certificate transfer in which the State of Design will remain the same, each transferor must, before such a transfer, notify the FAA in writing. This notification must include the applicable type certificate number, the name and address of the transferee, and the anticipated date of the transfer.

(c) For a type certificate transfer in which the State of Design is changing, a type certificate may only be transferred to or from a person subject to the authority of another State of Design if the United States has an agreement with that State of Design for the acceptance of the affected product for export and import. Each transferor must notify the FAA before such a transfer in a form and manner acceptable to the FAA. This notification must include the applicable type certificate number; the name, address, and country of residence of the transferee; and the anticipated date of the transfer.

(d) Before executing or terminating a licensing agreement that makes a type certificate available to another person, the type certificate holder must notify the FAA in writing. This notification must include the type certificate number addressed by the licensing agreement, the name and address of the licensee, the extent of authority granted the licensee, and the anticipated date of the agreement.

[Doc. No. FAA-2006-25877, Amdt. 21-92, 74 FR 53386, Oct. 16, 2009; Doc. No. FAA-2018-0119, Amdt. 21-101, 83 FR 9169, Mar. 5, 2018]

21.49 Availability

The holder of a type certificate shall make the certificate available for examination upon the request of the Administrator or the National Transportation Safety Board

[Doc. No. 5085, 29 FR 14564, Oct. 24, 1964, as amended by Doc. No. 8084, 32 FR 5769, Apr. 11, 1967]

21.50 Instructions for continued airworthiness and manufacturer's maintenance manuals having airworthiness limitations sections

(a) The holder of a type certificate for a rotorcraft for which a Rotorcraft Maintenance Manual containing an "Airworthiness Limitations" section has been issued under 27.1529 (a)(2) or 29.1529 (a)(2) of this chapter, and who obtains approval of changes to any replacement time, inspection interval, or related procedure in that section of the manual, must make those changes available upon request to any operator of the same type of rotorcraft

(b) The holder of a design approval, including either a type certificate or supplemental type certificate for an aircraft, aircraft engine, or propeller for which application was made after January 28, 1981, must furnish at least one set of complete Instructions for Continued Airworthiness to the owner of each type aircraft, aircraft engine, or propeller upon its delivery, or upon issuance of the first standard airworthiness certificate for the affected aircraft, whichever occurs later. The Instructions for Continued Airworthiness must be prepared in accordance with 23.1529, 25.1529, 25.1729, 27.1529, 29.1529, 31.82, 33.4, 35.4, or part 26 of this subchapter, or as specified in the applicable airworthiness criteria for special classes of aircraft defined in § 21.17(b), as applicable. If the holder of a design approval chooses to designate parts as commercial, it must include in the Instructions for Continued Airworthiness a list of commercial parts submitted in accordance with the provisions of paragraph (c) of this section. Thereafter, the holder of a design approval must make those instructions available to any other person required by this chapter to comply with any of the terms of those instructions. In addition, changes to the Instructions for Continued Airworthiness shall be made available to any person required by this chapter to comply with any of those instructions.

(c) To designate commercial parts, the holder of a design approval, in a manner acceptable to the FAA, must submit:

(1) A Commercial Parts List;

(2) Data for each part on the List showing that:

(i) The failure of the commercial part, as installed in the product, would not degrade the level of safety of the product; and

(ii) The part is produced only under the commercial part manufacturer's specification and marked only with the commercial part manufacturer's markings; and

(3) Any other data necessary for the FAA to approve the List

[Amdt. 21-23, 33 FR 14105, Sept. 18, 1968, as amended by Amdt. 21-51, 45 FR 60170, Sept. 11, 1980; Amdt. 21-60, 52 FR 8042, Mar. 13, 1987; Amdt. 21-90, 72 FR 63404, Nov. 8, 2007; Amdt. 21-92, 74 FR 53386, Oct. 16, 2009; Doc. No. FAA-2015-1621, Amdt. 21-100, 81 FR 96689, Dec. 30, 2016]

21.51 Duration

A type certificate is effective until surrendered, suspended, revoked, or a termination date is otherwise established by the FAA

[Doc. No. 5085, 29 FR 14564, Oct. 24, 1964, as amended by Amdt. 21-92, 74 FR 53386, Oct. 16, 2009; Amdt. 21-92A, 75 FR 9095, Mar. 1, 2010]

21.53 Statement of conformity

(a) Each applicant must provide, in a form and manner acceptable to the FAA, a statement that each aircraft engine or propeller presented for type certification conforms to its type design

(b) Each applicant must submit a statement of conformity to the FAA for each aircraft or part thereof presented to the FAA for tests. This statement of conformity must include a statement that the applicant has complied with 21.33(a) (unless otherwise authorized under that paragraph)

[Amdt. 21-17, 32 FR 14926, Oct. 28, 1967, as amended by Amdt. 21-92, 74 FR 53386, Oct. 16, 2009]

21.55 Responsibility of type certificate holders to provide written licensing agreements

A type certificate holder who allows a person to use the type certificate to manufacture a new aircraft, aircraft engine, or propeller must provide that person with a written licensing agreement acceptable to the FAA

[Doc. No. FAA-2003-14825, 71 FR 52258, Sept. 1, 2006]

Subpart C — Provisional Type Certificates

Source: Docket No. 5085, 29 FR 14566, Oct. 24, 1964, unless otherwise noted

21.71 Applicability

This subpart prescribes—

(a) Procedural requirements for the issue of provisional type certificates, amendments to provisional type certificates, and provisional amendments to type certificates; and

(b) Rules governing the holders of those certificates

21.73 Eligibility

(a) Any manufacturer of aircraft manufactured within the United States who is a United States citizen may apply for Class I or Class II provisional type certificates, for amendments to provisional type certificates held by him, and for provisional amendments to type certificates held by him

(b) Any manufacturer of aircraft in a State of Manufacture subject to the provisions of an agreement with the United States for the acceptance of those aircraft for export and import may apply for a Class II provisional type certificate, for amendments to provisional type certificates held by him, and for provisional amendments to type certificates held by him

(c) An aircraft engine manufacturer who is a United States citizen and who has altered a type certificated aircraft by installing different type certificated aircraft engines manufactured by him within the United States may apply for a Class I provisional type certificate for the aircraft, and for amendments to Class I provisional type certificates held by him, if the basic aircraft, before alteration, was type certificated in the normal, utility, acrobatic, commuter, or transport category

[Doc. No. 5085, 29 FR 14566, Oct. 24, 1964, as amended by Amdt. 21–12, 31 FR 13380, Oct. 15, 1966; Amdt. 21–59, 52 FR 1836, Jan. 15, 1987; Amdt. 21–92, 74 FR 53387, Oct. 16, 2009]

21.75   Application

Each applicant for a provisional type certificate, for an amendment thereto, or for a provisional amendment to a type certificate must apply to the FAA and provide the information required by this subpart.

[Doc. No. FAA-2006-25877, Amdt. 21-92, 74 FR 53387, Oct. 16, 2009; Doc. No. FAA-2018-0119, Amdt. 21-101, 83 FR 9169, Mar. 5, 2018]

21.77   Duration

(a) Unless sooner surrendered, superseded, revoked, or otherwise terminated, provisional type certificates and amendments thereto are effective for the periods specified in this section

(b) A Class I provisional type certificate is effective for 24 months after the date of issue

(c) A Class II provisional type certificate is effective for twelve months after the date of issue

(d) An amendment to a Class I or Class II provisional type certificate is effective for the duration of the amended certificate

(e) A provisional amendment to a type certificate is effective for six months after its approval or until the amendment of the type certificate is approved, whichever is first

[Doc. No. 5085, 29 FR 14566, Oct. 24, 1964 as amended by Amdt. 21–7, 30 FR 14311, Nov. 16, 1965]

21.79   Transferability

Provisional type certificates are not transferable

21.81   Requirements for issue and amendment of Class I provisional type certificates

(a) An applicant is entitled to the issue or amendment of a Class I provisional type certificate if he shows compliance with this section and the Administrator finds that there is no feature, characteristic, or condition that would make the aircraft unsafe when operated in accordance with the limitations established in paragraph (e) of this section and in 91.317 of this chapter

(b) The applicant must apply for the issue of a type or supplemental type certificate for the aircraft

(c) The applicant must certify that—

(1) The aircraft has been designed and constructed in accordance with the airworthiness requirements applicable to the issue of the type or supplemental type certificate applied for;

(2) The aircraft substantially meets the applicable flight characteristic requirements for the type or supplemental type certificate applied for; and

(3) The aircraft can be operated safely under the appropriate operating limitations specified in paragraph (a) of this section

(d) The applicant must submit a report showing that the aircraft had been flown in all maneuvers necessary to show compliance with the flight requirements for the issue of the type or supplemental type certificate applied for, and to establish that the aircraft can be operated safely in accordance with the limitations contained in this subchapter

(e) The applicant must establish all limitations required for the issue of the type or supplemental type certificate applied for, including limitations on weights, speeds, flight maneuvers, loading, and operation of controls and equipment unless, for each limitation not so established, appropriate operating restrictions are established for the aircraft

(f) The applicant must establish an inspection and maintenance program for the continued airworthiness of the aircraft

(g) The applicant must show that a prototype aircraft has been flown for at least 50 hours under an experimental certificate issued under 21.191 through 21.195, or under the auspices of an Armed Force of the United States. However, in the case of an amendment to a provisional type certificate, the Administrator may reduce the number of required flight hours

[Doc. No. 5085, 29 FR 14566, Oct. 24, 1964, as amended by Amdt. 21–66, 54 FR 34329, Aug. 18, 1989]

21.83   Requirements for issue and amendment of Class II provisional type certificates

(a) An applicant who manufactures aircraft within the United States is entitled to the issue or amendment of a Class II provisional type certificate if he shows compliance with this section and the Administrator finds that there is no feature, characteristic, or condition that would make the aircraft unsafe when operated in accordance with the limitations in paragraph (h) of this section, and 91.317 and 121.207 of this chapter

(b) An applicant who manufactures aircraft in a country with which the United States has an agreement for the acceptance of those aircraft for export and import is entitled to the issue or amendment of a Class II provisional type certificate if the country in which the aircraft was manufactured certifies that the applicant has shown compliance with this section, that the aircraft meets the requirements of paragraph (f) of this section and that there is no feature, characteristic, or condition that would make the aircraft unsafe when operated in accordance with the limitations in paragraph (h) of this section and 91.317 and 121.207 of this chapter

(c) The applicant must apply for a type certificate, in the transport category, for the aircraft

(d) The applicant must hold a U.S. type certificate for at least one other aircraft in the same transport category as the subject aircraft

(e) The FAA's official flight test program or the flight test program conducted by the authorities of the country in which the aircraft was manufactured, with respect to the issue of a type certificate for that aircraft, must be in progress

(f) The applicant or, in the case of a foreign manufactured aircraft, the country in which the aircraft was manufactured, must certify that—

(1) The aircraft has been designed and constructed in accordance with the airworthiness requirements applicable to the issue of the type certificate applied for;

(2) The aircraft substantially complies with the applicable flight characteristic requirements for the type certificate applied for; and

(3) The aircraft can be operated safely under the appropriate operating limitations in this subchapter

(g) The applicant must submit a report showing that the aircraft has been flown in all maneuvers necessary to show compliance with the flight requirements for the issue of the type certificate and to establish that the aircraft can be operated safely in accordance with the limitations in this subchapter

(h) The applicant must prepare a provisional aircraft flight manual containing all limitations required for the issue of the type certificate applied for, including limitations on weights, speeds, flight maneuvers, loading, and operation of controls and equipment unless, for each limitation not so established, appropriate operating restrictions are established for the aircraft

(i) The applicant must establish an inspection and maintenance program for the continued airworthiness of the aircraft

(j) The applicant must show that a prototype aircraft has been flown for at least 100 hours. In the case of an amendment to a provisional type certificate, the Administrator may reduce the number of required flight hours

[Amdt. 21–12, 31 FR 13386, Oct. 15, 1966, as amended by Amdt. 21–66, 54 FR 34329, Aug. 18, 1989]

21.85   Provisional amendments to type certificates

(a) An applicant who manufactures aircraft within the United States is entitled to a provisional amendment to a type certificate if he shows compliance with this section and the Administrator finds that there is no feature, characteristic, or condition that would make the aircraft unsafe when operated under the appropriate limitations contained in this subchapter

(b) An applicant who manufactures aircraft in a foreign country with which the United States has an agreement for the acceptance of those aircraft for export and import is entitled to a provisional amendment to a type certificate if the country in which the aircraft was manufactured certifies that the applicant has shown compliance with this section, that the aircraft meets the requirements of paragraph (e) of this section and that there is no feature, characteristic, or condition that would make the aircraft unsafe when operated under the appropriate limitations contained in this subchapter

(c) The applicant must apply for an amendment to the type certificate

(d) The FAA's official flight test program or the flight test program conducted by the authorities of the country in which the aircraft was manufactured, with respect to the amendment of the type certificate, must be in progress

(e) The applicant or, in the case of foreign manufactured aircraft, the country in which the aircraft was manufactured, must certify that—

(1) The modification involved in the amendment to the type certificate has been designed and constructed in accordance with the airworthiness requirements applicable to the issue of the type certificate for the aircraft;

(2) The aircraft substantially complies with the applicable flight characteristic requirements for the type certificate; and

(3) The aircraft can be operated safely under the appropriate operating limitations in this subchapter

(f) The applicant must submit a report showing that the aircraft incorporating the modifications involved has been flown in all maneuvers necessary to show compliance with the flight requirements applicable to those modifications and to establish that the aircraft can be operated safely in accordance with the limitations specified in 91.317 and 121.207 of this chapter

(g) The applicant must establish and publish, in a provisional aircraft flight manual or other document and on appropriate placards, all limitations required for the issue of the type certificate applied for, including weight, speed, flight maneuvers, loading, and operation of controls and equipment, unless, for each limitation not so established, appropriate operating restrictions are established for the aircraft

(h) The applicant must establish an inspection and maintenance program for the continued airworthiness of the aircraft

(i) The applicant must operate a prototype aircraft modified in accordance with the corresponding amendment to the type certificate for the number of hours found necessary by the Administrator

[Amdt. 21–12, 31 FR 13388, Oct. 15, 1966, as amended by Amdt. 21–66, 54 FR 34329, Aug. 18, 1989]

Subpart D — Changes to Type Certificates

Source: Docket No. 5085, 29 FR 14567, Oct. 24, 1964, unless otherwise noted

21.91   Applicability

This subpart prescribes procedural requirements for the approval of changes to type certificates

21.93   Classification of changes in type design

(a) In addition to changes in type design specified in paragraph (b) of this section, changes in type design are classified as minor and major. A "minor change" is one that has no appreciable effect on the weight, balance, structural strength, reliability, operational characteristics, or other characteristics affecting the airworthiness of the product. All other changes are "major changes" (except as provided in paragraph (b) of this section)

(b) For the purpose of complying with Part 36 of this chapter, and except as provided in paragraphs (b)(2), (b)(3), and (b)(4) of this section, any voluntary change in the type design of an aircraft that may increase the noise levels of that aircraft is an "acoustical change" (in addition to being a minor or major change as classified in paragraph (a) of this section) for the following aircraft:

(1) Transport category large airplanes

(2) Jet (Turbojet powered) airplanes (regardless of category). For airplanes to which this paragraph applies, "acoustical changes" do not include changes in type design that are limited to one of the following—

    (i) Gear down flight with one or more retractable landing gear down during the entire flight, or

    (ii) Spare engine and nacelle carriage external to the skin of the airplane (and return of the pylon or other external mount), or

    (iii) Time-limited engine and/or nacelle changes, where the change in type design specifies that the airplane may not be operated for a period of more than 90 days unless compliance with the applicable acoustical change provisions of Part 36 of this chapter is shown for that change in type design

(3) Propeller driven commuter category and small airplanes in the primary, normal, utility, acrobatic, transport, and restricted categories, except for airplanes that are:

    (i) Designated for "agricultural aircraft operations" (as defined in 137.3 of this chapter, effective January 1, 1966) to which 36.1583 of this chapter does not apply, or

    (ii) Designated for dispensing fire fighting materials to which 36.1583 of this chapter does not apply, or

    (iii) U.S. registered, and that had flight time prior to January 1, 1955 or

    (iv) Land configured aircraft reconfigured with floats or skis. This reconfiguration does not permit further exception from the requirements of this section upon any acoustical change not enumerated in 21.93(b)

(4) Helicopters except:

    (i) Those helicopters that are designated exclusively:

      (A) For "agricultural aircraft operations", as defined in 137.3 of this chapter, as effective on January 1, 1966;

      (B) For dispensing fire fighting materials; or

      (C) For carrying external loads, as defined in 133.1(b) of this chapter, as effective on December 20, 1976

    (ii) Those helicopters modified by installation or removal of external equipment. For purposes of this paragraph, "external equipment" means any instrument, mechanism, part, apparatus, appurtenance, or accessory that is attached to, or extends from, the helicopter exterior but is not used nor is intended to be used in operating or controlling a helicopter in flight and is not part of an airframe or engine. An "acoustical change" does not include:

      (A) Addition or removal of external equipment;

      (B) Changes in the airframe made to accommodate the addition or removal of external equipment, to provide for an external load attaching means, to facilitate the use of external equipment or external loads, or to facilitate the safe operation of the helicopter with external equipment mounted to, or external loads carried by, the helicopter;

      (C) Reconfiguration of the helicopter by the addition or removal of floats and skis;

      (D) Flight with one or more doors and/or windows removed or in an open position; or

(E) Any changes in the operational limitations placed on the helicopter as a consequence of the addition or removal of external equipment, floats, and skis, or flight operations with doors and/or windows removed or in an open position

(5) Tiltrotors

(c) For purposes of complying with part 34 of this chapter, any voluntary change in the type design of the airplane or engine which may increase fuel venting or exhaust emissions is an "emissions change."

[Amdt. 21–27, 34 FR 18363, Nov. 18, 1969]

Editorial Note: ForFederal Registercitations affecting 21.93, see the List of CFR Sections Affected, which appears in the Finding Aids section of the printed volume and on GPO Access

21.95 Approval of minor changes in type design

Minor changes in a type design may be approved under a method acceptable to the Administrator before submitting to the Administrator any substantiating or descriptive data

21.97 Approval of major changes in type design

(a) An applicant for approval of a major change in type design must—

(1) Provide substantiating data and necessary descriptive data for inclusion in the type design;

(2) Show that the change and areas affected by the change comply with the applicable requirements of this subchapter, and provide the FAA the means by which such compliance has been shown; and

(3) Provide a statement certifying that the applicant has complied with the applicable requirements

(b) Approval of a major change in the type design of an aircraft engine is limited to the specific engine configuration upon which the change is made unless the applicant identifies in the necessary descriptive data for inclusion in the type design the other configurations of the same engine type for which approval is requested and shows that the change is compatible with the other configurations

[Amdt. 21-40, 39 FR 35459, Oct. 1, 1974, as amended by Amdt. 21-92, 74 FR 53387, Oct. 16, 2009; Amdt. 21-96, 77 FR 71695, Dec. 4, 2012]

21.99 Required design changes

(a) When an Airworthiness Directive is issued under Part 39 the holder of the type certificate for the product concerned must—

(1) If the Administrator finds that design changes are necessary to correct the unsafe condition of the product, and upon his request, submit appropriate design changes for approval; and

(2) Upon approval of the design changes, make available the descriptive data covering the changes to all operators of products previously certificated under the type certificate

(b) In a case where there are no current unsafe conditions, but the Administrator or the holder of the type certificate finds through service experience that changes in type design will contribute to the safety of the product, the holder of the type certificate may submit appropriate design changes for approval. Upon approval of the changes, the manufacturer shall make information on the design changes available to all operators of the same type of product

[Doc. No. 5085, 29 FR 14567, Oct. 24, 1964, as amended by Amdt. 21-3, 30 FR 8826, July 24, 1965]

21.101 Designation of applicable regulations

(a) An applicant for a change to a type certificate must show that the change and areas affected by the change comply with the airworthiness requirements applicable to the category of the product in effect on the date of the application for the change and with parts 34 and 36 of this chapter. Exceptions are detailed in paragraphs (b) and (c) of this section.

(b) Except as provided in paragraph (g) of this section, if paragraphs (b) (1), (2), or (3) of this section apply, an applicant may show that the

change and areas affected by the change comply with an earlier amendment of a regulation required by paragraph (a) of this section, and of any other regulation the FAA finds is directly related. However, the earlier amended regulation may not precede either the corresponding regulation included by reference in the type certificate, or any regulation in 25.2, 27.2, or 29.2 of this chapter that is related to the change. The applicant may show compliance with an earlier amendment of a regulation for any of the following:

(1) A change that the Administrator finds not to be significant. In determining whether a specific change is significant, the Administrator considers the change in context with all previous relevant design changes and all related revisions to the applicable regulations incorporated in the type certificate for the product. Changes that meet one of the following criteria are automatically considered significant:

(i) The general configuration or the principles of construction are not retained

(ii) The assumptions used for certification of the product to be changed do not remain valid

(2) Each area, system, component, equipment, or appliance that the Administrator finds is not affected by the change

(3) Each area, system, component, equipment, or appliance that is affected by the change, for which the FAA finds that compliance with a regulation described in paragraph (a) of this section would not contribute materially to the level of safety of the product or would be impractical.

(c) An applicant for a change to an aircraft (other than a rotorcraft) of 6,000 pounds or less maximum weight, to a non-turbine rotorcraft of 3,000 pounds or less maximum weight, to a level 1 low-speed airplane, or to a level 2 low-speed airplane may show that the change and areas affected by the change comply with the regulations included in the type certificate. However, if the FAA finds that the change is significant in an area, the FAA may designate compliance with an amendment to the regulation incorporated by reference in the type certificate that applies to the change and any regulation that the FAA finds is directly related, unless the FAA also finds that compliance with that amendment or regulation would not contribute materially to the level of safety of the product or would be impractical.

(d) If the Administrator finds that the regulations in effect on the date of the application for the change do not provide adequate standards with respect to the proposed change because of a novel or unusual design feature, the applicant must also comply with special conditions, and amendments to those special conditions, prescribed under the provisions of 21.16, to provide a level of safety equal to that established by the regulations in effect on the date of the application for the change

(e) An application for a change to a type certificate for a transport category aircraft is effective for 5 years, and an application for a change to any other type certificate is effective for 3 years. If the change has not been approved, or if it is clear that it will not be approved under the time limit established under this paragraph, the applicant may do either of the following:

(1) File a new application for a change to the type certificate and comply with all the provisions of paragraph (a) of this section applicable to an original application for a change

(2) File for an extension of the original application and comply with the provisions of paragraph (a) of this section. The applicant must then select a new application date. The new application date may not precede the date the change is approved by more than the time period established under this paragraph (e)

(f) For aircraft certificated under 21.17(b), 21.24, 21.25, and 21.27 the airworthiness requirements applicable to the category of the product in effect on the date of the application for the change include each airworthiness requirement that the Administrator finds to be appropriate for the type certification of the aircraft in accordance with those sections

(g) Notwithstanding paragraph (b) of this section, for transport category airplanes, the applicant must show compliance with each applicable provision of part 26 of this chapter, unless the applicant has elected or was required to comply with a corresponding amendment to part 25 of this chapter that was issued on or after the date of the applicable part 26 provision

[Doc. No. 28903, 65 FR 36266, June 7, 2000, as amended by Amdt. 21-90, 72 FR 63404, Nov. 8, 2007; Amdt. 21-96, 77 FR 71695, Dec. 4, 2012; Doc. No. FAA-2015-1621, Amdt. 21-100, 81 FR 96689, Dec. 30, 2016]

Subpart E — Supplemental Type Certificates

Source: Docket No. 5085, 29 FR 14568, Oct. 24, 1964, unless otherwise noted

21.111   Applicability

This subpart prescribes procedural requirements for the issue of supplemental type certificates

21.113   Requirement for supplemental type certificate

(a) If a person holds the TC for a product and alters that product by introducing a major change in type design that does not require an application for a new TC under §21.19, that person must apply to the FAA either for an STC, or to amend the original type certificate under subpart D of this part.

(b) If a person does not hold the TC for a product and alters that product by introducing a major change in type design that does not require an application for a new TC under §21.19, that person must apply to the FAA for an STC.

(c) The application for an STC must be made in the form and manner prescribed by the FAA.

[Doc. No. FAA-2006-25877, Amdt. 21-92, 74 FR 53387, Oct. 16, 2009; Doc. No. FAA-2018-0119, Amdt. 21-101, 83 FR 9169, Mar. 5, 2018]

21.115   Applicable requirements

(a) Each applicant for a supplemental type certificate must show that the altered product meets applicable requirements specified in 21.101 and, in the case of an acoustical change described in 21.93(b), show compliance with the applicable noise requirements of part 36 of this chapter and, in the case of an emissions change described in 21.93(c), show compliance with the applicable fuel venting and exhaust emissions requirements of part 34 of this chapter

(b) Each applicant for a supplemental type certificate must meet 21.33 and 21.53 with respect to each change in the type design

[Amdt. 21–17, 32 FR 14927, Oct. 28, 1967, as amended by Amdt. 21–42, 40 FR 1033, Jan. 6, 1975; Amdt. 21–52A, 45 FR 79009, Nov. 28, 1980; Amdt. 21–61, 53 FR 3540, Feb. 5, 1988; Amdt. 21–68, 55 FR 32860, Aug. 10, 1990; Amdt. 21–71, 57 FR 42854, Sept. 16, 1992; Amdt. 21–77, 65 FR 36266, June 7, 2000]

21.117   Issue of supplemental type certificates

(a) An applicant is entitled to a supplemental type certificate if the FAA finds that the applicant meets the requirements of 21.113 and 21.115

(b) A supplemental type certificate consists of—

(1) The approval by the FAA of a change in the type design of the product; and

(2) The type certificate previously issued for the product

[Docket No. 5085, 29 FR 14568, Oct. 24, 1964, as amended by Amdt. 21–92, 74 FR 53387, Oct. 16, 2009]

21.119   Privileges

The holder of a supplemental type certificate may—

(a) In the case of aircraft, obtain airworthiness certificates;

(b) In the case of other products, obtain approval for installation on certificated aircraft; and

(c) Obtain a production certificate in accordance with the requirements of subpart G of this part for the change in the type design approved by the supplemental type certificate

[Docket No. 5085, 29 FR 14568, Oct. 24, 1964, as amended by Amdt. 21–92, 74 FR 53387, Oct. 16, 2009]

21.120   Responsibility of supplemental type certificate holders to provide written permission for alterations

A supplemental type certificate holder who allows a person to use the supplemental type certificate to alter an aircraft, aircraft engine, or propeller must provide that person with written permission acceptable to the FAA

[Doc. No. FAA–2003–14825, 71 FR 52258, Sept. 1, 2006]

Subpart F — Production Under Type Certificate Only

Source: Docket No. 5085, 29 FR 14568, Oct. 24, 1964, unless otherwise noted

21.121   Applicability

This subpart prescribes rules for production under a type certificate only

21.122   Location of or change to manufacturing facilities

(a) A type certificate holder may utilize manufacturing facilities located outside of the United States if the FAA finds no undue burden in administering the applicable requirements of Title 49 U.S.C. and this subchapter

(b) The type certificate holder must obtain FAA approval before making any changes to the location of any of its manufacturing facilities

(c) The type certificate holder must immediately notify the FAA, in writing, of any change to the manufacturing facilities that may affect the inspection, conformity, or airworthiness of its product or article

[Doc. No. FAA–2006–25877, 74 FR 53387, Oct. 16, 2009, as amended by Amdt. 21–92A, 75 FR 9095, Mar. 1, 2010]

21.123   Production under type certificate

Each manufacturer of a product being manufactured under a type certificate must—

(a) Maintain at the place of manufacture all information and data specified in 21.31 and 21.41;

(b) Make each product and article thereof available for inspection by the FAA;

(c) Maintain records of the completion of all inspections and tests required by 21.127, 21.128, and 21.129 for at least 5 years for the products and articles thereof manufactured under the approval and at least 10 years for critical components identified under 45.15(c) of this chapter;

(d) Allow the FAA to make any inspection or test, including any inspection or test at a supplier facility, necessary to determine compliance with this subchapter;

(e) Mark the product in accordance with part 45 of this chapter, including any critical parts;

(f) Identify any portion of that product (e.g., sub-assemblies, component parts, or replacement articles) that leave the manufacturer's facility as FAA approved with the manufacturer's part number and name, trademark, symbol, or other FAA-approved manufacturer's identification; and

(g) Except as otherwise authorized by the FAA, obtain a production certificate for that product in accordance with subpart G of this part within 6 months after the date of issuance of the type certificate

[Doc. No. FAA-2006-25877, 74 FR 53387, Oct. 16, 2009]

21.125   [Reserved]

21.127   Tests: aircraft

(a) Each person manufacturing aircraft under a type certificate only shall establish an approved production flight test procedure and flight check-off form, and in accordance with that form, flight test each aircraft produced

(b) Each production flight test procedure must include the following:

  (1) An operational check of the trim, controllability, or other flight characteristics to establish that the production aircraft has the same range and degree of control as the prototype aircraft

  (2) An operational check of each part or system operated by the crew while in flight to establish that, during flight, instrument readings are within normal range

  (3) A determination that all instruments are properly marked, and that all placards and required flight manuals are installed after flight test

  (4) A check of the operational characteristics of the aircraft on the ground

  (5) A check on any other items peculiar to the aircraft being tested that can best be done during the ground or flight operation of the aircraft

21.128 Tests: aircraft engines

(a) Each person manufacturing aircraft engines under a type certificate only shall subject each engine (except rocket engines for which the manufacturer must establish a sampling technique) to an acceptable test run that includes the following:

  (1) Break-in runs that include a determination of fuel and oil consumption and a determination of power characteristics at rated maximum continuous power or thrust and, if applicable, at rated takeoff power or thrust

  (2) At least five hours of operation at rated maximum continuous power or thrust. For engines having a rated takeoff power or thrust higher than rated maximum continuous power or thrust, the five-hour run must include 30 minutes at rated takeoff power or thrust

(b) The test runs required by paragraph (a) of this section may be made with the engine appropriately mounted and using current types of power and thrust measuring equipment

[Doc. No. 5085, 29 FR 14568, Oct. 24, 1964, as amended by Amdt. 21–5, 32 FR 3735, Mar. 4, 1967]

21.129 Tests: propellers

Each person manufacturing propellers under a type certificate only shall give each variable pitch propeller an acceptable functional test to determine if it operates properly throughout the normal range of operation

21.130 Statement of Conformity

Each holder or licensee of a type certificate who manufactures a product under this subpart must provide, in a form and manner acceptable to the FAA, a statement that the product for which the type certificate has been issued conforms to its type certificate and is in a condition for safe operation

[Doc. No. FAA–2006–25877, 74 FR 53387, Oct. 16, 2009]

Subpart G — Production Certificates

Source: Docket No. FAA-2006-25877, 74 FR 53387, Oct. 16, 2009, unless otherwise noted

21.131 Applicability

This subpart prescribes—

(a) Procedural requirements for issuing production certificates; and

(b) Rules governing holders of those certificates

21.132 Eligibility

Any person may apply for a production certificate if that person holds, for the product concerned—

(a) A current type certificate,

(b) A supplemental type certificate, or

(c) Rights to the benefits of that type certificate or supplemental type certificate under a licensing agreement

21.133 Application

Each applicant must apply for a production certificate in a form and manner prescribed by the FAA

21.135 Organization

(a) Each applicant for or holder of a production certificate must provide the FAA with a document—

  (1) Describing how its organization will ensure compliance with the provisions of this subpart;

  (2) Describing assigned responsibilities, delegated authorities, and the functional relationship of those responsible for quality to management and other organizational components; and

  (3) Identifying an accountable manager.

(b) The accountable manager specified in paragraph (a) of this section must be responsible within the applicant's or production approval holder's organization for, and have authority over, all production operations conducted under this part. The accountable manager must confirm that the procedures described in the quality manual required by 21.138 are in place and that the production approval holder satisfies the requirements of the applicable regulations of subchapter C, Aircraft. The accountable manager must serve as the primary contact with the FAA.

[Doc. No. FAA-2013-0933, Amdt. 21-98, 80 FR 59031, Oct. 1, 2015]

21.137 Quality system

Each applicant for or holder of a production certificate must establish and describe in writing a quality system that ensures that each product and article conforms to its approved design and is in a condition for safe operation. This quality system must include:

(a) Design data control. Procedures for controlling design data and subsequent changes to ensure that only current, correct, and approved data is used

(b) Document control. Procedures for controlling quality system documents and data and subsequent changes to ensure that only current, correct, and approved documents and data are used

(c) Supplier control. Procedures that—

  (1) Ensure that each supplier-provided product, article, or service conforms to the production approval holder's requirements; and

  (2) Establish a supplier-reporting process for products, articles, or services that have been released from or provided by the supplier and subsequently found not to conform to the production approval holder's requirements.

(d) Manufacturing process control. Procedures for controlling manufacturing processes to ensure that each product and article conforms to its approved design

(e) Inspecting and testing. Procedures for inspections and tests used to ensure that each product and article conforms to its approved design. These procedures must include the following, as applicable:

  (1) A flight test of each aircraft produced unless that aircraft will be exported as an unassembled aircraft

  (2) A functional test of each aircraft engine and each propeller produced

(f) Inspection, measuring, and test equipment control. Procedures to ensure calibration and control of all inspection, measuring, and test equipment used in determining conformity of each product and article to its approved design. Each calibration standard must be traceable to a standard acceptable to the FAA

(g) Inspection and test status. Procedures for documenting the inspection and test status of products and articles supplied or manufactured to the approved design

(h) Nonconforming product and article control

  (1) Procedures to ensure that only products or articles that conform to their approved design are installed on a type-certificated product. These procedures must provide for the identifica-

tion, documentation, evaluation, segregation, and disposition of nonconforming products and articles. Only authorized individuals may make disposition determinations

(2) Procedures to ensure that discarded articles are rendered unusable

(i) **Corrective and preventive actions.** Procedures for implementing corrective and preventive actions to eliminate the causes of an actual or potential nonconformity to the approved design or noncompliance with the approved quality system

(j) **Handling and storage.** Procedures to prevent damage and deterioration of each product and article during handling, storage, preservation, and packaging

(k) **Control of quality records.** Procedures for identifying, storing, protecting, retrieving, and retaining quality records. A production approval holder must retain these records for at least 5 years for the products and articles manufactured under the approval and at least 10 years for critical components identified under 45.15(c) of this chapter

(l) **Internal audits.** Procedures for planning, conducting, and documenting internal audits to ensure compliance with the approved quality system. The procedures must include reporting results of internal audits to the manager responsible for implementing corrective and preventive actions

(m) **In-service feedback.** Procedures for receiving and processing feedback on in-service failures, malfunctions, and defects. These procedures must include a process for assisting the design approval holder to—

(1) Address any in-service problem involving design changes; and

(2) Determine if any changes to the Instructions for Continued Airworthiness are necessary

(n) **Quality escapes.** Procedures for identifying, analyzing, and initiating appropriate corrective action for products or articles that have been released from the quality system and that do not conform to the applicable design data or quality system requirements

(o) **Issuing authorized release documents.** Procedures for issuing authorized release documents for aircraft engines, propellers, and articles if the production approval holder intends to issue those documents. These procedures must provide for the selection, appointment, training, management, and removal of individuals authorized by the production approval holder to issue authorized release documents. Authorized release documents may be issued for new aircraft engines, propellers, and articles manufactured by the production approval holder; and for used aircraft engines, propellers, and articles when rebuilt, or altered, in accordance with 43.3(j) of this chapter. When a production approval holder issues an authorized release document for the purpose of export, the production approval holder must comply with the procedures applicable to the export of new and used aircraft engines, propellers, and articles specified in 21.331 and the responsibilities of exporters specified in 21.335.

[Docket No. FAA-2006-25877, Amdt. 21-92, 74 FR 53387, Oct. 16, 2009, as amended by Doc. No. FAA-2013-0933, Amdt. 21-98, 80 FR 59031, Oct. 1, 2015; Amdt. 21-98A, 80 FR 59031, Dec. 17, 2015]

21.138   Quality manual

Each applicant for or holder of a production certificate must provide a manual describing its quality system to the FAA for approval. The manual must be in the English language and retrievable in a form acceptable to the FAA

21.139   Location of or change to manufacturing facilities

(a) An applicant may obtain a production certificate for manufacturing facilities located outside of the United States if the FAA finds no undue burden in administering the applicable requirements of Title 49 U.S.C. and this subchapter

(b) The production certificate holder must obtain FAA approval before making any changes to the location of any of its manufacturing facilities

(c) The production certificate holder must immediately notify the FAA, in writing, of any change to the manufacturing facilities that may affect the inspection, conformity, or airworthiness of its product or article

21.140   Inspections and tests

Each applicant for or holder of a production certificate must allow the FAA to inspect its quality system, facilities, technical data, and any manufactured products or articles and witness any tests, including any inspections or tests at a supplier facility, necessary to determine compliance with this subchapter

21.141   Issuance

The FAA issues a production certificate after finding that the applicant complies with the requirements of this subpart

21.142   Production limitation record

The FAA issues a production limitation record as part of a production certificate. The record lists the type certificate number and model of every product that the production certificate holder is authorized to manufacture, and identifies every interface component that the production certificate holder is authorized to manufacture and install under this part.

[Doc. No. FAA-2013-0933, Amdt. 21-98, 80 FR 59031, Oct. 1, 2015, as amended by Amdt. 21-98A, 80 FR 59031, Dec. 17, 2015]

21.143   Duration

A production certificate is effective until surrendered, suspended, revoked, or the FAA otherwise establishes a termination date

21.144   Transferability

The holder of a production certificate may not transfer the production certificate

21.145   Privileges

(a) The holder of a production certificate may—

(1) Obtain an aircraft airworthiness certificate without further showing, except that the FAA may inspect the aircraft for conformity with the type design; or

(2) In the case of other products, obtain approval from the FAA for installation on type-certificated aircraft

(b) Notwithstanding the provisions of 147.3 of this chapter, the holder of a production certificate for a primary category aircraft, or for a normal, utility, or acrobatic category aircraft of a type design that is eligible for a special airworthiness certificate in the primary category under 21.184(c), may—

(1) Conduct training for persons in the performance of a special inspection and preventive maintenance program approved as a part of the aircraft's type design under 21.24(b), provided a person holding a mechanic certificate with appropriate airframe and powerplant ratings issued under part 65 of this chapter gives the training; and

(2) Issue a certificate of competency to persons successfully completing the approved training program, provided the certificate specifies the aircraft make and model to which the certificate applies

21.146   Responsibility of holder

The holder of a production certificate must—

(a) Amend the document required by 21.135 as necessary to reflect changes in the organization and provide these amendments to the FAA

(b) Maintain the quality system in compliance with the data and procedures approved for the production certificate;

(c) Ensure that each completed product or article for which a production certificate has been issued, including primary category aircraft assembled under a production certificate by another person from a kit provided by the holder of the production certificate, presented for airworthiness certification or approval conforms to its approved design and is in a condition for safe operation;

(d) Mark the product or article for which a certificate or approval has been issued. Marking must be in accordance with part 45 of this chapter, including any critical parts;

(e) Identify any portion of the product or article (e.g., sub-assemblies, component parts, or replacement articles) that leave the manufacturer's facility as FAA approved with the manufacturer's part number and name, trademark, symbol, or other FAA approved manufacturer's identification;

(f) Have access to type design data necessary to determine conformity and airworthiness for each product and article produced under the production certificate;

(g) Retain its production certificate and make it available to the FAA upon request; and

(h) Make available to the FAA information regarding all delegation of authority to suppliers

21.147 Amendment of production certificates

(a) A holder of a production certificate must apply for an amendment to a production certificate in a form and manner prescribed by the FAA.

(b) An applicant for an amendment to a production certificate to add a type certificate or model, or both, must comply with 21.137, 21.138, and 21.150.

(c) An applicant may apply to amend its production limitation record to allow the manufacture and installation of an interface component, provided—

(1) The applicant owns or has a license to use the design and installation data for the interface component and makes that data available to the FAA upon request;

(2) The applicant manufactures the interface component;

(3) The applicant's product conforms to its approved type design and the interface component conforms to its approved type design;

(4) The assembled product with the installed interface component is in a condition for safe operation; and

(5) The applicant complies with any other conditions and limitations the FAA considers necessary.

[Doc. No. FAA-2013-0933, Amdt. 21-98, 80 FR 59031, Oct. 1, 2015, as amended by Amdt. 21-98A, 80 FR 59031, Dec. 17, 2015]

21.150 Changes in quality system

After the issuance of a production certificate—

(a) Each change to the quality system is subject to review by the FAA; and

(b) The holder of a production certificate must immediately notify the FAA, in writing, of any change that may affect the inspection, conformity, or airworthiness of its product or article

Subpart H — Airworthiness Certificates

Source: Docket No. 5085, 29 FR 14569, Oct. 24, 1964, unless otherwise noted

21.171 Applicability

This subpart prescribes procedural requirements for the issue of airworthiness certificates

21.173 Eligibility

Any registered owner of a U.S.-registered aircraft (or the agent of the owner) may apply for an airworthiness certificate for that aircraft. An application for an airworthiness certificate must be made in a form and manner acceptable to the Administrator, and may be submitted to any FAA office

[Amdt. 21-26, 34 FR 15244, Sept. 30, 1969]

21.175 Airworthiness certificates: classification

(a) Standard airworthiness certificates are airworthiness certificates issued for aircraft type certificated in the normal, utility, acrobatic, commuter, or transport category, and for manned free balloons, and for aircraft designated by the Administrator as special classes of aircraft

(b) Special airworthiness certificates are primary, restricted, limited, light-sport, and provisional airworthiness certificates, special flight permits, and experimental certificates

[Amdt. 21-21, 33 FR 6858, May 7, 1968, as amended by Amdt. 21-60, 52 FR 8043, Mar. 13, 1987; Amdt. 21-70, 57 FR 41368, Sept. 9, 1992; Amdt. 21-85, 69 FR 44861, July 27, 2004]

21.177 Amendment or modification

An airworthiness certificate may be amended or modified only upon application to the Administrator

21.179 Transferability

An airworthiness certificate is transferred with the aircraft

21.181 Duration

(a) Unless sooner surrendered, suspended, revoked, or a termination date is otherwise established by the Administrator, airworthiness certificates are effective as follows:

(1) Standard airworthiness certificates, special airworthiness certificates—primary category, and airworthiness certificates issued for restricted or limited category aircraft are effective as long as the maintenance, preventive maintenance, and alterations are performed in accordance with Parts 43 and 91 of this chapter and the aircraft are registered in the United States

(2) A special flight permit is effective for the period of time specified in the permit

(3) A special airworthiness certificate in the light-sport category is effective as long as—

(i) The aircraft meets the definition of a light-sport aircraft;

(ii) The aircraft conforms to its original configuration, except for those alterations performed in accordance with an applicable consensus standard and authorized by the aircraft's manufacturer or a person acceptable to the FAA;

(iii) The aircraft has no unsafe condition and is not likely to develop an unsafe condition; and

(iv) The aircraft is registered in the United States

(4) An experimental certificate for research and development, showing compliance with regulations, crew training, or market surveys is effective for 1 year after the date of issue or renewal unless the FAA prescribes a shorter period. The duration of an experimental certificate issued for operating amateur-built aircraft, exhibition, air-racing, operating primary kit-built aircraft, or operating light-sport aircraft is unlimited, unless the FAA establishes a specific period for good cause

(b) The owner, operator, or bailee of the aircraft shall, upon request, make it available for inspection by the Administrator

(c) Upon suspension, revocation, or termination by order of the Administrator of an airworthiness certificate, the owner, operator, or bailee of an aircraft shall, upon request, surrender the certificate to the Administrator

[Amdt. 21-21, 33 FR 6858, May 7, 1968, as amended by Amdt. 21-49, 44 FR 46781, Aug. 9, 1979; Amdt. 21-70, 57 FR 41368, Sept. 9, 1992; Amdt. 21-85, 69 FR 44861, July 27, 2004]

21.182 Aircraft identification

(a) Except as provided in paragraph (b) of this section, each applicant for an airworthiness certificate under this subpart must show that his aircraft is identified as prescribed in 45.11

FAR 21

(b) Paragraph (a) of this section does not apply to applicants for the following:

  (1) A special flight permit

  (2) An experimental certificate for an aircraft not issued for the purpose of operating amateur-built aircraft, operating primary kit-built aircraft, or operating light-sport aircraft

  (3) A change from one airworthiness classification to another, for an aircraft already identified as prescribed in 45.11

[Amdt. 21–13, 32 FR 188, Jan. 10, 1967, as amended by Amdt. 21–51, 45 FR 60170, Sept. 11, 1980; Amdt. 21–70, 57 FR 41368, Sept. 9, 1992; Amdt. 21–85, 69 FR 44862, July 27, 2004]

21.183 Issue of standard airworthiness certificates for normal, utility, acrobatic, commuter, and transport category aircraft; manned free balloons; and special classes of aircraft

(a) New aircraft manufactured under a production certificate. An applicant for a standard airworthiness certificate for a new aircraft manufactured under a production certificate is entitled to a standard airworthiness certificate without further showing, except that the Administrator may inspect the aircraft to determine conformity to the type design and condition for safe operation

(b) New aircraft manufactured under type certificate only. An applicant for a standard airworthiness certificate for a new aircraft manufactured under a type certificate only is entitled to a standard airworthiness certificate upon presentation, by the holder or licensee of the type certificate, of the statement of conformity prescribed in 21.130 if the Administrator finds after inspection that the aircraft conforms to the type design and is in condition for safe operation

(c) Import aircraft. An applicant for a standard airworthiness certificate for an import aircraft is entitled to that certificate if—

  (1) The aircraft is type certificated in accordance with 21.21 or 21.29 and produced under the authority of another State of Manufacture;

  (2) The State of Manufacture certifies, in accordance with the export provisions of an agreement with the United States for import of that aircraft, that the aircraft conforms to the type design and is in condition for safe operations; and

  (3) The FAA finds that the aircraft conforms to the type design and is in condition for safe operation

(d) Used aircraft and surplus aircraft of the U.S. Armed Forces. An applicant for a standard airworthiness certificate for a used aircraft or surplus aircraft of the U.S. Armed Forces is entitled to a standard airworthiness certificate if—

  (1) The applicant presents evidence to the FAA that the aircraft conforms to a type design approved under a type certificate or a supplemental type certificate and to applicable Airworthiness Directives;

  (2) The aircraft (except an experimentally certificated aircraft that previously had been issued a different airworthiness certificate under this section) has been inspected in accordance with the performance rules for 100-hour inspections set forth in 43.15 of this chapter, or an equivalent performance standard acceptable to the FAA, and found airworthy by—

    (i) The manufacturer;

    (ii) The holder of a repair station certificate as provided in Part 145 of this chapter;

    (iii) The holder of a mechanic certificate as authorized in Part 65 of this chapter; or

    (iv) The holder of a certificate issued under Part 121 of this chapter, and having a maintenance and inspection organization appropriate to the aircraft type; and

  (3) The FAA finds after inspection, that the aircraft conforms to the type design, and is in condition for safe operation

(e) Noise requirements. Notwithstanding all other provisions of this section, the following must be complied with for the original issuance of a standard airworthiness certificate:

  (1) For transport category large airplanes and jet (turbojet powered) airplanes that have not had any flight time before the dates specified in 36.1(d), no standard airworthiness certificate is originally issued under this section unless the Administrator finds that the type design complies with the noise requirements in 36.1(d) in addition to the applicable airworthiness requirements in this section. For import airplanes, compliance with this paragraph is shown if the country in which the airplane was manufactured certifies, and the Administrator finds, that 36.1(d) (or the applicable airplane noise requirements of the country in which the airplane was manufactured and any other requirements the Administrator may prescribe to provide noise levels no greater than those provided by compliance with 36.1(d)) and paragraph (c) of this section are complied with

  (2) For normal, utility, acrobatic, commuter, or transport category propeller driven small airplanes (except for those airplanes that are designed for "agricultural aircraft operations" (as defined in 137.3 of this chapter, as effective on January 1, 1966) or for dispensing fire fighting materials to which 36.1583 of this chapter does not apply) that have not had any flight time before the applicable date specified in Part 36 of this chapter, no standard airworthiness certificate is originally issued under this section unless the applicant shows that the type design complies with the applicable noise requirements of Part 36 of this chapter in addition to the applicable airworthiness requirements in this section. For import airplanes, compliance with this paragraph is shown if the country in which the airplane was manufactured certifies, and the Administrator finds, that the applicable requirements of Part 36 of this chapter (or the applicable airplane noise requirements of the country in which the airplane was manufactured and any other requirements the Administrator may prescribe to provide noise levels no greater than those provided by compliance with the applicable requirements of Part 36 of this chapter) and paragraph (c) of this section are complied with

(f) Passenger emergency exit requirements. Notwithstanding all other provisions of this section, each applicant for issuance of a standard airworthiness certificate for a transport category airplane manufactured after October 16, 1987, must show that the airplane meets the requirements of 25.807(c)(7) in effect on July 24, 1989. For the purposes of this paragraph, the date of manufacture of an airplane is the date the inspection acceptance records reflect that the airplane is complete and meets the FAA-approved type design data

(g) Fuel venting and exhaust emission requirements. Notwithstanding all other provisions of this section, and irrespective of the date of application, no airworthiness certificate is issued, on and after the dates specified in part 34 for the airplanes specified therein, unless the airplane complies with the applicable requirements of that part

(h) New aircraft manufactured under the provisions of 21.6(b) . An applicant for a standard airworthiness certificate for a new aircraft manufactured under the provisions of 21.6(b) is entitled to a standard airworthiness certificate if—

  (1) The applicant presents evidence to the FAA that the aircraft conforms to a type design approved under a type certificate or supplemental type certificate and to applicable Airworthiness Directives;

  (2) The aircraft has been inspected in accordance with the performance rules for a 100-hour inspections set forth in 43.15 of this chapter and found airworthy by a person specified in paragraph (d)(2) of this section; and

  (3) The FAA finds after inspection, that the aircraft conforms to the type design, and is in condition for safe operation

[Amdt. 21–17, 32 FR 14927, Oct. 28, 1967]

Editorial Note: ForFederal Registercitations affecting 21.183, see the List of CFR Sections Affected, which appears in the Finding Aids section of the printed volume and at www.fdsys.gov.

21.184 Issue of special airworthiness certificates for primary category aircraft

(a) New primary category aircraft manufactured under a production certificate. An applicant for an original, special airworthiness certificate-primary category for a new aircraft that meets the criteria of 21.24(a)(1), manufactured under a production certificate, including aircraft assembled by another person from a kit provided by the holder of the production certificate and under the supervision and quality control of that holder, is entitled to a special airworthiness certificate without further showing, except that the Administrator may inspect the aircraft to determine conformity to the type design and condition for safe operation

(b) Imported aircraft. An applicant for a special airworthiness certificate-primary category for an imported aircraft type certificated under 21.29 is entitled to a special airworthiness certificate if the civil airworthiness authority of the country in which the aircraft was manufactured certifies, and the Administrator finds after inspection, that the aircraft conforms to an approved type design that meets the criteria of 21.24(a)(1) and is in a condition for safe operation

(c) Aircraft having a current standard airworthiness certificate. An applicant for a special airworthiness certificate-primary category, for an aircraft having a current standard airworthiness certificate that meets the criteria of 21.24(a)(1), may obtain the primary category certificate in exchange for its standard airworthiness certificate through the supplemental type certification process. For the purposes of this paragraph, a current standard airworthiness certificate means that the aircraft conforms to its approved normal, utility, or acrobatic type design, complies with all applicable airworthiness directives, has been inspected and found airworthy within the last 12 calendar months in accordance with 91.409(a)(1) of this chapter, and is found to be in a condition for safe operation by the Administrator

(d) Other aircraft. An applicant for a special airworthiness certificate-primary category for an aircraft that meets the criteria of 21.24(a)(1), and is not covered by paragraph (a), (b), or (c) of this section, is entitled to a special airworthiness certificate if—

    (1) The applicant presents evidence to the Administrator that the aircraft conforms to an approved primary, normal, utility, or acrobatic type design, including compliance with all applicable airworthiness directives;

    (2) The aircraft has been inspected and found airworthy within the past 12 calendar months in accordance with 91.409(a)(1) of this chapter and;

    (3) The aircraft is found by the Administrator to conform to an approved type design and to be in a condition for safe operation

(e) Multiple-category airworthiness certificates in the primary category and any other category will not be issued; a primary category aircraft may hold only one airworthiness certificate

[Doc. No. 23345, 57 FR 41368, Sept. 9, 1992, as amended by Amdt. 21–70, 57 FR 43776, Sept. 22, 1992]

21.185 Issue of airworthiness certificates for restricted category aircraft

(a) Aircraft manufactured under a production certificate or type certificate. An applicant for the original issue of a restricted category airworthiness certificate for an aircraft type certificated in the restricted category, that was not previously type certificated in any other category, must comply with the appropriate provisions of 21.183

(b) Other aircraft. An applicant for a restricted category airworthiness certificate for an aircraft type certificated in the restricted category, that was either a surplus aircraft of the Armed Forces or previously type certificated in another category, is entitled to an airworthiness certificate if the aircraft has been inspected by the FAA and found by him to be in a good state of preservation and repair and in a condition for safe operation

(c) Import aircraft. An applicant for the original issue of a special airworthiness certificate for a restricted category import aircraft is entitled to that certificate if—

    (1) The aircraft is type-certificated in accordance with 21.25 or 21.29 and produced under the authority of another State of Manufacture;

    (2) The State of Manufacture certifies, in accordance with the export provisions of an agreement with the United States for import of that aircraft that the aircraft conforms to the type design and is in condition for safe operation; and

    (3) The FAA finds that the aircraft conforms to the type design and is in condition for safe operation

(d) Noise requirements. For propeller-driven small airplanes (except airplanes designed for "agricultural aircraft operations," as defined in 137.3 of this chapter, as effective on January 1, 1966, or for dispensing fire fighting materials) that have not had any flight time before the applicable date specified in Part 36 of this chapter, and notwithstanding the other provisions of this section, no original restricted category airworthiness certificate is issued under this section unless the FAA finds that the type design complies with the applicable noise requirements of Part 36 of this chapter in addition to the applicable airworthiness requirements of this section. For import airplanes, compliance with this paragraph is shown if the country in which the airplane was manufactured certifies, and the FAA finds, that the applicable requirements of Part 36 of this chapter (or the applicable airplane noise requirements of the country in which the airplane was manufactured and any other requirements the FAA may prescribe to provide noise levels no greater than those provided by compliance with the applicable requirements of Part 36 of this chapter) and paragraph (c) of this section are complied with

[Amdt. 21–10, 31 FR 9211, July 6, 1966; as amended by Amdt. 21–32, 35 FR 10202, June 23, 1970; Amdt. 21–42, 40 FR 1034, Jan. 6, 1975; Amdt. 21–92, 74 FR 53389, Oct. 16, 2009; Amdt. 21–92, 74 FR 53389, Oct. 16, 2009; Amdt. 21–92A, 75 FR 9095, Mar. 1, 2010]

21.187 Issue of multiple airworthiness certification

(a) An applicant for an airworthiness certificate in the restricted category, and in one or more other categories except primary category, is entitled to the certificate, if—

    (1) He shows compliance with the requirements for each category, when the aircraft is in the configuration for that category; and

    (2) He shows that the aircraft can be converted from one category to another by removing or adding equipment by simple mechanical means

(b) The operator of an aircraft certificated under this section shall have the aircraft inspected by the Administrator, or by a certificated mechanic with an appropriate airframe rating, to determine airworthiness each time the aircraft is converted from the restricted category to another category for the carriage of passengers for compensation or hire, unless the Administrator finds this unnecessary for safety in a particular case

(c) The aircraft complies with the applicable requirements of part 34

[Doc. No. 5085, 29 FR 14569, Oct. 24, 1964, as amended by Amdt. 21–68, 55 FR 32860, Aug. 10, 1990; Amdt. 21–70, 57 FR 41369, Sept. 9, 1992]

21.189 Issue of airworthiness certificate for limited category aircraft

(a) An applicant for an airworthiness certificate for an aircraft in the limited category is entitled to the certificate when—

    (1) He shows that the aircraft has been previously issued a limited category type certificate and that the aircraft conforms to that type certificate; and

    (2) The Administrator finds, after inspection (including a flight check by the applicant), that the aircraft is in a good state of preservation and repair and is in a condition for safe operation

FAR 21

(b) The Administrator prescribes limitations and conditions necessary for safe operation

[Doc. No. 5085, 29 FR 14570, Oct. 24, 1964, as amended by Amdt. 21–4, 30 FR 9437, July 29, 1965]

21.190 Issue of a special airworthiness certificate for a light-sport category aircraft

(a) Purpose. The FAA issues a special airworthiness certificate in the light-sport category to operate a light-sport aircraft, other than a gyroplane

(b) Eligibility. To be eligible for a special airworthiness certificate in the light-sport category:

(1) An applicant must provide the FAA with—

    (i)   The aircraft's operating instructions;

    (ii) The aircraft's maintenance and inspection procedures;

    (iii) The manufacturer's statement of compliance as described in paragraph (c) of this section; and

    (iv) The aircraft's flight training supplement

(2) The aircraft must not have been previously issued a standard, primary, restricted, limited, or provisional airworthiness certificate, or an equivalent airworthiness certificate issued by a foreign civil aviation authority

(3) The aircraft must be inspected by the FAA and found to be in a condition for safe operation

(c) Manufacturer's statement of compliance for light-sport category aircraft. The manufacturer's statement of compliance required in paragraph (b)(1)(iii) of this section must—

(1) Identify the aircraft by make and model, serial number, class, date of manufacture, and consensus standard used;

(2) State that the aircraft meets the provisions of the identified consensus standard;

(3) State that the aircraft conforms to the manufacturer's design data, using the manufacturer's quality assurance system that meets the identified consensus standard;

(4) State that the manufacturer will make available to any interested person the following documents that meet the identified consensus standard:

    (i)   The aircraft's operating instructions

    (ii) The aircraft's maintenance and inspection procedures

    (iii) The aircraft's flight training supplement

(5) State that the manufacturer will monitor and correct safety-of-flight issues through the issuance of safety directives and a continued airworthiness system that meets the identified consensus standard;

(6) State that at the request of the FAA, the manufacturer will provide unrestricted access to its facilities; and

(7) State that the manufacturer, in accordance with a production acceptance test procedure that meets an applicable consensus standard has—

    (i)   Ground and flight tested the aircraft;

    (ii) Found the aircraft performance acceptable; and

    (iii) Determined that the aircraft is in a condition for safe operation

(d) Light-sport aircraft manufactured outside the United States. For aircraft manufactured outside of the United States to be eligible for a special airworthiness certificate in the light-sport category, an applicant must meet the requirements of paragraph (b) of this section and provide to the FAA evidence that—

(1) The aircraft was manufactured in a country with which the United States has a Bilateral Airworthiness Agreement concerning airplanes or Bilateral Aviation Safety Agreement with associated Implementation Procedures for Airworthiness concerning airplanes, or an equivalent airworthiness agreement; and

(2) The aircraft is eligible for an airworthiness certificate, flight authorization, or other similar certification in its country of manufacture

[Amdt. 21–85, 69 FR 44862, July 27, 2004]

21.191 Experimental certificates

Experimental certificates are issued for the following purposes:

(a) Research and development. Testing new aircraft design concepts, new aircraft equipment, new aircraft installations, new aircraft operating techniques, or new uses for aircraft

(b) Showing compliance with regulations. Conducting flight tests and other operations to show compliance with the airworthiness regulations including flights to show compliance for issuance of type and supplemental type certificates, flights to substantiate major design changes, and flights to show compliance with the function and reliability requirements of the regulations

(c) Crew training. Training of the applicant's flight crews

(d) Exhibition. Exhibiting the aircraft's flight capabilities, performance, or unusual characteristics at air shows, motion picture, television, and similar productions, and the maintenance of exhibition flight proficiency, including (for persons exhibiting aircraft) flying to and from such air shows and productions

(e) Air racing. Participating in air races, including (for such participants) practicing for such air races and flying to and from racing events

(f) Market surveys. Use of aircraft for purposes of conducting market surveys, sales demonstrations, and customer crew training only as provided in 21.195

(g) Operating amateur-built aircraft. Operating an aircraft the major portion of which has been fabricated and assembled by persons who undertook the construction project solely for their own education or recreation

(h) Operating primary kit-built aircraft. Operating a primary category aircraft that meets the criteria of 21.24(a)(1) that was assembled by a person from a kit manufactured by the holder of a production certificate for that kit, without the supervision and quality control of the production certificate holder under 21.184(a)

(i) Operating light-sport aircraft. Operating a light-sport aircraft that—

(1) Has not been issued a U.S. or foreign airworthiness certificate and does not meet the provisions of 103.1 of this chapter. An experimental certificate will not be issued under this paragraph for these aircraft after January 31, 2008;

(2) Has been assembled—

    (i)   From an aircraft kit for which the applicant can provide the information required by 21.193(e); and

    (ii) In accordance with manufacturer's assembly instructions that meet an applicable consensus standard; or

(3) Has been previously issued a special airworthiness certificate in the light-sport category under 21.190

[Amdt. 21–21, 38 FR 6858, May 7, 1968, as amended by Amdt. 21–57, 49 FR 39651, Oct. 9, 1984; Amdt. 21–70, 57 FR 41369, Sept. 9, 1992; Amdt. 21–85, 69 FR 44862, July 27, 2004; Amdt. 21–85, 69 FR 53336, Sept. 1, 2004]

21.193 Experimental certificates: general

An applicant for an experimental certificate must submit the following information:

(a) A statement, in a form and manner prescribed by the Administrator setting forth the purpose for which the aircraft is to be used

(b) Enough data (such as photographs) to identify the aircraft

(c) Upon inspection of the aircraft, any pertinent information found necessary by the Administrator to safeguard the general public

(d) In the case of an aircraft to be used for experimental purposes—

(1) The purpose of the experiment;

(2) The estimated time or number of flights required for the experiment;

(3) The areas over which the experiment will be conducted; and

(4) Except for aircraft converted from a previously certificated type without appreciable change in the external configuration, three-view drawings or three-view dimensioned photographs of the aircraft

(e) In the case of a light-sport aircraft assembled from a kit to be certificated in accordance with 21.191(i)(2), an applicant must provide the following:

(1) Evidence that an aircraft of the same make and model was manufactured and assembled by the aircraft kit manufacturer and issued a special airworthiness certificate in the light-sport category

(2) The aircraft's operating instructions

(3) The aircraft's maintenance and inspection procedures

(4) The manufacturer's statement of compliance for the aircraft kit used in the aircraft assembly that meets 21.190(c), except that instead of meeting 21.190(c)(7), the statement must identify assembly instructions for the aircraft that meet an applicable consensus standard

(5) The aircraft's flight training supplement

(6) In addition to paragraphs (e)(1) through (e)(5) of this section, for an aircraft kit manufactured outside of the United States, evidence that the aircraft kit was manufactured in a country with which the United States has a Bilateral Airworthiness Agreement concerning airplanes or a Bilateral Aviation Safety Agreement with associated Implementation Procedures for Airworthiness concerning airplanes, or an equivalent airworthiness agreement

[Docket No. 5085, 29 FR 14569, Oct. 24, 1964, as amended by Amdt. 21–85, 69 FR 44862, July 27, 2004]

21.195 Experimental certificates: Aircraft to be used for market surveys, sales demonstrations, and customer crew training

(a) A manufacturer of aircraft manufactured within the United States may apply for an experimental certificate for an aircraft that is to be used for market surveys, sales demonstrations, or customer crew training

(b) A manufacturer of aircraft engines who has altered a type certificated aircraft by installing different engines, manufactured by him within the United States, may apply for an experimental certificate for that aircraft to be used for market surveys, sales demonstrations, or customer crew training, if the basic aircraft, before alteration, was type certificated in the normal, acrobatic, commuter, or transport category

(c) A person who has altered the design of a type certificated aircraft may apply for an experimental certificate for the altered aircraft to be used for market surveys, sales demonstrations, or customer crew training if the basic aircraft, before alteration, was type certificated in the normal, utility, acrobatic, or transport category

(d) An applicant for an experimental certificate under this section is entitled to that certificate if, in addition to meeting the requirements of 21.193—

(1) He has established an inspection and maintenance program for the continued airworthiness of the aircraft; and

(2) The applicant shows that the aircraft has been flown for at least 50 hours, or for at least 5 hours if it is a type certificated aircraft which has been modified. The FAA may reduce these operational requirements if the applicant provides adequate justification

[Amdt. 21–21, 33 FR 6858, May 7, 1968, as amended by Amdt. 21–28, 35 FR 2818, Feb. 11, 1970; Amdt. 21–57, 49 FR 39651, Oct. 9, 1984; Amdt. 21–59, 52 FR 1836, Jan. 15, 1987; Amtd. 21–92, 74 FR 53389, Oct. 16, 2009]

21.197 Special flight permits

(a) A special flight permit may be issued for an aircraft that may not currently meet applicable airworthiness requirements but is capable of safe flight, for the following purposes:

(1) Flying the aircraft to a base where repairs, alterations, or maintenance are to be performed, or to a point of storage

(2) Delivering or exporting the aircraft

(3) Production flight testing new production aircraft

(4) Evacuating aircraft from areas of impending danger

(5) Conducting customer demonstration flights in new production air-craft that have satisfactorily completed production flight tests

(b) A special flight permit may also be issued to authorize the operation of an aircraft at a weight in excess of its maximum certificated takeoff weight for flight beyond the normal range over water, or over land areas where adequate landing facilities or appropriate fuel is not available. The excess weight that may be authorized under this paragraph is limited to the additional fuel, fuel-carrying facilities, and navigation equipment necessary for the flight

(c) Upon application, as prescribed in 91.1017 or 119.51 of this chapter, a special flight permit with a continuing authorization may be issued for aircraft that may not meet applicable airworthiness requirements but are capable of safe flight for the purpose of flying aircraft to a base where maintenance or alterations are to be performed. The permit issued under this paragraph is an authorization, including conditions and limitations for flight, which is set forth in the certificate holder's operations specifications. The permit issued under this paragraph may be issued to—

(1) Certificate holders authorized to conduct operations under Part 119 of this chapter, that have an approved program for continuing flight authorization; or

(2) Management specification holders authorized to conduct operations under part 91, subpart K of this chapter for those aircraft they operate and maintain under a continuous airworthiness maintenance program prescribed by 91.1411 of this chapter. The permit issued under this paragraph is an authorization, including any conditions and limitations for flight, which is set forth in the certificate holder's operations specifications

(3) Management specification holders authorized to conduct operations under part 91, subpart K, for those aircraft they operate and maintain under a continuous airworthiness maintenance program prescribed by 91.1411 of this part

[Doc. No. 5085, 29 FR 14570, Oct. 24, 1964, as amended by Amdt. 21–21, 33 FR 6859, May 7, 1968; Amdt. 21–51, 45 FR 60170, Sept. 11, 1980; Amdt. 21–54, 46 FR 37878, July 23, 1981; Amdt. 21–79, 66 FR 21066, Apr. 27, 2001; Amdt. 21–84, 68 FR 54559, Sept. 17, 2003; Amdt. 21–87, 71 FR 536, Jan. 4, 2006; Amdt. 21–92, 74 FR 53389, Oct. 16, 2009]

21.199 Issue of special flight permits

(a) Except as provided in 21.197(c), an applicant for a special flight permit must submit a statement in a form and manner prescribed by the Administrator, indicating—

(1) The purpose of the flight

(2) The proposed itinerary

(3) The crew required to operate the aircraft and its equipment, e.g., pilot, co-pilot, navigator, etc

(4) The ways, if any, in which the aircraft does not comply with the applicable airworthiness requirements

(5) Any restriction the applicant considers necessary for safe operation of the aircraft

(6) Any other information considered necessary by the Administrator for the purpose of prescribing operating limitations

(b) The Administrator may make, or require the applicant to make appropriate inspections or tests necessary for safety

[Doc. No. 5085, 29 FR 14570, Oct. 24, 1964, as amended by Amdt. 21–21, 33 FR 6859, May 7, 1968; Amdt. 21–22, 33 FR 11901, Aug. 22, 1968]

Subpart I — Provisional Airworthiness Certificates

Source: Docket No. 5085, 29 FR 14571, Oct. 24, 1964, unless otherwise noted

21.211   Applicability

This subpart prescribes procedural requirements for the issue of provisional airworthiness certificates

21.213   Eligibility

(a) A manufacturer who is a United States citizen may apply for a Class I or Class II provisional airworthiness certificate for aircraft manufactured by him within the U.S

(b) Any holder of an air carrier operating certificate under Part 121 of this chapter who is a United States citizen may apply for a Class II provisional airworthiness certificate for transport category aircraft that meet either of the following:

(1) The aircraft has a current Class II provisional type certificate or an amendment thereto

(2) The aircraft has a current provisional amendment to a type certificate that was preceded by a corresponding Class II provisional type certificate

(c) An aircraft engine manufacturer who is a United States citizen and who has altered a type certificated aircraft by installing different type certificated engines, manufactured by him within the United States, may apply for a Class I provisional airworthiness certificate for that aircraft, if the basic aircraft, before alteration, was type certificated in the normal, utility, acrobatic, commuter, or transport category

[Doc. No. 5085, 29 FR 14571, Oct. 24, 1964, as amended by Amdt. 21–59, 52 FR 1836, Jan. 15, 1987; Amdt. 21–79, 66 FR 21066, Apr. 27, 2001]

21.215   Application

Applications for provisional airworthiness certificates must be submitted to the FAA. The application must be accompanied by the pertinent information specified in this subpart.

[Amdt. 21-67, 54 FR 39291, Sept. 25, 1989; 54 FR 52872, Dec. 22, 1989; Doc. No. FAA-2018-0119, Amdt. 21-101, 83 FR 9169, Mar. 5, 2018]

21.217   Duration

Unless sooner surrendered, superseded, revoked, or otherwise terminated, provisional airworthiness certificates are effective for the duration of the corresponding provisional type certificate, amendment to a provisional type certificate, or provisional amendment to the type certificate

21.219   Transferability

Class I provisional airworthiness certificates are not transferable. Class II provisional airworthiness certificates may be transferred to an air carrier eligible to apply for a certificate under 21.213(b)

21.221   Class I provisional airworthiness certificates

(a) Except as provided in 21.225, an applicant is entitled to a Class I provisional airworthiness certificate for an aircraft for which a Class I provisional type certificate has been issued if—

(1) He meets the eligibility requirements of 21.213 and he complies with this section; and

(2) The Administrator finds that there is no feature, characteristic or condition of the aircraft that would make the aircraft unsafe when operated in accordance with the limitations established in 21.81(e) and 91.317 of this subchapter

(b) The manufacturer must hold a provisional type certificate for the aircraft

(c) The manufacturer must submit a statement that the aircraft conforms to the type design corresponding to the provisional type certificate and has been found by him to be in safe operating condition under all applicable limitations

(d) The aircraft must be flown at least five hours by the manufacturer

(e) The aircraft must be supplied with a provisional aircraft flight manual or other document and appropriate placards containing the limitations established by 21.81(e) and 91.317

[Doc. No. 5085, 29 FR 14571, Oct. 24, 1964, as amended by Amdt. 21–66, 54 FR 34329, Aug. 18, 1989]

21.223   Class II provisional airworthiness certificates

(a) Except as provided in 21.225, an applicant is entitled to a Class II provisional airworthiness certificate for an aircraft for which a Class II provisional type certificate has been issued if—

(1) He meets the eligibility requirements of 21.213 and he complies with this section; and

(2) The Administrator finds that there is no feature, characteristic, or condition of the aircraft that would make the aircraft unsafe when operated in accordance with the limitations established in 21.83(h), 91.317, and 121.207 of this chapter

(b) The applicant must show that a Class II provisional type certificate for the aircraft has been issued to the manufacturer

(c) The applicant must submit a statement by the manufacturer that the aircraft has been manufactured under a quality system adequate to ensure that the aircraft conforms to the type design corresponding with the provisional type certificate

(d) The applicant must submit a statement that the aircraft has been found by him to be in a safe operating condition under the applicable limitations

(e) The aircraft must be flown at least five hours by the manufacturer

(f) The aircraft must be supplied with a provisional aircraft flight manual containing the limitations established by 21.83(h), 91.317, and 121.207 of this chapter

[Doc. No. 5085, 29 FR 14571, Oct. 24, 1964, as amended by Amdt. 21–12, 31 FR 13389, Oct. 15, 1966; Amdt. 21–66, 54 FR 34329, Aug. 18, 1989; Amdt. 21-92, 74 FR 53389, Oct. 16, 2009]

21.225   Provisional airworthiness certificates corresponding with provisional amendments to type certificates

(a) An applicant is entitled to a Class I or a Class II provisional airworthiness certificate, for an aircraft, for which a provisional amendment to the type certificate has been issued, if—

(1) He meets the eligibility requirements of 21.213 and he complies with this section; and

(2) The Administrator finds that there is no feature, characteristic, or condition of the aircraft, as modified in accordance with the provisionally amended type certificate, that would make the aircraft unsafe when operated in accordance with the applicable limitations established in 21.85(g), 91.317, and 121.207 of this chapter

(b) The applicant must show that the modification was made under a quality system adequate to ensure that the modification conforms to the provisionally amended type certificate

(c) The applicant must submit a statement that the aircraft has been found by him to be in a safe operating condition under the applicable limitations

(d) The aircraft must be flown at least five hours by the manufacturer

(e) The aircraft must be supplied with a provisional aircraft flight manual or other document and appropriate placards containing the limitations required by 21.85(g), 91.317, and 121.207 of this chapter

[Doc. No. 5085, 29 FR 14571, Oct. 24, 1964, as amended by Amdt. 21–12, 31 FR 13389, Oct. 15, 1966; Amdt. 21–66, 54 FR 34329, Aug. 18, 1989; Amdt. 21-92, 74 FR 53389, Oct. 16, 2009]

Subpart J — [Reserved]

Subpart K — Parts Manufacturer Approvals

Source: Docket No. FAA–2006–25877, 74 FR 53390, Oct. 16, 2009, unless otherwise noted

21.301   Applicability

This subpart prescribes—

(a) Procedural requirements for issuing PMAs; and

(b) Rules governing holders of PMAs

21.303   Application

(a) The applicant for a PMA must apply in a form and manner prescribed by the FAA, and include the following:

   (1) The identity of the product on which the article is to be installed

   (2) The name and address of the manufacturing facilities at which these articles are to be manufactured

   (3) The design of the article, which consists of—

      (i) Drawings and specifications necessary to show the configuration of the article; and

      (ii) Information on dimensions, materials, and processes necessary to define the structural strength of the article

   (4) Test reports and computations necessary to show that the design of the article meets the airworthiness requirements of this subchapter. The test reports and computations must be applicable to the product on which the article is to be installed, unless the applicant shows that the design of the article is identical to the design of a article that is covered under a type certificate. If the design of the article was obtained by a licensing agreement, the applicant must provide evidence of that agreement

   (5) An applicant for a PMA based on test reports and computations must provide a statement certifying that the applicant has complied with the airworthiness requirements of this subchapter

(b) Each applicant for a PMA must make all inspections and tests necessary to determine—

   (1) Compliance with the applicable airworthiness requirements;

   (2) That materials conform to the specifications in the design;

   (3) That the article conforms to its approved design; and

   (4) That the manufacturing processes, construction, and assembly conform to those specified in the design

21.305   Organization

(a) Each applicant for or holder of a PMA must provide the FAA with a document—

   (1) Describing how its organization will ensure compliance with the provisions of this subpart;

   (2) Describing assigned responsibilities, delegated authorities, and the functional relationship of those responsible for quality to management and other organizational components; and

   (3) Identifying an accountable manager.

(b) The accountable manager specified in paragraph (a) of this section must be responsible within the applicant's or production approval holder's organization for, and have authority over, all production operations conducted under this part. The accountable manager must confirm that the procedures described in the quality manual required by §21.308 are in place and that the production approval holder satisfies the requirements of the applicable regulations of subchapter C, Aircraft. The accountable manager must serve as the primary contact with the FAA.

[Doc. No. FAA-2013-0933, Amdt. 21-98, 80 FR 59031, Oct. 1, 2015]

21.307   Quality system

Each applicant for or holder of a PMA must establish a quality system that meets the requirements of 21.137

21.308   Quality manual

Each applicant for or holder of a PMA must provide a manual describing its quality system to the FAA for approval. The manual must be in the English language and retrievable in a form acceptable to the FAA

21.309   Location of or change to manufacturing facilities

(a) An applicant may obtain a PMA for manufacturing facilities located outside of the United States if the FAA finds no undue burden in administering the applicable requirements of Title 49 U.S.C. and this subchapter

(b) The PMA holder must obtain FAA approval before making any changes to the location of any of its manufacturing facilities

(c) The PMA holder must immediately notify the FAA, in writing, of any change to the manufacturing facilities that may affect the inspection, conformity, or airworthiness of its PMA article

21.310   Inspections and tests

(a) Each applicant for or holder of a PMA must allow the FAA to inspect its quality system, facilities, technical data, and any manufactured articles and witness any tests, including any inspections or tests at a supplier facility, necessary to determine compliance with this subchapter

(b) Unless otherwise authorized by the FAA, the applicant or holder—

   (1) May not present any article to the FAA for an inspection or test unless compliance with 21.303(b)(2) through (4) has been shown for that article; and

   (2) May not make any change to an article between the time that compliance with 21.303(b)(2) through (4) is shown for that article and the time that the article is presented to the FAA for the inspection or test

21.311   Issuance

The FAA issues a PMA after finding that the applicant complies with the requirements of this subpart and the design complies with the requirements of this chapter applicable to the product on which the article is to be installed

21.313   Duration

A PMA is effective until surrendered, withdrawn, or the FAA otherwise terminates it

21.314   Transferability

The holder of a PMA may not transfer the PMA

21.316   Responsibility of holder

Each holder of a PMA must—

(a) Amend the document required by 21.305 as necessary to reflect changes in the organization and provide these amendments to the FAA;

(b) Maintain the quality system in compliance with the data and procedures approved for the PMA;

(c) Ensure that each PMA article conforms to its approved design and is in a condition for safe operation;

(d) Mark the PMA article for which an approval has been issued. Marking must be in accordance with part 45 of this chapter, including any critical parts;

(e) Identify any portion of the PMA article (e.g., sub-assemblies, component parts, or replacement articles) that leave the manufacturer's facility as FAA approved with the manufacturer's part number and name, trademark, symbol, or other FAA approved manufacturer's identification;

(f) Have access to design data necessary to determine conformity and airworthiness for each article produced under the PMA;

(g) Retain each document granting PMA and make it available to the FAA upon request; and

(h) Make available to the FAA information regarding all delegation of authority to suppliers

21.319   Design changes

(a) Classification of design changes

   (1) A "minor change" to the design of an article produced under a PMA is one that has no appreciable effect on the approval basis

   (2) A "major change" to the design of an article produced under a PMA is any change that is not minor

(b) Approval of design changes

   (1) Minor changes to the basic design of a PMA may be approved using a method acceptable to the FAA

   (2) The PMA holder must obtain FAA approval of any major change before including it in the design of an article produced under a PMA

21.320   Changes in quality system

After the issuance of a PMA—

(a) Each change to the quality system is subject to review by the FAA; and

(b) The holder of the PMA must immediately notify the FAA, in writing, of any change that may affect the inspection, conformity, or airworthiness of its article

Subpart L — Export Airworthiness Approvals

Source: 74 FR 53391, Oct. 16, 2009, unless otherwise noted

21.321   Applicability

This subpart prescribes—

(a) Procedural requirements for issuing export airworthiness approvals; and

(b) Rules governing the holders of those approvals

21.325   Export airworthiness approvals

(a) An export airworthiness approval for an aircraft is issued in the form of an export certificate of airworthiness. This certificate does not authorize operation of that aircraft

(b) The FAA prescribes the form and manner in which an export airworthiness approval for an aircraft engine, propeller, or article is issued

(c) If the FAA finds no undue burden in administering the applicable requirements of Title 49 U.S.C. and this subchapter, an export airworthiness approval may be issued for a product or article located outside of the United States

21.327   Application

Any person may apply for an export airworthiness approval. Each applicant must apply in a form and manner prescribed by the FAA

21.329   Issuance of export certificates of airworthiness

(a) A person may obtain from the FAA an export certificate of airworthiness for an aircraft if—

   (1) A new or used aircraft manufactured under subpart F or G of this part meets the airworthiness requirements under subpart H of this part for a—

      (i) Standard airworthiness certificate; or

      (ii) Special airworthiness certificate in either the "primary" or the "restricted" category; or

   (2) A new or used aircraft not manufactured under subpart F or G of this part has a valid—

      (i) Standard airworthiness certificate; or

      (ii) Special airworthiness certificate in either the "primary" or the "restricted" category

(b) An aircraft need not meet a requirement specified in paragraph (a) of this section, as applicable, if—

   (1) The importing country or jurisdiction accepts, in a form and manner acceptable to the FAA, a deviation from that requirement; and

   (2) The export certificate of airworthiness lists as an exception any difference between the aircraft to be exported and its type design

21.331   Issuance of export airworthiness approvals for aircraft engines, propellers, and articles

(a) A person may obtain from the FAA an export airworthiness approval to export a new aircraft engine, propeller, or article that is manufactured under this part if it conforms to its approved design and is in a condition for safe operation

(b) A new aircraft engine, propeller, or article need not meet a requirement of paragraph (a) of this section if—

   (1) The importing country or jurisdiction accepts, in a form and manner acceptable to the FAA, a deviation from that requirement; and

   (2) The export airworthiness approval lists as an exception any difference between the aircraft engine, propeller, or article to be exported and its approved design

(c) A person may obtain from the FAA an export airworthiness approval to export a used aircraft engine, propeller, or article if it conforms to its approved design and is in a condition for safe operation

(d) A used aircraft engine or propeller need not meet a requirement of paragraph (c) of this section if—

   (1) The importing country or jurisdiction accepts, in a form and manner acceptable to the FAA, a deviation from that requirement; and

   (2) The export airworthiness approval lists as an exception any difference between the used aircraft engine or propeller to be exported and its approved design

21.335   Responsibilities of exporters

Unless otherwise agreed to by the importing country or jurisdiction, each exporter must—

(a) Forward to the importing country or jurisdiction all documents specified by that country or jurisdiction;

(b) Preserve and package products and articles as necessary to protect them against corrosion and damage during transit or storage and state the duration of effectiveness of such preservation and packaging;

(c) Remove or cause to be removed any temporary installation incorporated on an aircraft for the purpose of export delivery and restore the aircraft to the approved configuration upon completion of the delivery flight;

(d) Secure all proper foreign entry clearances from all the countries or jurisdictions involved when conducting sales demonstrations or delivery flights; and

(e) When title to an aircraft passes or has passed to a foreign purchaser—

   (1) Request cancellation of the U.S. registration and airworthiness certificates from the FAA, giving the date of transfer of title, and the name and address of the foreign owner;

   (2) Return the Registration and Airworthiness Certificates to the FAA; and

   (3) Provide a statement to the FAA certifying that the U.S. identification and registration numbers have been removed from the aircraft in compliance with 45.33

Subpart M — [Reserved]

Subpart N — Acceptance of Aircraft Engines, Propellers, and Articles for Import

Source: 74 FR 53391, Oct. 16, 2009, unless otherwise noted

21.500 Acceptance of aircraft engines and propellers

An aircraft engine or propeller manufactured in a foreign country or jurisdiction meets the requirements for acceptance under this subchapter if—

(a) That country or jurisdiction is subject to the provisions of an agreement with the United States for the acceptance of that product;

(b) That product is marked in accordance with part 45 of this chapter; and

(c) The holder or licensee of a U.S. type certificate for that product furnishes with each such aircraft engine or propeller imported into the United States, an export airworthiness approval issued in accordance with the provisions of that agreement certifying that the individual aircraft engine or propeller —

  (1) Conforms to its U.S. type certificate and is in condition for safe operation; and

  (2) Has been subjected by the manufacturer to a final operational check

21.502 Acceptance of articles

An article (including an article produced under a letter of TSO design approval) manufactured in a foreign country or jurisdiction meets the requirements for acceptance under this subchapter if—

(a) That country or jurisdiction is subject to the provisions of an agreement with the United States for the acceptance of that article;

(b) That article is marked in accordance with part 45 of this chapter; and

(c) An export airworthiness approval has been issued in accordance with the provisions of that agreement for that article for import into the United States

Subpart O — Technical Standard Order Approvals

Source: Docket No. FAA–2006–25877, 74 FR 53392, Oct. 16, 2009, unless otherwise noted

21.601 Applicability and definitions

(a) This subpart prescribes—

  (1) Procedural requirements for issuing TSO authorizations;

  (2) Rules governing the holders of TSO authorizations; and

  (3) Procedural requirements for issuing letters of TSO design approval

(b) For the purposes of this subpart—

  (1) A TSO issued by the FAA is a minimum performance standard for specified articles used on civil aircraft;

  (2) A TSO authorization is an FAA design and production approval issued to the manufacturer of an article that has been found to meet a specific TSO;

  (3) A letter of TSO design approval is an FAA design approval for an article that has been found to meet a specific TSO in accordance with the procedures of 21.621;

  (4) An article manufactured under a TSO authorization, an FAA letter of acceptance as described in 21.613(b), or an article manufactured under a letter of TSO design approval described in 21.621 is an approved article for the purpose of meeting the regulations of this chapter that require the article to be approved; and

  (5) An article manufacturer is the person who controls the design and quality of the article produced (or to be produced, in the case of an application), including any related parts, processes, or services procured from an outside source

21.603 Application

(a) An applicant for a TSO authorization must apply in the form and manner prescribed by the FAA. The applicant must include the following documents in the application:

  (1) A statement of conformance certifying that the applicant has met the requirements of this subpart and that the article concerned meets the applicable TSO that is effective on the date of application for that article

  (2) One copy of the technical data required in the applicable TSO

(b) If the applicant anticipates a series of minor changes in accordance with 21.619, the applicant may set forth in its application the basic model number of the article and the part number of the components with open brackets after it to denote that suffix change letters or numbers (or combinations of them) will be added from time to time

(c) If the application is deficient, the applicant must, when requested by the FAA, provide any additional information necessary to show compliance with this part. If the applicant fails to provide the additional information within 30 days after the FAA's request, the FAA denies the application and notifies the applicant

[, as amended by Doc. No. FAA-2018-0119, Amdt. 21-101, 83 FR 9169, Mar. 5, 2018]

21.605 Organization

(a) Each applicant for or holder of a TSO authorization must provide the FAA with a document—

  (1) Describing how its organization will ensure compliance with the provisions of this subpart;

  (2) Describing assigned responsibilities, delegated authorities, and the functional relationship of those responsible for quality to management and other organizational components; and

  (3) Identifying an accountable manager.

(b) The accountable manager specified in paragraph (a) of this section must be responsible within the applicant's or production approval holder's organization for, and have authority over, all production operations conducted under this part. The accountable manager must confirm that the procedures described in the quality manual required by §21.608 are in place and that the production approval holder satisfies the requirements of the applicable regulations of subchapter C, Aircraft. The accountable manager must serve as the primary contact with the FAA.

[Doc. No. FAA-2013-0933, Amdt. 21-98, 80 FR 59032, Oct. 1, 2015]

21.607 Quality system

Each applicant for or holder of a TSO authorization must establish a quality system that meets the requirements of 21.137

21.608 Quality manual

Each applicant for or holder of a TSO authorization must provide a manual describing its quality system to the FAA for approval. The manual must be in the English language and retrievable in a form acceptable to the FAA

21.609 Location of or change to manufacturing facilities

(a) An applicant may obtain a TSO authorization for manufacturing facilities located outside of the United States if the FAA finds no undue burden in administering the applicable requirements of Title 49 U.S.C. and this subchapter

(b) The TSO authorization holder must obtain FAA approval before making any changes to the location of any of its manufacturing facilities

(c) The TSO authorization holder must immediately notify the FAA, in writing, of any change to the manufacturing facilities that may affect the inspection, conformity, or airworthiness of its product or article

21.610 Inspections and tests

Each applicant for or holder of a TSO authorization must allow the

FAA to inspect its quality system, facilities, technical data, and any manufactured articles and witness any tests, including any inspections or tests at a supplier facility, necessary to determine compliance with this subchapter

21.611   Issuance

If the FAA finds that the applicant complies with the requirements of this subchapter, the FAA issues a TSO authorization to the applicant (including all TSO deviations granted to the applicant)

21.613   Duration

(a) A TSO authorization or letter of TSO design approval is effective until surrendered, withdrawn, or otherwise terminated by the FAA

(b) If a TSO is revised or canceled, the holder of an affected FAA letter of acceptance of a statement of conformance, TSO authorization, or letter of TSO design approval may continue to manufacture articles that meet the original TSO without obtaining a new acceptance, authorization, or approval but must comply with the requirements of this chapter

21.614   Transferability

The holder of a TSO authorization or letter of TSO design approval may not transfer the TSO authorization or letter of TSO design approval

21.616   Responsibility of holder

Each holder of a TSO authorization must—

(a) Amend the document required by 21.605 as necessary to reflect changes in the organization and provide these amendments to the FAA

(b) Maintain a quality system in compliance with the data and procedures approved for the TSO authorization;

(c) Ensure that each manufactured article conforms to its approved design, is in a condition for safe operation, and meets the applicable TSO;

(d) Mark the TSO article for which an approval has been issued. Marking must be in accordance with part 45 of this chapter, including any critical parts;

(e) Identify any portion of the TSO article (e.g., sub-assemblies, component parts, or replacement articles) that leave the manufacturer's facility as FAA approved with the manufacturer's part number and name, trademark, symbol, or other FAA approved manufacturer's identification;

(f) Have access to design data necessary to determine conformity and airworthiness for each article produced under the TSO authorization. The manufacturer must retain this data until it no longer manufactures the article. At that time, copies of the data must be sent to the FAA;

(g) Retain its TSO authorization and make it available to the FAA upon request; and

(h) Make available to the FAA information regarding all delegation of authority to suppliers

21.618   Approval for deviation

(a) Each manufacturer who requests approval to deviate from any performance standard of a TSO must show that factors or design features providing an equivalent level of safety compensate for the standards from which a deviation is requested

(b) The manufacturer must send requests for approval to deviate, together with all pertinent data, to the FAA. If the article is manufactured under the authority of a foreign country or jurisdiction, the manufacturer must send requests for approval to deviate, together with all pertinent data, through the civil aviation authority of that country or jurisdiction to the FAA.

[Docket No. FAA-2006-25877, Amdt. 21-92, 74 FR 53392, Oct. 16, 2009, as amended by Doc. No. FAA-2018-0119, Amdt. 21-101, 83 FR 9169, Mar. 5, 2018]

21.619   Design changes

(a) Minor changes by the manufacturer holding a TSO authorization. The manufacturer of an article under an authorization issued under this part may make minor design changes (any change other than a major change) without further approval by the FAA. In this case, the changed article keeps the original model number (part numbers may be used to identify minor changes) and the manufacturer must forward to the FAA, any revised data that are necessary for compliance with 21.603(b).

(b) Major changes by the manufacturer holding a TSO authorization. Any design change by the manufacturer extensive enough to require a substantially complete investigation to determine compliance with a TSO is a major change. Before making a major change, the manufacturer must assign a new type or model designation to the article and apply for an authorization under 21.603

(c) Changes by persons other than the manufacturer . No design change by any person (other than the manufacturer who provided the statement of conformance for the article) is eligible for approval under this part unless the person seeking the approval is a manufacturer and applies under 21.603(a) for a separate TSO authorization. Persons other than a manufacturer may obtain approval for design changes under part 43 or under the applicable airworthiness regulations of this chapter

[Docket No. FAA-2006-25877, Amdt. 21-92, 74 FR 53392, Oct. 16, 2009, as amended by Doc. No. FAA-2018-0119, Amdt. 21-101, 83 FR 9169, Mar. 5, 2018]

21.620   Changes in quality system

After the issuance of a TSO authorization—

(a) Each change to the quality system is subject to review by the FAA; and

(b) The holder of the TSO authorization must immediately notify the FAA, in writing, of any change that may affect the inspection, conformity, or airworthiness of its article

21.621   Issue of letters of TSO design approval: Import articles

(a) The FAA may issue a letter of TSO design approval for an article—

(1) Designed and manufactured in a foreign country or jurisdiction subject to the export provisions of an agreement with the United States for the acceptance of these articles for import; and

(2) For import into the United States if—

(i) The State of Design certifies that the article has been examined, tested, and found to meet the applicable TSO or the applicable performance standards of the State of Design and any other performance standards the FAA may prescribe to provide a level of safety equivalent to that provided by the TSO; and

(ii) The manufacturer has provided to the FAA one copy of the technical data required in the applicable performance standard through its State of Design

(b) The FAA issues the letter of TSO design approval that lists any deviation granted under 21.618

[Doc. No. FAA–2006–25877, 74 FR 53392, Oct. 16, 2009, as amended by Amdt. 21–92A, 75 FR 9095, Mar. 1, 2010]

Subpart P — Special Federal Aviation Regulations

Source: Docket No. FAA–2011–0186, 76 FR 12555, Mar. 8, 2011, unless otherwise noted

21.700   SFAR No. 111—Lavatory Oxygen Systems

The requirements of 121.1500 of this chapter also apply to this part.

PART 23—AIRWORTHINESS STANDARDS: NORMAL CATEGORY AIRPLANES

Authority: 49 U.S.C. 106(f), 106(g), 40113, 44701-44702, 44704, Pub. L. 113-53, 127 Stat. 584 (49 U.S.C. 44704) note.

Source: Doc. No. FAA-2015-1621, Amdt. 23-64, 81 FR 96689, Dec. 30, 2016, unless otherwise noted.

23.1457 Cockpit voice recorders

(a) Each cockpit voice recorder required by the operating rules of this chapter must be approved and must be installed so that it will record the following:

(1) Voice communications transmitted from or received in the airplane by radio.

(2) Voice communications of flightcrew members on the flight deck.

(3) Voice communications of flightcrew members on the flight deck, using the airplane's interphone system.

(4) Voice or audio signals identifying navigation or approach aids introduced into a headset or speaker.

(5) Voice communications of flightcrew members using the passenger loudspeaker system, if there is such a system and if the fourth channel is available in accordance with the requirements of paragraph (c)(4)(ii) of this section.

(6) If datalink communication equipment is installed, all datalink communications, using an approved data message set. Datalink messages must be recorded as the output signal from the communications unit that translates the signal into usable data.

(b) The recording requirements of paragraph (a)(2) of this section must be met by installing a cockpit-mounted area microphone, located in the best position for recording voice communications originating at the first and second pilot stations and voice communications of other crewmembers on the flight deck when directed to those stations. The microphone must be so located and, if necessary, the preamplifiers and filters of the recorder must be so adjusted or supplemented, so that the intelligibility of the recorded communications is as high as practicable when recorded under flight cockpit noise conditions and played back. Repeated aural or visual playback of the record may be used in evaluating intelligibility.

(c) Each cockpit voice recorder must be installed so that the part of the communication or audio signals specified in paragraph (a) of this section obtained from each of the following sources is recorded on a separate channel:

(1) For the first channel, from each boom, mask, or handheld microphone, headset, or speaker used at the first pilot station.

(2) For the second channel from each boom, mask, or handheld microphone, headset, or speaker used at the second pilot station.

(3) For the third channel—from the cockpit-mounted area microphone.

(4) For the fourth channel from:

(i) Each boom, mask, or handheld microphone, headset, or speaker used at the station for the third and fourth crewmembers.

(ii) If the stations specified in paragraph (c)(4)(i) of this section are not required or if the signal at such a station is picked up by another channel, each microphone on the flight deck that is used with the passenger loudspeaker system, if its signals are not picked up by another channel.

(5) And that as far as is practicable all sounds received by the microphone listed in paragraphs (c)(1), (2), and (4) of this section must be recorded without interruption irrespective of the position of the interphone-transmitter key switch. The design shall ensure that sidetone for the flightcrew is produced only when the interphone, public address system, or radio transmitters are in use.

(d) Each cockpit voice recorder must be installed so that:

(1)

(i) It receives its electrical power from the bus that provides the maximum reliability for operation of the cockpit voice recorder without jeopardizing service to essential or emergency loads.

(ii) It remains powered for as long as possible without jeopardizing emergency operation of the airplane.

(2) There is an automatic means to simultaneously stop the recorder and prevent each erasure feature from functioning, within 10 minutes after crash impact.

(3) There is an aural or visual means for preflight checking of the recorder for proper operation.

(4) Any single electrical failure external to the recorder does not disable both the cockpit voice recorder and the flight data recorder.

(5) It has an independent power source—

(i) That provides 10 ±1 minutes of electrical power to operate both the cockpit voice recorder and cockpit-mounted area microphone;

(ii) That is located as close as practicable to the cockpit voice recorder; and

(iii) To which the cockpit voice recorder and cockpit-mounted area microphone are switched automatically in the event that all other power to the cockpit voice recorder is interrupted either by normal shutdown or by any other loss of power to the electrical power bus.

(6) It is in a separate container from the flight data recorder when both are required. If used to comply with only the cockpit voice recorder requirements, a combination unit may be installed.

(e) The recorder container must be located and mounted to minimize the probability of rupture of the container as a result of crash impact and consequent heat damage to the recorder from fire.

(1) Except as provided in paragraph (e)(2) of this section, the recorder container must be located as far aft as practicable, but need not be outside of the pressurized compartment, and may not be located where aft-mounted engines may crush the container during impact.

(2) If two separate combination digital flight data recorder and cockpit voice recorder units are installed instead of one cockpit voice recorder and one digital flight data recorder, the combination unit that is installed to comply with the cockpit voice recorder requirements may be located near the cockpit.

(f) If the cockpit voice recorder has a bulk erasure device, the installation must be designed to minimize the probability of inadvertent operation and actuation of the device during crash impact.

(g) Each recorder container must—

(1) Be either bright orange or bright yellow;

(2) Have reflective tape affixed to its external surface to facilitate its location under water; and

(3) Have an underwater locating device, when required by the operating rules of this chapter, on or adjacent to the container, which is secured in such manner that they are not likely to be separated during crash impact.

23.1459   Flight data recorders

(a) Each flight recorder required by the operating rules of this chapter must be installed so that—

(1) It is supplied with airspeed, altitude, and directional data obtained from sources that meet the aircraft level system requirements and the functionality specified in 23.2500;

(2) The vertical acceleration sensor is rigidly attached, and located longitudinally either within the approved center of gravity limits of the airplane, or at a distance forward or aft of these limits that does not exceed 25 percent of the airplane's mean aerodynamic chord;

(3)

(i) It receives its electrical power from the bus that provides the maximum reliability for operation of the flight data recorder without jeopardizing service to essential or emergency loads;

(ii) It remains powered for as long as possible without jeopardizing emergency operation of the airplane;

(4) There is an aural or visual means for preflight checking of the recorder for proper recording of data in the storage medium;

(5) Except for recorders powered solely by the engine-driven electrical generator system, there is an automatic means to simultaneously stop a recorder that has a data erasure feature and prevent each erasure feature from functioning, within 10 minutes after crash impact;

(6) Any single electrical failure external to the recorder does not disable both the cockpit voice recorder and the flight data recorder; and

(7) It is in a separate container from the cockpit voice recorder when both are required. If used to comply with only the flight data recorder requirements, a combination unit may be installed. If a combination unit is installed as a cockpit voice recorder to comply with 23.1457(e)(2), a combination unit must be used to comply with this flight data recorder requirement.

(b) Each non-ejectable record container must be located and mounted so as to minimize the probability of container rupture resulting from crash impact and subsequent damage to the record from fire. In meeting this requirement, the record container must be located as far aft as practicable, but need not be aft of the pressurized compartment, and may not be where aft-mounted engines may crush the container upon impact.

(c) A correlation must be established between the flight recorder readings of airspeed, altitude, and heading and the corresponding readings (taking into account correction factors) of the first pilot's instruments. The correlation must cover the airspeed range over which the airplane is to be operated, the range of altitude to which the airplane is limited, and 360 degrees of heading. Correlation may be established on the ground as appropriate.

(d) Each recorder container must—

(1) Be either bright orange or bright yellow;

(2) Have reflective tape affixed to its external surface to facilitate its location under water; and

(3) Have an underwater locating device, when required by the operating rules of this chapter, on or adjacent to the container, which is secured in such a manner that they are not likely to be separated during crash impact.

(e) Any novel or unique design or operational characteristics of the aircraft shall be evaluated to determine if any dedicated parameters must be recorded on flight recorders in addition to or in place of existing requirements.

23.1529   Instructions for continued airworthiness

The applicant must prepare Instructions for Continued Airworthiness, in accordance with appendix A of this part, that are acceptable to the Administrator. The instructions may be incomplete at type certification if a program exists to ensure their completion prior to delivery of the first airplane or issuance of a standard certificate of airworthiness, whichever occurs later.

Subpart A — General
23.2000   Applicability and definitions

(a) This part prescribes airworthiness standards for the issuance of type certificates, and changes to those certificates, for airplanes in the normal category.

(b) For the purposes of this part, the following definition applies:

Continued safe flight and landing means an airplane is capable of continued controlled flight and landing, possibly using emergency procedures, without requiring exceptional pilot skill or strength. Upon landing, some airplane damage may occur as a result of a failure condition.

23.2005   Certification of normal category airplanes

(a) Certification in the normal category applies to airplanes with a passenger-seating configuration of 19 or less and a maximum certificated takeoff weight of 19,000 pounds or less.

(b) Airplane certification levels are:

(1) Level 1—for airplanes with a maximum seating configuration of 0 to 1 passengers.

(2) Level 2—for airplanes with a maximum seating configuration of 2 to 6 passengers.

(3) Level 3—for airplanes with a maximum seating configuration of 7 to 9 passengers.

(4) Level 4—for airplanes with a maximum seating configuration of 10 to 19 passengers.

(c) Airplane performance levels are:

(1) Low speed—for airplanes with a V_{NO} and $V_{MO} \leq 250$ Knots Calibrated Airspeed (KCAS) and a $M_{MO} \leq 0.6$.

(2) High speed—for airplanes with a V_{NO} or $V_{MO} > 250$ KCAS or a $M_{MO} > 0.6$.

(d) Airplanes not certified for aerobatics may be used to perform any maneuver incident to normal flying, including—

(1) Stalls (except whip stalls); and

(2) Lazy eights, chandelles, and steep turns, in which the angle of bank is not more than 60 degrees.

(e) Airplanes certified for aerobatics may be used to perform maneuvers without limitations, other than those limitations established under subpart G of this part.

23.2010   Accepted means of compliance

(a) An applicant must comply with this part using a means of compliance, which may include consensus standards, accepted by the Administrator.

(b) An applicant requesting acceptance of a means of compliance must provide the means of compliance to the FAA in a form and manner acceptable to the Administrator.

Subpart B — Flight
Performance
23.2100   Weight and center of gravity

(a) The applicant must determine limits for weights and centers of gravity that provide for the safe operation of the airplane.

(b) The applicant must comply with each requirement of this subpart at critical combinations of weight and center of gravity within the airplane's range of loading conditions using tolerances acceptable to the Administrator.

(c) The condition of the airplane at the time of determining its empty weight and center of gravity must be well defined and easily repeatable.

23.2105   Performance data

(a) Unless otherwise prescribed, an airplane must meet the performance requirements of this subpart in—

(1) Still air and standard atmospheric conditions at sea level for all airplanes; and

(2) Ambient atmospheric conditions within the operating envelope for levels 1 and 2 high-speed and levels 3 and 4 airplanes.

(b) Unless otherwise prescribed, the applicant must develop the performance data required by this subpart for the following conditions:

(1) Airport altitudes from sea level to 10,000 feet (3,048 meters); and

(2) Temperatures above and below standard day temperature that are within the range of operating limitations, if those temperatures could have a negative effect on performance.

(c) The procedures used for determining takeoff and landing distances must be executable consistently by pilots of average skill in atmospheric conditions expected to be encountered in service.

(d) Performance data determined in accordance with paragraph (b) of this section must account for losses due to atmospheric conditions, cooling needs, and other demands on power sources.

23.2110   Stall speed

The applicant must determine the airplane stall speed or the minimum steady flight speed for each flight configuration used in normal operations, including takeoff, climb, cruise, descent, approach, and landing. The stall speed or minimum steady flight speed determination must account for the most adverse conditions for each flight configuration with power set at—

(a) Idle or zero thrust for propulsion systems that are used primarily for thrust; and

(b) A nominal thrust for propulsion systems that are used for thrust, flight control, and/or high-lift systems.

23.2115   Takeoff performance

(a) The applicant must determine airplane takeoff performance accounting for—

(1) Stall speed safety margins;

(2) Minimum control speeds; and

(3) Climb gradients.

(b) For single engine airplanes and levels 1, 2, and 3 low-speed multi-engine airplanes, takeoff performance includes the determination of ground roll and initial climb distance to 50 feet (15 meters) above the takeoff surface.

(c) For levels 1, 2, and 3 high-speed multiengine airplanes, and level 4 multiengine airplanes, takeoff performance includes a determination the following distances after a sudden critical loss of thrust—

    (1) An aborted takeoff at critical speed;

    (2) Ground roll and initial climb to 35 feet (11 meters) above the takeoff surface; and

    (3) Net takeoff flight path.

23.2120 Climb requirements

The design must comply with the following minimum climb performance out of ground effect:

(a) With all engines operating and in the initial climb configuration—

    (1) For levels 1 and 2 low-speed airplanes, a climb gradient of 8.3 percent for landplanes and 6.7 percent for seaplanes and amphibians; and

    (2) For levels 1 and 2 high-speed airplanes, all level 3 airplanes, and level 4 single-engines a climb gradient after takeoff of 4 percent.

(b) After a critical loss of thrust on multiengine airplanes—

    (1) For levels 1 and 2 low-speed airplanes that do not meet single-engine crashworthiness requirements, a climb gradient of 1.5 percent at a pressure altitude of 5,000 feet (1,524 meters) in the cruise configuration(s);

    (2) For levels 1 and 2 high-speed airplanes, and level 3 low-speed airplanes, a 1 percent climb gradient at 400 feet (122 meters) above the takeoff surface with the landing gear retracted and flaps in the takeoff configuration(s); and

    (3) For level 3 high-speed airplanes and all level 4 airplanes, a 2 percent climb gradient at 400 feet (122 meters) above the takeoff surface with the landing gear retracted and flaps in the approach configuration(s).

(c) For a balked landing, a climb gradient of 3 percent without creating undue pilot workload with the landing gear extended and flaps in the landing configuration(s).

23.2125 Climb information

(a) The applicant must determine climb performance at each weight, altitude, and ambient temperature within the operating limitations—

    (1) For all single-engine airplanes;

    (2) For levels 1 and 2 high-speed multiengine airplanes and level 3 multiengine airplanes, following a critical loss of thrust on takeoff in the initial climb configuration; and

    (3) For all multiengine airplanes, during the enroute phase of flight with all engines operating and after a critical loss of thrust in the cruise configuration.

(b) The applicant must determine the glide performance for single-engine airplanes after a complete loss of thrust.

23.2130 Landing

The applicant must determine the following, for standard temperatures at critical combinations of weight and altitude within the operational limits:

(a) The distance, starting from a height of 50 feet (15 meters) above the landing surface, required to land and come to a stop.

(b) The approach and landing speeds, configurations, and procedures, which allow a pilot of average skill to land within the published landing distance consistently and without causing damage or injury, and which allow for a safe transition to the balked landing conditions of this part accounting for:

    (1) Stall speed safety margin; and

    (2) Minimum control speeds.

Flight Characteristics

23.2135 Controllability

(a) The airplane must be controllable and maneuverable, without requiring exceptional piloting skill, alertness, or strength, within the operating envelope—

    (1) At all loading conditions for which certification is requested;

    (2) During all phases of flight;

    (3) With likely reversible flight control or propulsion system failure; and

    (4) During configuration changes.

(b) The airplane must be able to complete a landing without causing substantial damage or serious injury using the steepest approved approach gradient procedures and providing a reasonable margin below V_{ref} or above approach angle of attack.

(c) V_{MC} is the calibrated airspeed at which, following the sudden critical loss of thrust, it is possible to maintain control of the airplane. For multiengine airplanes, the applicant must determine V_{MC}, if applicable, for the most critical configurations used in takeoff and landing operations.

(d) If the applicant requests certification of an airplane for aerobatics, the applicant must demonstrate those aerobatic maneuvers for which certification is requested and determine entry speeds.

23.2140 Trim

(a) The airplane must maintain lateral and directional trim without further force upon, or movement of, the primary flight controls or corresponding trim controls by the pilot, or the flight control system, under the following conditions:

    (1) For levels 1, 2, and 3 airplanes in cruise.

    (2) For level 4 airplanes in normal operations.

(b) The airplane must maintain longitudinal trim without further force upon, or movement of, the primary flight controls or corresponding trim controls by the pilot, or the flight control system, under the following conditions:

    (1) Climb.

    (2) Level flight.

    (3) Descent.

    (4) Approach.

(c) Residual control forces must not fatigue or distract the pilot during normal operations of the airplane and likely abnormal or emergency operations, including a critical loss of thrust on multiengine airplanes.

23.2145 Stability

(a) Airplanes not certified for aerobatics must—

    (1) Have static longitudinal, lateral, and directional stability in normal operations;

    (2) Have dynamic short period and Dutch roll stability in normal operations; and

    (3) Provide stable control force feedback throughout the operating envelope.

(b) No airplane may exhibit any divergent longitudinal stability characteristic so unstable as to increase the pilot's workload or otherwise endanger the airplane and its occupants.

23.2150 Stall characteristics, stall warning, and spins

(a) The airplane must have controllable stall characteristics in straight flight, turning flight, and accelerated turning flight with a clear and distinctive stall warning that provides sufficient margin to prevent inadvertent stalling.

(b) Single-engine airplanes, not certified for aerobatics, must not have a tendency to inadvertently depart controlled flight.

(c) Levels 1 and 2 multiengine airplanes, not certified for aerobatics, must not have a tendency to inadvertently depart controlled flight from thrust asymmetry after a critical loss of thrust.

(d) Airplanes certified for aerobatics that include spins must have controllable stall characteristics and the ability to recover within one and one-half additional turns after initiation of the first control action from any point in a spin, not exceeding six turns or any greater number of turns for which certification is requested, while remaining within the operating limitations of the airplane.

(e) Spin characteristics in airplanes certified for aerobatics that includes spins must recover without exceeding limitations and may not result in unrecoverable spins—

(1) With any typical use of the flight or engine power controls; or

(2) Due to pilot disorientation or incapacitation.

23.2155 Ground and water handling characteristics

For airplanes intended for operation on land or water, the airplane must have controllable longitudinal and directional handling characteristics during taxi, takeoff, and landing operations.

23.2160 Vibration, buffeting, and high-speed characteristics

(a) Vibration and buffeting, for operations up to V_D/M_D, must not interfere with the control of the airplane or cause excessive fatigue to the flightcrew. Stall warning buffet within these limits is allowable.

(b) For high-speed airplanes and all airplanes with a maximum operating altitude greater than 25,000 feet (7,620 meters) pressure altitude, there must be no perceptible buffeting in cruise configuration at 1g and at any speed up to V_{MO}/M_{MO}, except stall buffeting.

(c) For high-speed airplanes, the applicant must determine the positive maneuvering load factors at which the onset of perceptible buffet occurs in the cruise configuration within the operational envelope. Likely inadvertent excursions beyond this boundary must not result in structural damage.

(d) High-speed airplanes must have recovery characteristics that do not result in structural damage or loss of control, beginning at any likely speed up to V_{MO}/M_{MO}, following—

(1) An inadvertent speed increase; and

(2) A high-speed trim upset for airplanes where dynamic pressure can impair the longitudinal trim system operation.

23.2165 Performance and flight characteristics requirements for flight in icing conditions

(a) An applicant who requests certification for flight in icing conditions defined in part 1 of appendix C to part 25 of this chapter, or an applicant who requests certification for flight in these icing conditions and any additional atmospheric icing conditions, must show the following in the icing conditions for which certification is requested under normal operation of the ice protection system(s):

(1) Compliance with each requirement of this subpart, except those applicable to spins and any that must be demonstrated at speeds in excess of—

(i) 250 knots CAS;

(ii) V_{MO}/M_{MO} or V_{NE}; or

(iii) A speed at which the applicant demonstrates the airframe will be free of ice accretion.

(2) The means by which stall warning is provided to the pilot for flight in icing conditions and non-icing conditions is the same.

(b) If an applicant requests certification for flight in icing conditions, the applicant must provide a means to detect any icing conditions for which certification is not requested and show the airplane's ability to avoid or exit those conditions.

(c) The applicant must develop an operating limitation to prohibit intentional flight, including takeoff and landing, into icing conditions for which the airplane is not certified to operate.

Subpart C — Structures

23.2200 Structural design envelope

The applicant must determine the structural design envelope, which describes the range and limits of airplane design and operational parameters for which the applicant will show compliance with the requirements of this subpart. The applicant must account for all airplane design and operational parameters that affect structural loads, strength, durability, and aeroelasticity, including:

(a) Structural design airspeeds, landing descent speeds, and any other airspeed limitation at which the applicant must show compliance to the requirements of this subpart. The structural design airspeeds must—

(1) Be sufficiently greater than the stalling speed of the airplane to safeguard against loss of control in turbulent air; and

(2) Provide sufficient margin for the establishment of practical operational limiting airspeeds.

(b) Design maneuvering load factors not less than those, which service history shows, may occur within the structural design envelope.

(c) Inertial properties including weight, center of gravity, and mass moments of inertia, accounting for—

(1) Each critical weight from the airplane empty weight to the maximum weight; and

(2) The weight and distribution of occupants, payload, and fuel.

(d) Characteristics of airplane control systems, including range of motion and tolerances for control surfaces, high lift devices, or other moveable surfaces.

(e) Each critical altitude up to the maximum altitude.

23.2205 Interaction of systems and structures

For airplanes equipped with systems that modify structural performance, alleviate the impact of this subpart's requirements, or provide a means of compliance with this subpart, the applicant must account for the influence and failure of these systems when showing compliance with the requirements of this subpart.

Structural Loads

23.2210 Structural design loads

(a) The applicant must:

(1) Determine the applicable structural design loads resulting from likely externally or internally applied pressures, forces, or moments that may occur in flight, ground and water operations, ground and water handling, and while the airplane is parked or moored.

(2) Determine the loads required by paragraph (a)(1) of this section at all critical combinations of parameters, on and within the boundaries of the structural design envelope.

(b) The magnitude and distribution of the applicable structural design loads required by this section must be based on physical principles.

23.2215 Flight load conditions

The applicant must determine the structural design loads resulting from the following flight conditions:

(a) Atmospheric gusts where the magnitude and gradient of these gusts are based on measured gust statistics.

(b) Symmetric and asymmetric maneuvers.

(c) Asymmetric thrust resulting from the failure of a powerplant unit.

23.2220 Ground and water load conditions

The applicant must determine the structural design loads resulting from taxi, takeoff, landing, and handling conditions on the applicable surface in normal and adverse attitudes and configurations.

23.2225 Component loading conditions

The applicant must determine the structural design loads acting on:

(a) Each engine mount and its supporting structure such that both are designed to withstand loads resulting from—

(1) Powerplant operation combined with flight gust and maneuver loads; and

(2) For non-reciprocating powerplants, sudden powerplant stoppage.

(b) Each flight control and high-lift surface, their associated system and supporting structure resulting from—

(1) The inertia of each surface and mass balance attachment;

(2) Flight gusts and maneuvers;

(3) Pilot or automated system inputs;

(4) System induced conditions, including jamming and friction; and

(5) Taxi, takeoff, and landing operations on the applicable surface, including downwind taxi and gusts occurring on the applicable surface.

(c) A pressurized cabin resulting from the pressurization differential—

(1) From zero up to the maximum relief pressure combined with gust and maneuver loads;

(2) From zero up to the maximum relief pressure combined with ground and water loads if the airplane may land with the cabin pressurized; and

(3) At the maximum relief pressure multiplied by 1.33, omitting all other loads.

23.2230 Limit and ultimate loads

The applicant must determine—

(a) The limit loads, which are equal to the structural design loads unless otherwise specified elsewhere in this part; and

(b) The ultimate loads, which are equal to the limit loads multiplied by a 1.5 factor of safety unless otherwise specified elsewhere in this part.

Structural Performance

23.2235 Structural strength

The structure must support:

(a) Limit loads without—

(1) Interference with the safe operation of the airplane; and

(2) Detrimental permanent deformation.

(b) Ultimate loads.

23.2240 Structural durability

(a) The applicant must develop and implement inspections or other procedures to prevent structural failures due to foreseeable causes of strength degradation, which could result in serious or fatal injuries, or extended periods of operation with reduced safety margins. Each of the inspections or other procedures developed under this section must be included in the Airworthiness Limitations Section of the Instructions for Continued Airworthiness required by 23.1529.

(b) For Level 4 airplanes, the procedures developed for compliance with paragraph (a) of this section must be capable of detecting structural damage before the damage could result in structural failure.

(c) For pressurized airplanes:

(1) The airplane must be capable of continued safe flight and landing following a sudden release of cabin pressure, including sudden releases caused by door and window failures.

(2) For airplanes with maximum operating altitude greater than 41,000 feet, the procedures developed for compliance with paragraph (a) of this section must be capable of detecting damage to the pressurized cabin structure before the damage could result in rapid decompression that would result in serious or fatal injuries.

(d) The airplane must be designed to minimize hazards to the airplane due to structural damage caused by high-energy fragments from an uncontained engine or rotating machinery failure.

23.2245 Aeroelasticity

(a) The airplane must be free from flutter, control reversal, and divergence—

(1) At all speeds within and sufficiently beyond the structural design envelope;

(2) For any configuration and condition of operation;

(3) Accounting for critical degrees of freedom; and

(4) Accounting for any critical failures or malfunctions.

(b) The applicant must establish tolerances for all quantities that affect flutter.

Design

23.2250 Design and construction principles

(a) The applicant must design each part, article, and assembly for the expected operating conditions of the airplane.

(b) Design data must adequately define the part, article, or assembly configuration, its design features, and any materials and processes used.

(c) The applicant must determine the suitability of each design detail and part having an important bearing on safety in operations.

(d) The control system must be free from jamming, excessive friction, and excessive deflection when the airplane is subjected to expected limit airloads.

(e) Doors, canopies, and exits must be protected against inadvertent opening in flight, unless shown to create no hazard when opened in flight.

23.2255 Protection of structure

(a) The applicant must protect each part of the airplane, including small parts such as fasteners, against deterioration or loss of strength due to any cause likely to occur in the expected operational environment.

(b) Each part of the airplane must have adequate provisions for ventilation and drainage.

(c) For each part that requires maintenance, preventive maintenance, or servicing, the applicant must incorporate a means into the aircraft design to allow such actions to be accomplished.

23.2260 Materials and processes

(a) The applicant must determine the suitability and durability of materials used for parts, articles, and assemblies, accounting for the effects of likely environmental conditions expected in service, the failure of which could prevent continued safe flight and landing.

(b) The methods and processes of fabrication and assembly used must produce consistently sound structures. If a fabrication process requires close control to reach this objective, the applicant must perform the process under an approved process specification.

(c) Except as provided in paragraphs (f) and (g) of this section, the applicant must select design values that ensure material strength with probabilities that account for the criticality of the structural element. Design values must account for the probability of structural failure due to material variability.

(d) If material strength properties are required, a determination of those properties must be based on sufficient tests of material meeting specifications to establish design values on a statistical basis.

(e) If thermal effects are significant on a critical component or structure under normal operating conditions, the applicant must determine those effects on allowable stresses used for design.

(f) Design values, greater than the minimums specified by this section, may be used, where only guaranteed minimum values are normally allowed, if a specimen of each individual item is tested before use to determine that the actual strength properties of that particular item will equal or exceed those used in the design.

(g) An applicant may use other material design values if approved by the Administrator.

23.2265 Special factors of safety

(a) The applicant must determine a special factor of safety for each critical design value for each part, article, or assembly for which that critical design value is uncertain, and for each part, article, or assembly that is—

(1) Likely to deteriorate in service before normal replacement; or

(2) Subject to appreciable variability because of uncertainties in manufacturing processes or inspection methods.

(b) The applicant must determine a special factor of safety using quality controls and specifications that account for each—

(1) Type of application;

(2) Inspection method;

(3) Structural test requirement;

(4) Sampling percentage; and

(5) Process and material control.

(c) The applicant must multiply the highest pertinent special factor of safety in the design for each part of the structure by each limit and ultimate load, or ultimate load only, if there is no corresponding limit load, such as occurs with emergency condition loading.

Structural Occupant Protection

23.2270 Emergency conditions

(a) The airplane, even when damaged in an emergency landing, must protect each occupant against injury that would preclude egress when—

(1) Properly using safety equipment and features provided for in the design;

(2) The occupant experiences ultimate static inertia loads likely to occur in an emergency landing; and

(3) Items of mass, including engines or auxiliary power units (APUs), within or aft of the cabin, that could injure an occupant, experience ultimate static inertia loads likely to occur in an emergency landing.

(b) The emergency landing conditions specified in paragraph (a)(1) and (a)(2) of this section, must—

(1) Include dynamic conditions that are likely to occur in an emergency landing; and

(2) Not generate loads experienced by the occupants, which exceed established human injury criteria for human tolerance due to restraint or contact with objects in the airplane.

(c) The airplane must provide protection for all occupants, accounting for likely flight, ground, and emergency landing conditions.

(d) Each occupant protection system must perform its intended function and not create a hazard that could cause a secondary injury to an occupant. The occupant protection system must not prevent occupant egress or interfere with the operation of the airplane when not in use.

(e) Each baggage and cargo compartment must—

(1) Be designed for its maximum weight of contents and for the critical load distributions at the maximum load factors corresponding to the flight and ground load conditions determined under this part;

(2) Have a means to prevent the contents of the compartment from becoming a hazard by impacting occupants or shifting; and

(3) Protect any controls, wiring, lines, equipment, or accessories whose damage or failure would affect safe operations.

Subpart D — Design and Construction

23.2300 Flight control systems

(a) The applicant must design airplane flight control systems to:

(1) Operate easily, smoothly, and positively enough to allow proper performance of their functions.

(2) Protect against likely hazards.

(b) The applicant must design trim systems, if installed, to:

(1) Protect against inadvertent, incorrect, or abrupt trim operation.

(2) Provide a means to indicate—

    (i) The direction of trim control movement relative to airplane motion;

    (ii) The trim position with respect to the trim range;

    (iii) The neutral position for lateral and directional trim; and

    (iv) The range for takeoff for all applicant requested center of gravity ranges and configurations.

23.2305 Landing gear systems

(a) The landing gear must be designed to—

(1) Provide stable support and control to the airplane during surface operation; and

(2) Account for likely system failures and likely operation environments (including anticipated limitation exceedances and emergency procedures).

(b) All airplanes must have a reliable means of stopping the airplane with sufficient kinetic energy absorption to account for landing. Airplanes that are required to demonstrate aborted takeoff capability must account for this additional kinetic energy.

(c) For airplanes that have a system that actuates the landing gear, there is—

(1) A positive means to keep the landing gear in the landing position; and

(2) An alternative means available to bring the landing gear in the landing position when a non-deployed system position would be a hazard.

23.2310 Buoyancy for seaplanes and amphibians

Airplanes intended for operations on water, must—

(a) Provide buoyancy of 80 percent in excess of the buoyancy required to support the maximum weight of the airplane in fresh water; and

(b) Have sufficient margin so the airplane will stay afloat at rest in calm water without capsizing in case of a likely float or hull flooding.

Occupant System Design Protection

23.2315 Means of egress and emergency exits

(a) With the cabin configured for takeoff or landing, the airplane is designed to:

(1) Facilitate rapid and safe evacuation of the airplane in conditions likely to occur following an emergency landing, excluding ditching for level 1, level 2 and single engine level 3 airplanes.

(2) Have means of egress (openings, exits or emergency exits), that can be readily located and opened from the inside and outside. The means of opening must be simple and obvious and marked inside and outside the airplane.

(3) Have easy access to emergency exits when present.

(b) Airplanes approved for aerobatics must have a means to egress the airplane in flight.

23.2320 Occupant physical environment

(a) The applicant must design the airplane to—

FAR 23

(1) Allow clear communication between the flightcrew and passengers;

(2) Protect the pilot and flight controls from propellers; and

(3) Protect the occupants from serious injury due to damage to windshields, windows, and canopies.

(b) For level 4 airplanes, each windshield and its supporting structure directly in front of the pilot must withstand, without penetration, the impact equivalent to a two-pound bird when the velocity of the airplane is equal to the airplane's maximum approach flap speed.

(c) The airplane must provide each occupant with air at a breathable pressure, free of hazardous concentrations of gases, vapors, and smoke during normal operations and likely failures.

(d) If a pressurization system is installed in the airplane, it must be designed to protect against—

(1) Decompression to an unsafe level; and

(2) Excessive differential pressure.

(e) If an oxygen system is installed in the airplane, it must—

(1) Effectively provide oxygen to each user to prevent the effects of hypoxia; and

(2) Be free from hazards in itself, in its method of operation, and its effect upon other components.

Fire and High Energy Protection

23.2325   Fire protection

(a) The following materials must be self-extinguishing—

(1) Insulation on electrical wire and electrical cable;

(2) For levels 1, 2, and 3 airplanes, materials in the baggage and cargo compartments inaccessible in flight; and

(3) For level 4 airplanes, materials in the cockpit, cabin, baggage, and cargo compartments.

(b) The following materials must be flame resistant—

(1) For levels 1, 2 and 3 airplanes, materials in each compartment accessible in flight; and

(2) Any equipment associated with any electrical cable installation and that would overheat in the event of circuit overload or fault.

(c) Thermal/acoustic materials in the fuselage, if installed, must not be a flame propagation hazard.

(d) Sources of heat within each baggage and cargo compartment that are capable of igniting adjacent objects must be shielded and insulated to prevent such ignition.

(e) For level 4 airplanes, each baggage and cargo compartment must—

(1) Be located where a fire would be visible to the pilots, or equipped with a fire detection system and warning system; and

(2) Be accessible for the manual extinguishing of a fire, have a built-in fire extinguishing system, or be constructed and sealed to contain any fire within the compartment.

(f) There must be a means to extinguish any fire in the cabin such that—

(1) The pilot, while seated, can easily access the fire extinguishing means; and

(2) For levels 3 and 4 airplanes, passengers have a fire extinguishing means available within the passenger compartment.

(g) Each area where flammable fluids or vapors might escape by leakage of a fluid system must—

(1) Be defined; and

(2) Have a means to minimize the probability of fluid and vapor ignition, and the resultant hazard, if ignition occurs.

(h) Combustion heater installations must be protected from uncontained fire.

23.2330   Fire protection in designated fire zones and adjacent areas

(a) Flight controls, engine mounts, and other flight structures within or adjacent to designated fire zones must be capable of withstanding the effects of a fire.

(b) Engines in a designated fire zone must remain attached to the airplane in the event of a fire.

(c) In designated fire zones, terminals, equipment, and electrical cables used during emergency procedures must be fire-resistant.

23.2335   Lightning protection

The airplane must be protected against catastrophic effects from lightning.

Subpart E — Powerplant
23.2400   Powerplant installation

(a) For the purpose of this subpart, the airplane powerplant installation must include each component necessary for propulsion, which affects propulsion safety, or provides auxiliary power to the airplane.

(b) Each airplane engine and propeller must be type certificated, except for engines and propellers installed on level 1 low-speed airplanes, which may be approved under the airplane type certificate in accordance with a standard accepted by the FAA that contains airworthiness criteria the Administrator has found appropriate and applicable to the specific design and intended use of the engine or propeller and provides a level of safety acceptable to the FAA.

(c) The applicant must construct and arrange each powerplant installation to account for—

(1) Likely operating conditions, including foreign object threats;

(2) Sufficient clearance of moving parts to other airplane parts and their surroundings;

(3) Likely hazards in operation including hazards to ground personnel; and

(4) Vibration and fatigue.

(d) Hazardous accumulations of fluids, vapors, or gases must be isolated from the airplane and personnel compartments, and be safely contained or discharged.

(e) Powerplant components must comply with their component limitations and installation instructions or be shown not to create a hazard.

23.2405   Automatic power or thrust control systems

(a) An automatic power or thrust control system intended for in-flight use must be designed so no unsafe condition will result during normal operation of the system.

(b) Any single failure or likely combination of failures of an automatic power or thrust control system must not prevent continued safe flight and landing of the airplane.

(c) Inadvertent operation of an automatic power or thrust control system by the flightcrew must be prevented, or if not prevented, must not result in an unsafe condition.

(d) Unless the failure of an automatic power or thrust control system is extremely remote, the system must—

(1) Provide a means for the flightcrew to verify the system is in an operating condition;

(2) Provide a means for the flightcrew to override the automatic function; and

(3) Prevent inadvertent deactivation of the system.

23.2410   Powerplant installation hazard assessment

The applicant must assess each powerplant separately and in relation to other airplane systems and installations to show that any hazard resulting from the likely failure of any powerplant system, component, or accessory will not—

(a) Prevent continued safe flight and landing or, if continued safe flight and landing cannot be ensured, the hazard has been minimized;

(b) Cause serious injury that may be avoided; and

(c) Require immediate action by any crewmember for continued operation of any remaining powerplant system.

23.2415   Powerplant ice protection

(a) The airplane design, including the induction and inlet system, must prevent foreseeable accumulation of ice or snow that adversely affects powerplant operation.

(b) The powerplant installation design must prevent any accumulation of ice or snow that adversely affects powerplant operation, in those icing conditions for which certification is requested.

23.2420   Reversing systems

Each reversing system must be designed so that—

(a) No unsafe condition will result during normal operation of the system; and

(b) The airplane is capable of continued safe flight and landing after any single failure, likely combination of failures, or malfunction of the reversing system.

23.2425   Powerplant operational characteristics

(a) The installed powerplant must operate without any hazardous characteristics during normal and emergency operation within the range of operating limitations for the airplane and the engine.

(b) The pilot must have the capability to stop the powerplant in flight and restart the powerplant within an established operational envelope.

23.2430   Fuel systems

(a) Each fuel system must—

(1) Be designed and arranged to provide independence between multiple fuel storage and supply systems so that failure of any one component in one system will not result in loss of fuel storage or supply of another system;

(2) Be designed and arranged to prevent ignition of the fuel within the system by direct lightning strikes or swept lightning strokes to areas where such occurrences are highly probable, or by corona or streamering at fuel vent outlets;

(3) Provide the fuel necessary to ensure each powerplant and auxiliary power unit functions properly in all likely operating conditions;

(4) Provide the flightcrew with a means to determine the total useable fuel available and provide uninterrupted supply of that fuel when the system is correctly operated, accounting for likely fuel fluctuations;

(5) Provide a means to safely remove or isolate the fuel stored in the system from the airplane;

(6) Be designed to retain fuel under all likely operating conditions and minimize hazards to the occupants during any survivable emergency landing. For level 4 airplanes, failure due to overload of the landing system must be taken into account; and

(7) Prevent hazardous contamination of the fuel supplied to each powerplant and auxiliary power unit.

(b) Each fuel storage system must—

(1) Withstand the loads under likely operating conditions without failure;

(2) Be isolated from personnel compartments and protected from hazards due to unintended temperature influences;

(3) Be designed to prevent significant loss of stored fuel from any vent system due to fuel transfer between fuel storage or supply systems, or under likely operating conditions;

(4) Provide fuel for at least one-half hour of operation at maximum continuous power or thrust; and

(5) Be capable of jettisoning fuel safely if required for landing.

(c) Each fuel storage refilling or recharging system must be designed to—

(1) Prevent improper refilling or recharging;

(2) Prevent contamination of the fuel stored during likely operating conditions; and

(3) Prevent the occurrence of any hazard to the airplane or to persons during refilling or recharging.

23.2435   Powerplant induction and exhaust systems

(a) The air induction system for each powerplant or auxiliary power unit and their accessories must—

(1) Supply the air required by that powerplant or auxiliary power unit and its accessories under likely operating conditions;

(2) Be designed to prevent likely hazards in the event of fire or backfire;

(3) Minimize the ingestion of foreign matter; and

(4) Provide an alternate intake if blockage of the primary intake is likely.

(b) The exhaust system, including exhaust heat exchangers for each powerplant or auxiliary power unit, must—

(1) Provide a means to safely discharge potential harmful material; and

(2) Be designed to prevent likely hazards from heat, corrosion, or blockage.

23.2440   Powerplant fire protection

(a) A powerplant, auxiliary power unit, or combustion heater that includes a flammable fluid and an ignition source for that fluid must be installed in a designated fire zone.

(b) Each designated fire zone must provide a means to isolate and mitigate hazards to the airplane in the event of fire or overheat within the zone.

(c) Each component, line, fitting, and control subject to fire conditions must—

(1) Be designed and located to prevent hazards resulting from a fire, including any located adjacent to a designated fire zone that may be affected by fire within that zone;

(2) Be fire resistant if carrying flammable fluids, gas, or air or required to operate in event of a fire; and

(3) Be fireproof or enclosed by a fire proof shield if storing concentrated flammable fluids.

(d) The applicant must provide a means to prevent hazardous quantities of flammable fluids from flowing into, within or through each designated fire zone. This means must—

(1) Not restrict flow or limit operation of any remaining powerplant or auxiliary power unit, or equipment necessary for safety;

(2) Prevent inadvertent operation; and

(3) Be located outside the fire zone unless an equal degree of safety is provided with a means inside the fire zone.

(e) A means to ensure the prompt detection of fire must be provided for each designated fire zone—

(1) On a multiengine airplane where detection will mitigate likely hazards to the airplane; or

(2) That contains a fire extinguisher.

(f) A means to extinguish fire within a fire zone, except a combustion heater fire zone, must be provided for—

(1) Any fire zone located outside the pilot's view;

(2) Any fire zone embedded within the fuselage, which must also include a redundant means to extinguish fire; and

(3) Any fire zone on a level 4 airplane.

Subpart F — Equipment

23.2500 Airplane level systems requirements

This section applies generally to installed equipment and systems unless a section of this part imposes requirements for a specific piece of equipment, system, or systems.

(a) The equipment and systems required for an airplane to operate safely in the kinds of operations for which certification is requested (Day VFR, Night VFR, IFR) must be designed and installed to—

(1) Meet the level of safety applicable to the certification and performance level of the airplane; and

(2) Perform their intended function throughout the operating and environmental limits for which the airplane is certificated.

(b) The systems and equipment not covered by paragraph (a), considered separately and in relation to other systems, must be designed and installed so their operation does not have an adverse effect on the airplane or its occupants.23.2505   Function and installation.

When installed, each item of equipment must function as intended.

23.2510 Equipment, systems, and installations

For any airplane system or equipment whose failure or abnormal operation has not been specifically addressed by another requirement in this part, the applicant must design and install each system and equipment, such that there is a logical and acceptable inverse relationship between the average probability and the severity of failure conditions to the extent that:

(a) Each catastrophic failure condition is extremely improbable;

(b) Each hazardous failure condition is extremely remote; and

(c) Each major failure condition is remote.

23.2515 Electrical and electronic system lightning protection

An airplane approved for IFR operations must meet the following requirements, unless an applicant shows that exposure to lightning is unlikely:

(a) Each electrical or electronic system that performs a function, the failure of which would prevent the continued safe flight and landing of the airplane, must be designed and installed such that—

(1) The function at the airplane level is not adversely affected during and after the time the airplane is exposed to lightning; and

(2) The system recovers normal operation of that function in a timely manner after the airplane is exposed to lightning unless the system's recovery conflicts with other operational or functional requirements of the system.

(b) Each electrical and electronic system that performs a function, the failure of which would significantly reduce the capability of the airplane or the ability of the flightcrew to respond to an adverse operating condition, must be designed and installed such that the system recovers normal operation of that function in a timely manner after the airplane is exposed to lightning.

23.2520 High-intensity Radiated Fields (HIRF) protection

(a) Each electrical and electronic systems that perform a function, the failure of which would prevent the continued safe flight and landing of the airplane, must be designed and installed such that—

(1) The function at the airplane level is not adversely affected during and after the time the airplane is exposed to the HIRF environment; and

(2) The system recovers normal operation of that function in a timely manner after the airplane is exposed to the HIRF environment, unless the system's recovery conflicts with other operational or functional requirements of the system.

(b) For airplanes approved for IFR operations, each electrical and electronic system that performs a function, the failure of which would significantly reduce the capability of the airplane or the ability of the flightcrew to respond to an adverse operating condi-

tion, must be designed and installed such that the system recovers normal operation of that function in a timely manner after the airplane is exposed to the HIRF environment.

23.2525 System power generation, storage, and distribution

The power generation, storage, and distribution for any system must be designed and installed to—

(a) Supply the power required for operation of connected loads during all intended operating conditions;

(b) Ensure no single failure or malfunction of any one power supply, distribution system, or other utilization system will prevent the system from supplying the essential loads required for continued safe flight and landing; and

(c) Have enough capacity, if the primary source fails, to supply essential loads, including non-continuous essential loads for the time needed to complete the function required for continued safe flight and landing.

23.2530 External and cockpit lighting

(a) The applicant must design and install all lights to minimize any adverse effects on the performance of flightcrew duties.

(b) Any position and anti-collision lights, if required by part 91 of this chapter, must have the intensities, flash rate, colors, fields of coverage, and other characteristics to provide sufficient time for another aircraft to avoid a collision.

(c) Any position lights, if required by part 91 of this chapter, must include a red light on the left side of the airplane, a green light on the right side of the airplane, spaced laterally as far apart as practicable, and a white light facing aft, located on an aft portion of the airplane or on the wing tips.

(d) Any taxi and landing lights must be designed and installed so they provide sufficient light for night operations.

(e) For seaplanes or amphibian airplanes, riding lights must provide a white light visible in clear atmospheric conditions.

23.2535 Safety equipment

Safety and survival equipment, required by the operating rules of this chapter, must be reliable, readily accessible, easily identifiable, and clearly marked to identify its method of operation.

23.2540 Flight in icing conditions

An applicant who requests certification for flight in icing conditions defined in part 1 of appendix C to part 25 of this chapter, or an applicant who requests certification for flight in these icing conditions and any additional atmospheric icing conditions, must show the following in the icing conditions for which certification is requested:

(a) The ice protection system provides for safe operation.

(b) The airplane design must provide protection from stalling when the autopilot is operating.

23.2545 Pressurized systems elements

Pressurized systems must withstand appropriate proof and burst pressures.

23.2550 Equipment containing high-energy rotors

Equipment containing high-energy rotors must be designed or installed to protect the occupants and airplane from uncontained fragments.

Subpart G — Flightcrew Interface and Other Information

23.2600 Flightcrew interface

(a) The pilot compartment, its equipment, and its arrangement to include pilot view, must allow each pilot to perform his or her duties, including taxi, takeoff, climb, cruise, descent, approach, landing, and perform any maneuvers within the operating envelope of the airplane, without excessive concentration, skill, alertness, or fatigue.

(b) The applicant must install flight, navigation, surveillance, and powerplant controls and displays so qualified flightcrew can monitor and perform defined tasks associated with the intended functions of systems and equipment. The system and equipment design must minimize flightcrew errors, which could result in additional hazards.

(c) For level 4 airplanes, the flightcrew interface design must allow for continued safe flight and landing after the loss of vision through any one of the windshield panels.

23.2605   Installation and operation

(a) Each item of installed equipment related to the flightcrew interface must be labelled, if applicable, as to it identification, function, or operating limitations, or any combination of these factors.

(b) There must be a discernible means of providing system operating parameters required to operate the airplane, including warnings, cautions, and normal indications to the responsible crewmember.

(c) Information concerning an unsafe system operating condition must be provided in a timely manner to the crewmember responsible for taking corrective action. The information must be clear enough to avoid likely crewmember errors.

23.2610   Instrument markings, control markings, and placards

(a) Each airplane must display in a conspicuous manner any placard and instrument marking necessary for operation.

(b) The design must clearly indicate the function of each cockpit control, other than primary flight controls.

(c) The applicant must include instrument marking and placard information in the Airplane Flight Manual.

23.2615   Flight, navigation, and powerplant instruments

(a) Installed systems must provide the flightcrew member who sets or monitors parameters for the flight, navigation, and powerplant, the information necessary to do so during each phase of flight. This information must—

(1) Be presented in a manner that the crewmember can monitor the parameter and determine trends, as needed, to operate the airplane; and

(2) Include limitations, unless the limitation cannot be exceeded in all intended operations.

(b) Indication systems that integrate the display of flight or powerplant parameters to operate the airplane or are required by the operating rules of this chapter must—

(1) Not inhibit the primary display of flight or powerplant parameters needed by any flightcrew member in any normal mode of operation; and

(2) In combination with other systems, be designed and installed so information essential for continued safe flight and landing will be available to the flightcrew in a timely manner after any single failure or probable combination of failures.

23.2620   Airplane flight manual

The applicant must provide an Airplane Flight Manual that must be delivered with each airplane.

(a) The Airplane Flight Manual must contain the following information—

(1) Airplane operating limitations;

(2) Airplane operating procedures;

(3) Performance information;

(4) Loading information; and

(5) Other information that is necessary for safe operation because of design, operating, or handling characteristics.

(b) The following sections of the Airplane Flight Manual must be approved by the FAA in a manner specified by the administrator—

(1) For low-speed, level 1 and 2 airplanes, those portions of the Airplane Flight Manual containing the information specified in paragraph (a)(1) of this section; and

(2) For high-speed level 1 and 2 airplanes and all level 3 and 4 airplanes, those portions of the Airplane Flight Manual containing the information specified in paragraphs (a)(1) thru (a)(4) of this section.

Appendix A to Part 23—Instructions for Continued Airworthiness

A23.1   General

(a) This appendix specifies requirements for the preparation of Instructions for Continued Airworthiness as required by this part.

(b) The Instructions for Continued Airworthiness for each airplane must include the Instructions for Continued Airworthiness for each engine and propeller (hereinafter designated "products"), for each appliance required by this chapter, and any required information relating to the interface of those appliances and products with the airplane. If Instructions for Continued Airworthiness are not supplied by the manufacturer of an appliance or product installed in the airplane, the Instructions for Continued Airworthiness for the airplane must include the information essential to the continued airworthiness of the airplane.

(c) The applicant must submit to the FAA a program to show how changes to the Instructions for Continued Airworthiness made by the applicant or by the manufacturers of products and appliances installed in the airplane will be distributed.

A23.2   Format

(a) The Instructions for Continued Airworthiness must be in the form of a manual or manuals as appropriate for the quantity of data to be provided.

(b) The format of the manual or manuals must provide for a practical arrangement.

A23.3   Content

The contents of the manual or manuals must be prepared in the English language. The Instructions for Continued Airworthiness must contain the following manuals or sections and information:

(a) Airplane maintenance manual or section.

(1) Introduction information that includes an explanation of the airplane's features and data to the extent necessary for maintenance or preventive maintenance.

(2) A description of the airplane and its systems and installations including its engines, propellers, and appliances.

(3) Basic control and operation information describing how the airplane components and systems are controlled and how they operate, including any special procedures and limitations that apply.

(4) Servicing information that covers details regarding servicing points, capacities of tanks, reservoirs, types of fluids to be used, pressures applicable to the various systems, location of access panels for inspection and servicing, locations of lubrication points, lubricants to be used, equipment required for servicing, tow instructions and limitations, mooring, jacking, and leveling information.

(b) Maintenance Instructions.

(1) Scheduling information for each part of the airplane and its engines, auxiliary power units, propellers, accessories, instruments, and equipment that provides the recommended periods at which they should be cleaned, inspected, adjusted, tested, and lubricated, and the degree of inspection, the applicable wear tolerances, and work recommended at these periods. However, the applicant may refer to an accessory, instrument, or equipment manufacturer as the source of this information

if the applicant shows that the item has an exceptionally high degree of complexity requiring specialized maintenance techniques, test equipment, or expertise. The recommended overhaul periods and necessary cross reference to the Airworthiness Limitations section of the manual must also be included. In addition, the applicant must include an inspection program that includes the frequency and extent of the inspections necessary to provide for the continued airworthiness of the airplane.

(2) Troubleshooting information describing probable malfunctions, how to recognize those malfunctions, and the remedial action for those malfunctions.

(3) Information describing the order and method of removing and replacing products and parts with any necessary precautions to be taken.

(4) Other general procedural instructions including procedures for system testing during ground running, symmetry checks, weighing and determining the center of gravity, lifting and shoring, and storage limitations.

(c) Diagrams of structural access plates and information needed to gain access for inspections when access plates are not provided.

(d) Details for the application of special inspection techniques including radiographic and ultrasonic testing where such processes are specified by the applicant.

(e) Information needed to apply protective treatments to the structure after inspection.

(f) All data relative to structural fasteners such as identification, discard recommendations, and torque values.

(g) A list of special tools needed.

(h) In addition, for level 4 airplanes, the following information must be furnished—

(1) Electrical loads applicable to the various systems;

(2) Methods of balancing control surfaces;

(3) Identification of primary and secondary structures; and

(4) Special repair methods applicable to the airplane.

A23.4 Airworthiness limitations section

The Instructions for Continued Airworthiness must contain a section titled Airworthiness Limitations that is segregated and clearly distinguishable from the rest of the document. This section must set forth each mandatory replacement time, structural inspection interval, and related structural inspection procedure required for type certification. If the Instructions for Continued Airworthiness consist of multiple documents, the section required by this paragraph must be included in the principal manual. This section must contain a legible statement in a prominent location that reads "The Airworthiness Limitations section is FAA approved and specifies maintenance required under 43.16 and 91.403 of Title 14 of the Code of Federal Regulations unless an alternative program has been FAA approved."

PART 26 — CONTINUED AIRWORTHINESS AND SAFETY IMPROVEMENTS FOR TRANSPORT CATEGORY AIRPLANES

Subpart A — General

26.1 Purpose and scope
26.3 Definitions
26.5 Applicability table

Subpart B — Enhanced Airworthiness Program for Airplane Systems

26.11 Electrical wiring interconnection systems (EWIS) maintenance program

Subpart C — Aging Airplane Safety — Widespread Fatigue Damage

26.21 Limit of validity

Subpart D — Fuel Tank Flammability

26.31 Definitions
26.33 Holders of type certificates: Fuel tank flammability
26.35 Changes to type certificates affecting fuel tank flammability
26.37 Pending type certification projects: Fuel tank flammability
26.39 Newly produced airplanes: Fuel tank flammability

Subpart E — Aging Airplane Safety — Damage Tolerance Data for Repairs and Alterations

26.41 Definitions
26.43 Holders of and applicants for type certificates—Repairs
26.45 Holders of type certificates—Alterations and repairs to alterations
26.47 Holders of and applicants for a supplemental type certificate—Alterations and repairs to alterations
26.49 Compliance plan

Authority: 49 U.S.C. 106(g), 40113, 44701, 44702 and 44704.

Source: Docket No. FAA–2004–18379, Amdt. No. 26–0, 72 FR 63409, Nov. 8, 2007, unless otherwise noted.

Subpart A — General

26.1 Purpose and scope

(a) This part establishes requirements for support of the continued airworthiness of and safety improvements for transport category airplanes. These requirements may include performing assessments, developing design changes, developing revisions to Instructions for Continued Airworthiness (ICA), and making necessary documentation available to affected persons. Requirements of this part that establish standards for design changes and revisions to the ICA are considered airworthiness requirements.

(b) Except as provided in paragraph (c) of this section, this part applies to the following persons, as specified in each subpart of this part:

(1) Holders of type certificates and supplemental type certificates.

(2) Applicants for type certificates and supplemental type certificates and changes to those certificates (including service bulletins describing design changes).

(3) Persons seeking design approval for airplane repairs, alterations, or modifications that may affect airworthiness.

(4) Holders of type certificates and their licensees producing new airplanes.

(c) An applicant for approval of a design change is not required to comply with any applicable airworthiness requirement of this part if the applicant elects or is required to comply with a correspond-

ing amendment to part 25 of this chapter that is adopted concurrently or after that airworthiness requirement.

(d) For the purposes of this part, the word "type certificate" does not include supplemental type certificates.

26.5 Applicability table

Table 1 of this section provides an overview of the applicability of this part. It provides guidance in identifying what sections apply to various types of entities. The specific applicability of each subpart and section is specified in the regulatory text.

[Doc. No. FAA–2006–24281, 75 FR 69782, Nov. 15, 2010]

TABLE 1—APPLICABILITY OF PART 26 RULES				
	Applicable Sections			
	Subpart B EAPAS/FTS	Subpart C Widespread Fatigue Damage	Subpart D Fuel Tank Flammability	Subpart E Damage Tolerance Data
Effective Date of Rule	December 10, 2007	January 14, 2011	December 26, 2008	January 11, 2008
Existing[1] TC Holders	26.11	26.21	26.33	26.43 26.45 26.49
Pending[1] TC Applicants	26.11	26.21	26.37	26.43 26.45
Future[2] TC Applicants	N/A	N/A	N/A	26.43
Existing[1] STC Holders	N/A	26.21	26.35	26.47 26.49
Pending[1] STC/ ATC Applicants	26.11	26.21	26.35	26.45 26.47 26.49
Future[2] STC/ ATC Applicants	26.11	26.21	26.35	26.45 26.47 26.49
Manufacturers	N/A		26.39	N/A

[1] As of the effective date of the identified rule.
[2] Application made after the effective date of the identified rule.

Subpart B — Enhanced Airworthiness Program for Airplane Systems

26.11 Electrical wiring interconnection systems (EWIS) maintenance program

(a) Except as provided in paragraph (g) of this section, this section applies to transport category, turbine-powered airplanes with a type certificate issued after January 1, 1958, that, as a result of the original certification, or later increase in capacity, have—

(1) A maximum type-certificated passenger capacity of 30 or more or

(2) A maximum payload capacity of 7,500 pounds or more.

(b) Holders of, and applicants for, type certificates, as identified in paragraph (d) of this section must develop Instructions for Continued Airworthiness (ICA) for the representative airplane's EWIS in accordance with part 25, Appendix H paragraphs H25.5(a)(1) and (b) of this subchapter in effect on December 10, 2007 for each affected type design, and submit those ICA for review and approval by the responsible Aircraft Certification Service office. For purposes of this section, the "representative airplane" is the configuration of each model series airplane that incorporates all variations of EWIS used in production on that series airplane, and all TC-holder-designed modifications mandated by airworthiness directive as of the effective date of this rule. Each person specified in paragraph (d) of this section must also review any fuel tank system ICA developed by that person to comply with SFAR 88 to ensure compatibility with the EWIS ICA, including minimizing redundant requirements.

(c) Applicants for amendments to type certificates and supplemental type certificates, as identified in paragraph (d) of this section, must:

   (1) Evaluate whether the design change for which approval is sought necessitates a revision to the ICA required by paragraph (b) of this section to comply with the requirements of Appendix H, paragraphs H25.5(a)(1) and (b). If so, the applicant must develop and submit the necessary revisions for review and approval by the responsible Aircraft Certification Service office.

   (2) Ensure that any revised EWIS ICA remain compatible with any fuel tank system ICA previously developed to comply with SFAR 88 and any redundant requirements between them are minimized.

(d) The following persons must comply with the requirements of paragraph (b) or (c) of this section, as applicable, before the dates specified.

   (1) Holders of type certificates (TC): December 10, 2009.

   (2) Applicants for TCs, and amendments to TCs (including service bulletins describing design changes), if the date of application was before December 10, 2007 and the certificate was issued on or after December 10, 2007: December 10, 2009 or the date the certificate is issued, whichever occurs later.

   (3) Unless compliance with 25.1729 of this subchapter is required or elected, applicants for amendments to TCs, if the application was filed on or after December 10, 2007: December 10, 2009, or the date of approval of the certificate, whichever occurs later.

   (4) Applicants for supplemental type certificates (STC), including changes to existing STCs, if the date of application was before December 10, 2007 and the certificate was issued on or after December 10, 2007: June 7, 2010, or the date of approval of the certificate, whichever occurs later.

   (5) Unless compliance with 25.1729 of this subchapter is required or elected, applicants for STCs, including changes to existing STCs, if the application was filed on or after December 10, 2007, June 7, 2010, or the date of approval of the certificate, whichever occurs later.

(e) Each person identified in paragraphs (d)(1), (d)(2), and (d)(4) of this section must submit to the responsible Aircraft Certification Service office for approval a compliance plan by March 10, 2008. The compliance plan must include the following information:

   (1) A proposed project schedule, identifying all major milestones, for meeting the compliance dates specified in paragraph (d) of this section.

   (2) A proposed means of compliance with this section, identifying all required submissions, including all compliance items as mandated in part 25, Appendix H paragraphs H25.5(a)(1) and (b) of this subchapter in effect on December 10, 2007, and all data to be developed to substantiate compliance.

   (3) A proposal for submitting a draft of all compliance items required by paragraph (e)(2) of this section for review by the responsible Aircraft Certification Service office not less than 60 days before the compliance time specified in paragraph (d) of this section.

   (4) A proposal for how the approved ICA will be made available to affected persons.

(f) Each person specified in paragraph (e) must implement the compliance plan, or later approved revisions, as approved in compliance with paragraph (e) of this section.

(g) This section does not apply to the following airplane models:

   (1) Lockheed L–188
   (2) Bombardier CL–44
   (3) Mitsubishi YS–11
   (4) British Aerospace BAC 1–11
   (5) Concorde
   (6) deHavilland D.H. 106 Comet 4C
   (7) VFW—Vereinigte Flugtechnische Werk VFW–614
   (8) Illyushin Aviation IL 96T
   (9) Bristol Aircraft Britannia 305
   (10) Handley Page Herald Type 300
   (11) Avions Marcel Dassault—Breguet Aviation Mercure 100C
   (12) Airbus Caravelle
   (13) Lockheed L–300

[Amdt. 26-0, 72 FR 63409, Nov. 8, 2007; 72 FR 68618, Dec. 5, 2007, as amended by Doc. No. FAA-2018-0119, Amdt. 26-7, 83 FR 9170, Mar. 5, 2018]

Subpart C — Aging Airplane Safety—Widespread Fatigue Damage

Source: Doc. No. FAA–2006–24281, 75 FR 69782, Nov. 15, 2010, unless otherwise noted.

26.21 Limit of validity

(a) Applicability. Except as provided in paragraph (g) of this section, this section applies to transport category, turbine-powered airplanes with a maximum takeoff gross weight greater than 75,000 pounds and a type certificate issued after January 1, 1958, regardless of whether the maximum takeoff gross weight is a result of an original type certificate or a later design change. This section also applies to transport category, turbine-powered airplanes with a type certificate issued after January 1, 1958, if a design change approval for which application is made after January 14, 2011 has the effect of reducing the maximum takeoff gross weight from greater than 75,000 pounds to 75,000 pounds or less.

(b) Limit of validity. Each person identified in paragraph (c) of this section must comply with the following requirements:

   (1) Establish a limit of validity of the engineering data that supports the structural maintenance program (hereafter referred to as LOV) that corresponds to the period of time, stated as a number of total accumulated flight cycles or flight hours or both, during which it is demonstrated that widespread fatigue damage will not occur in the airplane. This demonstration must include an evaluation of airplane structural configurations and be supported by test evidence and analysis at a minimum and, if available, service experience, or service experience and teardown inspection results, of high-time airplanes of similar structural design, accounting for differences in operating conditions and procedures. The airplane structural configurations to be evaluated include—

     (i) All model variations and derivatives approved under the type certificate; and

     (ii) All structural modifications to and replacements for the airplane structural configurations specified in paragraph (b)(1)(i) of this section, mandated by airworthiness directives as of January 14, 2011.

   (2) If the LOV depends on performance of maintenance actions for which service information has not been mandated by airworthiness directive as of January 14, 2011, submit the following to the responsible Aircraft Certification Service office:

     (i) For those maintenance actions for which service information has been issued as of the applicable compliance date specified in paragraph (c) of this section, a list identifying each of those actions.

     (ii) For those maintenance actions for which service information has not been issued as of the applicable compliance date specified in paragraph (c) of this section, a list identifying each of those actions and a binding schedule for providing in a timely manner the necessary service information for those actions. Once the responsible Aircraft Certification Service office approves this schedule, each person identified in paragraph (c) of this section must comply with that schedule.

   (3) Unless previously accomplished, establish an Airworthiness Limitations section (ALS) for each airplane structural configuration evaluated under paragraph (b)(1) of this section.

(4) Incorporate the applicable LOV established under paragraph (b)(1) of this section into the ALS for each airplane structural configuration evaluated under paragraph (b)(1) and submit it to the responsible Aircraft Certification Service office for approval.

(c) Persons who must comply and compliance dates. The following persons must comply with the requirements of paragraph (b) of this section by the specified date.

(1) Holders of type certificates (TC) of airplane models identified in Table 1 of this section: No later than the applicable date identified in Table 1 of this section.

(2) Applicants for TCs, if the date of application was before January 14, 2011: No later than the latest of the following dates:

    (i)   January 14, 2016;

    (ii) The date the certificate is issued; or

    (iii) The date specified in the plan approved under 25.571(b) for completion of the full-scale fatigue testing and demonstrating that widespread fatigue damage will not occur in the airplane structure.

(3) Applicants for amendments to TCs, with the exception of amendments to TCs specified in paragraphs (c)(6) or (c)(7) of this section, if the original TC was issued before January 14, 2011: No later than the latest of the following dates:

    (i)   January 14, 2016;

    (ii) The date the amended certificate is issued; or

    (iii) The date specified in the plan approved under 25.571(b) for completion of the full-scale fatigue testing and demonstrating that widespread fatigue damage will not occur in the airplane structure.

(4) Applicants for amendments to TCs, with the exception of amendments to TCs specified in paragraphs (c)(6) or (c)(7) of this section, if the application for the original TC was made before January 14, 2011 but the TC was not issued before January 14, 2011: No later than the latest of the following dates:

    (i)   January 14, 2016;

    (ii) The date the amended certificate is issued; or

    (iii) The date specified in the plan approved under 25.571(b) for completion of the full-scale fatigue testing and demonstrating that widespread fatigue damage will not occur in the airplane structure.

(5) Holders of either supplemental type certificates (STCs) or amendments to TCs that increase maximum takeoff gross weights from 75,000 pounds or less to greater than 75,000 pounds: No later than July 14, 2012.

(6) Applicants for either STCs or amendments to TCs that increase maximum takeoff gross weights from 75,000 pounds or less to greater than 75,000 pounds: No later than the latest of the following dates:

    (i)   July 14, 2012;

    (ii) The date the certificate is issued; or

    (iii) The date specified in the plan approved under 25.571(b) for completion of the full-scale fatigue testing and demonstrating that widespread fatigue damage will not occur in the airplane structure.

(7) Applicants for either STCs or amendments to TCs that decrease maximum takeoff gross weights from greater than 75,000 pounds to 75,000 pounds or less, if the date of application was after January 14, 2011: No later than the latest of the following dates:

    (i)   July 14, 2012;

    (ii) The date the certificate is issued; or

    (iii) The date specified in the plan approved under 25.571(b) for completion of the full-scale fatigue testing and demonstrating that widespread fatigue damage will not occur in the airplane structure.

(d) Compliance plan. Each person identified in paragraph (e) of this section must submit a compliance plan consisting of the following:

(1) A proposed project schedule, identifying all major milestones, for meeting the compliance dates specified in paragraph (c) of this section.

(2) A proposed means of compliance with paragraphs (b)(1) through (b)(4) of this section.

(3) A proposal for submitting a draft of all compliance items required by paragraph (b) of this section for review by the responsible Aircraft Certification Service office not less than 60 days before the compliance date specified in paragraph (c) of this section, as applicable.

(4) A proposal for how the LOV will be distributed.

(e) Compliance dates for compliance plans. The following persons must submit the compliance plan described in paragraph (d) of this section to the responsible Aircraft Certification Service office by the specified date.

(1) Holders of type certificates: No later than April 14, 2011.

(2) Applicants for TCs and amendments to TCs, with the exception of amendments to TCs specified in paragraphs (e)(4), (e)(5), or (e)(6) of this section, if the date of application was before January 14, 2011 but the TC or TC amendment was not issued before January 14, 2011: No later than April 14, 2011.

(3) Holders of either supplemental type certificates or amendments to TCs that increase maximum takeoff gross weights from 75,000 pounds or less to greater than 75,000 pounds: No later than April 14, 2011.

(4) Applicants for either STCs or amendments to TCs that increase maximum takeoff gross weights from 75,000 pounds or less to greater than 75,000 pounds, if the date of application was before January 14, 2011: No later than April 14, 2011.

(5) Applicants for either STCs or amendments to TCs that increase maximum takeoff gross weights from 75,000 pounds or less to greater than 75,000 pounds, if the date of application is on or after January 14, 2011: Within 90 days after the date of application.

(6) Applicants for either STCs or amendments to TCs that decrease maximum takeoff gross weights from greater than 75,000 pounds to 75,000 pounds or less, if the date of application is on or after January 14, 2011: Within 90 days after the date of application.

(f) Compliance plan implementation. Each affected person must implement the compliance plan as approved in compliance with paragraph (d) of this section.

(g) Exceptions. This section does not apply to the following airplane models:

(1) Bombardier BD–700

(2) Bombardier CL–44

(3) Gulfstream GV

(4) Gulfstream GV–SP

(5) British Aerospace, Aircraft Group, and Societe Nationale Industrielle Aerospatiale Concorde Type 1

(6) British Aerospace (Commercial Aircraft) Ltd., Armstrong Whitworth Argosy A.W. 650 Series 101

(7) British Aerospace Airbus, Ltd., BAC 1–11

(8) BAE Systems (Operations) Ltd., BAe 146

(9) BAE Systems (Operations) Ltd., Avro 146

(10) Lockheed 300–50A01 (USAF C141A)

(11) Boeing 707

(12) Boeing 720

(13) deHavilland D.H. 106 Comet 4C

(14) Ilyushin Aviation IL–96T

(15) Bristol Aircraft Britannia 305

(16) Avions Marcel Dassault-Breguet Aviation Mercure 100C

(17) Airbus Caravelle

(18) D & R Nevada, LLC, Convair Model 22

(19) D & R Nevada, LLC, Convair Model 23M

FAR 26

TABLE 1 — COMPLIANCE DATES FOR AFFECTED AIRPLANES	
AIRPLANE MODEL (ALL EXISTING[1] MODELS)	COMPLIANCE DATE (MONTHS AFTER JANUARY 14, 2011)
AIRBUS	
A300 Series	18
A310 Series, A300-600 Series	48
A318 Series	48
A319 Series	48
A320 Series	48
A321 Series	48
A330-200, -200 Freighter, -300 Series	48
A340-200, -300, -500, -600 Series	48
A380-800 Series	60
BOEING	
717	48
727 (All series)	18
737 (Classics): 737-100, -200, -200C, -300, -400, -500	18
737 (NG): 737-600, -700, -700C, -800, -900, -900ER	48
747 (Classics): 747-100, -100B, -100B SUD, -200B, -200C, -200F, -300, 747SP, 747SR	18
747-400: 747-400, -400D, -400F	48
757	48
767	48
777-200, -300	48
777-200LR, 777-300ER, 777F	60
BOMBARDIER	
CL-600: 2D15 (Regional Jet Series 705), 2D24 (Regional Jet Series 900)	60
EMBRAER	
ERJ 170	60
ERJ190	60
FOKKER	
F.28 Mark 0070, Mark 0100	18
LOCKHEED	
L-1011	18
188	18
382 (All Series)	18
MCDONNELL DOUGLAS	
DC-8, -8F	18
DC-9	18
MD-80 (DC-9-81, -82, -83, -87, MD-88)	18
MD-90	48
DC-10	18
MD-10	48
MD-11, -11F	48
All other airplane models listed on a Type Certificate as of January 14, 2011	60
[1]Type certificated as of January 14, 2011	

[Doc. No. FAA-2006-24281, 75 FR 69782, Nov. 15, 2010, as amended at 77 FR 30878, May 24, 2012; Doc. No. FAA-2018-0119, Amdt. 26-7, 83 FR 9169, Mar. 5, 2018]

26.23   Extended limit of validity

(a) Applicability. Any person may apply to extend a limit of validity of the engineering data that supports the structural maintenance program (hereafter referred to as LOV) approved under 25.571 of this subchapter, 26.21, or this section. Extending an LOV is a major design change. The applicant must comply with the relevant provisions of subparts D or E of part 21 of this subchapter and paragraph (b) of this section.

(b) Extended limit of validity. Each person applying for an extended LOV must comply with the following requirements:

(1) Establish an extended LOV that corresponds to the period of time, stated as a number of total accumulated flight cycles or flight hours or both, during which it is demonstrated that widespread fatigue damage will not occur in the airplane. This demonstration must include an evaluation of airplane structural configurations and be supported by test evidence and analysis at a minimum and, if available, service experience, or service experience and teardown inspection results, of high-time airplanes of similar structural design, accounting for differences in operating conditions and procedures. The airplane structural configurations to be evaluated include—

(i) All model variations and derivatives approved under the type certificate for which approval for an extension is sought; and

(ii) All structural modifications to and replacements for the airplane structural configurations specified in paragraph (b)(1)(i) of this section, mandated by airworthiness directive, up to the date of approval of the extended LOV.

(2) Establish a revision or supplement, as applicable, to the Airworthiness Limitations section (ALS) of the Instructions for Continued Airworthiness required by §25.1529 of this subchapter, and submit it to the responsible Aircraft Certification Service office for approval. The revised ALS or supplement to the ALS must include the applicable extended LOV established under paragraph (b)(1) of this section.

(3) Develop the maintenance actions determined by the WFD evaluation performed in paragraph (b)(1) of this section to be necessary to preclude WFD from occurring before the airplane reaches the proposed extended LOV. These maintenance actions must be documented as airworthiness limitation items in the ALS and submitted to the responsible Aircraft Certification Service office for approval.

[Docket No. FAA-2006-24281, 75 FR 69782, Nov. 15, 2010, as amended by Doc. No. FAA-2018-0119, Amdt. 26-7, 83 FR 9169, Mar. 5, 2018]

Subpart D — Fuel Tank Flammability

26.31   Definitions

For purposes of this subpart—

(a) Fleet Average Flammability Exposure has the meaning defined in Appendix N of part 25 of this chapter.

(b) Normally Emptied means a fuel tank other than a Main Fuel Tank. Main Fuel Tank is defined in 14 CFR 25.981(b).

26.33   Holders of type certificates: Fuel tank flammability

(a) Applicability. This section applies to U.S. type certificated transport category, turbine-powered airplanes, other than those designed solely for all-cargo operations, for which the State of Manufacture issued the original certificate of airworthiness or export airworthiness approval on or after January 1, 1992, that, as a result of original type certification or later increase in capacity have:

(1) A maximum type-certificated passenger capacity of 30 or more, or

(2) A maximum payload capacity of 7,500 pounds or more.

(b) Flammability Exposure Analysis.

(1) General. Within 150 days after December 26, 2008, holders of type certificates must submit for approval to the responsible

Aircraft Certification Service office a flammability exposure analysis of all fuel tanks defined in the type design, as well as all design variations approved under the type certificate that affect flammability exposure. This analysis must be conducted in accordance with Appendix N of part 25 of this chapter.

(2) Exception. This paragraph (b) does not apply to—

    (i) Fuel tanks for which the type certificate holder has notified the FAA under paragraph (g) of this section that it will provide design changes and service instructions for Flammability Reduction Means or an Ignition Mitigation Means (IMM) meeting the requirements of paragraph (c) of this section.

    (ii) Fuel tanks substantiated to be conventional unheated aluminum wing tanks.

(c) Design Changes. For fuel tanks with a Fleet Average Flammability Exposure exceeding 7 percent, one of the following design changes must be made.

(1) Flammability Reduction Means (FRM) . A means must be provided to reduce the fuel tank flammability.

    (i) Fuel tanks that are designed to be Normally Emptied must meet the flammability exposure criteria of Appendix M of part 25 of this chapter if any portion of the tank is located within the fuselage contour.

    (ii) For all other fuel tanks, the FRM must meet all of the requirements of Appendix M of part 25 of this chapter, except, instead of complying with paragraph M25.1 of this appendix, the Fleet Average Flammability Exposure may not exceed 7 percent.

(2) Ignition Mitigation Means (IMM). A means must be provided to mitigate the effects of an ignition of fuel vapors within the fuel tank such that no damage caused by an ignition will prevent continued safe flight and landing.

(d) Service Instructions. No later than December 27, 2010, holders of type certificates required by paragraph (c) of this section to make design changes must meet the requirements specified in either paragraph (d)(1) or (d)(2) of this section. The required service instructions must identify each airplane subject to the applicability provisions of paragraph (a) of this section.

(1) FRM. The type certificate holder must submit for approval by the responsible Aircraft Certification Service office design changes and service instructions for installation of fuel tank flammability reduction means (FRM) meeting the criteria of paragraph (c) of this section.

(2) IMM. The type certificate holder must submit for approval by the responsible Aircraft Certification Service office design changes and service instructions for installation of fuel tank IMM that comply with 14 CFR 25.981(c) in effect on December 26, 2008.

(e) Instructions for Continued Airworthiness (ICA). No later than December 27, 2010, holders of type certificates required by paragraph (c) of this section to make design changes must submit for approval by the responsible Aircraft Certification Service office, critical design configuration control limitations (CDCCL), inspections, or other procedures to prevent increasing the flammability exposure of any tanks equipped with FRM above that permitted under paragraph (c)(1) of this section and to prevent degradation of the performance of any IMM provided under paragraph (c)(2) of this section. These CDCCL, inspections, and procedures must be included in the Airworthiness Limitations Section (ALS) of the ICA required by 14 CFR 25.1529 or paragraph (f) of this section. Unless shown to be impracticable, visible means to identify critical features of the design must be placed in areas of the airplane where foreseeable maintenance actions, repairs, or alterations may compromise the critical design configuration limitations. These visible means must also be identified as a CDCCL.

(f) Airworthiness Limitations. Unless previously accomplished, no later than December 27, 2010, holders of type certificates affected by this section must establish an ALS of the maintenance manual or ICA for each airplane configuration evaluated under paragraph (b)(1) of this section and submit it to the responsible Aircraft Certification Service office for approval. The ALS must include a section that contains the CDCCL, inspections, or other procedures developed under paragraph (e) of this section.

(g) Compliance Plan for Flammability Exposure Analysis. Within 90 days after December 26, 2008, each holder of a type certificate required to comply with paragraph (b) of this section must submit to the responsible Aircraft Certification Service office a compliance plan consisting of the following:

(1) A proposed project schedule for submitting the required analysis, or a determination that compliance with paragraph (b) of this section is not required because design changes and service instructions for FRM or IMM will be developed and made available as required by this section.

(2) A proposed means of compliance with paragraph (b) of this section, if applicable.

(h) Compliance Plan for Design Changes and Service Instructions. Within 210 days after December 26, 2008, each holder of a type certificate required to comply with paragraph (d) of this section must submit to the responsible Aircraft Certification Service office a compliance plan consisting of the following:

(1) A proposed project schedule, identifying all major milestones, for meeting the compliance dates specified in paragraphs (d), (e) and (f) of this section.

(2) A proposed means of compliance with paragraphs (d), (e) and (f) of this section.

(3) A proposal for submitting a draft of all compliance items required by paragraphs (d), (e) and (f) of this section for review by the responsible Aircraft Certification Service office not less than 60 days before the compliance times specified in those paragraphs.

(4) A proposal for how the approved service information and any necessary modification parts will be made available to affected persons.

(i) Each affected type certificate holder must implement the compliance plans, or later revisions, as approved under paragraph (g) and (h) of this section.

[Doc. No. FAA-2005-22997, 73 FR 42499, July 21, 2008, as amended by Amdt. 26-3, 74 FR 31619, July 2, 2009; Doc. No. FAA-2018-0119, Amdt. 26-7, 83 FR 9169, Mar. 5, 2018]

26.35 Changes to type certificates affecting fuel tank flammability

(a) Applicability. This section applies to holders and applicants for approvals of the following design changes to any airplane subject to 14 CFR 26.33(a):

(1) Any fuel tank designed to be Normally Emptied if the fuel tank installation was approved pursuant to a supplemental type certificate or a field approval before December 26, 2008;

(2) Any fuel tank designed to be Normally Emptied if an application for a supplemental type certificate or an amendment to a type certificate was made before December 26, 2008 and if the approval was not issued before December 26, 2008; and

(3) If an application for a supplemental type certificate or an amendment to a type certificate is made on or after December 26, 2008, any of the following design changes:

    (i) Installation of a fuel tank designed to be Normally Emptied,

    (ii) Changes to existing fuel tank capacity, or

    (iii) Changes that may increase the flammability exposure of an existing fuel tank for which FRM or IMM is required by 26.33(c).

FAR 26

(b) Flammability Exposure Analysis.

    (1) General. By the times specified in paragraphs (b)(1)(i) and (b)(1)(ii) of this section, each person subject to this section must submit for approval a flammability exposure analysis of the auxiliary fuel tanks or other affected fuel tanks, as defined in the type design, to the responsible Aircraft Certification Service office. This analysis must be conducted in accordance with Appendix N of part 25 of this chapter.

        (i) Holders of supplemental type certificates and field approvals: Within 12 months of December 26, 2008,

        (ii) Applicants for supplemental type certificates and for amendments to type certificates: Within 12 months after December 26, 2008, or before the certificate is issued, whichever occurs later.

    (2) Exception. This paragraph does not apply to—

        (i) Fuel tanks for which the type certificate holder, supplemental type certificate holder, or field approval holder has notified the FAA under paragraph (f) of this section that it will provide design changes and service instructions for an IMM meeting the requirements of 25.981(c) in effect December 26, 2008; and

        (ii) Fuel tanks substantiated to be conventional unheated aluminum wing tanks.

(c) Impact Assessment. By the times specified in paragraphs (c)(1) and (c)(2) of this section, each person subject to paragraph (a)(1) of this section holding an approval for installation of a Normally Emptied fuel tank on an airplane model listed in Table 1 of this section, and each person subject to paragraph (a)(3)(iii) of this section, must submit for approval to the responsible Aircraft Certification Service office an assessment of the fuel tank system, as modified by their design change. The assessment must identify any features of the design change that compromise any critical design configuration control limitation (CDCCL) applicable to any airplane on which the design change is eligible for installation.

    (1) Holders of supplemental type certificates and field approvals: Before June 26, 2011.

    (2) Applicants for supplemental type certificates and for amendments to type certificates: Before June 26, 2011 or before the certificate is issued, whichever occurs later.

TABLE 1	
Model—Boeing	Model—Airbus
747 Series	A318, A319, A320, A321 Series
737 Series	A300, A310 Series
777 Series	A330, A340 Series
767 Series	
757 Series	

(d) Design Changes and Service Instructions. By the times specified in paragraph (e) of this section, each person subject to this section must meet the requirements of paragraphs (d)(1) or (d)(2) of this section, as applicable.

    (1) For holders and applicants subject to paragraph (a)(1) or (a)(3)(iii) of this section, if the assessment required by paragraph (c) of this section identifies any features of the design change that compromise any CDCCL applicable to any airplane on which the design change is eligible for installation, the holder or applicant must submit for approval by the responsible Aircraft Certification Service office design changes and service instructions for Flammability Impact Mitigation Means (FIMM) that would bring the design change into compliance with the CDCCL. Any fuel tank modified as required by this paragraph must also be evaluated as required by paragraph (b) of this section.

    (2) Applicants subject to paragraph (a)(2), or (a)(3)(i) of this sec-

tion must comply with the requirements of 14 CFR 25.981, in effect on December 26, 2008.

    (3) Applicants subject to paragraph (a)(3)(ii) of this section must comply with the requirements of 14 CFR 26.33.

(e) Compliance Times for Design Changes and Service Instructions. The following persons subject to this section must comply with the requirements of paragraph (d) of this section at the specified times.

    (1) Holders of supplemental type certificates and field approvals: Before December 26, 2012.

    (2) Applicants for supplemental type certificates and for amendments to type certificates: Before December 26, 2012, or before the certificate is issued, whichever occurs later.

(f) Compliance Planning. By the applicable date specified in Table 2 of this section, each person subject to paragraph (a)(1) of this section must submit for approval by the responsible Aircraft Certification Service office compliance plans for the flammability exposure analysis required by paragraph (b) of this section, the impact assessment required by paragraph (c) of this section, and the design changes and service instructions required by paragraph (d) of this section. Each person's compliance plans must include the following:

    (1) A proposed project schedule for submitting the required analysis or impact assessment.

    (2) A proposed means of compliance with paragraph (d) of this section.

    (3) For the requirements of paragraph (d) of this section, a proposal for submitting a draft of all design changes, if any are required, and Airworthiness Limitations (including CDCCLs) for review by the responsible Aircraft Certification Service office not less than 60 days before the compliance time specified in paragraph (e) of this section.

    (4) For the requirements of paragraph (d) of this section, a proposal for how the approved service information and any necessary modification parts will be made available to affected persons.

TABLE 2—COMPLIANCE PLANNING DATES		
STC and Field Approval Holders		
Flammability exposure analysis plan	Impact assessment plan	Design changes and service instructions plan
March 26, 2009	February 26, 2011	August 26, 2011

(g) Each person subject to this section must implement the compliance plans, or later revisions, as approved under paragraph (f) of this section.

[Doc. No. FAA-2005-22997, 73 FR 42499, July 21, 2008, as amended by Amdt. 26-3, 74 FR 31619, July 2, 2009; Doc. No. FAA-2018-0119, Amdt. 26-7, 83 FR 9170, Mar. 5, 2018]

26.37 Pending type certification projects: Fuel tank flammability

(a) Applicability. This section applies to any new type certificate for a transport category airplane, if the application was made before December 26, 2008, and if the certificate was not issued before December 26, 2008. This section applies only if the airplane would have—

    (1) A maximum type-certificated passenger capacity of 30 or more, or

    (2) A maximum payload capacity of 7,500 pounds or more.

(b) If the application was made on or after June 6, 2001, the requirements of 14 CFR 25.981 in effect on December 26, 2008, apply.

[Doc. No. FAA-2005-22997, 73 FR 42499, July 21, 2008, as amended by Amdt. 26-3, 74 FR 31619, July 2, 2009]

26.39 Newly produced airplanes: Fuel tank flammability

(a) Applicability: This section applies to Boeing model airplanes specified in Table 1 of this section, including passenger and cargo versions of each model, when application is made for original certificates of airworthiness or export airworthiness approvals after December 27, 2010.

TABLE 1
Model—Boeing
747 Series
737 Series
777 Series
767 Series

(b) Any fuel tank meeting all of the criteria stated in paragraphs (b)(1), (b)(2) and (b)(3) of this section must have flammability reduction means (FRM) or ignition mitigation means (IMM) that meet the requirements of 14 CFR 25.981 in effect on December 26, 2008.

(1) The fuel tank is Normally Emptied.

(2) Any portion of the fuel tank is located within the fuselage contour.

(3) The fuel tank exceeds a Fleet Average Flammability Exposure of 7 percent.

(c) All other fuel tanks that exceed an Fleet Average Flammability Exposure of 7 percent must have an IMM that meets 14 CFR 25.981(d) in effect on December 26, 2008, or an FRM that meets all of the requirements of Appendix M to this part, except instead of complying with paragraph M25.1 of that appendix, the Fleet Average Flammability Exposure may not exceed 7 percent.

[Doc. No. FAA–2005–22997, 73 FR 42499, July 21, 2008, as amended by Amdt. 26–3, 74 FR 31619, July 2, 2009]

Subpart E — Aging Airplane Safety—Damage Tolerance Data for Repairs and Alterations

Source: Doc. No. FAA–2005–21693, 72 FR 70505, Dec. 12, 2007

26.41   Definitions

Affects (or Affected) means structure has been physically repaired, altered, or modified, or the structural loads acting on the structure have been increased or redistributed.

Baseline structure means structure that is designed under the original type certificate or amended type certificate for that airplane model.

Damage Tolerance Evaluation (DTE) means a process that leads to a determination of maintenance actions necessary to detect or preclude fatigue cracking that could contribute to a catastrophic failure. As applied to repairs and alterations, a DTE includes the evaluation both of the repair or alteration and of the fatigue critical structure affected by the repair or alteration.

Damage Tolerance Inspection (DTI) means the inspection developed as a result of a DTE. A DTI includes the areas to be inspected, the inspection method, the inspection procedures, including acceptance and rejection criteria, the threshold, and any repeat intervals associated with those inspections. The DTI may specify a time limit when a repair or alteration needs to be replaced or modified. If the DTE concludes that DT-based supplemental structural inspections are not necessary, the DTI contains a statement to that effect.

DT data mean DTE documentation and the DTI.

DTE documentation means data that identify the evaluated fatigue critical structure, the basic assumptions applied in a DTE, and the results of a DTE.

Fatigue critical structure means airplane structure that is susceptible to fatigue cracking that could contribute to a catastrophic failure, as determined in accordance with 25.571 of this chapter. Fatigue critical structure includes structure, which, if repaired or altered, could be susceptible to fatigue cracking and contribute to a catastrophic failure. Such structure may be part of the baseline structure or part of an alteration.

Implementation schedule consists of documentation that establishes the timing for accomplishing the necessary actions for developing DT data for repairs and alterations, and for incorporating those data into an operator's continuing airworthiness maintenance program. The documentation must identify times when actions must be taken as specific numbers of airplane flight hours, flight cycles, or both.

Published repair data mean instructions for accomplishing repairs, which are published for general use in structural repair manuals and service bulletins (or equivalent types of documents).

26.43   Holders of and applicants for type certificates—Repairs

(a) Applicability. Except as specified in paragraph (g) of this section, this section applies to transport category, turbine powered airplane models with a type certificate issued after January 1, 1958, that as a result of original type certification or later increase in capacity have—

(1) A maximum type certificated passenger seating capacity of 30 or more; or

(2) A maximum payload capacity of 7,500 pounds or more.

(b) List of fatigue critical baseline structure. For airplanes specified in paragraph (a) of this section, the holder of or applicant for a type certificate must—

(1) Identify fatigue critical baseline structure for all airplane model variations and derivatives approved under the type certificate; and

(2) Develop and submit to the responsible Aircraft Certification Service office for review and approval, a list of the structure identified under paragraph (b)(1) of this section and, upon approval, make the list available to persons required to comply with 26.47 and 121.1109 and 129.109 of this chapter.

(c) Existing and future published repair data. For repair data published by a holder of a type certificate that is current as of January 11, 2008 and for all later published repair data, the holder of a type certificate must—

(1) Review the repair data and identify each repair specified in the data that affects fatigue critical baseline structure identified under paragraph (b)(1) of this section;

(2) Perform a DTE and develop the DTI for each repair identified under paragraph (c)(1) of this section, unless previously accomplished;

(3) Submit the DT data to the responsible Aircraft Certification Service office or its properly authorized designees for review and approval; and

(4) Upon approval, make the DTI available to persons required to comply with 121.1109 and 129.109 of this chapter.

(d) Future repair data not published. For repair data developed by a holder of a type certificate that are approved after January 11, 2008 and are not published, the type certificate holder must accomplish the following for repairs specified in the repair data that affect fatigue critical baseline structure:

(1) Perform a DTE and develop the DTI.

(2) Submit the DT data required in paragraph (d)(1) of this section for review and approval by the responsible Aircraft Certification Service office or its properly authorized designees.

(3) Upon approval, make the approved DTI available to persons required to comply with 121.1109 and 129.109 of this chapter.

(e) Repair Evaluation Guidelines. Except for airplane models whose type certificate is issued after January 11, 2008, holders of a type certificate for each airplane model subject to this section must—

(1) Develop repair evaluation guidelines for operators' use that include—

(i) A process for conducting surveys of affected airplanes that will enable identification and documentation of all existing repairs that affect fatigue critical baseline structure identified under paragraph (b)(1) of this section and 26.45(b)(2);

FAR 26

(ii) A process that will enable operators to obtain the DTI for repairs identified under paragraph (e)(1)(i) of this section; and

(iii) An implementation schedule for repairs covered by the repair evaluation guidelines. The implementation schedule must identify times when actions must be taken as specific numbers of airplane flight hours, flight cycles, or both.

(2) Submit the repair evaluation guidelines to the responsible Aircraft Certification Service office for review and approval.

(3) Upon approval, make the guidelines available to persons required to comply with 121.1109 and 129.109 of this chapter.

(4) If the guidelines direct the operator to obtain assistance from the holder of a type certificate, make such assistance available in accordance with the implementation schedule.

(f) Compliance times. Holders of type certificates must submit the following to the responsible Aircraft Certification Service office or its properly authorized designees for review and approval by the specified compliance time:

(1) The identified list of fatigue critical baseline structure required by paragraph (b)(2) of this section must be submitted no later than 180 days after January 11, 2008 or before issuance of the type certificate, whichever occurs later.

(2) For published repair data that are current as of January 11, 2008, the DT data required by paragraph (c)(3) of this section must be submitted by June 30, 2009.

(3) For repair data published after January 11, 2008, the DT data required by paragraph (c)(3) of this section must be submitted before FAA approval of the repair data.

(4) For unpublished repair data developed after January 11, 2008, the DT data required by paragraph (d)(1) of this section must be submitted within 12 months of the airplane's return to service or in accordance with a schedule approved by the responsible Aircraft Certification Service office.

(5) The repair evaluation guidelines required by paragraph (e)(1) of this section must be submitted by December 30, 2009.

(g) Exceptions. The requirements of this section do not apply to the following transport category airplane models:

(1) Convair CV–240, 340, 440, if modified to include turbine engines.

(2) Vickers Armstrong Viscount, TCDS No. A–814.

(3) Douglas DC–3, if modified to include turbine engines, TCDS No. A–618.

(4) Bombardier CL–44, TCDS No. 1A20.

(5) Mitsubishi YS–11, TCDS No. A1PC.

(6) British Aerospace BAC 1–11, TCDS No. A5EU.

(7) Concorde, TCDS No. A45EU.

(8) deHavilland D.H. 106 Comet 4C, TCDS No. 7A10.

(9) deHavilland DHC–7, TCDS No. A20EA.

(10) VFW-Vereinigte Flugtechnische Werk VFW–614, TCDS No. A39EU.

(11) Illyushin Aviation IL 96T, TCDS No. A54NM.

(12) Bristol Aircraft Britannia 305, TCDS No. 7A2.

(13) Handley Page Herald Type 300, TCDS No. A21N.

(14) Avions Marcel Dassault—Breguet Aviation Mercure 100C, TCDS No. A40EU.

(15) Airbus Caravelle, TCDS No. 7A6.

(16) Lockheed L–300, TCDS No. A2S0.

(17) Boeing 707–100/–200, TCDS No. 4A21.

(18) Boeing 707–300/–400, TCDS No. 4A26.

(19) Boeing 720, TCDS No. 4A28.

[Doc. No. FAA-2005-21693, 72 FR 70505, Dec. 12, 2007, as amended by Amdt. 26-4, 75 FR 11734, Mar. 12, 2010; Doc. No. FAA-2018-0119, Amdt. 26-7, 83 FR 9170, Mar. 5, 2018]

26.45 Holders of type certificates—Alterations and repairs to alterations

(a) Applicability. This section applies to transport category airplanes subject to 26.43.

(b) Fatigue critical alteration structure. For existing and future alteration data developed by the holder of a type certificate, the holder must—

(1) Review alteration data and identify all alterations that affect fatigue critical baseline structure identified under 26.43(b)(1);

(2) For each alteration identified under paragraph (b)(1) of this section, identify any fatigue critical alteration structure;

(3) Develop and submit to the responsible Aircraft Certification Service office for review and approval a list of the structure identified under paragraph (b)(2) of this section; and

(4) Upon approval, make the list required in paragraph (b)(3) of this section available to persons required to comply with 121.1109 and 129.109 of this chapter.

(c) DT Data. For existing and future alteration data developed by the holder of a type certificate that affect fatigue critical baseline structure identified under 26.43(b)(1), unless previously accomplished, the holder must—

(1) Perform a DTE and develop the DTI for the alteration and fatigue critical baseline structure that is affected by the alteration;

(2) Submit the DT data developed in accordance with paragraphs (c)(1) of this section to the responsible Aircraft Certification Service office or its properly authorized designees for review and approval; and

(3) Upon approval, make the DTI available to persons required to comply with 121.1109 and 129.109 of this chapter.

(d) DT Data for Repairs Made to Alterations. For existing and future repair data developed by a holder of a type certificate, the type certificate holder must—

(1) Review the repair data, and identify each repair that affects any fatigue critical alteration structure identified under paragraph (b)(2) of this section;

(2) For each repair identified under paragraph (d)(1) of this section, unless previously accomplished, perform a DTE and develop DTI;

(3) Submit the DT data developed in accordance with paragraph (d)(2) of this section to the responsible Aircraft Certification Service office or its properly authorized designees for review and approval; and

(4) Upon approval, make the DTI available to persons required to comply with 121.1109 and 129.109 of this chapter.

(e) Compliance times. Holders of type certificates must submit the following to the responsible Aircraft Certification Service office or its properly authorized designees for review and approval by the specified compliance time:

(1) The list of fatigue critical alteration structure identified under paragraph (b)(3) of this section must be submitted—

(i) No later than 360 days after January 11, 2008, for alteration data approved before January 11, 2008.

(ii) No later than 360 days after March 12, 2010 or before initial approval of the alteration data, whichever occurs later, for alteration data approved on or after January 11, 2008.

(2) For alteration data developed and approved before January 11, 2008, the DT data required by paragraph (c)(2) of this section must be submitted by June 30, 2009.

(3) For alteration data approved on or after January 11, 2008, DT data required by paragraph (c)(2) of this section must be submitted before initial approval of the alteration data.

(4) For repair data developed and approved before January 11, 2008, the DT data required by paragraph (d)(2) of this section must be submitted by June 30, 2009.

(5) For repair data developed and approved after January 11, 2008, the DT data required by paragraph (d)(2) of this section must be submitted within 12 months after initial approval of the repair data and before making the DT data available to persons required to comply with 121.1109 and 129.109 of this chapter.

[Doc. No. FAA-2005-21693, 72 FR 70505, Dec. 12, 2007, as amended by Amdt. 26-4, 75 FR 11734, Mar. 12, 2010; Doc. No. FAA-2018-0119, Amdt. 26-7, 83 FR 9170, Mar. 5, 2018]

26.47 Holders of and applicants for a supplemental type certificate—Alterations and repairs to alterations

(a) Applicability. This section applies to transport category airplanes subject to 26.43.

(b) Fatigue critical alteration structure. For existing structural alteration data approved under a supplemental certificate, the holder of the supplemental certificate must—

(1) Review the alteration data and identify all alterations that affect fatigue critical baseline structure identified under 26.43(b)(1);

(2) For each alteration identified under paragraph (b)(1) of this section, identify any fatigue critical alteration structure;

(3) Develop and submit to the responsible Aircraft Certification Service office for review and approval a list of the structure identified under paragraph (b)(2) of this section; and

(4) Upon approval, make the list required in paragraph (b)(3) of this section available to persons required to comply with 121.1109 and 129.109 of this chapter.

(c) DT Data. For existing and future alteration data developed by the holder of a supplemental type certificate that affect fatigue critical baseline structure identified under 26.43(b)(1), unless previously accomplished, the holder of a supplemental type certificate must—

(1) Perform a DTE and develop the DTI for the alteration and fatigue critical baseline structure that is affected by the alteration;

(2) Submit the DT data developed in accordance with paragraphs (c)(1) of this section to the responsible Aircraft Certification Service office or its properly authorized designees for review and approval; and

(3) Upon approval, make the DTI available to persons required to comply with 121.1109 and 129.109 of this chapter.

(d) DT Data for Repairs Made to Alterations. For existing and future repair data developed by the holder of a supplemental holder of a supplemental type certificate, the holder of a supplemental type certificate must—

(1) Review the repair data, and identify each repair that affects any fatigue critical alteration structure identified under paragraph (b)(2) of this section;

(2) For each repair identified under paragraph (d)(1) of this section, unless previously accomplished, perform a DTE and develop DTI;

(3) Submit the DT data developed in accordance with paragraph (d)(2) of this section to the responsible Aircraft Certification Service office or its properly authorized designees for review and approval; and

(4) Upon approval, make the DTI available to persons required to comply with 121.1109 and 129.109 of this chapter.

(e) Compliance times. Holders of supplemental type certificates must submit the following to the responsible Aircraft Certification Service office or its properly authorized designees for review and approval by the specified compliance time:

(1) The list of fatigue critical alteration structure required by paragraph (b)(3) of this section must be submitted no later than 360 days after January 11, 2008.

(2) For alteration data developed and approved before January 11, 2008, the DT data required by paragraph (c)(2) of this section must be submitted by June 30, 2009.

(3) For alteration data developed after January 11, 2008, the DT data required by paragraph (c)(2) of this section must be submitted before approval of the alteration data and making it

available to persons required to comply with 121.1109 and 129.109 of this chapter.

(4) For repair data developed and approved before January 11, 2008, the DT data required by paragraph (d)(2) of this section must be submitted by June 30, 2009.

(5) For repair data developed and approved after January 11, 2008, the DT data required by paragraph (d)(2) of this section, must be submitted within 12 months after initial approval of the repair data and before making the DT data available to persons required to comply with 121.1109 and 129.109 of this chapter.

[Docket No. FAA-2005-21693, 72 FR 70505, Dec. 12, 2007, as amended by Doc. No. FAA-2018-0119, Amdt. 26-7, 83 FR 9170, Mar. 5, 2018]

26.49 Compliance plan

(a) Compliance plan. Except for applicants for type certificates and supplemental type certificates whose applications are submitted after January 11, 2008, each person identified in 26.43, 26.45, and 26.47, must submit a compliance plan consisting of the following:

(1) A project schedule identifying all major milestones for meeting the compliance times specified in 26.43(f), 26.45(e), and 26.47(e), as applicable.

(2) A proposed means of compliance with 26.43, 26.45, and 26.47, as applicable.

(3) A plan for submitting a draft of all compliance items required by this subpart for review by the FAA Oversight Office not less than 60 days before the applicable compliance date.

(b) Compliance dates for compliance plans. The following persons must submit the compliance plan described in paragraph (a) of this section to the FAA Oversight Office for approval on the following schedule:

(1) For holders of type certificates, no later than 90 days after January 11, 2008.

(2) For holders of supplemental type certificates no later than 180 days after January 11, 2008.

(3) For applicants for changes to type certificates whose application are submitted before January 11, 2008, no later than 180 days after January 11, 2008.

(c) Compliance Plan Implementation. Each affected person must implement the compliance plan as approved in compliance with paragraph (a) of this section.

[Docket No. FAA-2005-21693, 72 FR 70505, Dec. 12, 2007, as amended by Doc. No. FAA-2018-0119, Amdt. 26-7, 83 FR 9170, Mar. 5, 2018]

FAR 26

PART 27 — AIRWORTHINESS STANDARDS: NORMAL CATEGORY ROTORCRAFT

FAR
27

Lights

Safety Equipment

Subpart G — Operating Limitations and Information

Operating Limitations

Markings and Placards

Rotorcraft Flight Manual and Approved Manual Material

Appendix A to Part 27 — Instructions for Continued Airworthiness

Appendix B to Part 27 — Airworthiness Criteria for Helicopter Instrument Flight

Appendix C to Part 27 — Criteria for Category A

Appendix D to Part 27 — HIRF Environments and Equipment HIRF Test Levels

Authority: 49 U.S.C. 106(f), 106(g), 40113, 44701-44702, 44704.

Source: Docket No. 5074, 29 FR 15695, Nov. 24, 1964, unless otherwise noted.

Subpart A — General

27.1 Applicability

(a) This part prescribes airworthiness standards for the issue of type certificates, and changes to those certificates, for normal category rotorcraft with maximum weights of 7,000 pounds or less and nine or less passenger seats.

(b) Each person who applies under Part 21 for such a certificate or change must show compliance with the applicable requirements of this part.

(c) Multiengine rotorcraft may be type certified as Category A provided the requirements referenced in appendix C of this part are met.

[Doc. No. 5074, 29 FR 15695, Nov. 24, 1964, as amended by Amdt. 27–33, 61 FR 21906, May 10, 1996; Amdt. 27–37, 64 FR 45094, Aug. 18, 1999]

27.2 Special retroactive requirements

(a) For each rotorcraft manufactured after September 16, 1992, each applicant must show that each occupant's seat is equipped with a safety belt and shoulder harness that meets the requirements of paragraphs (a), (b), and (c) of this section.

(1) Each occupant's seat must have a combined safety belt and shoulder harness with a single-point release. Each pilot's combined safety belt and shoulder harness must allow each pilot, when seated with safety belt and shoulder harness fastened, to perform all functions necessary for flight operations. There must be a means to secure belts and harnesses, when not in use, to prevent interference with the operation of the rotorcraft and with rapid egress in an emergency.

(2) Each occupant must be protected from serious head injury by a safety belt plus a shoulder harness that will prevent the head from contacting any injurious object.

(3) The safety belt and shoulder harness must meet the static and dynamic strength requirements, if applicable, specified by the rotorcraft type certification basis.

(4) For purposes of this section, the date of manufacture is either—

    (i) The date the inspection acceptance records, or equivalent, reflect that the rotorcraft is complete and meets the FAA-Approved Type Design Data; or

    (ii) The date the foreign civil airworthiness authority certifies that the rotorcraft is complete and issues an original standard airworthiness certificate, or equivalent, in that country.

(b) For rotorcraft with a certification basis established prior to October 18, 1999—

(1) The maximum passenger seat capacity may be increased to eight or nine provided the applicant shows compliance with all the airworthiness requirements of this part in effect on October 18, 1999.

(2) The maximum weight may be increased to greater than 6,000 pounds provided—

    (i) The number of passenger seats is not increased above the maximum number certificated on October 18, 1999, or

    (ii) The applicant shows compliance with all of the airworthiness requirements of this part in effect on October 18, 1999.

[Doc. No. 26078, 56 FR 41051, Aug. 16, 1991, as amended by Amdt. 27–37, 64 FR 45094, Aug. 18, 1999]

Subpart B — Flight

General

27.21 Proof of compliance

Each requirement of this subpart must be met at each appropriate combination of weight and center of gravity within the range of loading conditions for which certification is requested. This must be shown—

(a) By tests upon a rotorcraft of the type for which certification is requested, or by calculations based on, and equal in accuracy to, the results of testing; and

(b) By systematic investigation of each required combination of weight and center of gravity if compliance cannot be reasonably inferred from combinations investigated.

[Doc. No. 5074, 29 FR 15695, Nov. 24, 1964, as amended by Amdt. 27–21, 49 FR 44432, Nov. 6, 1984]

27.25 Weight limits

(a) *Maximum weight.* The maximum weight (the highest weight at which compliance with each applicable requirement of this part is shown) must be established so that it is—

(1) Not more than—

  (i) The highest weight selected by the applicant;

  (ii) The design maximum weight (the highest weight at which compliance with each applicable structural loading condition of this part is shown);

  (iii) The highest weight at which compliance with each applicable flight requirement of this part is shown; or

  (iv) The highest weight in which the provisions of 27.87 or 27.143(c)(1), or combinations thereof, are demonstrated if the weights and operating conditions (altitude and temperature) prescribed by those requirements cannot be met; and

(2) Not less than the sum of—

  (i) The empty weight determined under 27.29; and

  (ii) The weight of usable fuel appropriate to the intended operation with full payload;

  (iii) The weight of full oil capacity; and

  (iv) For each seat, an occupant weight of 170 pounds or any lower weight for which certification is requested.

(b) *Minimum weight.* The minimum weight (the lowest weight at which compliance with each applicable requirement of this part is shown) must be established so that it is—

(1) Not more than the sum of—

  (i) The empty weight determined under 27.29; and

  (ii) The weight of the minimum crew necessary to operate the rotorcraft, assuming for each crewmember a weight no more than 170 pounds, or any lower weight selected by the applicant or included in the loading instructions; and

(2) Not less than—

  (i) The lowest weight selected by the applicant;

  (ii) The design minimum weight (the lowest weight at which compliance with each applicable structural loading condition of this part is shown); or

  (iii) The lowest weight at which compliance with each applicable flight requirement of this part is shown.

(c) *Total weight with jettisonable external load.* A total weight for the rotorcraft with a jettisonable external load attached that is greater than the maximum weight established under paragraph (a) of this section may be established for any rotorcraft-load combination if—

(1) The rotorcraft-load combination does not include human external cargo,

(2) Structural component approval for external load operations under either 27.865 or under equivalent operational standards is obtained,

(3) The portion of the total weight that is greater than the maximum weight established under paragraph (a) of this section is made up only of the weight of all or part of the jettisonable external load.

(4) Structural components of the rotorcraft are shown to comply with the applicable structural requirements of this part under the increased loads and stresses caused by the weight increase over that established under paragraph (a) of this section, and

(5) Operation of the rotorcraft at a total weight greater than the maximum certificated weight established under paragraph (a) of this section is limited by appropriate operating limitations under 27.865(a) and (d) of this part.

(Secs. 313(a), 601, 603, 604, and 605 of the Federal Aviation Act of 1958 (49 U.S.C. 1354(a), 1421, 1423, 1424, and 1425); and sec. 6(c) of the Dept. of Transportation Act (49 U.S.C. 1655(c)))

[Doc. No. 5074, 29 FR 15695, Nov. 29, 1964, as amended by Amdt. 27–11, 41 FR 55468, Dec. 20, 1976; Amdt. 25–42, 43 FR 2324, Jan. 16, 1978; Amdt. 27–36, 64 FR 43019, Aug. 6, 1999; Amdt. No. 27–44, 73 FR 10998, Feb. 29, 2008; 73 FR 33876, June 16, 2008]

27.27 Center of gravity limits

The extreme forward and aft centers of gravity and, where critical, the extreme lateral centers of gravity must be established for each weight established under 27.25. Such an extreme may not lie beyond—

(a) The extremes selected by the applicant;

(b) The extremes within which the structure is proven; or

(c) The extremes within which compliance with the applicable flight requirements is shown.

[Amdt. 27–2, 33 FR 962, Jan. 26, 1968]

27.29 Empty weight and corresponding center of gravity

(a) The empty weight and corresponding center of gravity must be determined by weighing the rotorcraft without the crew and payload, but with—

(1) Fixed ballast;

(2) Unusable fuel; and

(3) Full operating fluids, including—

  (i) Oil;

  (ii) Hydraulic fluid; and

  (iii) Other fluids required for normal operation of roto-craft systems, except water intended for injection in the engines.

(b) The condition of the rotorcraft at the time of determining empty weight must be one that is well defined and can be easily repeated, particularly with respect to the weights of fuel, oil, coolant, and installed equipment.

(Secs. 313(a), 601, 603, 604, and 605 of the Federal Aviation Act of 1958 (49 U.S.C. 1354(a), 1421, 1423, 1424, and 1425); and sec. 6(c) of the Dept. of Transportation Act (49 U.S.C. 1655(c)))

[Doc. No. 5074, 29 FR 15695, Nov. 24, 1964, as amended by Amdt. 27–14, 43 FR 2324, Jan. 16, 1978]

27.31 Removable ballast

Removable ballast may be used in showing compliance with the flight requirements of this subpart.

27.33 Main rotor speed and pitch limits

(a) *Main rotor speed limits.* A range of main rotor speeds must be established that—

(1) With power on, provides adequate margin to accommodate the variations in rotor speed occurring in any appropriate maneuver, and is consistent with the kind of governor or synchronizer used; and

(2) With power off, allows each appropriate autorotative maneuver to be performed throughout the ranges of airspeed and weight for which certification is requested.

(b) *Normal main rotor high pitch limits (power on).* For rotorcraft, except helicopters required to have a main rotor low speed warning under paragraph (e) of this section. It must be shown, with power on and without exceeding approved engine maximum limitations, that main rotor speeds substantially less than the minimum approved main rotor speed will not occur under any sustained flight condition. This must be met by—

(1) Appropriate setting of the main rotor high pitch stop;

(2) Inherent rotorcraft characteristics that make unsafe low main rotor speeds unlikely; or

(3) Adequate means to warn the pilot of unsafe main rotor speeds.

(c) Normal main rotor low pitch limits (power off). It must be shown, with power off, that—

(1) The normal main rotor low pitch limit provides sufficient rotor speed, in any autorotative condition, under the most critical combinations of weight and airspeed; and

(2) It is possible to prevent overspeeding of the rotor without exceptional piloting skill.

(d) Emergency high pitch. If the main rotor high pitch stop is set to meet paragraph (b)(1) of this section, and if that stop cannot be exceeded inadvertently, additional pitch may be made available for emergency use.

(e) Main rotor low speed warning for helicopters. For each single engine helicopter, and each multiengine helicopter that does not have an approved device that automatically increases power on the operating engines when one engine fails, there must be a main rotor low speed warning which meets the following requirements:

(1) The warning must be furnished to the pilot in all flight conditions, including power-on and power-off flight, when the speed of a main rotor approaches a value that can jeopardize safe flight.

(2) The warning may be furnished either through the inherent aerodynamic qualities of the helicopter or by a device.

(3) The warning must be clear and distinct under all conditons, and must be clearly distinguishable from all other warnings. A visual device that requires the attention of the crew within the cockpit is not acceptable by itself.

(4) If a warning device is used, the device must automatically deactivate and reset when the low-speed condition is corrected. If the device has an audible warning, it must also be equipped with a means for the pilot to manually silence the audible warning before the low-speed condition is corrected.

(Secs. 313(a), 601, 603, 604, and 605 of the Federal Aviation Act of 1958 (49 U.S.C. 1354(a), 1421, 1423, 1424, and 1425); and sec. 6(c) of the Dept. of Transportation Act (49 U.S.C. 1655(c)))

[Doc. No. 5074, 29 FR 15695, Nov. 24, 1964, as amended by Amdt. 27–2, 33 FR 962, Jan. 26, 1968; Amdt. 27–14, 43 FR 2324, Jan. 16, 1978]

Performance

27.45 General

(a) Unless otherwise prescribed, the performance requirements of this subpart must be met for still air and a standard atmosphere.

(b) The performance must correspond to the engine power available under the particular ambient atmospheric conditions, the particular flight condition, and the relative humidity specified in paragraphs (d) or (e) of this section, as appropriate.

(c) The available power must correspond to engine power, not exceeding the approved power, less—

(1) Installation losses; and

(2) The power absorbed by the accessories and services appropriate to the particular ambient atmospheric conditions and the particular flight condition.

(d) For reciprocating engine-powered rotorcraft, the performance, as affected by engine power, must be based on a relative humidity of 80 percent in a standard atmosphere.

(e) For turbine engine-powered rotorcraft, the performance, as affected by engine power, must be based on a relative humidity of—

(1) 80 percent, at and below standard temperature; and

(2) 34 percent, at and above standard temperature plus 50 degrees F. Between these two temperatures, the relative humidity must vary linearly.

(f) For turbine-engine-powered rotorcraft, a means must be provided to permit the pilot to determine prior to takeoff that each engine is capable of developing the power necessary to achieve the applicable rotorcraft performance prescribed in this subpart.

(Secs. 313(a), 601, 603, 604, and 605 of the Federal Aviation Act of 1958 (49 U.S.C. 1354(a), 1421, 1423, 1424, and 1425); and sec. 6(c) of the Dept. of Transportation Act (49 U.S.C. 1655(c)))

[Amdt. 27–14, 43 FR 2324, Jan. 16, 1978, as amended by Amdt. 27–21, 49 FR 44432, Nov. 6, 1984]

27.49 Performance at minimum operating speed

(a) For helicopters—

(1) The hovering ceiling must be determined over the ranges of weight, altitude, and temperature for which certification is requested, with—

(i)   Takeoff power;

(ii) The landing gear extended; and

(iii) The helicopter in-ground effect at a height consistent with normal takeoff procedures; and

(2) The hovering ceiling determined under paragraph (a)(1) of this section must be at least—

(i)   For reciprocating engine powered helicopters, 4,000 feet at maximum weight with a standard atmosphere;

(ii) For turbine engine powered helicopters, 2,500 feet pressure altitude at maximum weight at a temperature of standard plus 22 °C (standard plus 40 °F).

(3) The out-of-ground effect hovering performance must be determined over the ranges of weight, altitude, and temperature for which certification is requested, using takeoff power.

(b) For rotorcraft other than helicopters, the steady rate of climb at the minimum operating speed must be determined over the ranges of weight, altitude, and temperature for which certification is requested, with—

(1) Takeoff power; and

(2) The landing gear extended.

[Amdt. No. 27–44, 73 FR 10998, Feb. 29, 2008]

27.51 Takeoff

The takeoff, with takeoff power and r.p.m. at the most critical center of gravity, and with weight from the maximum weight at sea level to the weight for which takeoff certification is requested for each altitude covered by this section—

(a) May not require exceptional piloting skill or exceptionally favorable conditions throughout the ranges of altitude from standard sea level conditions to the maximum altitude for which takeoff and landing certification is requested, and

(b) Must be made in such a manner that a landing can be made safely at any point along the flight path if an engine fails. This must be demonstrated up to the maximum altitude for which takeoff and landing certification is requested or 7,000 feet density altitude, whichever is less.

[Amdt. No. 27–44, 73 FR 10999, Feb. 29, 2008]

27.65 Climb: all engines operating

(a) For rotorcraft other than helicopters—

(1) The steady rate of climb, at V_y, must be determined—

(i)   With maximum continuous power on each engine;

(ii) With the landing gear retracted; and

(iii) For the weights, altitudes, and temperatures for which certification is requested; and

(2) The climb gradient, at the rate of climb determined in accordance with paragraph (a)(1) of this section, must be either—

(i)   At least 1:10 if the horizontal distance required to take off and climb over a 50-foot obstacle is determined for each weight, altitude, and temperature within the range for which certification is requested; or

(ii) At least 1:6 under standard sea level conditions.

(b) Each helicopter must meet the following requirements:

FAR 27

(1) V_Y must be determined—

    (i)   For standard sea level conditions;

    (ii) At maximum weight; and

    (iii) With maximum continuous power on each engine.

(2) The steady rate of climb must be determined—

    (i)   At the climb speed selected by the applicant at or below V_{NE};

    (ii) Within the range from sea level up to the maximum altitude for which certification is requested;

    (iii) For the weights and temperatures that correspond to the altitude range set forth in paragraph (b)(2)(ii) of this section and for which certification is requested; and

    (iv) With maximum continuous power on each engine.

(Secs. 313(a), 601, 603, 604, and 605 of the Federal Aviation Act of 1958 (49 U.S.C. 1354(a), 1421, 1423, 1424, and 1425); and sec. 6(c) of the Dept. of Transportation Act (49 U.S.C. 1655(c)))

[Doc. No. 5074, 29 FR 15695, Nov. 24, 1964, as amended by Amdt. 27–14, 43 FR 2324, Jan. 16, 1978; Amdt. 27–33, 61 FR 21907, May 10, 1996]

27.67 Climb: one engine inoperative

For multiengine helicopters, the steady rate of climb (or descent), at V y (or at the speed for minimum rate of descent), must be determined with—

(a) Maximum weight;

(b) The critical engine inoperative and the remaining engines at either—

    (1) Maximum continuous power and, for helicopters for which certification for the use of 30-minute OEI power is requested, at 30-minute OEI power; or

    (2) Continuous OEI power for helicopters for which certification for the use of continuous OEI power is requested.

(Secs. 313(a), 601, 603, 604, and 605 of the Federal Aviation Act of 1958 (49 U.S.C. 1354(a), 1421, 1423, 1424, and 1425); and sec. 6(c) of the Dept. of Transportation Act (49 U.S.C. 1655(c)))

[Doc. No 5074, 29 FR 15695, Nov. 24, 1964, as amended by Amdt. 27–23, 53 FR 34210, Sept. 2, 1988]

27.71 Autorotation performance

For single-engine helicopters and multiengine helicopters that do not meet the Category A engine isolation requirements of Part 29 of this chapter, the minimum rate of descent airspeed and the best angle-of-glide airspeed must be determined in autorotation at—

(a) Maximum weight; and

(b) Rotor speed(s) selected by the applicant.

[Amdt. 27–21, 49 FR 44433, Nov. 6, 1984]

27.73 Performance at minimum operating speed

(a) For helicopters—

    (1) The hovering ceiling must be determined over the ranges of weight, altitude, and temperature for which certification is requested, with—

        (i)   Takeoff power;

        (ii) The landing gear extended; and

        (iii) The helicopter in ground effect at a height consistent with normal takeoff procedures; and

    (2) The hovering ceiling determined under paragraph (a)(1) of this section must be at least—

        (i)   For reciprocating engine powered helicopters, 4,000 feet at maximum weight with a standard atmosphere; or

        (ii) For turbine engine powered helicopters, 2,500 feet pressure altitude at maximum weight at a temperature of standard +40 degrees F.

(b) For rotorcraft other than helicopters, the steady rate of climb at the minimum operating speed must be determined, over the ranges of weight, altitude, and temperature for which certification is requested, with—

    (1) Takeoff power; and

    (2) The landing gear extended.

27.75 Landing

(a) The rotorcraft must be able to be landed with no excessive vertical acceleration, no tendency to bounce, nose over, ground loop, porpoise, or water loop, and without exceptional piloting skill or exceptionally favorable conditions, with—

    (1) Approach or autorotation speeds appropriate to the type of rotorcraft and selected by the applicant;

    (2) The approach and landing made with—

        (i)   Power off, for single engine rotorcraft and entered from steady state autorotation; or

        (ii) One-engine inoperative (OEI) for multiengine rotorcraft, with each operating engine within approved operating limitations, and entered from an established OEI approach.

(b) Multiengine rotorcraft must be able to be landed safely after complete power failure under normal operating conditions.

[Doc. No. 5074, 29 FR 15695, Nov. 24, 1964, as amended by Amdt. 27–14, 43 FR 2324, Jan. 16, 1978; Amdt. No. 27–44, 73 FR 10999, Feb. 29, 2008]

27.87 Height-speed envelope

(a) If there is any combination of height and forward speed (including hover) under which a safe landing cannot be made under the applicable power failure condition in paragraph (b) of this section, a limiting height-speed envelope must be established (including all pertinent information) for that condition, throughout the ranges of—

    (1) Altitude, from standard sea level conditions to the maximum altitude capability of the rotorcraft, or 7000 feet density altitude, whichever is less; and

    (2) Weight, from the maximum weight at sea level to the weight selected by the applicant for each altitude covered by paragraph (a)(1) of this section. For helicopters, the weight at altitudes above sea level may not be less than the maximum weight or the highest weight allowing hovering out-of-ground effect, whichever is lower.

(b) The applicable power failure conditions are—

    (1) For single-engine helicopters, full autorotation;

    (2) For multiengine helicopters, OEI (where engine isolation features ensure continued operation of the remaining engines), and the remaining engine(s) within approved limits and at the minimum installed specification power available for the most critical combination of approved ambient temperature and pressure altitude resulting in 7000 feet density altitude or the maximum altitude capability of the helicopter, whichever is less, and

    (3) For other rotorcraft, conditions appropriate to the type.

(Secs. 313(a), 601, 603, 604, Federal Aviation Act of 1958 (49 U.S.C. 1354(a), 1421, 1423, 1424), sec. 6(c), Dept. of Transportation Act (49 U.S.C. 1655(c)))

[Doc. No. 5074, 29 FR 15695, Nov. 24, 1964, as amended by Amdt. 27–14, 43 FR 2324, Jan. 16, 1978; Amdt. 27–21, 49 FR 44433, Nov. 6, 1984; Amdt. No. 27–44, 73 FR 10999, Feb. 29, 2008]

Flight Characteristics

27.141 General

The rotorcraft must—

(a) Except as specifically required in the applicable section, meet the flight characteristics requirements of this subpart—

    (1) At the altitudes and temperatures expected in operation;

    (2) Under any critical loading condition within the range of weights and centers of gravity for which certification is requested;

    (3) For power-on operations, under any condition of speed, power, and rotor r.p.m. for which certification is requested; and

(4) For power-off operations, under any condition of speed and rotor r.p.m. for which certification is requested that is attainable with the controls rigged in accordance with the approved rigging instructions and tolerances;

(b) Be able to maintain any required flight condition and make a smooth transition from any flight condition to any other flight condition without exceptional piloting skill, alertness, or strength, and without danger of exceeding the limit load factor under any operating condition probable for the type, including—

(1) Sudden failure of one engine, for multiengine rotorcraft meeting Transport Category A engine isolation requirements of Part 29 of this chapter;

(2) Sudden, complete power failure for other rotorcraft; and

(3) Sudden, complete control system failures specified in 27.695 of this part; and

(c) Have any additional characteristic required for night or instrument operation, if certification for those kinds of operation is requested. Requirements for helicopter instrument flight are contained in appendix B of this part.

[Doc. No. 5074, 29 FR 15695, Nov. 24, 1964, as amended by Amdt. 27–2, 33 FR 962, Jan. 26, 1968; Amdt. 27–11, 41 FR 55468, Dec. 20, 1976; Amdt. 27–19, 48 FR 4389, Jan. 31, 1983; Amdt. 27–21, 49 FR 44433, Nov. 6, 1984]

27.143 Controllability and maneuverability

(a) The rotorcraft must be safely controllable and maneuverable—

(1) During steady flight; and

(2) During any maneuver appropriate to the type, including—

  (i)   Takeoff;

  (ii) Climb;

  (iii) Level flight;

  (iv) Turning flight;

  (v)   Autorotation;

  (vi) Landing (power on and power off); and

  (vii) Recovery to power-on flight from a balked autorotative approach.

(b) The margin of cyclic control must allow satisfactory roll and pitch control at V_{NE} with—

(1) Critical weight;

(2) Critical center of gravity;

(3) Critical rotor r.p.m.; and

(4) Power off (except for helicopters demonstrating compliance with paragraph (f) of this section) and power on.

(c) Wind velocities from zero to at least 17 knots, from all azimuths, must be established in which the rotorcraft can be operated without loss of control on or near the ground in any maneuver appropriate to the type (such as crosswind takeoffs, sideward flight, and rearward flight)—

(1) With altitude, from standard sea level conditions to the maximum takeoff and landing altitude capability of the rotorcraft or 7000 feet density altitude, whichever is less; with—

  (i)   Critical Weight;

  (ii) Critical center of gravity;

  (iii) Critical rotor r.p.m.;

(2) For takeoff and landing altitudes above 7000 feet density altitude with–

  (i)   Weight selected by the applicant;

  (ii) Critical center of gravity; and

  (iii) Critical rotor r.p.m.

(d) Wind velocities from zero to at least 17 knots, from all azimuths, must be established in which the rotorcraft can be operated without loss of control out-of-ground-effect, with—

(1) Weight selected by the applicant;

(2) Critical center of gravity;

(3) Rotor r.p.m. selected by the applicant; and

(4) Altitude, from standard sea level conditions to the maximum takeoff and landing altitude capability of the rotorcraft.

(e) The rotorcraft, after

(1) failure of one engine in the case of multiengine rotorcraft that meet Transport Category A engine isolation requirements, or

(2) complete engine failure in the case of other rotorcraft, must be controllable over the range of speeds and altitudes for which certification is requested when such power failure occurs with maximum continuous power and critical weight. No corrective action time delay for any condition following power failure may be less than—

  (i) For the cruise condition, one second, or normal pilot reaction time (whichever is greater); and

  (ii) For any other condition, normal pilot reaction time.

(f) For helicopters for which a V_{NE} (power-off) is established under 27.1505(c), compliance must be demonstrated with the following requirements with critical weight, critical center of gravity, and critical rotor r.p.m.:

(1) The helicopter must be safely slowed to V_{NE} (power-off), without exceptional pilot skill, after the last operating engine is made inoperative at power-on V_{NE}.

(2) At a speed of 1.1 V_{NE} (power-off), the margin of cyclic control must allow satisfactory roll and pitch control with power off.

(Secs. 313(a), 601, 603, 604, and 605 of the Federal Aviation Act of 1958 (49 U.S.C. 1354(a), 1421, 1423, 1424, and 1425); and sec. 6(c) of the Dept. of Transportation Act (49 U.S.C. 1655(c)))

[Doc. No. 5074, 29 FR 15695, Nov. 24, 1964, as amended by Amdt. 27–2, 33 FR 963, Jan. 26, 1968; Amdt. 27–14, 43 FR 2325, Jan. 16, 1978; Amdt. 27–21, 49 FR 44433, Nov. 6, 1984; Amdt. No. 27–44, 73 FR 10999, Feb. 29, 2008]

27.151 Flight controls

(a) Longitudinal, lateral, directional, and collective controls may not exhibit excessive breakout force, friction, or preload.

(b) Control system forces and free play may not inhibit a smooth, direct rotorcraft response to control system input.

[Amdt. 27–21, 49 FR 44433, Nov. 6, 1984]

27.161 Trim control

The trim control—

(a) Must trim any steady longitudinal, lateral, and collective control forces to zero in level flight at any appropriate speed; and

(b) May not introduce any undesirable discontinuities in control force gradients.

[Doc. No. 5074, 29 FR 15695, Nov. 24, 1964, as amended by Amdt. 27–21, 49 FR 44433, Nov. 6, 1984]

27.171 Stability: general

The rotorcraft must be able to be flown, without undue pilot fatigue or strain, in any normal maneuver for a period of time as long as that expected in normal operation. At least three landings and takeoffs must be made during this demonstration.

27.173 Static longitudinal stability

(a) The longitudinal control must be designed so that a rearward movement of the control is necessary to obtain an airspeed less than the trim speed, and a forward movement of the control is necessary to obtain an airspeed more than the trim speed.

(b) Throughout the full range of altitude for which certification is requested, with the throttle and collective pitch held constant during the maneuvers specified in 27.175(a) through (d), the slope of the control position versus airspeed curve must be positive. However, in limited flight conditions or modes of operation determined by the Administrator to be acceptable, the slope of the control position versus airspeed curve may be neutral or negative if the rotorcraft possesses flight characteristics that allow the pilot to maintain airspeed within ±5 knots of the desired trim airspeed without exceptional piloting skill or alertness.

[Amdt. 27–21, 49 FR 44433, Nov. 6, 1984, as amended by Amdt. No. 27–44, 73 FR 10999, Feb. 29, 2008]

27.175   Demonstration of static longitudinal stability

(a) Climb. Static longitudinal stability must be shown in the climb condition at speeds from V_y – 10 kt to V_y + 10 kt with—

(1) Critical weight;

(2) Critical center of gravity;

(3) Maximum continuous power;

(4) The landing gear retracted; and

(5) The rotorcraft trimmed at V_Y.

(b) Cruise. Static longitudinal stability must be shown in the cruise condition at speeds from 0.8 V_{NE} - 10 kt to 0.8 V_{NE} + 10 kt or, if V_H is less than 0.8 V_{NE}, from V_H - 10 kt to V_H + 10 kt, with—

(1) Critical weight;

(2) Critical center of gravity;

(3) Power for level flight at 0.8 V_{NE} or V_H, whichever is less;

(4) The landing gear retracted; and

(5) The rotorcraft trimmed at 0.8 V_{NE} or V_H, whichever is less.

(c) V_{NE}. Static longitudinal stability must be shown at speeds from V_{NE}–20 kt to V_{NE} with—

(1) Critical weight;

(2) Critical center of gravity;

(3) Power required for level flight at V_{NE} – 10 kt or maximum continuous power, whichever is less;

(4) The landing gear retracted; and

(5) The rotorcraft trimmed at V_{NE} – 10 kt.

(d) Autorotation. Static longitudinal stability must be shown in autorotation at—

(1) Airspeeds from the minimum rate of descent airspeed–10 kt to the minimum rate of descent airspeed + 10 kt, with—

   (i) Critical weight;

   (ii) Critical center of gravity;

   (iii) The landing gear extended; and

   (iv) The rotorcraft trimmed at the minimum rate of descent airspeed.

(2) Airspeeds from best angle-of-glide airspeed–10 kt to the best angle-of-glide airspeed + 10 kt, with—

   (i) Critical weight;

   (ii) Critical center of gravity;

   (iii) The landing gear retracted; and

   (iv) The rotorcraft trimmed at the best angle-of-glide airspeed.

(Secs. 313(a), 601, 603, 604, and 605 of the Federal Aviation Act of 1958 (49 U.S.C. 1354(a), 1421, 1423, 1424, and 1425); and sec. 6(c) of the Dept. of Transportation Act (49 U.S.C. 1655(c)))

[Doc. No. 5074, 29 FR 15695, Nov. 24, 1964, as amended by Amdt. 27–2, 33 FR 963, Jan. 26, 1968; Amdt. 27–11, 41 FR 55468, Dec. 20, 1976; Amdt. 27–14, 43 FR 2325, Jan. 16, 1978; Amdt. 27–21, 49 FR 44433, Nov. 6, 1984; Amdt. 27–34, 62 FR 46173, Aug. 29, 1997; Amdt. No. 27–44, 73 FR 10999, Feb. 29, 2008]

27.177   Static directional stability

(a) The directional controls must operate in such a manner that the sense and direction of motion of the rotorcraft following control displacement are in the direction of the pedal motion with the throttle and collective controls held constant at the trim conditions specified in 27.175(a), (b), and (c). Sideslip angles must increase with steadily increasing directional control deflection for sideslip angles up to the lesser of—

(1) ±25 degrees from trim at a speed of 15 knots less than the speed for minimum rate of descent varying linearly to ±10 degrees from trim at V_{NE};

(2) The steady state sideslip angles established by 27.351;

(3) A sideslip angle selected by the applicant, which corresponds to a sideforce of at least 0.1g; or

(4) The sideslip angle attained by maximum directional control input.

(b) Sufficient cues must accompany the sideslip to alert the pilot when the aircraft is approaching the sideslip limits.

(c) During the maneuver specified in paragraph (a) of this section, the sideslip angle versus directional control position curve may have a negative slope within a small range of angles around trim, provided the desired heading can be maintained without exceptional piloting skill or alertness.

[Amdt. No. 27–44, 73 FR 11000, Feb. 29, 2008]

Ground and Water Handling Characteristics
27.231   General

The rotorcraft must have satisfactory ground and water handling characteristics, including freedom from uncontrollable tendencies in any condition expected in operation.

27.235   Taxiing condition

The rotorcraft must be designed to withstand the loads that would occur when the rotorcraft is taxied over the roughest ground that may reasonably be expected in normal operation.

27.239   Spray characteristics

If certification for water operation is requested, no spray characteristics during taxiing, takeoff, or landing may obscure the vision of the pilot or damage the rotors, propellers, or other parts of the rotorcraft.

27.241   Ground resonance

The rotorcraft may have no dangerous tendency to oscillate on the ground with the rotor turning.

Miscellaneous Flight Requirements
27.251   Vibration

Each part of the rotorcraft must be free from excessive vibration under each appropriate speed and power condition.

Subpart C — Strength Requirements
General
27.301   Loads

(a) Strength requirements are specified in terms of limit loads (the maximum loads to be expected in service) and ultimate loads (limit loads multiplied by prescribed factors of safety). Unless otherwise provided, prescribed loads are limit loads.

(b) Unless otherwise provided, the specified air, ground, and water loads must be placed in equilibrium with inertia forces, considering each item of mass in the rotorcraft. These loads must be distributed to closely approximate or conservatively represent actual conditions.

(c) If deflections under load would significantly change the distribution of external or internal loads, this redistribution must be taken into account.

27.303   Factor of safety

Unless otherwise provided, a factor of safety of 1.5 must be used. This factor applies to external and inertia loads unless its application to the resulting internal stresses is more conservative.

27.305 Strength and deformation

(a) The structure must be able to support limit loads without detrimental or permanent deformation. At any load up to limit loads, the deformation may not interfere with safe operation.

(b) The structure must be able to support ultimate loads without failure. This must be shown by—

(1) Applying ultimate loads to the structure in a static test for at least three seconds; or

(2) Dynamic tests simulating actual load application.

27.307 Proof of structure

(a) Compliance with the strength and deformation requirements of this subpart must be shown for each critical loading condition accounting for the environment to which the structure will be exposed in operation. Structural analysis (static or fatigue) may be used only if the structure conforms to those structures for which experience has shown this method to be reliable. In other cases, substantiating load tests must be made.

(b) Proof of compliance with the strength requirements of this subpart must include—

(1) Dynamic and endurance tests of rotors, rotor drives, and rotor controls;

(2) Limit load tests of the control system, including control surfaces;

(3) Operation tests of the control system;

(4) Flight stress measurement tests;

(5) Landing gear drop tests; and

(6) Any additional test required for new or unusual design features.

(Secs. 604, 605, 72 Stat. 778, 49 U.S.C. 1424, 1425)

[Doc. No. 5074, 29 FR 15695, Nov. 24, 1964, as amended by Amdt. 27–3, 33 FR 14105, Sept. 18, 1968; Amdt. 27–26, 55 FR 7999, Mar. 6, 1990]

27.309 Design limitations

The following values and limitations must be established to show compliance with the structural requirements of this subpart:

(a) The design maximum weight.

(b) The main rotor r.p.m. ranges power on and power off.

(c) The maximum forward speeds for each main rotor r.p.m. within the ranges determined under paragraph (b) of this section.

(d) The maximum rearward and sideward flight speeds.

(e) The center of gravity limits corresponding to the limitations determined under paragraphs (b), (c), and (d) of this section.

(f) The rotational speed ratios between each powerplant and each connected rotating component.

(g) The positive and negative limit maneuvering load factors.

Flight Loads

27.321 General

(a) The flight load factor must be assumed to act normal to the longitudinal axis of the rotorcraft, and to be equal in magnitude and opposite in direction to the rotorcraft inertia load factor at the center of gravity.

(b) Compliance with the flight load requirements of this subpart must be shown—

(1) At each weight from the design minimum weight to the design maximum weight; and

(2) With any practical distribution of disposable load within the operating limitations in the Rotorcraft Flight Manual.

[Doc. No. 5074, 29 FR 15695, Nov. 24, 1964, as amended by Amdt. 27–11, 41 FR 55468, Dec. 20, 1976]

27.337 Limit maneuvering load factor

The rotorcraft must be designed for—

(a) A limit maneuvering load factor ranging from a positive limit of 3.5 to a negative limit of –1.0; or

(b) Any positive limit maneuvering load factor not less than 2.0 and any negative limit maneuvering load factor of not less than –0.5 for which—

(1) The probability of being exceeded is shown by analysis and flight tests to be extremely remote; and

(2) The selected values are appropriate to each weight condition between the design maximum and design minimum weights.

[Amdt. 27–26, 55 FR 7999, Mar. 6, 1990]

27.339 Resultant limit maneuvering loads

The loads resulting from the application of limit maneuvering load factors are assumed to act at the center of each rotor hub and at each auxiliary lifting surface, and to act in directions, and with distributions of load among the rotors and auxiliary lifting surfaces, so as to represent each critical maneuvering condition, including power-on and power-off flight with the maximum design rotor tip speed ratio. The rotor tip speed ratio is the ratio of the rotorcraft flight velocity component in the plane of the rotor disc to the rotational tip speed of the rotor blades, and is expressed as follows:

$$\mu = \frac{V \cos a}{\Omega R}$$

where—

V = The airspeed along flight path (f.p.s.);

a = The angle between the projection, in the plane of symmetry, of the axis of no feathering and a line perpendicular to the flight path (radians, positive when axis is pointing aft);

Ω (omega) = The angular velocity of rotor (radians per second); and

R = The rotor radius (ft).

[Doc. No. 5074, 29 FR 15695, Nov. 24, 1964, as amended by Amdt. 27–11, 41 FR 55469, Dec. 20, 1976]

27.341 Gust loads

The rotorcraft must be designed to withstand, at each critical airspeed including hovering, the loads resulting from a vertical gust of 30 feet per second.

27.351 Yawing conditions

(a) Each rotorcraft must be designed for the loads resulting from the maneuvers specified in paragraphs (b) and (c) of this section with—

(1) Unbalanced aerodynamic moments about the center of gravity which the aircraft reacts to in a rational or conservative manner considering the principal masses furnishing the reacting inertia forces; and

(2) Maximum main rotor speed.

(b) To produce the load required in paragraph (a) of this section, in unaccelerated flight with zero yaw, at forward speeds from zero up to 0.6 V_{NE}—

(1) Displace the cockpit directional control suddenly to the maximum deflection limited by the control stops or by the maximum pilot force specified in 27.397(a);

(2) Attain a resulting sideslip angle or 90°, whichever is less; and

(3) Return the directional control suddenly to neutral.

(c) To produce the load required in paragraph (a) of this section, in unaccelerated flight with zero yaw, at forward speeds from 0.6 V_{NE} up to V_{NE} or V_H, whichever is less—

(1) Displace the cockpit directional control suddenly to the maximum deflection limited by the control stops or by the maximum pilot force specified in 27.397(a);

(2) Attain a resulting sideslip angle or 15°, whichever is less, at the lesser speed of V_{NE} or V_H;

(3) Vary the sideslip angles of paragraphs (b)(2) and (c)(2) of this section directly with speed; and

(4) Return the directional control suddenly to neutral.

[Amdt. 27–26, 55 FR 7999, Mar. 6, 1990, as amended by Amdt. 27–34, 62 FR 46173, Aug. 29, 1997]

27.361 Engine torque

(a) For turbine engines, the limit torque may not be less than the highest of—

(1) The mean torque for maximum continuous power multiplied by 1.25;

(2) The torque required by 27.923;

(3) The torque required by 27.927; or

(4) The torque imposed by sudden engine stoppage due to malfunction or structural failure (such as compressor jamming).

(b) For reciprocating engines, the limit torque may not be less than the mean torque for maximum continuous power multiplied by—

(1) 1.33, for engines with five or more cylinders; and

(2) Two, three, and four, for engines with four, three, and two cylinders, respectively.

[Amdt. 27–23, 53 FR 34210, Sept. 2, 1988]

Control Surface and System Loads

27.391 General

Each auxiliary rotor, each fixed or movable stabilizing or control surface, and each system operating any flight control must meet the requirements of 27.395, 27.397, 27.399, 27.411, and 27.427.

[Amdt. 27–26, 55 FR 7999, Mar. 6, 1990, as amended by Amdt. 27–34, 62 FR 46173, Aug. 29, 1997]

27.395 Control system

(a) The part of each control system from the pilot's controls to the control stops must be designed to withstand pilot forces of not less than—

(1) The forces specified in 27.397; or

(2) If the system prevents the pilot from applying the limit pilot forces to the system, the maximum forces that the system allows the pilot to apply, but not less than 0.60 times the forces specified in 27.397.

(b) Each primary control system, including its supporting structure, must be designed as follows:

(1) The system must withstand loads resulting from the limit pilot forces prescribed in 27.397.

(2) Notwithstanding paragraph (b)(3) of this section, when power-operated actuator controls or power boost controls are used, the system must also withstand the loads resulting from the force output of each normally energized power device, including any single power boost or actuator system failure.

(3) If the system design or the normal operating loads are such that a part of the system cannot react to the limit pilot forces prescribed in 27.397, that part of the system must be designed to withstand the maximum loads that can be obtained in normal operation. The minimum design loads must, in any case, provide a rugged system for service use, including consideration of fatigue, jamming, ground gusts, control inertia, and friction loads. In the absence of rational analysis, the design loads resulting from 0.60 of the specified limit pilot forces are acceptable minimum design loads.

(4) If operational loads may be exceeded through jamming, ground gusts, control inertia, or friction, the system must withstand the limit pilot forces specified in 27.397, without yielding.

[Doc. No. 5074, 29 FR 15695, Nov. 24, 1964, as amended by Amdt. 27–26, 55 FR 7999, Mar. 6, 1990]

27.397 Limit pilot forces and torques

(a) Except as provided in paragraph (b) of this section, the limit pilot forces are as follows:

(1) For foot controls, 130 pounds.

(2) For stick controls, 100 pounds fore and aft, and 67 pounds laterally.

(b) For flap, tab, stabilizer, rotor brake, and landing gear operating controls, the follows apply (R=radius in inches):

(1) Crank, wheel, and lever controls, $[1+R]/3 \times 50$ pounds, but not less than 50 pounds nor more than 100 pounds for hand operated controls or 130 pounds for foot operated controls, applied at any angle within 20 degrees of the plane of motion of the control.

(2) Twist controls, 80R inch-pounds.

[Amdt. 27–11, 41 FR 55469, Dec. 20, 1976, as amended by Amdt. 27–40, 66 FR 23538, May 9, 2001]

27.399 Dual control system

Each dual primary flight control system must be designed to withstand the loads that result when pilot forces of 0.75 times those obtained under 27.395 are applied—

(a) In opposition; and

(b) In the same direction.

27.411 Ground clearance: tail rotor guard

(a) It must be impossible for the tail rotor to contact the landing surface during a normal landing.

(b) If a tail rotor guard is required to show compliance with paragraph (a) of this section—

(1) Suitable design loads must be established for the guard; and

(2) The guard and its supporting structure must be designed to withstand those loads.

27.427 Unsymmetrical loads

(a) Horizontal tail surfaces and their supporting structure must be designed for unsymmetrical loads arising from yawing and rotor wake effects in combination with the prescribed flight conditions.

(b) To meet the design criteria of paragraph (a) of this section, in the absence of more rational data, both of the following must be met:

(1) One hundred percent of the maximum loading from the symmetrical flight conditions acts on the surface on one side of the plane of symmetry, and no loading acts on the other side.

(2) Fifty percent of the maximum loading from the symmetrical flight conditions acts on the surface on each side of the plane of symmetry but in opposite directions.

(c) For empennage arrangements where the horizontal tail surfaces are supported by the vertical tail surfaces, the vertical tail surfaces and supporting structure must be designed for the combined vertical and horizontal surface loads resulting from each prescribed flight condition, considered separately. The flight conditions must be selected so the maximum design loads are obtained on each surface. In the absence of more rational data, the unsymmetrical horizontal tail surface loading distributions described in this section must be assumed.

[Amdt. 27–26, 55 FR 7999, Mar. 6, 1990, as amended by Amdt. 27–27, 55 FR 38966, Sept. 21, 1990]

Ground Loads

27.471 General

(a) Loads and equilibrium. For limit ground loads—

(1) The limit ground loads obtained in the landing conditions in this part must be considered to be external loads that would occur in the rotorcraft structure if it were acting as a rigid body; and

(2) In each specified landing condition, the external loads must be placed in equilibrium with linear and angular inertia loads in a rational or conservative manner.

(b) Critical centers of gravity. The critical centers of gravity within the range for which certification is requested must be selected so that the maximum design loads are obtained in each landing gear element.

27.473 Ground loading conditions and assumptions

(a) For specified landing conditions, a design maximum weight must be used that is not less than the maximum weight. A rotor lift may be assumed to act through the center of gravity throughout the landing impact. This lift may not exceed two-thirds of the design maximum weight.

(b) Unless otherwise prescribed, for each specified landing condition, the rotorcraft must be designed for a limit load factor of not less than the limit inertia load factor substantiated under 27.725.

[Amdt. 27–2, 33 FR 963, Jan. 26, 1968]

27.475 Tires and shock absorbers

Unless otherwise prescribed, for each specified landing condition, the tires must be assumed to be in their static position and the shock absorbers to be in their most critical position.

27.477 Landing gear arrangement

Sections 27.235, 27.479 through 27.485, and 27.493 apply to landing gear with two wheels aft, and one or more wheels forward, of the center of gravity.

27.479 Level landing conditions

(a) Attitudes. Under each of the loading conditions prescribed in paragraph (b) of this section, the rotorcraft is assumed to be in each of the following level landing attitudes:

(1) An attitude in which all wheels contact the ground simultaneously.

(2) An attitude in which the aft wheels contact the ground with the forward wheels just clear of the ground.

(b) Loading conditions. The rotorcraft must be designed for the following landing loading conditions:

(1) Vertical loads applied under 27.471.

(2) The loads resulting from a combination of the loads applied under paragraph (b)(1) of this section with drag loads at each wheel of not less than 25 percent of the vertical load at that wheel.

(3) If there are two wheels forward, a distribution of the loads applied to those wheels under paragraphs (b)(1) and (2) of this section in a ratio of 40:60.

(c) Pitching moments. Pitching moments are assumed to be resisted by—

(1) In the case of the attitude in paragraph (a)(1) of this section, the forward landing gear; and

(2) In the case of the attitude in paragraph (a)(2) of this section, the angular inertia forces.

[Doc. No. 5074, 29 FR 15695, Nov. 24, 1964; 29 FR 17885, Dec. 17, 1964]

27.481 Tail-down landing conditions

(a) The rotorcraft is assumed to be in the maximum nose-up attitude allowing ground clearance by each part of the rotorcraft.

(b) In this attitude, ground loads are assumed to act perpendicular to the ground.

27.483 One-wheel landing conditions

For the one-wheel landing condition, the rotorcraft is assumed to be in the level attitude and to contact the ground on one aft wheel. In this attitude—

(a) The vertical load must be the same as that obtained on that side under 27.479(b)(1); and

(b) The unbalanced external loads must be reacted by rotorcraft inertia.

27.485 Lateral drift landing conditions

(a) The rotorcraft is assumed to be in the level landing attitude, with—

(1) Side loads combined with one-half of the maximum ground reactions obtained in the level landing conditions of 27.479 (b)(1); and

(2) The loads obtained under paragraph (a)(1) of this section applied—

(i) At the ground contact point; or

(ii) For full-swiveling gear, at the center of the axle.

(b) The rotorcraft must be designed to withstand, at ground contact—

(1) When only the aft wheels contact the ground, side loads of 0.8 times the vertical reaction acting inward on one side, and 0.6 times the vertical reaction acting outward on the other side, all combined with the vertical loads specified in paragraph (a) of this section; and

(2) When all wheels contact the ground simultaneously—

(i) For the aft wheels, the side loads specified in paragraph (b)(1) of this section; and

(ii) For the forward wheels, a side load of 0.8 times the vertical reaction combined with the vertical load specified in paragraph (a) of this section.

27.493 Braked roll conditions

Under braked roll conditions with the shock absorbers in their static positions—

(a) The limit vertical load must be based on a load factor of at least—

(1) 1.33, for the attitude specified in 27.479(a)(1); and

(2) 1.0 for the attitude specified in 27.479(a)(2); and

(b) The structure must be designed to withstand at the ground contact point of each wheel with brakes, a drag load at least the lesser of—

(1) The vertical load multiplied by a coefficient of friction of 0.8; and

(2) The maximum value based on limiting brake torque.

27.497 Ground loading conditions: landing gear with tail wheels

(a) General. Rotorcraft with landing gear with two wheels forward, and one wheel aft, of the center of gravity must be designed for loading conditions as prescribed in this section.

(b) Level landing attitude with only the forward wheels contacting the ground. In this attitude—

(1) The vertical loads must be applied under 27.471 through 27.475;

(2) The vertical load at each axle must be combined with a drag load at that axle of not less than 25 percent of that vertical load; and

(3) Unbalanced pitching moments are assumed to be resisted by angular inertia forces.

(c) Level landing attitude with all wheels contacting the ground simultaneously. In this attitude, the rotorcraft must be designed for landing loading conditions as prescribed in paragraph (b) of this section.

(d) Maximum nose-up attitude with only the rear wheel contacting the ground. The attitude for this condition must be the maximum nose-up attitude expected in normal operation, including autorotative landings. In this attitude—

(1) The appropriate ground loads specified in paragraphs (b)(1) and (2) of this section must be determined and applied, using a rational method to account for the moment arm between the rear wheel ground reaction and the rotorcraft center of gravity; or

(2) The probability of landing with initial contact on the rear wheel must be shown to be extremely remote.

(e) Level landing attitude with only one forward wheel contacting the ground. In this attitude, the rotorcraft must be designed for ground loads as specified in paragraphs (b)(1) and (3) of this section.

(f) Side loads in the level landing attitude. In the attitudes specified in paragraphs (b) and (c) of this section, the following apply:

(1) The side loads must be combined at each wheel with one-half of the maximum vertical ground reactions obtained for that wheel under paragraphs (b) and (c) of this section. In this condition, the side loads must be—

   (i) For the forward wheels, 0.8 times the vertical reaction (on one side) acting inward, and 0.6 times the vertical reaction (on the other side) acting outward; and

   (ii) For the rear wheel, 0.8 times the vertical reaction.

(2) The loads specified in paragraph (f)(1) of this section must be applied—

   (i) At the ground contact point with the wheel in the trailing position (for non-full swiveling landing gear or for full swiveling landing gear with a lock, steering device, or shimmy damper to keep the wheel in the trailing position); or

   (ii) At the center of the axle (for full swiveling landing gear without a lock, steering device, or shimmy damper).

(g) Braked roll conditions in the level landing attitude. In the attitudes specified in paragraphs (b) and (c) of this section, and with the shock absorbers in their static positions, the rotorcraft must be designed for braked roll loads as follows:

(1) The limit vertical load must be based on a limit vertical load factor of not less than—

   (i) 1.0, for the attitude specified in paragraph (b) of this section; and

   (ii) 1.33, for the attitude specified in paragraph (c) of this section.

(2) For each wheel with brakes, a drag load must be applied, at the ground contact point, of not less than the lesser of—

   (i) 0.8 times the vertical load; and

   (ii) The maximum based on limiting brake torque.

(h) Rear wheel turning loads in the static ground attitude. In the static ground attitude, and with the shock absorbers and tires in their static positions, the rotorcraft must be designed for rear wheel turning loads as follows:

(1) A vertical ground reaction equal to the static load on the rear wheel must be combined with an equal sideload.

(2) The load specified in paragraph (h)(1) of this section must be applied to the rear landing gear—

   (i) Through the axle, if there is a swivel (the rear wheel being assumed to be swiveled 90 degrees to the longitudinal axis of the rotorcraft); or

   (ii) At the ground contact point, if there is a lock, steering device or shimmy damper (the rear wheel being assumed to be in the trailing position).

(i) Taxiing condition. The rotorcraft and its landing gear must be designed for loads that would occur when the rotorcraft is taxied over the roughest ground that may reasonably be expected in normal operation.

27.501 Ground loading conditions: landing gear with skids

(a) General. Rotorcraft with landing gear with skids must be designed for the loading conditions specified in this section. In showing compliance with this section, the following apply:

(1) The design maximum weight, center of gravity, and load factor must be determined under 27.471 through 27.475.

(2) Structural yielding of elastic spring members under limit loads is acceptable.

(3) Design ultimate loads for elastic spring members need not exceed those obtained in a drop test of the gear with—

   (i) A drop height of 1.5 times that specified in 27.725; and

   (ii) An assumed rotor lift of not more than 1.5 times that used in the limit drop tests prescribed in 27.725.

(4) Compliance with paragraphs (b) through (e) of this section must be shown with—

   (i) The gear in its most critically deflected position for the landing condition being considered; and

   (ii) The ground reactions rationally distributed along the bottom of the skid tube.

(b) Vertical reactions in the level landing attitude. In the level attitude, and with the rotorcraft contacting the ground along the bottom of both skids, the vertical reactions must be applied as prescribed in paragraph (a) of this section.

(c) Drag reactions in the level landing attitude. In the level attitude, and with the rotorcraft contacting the ground along the bottom of both skids, the following apply:

(1) The vertical reactions must be combined with horizontal drag reactions of 50 percent of the vertical reaction applied at the ground.

(2) The resultant ground loads must equal the vertical load specified in paragraph (b) of this section.

(d) Sideloads in the level landing attitude. In the level attitude, and with the rotorcraft contacting the ground along the bottom of both skids, the following apply:

(1) The vertical ground reaction must be—

   (i) Equal to the vertical loads obtained in the condition specified in paragraph (b) of this section; and

   (ii) Divided equally among the skids.

(2) The vertical ground reactions must be combined with a horizontal sideload of 25 percent of their value.

(3) The total sideload must be applied equally between the skids and along the length of the skids.

(4) The unbalanced moments are assumed to be resisted by angular inertia.

(5) The skid gear must be investigated for—

   (i) Inward acting sideloads; and

   (ii) Outward acting sideloads.

(e) One-skid landing loads in the level attitude. In the level attitude, and with the rotorcraft contacting the ground along the bottom of one skid only, the following apply:

(1) The vertical load on the ground contact side must be the same as that obtained on that side in the condition specified in paragraph (b) of this section.

(2) The unbalanced moments are assumed to be resisted by angular inertia.

(f) Special conditions. In addition to the conditions specified in paragraphs (b) and (c) of this section, the rotorcraft must be designed for the following ground reactions:

(1) A ground reaction load acting up and aft at an angle of 45 degrees to the longitudinal axis of the rotorcraft. This load must be—

   (i) Equal to 1.33 times the maximum weight;

   (ii) Distributed symmetrically among the skids;

   (iii) Concentrated at the forward end of the straight part of the skid tube; and

   (iv) Applied only to the forward end of the skid tube and its attachment to the rotorcraft.

(2) With the rotorcraft in the level landing attitude, a vertical ground reaction load equal to one-half of the vertical load determined under paragraph (b) of this section. This load must be—

   (i) Applied only to the skid tube and its attachment to the rotorcraft; and

   (ii) Distributed equally over 33.3 percent of the length between the skid tube attachments and centrally located midway between the skid tube attachments.

[Doc. No. 5074, 29 FR 15695, Nov. 24, 1964, as amended by Amdt. 27-2, 33 FR 963, Jan. 26, 1968; Amdt. 27–26, 55 FR 8000, Mar. 6, 1990]

27.505 Ski landing conditions

If certification for ski operation is requested, the rotorcraft, with skis, must be designed to withstand the following loading conditions (where P is the maximum static weight on each ski with the rotorcraft at design maximum weight, and n is the limit load factor determined under 27.473(b).

(a) Up-load conditions in which—

  (1) A vertical load of Pn and a horizontal load of Pn/4 are simultaneously applied at the pedestal bearings; and

  (2) A vertical load of 1.33 P is applied at the pedestal bearings.

(b) A side-load condition in which a side load of 0.35 Pn is applied at the pedestal bearings in a horizontal plane perpendicular to the centerline of the rotorcraft.

(c) A torque-load condition in which a torque load of 1.33 P (in foot pounds) is applied to the ski about the vertical axis through the centerline of the pedestal bearings.

Water Loads

27.521 Float landing conditions

If certification for float operation is requested, the rotorcraft, with floats, must be designed to withstand the following loading conditions (where the limit load factor is determined under 27.473(b) or assumed to be equal to that determined for wheel landing gear):

(a) Up-load conditions in which—

  (1) A load is applied so that, with the rotorcraft in the static level attitude, the resultant water reaction passes vertically through the center of gravity; and

  (2) The vertical load prescribed in paragraph (a)(1) of this section is applied simultaneously with an aft component of 0.25 times the vertical component.

(b) A side-load condition in which—

  (1) A vertical load of 0.75 times the total vertical load specified in paragraph (a)(1) of this section is divided equally among the floats; and

  (2) For each float, the load share determined under paragraph (b)(1) of this section, combined with a total side load of 0.25 times the total vertical load specified in paragraph (b)(1) of this section, is applied to that float only.

Main Component Requirements

27.547 Main rotor structure

(a) Each main rotor assembly (including rotor hubs and blades) must be designed as prescribed in this section.

(b) [Reserved]

(c) The main rotor structure must be designed to withstand the following loads prescribed in 27.337 through 27.341:

  (1) Critical flight loads.

  (2) Limit loads occurring under normal conditions of autorotation. For this condition, the rotor r.p.m. must be selected to include the effects of altitude.

(d) The main rotor structure must be designed to withstand loads simulating—

  (1) For the rotor blades, hubs, and flapping hinges, the impact force of each blade against its stop during ground operation; and

  (2) Any other critical condition expected in normal operation.

(e) The main rotor structure must be designed to withstand the limit torque at any rotational speed, including zero. In addition:

  (1) The limit torque need not be greater than the torque defined by a torque limiting device (where provided), and may not be less than the greater of—

    (i) The maximum torque likely to be transmitted to the rotor structure in either direction; and

    (ii) The limit engine torque specified in 27.361.

  (2) The limit torque must be distributed to the rotor blades in a rational manner.

(Secs. 604, 605, 72 Stat. 778, 49 U.S.C. 1424, 1425)
[Doc. No. 5074, 29 FR 15695, Nov. 24, 1964, as amended by Amdt. 27–3, 33 FR 14105, Sept. 18, 1968]

27.549 Fuselage, landing gear, and rotor pylon structures

(a) Each fuselage, landing gear, and rotor pylon structure must be designed as prescribed in this section. Resultant rotor forces may be represented as a single force applied at the rotor hub attachment point.

(b) Each structure must be designed to withstand—

  (1) The critical loads prescribed in 27.337 through 27.341;

  (2) The applicable ground loads prescribed in 27.235, 27.471 through 27.485, 27.493, 27.497, 27.501, 27.505, and 27.521; and

  (3) The loads prescribed in 27.547 (d)(2) and (e).

(c) Auxiliary rotor thrust, and the balancing air and inertia loads occurring under accelerated flight conditions, must be considered.

(d) Each engine mount and adjacent fuselage structure must be designed to withstand the loads occurring under accelerated flight and landing conditions, including engine torque.

(Secs. 604, 605, 72 Stat. 778, 49 U.S.C. 1424, 1425)
[Doc. No. 5074, 29 FR 15695, Nov. 24, 1964, as amended by Amdt. 27–3, 33 FR 14105, Sept. 18, 1968]

Emergency Landing Conditions

27.561 General

(a) The rotorcraft, although it may be damaged in emergency landing conditions on land or water, must be designed as prescribed in this section to protect the occupants under those conditions.

(b) The structure must be designed to give each occupant every reasonable chance of escaping serious injury in a crash landing when—

  (1) Proper use is made of seats, belts, and other safety design provisions;

  (2) The wheels are retracted (where applicable); and

  (3) Each occupant and each item of mass inside the cabin that could injure an occupant is restrained when subjected to the following ultimate inertial load factors relative to the surrounding structure:

    (i) Upward—4g.

    (ii) Forward—16g.

    (iii) Sideward—8g.

    (iv) Downward—20g, after intended displacement of the seat device.

    (v) Rearward—1.5g.

(c) The supporting structure must be designed to restrain, under any ultimate inertial load up to those specified in this paragraph, any item of mass above and/or behind the crew and passenger compartment that could injure an occupant if it came loose in an emergency landing. Items of mass to be considered include, but are not limited to, rotors, transmissions, and engines. The items of mass must be restrained for the following ultimate inertial load factors:

  (1) Upward—1.5g.

  (2) Forward—12g.

  (3) Sideward—6g.

  (4) Downward—12g.

  (5) Rearward—1.5g

(d) Any fuselage structure in the area of internal fuel tanks below the passenger floor level must be designed to resist the following ultimate inertial factors and loads and to protect the fuel tanks from rupture when those loads are applied to that area:

    (i) Upward—1.5g.

    (ii) Forward—4.0g.

    (iii) Sideward—2.0g.

    (iv) Downward—4.0g.

[Doc. No. 5074, 29 FR 15695, Nov. 24, 1964, as amended by Amdt. 27–25, 54 FR 47318, Nov. 13, 1989; Amdt. 27–30, 59 FR 50386, Oct. 3, 1994; Amdt. 27–32, 61 FR 10438, Mar. 13, 1996]

27.562   Emergency landing dynamic conditions

(a) The rotorcraft, although it may be damaged in an emergency crash landing, must be designed to reasonably protect each occupant when—

(1) The occupant properly uses the seats, safety belts, and shoulder harnesses provided in the design; and

(2) The occupant is exposed to the loads resulting from the conditions prescribed in this section.

(b) Each seat type design or other seating device approved for crew or passenger occupancy during takeoff and landing must successfully complete dynamic tests or be demonstrated by rational analysis based on dynamic tests of a similar type seat in accordance with the following criteria. The tests must be conducted with an occupant, simulated by a 170-pound anthropomorphic test dummy (ATD), as defined by 49 CFR 572, subpart B, or its equivalent, sitting in the normal upright position.

(1) A change in downward velocity of not less than 30 feet per second when the seat or other seating device is oriented in its nominal position with respect to the rotorcraft's reference system, the rotorcraft's longitudinal axis is canted upward 60° with respect to the impact velocity vector, and the rotorcraft's lateral axis is perpendicular to a vertical plane containing the impact velocity vector and the rotorcraft's longitudinal axis. Peak floor deceleration must occur in not more than 0.031 seconds after impact and must reach a minimum of 30g's.

(2) A change in forward velocity of not less than 42 feet per second when the seat or other seating device is oriented in its nominal position with respect to the rotorcraft's reference system, the rotorcraft's longitudinal axis is yawed 10° either right or left of the impact velocity vector (whichever would cause the greatest load on the shoulder harness), the rotorcraft's lateral axis is contained in a horizontal plane containing the impact velocity vector, and the rotorcraft's vertical axis is perpendicular to a horizontal plane containing the impact velocity vector. Peak floor deceleration must occur in not more than 0.071 seconds after impact and must reach a minimum of 18.4g's.

(3) Where floor rails or floor or sidewall attachment devices are used to attach the seating devices to the airframe structure for the conditions of this section, the rails or devices must be misaligned with respect to each other by at least 10° vertically (i.e., pitch out of parallel) and by at least a 10° lateral roll, with the directions optional, to account for possible floor warp.

(c) Compliance with the following must be shown:

(1) The seating device system must remain intact although it may experience separation intended as part of its design.

(2) The attachment between the seating device and the airframe structure must remain intact, although the structure may have exceeded its limit load.

(3) The ATD's shoulder harness strap or straps must remain on or in the immediate vicinity of the ATD's shoulder during the impact.

(4) The safety belt must remain on the ATD's pelvis during the impact.

(5) The ATD's head either does not contact any portion of the crew or passenger compartment, or if contact is made, the head impact does not exceed a head injury criteria (HIC) of 1,000 as determined by this equation.

$$HIC = (t_2 - t_1)\left[\frac{1}{(t_2 - t_1)}\int_{t_1}^{t_2} a(t)dt\right]^{2.5}$$

Where:

a(t) is the resultant acceleration at the center of gravity of the head form expressed as a multiple of g (the acceleration of gravity) and $t_2 - t_1$ is the time duration, in seconds, of major head impact, not to exceed 0.05 seconds.

(6) Loads in individual upper torso harness straps must not exceed 1,750 pounds. If dual straps are used for retaining the upper torso, the total harness strap loads must not exceed 2,000 pounds.

(7) The maximum compressive load measured between the pelvis and the lumbar column of the ATD must not exceed 1,500 pounds.

(d) An alternate approach that achieves an equivalent or greater level of occupant protection, as required by this section, must be substantiated on a rational basis.

[Amdt. 27–25, 54 FR 47318, Nov. 13, 1989]

27.563   Structural ditching provisions

If certification with ditching provisions is requested, structural strength for ditching must meet the requirements of this section and 27.801(e).

(a) Forward speed landing conditions. The rotorcraft must initially contact the most critical wave for reasonably probable water conditions at forward velocities from zero up to 30 knots in likely pitch, roll, and yaw attitudes. The rotorcraft limit vertical descent velocity may not be less than 5 feet per second relative to the mean water surface. Rotor lift may be used to act through the center of gravity throughout the landing impact. This lift may not exceed two-thirds of the design maximum weight. A maximum forward velocity of less than 30 knots may be used in design if it can be demonstrated that the forward velocity selected would not be exceeded in a normal one-engine-out touchdown.

(b) Auxiliary or emergency float conditions —

(1) Floats fixed or deployed before initial water contact. In addition to the landing loads in paragraph (a) of this section, each auxiliary or emergency float, of its support and attaching structure in the airframe or fuselage, must be designed for the load developed by a fully immersed float unless it can be shown that full immersion is unlikely. If full immersion is unlikely, the highest likely float buoyancy load must be applied. The highest likely buoyancy load must include consideration of a partially immersed float creating restoring moments to compensate the upsetting moments caused by side wind, unsymmetrical rotorcraft loading, water wave action, rotorcraft inertia, and probable structural damage and leakage considered under 27.801(d). Maximum roll and pitch angles determined from compliance with 27.801(d) may be used, if significant, to determine the extent of immersion of each float. If the floats are deployed in flight, appropriate air loads derived from the flight limitations with the floats deployed shall be used in substantiation of the floats and their attachment to the rotorcraft. For this purpose, the design airspeed for limit load is the float deployed airspeed operating limit multiplied by 1.11.

(2) Floats deployed after initial water contact. Each float must be designed for full or partial immersion perscribed in paragraph (b)(1) of this section. In addition, each float must be designed for combined vertical and drag loads using a relative limit speed of 20 knots between the rotorcraft and the water. The vertical load may not be less than the highest likely buoyancy load determined under paragraph (b)(1) of this section.

[Amdt. 27–26, 55 FR 8000, Mar. 6, 1990]

Fatigue Evaluation

27.571   Fatigue evaluation of flight structure

(a) General. Each portion of the flight structure (the flight structure includes rotors, rotor drive systems between the engines and the rotor hubs, controls, fuselage, landing gear, and their related primary attachments), the failure of which could be catastrophic, must be identified and must be evaluated under paragraph (b), (c), (d), or (e) of this section. The following apply to each fatigue evaluation:

(1) The procedure for the evaluation must be approved.

(2) The locations of probable failure must be determined.

(3) Inflight measurement must be included in determining the following:

   (i) Loads or stresses in all critical conditions throughout the range of limitations in 27.309, except that maneuvering load factors need not exceed the maximum values expected in operation.

   (ii) The effect of altitude upon these loads or stresses.

(4) The loading spectra must be as severe as those expected in operation including, but not limited to, external cargo operations, if applicable, and ground-air-ground cycles. The loading spectra must be based on loads or stresses determined under paragraph (a)(3) of this section.

(b) Fatigue tolerance evaluation. It must be shown that the fatigue tolerance of the structure ensures that the probability of catastrophic fatigue failure is extremely remote without establishing replacement times, inspection intervals or other procedures under section A27.4 of appendix A.

(c) Replacement time evaluation. it must be shown that the probability of catastrophic fatigue failure is extremely remote within a replacement time furnished under section A27.4 of appendix A.

(d) Fail-safe evaluation. The following apply to fail-safe evaluation:

(1) It must be shown that all partial failures will become readily detectable under inspection procedures furnished under section A27.4 of appendix A.

(2) The interval between the time when any partial failure becomes readily detectable under paragraph (d)(1) of this section, and the time when any such failure is expected to reduce the remaining strength of the structure to limit or maximum attainable loads (whichever is less), must be determined.

(3) It must be shown that the interval determined under paragraph (d)(2) of this section is long enough, in relation to the inspection intervals and related procedures furnished under section A27.4 of appendix A, to provide a probability of detection great enough to ensure that the probability of catastrophic failure is extremely remote.

(e) Combination of replacement time and failsafe evaluations. A component may be evaluated under a combination of paragraphs (c) and (d) of this section. For such component it must be shown that the probability of catastrophic failure is extremely remote with an approved combination of replacement time, inspection intervals, and related procedures furnished under section A27.4 of appendix A.

(Secs. 313(a), 601, 603, 604, and 605, 72 Stat. 752, 775, and 778, (49 U.S.C. 1354(a), 1421, 1423, 1424, and 1425; sec. 6(c), 49 U.S.C. 1655(c)))

[Amdt. 27–3, 33 FR 14106, Sept. 18, 1968, as amended by Amdt. 27–12, 42 FR 15044, Mar. 17, 1977; Amdt. 27–18, 45 FR 60177, Sept. 11 1980; Amdt. 27–26, 55 FR 8000, Mar. 6, 1990]

27.573 Damage tolerance and fatigue evaluation of composite rotorcraft structures

(a) Each applicant must evaluate the composite rotorcraft structure under the damage tolerance standards of paragraph (d) of this section unless the applicant establishes that a damage tolerance evaluation is impractical within the limits of geometry, inspectability, and good design practice. If an applicant establishes that it is impractical within the limits of geometry, inspectability, and good design practice, the applicant must do a fatigue evaluation in accordance with paragraph (e) of this section.

(b) The methodology used to establish compliance with this section must be submitted to and approved by the Administrator.

(c) Definitions:

(1) Catastrophic failure is an event that could prevent continued safe flight and landing.

(2) Principal Structural Elements (PSEs) are structural elements that contribute significantly to the carrying of flight or ground loads, the failure of which could result in catastrophic failure of the rotorcraft.

(3) Threat Assessment is an assessment that specifies the locations, types, and sizes of damage, considering fatigue, environmental effects, intrinsic and discrete flaws, and impact or other accidental damage (including the discrete source of the accidental damage) that may occur during manufacture or operation.

(d) Damage Tolerance Evaluation:

(1) Each applicant must show that catastrophic failure due to static and fatigue loads, considering the intrinsic or discrete manufacturing defects or accidental damage, is avoided throughout the operational life or prescribed inspection intervals of the rotorcraft by performing damage tolerance evaluations of the strength of composite PSEs and other parts, detail design points, and fabrication techniques. Each applicant must account for the effects of material and process variability along with environmental conditions in the strength and fatigue evaluations. Each applicant must evaluate parts that include PSEs of the airframe, main and tail rotor drive systems, main and tail rotor blades and hubs, rotor controls, fixed and movable control surfaces, engine and transmission mountings, landing gear, other parts, detail design points, and fabrication techniques deemed critical by the FAA. Each damage tolerance evaluation must include:

   (i) The identification of all PSEs;

   (ii) In-flight and ground measurements for determining the loads or stresses for all PSEs for all critical conditions throughout the range of limits in 27.309 (including altitude effects), except that maneuvering load factors need not exceed the maximum values expected in service;

   (iii) The loading spectra as severe as those expected in service based on loads or stresses determined under paragraph (d)(1)(ii) of this section, including external load operations, if applicable, and other operations including high-torque events;

   (iv) A threat assessment for all PSEs that specifies the locations, types, and sizes of damage, considering fatigue, environmental effects, intrinsic and discrete flaws, and impact or other accidental damage (including the discrete source of the accidental damage) that may occur during manufacture or operation; and

   (v) An assessment of the residual strength and fatigue characteristics of all PSEs that supports the replacement times and inspection intervals established under paragraph (d)(2) of this section.

(2) Each applicant must establish replacement times, inspections, or other procedures for all PSEs to require the repair or replacement of damaged parts before a catastrophic failure. These replacement times, inspections, or other procedures must be included in the Airworthiness Limitations Section of the Instructions for Continued Airworthiness required by 27.1529.

   (i) Replacement times for PSEs must be determined by tests, or by analysis supported by tests, and must show that the structure is able to withstand the repeated loads of variable magnitude expected in-service. In establishing these replacement times, the following items must be considered:

      (A) Damage identified in the threat assessment required by paragraph (d)(1)(iv) of this section;

      (B) Maximum acceptable manufacturing defects and in-service damage (i.e., those that do not lower the residual strength below ultimate design loads and those that can be repaired to restore ultimate strength); and

    (C) Ultimate load strength capability after applying repeated loads.

  (ii) Inspection intervals for PSEs must be established to reveal any damage identified in the threat assessment required by paragraph (d)(1)(iv) of this section that may occur from fatigue or other in-service causes before such damage has grown to the extent that the component cannot sustain the required residual strength capability. In establishing these inspection intervals, the following items must be considered:

    (A) The growth rate, including no-growth, of the damage under the repeated loads expected in-service determined by tests or analysis supported by tests;

    (B) The required residual strength for the assumed damage established after considering the damage type, inspection interval, detectability of damage, and the techniques adopted for damage detection. The minimum required residual strength is limit load; and

    (C) Whether the inspection will detect the damage growth before the minimum residual strength is reached and restored to ultimate load capability, or whether the component will require replacement.

(3) Each applicant must consider the effects of damage on stiffness, dynamic behavior, loads, and functional performance on all PSEs when substantiating the maximum assumed damage size and inspection interval.

(e) Fatigue Evaluation: If an applicant establishes that the damage tolerance evaluation described in paragraph (d) of this section is impractical within the limits of geometry, inspectability, or good design practice, the applicant must do a fatigue evaluation of the particular composite rotorcraft structure and:

(1) Identify all PSEs considered in the fatigue evaluation;

(2) Identify the types of damage for all PSEs considered in the fatigue evaluation;

(3) Establish supplemental procedures to minimize the risk of catastrophic failure associated with the damages identified in paragraph (d) of this section; and

(4) Include these supplemental procedures in the Airworthiness Limitations section of the Instructions for Continued Airworthiness required by 27.1529.

[Doc. No. FAA–2009–0660, 76 FR 74663, Dec. 1, 2011]

Subpart D — Design and Construction

General

27.601 Design

(a) The rotorcraft may have no design features or details that experience has shown to be hazardous or unreliable.

(b) The suitability of each questionable design detail and part must be established by tests.

27.602 Critical parts

(a) Critical part. A critical part is a part, the failure of which could have a catastrophic effect upon the rotorcraft, and for which critical characteristics have been identified which must be controlled to ensure the required level of integrity.

(b) If the type design includes crtical parts, a critical parts list shall be established. Procedures shall be established to define the critical design characteristics, identify processes that affect those characteristics, and identify the design change and process change controls necessary for showing compliance with the quality assurance requirements of part 21 of this chapter.

[Doc. No. 29311, 64 FR 46232, Aug. 24, 1999]

27.603 Materials

The suitability and durability of materials used for parts, the failure of which could adversely affect safety, must—

(a) Be established on the basis of experience or tests;

(b) Meet approved specifications that ensure their having the strength and other properties assumed in the design data; and

(c) Take into account the effects of environmental conditions, such as temperature and humidity, expected in service.

(Secs. 313(a), 601, 603, 604, Federal Aviation Act of 1958 (49 U.S.C. 1354(a), 1421, 1423, 1424); and sec. 6(c) of the Dept. of Transportation Act (49 U.S.C. 1655(c)))

[Doc. No. 5074, 29 FR 15695, Nov. 24, 1964, as amended by Amdt. 27–11, 41 FR 55469, Dec. 20, 1976; Amdt. 27–16, 43 FR 50599, Oct. 30, 1978]

27.605 Fabrication methods

(a) The methods of fabrication used must produce consistently sound structures. If a fabrication process (such as gluing, spot welding, or heat-treating) requires close control to reach this objective, the process must be performed according to an approved process specification.

(b) Each new aircraft fabrication method must be substantiated by a test program.

(Secs. 313(a), 601, 603, 604, and 605 of the Federal Aviation Act of 1958 (49 U.S.C. 1354(a), 1421, 1423, 1424 and 1425); sec. 6(c) of the Dept. of Transportation Act (49 U.S.C. 1655(c)))

[Doc. No. 5074, 29 FR 15695, Nov. 24, 1964, as amended by Amdt. 27–16, 43 FR 50599, Oct. 30, 1978]

27.607 Fasteners

(a) Each removable bolt, screw, nut, pin, or other fastener whose loss could jeopardize the safe operation of the rotorcraft must incorporate two separate locking devices. The fastener and its locking devices may not be adversely affected by the environmental conditions associated with the particular installation.

(b) No self-locking nut may be used on any bolt subject to rotation in operation unless a nonfriction locking device is used in addition to the self-locking device.

[Amdt. 27–4, 33 FR 14533, Sept. 27, 1968]

27.609 Protection of structure

Each part of the structure must—

(a) Be suitably protected against deterioration or loss of strength in service due to any cause, including—

  (1) Weathering;

  (2) Corrosion; and

  (3) Abrasion; and

(b) Have provisions for ventilation and drainage where necessary to prevent the accumulation of corrosive, flammable, or noxious fluids.

27.610 Lightning and static electricity protection

(a) The rotorcraft must be protected against catastrophic effects from lightning.

(b) For metallic components, compliance with paragraph (a) of this section may be shown by—

  (1) Electrically bonding the components properly to the airframe; or

  (2) Designing the components so that a strike will not endanger the rotorcraft.

(c) For nonmetallic components, compliance with paragraph (a) of this section may be shown by—

  (1) Designing the components to minimize the effect of a strike; or

  (2) Incorporating acceptable means of diverting the resulting electrical current so as not to endanger the rotorcraft.

(d) The electrical bonding and protection against lightning and static electricity must—

 (1) Minimize the accumulation of electrostatic charge;

 (2) Minimize the risk of electric shock to crew, passengers, and service and maintenance personnel using normal precautions;

 (3) Provide an electrical return path, under both normal and fault conditions, on rotorcraft having grounded electrical systems; and

 (4) Reduce to an acceptable level the effects of static electricity on the functioning of essential electrical and electronic equipment.

[Amdt. 27–21, 49 FR 44433, Nov. 6, 1984, as amended by Amdt. 27–37, 64 FR 45094, Aug. 18, 1999; Amdt. 27–46, 76 FR 33135, June 8, 2011]

27.611　Inspection provisions

There must be means to allow the close examination of each part that requires—

(a) Recurring inspection;

(b) Adjustment for proper alignment and functioning; or

(c) Lubrication.

27.613　Material strength properties and design values

(a) Material strength properties must be based on enough tests of material meeting specifications to establish design values on a statistical basis.

(b) Design values must be chosen to minimize the probability of structural failure due to material variability. Except as provided in paragraphs (d) and (e) of this section, compliance with this paragraph must be shown by selecting design values that assure material strength with the following probability—

 (1) Where applied loads are eventually distributed through a single member within an assembly, the failure of which would result in loss of structural integrity of the component, 99 percent probability with 95 percent confidence; and

 (2) For redundant structure, those in which the failure of individual elements would result in applied loads being safely distributed to other load-carrying members, 90 percent probability with 95 percent confidence.

(c) The strength, detail design, and fabrication of the structure must minimize the probability of disastrous fatigue failure, particularly at points of stress concentration.

(d) Design values may be those contained in the following publications (available from the Naval Publications and Forms Center, 5801 Tabor Avenue, Philadelphia, Pennsylvania 19120) or other values approved by the Administrator:

 (1) MIL-HDBK-5, "Metallic Materials and Elements for Flight Vehicle Structure".

 (2) MIL-HDBK-17, "Plastics for Flight Vehicles".

 (3) ANC-18, "Design of Wood Aircraft Structures".

 (4) MIL-HDBK-23, "Composite Construction for Flight Vehicles".

(e) Other design values may be used if a selection of the material is made in which a specimen of each individual item is tested before use and it is determined that the actual strength properties of that particular item will equal or exceed those used in design.

(Secs. 313(a), 601, 603, 604, Federal Aviation Act of 1958 (49 U.S.C. 1354(a), 1421, 1423, 1424), sec. 6(c), Dept. of Transportation Act (49 U.S.C. 1655(c)))

[Doc. No. 5074, 29 FR 15695, Nov. 24, 1964, as amended by Amdt. 27–16, 43 FR 50599, Oct. 30, 1978; Amdt. 27–26, 55 FR 8000, Mar. 6, 1990]

27.619　Special factors

(a) The special factors prescribed in 27.621 through 27.625 apply to each part of the structure whose strength is—

 (1) Uncertain;

 (2) Likely to deteriorate in service before normal replacement; or

 (3) Subject to appreciable variability due to—

　(i) Uncertainties in manufacturing processes; or

　(ii) Uncertainties in inspection methods.

(b) For each part to which 27.621 through 27.625 apply, the factor of safety prescribed in 27.303 must be multiplied by a special factor equal to—

 (1) The applicable special factors prescribed in 27.621 through 27.625; or

 (2) Any other factor great enough to ensure that the probability of the part being understrength because of the uncertainties specified in paragraph (a) of this section is extremely remote.

27.621　Casting factors

(a) General. The factors, tests, and inspections specified in paragraphs (b) and (c) of this section must be applied in addition to those necessary to establish foundry quality control. The inspections must meet approved specifications. Paragraphs (c) and (d) of this section apply to structural castings except castings that are pressure tested as parts of hydraulic or other fluid systems and do not support structural loads.

(b) Bearing stresses and surfaces. The casting factors specified in paragraphs (c) and (d) of this section—

 (1) Need not exceed 1.25 with respect to bearing stresses regardless of the method of inspection used; and

 (2) Need not be used with respect to the bearing surfaces of a part whose bearing factor is larger than the applicable casting factor.

(c) Critical castings. For each casting whose failure would preclude continued safe flight and landing of the rotorcraft or result in serious injury to any occupant, the following apply:

 (1) Each critical casting must—

　(i) Have a casting factor of not less than 1.25; and

　(ii) Receive 100 percent inspection by visual, radiographic, and magnetic particle (for ferromagnetic materials) or penetrant (for nonferromagnetic materials) inspection methods or approved equivalent inspection methods.

 (2) For each critical casting with a casting factor less than 1.50, three sample castings must be static tested and shown to meet—

　(i) The strength requirements of 27.305 at an ultimate load corresponding to a casting factor of 1.25; and

　(ii) The deformation requirements of 27.305 at a load of 1.15 times the limit load.

(d) Noncritical castings. For each casting other than those specified in paragraph (c) of this section, the following apply:

 (1) Except as provided in paragraphs (d)(2) and (3) of this section, the casting factors and corresponding inspections must meet the following table:

CASTING FACTOR	INSPECTION
2.0 or greater	100 percent visual.
Less than 2.0, greater than 1.5	100 percent visual, and magnetic particle (ferromagnetic materials), penetrant (nonferromagnetic materials), or approved equivalent inspection methods.
1.25 through 1.50	100 percent visual, and magnetic particle (ferromagnetic materials). penetrant (nonferromagnetic materials), and radiographic or approved equivalent inspection methods.

 (2) The percentage of castings inspected by nonvisual methods may be reduced below that specified in paragraph (d)(1) of this section when an approved quality control procedure is established.

(3) For castings procured to a specification that guarantees the mechanical properties of the material in the casting and provides for demonstration of these properties by test of coupons cut from the castings on a sampling basis—

    (i) A casting factor of 1.0 may be used; and

    (ii) The castings must be inspected as provided in paragraph (d)(1) of this section for casting factors of "1.25 through 1.50" and tested under paragraph (c)(2) of this section.

[Doc. No. 5074, 29 FR 15695, Nov. 24, 1964, as amended by Amdt. 27–34, 62 FR 46173, Aug. 29, 1997]

27.623   Bearing factors

(a) Except as provided in paragraph (b) of this section, each part that has clearance (free fit), and that is subject to pounding or vibration, must have a bearing factor large enough to provide for the effects of normal relative motion.

(b) No bearing factor need be used on a part for which any larger special factor is prescribed.

27.625   Fitting factors

For each fitting (part or terminal used to join one structural member to another) the following apply:

(a) For each fitting whose strength is not proven by limit and ultimate load tests in which actual stress conditions are simulated in the fitting and surrounding structures, a fitting factor of at least 1.15 must be applied to each part of—

    (1) The fitting;

    (2) The means of attachment; and

    (3) The bearing on the joined members.

(b) No fitting factor need be used—

    (1) For joints made under approved practices and based on comprehensive test data (such as continuous joints in metal plating, welded joints, and scarf joints in wood); and

    (2) With respect to any bearing surface for which a larger special factor is used.

(c) For each integral fitting, the part must be treated as a fitting up to the point at which the section properties become typical of the member.

(d) Each seat, berth, litter, safety belt, and harness attachment to the structure must be shown by analysis, tests, or both, to be able to withstand the inertia forces prescribed in 27.561(b)(3) multiplied by a fitting factor of 1.33.

[Doc. No. 5074, 29 FR 15695, Nov. 24, 1964, as amended by Amdt. 27–35, 63 FR 43285, Aug. 12, 1998]

27.629   Flutter

Each aerodynamic surface of the rotorcraft must be free from flutter under each appropriate speed and power condition.

[Doc. No. 5074, 29 FR 15695, Nov. 24, 1964, as amended by Amdt. 27–26, 55 FR 8000, Mar. 6, 1990]

Rotors

27.653   Pressure venting and drainage of rotor blades

(a) For each rotor blade—

    (1) There must be means for venting the internal pressure of the blade;

    (2) Drainage holes must be provided for the blade; and

    (3) The blade must be designed to prevent water from becoming trapped in it.

(b) Paragraphs (a)(1) and (2) of this section does not apply to sealed rotor blades capable of withstanding the maximum pressure differentials expected in service.

[Amdt. 27–2, 33 FR 963, Jan. 26, 1968]

27.659   Mass balance

(a) The rotors and blades must be mass balanced as necessary to—

    (1) Prevent excessive vibration; and

    (2) Prevent flutter at any speed up to the maximum forward speed.

(b) The structural integrity of the mass balance installation must be substantiated.

[Amdt. 27–2, 33 FR 963, Jan. 26, 1968]

27.661   Rotor blade clearance

There must be enough clearance between the rotor blades and other parts of the structure to prevent the blades from striking any part of the structure during any operating condition.

[Amdt. 27–2, 33 FR 963, Jan. 26, 1968]

27.663   Ground resonance prevention means

(a) The reliability of the means for preventing ground resonance must be shown either by analysis and tests, or reliable service experience, or by showing through analysis or tests that malfunction or failure of a single means will not cause ground resonance.

(b) The probable range of variations, during service, of the damping action of the ground resonance prevention means must be established and must be investigated during the test required by 27.241.

[Amdt. 27–2, 33 FR 963, Jan. 26, 1968, as amended by Amdt. 27–26, 55 FR 8000, Mar. 6, 1990]

Control Systems

27.671   General

(a) Each control and control system must operate with the ease, smoothness, and positiveness appropriate to its function.

(b) Each element of each flight control system must be designed, or distinctively and permanently marked, to minimize the probability of any incorrect assembly that could result in the malfunction of the system.

27.672   Stability augmentation, automatic, and power-operated systems

If the functioning of stability augmentation or other automatic or power-operated systems is necessary to show compliance with the flight characteristics requirements of this part, such systems must comply with 27.671 of this part and the following:

(a) A warning which is clearly distinguishable to the pilot under expected flight conditions without requiring the pilot's attention must be provided for any failure in the stability augmentation system or in any other automatic or power-operated system which could result in an unsafe condition if the pilot is unaware of the failure. Warning systems must not activate the control systems.

(b) The design of the stability augmentation system or of any other automatic or power-operated system must allow initial counteraction of failures without requiring exceptional pilot skill or strength by overriding the failure by movement of the flight controls in the normal sense and deactivating the failed system.

(c) It must be shown that after any single failure of the stability augmentation system or any other automatic or power-operated system—

    (1) The rotorcraft is safely controllable when the failure or malfunction occurs at any speed or altitude within the approved operating limitations;

    (2) The controllability and maneuverability requirements of this part are met within a practical operational flight envelope (for example, speed, altitude, normal acceleration, and rotorcraft configurations) which is described in the Rotorcraft Flight Manual; and

    (3) The trim and stability characteristics are not impaired below a level needed to permit continued safe flight and landing.

[Amdt. 27–21, 49 FR 44433, Nov. 6, 1984; 49 FR 47594, Dec. 6, 1984]

27.673 Primary flight control

Primary flight controls are those used by the pilot for immediate control of pitch, roll, yaw, and vertical motion of the rotorcraft.

[Amdt. 27–21, 49 FR 44434, Nov. 6, 1984]

27.674 Interconnected controls

Each primary flight control system must provide for safe flight and landing and operate independently after a malfunction, failure, or jam of any auxiliary interconnected control.

[Amdt. 27–26, 55 FR 8001, Mar. 6, 1990]

27.675 Stops

(a) Each control system must have stops that positively limit the range of motion of the pilot's controls.

(b) Each stop must be located in the system so that the range of travel of its control is not appreciably affected by—

(1) Wear;

(2) Slackness; or

(3) Takeup adjustments.

(c) Each stop must be able to withstand the loads corresponding to the design conditions for the system.

(d) For each main rotor blade—

(1) Stops that are appropriate to the blade design must be provided to limit travel of the blade about its hinge points; and

(2) There must be means to keep the blade from hitting the droop stops during any operation other than starting and stopping the rotor.

(Secs. 313(a), 601, 603, 604, Federal Aviation Act of 1958 (49 U.S.C. 1354(a), 1421, 1423, 1424), sec. 6(c), Dept. of Transportation Act (49 U.S.C. 1655(c)))

[Doc. No. 5074, 29 FR 15695, Nov. 24, 1964, as amended by Amdt. 27–16, 43 FR 50599, Oct. 30, 1978]

27.679 Control system locks

If there is a device to lock the control system with the rotorcraft on the ground or water, there must be means to—

(a) Give unmistakable warning to the pilot when the lock is engaged; and

(b) Prevent the lock from engaging in flight.

27.681 Limit load static tests

(a) Compliance with the limit load requirements of this part must be shown by tests in which—

(1) The direction of the test loads produces the most severe loading in the control system; and

(2) Each fitting, pulley, and bracket used in attaching the system to the main structure is included.

(b) Compliance must be shown (by analyses or individual load tests) with the special factor requirements for control system joints subject to angular motion.

27.683 Operation tests

It must be shown by operation tests that, when the controls are operated from the pilot compartment with the control system loaded to correspond with loads specified for the system, the system is free from—

(a) Jamming;

(b) Excessive friction; and

(c) Excessive deflection.

27.685 Control system details

(a) Each detail of each control system must be designed to prevent jamming, chafing, and interference from cargo, passengers, loose objects or the freezing of moisture.

(b) There must be means in the cockpit to prevent the entry of foreign objects into places where they would jam the system.

(c) There must be means to prevent the slapping of cables or tubes against other parts.

(d) Cable systems must be designed as follows:

(1) Cables, cable fittings, turnbuckles, splices, and pulleys must be of an acceptable kind.

(2) The design of the cable systems must prevent any hazardous change in cable tension throughout the range of travel under any operating conditions and temperature variations.

(3) No cable smaller than three thirty-seconds of an inch diameter may be used in any primary control system.

(4) Pulley kinds and sizes must correspond to the cables with which they are used. The pulley cable combinations and strength values which must be used are specified in Military Handbook MIL-HDBK-5C, Vol. 1 & Vol. 2, Metallic Materials and Elements for Flight Vehicle Structures, (Sept. 15, 1976, as amended through December 15, 1978). This incorporation by reference was approved by the Director of the Federal Register in accordance with 5 U.S.C. section 552(a) and 1 CFR part 51. Copies may be obtained from the Naval Publications and Forms Center, 5801 Tabor Avenue, Philadelphia, Pennsylvania, 19120. Copies may be inspected at the National Archives and Records Administration (NARA). For information on the availability of this material at NARA, call 202-741-6030, or go to: http://www.archives.gov/federal-register/cfr/ibr-locations.html

(5) Pulleys must have close fitting guards to prevent the cables from being displaced or fouled.

(6) Pulleys must lie close enough to the plane passing through the cable to prevent the cable from rubbing against the pulley flange.

(7) No fairlead may cause a change in cable direction of more than 3°.

(8) No clevis pin subject to load or motion and retained only by cotter pins may be used in the control system.

(9) Turnbuckles attached to parts having angular motion must be installed to prevent binding throughout the range of travel.

(10) There must be means for visual inspection at each fairlead, pulley, terminal, and turnbuckle.

(e) Control system joints subject to angular motion must incorporate the following special factors with respect to the ultimate bearing strength of the softest material used as a bearing:

(1) 3.33 for push-pull systems other than ball and roller bearing systems.

(2) 2.0 for cable systems.

(f) For control system joints, the manufacturer's static, non-Brinell rating of ball and roller bearings must not be exceeded.

[Doc. No. 5074, 29 FR 15695, Nov. 24, 1964, as amended by Amdt. 27-11, 41 FR 55469, Dec. 20, 1976; Amdt. 27-26, 55 FR 8001, Mar. 6, 1990; 69 FR 18803, Apr. 9, 2004; Doc. No. FAA-2018-0119, Amdt. 27-49, 83 FR 9170, Mar. 5, 2018]

27.687 Spring devices

(a) Each control system spring device whose failure could cause flutter or other unsafe characteristics must be reliable.

(b) Compliance with paragraph (a) of this section must be shown by tests simulating service conditions.

27.691 Autorotation control mechanism

Each main rotor blade pitch control mechanism must allow rapid entry into autorotation after power failure.

27.695 Power boost and power-operated control system

(a) If a power boost or power-operated control system is used, an alternate system must be immediately available that allows continued safe flight and landing in the event of—

(1) Any single failure in the power portion of the system; or

(2) The failure of all engines.

(b) Each alternate system may be a duplicate power portion or a manually operated mechanical system. The power portion includes the power source (such as hydraulic pumps), and such items as valves, lines, and actuators.

(c) The failure of mechanical parts (such as piston rods and links), and the jamming of power cylinders, must be considered unless they are extremely improbable.

Landing Gear

27.723   Shock absorption tests

The landing inertia load factor and the reserve energy absorption capacity of the landing gear must be substantiated by the tests prescribed in 27.725 and 27.727, respectively. These tests must be conducted on the complete rotorcraft or on units consisting of wheel, tire, and shock absorber in their proper relation.

27.725   Limit drop test

The limit drop test must be conducted as follows:

(a) The drop height must be—

(1) 13 inches from the lowest point of the landing gear to the ground; or

(2) Any lesser height, not less than eight inches, resulting in a drop contact velocity equal to the greatest probable sinking speed likely to occur at ground contact in normal power-off landings.

(b) If considered, the rotor lift specified in 27.473(a) must be introduced into the drop test by appropriate energy absorbing devices or by the use of an effective mass.

(c) Each landing gear unit must be tested in the attitude simulating the landing condition that is most critical from the standpoint of the energy to be absorbed by it.

(d) When an effective mass is used in showing compliance with paragraph (b) of this section, the following formula may be used instead of more rational computations:

$$W_e = W \times \frac{[h + (1 - L)\,d]}{h+d}\;;\; \text{and}$$

$$n = n_j \frac{W_e}{W} + L$$

where:

W_e = the effective weight to be used in the drop test (lbs.);

$W = W_M$ for main gear units (lbs.), equal to the static reaction on the particular unit with the rotorcraft in the most critical attitude. A rational method may be used in computing a main gear static reaction, taking into consideration the moment arm between the main wheel reaction and the rotorcraft center of gravity.

$W = W_N$ for nose gear units (lbs.), equal to the vertical component of the static reaction that would exist at the nose wheel, assuming that the mass of the rotorcraft acts at the center of gravity and exerts a force of 1.0 g downward and 0.25 g forward.

$W = W_T$ for tailwheel units (lbs.), equal to whichever of the following is critical:

(1) The static weight on the tailwheel with the rotorcraft resting on all wheels; or

(2) The vertical component of the ground reaction that would occur at the tailwheel, assuming that the mass of the rotorcraft acts at the center of gravity and exerts a force of l g downward with the rotorcraft in the maximum nose-up attitude considered in the nose-up landing conditions.

h = specified free drop height (inches).

L = ration of assumed rotor lift to the rotorcraft weight.

d = deflection under impact of the tire (at the proper inflation pressure) plus the vertical component of the axle travels (inches) relative to the drop mass.

n = limit inertia load factor.

n_j = the load factor developed, during impact, on the mass used in the drop test (i.e., the acceleration dv/dt in g 's recorded in the drop test plus 1.0).

27.727   Reserve energy absorption drop test

The reserve energy absorption drop test must be conducted as follows:

(a) The drop height must be 1.5 times that specified in 27.725(a).

(b) Rotor lift, where considered in a manner similar to that prescribed in 27.725(b), may not exceed 1.5 times the lift allowed under that paragraph.

(c) The landing gear must withstand this test without collapsing. Collapse of the landing gear occurs when a member of the nose, tail, or main gear will not support the rotorcraft in the proper attitude or allows the rotorcraft structure, other than the landing gear and external accessories, to impact the landing surface.

[Doc. No. 5074, 29 FR 15695, Nov. 24, 1964, as amended by Amdt. 27–26, 55 FR 8001, Mar. 6, 1990]

27.729   Retracting mechanism

For rotorcraft with retractable landing gear, the following apply:

(a) Loads. The landing gear, retracting mechansim, wheel-well doors, and supporting structure must be designed for—

(1) The loads occurring in any maneuvering condition with the gear retracted;

(2) The combined friction, inertia, and air loads occurring during retraction and extension at any airspeed up to the design maximum landing gear operating speed; and

(3) The flight loads, including those in yawed flight, occurring with the gear extended at any airspeed up to the design maximum landing gear extended speed.

(b) Landing gear lock. A positive means must be provided to keep the gear extended.

(c) Emergency operation. When other than manual power is used to operate the gear, emergency means must be provided for extending the gear in the event of—

(1) Any reasonably probable failure in the normal retraction system; or

(2) The failure of any single source of hydraulic, electric, or equivalent energy.

(d) Operation tests. The proper functioning of the retracting mechanism must be shown by operation tests.

(e) Position indicator. There must be a means to indicate to the pilot when the gear is secured in the extreme positions.

(f) Control. The location and operation of the retraction control must meet the requirements of 27.777 and 27.779.

(g) Landing gear warning. An aural or equally effective landing gear warning device must be provided that functions continuously when the rotorcraft is in a normal landing mode and the landing gear is not fully extended and locked. A manual shutoff capability must be provided for the warning device and the warning system must automatically reset when the rotorcraft is no longer in the landing mode.

[Amdt. 27–21, 49 FR 44434, Nov. 6, 1984]

27.731   Wheels

(a) Each landing gear wheel must be approved.

(b) The maximum static load rating of each wheel may not be less than the corresponding static ground reaction with—

(1) Maximum weight; and

(2) Critical center of gravity.

(c) The maximum limit load rating of each wheel must equal or exceed the maximum radial limit load determined under the applicable ground load requirements of this part.

27.733 Tires

(a) Each landing gear wheel must have a tire—

    (1) That is a proper fit on the rim of the wheel; and

    (2) Of the proper rating.

(b) The maximum static load rating of each tire must equal or exceed the static ground reaction obtained at its wheel, assuming—

    (1) The design maximum weight; and

    (2) The most unfavorable center of gravity.

(c) Each tire installed on a retractable landing gear system must, at the maximum size of the tire type expected in service, have a clearance to surrounding structure and systems that is adequate to prevent contact between the tire and any part of the structure or systems.

[Doc. No. 5074, 29 FR 15695, Nov. 24, 1964, as amended by Amdt. 27–11, 41 FR 55469, Dec. 20, 1976]

27.735 Brakes

For rotorcraft with wheel-type landing gear, a braking device must be installed that is—

(a) Controllable by the pilot;

(b) Usable during power-off landings; and

(c) Adequate to—

    (1) Counteract any normal unbalanced torque when starting or stopping the rotor; and

    (2) Hold the rotorcraft parked on a 10-degree slope on a dry, smooth pavement.

[Doc. No. 5074, 29 FR 15695, Nov. 24, 1964, as amended by Amdt. 27–21, 49 FR 44434, Nov. 6, 1984]

27.737 Skis

The maximum limit load rating of each ski must equal or exceed the maximum limit load determined under the applicable ground load requirements of this part.

Floats and Hulls

27.751 Main float buoyancy

(a) For main floats, the buoyancy necessary to support the maximum weight of the rotorcraft in fresh water must be exceeded by—

    (1) 50 percent, for single floats; and

    (2) 60 percent, for multiple floats.

(b) Each main float must have enough water-tight compartments so that, with any single main float compartment flooded, the main floats will provide a margin of positive stability great enough to minimize the probability of capsizing.

[Doc. No. 5074, 29 FR 15695, Nov. 24, 1964, as amended by Amdt. 27–2, 33 FR 963, Jan. 26, 1968]

27.753 Main float design

(a) Bag floats. Each bag float must be designed to withstand—

    (1) The maximum pressure differential that might be developed at the maximum altitude for which certification with that float is requested; and

    (2) The vertical loads prescribed in 27.521(a), distributed along the length of the bag over three-quarters of its projected area.

(b) Rigid floats. Each rigid float must be able to withstand the vertical, horizontal, and side loads prescribed in 27.521. These loads may be distributed along the length of the float.

27.755 Hulls

For each rotorcraft, with a hull and auxiliary floats, that is to be approved for both taking off from and landing on water, the hull and auxiliary floats must have enough watertight compartments so that, with any single compartment flooded, the buoyancy of the hull and auxiliary floats (and wheel tires if used) provides a margin of positive stability great enough to minimize the probability of capsizing.

Personnel and Cargo Accommodations

27.771 Pilot compartment

For each pilot compartment—

(a) The compartment and its equipment must allow each pilot to perform his duties without unreasonable concentration or fatigue;

(b) If there is provision for a second pilot, the rotorcraft must be controllable with equal safety from either pilot seat; and

(c) The vibration and noise characteristics of cockpit appurtenances may not interfere with safe operation.

27.773 Pilot compartment view

(a) Each pilot compartment must be free from glare and reflections that could interfere with the pilot's view, and designed so that—

    (1) Each pilot's view is sufficiently extensive, clear, and undistorted for safe operation; and

    (2) Each pilot is protected from the elements so that moderate rain conditions do not unduly impair his view of the flight path in normal flight and while landing.

(b) If certification for night operation is requested, compliance with paragraph (a) of this section must be shown by ground or night flight tests.

(c) A vision system with a transparent display surface located in the pilot's outside field of view, such as a head up-display, head mounted display, or other equivalent display, must meet the following requirements:

    (1) While the vision system display is in operation, it must compensate for interference with the pilot's outside field of view such that the combination of what is visible in the display and what remains visible through and around it, allows the pilot compartment to satisfy the requirements of paragraphs (a)(1) and (b) of this section.

    (2) The pilot's view of the external scene may not be distorted by the transparent display surface or by the vision system imagery. When the vision system displays imagery or any symbology that is referenced to the imagery and outside scene topography, including attitude symbology, flight path vector, and flight path angle reference cue, that imagery and symbology must be aligned with, and scaled to, the external scene.

    (3) The vision system must provide a means to allow the pilot using the display to immediately deactivate and reactivate the vision system imagery, on demand, without removing the pilot's hands from the primary flight and power controls, or their equivalent.

    (4) When the vision system is not in operation it must permit the pilot compartment to satisfy the requirements of paragraphs (a)(1) and (b) of this section.

[Doc. No. 5074, 29 FR 15695, Nov. 24, 1964, as amended by Docket FAA-2013-0485, Amdt. 27–48, 81 FR 90170, Dec. 13, 2016; Docket FAA-2016-9275, Amdt. 27–50, 83 FR 9423, Mar. 6, 2018]

27.775 Windshields and windows

Windshields and windows must be made of material that will not break into dangerous fragments.

[Amdt. 27–27, 55 FR 38966, Sept. 21, 1990]

27.777 Cockpit controls

Cockpit controls must be—

(a) Located to provide convenient operation and to prevent confusion and inadvertent operation; and

(b) Located and arranged with respect to the pilots' seats so that there is full and unrestricted movement of each control without interference from the cockpit structure or the pilot's clothing when pilots from 5'2" to 6'0" in height are seated.

27.779 Motion and effect of cockpit controls

Cockpit controls must be designed so that they operate in accordance with the following movements and actuation:

(a) Flight controls, including the collective pitch control, must operate with a sense of motion which corresponds to the effect on the rotorcraft.

(b) Twist-grip engine power controls must be designed so that, for lefthand operation, the motion of the pilot's hand is clockwise to increase power when the hand is viewed from the edge containing the index finger. Other engine power controls, excluding the collective control, must operate with a forward motion to increase power.

(c) Normal landing gear controls must operate downward to extend the landing gear.

[Amdt. 27–21, 49 FR 44434, Nov. 6, 1984]

27.783   Doors

(a) Each closed cabin must have at least one adequate and easily accessible external door.

(b) Each external door must be located where persons using it will not be endangered by the rotors, propellers, engine intakes, and exhausts when appropriate operating procedures are used. If opening procedures are required, they must be marked inside, on or adjacent to the door opening device.

[Doc. No. 5074, 29 FR 15695, Nov. 24, 1964, as amended by Amdt. 27–26, 55 FR 8001, Mar. 6, 1990]

27.785   Seats, berths, litters, safety belts, and harnesses

(a) Each seat, safety belt, harness, and adjacent part of the rotorcraft at each station designated for occupancy during takeoff and landing must be free of potentially injurious objects, sharp edges, protuberances, and hard surfaces and must be designed so that a person making proper use of these facilities will not suffer serious injury in an emergency landing as a result of the static inertial load factors specified in 27.561(b) and dynamic conditions specified in 27.562.

(b) Each occupant must be protected from serious head injury by a safety belt plus a shoulder harness that will prevent the head from contacting any injurious object except as provided for in 27.562(c)(5). A shoulder harness (upper torso restraint), in combination with the safety belt, constitutes a torso restraint system as described in TSO–C114.

(c) Each occupant's seat must have a combined safety belt and shoulder harness with a single-point release. Each pilot's combined safety belt and shoulder harness must allow each pilot when seated with safety belt and shoulder harness fastened to perform all functions necessary for flight operations. There must be a means to secure belts and harnesses, when not in use, to prevent interference with the operation of the rotorcraft and with rapid egress in an emergency.

(d) If seat backs do not have a firm handhold, there must be hand grips or rails along each aisle to enable the occupants to steady themselves while using the aisle in moderately rough air.

(e) Each projecting object that could injure persons seated or moving about in the rotorcraft in normal flight must be padded.

(f) Each seat and its supporting structure must be designed for an occupant weight of at least 170 pounds considering the maximum load factors, inertial forces, and reactions between occupant, seat, and safety belt or harness corresponding with the applicable flight and ground load conditions, including the emergency landing conditions of 27.561(b). In addition—

   (1) Each pilot seat must be designed for the reactions resulting from the application of the pilot forces prescribed in 27.397; and

   (2) The inertial forces prescribed in 27.561(b) must be multiplied by a factor of 1.33 in determining the strength of the attachment of—

      (i)   Each seat to the structure; and

      (ii) Each safety belt or harness to the seat or structure.

(g) When the safety belt and shoulder harness are combined, the rated strength of the safety belt and shoulder harness may not be less than that corresponding to the inertial forces specified in 27.561(b), considering the occupant weight of at least 170 pounds, considering the dimensional characteristics of the restraint system installation, and using a distribution of at least a 60-percent load to the safety belt and at least a 40-percent load to the shoulder harness. If the safety belt is capable of being used without the shoulder harness, the inertial forces specified must be met by the safety belt alone.

(h) When a headrest is used, the headrest and its supporting structure must be designed to resist the inertia forces specified in 27.561, with a 1.33 fitting factor and a head weight of at least 13 pounds.

(i) Each seating device system includes the device such as the seat, the cushions, the occupant restraint system, and attachment devices.

(j) Each seating device system may use design features such as crushing or separation of certain parts of the seats to reduce occupant loads for the emergency landing dynamic conditions of 27.562; otherwise, the system must remain intact and must not interfere with rapid evacuation of the rotorcraft.

(k) For the purposes of this section, a litter is defined as a device designed to carry a nonambulatory person, primarily in a recumbent position, into and on the rotorcraft. Each berth or litter must be designed to withstand the load reaction of an occupant weight of at least 170 pounds when the occupant is subjected to the forward inertial factors specified in 27.561(b). A berth or litter installed within 15° or less of the longitudinal axis of the rotorcraft must be provided with a padded end-board, cloth diaphram, or equivalent means that can withstand the forward load reaction. A berth or litter oriented greater than 15° with the longitudinal axis of the rotorcraft must be equipped with appropriate restraints, such as straps or safety belts, to withstand the forward load reaction. In addition—

   (1) The berth or litter must have a restraint system and must not have corners or other protuberances likely to cause serious injury to a person occupying it during emergency landing conditions; and

   (2) The berth or litter attachment and the occupant restraint system attachments to the structure must be designed to withstand the critical loads resulting from flight and ground load conditions and from the conditions prescribed in 27.561(b). The fitting factor required by 27.625(d) shall be applied.

[Amdt. 27–21, 49 FR 44434, Nov. 6, 1984, as amended by Amdt. 27–25, 54 FR 47319, Nov. 13, 1989; Amdt. 27–35, 63 FR 43285, Aug. 12, 1998]

27.787   Cargo and baggage compartments

(a) Each cargo and baggage compartment must be designed for its placarded maximum weight of contents and for the critical load distributions at the appropriate maximum load factors corresponding to the specified flight and ground load conditions, except the emergency landing conditions of 27.561.

(b) There must be means to prevent the contents of any compartment from becoming a hazard by shifting under the loads specified in paragraph (a) of this section.

(c) Under the emergency landing conditions of 27.561, cargo and baggage compartments must—

   (1) Be positioned so that if the contents break loose they are unlikely to cause injury to the occupants or restrict any of the escape facilities provided for use after an emergency landing; or

   (2) Have sufficient strength to withstand the conditions specified in 27.561 including the means of restraint, and their attachments, required by paragraph (b) of this section. Sufficient strength must be provided for the maximum authorized weight of cargo and baggage at the critical loading distribution.

(d) If cargo compartment lamps are installed, each lamp must be installed so as to prevent contact between lamp bulb and cargo.

[Doc. No. 5074, 29 FR 15695, Nov. 24, 1964, as amended by Amdt. 27–11, 41 FR 55469, Dec. 20, 1976; Amdt. 27–27, 55 FR 38966, Sept. 21, 1990]

27.801 Ditching

(a) If certification with ditching provisions is requested, the rotorcraft must meet the requirements of this section and 27.807(d), 27.1411 and 27.1415.

(b) Each practicable design measure, compatible with the general characteristics of the rotorcraft, must be taken to minimize the probability that in an emergency landing on water, the behavior of the rotorcraft would cause immediate injury to the occupants or would make it impossible for them to escape.

(c) The probable behavior of the rotorcraft in a water landing must be investigated by model tests or by comparison with rotorcraft of similar configuration for which the ditching characteristics are known. Scoops, flaps, projections, and any other factor likely to affect the hydrodynamic characteristics of the rotorcraft must be considered.

(d) It must be shown that, under reasonably probable water conditions, the flotation time and trim of the rotorcraft will allow the occupants to leave the rotorcraft and enter the life rafts required by 27.1415. If compliance with this provision is shown by buoyancy and trim computations, appropriate allowances must be made for probable structural damage and leakage. If the rotorcraft has fuel tanks (with fuel jettisoning provisions) that can reasonably be expected to withstand a ditching without leakage, the jettisonable volume of fuel may be considered as buoyancy volume.

(e) Unless the effects of the collapse of external doors and windows are accounted for in the investigation of the probable behavior of the rotorcraft in a water landing (as prescribed in paragraphs (c) and (d) of this section), the external doors and windows must be designed to withstand the probable maximum local pressures.

[Amdt. 27–11, 41 FR 55469, Dec. 20, 1976]

27.805 Flight crew emergency exits

(a) For rotorcraft with passenger emergency exits that are not convenient to the flight crew, there must be flight crew emergency exits, on both sides of the rotorcraft or as a top hatch in the flight crew area.

(b) Each flight crew emergency exit must be of sufficient size and must be located so as to allow rapid evacuation of the flight crew. This must be shown by test.

(c) Each flight crew emergency exit must not be obstructed by water or flotation devices after an emergency landing on water. This must be shown by test, demonstration, or analysis.

[Doc. No. 29247, 64 FR 45094, Aug. 18, 1999]

27.807 Emergency exits

(a) Number and location.

(1) There must be at least one emergency exit on each side of the cabin readily accessible to each passenger. One of these exits must be usable in any probable attitude that may result from a crash;

(2) Doors intended for normal use may also serve as emergency exits, provided that they meet the requirements of this section; and

(3) If emergency flotation devices are installed, there must be an emergency exit accessible to each passenger on each side of the cabin that is shown by test, demonstration, or analysis to;

(i) Be above the waterline; and

(ii) Open without interference from flotation devices, whether stowed or deployed.

(b) Type and operation. Each emergency exit prescribed by paragraph (a) of this section must—

(1) Consist of a movable window or panel, or additional external door, providing an unobstructed opening that will admit a 19-by 26-inch ellipse;

(2) Have simple and obvious methods of opening, from the inside and from the outside, which do not require exceptional effort;

(3) Be arranged and marked so as to be readily located and opened even in darkness; and

(4) Be reasonably protected from jamming by fuselage deformation.

(c) Tests. The proper functioning of each emergency exit must be shown by test.

(d) Ditching emergency exits for passengers. If certification with ditching provisions is requested, the markings required by paragraph (b)(3) of this section must be designed to remain visible if the rotorcraft is capsized and the cabin is submerged.

[Doc. No. 29247, 64 FR 45094, Aug. 18, 1999]

27.831 Ventilation

(a) The ventilating system for the pilot and passenger compartments must be designed to prevent the presence of excessive quantities of fuel fumes and carbon monoxide.

(b) The concentration of carbon monoxide may not exceed one part in 20,000 parts of air during forward flight or hovering in still air. If the concentration exceeds this value under other conditions, there must be suitable operating restrictions.

27.833 Heaters

Each combustion heater must be approved.

[Amdt. 27–23, 53 FR 34210, Sept. 2, 1988]

Fire Protection

27.853 Compartment interiors

For each compartment to be used by the crew or passengers—

(a) The materials must be at least flame-resistant;

(b) [Reserved]

(c) If smoking is to be prohibited, there must be a placard so stating, and if smoking is to be allowed—

(1) There must be an adequate number of self-contained, removable ashtrays; and

(2) Where the crew compartment is separated from the passenger compartment, there must be at least one illuminated sign (using either letters or symbols) notifying all passengers when smoking is prohibited. Signs which notify when smoking is prohibited must—

(i) When illuminated, be legible to each passenger seated in the passenger cabin under all probable lighting conditions; and

(ii) Be so constructed that the crew can turn the illumination on and off.

[Amdt. 27–17, 45 FR 7755, Feb. 4, 1980, as amended by Amdt. 27–37, 64 FR 45095, Aug. 18, 1999]

27.855 Cargo and baggage compartments

(a) Each cargo and baggage compartment must be constructed of, or lined with, materials that are at least—

(1) Flame resistant, in the case of compartments that are readily accessible to a crewmember in flight; and

(2) Fire resistant, in the case of other compartments.

(b) No compartment may contain any controls, wiring, lines, equipment, or accessories whose damage or failure would affect safe operation, unless those items are protected so that—

(1) They cannot be damaged by the movement of cargo in the compartment; and

(2) Their breakage or failure will not create a fire hazard.

27.859 Heating systems

(a) General. For each heating system that involves the passage of cabin air over, or close to, the exhaust manifold, there must be means to prevent carbon monoxide from entering any cabin or pilot compartment.

(b) Heat exchangers. Each heat exchanger must be—

(1) Of suitable materials;

(2) Adequately cooled under all conditions; and

(3) Easily disassembled for inspection.

(c) Combustion heater fire protection. Except for heaters which incorporate designs to prevent hazards in the event of fuel leakage in the heater fuel system, fire within the ventilating air passage, or any other heater malfunction, each heater zone must incorporate the fire protection features of the applicable requirements of 27.1183, 27.1185, 27.1189, 27.1191, and be provided with—

    (1) Approved, quick-acting fire detectors in numbers and locations ensuring prompt detection of fire in the heater region.

    (2) Fire extinguisher systems that provide at least one adequate discharge to all areas of the heater region.

    (3) Complete drainage of each part of each zone to minimize the hazards resulting from failure or malfunction of any component containing flammable fluids. The drainage means must be—

        (i) Effective under conditions expected to prevail when drainage is needed; and

        (ii) Arranged so that no discharged fluid will cause an additional fire hazard.

    (4) Ventilation, arranged so that no discharged vapors will cause an additional fire hazard.

(d) Ventilating air ducts. Each ventilating air duct passing through any heater region must be fireproof.

    (1) Unless isolation is provided by fireproof valves or by equally effective means, the ventilating air duct downstream of each heater must be fireproof for a distance great enough to ensure that any fire originating in the heater can be contained in the duct.

    (2) Each part of any ventilating duct passing through any region having a flammable fluid system must be so constructed or isolated from that system that the malfunctioning of any component of that system cannot introduce flammable fluids or vapors into the ventilating airstream.

(e) Combustion air ducts. Each combustion air duct must be fireproof for a distance great enough to prevent damage from backfiring or reverse flame propagation.

    (1) No combustion air duct may connect with the ventilating airstream unless flames from backfires or reverse burning cannot enter the ventilating airstream under any operating condition, including reverse flow or malfunction of the heater or its associated components.

    (2) No combustion air duct may restrict the prompt relief of any backfire that, if so restricted, could cause heater failure.

(f) Heater control: General. There must be means to prevent the hazardous accumulation of water or ice on or in any heater control component, control system tubing, or safety control.

(g) Heater safety controls. For each combustion heater, safety control means must be provided as follows:

    (1) Means independent of the components provided for the normal continuous control of air temperature, airflow, and fuel flow must be provided for each heater to automatically shut off the ignition and fuel supply of that heater at a point remote from that heater when any of the following occurs:

        (i) The heat exchanger temperature exceeds safe limits.

        (ii) The ventilating air temperature exceeds safe limits.

        (iii) The combustion airflow becomes inadequate for safe operation.

        (iv) The ventilating airflow becomes inadequate for safe operation.

    (2) The means of complying with paragraph (g)(1) of this section for any individual heater must—

        (i) Be independent of components serving any other heater, the heat output of which is essential for safe operation; and

        (ii) Keep the heater off until restarted by the crew.

    (3) There must be means to warn the crew when any heater, the heat output of which is essential for safe operation, has been

shut off by the automatic means prescribed in paragraph (g)(1) of this section.

(h) Air intakes. Each combustion and ventilating air intake must be located so that no flammable fluids or vapors can enter the heater system—

    (1) During normal operation; or

    (2) As a result of the malfunction of any other component.

(i) Heater exhaust. Each heater exhaust system must meet the requirements of 27.1121 and 27.1123.

    (1) Each exhaust shroud must be sealed so that no flammable fluids or hazardous quantities of vapors can reach the exhaust system through joints.

    (2) No exhaust system may restrict the prompt relief of any backfire that, if so restricted, could cause heater failure.

(j) Heater fuel systems. Each heater fuel system must meet the powerplant fuel system requirements affecting safe heater operation. Each heater fuel system component in the ventilating airstream must be protected by shrouds so that no leakage from those components can enter the ventilating airstream.

(k) Drains. There must be means for safe drainage of any fuel that might accumulate in the combustion chamber or the heat exchanger.

    (1) Each part of any drain that operates at high temperatures must be protected in the same manner as heater exhausts.

    (2) Each drain must be protected against hazardous ice accumulation under any operating condition.

[Doc. No. 5074, 29 FR 15695, Nov. 24, 1964, as amended by Amdt. 27–23, 53 FR 34211, Sept. 2, 1988]

27.861   Fire protection of structure, controls, and other parts

Each part of the structure, controls, rotor mechanism, and other parts essential to a controlled landing that would be affected by powerplant fires must be fireproof or protected so they can perform their essential functions for at least 5 minutes under any foreseeable powerplant fire conditions.

[Amdt. 27–26, 55 FR 8001, Mar. 6, 1990]

27.863   Flammable fluid fire protection

(a) In each area where flammable fluids or vapors might escape by leakage of a fluid system, there must be means to minimize the probability of ignition of the fluids and vapors, and the resultant hazards if ignition does occur.

(b) Compliance with paragraph (a) of this section must be shown by analysis or tests, and the following factors must be considered:

    (1) Possible sources and paths of fluid leakage, and means of detecting leakage.

    (2) Flammability characteristics of fluids, including effects of any combustible or absorbing materials.

    (3) Possible ignition sources, including electrical faults, overheating of equipment, and malfunctioning of protective devices.

    (4) Means available for controlling or extinguishing a fire, such as stopping flow of fluids, shutting down equipment, fireproof containment, or use of extinguishing agents.

    (5) Ability of rotorcraft components that are critical to safety of flight to withstand fire and heat.

(c) If action by the flight crew is required to prevent or counteract a fluid fire (e.g. equipment shutdown or actuation of a fire extinguisher) quick acting means must be provided to alert the crew.

(d) Each area where flammable fluids or vapors might escape by leakage of a fluid system must be identified and defined.

(Secs. 313(a), 601, 603, 604, Federal Aviation Act of 1958 (49 U.S.C. 1354(a), 1421, 1423, 1424), sec. 6(c), Dept. of Transportation Act (49 U.S.C. 1655(c)))

[Amdt. 27–16, 43 FR 50599, Oct. 30, 1978]

External Loads

27.865 External loads

(a) It must be shown by analysis, test, or both, that the rotorcraft external load attaching means for rotorcraft-load combinations to be used for nonhuman external cargo applications can withstand a limit static load equal to 2.5, or some lower load factor approved under 27.337 through 27.341, multiplied by the maximum external load for which authorization is requested. It must be shown by analysis, test, or both that the rotorcraft external load attaching means and corresponding personnel carrying device system for rotorcraft-load combinations to be used for human external cargo applications can withstand a limit static load equal to 3.5 or some lower load factor, not less than 2.5, approved under 27.337 through 27.341, multiplied by the maximum external load for which authorization is requested. The load for any rotorcraft-load combination class, for any external cargo type, must be applied in the vertical direction. For jettisonable external loads of any applicable external cargo type, the load must also be applied in any direction making the maximum angle with the vertical that can be achieved in service but not less than 30°. However, the 30° angle may be reduced to a lesser angle if—

   (1) An operating limitation is established limiting external load operations to such angles for which compliance with this paragraph has been shown; or

   (2) It is shown that the lesser angle can not be exceeded in service.

(b) The external load attaching means, for jettisonable rotorcraft-load combinations, must include a quick-release system to enable the pilot to release the external load quickly during flight. The quick-release system must consist of a primary quick release subsystem and a backup quick release subsystem that are isolated from one another. The quick-release system, and the means by which it is controlled, must comply with the following:

   (1) A control for the primary quick release subsystem must be installed either on one of the pilot's primary controls or in an equivalently accessible location and must be designed and located so that it may be operated by either the pilot or a crewmember without hazardously limiting the ability to control the rotorcraft during an emergency situation.

   (2) A control for the backup quick release subsystem, readily accessible to either the pilot or another crewmember, must be provided.

   (3) Both the primary and backup quick release subsystems must—

      (i) Be reliable, durable, and function properly with all external loads up to and including the maximum external limit load for which authorization is requested.

      (ii) Be protected against electromagnetic interference (EMI) from external and internal sources and against lightning to prevent inadvertent load release.

         (A) The minimum level of protection required for jettisonable rotorcraft-load combinations used for nonhuman external cargo is a radio frequency field strength of 20 volts per meter.

         (B) The minimum level of protection required for jettisonable rotorcraft-load combinations used for human external cargo is a radio frequency field strength of 200 volts per meter.

      (iii) Be protected against any failure that could be induced by a failure mode of any other electrical or mechanical rotorcraft system.

(c) For rotorcraft-load combinations to be used for human external cargo applications, the rotorcraft must—

   (1) For jettisonable external loads, have a quick-release system that meets the requirements of paragraph (b) of this section and that—

      (i) Provides a dual actuation device for the primary quick release subsystem, and

      (ii) Provides a separate dual actuation device for the backup quick release subsystem;

   (2) Have a reliable, approved personnel carrying device system that has the structural capability and personnel safety features essential for external occupant safety;

   (3) Have placards and markings at all appropriate locations that clearly state the essential system operating instructions and, for the personnel carrying device system, the ingress and egress instructions;

   (4) Have equipment to allow direct intercommunication among required crewmembers and external occupants; and

   (5) Have the appropriate limitations and procedures incorporated in the flight manual for conducting human external cargo operations.

(d) The critically configured jettisonable external loads must be shown by a combination of analysis, ground tests, and flight tests to be both transportable and releasable throughout the approved operational envelope without hazard to the rotorcraft during normal flight conditions. In addition, these external loads must be shown to be releasable without hazard to the rotorcraft during emergency flight conditions.

(e) A placard or marking must be installed next to the external-load attaching means clearly stating any operational limitations and the maximum authorized external load as demonstrated under 27.25 and this section.

(f) The fatigue evaluation of 27.571 of this part does not apply to rotorcraft-load combinations to be used for nonhuman external cargo except for the failure of critical structural elements that would result in a hazard to the rotorcraft. For rotorcraft-load combinations to be used for human external cargo, the fatigue evaluation of 27.571 of this part applies to the entire quick release and personnel carrying device structural systems and their attachments.

[Amdt. 27–11, 41 FR 55469, Dec. 20, 1976; as amended by Amdt. 27–26, 55 FR 8001, Mar. 6, 1990; Amdt. 27–36, 64 FR 43019, Aug. 6, 1999]

Miscellaneous

27.871 Leveling marks

There must be reference marks for leveling the rotorcraft on the ground.

27.873 Ballast provisions

Ballast provisions must be designed and constructed to prevent inadvertent shifting of ballast in flight.

Subpart E — Powerplant

General

27.901 Installation

(a) For the purpose of this part, the powerplant installation includes each part of the rotorcraft (other than the main and auxiliary rotor structures) that—

   (1) Is necessary for propulsion;

   (2) Affects the control of the major propulsive units; or

   (3) Affects the safety of the major propulsive units between normal inspections or overhauls.

(b) For each powerplant installation—

   (1) Each component of the installation must be constructed, arranged, and installed to ensure its continued safe operation between normal inspections or overhauls for the range of temperature and altitude for which approval is requested;

   (2) Accessibility must be provided to allow any inspection and maintenance necessary for continued airworthiness;

   (3) Electrical interconnections must be provided to prevent differences of potential between major components of the installation and the rest of the rotorcraft;

(4) Axial and radial expansion of turbine engines may not affect the safety of the installation; and

(5) Design precautions must be taken to minimize the possibility of incorrect assembly of components and equipment essential to safe operation of the rotorcraft, except where operation with the incorrect assembly can be shown to be extremely improbable.

(c) The installation must comply with—

(1) The installation instructions provided under 33.5 of this chapter; and

(2) The applicable provisions of this subpart.

(Secs. 313(a), 601, and 603, 72 Stat. 752, 775, 49 U.S.C. 1354(a), 1421, and 1423; sec. 6(c), 49 U.S.C. 1655(c))

[Doc. No. 5074, 29 FR 15695, Nov. 24, 1964, as amended by Amdt. 27–2, 33 FR 963, Jan. 26, 1968; Amdt. 27–12, 42 FR 15044, Mar. 17, 1977; Amdt. 27–23, 53 FR 34211, Sept. 2, 1988]

27.903   Engines

(a) *Engine type certification.* Each engine must have an approved type certificate. Reciprocating engines for use in helicopters must be qualified in accordance with 33.49(d) of this chapter or be otherwise approved for the intended usage.

(b) *Engine or drive system cooling fan blade protection.*

(1) If an engine or rotor drive system cooling fan is installed, there must be a means to protect the rotorcraft and allow a safe landing if a fan blade fails. This must be shown by showing that—

(i)   The fan blades are contained in case of failure;

(ii) Each fan is located so that a failure will not jeopardize safety; or

(iii) Each fan blade can withstand an ultimate load of 1.5 times the centrifugal force resulting from operation limited by the following:

(A) For fans driven directly by the engine—

(1) The terminal engine r.p.m. under uncontrolled conditions; or

(2) An overspeed limiting device.

(B) For fans driven by the rotor drive system, the maximum rotor drive system rotational speed to be expected in service, including transients.

(2) Unless a fatigue evaluation under 27.571 is conducted, it must be shown that cooling fan blades are not operating at resonant conditions within the operating limits of the rotorcraft.

(c) *Turbine engine installation.* For turbine engine installations, the powerplant systems associated with engine control devices, systems, and instrumentation must be designed to give reasonable assurance that those engine operating limitations that adversely affect turbine rotor structural integrity will not be exceeded in service.

(d) *Restart capability:* A means to restart any engine in flight must be provided.

(1) Except for the in-flight shutdown of all engines, engine restart capability must be demonstrated throughout a flight envelope for the rotorcraft.

(2) Following the in-flight shutdown of all engines, in-flight engine restart capability must be provided.

[Doc. No. 5074, 29 FR 15695, Nov. 24, 1964, as amended by Amdt. 27–11, 41 FR 55469, Dec. 20, 1976; Amdt. 27–23, 53 FR 34211, Sept. 2, 1988; Amdt. No. 27–44, 73 FR 11000, Feb. 29, 2008]

27.907   Engine vibration

(a) Each engine must be installed to prevent the harmful vibration of any part of the engine or rotorcraft.

(b) The addition of the rotor and the rotor drive system to the engine may not subject the principal rotating parts of the engine to excessive vibration stresses. This must be shown by a vibration investigation.

(c) No part of the rotor drive system may be subjected to excessive vibration stresses.

Rotor Drive System

27.917   Design

(a) Each rotor drive system must incorporate a unit for each engine to automatically disengage that engine from the main and auxiliary rotors if that engine fails.

(b) Each rotor drive system must be arranged so that each rotor necessary for control in autorotation will continue to be driven by the main rotors after disengagement of the engine from the main and auxiliary rotors.

(c) If a torque limiting device is used in the rotor drive system, it must be located so as to allow continued control of the rotorcraft when the device is operating.

(d) The rotor drive system includes any part necessary to transmit power from the engines to the rotor hubs. This includes gear boxes, shafting, universal joints, couplings, rotor brake assemblies, clutches, supporting bearings for shafting, any attendant accessory pads or drives, and any cooling fans that are a part of, attached to, or mounted on the rotor drive system.

[Doc. No. 5074, 29 FR 15695, Nov. 24, 1964, as amended by Amdt. 27–11, 41 FR 55469, Dec. 20, 1976]

27.921   Rotor brake

If there is a means to control the rotation of the rotor drive system independently of the engine, any limitations on the use of that means must be specified, and the control for that means must be guarded to prevent inadvertent operation.

27.923   Rotor drive system and control mechanism tests

(a) Each part tested as prescribed in this section must be in a serviceable condition at the end of the tests. No intervening disassembly which might affect test results may be conducted.

(b) Each rotor drive system and control mechanism must be tested for not less than 100 hours. The test must be conducted on the rotorcraft, and the torque must be absorbed by the rotors to be installed, except that other ground or flight test facilities with other appropriate methods of torque absorption may be used if the conditions of support and vibration closely simulate the conditions that would exist during a test on the rotorcraft.

(c) A 60-hour part of the test prescribed in paragraph (b) of this section must be run at not less than maximum continuous torque and the maximum speed for use with maximum continuous torque. In this test, the main rotor controls must be set in the position that will give maximum longitudinal cyclic pitch change to simulate forward flight. The auxiliary rotor controls must be in the position for normal operation under the conditions of the test.

(d) A 30-hour or, for rotorcraft for which the use of either 30-minute OEI power or continuous OEI power is requested, a 25-hour part of the test prescribed in paragraph (b) of this section must be run at not less than 75 percent of maximum continuous torque and the minimum speed for use with 75 percent of maximum continuous torque. The main and auxiliary rotor controls must be in the position for normal operation under the conditions of the test.

(e) A 10-hour part of the test prescribed in paragraph (b) of this section must be run at not less than takeoff torque and the maximum speed for use with takeoff torque. The main and auxiliary rotor controls must be in the normal position for vertical ascent.

(1) For multiengine rotorcraft for which the use of 2½ minute OEI power is requested, 12 runs during the 10-hour test must be conducted as follows:

(i)   Each run must consist of at least one period of 2½ minutes with takeoff torque and the maximum speed for use with takeoff torque on all engines.

(ii) Each run must consist of at least one period for each engine in sequence, during which that engine simulates a power failure and the remaining engines are run at 2½ minute OEI torque and the maximum speed for use with 2½ minute OEI torque for 2½ minutes.

(2) For multiengine turbine-powered rotorcraft for which the use of 30-second and 2-minute OEI power is requested, 10 runs must be conducted as follows:

(i) Immediately following a takeoff run of at least 5 minutes, each power source must simulate a failure, in turn, and apply the maximum torque and the maximum speed for use with 30-second OEI power to the remaining affected drive system power inputs for not less than 30 seconds, followed by application of the maximum torque and the maximum speed for use with 2-minute OEI power for not less than 2 minutes. At least one run sequence must be conducted from a simulated "flight idle" condition. When conducted on a bench test, the test sequence must be conducted following stabilization at takeoff power.

(ii) For the purpose of this paragraph, an affected power input includes all parts of the rotor drive system which can be adversely affected by the application of higher or asymmetric torque and speed prescribed by the test.

(iii) This test may be conducted on a representative bench test facility when engine limitations either preclude repeated use of this power or would result in premature engine removal during the test. The loads, the vibration frequency, and the methods of application to the affected rotor drive system components must be representative of rotorcraft conditions. Test components must be those used to show compliance with the remainder of this section.

(f) The parts of the test prescribed in paragraphs (c) and (d) of this section must be conducted in intervals of not less than 30 minutes and may be accomplished either on the ground or in flight. The part of the test prescribed in paragraph (e) of this section must be conducted in intervals of not less than five minutes.

(g) At intervals of not more than five hours during the tests prescribed in paragraphs (c), (d), and (e) of this section, the engine must be stopped rapidly enough to allow the engine and rotor drive to be automatically disengaged from the rotors.

(h) Under the operating conditions specified in paragraph (c) of this section, 500 complete cycles of lateral control, 500 complete cycles of longitudinal control of the main rotors, and 500 complete cycles of control of each auxiliary rotor must be accomplished. A "complete cycle" involves movement of the controls from the neutral position, through both extreme positions, and back to the neutral position, except that control movements need not produce loads or flapping motions exceeding the maximum loads or motions encountered in flight. The cycling may be accomplished during the testing prescribed in paragraph (c) of this section.

(i) At least 200 start-up clutch engagements must be accomplished—

(1) So that the shaft on the driven side of the clutch is accelerated; and

(2) Using a speed and method selected by the applicant.

(j) For multiengine rotorcraft for which the use of 30-minute OEI power is requested, five runs must be made at 30-minute OEI torque and the maximum speed for use with 30-minute OEI torque, in which each engine, in sequence, is made inoperative and the remaining engine(s) is run for a 30-minute period.

(k) For multiengine rotorcraft for which the use of continuous OEI power is requested, five runs must be made at continuous OEI torque and the maximum speed for use with continuous OEI torque, in which each engine, in sequence, is made inoperative and the remaining engine(s) is run for a 1-hour period.

(Secs. 313(a), 601, and 603, 72 Stat. 752, 775, 49 U.S.C. 1354(a), 1421, and 1423; sec. 6(c), 49 U.S.C. 1655(c))

[Doc. No. 5074, 29 FR 15695, Nov. 24, 1964, as amended by Amdt. 27–2, 33 FR 963, Jan. 26, 1968; Amdt. 27–12, 42 FR 15044, Mar. 17, 1977; Amdt. 27–23, 53 FR 34212, Sept. 2, 1988; Amdt. 27–29, 59 FR 47767, Sept. 16, 1994]

27.927 Additional tests

(a) Any additional dynamic, endurance, and operational tests, and vibratory investigations necessary to determine that the rotor drive mechanism is safe, must be performed.

(b) If turbine engine torque output to the transmission can exceed the highest engine or transmission torque rating limit, and that output is not directly controlled by the pilot under normal operating conditions (such as where the primary engine power control is accomplished through the flight control), the following test must be made:

(1) Under conditions associated with all engines operating, make 200 applications, for 10 seconds each, or torque that is at least equal to the lesser of—

(i) The maximum torque used in meeting 27.923 plus 10 percent; or

(ii) The maximum attainable torque output of the engines, assuming that torque limiting devices, if any, function properly.

(2) For multiengine rotorcraft under conditions associated with each engine, in turn, becoming inoperative, apply to the remaining transmission torque inputs the maximum torque attainable under probable operating conditions, assuming that torque limiting devices, if any, function properly. Each transmission input must be tested at this maximum torque for at least 15 minutes.

(3) The tests prescribed in this paragraph must be conducted on the rotorcraft at the maximum rotational speed intended for the power condition of the test and the torque must be absorbed by the rotors to be installed, except that other ground or flight test facilities with other appropriate methods of torque absorption may be used if the conditions of support and vibration closely simulate the conditions that would exist during a test on the rotorcraft.

(c) It must be shown by tests that the rotor drive system is capable of operating under autorotative conditions for 15 minutes after the loss of pressure in the rotor drive primary oil system.

(Secs. 313(a), 601, and 603, 72 Stat. 752, 775, 49 U.S.C. 1354(a), 1421, and 1423; sec. 6(c), 49 U.S.C. 1655(c))

[Amdt. 27–2, 33 FR 963, Jan. 26, 1968, as amended by Amdt. 27–12, 42 FR 15045, Mar. 17, 1977; Amdt. 27–23, 53 FR 34212, Sept. 2, 1988]

27.931 Shafting critical speed

(a) The critical speeds of any shafting must be determined by demonstration except that analytical methods may be used if reliable methods of analysis are available for the particular design.

(b) If any critical speed lies within, or close to, the operating ranges for idling, power on, and autorotative conditions, the stresses occurring at that speed must be within safe limits. This must be shown by tests.

(c) If analytical methods are used and show that no critical speed lies within the permissible operating ranges, the margins between the calculated critical speeds and the limits of the allowable operating ranges must be adequate to allow for possible variations between the computed and actual values.

27.935 Shafting joints

Each universal joint, slip joint, and other shafting joints whose lubrication is necessary for operation must have provision for lubrication.

27.939 Turbine engine operating characteristics

(a) Turbine engine operating characteristics must be investigated in flight to determine that no adverse characteristics (such as stall, surge, or flameout) are present, to a hazardous degree, during normal and emergency operation within the range of operating limitations of the rotorcraft and of the engine.

(b) The turbine engine air inlet system may not, as a result of airflow distortion during normal operation, cause vibration harmful to the engine.

(c) For governor-controlled engines, it must be shown that there exists no hazardous torsional instability of the drive system associated with critical combinations of power, rotational speed, and control displacement.

[Amdt. 27–1, 32 FR 6914, May 5, 1967, as amended by Amdt. 27–11, 41 FR 55469, Dec. 20, 1976]

Fuel System

27.951 General

(a) Each fuel system must be constructed and arranged to ensure a flow of fuel at a rate and pressure established for proper engine functioning under any likely operating condition, including the maneuvers for which certification is requested.

(b) Each fuel system must be arranged so that—

(1) No fuel pump can draw fuel from more than one tank at a time; or

(2) There are means to prevent introducing air into the system.

(c) Each fuel system for a turbine engine must be capable of sustained operation throughout its flow and pressure range with fuel initially saturated with water at 80 °F. and having 0.75cc of free water per gallon added and cooled to the most critical condition for icing likely to be encountered in operation.

[Doc. No. 5074, 29 FR 15695, Nov. 24, 1964, as amended by Amdt. 27–9, 39 FR 35461, Oct. 1, 1974]

27.952 Fuel system crash resistance

Unless other means acceptable to the Administrator are employed to minimize the hazard of fuel fires to occupants following an otherwise survivable impact (crash landing), the fuel systems must incorporate the design features of this section. These systems must be shown to be capable of sustaining the static and dynamic deceleration loads of this section, considered as ultimate loads acting alone, measured at the system component's center of gravity, without structural damage to system components, fuel tanks, or their attachments that would leak fuel to an ignition source.

(a) Drop test requirements. Each tank, or the most critical tank, must be drop-tested as follows:

(1) The drop height must be at least 50 feet.

(2) The drop impact surface must be nondeforming.

(3) The tank must be filled with water to 80 percent of the normal, full capacity.

(4) The tank must be enclosed in a surrounding structure representative of the installation unless it can be established that the surrounding structure is free of projections or other design features likely to contribute to rupture of the tank.

(5) The tank must drop freely and impact in a horizontal position ±10°.

(6) After the drop test, there must be no leakage.

(b) Fuel tank load factors. Except for fuel tanks located so that tank rupture with fuel release to either significant ignition sources, such as engines, heaters, and auxiliary power units, or occupants is extremely remote, each fuel tank must be designed and installed to retain its contents under the following ultimate inertial load factors, acting alone.

(1) For fuel tanks in the cabin:

(i) Upward—4g.

(ii) Forward—16g.

(iii) Sideward—8g.

(iv) Downward—20g.

(2) For fuel tanks located above or behind the crew or passenger compartment that, if loosened, could injure an occupant in an emergency landing:

(i) Upward—1.5g.

(ii) Forward—8g.

(iii) Sideward—2g.

(iv) Downward—4g.

(3) For fuel tanks in other areas:

(i) Upward—1.5g.

(ii) Forward—4g.

(iii) Sideward—2g.

(iv) Downward—4g.

(c) Fuel line self-sealing breakaway couplings. Self-sealing breakaway couplings must be installed unless hazardous relative motion of fuel system components to each other or to local rotorcraft structure is demonstrated to be extremely improbable or unless other means are provided. The couplings or equivalent devices must be installed at all fuel tank-to-fuel line connections, tank-to-tank interconnects, and at other points in the fuel system where local structural deformation could lead to the release of fuel.

(1) The design and construction of self-sealing breakaway couplings must incorporate the following design features:

(i) The load necessary to separate a breakaway coupling must be between 25 to 50 percent of the minimum ultimate failure load (ultimate strength) of the weakest component in the fluid-carrying line. The separation load must in no case be less than 300 pounds, regardless of the size of the fluid line.

(ii) A breakaway coupling must separate whenever its ultimate load (as defined in paragraph (c)(1)(i) of this section) is applied in the failure modes most likely to occur.

(iii) All breakaway couplings must incorporate design provisions to visually ascertain that the coupling is locked together (leak-free) and is open during normal installation and service.

(iv) All breakaway couplings must incorporate design provisions to prevent uncoupling or unintended closing due to operational shocks, vibrations, or accelerations.

(v) No breakaway coupling design may allow the release of fuel once the coupling has performed its intended function.

(2) All individual breakaway couplings, coupling fuel feed systems, or equivalent means must be designed, tested, installed, and maintained so that inadvertent fuel shutoff in flight is improbable in accordance with 27.955(a) and must comply with the fatigue evaluation requirements of 27.571 without leaking.

(3) Alternate, equivalent means to the use of breakaway couplings must not create a survivable impact-induced load on the fuel line to which it is installed greater than 25 to 50 percent of the ultimate load (strength) of the weakest component in the line and must comply with the fatigue requirements of 27.571 without leaking.

(d) Frangible or deformable structural attachments. Unless hazardous relative motion of fuel tanks and fuel system components to local rotorcraft structure is demonstrated to be extremely improbable in an otherwise survivable impact, frangible or locally deformable attachments of fuel tanks and fuel system components to local rotorcraft structure must be used. The attachment of fuel tanks and fuel system components to local rotorcraft structure, whether frangible or locally deformable, must be designed such that its separation or relative local deformation will occur without rupture or local tear-out of the fuel tank or fuel system components that will cause fuel leakage. The ultimate strength of frangible or deformable attachments must be as follows:

(1) The load required to separate a frangible attachment from its support structure, or deform a locally deformable attachment relative to its support structure, must be between 25 and 50 percent of the minimum ultimate load (ultimate strength) of the weakest component in the attached system. In no case may the load be less than 300 pounds.

(2) A frangible or locally deformable attachment must separate or locally deform as intended whenever its ultimate load (as defined in paragraph (d)(1) of this section) is applied in the modes most likely to occur.

(3) All frangible or locally deformable attachments must comply with the fatigue requirements of 27.571.

(e) *Separation of fuel and ignition sources.* To provide maximum crash resistance, fuel must be located as far as practicable from all occupiable areas and from all potential ignition sources.

(f) *Other basic mechanical design criteria.* Fuel tanks, fuel lines, electrical wires, and electrical devices must be designed, constructed, and installed, as far as practicable, to be crash resistant.

(g) *Rigid or semirigid fuel tanks.* Rigid or semirigid fuel tank or bladder walls must be impact and tear resistant.

[Doc. No. 26352, 59 FR 50386, Oct. 3, 1994]

27.953 Fuel system independence

(a) Each fuel system for multiengine rotorcraft must allow fuel to be supplied to each engine through a system independent of those parts of each system supplying fuel to other engines. However, separate fuel tanks need not be provided for each engine.

(b) If a single fuel tank is used on a multiengine rotorcraft, the following must be provided:

(1) Independent tank outlets for each engine, each incorporating a shutoff valve at the tank. This shutoff valve may also serve as the firewall shutoff valve required by 27.995 if the line between the valve and the engine compartment does not contain a hazardous amount of fuel that can drain into the engine compartment.

(2) At least two vents arranged to minimize the probability of both vents becoming obstructed simultaneously.

(3) Filler caps designed to minimize the probability of incorrect installation or inflight loss.

(4) A fuel system in which those parts of the system from each tank outlet to any engine are independent of each part of each system supplying fuel to other engines.

27.954 Fuel system lightning protection

The fuel system must be designed and arranged to prevent the ignition of fuel vapor within the system by—

(a) Direct lightning strikes to areas having a high probability of stroke attachment;

(b) Swept lightning strokes to areas where swept strokes are highly probable; or

(c) Corona and streamering at fuel vent outlets.

[Amdt. 27–23, 53 FR 34212, Sept. 2, 1988]

27.955 Fuel flow

(a) *General.* The fuel system for each engine must be shown to provide the engine with at least 100 percent of the fuel required under each operating and maneuvering condition to be approved for the rotorcraft including, as applicable, the fuel required to operate the engine(s) under the test conditions required by 27.927. Unless equivalent methods are used, compliance must be shown by test during which the following provisions are met except that combinations of conditions which are shown to be improbable need not be considered.

(1) The fuel pressure, corrected for critical accelerations, must be within the limits specified by the engine type certificate data sheet.

(2) The fuel level in the tank may not exceed that established as the unusable fuel supply for that tank under 27.959, plus the minimum additional fuel necessary to conduct the test.

(3) The fuel head between the tank outlet and the engine inlet must be critical with respect to rotorcraft flight attitudes.

(4) The critical fuel pump (for pump-fed systems) is installed to produce (by actual or simulated failure) the critical restriction to fuel flow to be expected from pump failure.

(5) Critical values of engine rotation speed, electrical power, or other sources of fuel pump motive power must be applied.

(6) Critical values of fuel properties which adversely affect fuel flow must be applied.

(7) The fuel filter required by 27.997 must be blocked to the degree necessary to simulate the accumulation of fuel contamination required to activate the indicator required by 27.1305(q).

(b) *Fuel transfer systems.* If normal operation of the fuel system requires fuel to be transferred to an engine feed tank, the transfer must occur automatically via a system which has been shown to maintain the fuel level in the engine feed tank within acceptable limits during flight or surface operation of the rotorcraft.

(c) *Multiple fuel tanks.* If an engine can be supplied with fuel from more than one tank, the fuel systems must, in addition to having appropriate manual switching capability, be designed to prevent interruption of fuel flow to that engine, without attention by the flightcrew, when any tank supplying fuel to that engine is depleted of usable fuel during normal operation, and any other tank that normally supplies fuel to the engine alone contains usable fuel.

[Amdt. 27–23, 53 FR 34212, Sept. 2, 1988]

27.959 Unusable fuel supply

The unusable fuel supply for each tank must be established as not less than the quantity at which the first evidence of malfunction occurs under the most adverse fuel feed condition occurring under any intended operations and flight maneuvers involving that tank.

27.961 Fuel system hot weather operation

Each suction lift fuel system and other fuel systems with features conducive to vapor formation must be shown by test to operate satisfactorily (within certification limits) when using fuel at a temperature of 110°F under critical operating conditions including, if applicable, the engine operating conditions defined by 27.927 (b)(1) and (b)(2).

[Amdt. 27–23, 53 FR 34212, Sept. 2, 1988]

27.963 Fuel tanks: general

(a) Each fuel tank must be able to withstand, without failure, the vibration, inertia, fluid, and structural loads to which it may be subjected in operation.

(b) Each fuel tank of 10 gallons or greater capacity must have internal baffles, or must have external support to resist surging.

(c) Each fuel tank must be separated from the engine compartment by a firewall. At least one-half inch of clear airspace must be provided between the tank and the firewall.

(d) Spaces adjacent to the surfaces of fuel tanks must be ventilated so that fumes cannot accumulate in the tank compartment in case of leakage. If two or more tanks have interconnected outlets, they must be considered as one tank, and the airspaces in those tanks must be interconnected to prevent the flow of fuel from one tank to another as a result of a difference in pressure between those airspaces.

(e) The maximum exposed surface temperature of any component in the fuel tank must be less, by a safe margin as determined by the Administrator, than the lowest expected autoignition temperature of the fuel or fuel vapor in the tank. Compliance with this requirement must be shown under all operating conditions and under all failure or malfunction conditions of all components inside the tank.

(f) Each fuel tank installed in personnel compartments must be isolated by fume-proof and fuel-proof enclosures that are drained and vented to the exterior of the rotorcraft. The design and construction of the enclosures must provide necessary protection for the tank, must be crash resistant during a survivable impact in accordance with 27.952, and must be adequate to withstand loads and abrasions to be expected in personnel compartments.

(g) Each flexible fuel tank bladder or liner must be approved or shown to be suitable for the particular application and must be puncture resistant. Puncture resistance must be shown by meeting the TSO-C80, paragraph 16.0, requirements using a minimum puncture force of 370 pounds.

(h) Each integral fuel tank must have provisions for inspection and repair of its interior.

[Doc. No. 5074, 29 FR 15695, Nov. 24, 1964, as amended by Amdt. 27–23, 53 FR 34213, Sept. 2, 1988; Amdt. 27–30, 59 FR 50387, Oct. 3, 1994]

27.965 Fuel tank tests

(a) Each fuel tank must be able to withstand the applicable pressure tests in this section without failure or leakage. If practicable, test pressures may be applied in a manner simulating the pressure distribution in service.

(b) Each conventional metal tank, nonmetallic tank with walls that are not supported by the rotorcraft structure, and integral tank must be subjected to a pressure of 3.5 p.s.i. unless the pressure developed during maximum limit acceleration or emergency deceleration with a full tank exceeds this value, in which case a hydrostatic head, or equivalent test, must be applied to duplicate the acceleration loads as far as possible. However, the pressure need not exceed 3.5 p.s.i. on surfaces not exposed to the acceleration loading.

(c) Each nonmetallic tank with walls supported by the rotorcraft structure must be subjected to the following tests:

(1) A pressure test of at least 2.0 p.s.i. This test may be conducted on the tank alone in conjunction with the test specified in paragraph (c)(2) of this section.

(2) A pressure test, with the tank mounted in the rotorcraft structure, equal to the load developed by the reaction of the contents, with the tank full, during maximum limit acceleration or emergency deceleration. However, the pressure need not exceed 2.0 p.s.i. on surfaces not exposed to the acceleration loading.

(d) Each tank with large unsupported or unstiffened flat areas, or with other features whose failure or deformation could cause leakage, must be subjected to the following test or its equivalent:

(1) Each complete tank assembly and its support must be vibration tested while mounted to simulate the actual installation.

(2) The tank assembly must be vibrated for 25 hours while two-thirds full of any suitable fluid. The amplitude of vibration may not be less than one thirty-second of an inch, unless otherwise substantiated.

(3) The test frequency of vibration must be as follows:

(i) If no frequency of vibration resulting from any r.p.m. within the normal operating range of engine or rotor system speeds is critical, the test frequency of vibration, in number of cycles per minute must, unless a frequency based on a more rational calculation is used, be the number obtained by averaging the maximum and minimum power-on engine speeds (r.p.m.) for reciprocating engine powered rotorcraft or 2,000 c.p.m. for turbine engine powered rotorcraft.

(ii) If only one frequency of vibration resulting from any r.p.m. within the normal operating range of engine or rotor system speeds is critical, that frequency of vibration must be the test frequency.

(iii) If more than one frequency of vibration resulting from any r.p.m. within the normal operating range of engine or rotor system speeds is critical, the most critical of these frequencies must be the test frequency.

(4) Under paragraphs (d)(3)(ii) and (iii) of this section, the time of test must be adjusted to accomplish the same number of vibration cycles as would be accomplished in 25 hours at the frequency specified in paragraph (d)(3)(i) of this section.

(5) During the test, the tank assembly must be rocked at the rate of 16 to 20 complete cycles per minute through an angle of 15 degrees on both sides of the horizontal (30 degrees total), about the most critical axis, for 25 hours. If motion about more than one axis is likely to be critical, the tank must be rocked about each critical axis for 121/2 hours.

(Secs. 313(a), 601, and 603, 72 Stat. 752, 775, 49 U.S.C. 1354(a), 1421, and 1423; sec. 6(c), 49 U.S.C. 1655(c))
[Amdt. 27–12, 42 FR 15045, Mar. 17, 1977]

27.967 Fuel tank installation

(a) Each fuel tank must be supported so that tank loads are not concentrated on unsupported tank surfaces. In addition—

(1) There must be pads, if necessary, to prevent chafing between each tank and its supports;

(2) The padding must be nonabsorbent or treated to prevent the absorption of fuel;

(3) If flexible tank liners are used, they must be supported so that it is not necessary for them to withstand fluid loads; and

(4) Each interior surface of tank compartments must be smooth and free of projections that could cause wear of the liner unless—

(i) There are means for protection of the liner at those points; or

(ii) The construction of the liner itself provides such protection.

(b) Any spaces adjacent to tank surfaces must be adequately ventilated to avoid accumulation of fuel or fumes in those spaces due to minor leakage. If the tank is in a sealed compartment, ventilation may be limited to drain holes that prevent clogging and excessive pressure resulting from altitude changes. If flexible tank liners are installed, the venting arrangement for the spaces between the liner and its container must maintain the proper relationship to tank vent pressures for any expected flight condition.

(c) The location of each tank must meet the requirements of 27.1185 (a) and (c).

(d) No rotorcraft skin immediately adjacent to a major air outlet from the engine compartment may act as the wall of the integral tank.

[Doc. No. 26352, 59 FR 50387, Oct. 3, 1994]

27.969 Fuel tank expansion space

Each fuel tank or each group of fuel tanks with interconnected vent systems must have an expansion space of not less than 2 percent of the tank capacity. It must be impossible to fill the fuel tank expansion space inadvertently with the rotorcraft in the normal ground attitude.

[Amdt. 27–23, 53 FR 34213, Sept. 2, 1988]

27.971 Fuel tank sump

(a) Each fuel tank must have a drainable sump with an effective capacity in any ground attitude to be expected in service of 0.25 percent of the tank capacity or 1/16 gallon, whichever is greater, unless—

(1) The fuel system has a sediment bowl or chamber that is accessible for preflight drainage and has a minimum capacity of 1 ounce for every 20 gallons of fuel tank capacity; and

(2) Each fuel tank drain is located so that in any ground attitude to be expected in service, water will drain from all parts of the tank to the sediment bowl or chamber.

(b) Each sump, sediment bowl, and sediment chamber drain required by this section must comply with the drain provisions of 27.999(b).

[Amdt. 27–23, 53 FR 34213, Sept. 2, 1988]

27.973 Fuel tank filler connection

(a) Each fuel tank filler connection must prevent the entrance of fuel into any part of the rotorcraft other than the tank itself during normal operations and must be crash resistant during a survivable impact in accordance with 27.952(c). In addition—

(1) Each filler must be marked as prescribed in 27.1557(c)(1);

(2) Each recessed filler connection that can retain any appreciable quantity of fuel must have a drain that discharges clear of the entire rotorcraft; and

(3) Each filler cap must provide a fuel-tight seal under the fluid pressure expected in normal operation and in a survivable impact.

(b) Each filler cap or filler cap cover must warn when the cap is not fully locked or seated on the filler connection.

[Doc. No. 26352, 59 FR 50387, Oct. 3, 1994]

27.975 Fuel tank vents

(a) Each fuel tank must be vented from the top part of the expansion space so that venting is effective under all normal flight conditions. Each vent must minimize the probability of stoppage by dirt or ice.

(b) The venting system must be designed to minimize spillage of fuel through the vents to an ignition source in the event of a rollover during landing, ground operation, or a survivable impact.

[Doc. No. 5074, 29 FR 15695, Nov. 24, 1964, as amended by Amdt. 27–23, 53 FR 34213, Sept. 2, 1988; Amdt. 27–30, 59 FR 50387, Oct. 3, 1994; Amdt. 27–35, 63 FR 43285, Aug. 12, 1998]

27.977 Fuel tank outlet

(a) There must be a fuel stainer for the fuel tank outlet or for the booster pump. This strainer must—

(1) For reciprocating engine powered rotorcraft, have 8 to 16 meshes per inch; and

(2) For turbine engine powered rotorcraft, prevent the passage of any object that could restrict fuel flow or damage any fuel system component.

(b) The clear area of each fuel tank outlet strainer must be at least five times the area of the outlet line.

(c) The diameter of each strainer must be at least that of the fuel tank outlet.

(d) Each finger strainer must be accessible for inspection and cleaning.

[Amdt. 27–11, 41 FR 55470, Dec. 20, 1976]

Fuel System Components

27.991 Fuel pumps

Compliance with 27.955 may not be jeopardized by failure of—

(a) Any one pump except pumps that are approved and installed as parts of a type certificated engine; or

(b) Any component required for pump operation except, for engine driven pumps, the engine served by that pump.

[Amdt. 27–23, 53 FR 34213, Sept. 2, 1988]

27.993 Fuel system lines and fittings

(a) Each fuel line must be installed and supported to prevent excessive vibration and to withstand loads due to fuel pressure and accelerated flight conditions.

(b) Each fuel line connected to components of the rotorcraft between which relative motion could exist must have provisions for flexibility.

(c) Flexible hose must be approved.

(d) Each flexible connection in fuel lines that may be under pressure or subjected to axial loading must use flexible hose assemblies.

(e) No flexible hose that might be adversely affected by high temperatures may be used where excessive temperatures will exist during operation or after engine shutdown.

[Doc. No. 5074, 29 FR 15695, Nov. 24, 1964, as amended by Amdt. 27–2, 33 FR 964, Jan. 26, 1968]

27.995 Fuel valves

(a) There must be a positive, quick-acting valve to shut off fuel to each engine individually.

(b) The control for this valve must be within easy reach of appropriate crewmembers.

(c) Where there is more than one source of fuel supply there must be means for independent feeding from each source.

(d) No shutoff valve may be on the engine side of any firewall.

27.997 Fuel strainer or filter

There must be a fuel strainer or filter between the fuel tank outlet and the inlet of the first fuel system component which is susceptible to fuel contamination, including but not limited to the fuel metering device or an engine positive displacement pump, whichever is nearer the fuel tank outlet. This fuel strainer or filter must—

(a) Be accessible for draining and cleaning and must incorporate a screen or element which is easily removable;

(b) Have a sediment trap and drain except that it need not have a drain if the strainer or filter is easily removable for drain purposes;

(c) Be mounted so that its weight is not supported by the connecting lines or by the inlet or outlet connections of the strainer or filter itself, unless adequate strength margins under all loading conditions are provided in the lines and connections; and

(d) Provide a means to remove from the fuel any contaminant which would jeopardize the flow of fuel through rotorcraft or engine fuel system components required for proper rotorcraft fuel system or engine fuel system operation.

[Amdt. No. 27–9, 39 FR 35461, Oct. 1, 1974, as amended by Amdt. 27–20, 49 FR 6849, Feb. 23, 1984; Amdt. 27–23, 53 FR 34213, Sept. 2, 1988]

27.999 Fuel system drains

(a) There must be at least one accessible drain at the lowest point in each fuel system to completely drain the system with the rotorcraft in any ground attitude to be expected in service.

(b) Each drain required by paragraph (a) of this section must—

(1) Discharge clear of all parts of the rotorcraft;

(2) Have manual or automatic means to assure positive closure in the off position; and

(3) Have a drain valve—

(i) That is readily accessible and which can be easily opened and closed; and

(ii) That is either located or protected to prevent fuel spillage in the event of a landing with landing gear retracted.

[Doc. No. 574, 29 FR 15695, Nov. 24, 1964, as amended by Amdt. 27–11, 41 FR 55470, Dec. 20, 1976; Amdt. 27–23, 53 FR 34213, Sept. 2, 1988]

Oil System

27.1011 Engines: General

(a) Each engine must have an independent oil system that can supply it with an appropriate quantity of oil at a temperature not above that safe for continuous operation.

(b) The usable oil capacity of each system may not be less than the product of the endurance of the rotorcraft under critical operating conditions and the maximum oil consumption of the engine under the same conditions, plus a suitable margin to ensure adequate circulation and cooling. Instead of a rational analysis of endurance and consumption, a usable oil capacity of one gallon for each 40 gallons of usable fuel may be used.

(c) The oil cooling provisions for each engine must be able to maintain the oil inlet temperature to that engine at or below the maximum established value. This must be shown by flight tests.

[Doc. No. 5074, 29 FR 15695, Nov. 24, 1964, as amended by Amdt. 27–23, 53 FR 34213, Sept. 2, 1988]

27.1013 Oil tanks

Each oil tank must be designed and installed so that—

(a) It can withstand, without failure, each vibration, inertia, fluid, and structural load expected in operation;

(b) [Reserved]

(c) Where used with a reciprocating engine, it has an expansion space of not less than the greater of 10 percent of the tank capacity or 0.5 gallon, and where used with a turbine engine, it has an expansion space of not less than 10 percent of the tank capacity.

(d) It is impossible to fill the tank expansion space inadvertently with the rotorcraft in the normal ground attitude;

(e) Adequate venting is provided; and

(f) There are means in the filler opening to prevent oil overflow from entering the oil tank compartment.

[Doc. No. 5074, 29 FR 15695, Nov. 24, 1964, as amended by Amdt. 27–9, 39 FR 35461, Oct. 1, 1974]

FAR 27

27.1015 Oil tank tests

Each oil tank must be designed and installed so that it can withstand, without leakage, an internal pressure of 5 p.s.i., except that each pressurized oil tank used with a turbine engine must be designed and installed so that it can withstand, without leakage, an internal pressure of 5 p.s.i., plus the maximum operating pressure of the tank.

[Amdt. 27–9, 39 FR 35462, Oct. 1, 1974]

27.1017 Oil lines and fittings

(a) Each oil line must be supported to prevent excessive vibration.

(b) Each oil line connected to components of the rotorcraft between which relative motion could exist must have provisions for flexibility.

(c) Flexible hose must be approved.

(d) Each oil line must have an inside diameter of not less than the inside diameter of the engine inlet or outlet. No line may have splices between connections.

27.1019 Oil strainer or filter

(a) Each turbine engine installation must incorporate an oil strainer or filter through which all of the engine oil flows and which meets the following requirements:

(1) Each oil strainer or filter that has a bypass must be constructed and installed so that oil will flow at the normal rate through the rest of the system with the strainer or filter completely blocked.

(2) The oil strainer or filter must have the capacity (with respect to operating limitations established for the engine) to ensure that engine oil system functioning is not impaired when the oil is contaminated to a degree (with respect to particle size and density) that is greater than that established for the engine under Part 33 of this chapter.

(3) The oil strainer or filter, unless it is installed at an oil tank outlet, must incorporate a means to indicate contamination before it reaches the capacity established in accordance with paragraph (a)(2) of this section.

(4) The bypass of a strainer or filter must be constructed and installed so that the release of collected contaminants is minimized by appropriate location of the bypass to ensure that collected contaminants are not in the bypass flow path.

(5) An oil strainer or filter that has no bypass, except one that is installed at an oil tank outlet, must have a means to connect it to the warning system required in 27.1305(r).

(b) Each oil strainer or filter in a powerplant installation using reciprocating engines must be constructed and installed so that oil will flow at the normal rate through the rest of the system with the strainer or filter element completely blocked.

[Amdt. 27–9, 39 FR 35462, Oct. 1, 1974, as amended by Amdt. 27–20, 49 FR 6849, Feb. 23, 1984; Amdt. 27–23, 53 FR 34213, Sept. 2, 1988]

27.1021 Oil system drains

A drain (or drains) must be provided to allow safe drainage of the oil system. Each drain must—

(a) Be accessible; and

(b) Have manual or automatic means for positive locking in the closed position.

[Amdt. 27–20, 49 FR 6849, Feb. 23, 1984]

27.1027 Transmissions and gearboxes: General

(a) The lubrication system for components of the rotor drive system that require continuous lubrication must be sufficiently independent of the lubrication systems of the engine(s) to ensure lubrication during autorotation.

(b) Pressure lubrication systems for transmissions and gearboxes must comply with the engine oil system requirements of 27.1013 (except paragraph (c)), 27.1015, 27.1017, 27.1021, and 27.1337(d).

(c) Each pressure lubrication system must have an oil strainer or filte through which all of the lubricant flows and must—

(1) Be designed to remove from the lubricant any contaminan which may damage transmission and drive system compo nents or impede the flow of lubricant to a hazardous degree;

(2) Be equipped with a means to indicate collection of contami nants on the filter or strainer at or before opening of the bypas required by paragraph (c)(3) of this section; and

(3) Be equipped with a bypass constructed and installed so that—

(i)   The lubricant will flow at the normal rate through the rest of the system with the strainer or filter completely blocked; and

(ii) The release of collected contaminants is minimized by appropriate location of the bypass to ensure that collected contaminants are not in the bypass flowpath.

(d) For each lubricant tank or sump outlet supplying lubrication to rotor drive systems and rotor drive system components, a screen must be provided to prevent entrance into the lubrication system of any object that might obstruct the flow of lubricant from the outlet to the filter required by paragraph (c) of this section. The requirements of paragraph (c) do not apply to screens installed a lubricant tank or sump outlets.

(e) Splash-type lubrication systems for rotor drive system gearboxes must comply with 27.1021 and 27.1337(d).

[Amdt. 27–23, 53 FR 34213, Sept. 2, 1988, as amended by Amdt 27–37, 64 FR 45095, Aug. 18, 1999]

Cooling

27.1041 General

(a) Each powerplant cooling system must be able to maintain the temperatures of powerplant components within the limits established for these components under critical surface (ground or water) and flight operating conditions for which certification is required and after normal shutdown. Powerplant components to be considered include but may not be limited to engines, roto drive system components, auxiliary power units, and the cooling or lubricating fluids used with these components.

(b) Compliance with paragraph (a) of this section must be shown in tests conducted under the conditions prescribed in that paragraph

[Doc. No. 5074, 29 FR 15695, Nov. 24, 1964, as amended by Amdt 27–23, 53 FR 34213, Sept. 2, 1988]

27.1043 Cooling tests

(a) General. For the tests prescribed in 27.1041(b), the following apply:

(1) If the tests are conducted under conditions deviating from the maximum ambient atmospheric temperature specified in paragraph (b) of this section, the recorded powerplant temperatures must be corrected under paragraphs (c) and (d) of this section unless a more rational correction method is applicable.

(2) No corrected temperature determined under paragraph (a)(1) of this section may exceed established limits.

(3) For reciprocating engines, the fuel used during the cooling tests must be of the minimum grade approved for the engines, and the mixture settings must be those normally used in the flight stages for which the cooling tests are conducted.

(4) The test procedures must be as prescribed in 27.1045.

(b) Maximum ambient atmospheric temperature. A maximum ambient atmospheric temperature corresponding to sea level conditions of at least 100 degrees F. must be established. The assumed temperature lapse rate is 3.6 degrees F. per thousand feet of altitude above sea level until a temperature of −69.7 degrees F. is reached, above which altitude the temperature is considered constant at −69.7 degrees F. However, for winterization installations, the applicant may select a maximum ambient atmospheric temperature corresponding to sea level conditions of less than 100 degrees F.

(c) Correction factor (except cylinder barrels). Unless a more rational correction applies, temperatures of engine fluids and powerplant components (except cylinder barrels) for which temperature limits are established, must be corrected by adding to them the difference between the maximum ambient atmospheric temperature and the temperature of the ambient air at the time of the first occurrence of the maximum component or fluid temperature recorded during the cooling test.

(d) Correction factor for cylinder barrel temperatures. Cylinder barrel temperatures must be corrected by adding to them 0.7 times the difference between the maximum ambient atmospheric temperature and the temperature of the ambient air at the time of the first occurrence of the maximum cylinder barrel temperature recorded during the cooling test.

(Secs. 313(a), 601, 603, 604, and 605 of the Federal Aviation Act of 1958 (49 U.S.C. 1354(a), 1421, 1423, 1424, and 1425); and sec. 6(c) of the Dept. of Transportation Act (49 U.S.C. 1655(c)))

[Doc. No. 5074, 29 FR 15695, Nov. 24, 1964, as amended by Amdt. 27–11, 41 FR 55470, Dec. 20, 1976; Amdt. 27–14, 43 FR 2325, Jan. 16, 1978]

27.1045 Cooling test procedures

(a) General. For each stage of flight, the cooling tests must be conducted with the rotorcraft—

(1) In the configuration most critical for cooling; and

(2) Under the conditions most critical for cooling.

(b) Temperature stabilization. For the purpose of the cooling tests, a temperature is "stabilized" when its rate of change is less than two degrees F. per minute. The following component and engine fluid temperature stabilization rules apply:

(1) For each rotorcraft, and for each stage of flight—

(i) The temperatures must be stabilized under the conditions from which entry is made into the stage of flight being investigated; or

(ii) If the entry condition normally does not allow temperatures to stabilize, operation through the full entry condition must be conducted before entry into the stage of flight being investigated in order to allow the temperatures to attain their natural levels at the time of entry.

(2) For each helicopter during the takeoff stage of flight, the climb at takeoff power must be preceded by a period of hover during which the temperatures are stabilized.

(c) Duration of test. For each stage of flight the tests must be continued until—

(1) The temperatures stabilize or 5 minutes after the occurrence of the highest temperature recorded, as appropriate to the test condition;

(2) That stage of flight is completed; or

(3) An operating limitation is reached.

[Doc. No. 5074, 29 FR 15695, Nov. 24, 1964, as amended by Amdt. 27–23, 53 FR 34214, Sept. 2, 1988]

Induction System

27.1091 Air induction

(a) The air induction system for each engine must supply the air required by that engine under the operating conditions and maneuvers for which certification is requested.

(b) Each cold air induction system opening must be outside the cowling if backfire flames can emerge.

(c) If fuel can accumulate in any air induction system, that system must have drains that discharge fuel—

(1) Clear of the rotorcraft; and

(2) Out of the path of exhaust flames.

(d) For turbine engine powered rotorcraft—

(1) There must be means to prevent hazardous quantities of fuel leakage or overflow from drains, vents, or other components of flammable fluid systems from entering the engine intake system; and

(2) The air inlet ducts must be located or protected so as to minimize the ingestion of foreign matter during takeoff, landing, and taxiing.

[Doc. No. 5074, 29 FR 15695, Nov. 24, 1964, as amended by Amdt. 27–2, 33 FR 964, Jan. 26, 1968; Amdt. 27–23, 53 FR 34214, Sept. 2, 1988]

27.1093 Induction system icing protection

(a) Reciprocating engines. Each reciprocating engine air induction system must have means to prevent and eliminate icing. Unless this is done by other means, it must be shown that, in air free of visible moisture at a temperature of 30 degrees F., and with the engines at 75 percent of maximum continuous power—

(1) Each rotorcraft with sea level engines using conventional venturi carburetors has a preheater that can provide a heat rise of 90 degrees F.;

(2) Each rotorcraft with sea level engines using carburetors tending to prevent icing has a sheltered alternate source of air, and that the preheat supplied to the alternate air intake is not less than that provided by the engine cooling air downstream of the cylinders;

(3) Each rotorcraft with altitude engines using conventional venturi carburetors has a preheater capable of providing a heat rise of 120 degrees F.; and

(4) Each rotorcraft with altitude engines using carburetors tending to prevent icing has a preheater that can provide a heat rise of—

(i) 100 degrees F.; or

(ii) If a fluid deicing system is used, at least 40 degrees F.

(b) Turbine engine.

(1) It must be shown that each turbine engine and its air inlet system can operate throughout the flight power range of the engine (including idling)—

(i) Without accumulating ice on engine or inlet system components that would adversely affect engine operation or cause a serious loss of power under the icing conditions specified in appendix C of Part 29 of this chapter; and

(ii) In snow, both falling and blowing, without adverse effect on engine operation, within the limitations established for the rotorcraft.

(2) Each turbine engine must idle for 30 minutes on the ground, with the air bleed available for engine icing protection at its critical condition, without adverse effect, in an atmosphere that is at a temperature between 15° and 30 °F (between −9° and −1 °C) and has a liquid water content not less than 0.3 gram per cubic meter in the form of drops having a mean effective diameter not less than 20 microns, followed by momentary operation at takeoff power or thrust. During the 30 minutes of idle operation, the engine may be run up periodically to a moderate power or thrust setting in a manner acceptable to the Administrator.

(c) Supercharged reciprocating engines. For each engine having superchargers to pressurize the air before it enters the carburetor, the heat rise in the air caused by that supercharging at any altitude may be utilized in determining compliance with paragraph (a) of this section if the heat rise utilized is that which will be available, automatically, for the applicable altitude and operating condition because of supercharging.

(Secs. 313(a), 601, and 603, 72 Stat. 752, 775, 49 U.S.C. 1354(a), 1421, and 1423; sec. 6(c), 49 U.S.C. 1655(c))

[Doc. No. 5074, 29 FR 15695, Nov. 24, 1964, as amended by Amdt. 27–11, 41 FR 55470, Dec. 20, 1976; Amdt. 27–12, 42 FR 15045, Mar. 17, 1977; Amdt. 27–20, 49 FR 6849, Feb. 23, 1984; Amdt. 27–23, 53 FR 34214, Sept. 2, 1988]

FAR 27

Exhaust System

27.1121 General

For each exhaust system—

(a) There must be means for thermal expansion of manifolds and pipes;

(b) There must be means to prevent local hot spots;

(c) Exhaust gases must discharge clear of the engine air intake, fuel system components, and drains;

(d) Each exhaust system part with a surface hot enough to ignite flammable fluids or vapors must be located or shielded so that leakage from any system carrying flammable fluids or vapors will not result in a fire caused by impingement of the fluids or vapors on any part of the exhaust system including shields for the exhaust system;

(e) Exhaust gases may not impair pilot vision at night due to glare;

(f) If significant traps exist, each turbine engine exhaust system must have drains discharging clear of the rotorcraft, in any normal ground and flight attitudes, to prevent fuel accumulation after the failure of an attempted engine start;

(g) Each exhaust heat exchanger must incorporate means to prevent blockage of the exhaust port after any internal heat exchanger failure.

(Secs. 313(a), 601, and 603, 72 Stat. 752, 775, 49 U.S.C. 1354(a), 1421, and 1423; sec. 6(c), 49 U.S.C. 1655(c))

[Doc. No. 5074, 29 FR 15695, Nov. 24, 1964 as amended by Amdt. 27–12, 42 FR 15045, Mar. 17, 1977]

27.1123 Exhaust piping

(a) Exhaust piping must be heat and corrosion resistant, and must have provisions to prevent failure due to expansion by operating temperatures.

(b) Exhaust piping must be supported to withstand any vibration and inertia loads to which it would be subjected in operations.

(c) Exhaust piping connected to components between which relative motion could exist must have provisions for flexibility.

[Amdt. 27–11, 41 FR 55470, Dec. 20, 1976]

Powerplant Controls and Accessories

27.1141 Powerplant controls: general

(a) Powerplant controls must be located and arranged under 27.777 and marked under 27.1555.

(b) Each flexible powerplant control must be approved.

(c) Each control must be able to maintain any set position without—

(1) Constant attention; or

(2) Tendency to creep due to control loads or vibration.

(d) Controls of powerplant valves required for safety must have—

(1) For manual valves, positive stops or in the case of fuel valves suitable index provisions, in the open and closed position; and

(2) For power-assisted valves, a means to indicate to the flight crew when the valve—

(i) Is in the fully open or fully closed position; or

(ii) Is moving between the fully open and fully closed position.

(e) For turbine engine powered rotorcraft, no single failure or malfunction, or probable combination thereof, in any powerplant control system may cause the failure of any powerplant function necessary for safety.

(Secs. 313(a), 601, and 603, 72 Stat. 752, 775, 49 U.S.C. 1354(a), 1421, and 1423; sec. 6(c), 49 U.S.C. 1655(c))

[Doc. No. 5074, 29 FR 15695, Nov. 24, 1964, as amended by Amdt. 27–12, 42 FR 15045, Mar. 17, 1977; Amdt. 27–23, 53 FR 34214, Sept. 2, 1988; Amdt. 27–33, 61 FR 21907, May 10, 1996]

27.1143 Engine controls

(a) There must be a separate power control for each engine.

(b) Power controls must be grouped and arranged to allow—

(1) Separate control of each engine; and

(2) Simultaneous control of all engines.

(c) Each power control must provide a positive and immediately responsive means of controlling its engine.

(d) If a power control incorporates a fuel shutoff feature, the control must have a means to prevent the inadvertent movement of the control into the shutoff position. The means must—

(1) Have a positive lock or stop at the idle position; and

(2) Require a separate and distinct operation to place the control in the shutoff position.

(e) For rotorcraft to be certificated for a 30-second OEI power rating, a means must be provided to automatically activate and control the 30-second OEI power and prevent any engine from exceeding the installed engine limits associated with the 30-second OEI power rating approved for the rotorcraft.

[Doc. No. 5074, 29 FR 15695, Nov. 24, 1964, as amended by Amdt. 27–11, 41 FR 55470, Dec. 20, 1976; Amdt. 27–23, 53 FR 34214, Sept. 2, 1988; Amdt. 27–29, 59 FR 47767, Sept. 16, 1994]

27.1145 Ignition switches

(a) There must be means to quickly shut off all ignition by the grouping of switches or by a master ignition control.

(b) Each group of ignition switches, except ignition switches for turbine engines for which continuous ignition is not required, and each master ignition control must have a means to prevent its inadvertent operation.

(Secs. 313(a), 601, and 603, 72 Stat. 752, 775, 49 U.S.C. 1354(a), 1421, and 1423; sec. 6(c), 49 U.S.C. 1655(c))

[Doc. No. 5074, 29 FR 15695, Nov. 24, 1964, as amended by Amdt. 27–12, 42 FR 15045, Mar. 17, 1977]

27.1147 Mixture controls

If there are mixture controls, each engine must have a separate control and the controls must be arranged to allow—

(a) Separate control of each engine; and

(b) Simultaneous control of all engines.

27.1151 Rotor brake controls

(a) It must be impossible to apply the rotor brake inadvertently in flight.

(b) There must be means to warn the crew if the rotor brake has not been completely released before takeoff.

[Doc. No. 28008, 61 FR 21907, May 10, 1996]

27.1163 Powerplant accessories

(a) Each engine-mounted accessory must—

(1) Be approved for mounting on the engine involved;

(2) Use the provisions on the engine for mounting; and

(3) Be sealed in such a way as to prevent contamination of the engine oil system and the accessory system.

(b) Unless other means are provided, torque limiting means must be provided for accessory drives located on any component of the transmission and rotor drive system to prevent damage to these components from excessive accessory load.

[Amdt. 27–2, 33 FR 964, Jan. 26, 1968, as amended by Amdt. 27–20, 49 FR 6849, Feb. 23, 1984; Amdt. 27–23, 53 FR 34214, Sept. 2, 1988]

Powerplant Fire Protection

27.1183 Lines, fittings, and components

(a) Except as provided in paragraph (b) of this section, each line, fitting, and other component carrying flammable fluid in any area subject to engine fire conditions must be fire resistant, except that flammable fluid tanks and supports which are part of and attached to the engine must be fireproof or be enclosed by a fireproof shield unless damage by fire to any non-fireproof part will not cause leakage or spillage of flammable fluid. Components must be shielded or located so as to safeguard against the ignition of leaking flammable fluid. An integral oil sump of less than 25-quart capacity on a reciprocating engine need not be fireproof nor be enclosed by a fireproof shield.

(b) Paragraph (a) does not apply to—

(1) Lines, fittings, and components which are already approved as part of a type certificated engine; and

(2) Vent and drain lines, and their fittings, whose failure will not result in, or add to, a fire hazard.

(c) Each flammable fluid drain and vent must discharge clear of the induction system air inlet.

[Doc. No. 5074, 29 FR 15695, Nov. 24, 1964, as amended by Amdt. 27–1, 32 FR 6914, May 5, 1967; Amdt. 27–9, 39 FR 35462, Oct. 1, 1974; Amdt. 27–20, 49 FR 6849, Feb. 23, 1984]

27.1185 Flammable fluids

(a) Each fuel tank must be isolated from the engines by a firewall or shroud.

(b) Each tank or reservoir, other than a fuel tank, that is part of a system containing flammable fluids or gases must be isolated from the engine by a firewall or shroud, unless the design of the system, the materials used in the tank and its supports, the shutoff means, and the connections, lines and controls provide a degree of safety equal to that which would exist if the tank or reservoir were isolated from the engines.

(c) There must be at least one-half inch of clear airspace between each tank and each firewall or shroud isolating that tank, unless equivalent means are used to prevent heat transfer from each engine compartment to the flammable fluid.

(d) Absorbent materials close to flammable fluid system components that might leak must be covered or treated to prevent the absorption of hazardous quantities of fluids.

[Doc. No. 5074, 29 FR 15695, Nov. 24, 1964, as amended by Amdt. 27–2, 33 FR 964, Jan. 26, 1968; Amdt. 27–11, 41 FR 55470, Dec. 20, 1976; Amdt. 27–37, 64 FR 45095, Aug. 18, 1999]

27.1187 Ventilation and drainage

Each compartment containing any part of the powerplant installation must have provision for ventilation and drainage of flammable fluids. The drainage means must be—

(a) Effective under conditions expected to prevail when drainage is needed, and

(b) Arranged so that no discharged fluid will cause an additional fire hazard.

[Doc. No. 29247, 64 FR 45095, Aug. 18, 1999]

27.1189 Shutoff means

(a) There must be means to shut off each line carrying flammable fluids into the engine compartment, except—

(1) Lines, fittings, and components forming an intergral part of an engine;

(2) For oil systems for which all components of the system, including oil tanks, are fireproof or located in areas not subject to engine fire conditions; and

(3) For reciprocating engine installations only, engine oil system lines in installation using engines of less than 500 cu. in. displacement.

(b) There must be means to guard against inadvertent operation of each shutoff, and to make it possible for the crew to reopen it in flight after it has been closed.

(c) Each shutoff valve and its control must be designed, located, and protected to function properly under any condition likely to result from an engine fire.

[Doc. No. 5074, 29 FR 15695, Nov. 24, 1964, as amended by Amdt. 27–2, 33 FR 964, Jan. 26, 1968; Amdt. 27–20, 49 FR 6850, Feb. 23, 1984; Amdt. 27–23, 53 FR 34214, Sept. 2, 1988]

27.1191 Firewalls

(a) Each engine, including the combustor, turbine, and tailpipe sections of turbine engines must be isolated by a firewall, shroud, or equivalent means, from personnel compartments, structures, controls, rotor mechanisms, and other parts that are—

(1) Essential to a controlled landing: and

(2) Not protected under 27.861.

(b) Each auxiliary power unit and combustion heater, and any other combustion equipment to be used in flight, must be isolated from the rest of the rotorcraft by firewalls, shrouds, or equivalent means.

(c) In meeting paragraphs (a) and (b) of this section, account must be taken of the probable path of a fire as affected by the airflow in normal flight and in autorotation.

(d) Each firewall and shroud must be constructed so that no hazardous quantity of air, fluids, or flame can pass from any engine compartment to other parts of the rotorcraft.

(e) Each opening in the firewall or shroud must be sealed with close-fitting, fireproof grommets, bushings, or firewall fittings.

(f) Each firewall and shroud must be fireproof and protected against corrosion.

[Doc. No. 5074, 29 FR 15695, Nov. 24, 1964, as amended by Amdt. 27–2, 22 FR 964, Jan. 26, 1968]

27.1193 Cowling and engine compartment covering

(a) Each cowling and engine compartment covering must be constructed and supported so that it can resist the vibration, inertia, and air loads to which it may be subjected in operation.

(b) There must be means for rapid and complete drainage of each part of the cowling or engine compartment in the normal ground and flight attitudes.

(c) No drain may discharge where it might cause a fire hazard.

(d) Each cowling and engine compartment covering must be at least fire resistant.

(e) Each part of the cowling or engine compartment covering subject to high temperatures due to its nearness to exhaust system parts or exhaust gas impingement must be fireproof.

(f) A means of retaining each openable or readily removable panel, cowling, or engine or rotor drive system covering must be provided to preclude hazardous damage to rotors or critical control components in the event of structural or mechanical failure of the normal retention means, unless such failure is extremely improbable.

[Doc. No. 5074, 29 FR 15695, Nov. 24, 1964, as amended by Amdt. 27–23, 53 FR 34214, Sept. 2, 1988]

27.1194 Other surfaces

All surfaces aft of, and near, powerplant compartments, other than tail surfaces not subject to heat, flames, or sparks emanating from a powerplant compartment, must be at least fire resistant.

[Amdt. 27–2, 33 FR 964, Jan. 26, 1968]

27.1195 Fire detector systems

Each turbine engine powered rotorcraft must have approved quick-acting fire detectors in numbers and locations insuring prompt detection of fire in the engine compartment which cannot be readily observed in flight by the pilot in the cockpit.

[Amdt. 27–5, 36 FR 5493, Mar. 24, 1971]

Subpart F — Equipment

General

27.1301 Function and installation

Each item of installed equipment must—

(a) Be of a kind and design appropriate to its intended function;

(b) Be labeled as to its identification, function, or operating limitations, or any applicable combination of these factors;

(c) Be installed according to limitations specified for that equipment; and

(d) Function properly when installed.

27.1303   Flight and navigation instruments

The following are the required flight and navigation instruments:

(a) An airspeed indicator.

(b) An altimeter.

(c) A magnetic direction indicator.

27.1305   Powerplant instruments

The following are the required powerplant instruments:

(a) A carburetor air temperature indicator, for each engine having a preheater that can provide a heat rise in excess of 60 °F.

(b) A cylinder head temperature indicator, for each—

   (1) Air cooled engine;

   (2) Rotorcraft with cooling shutters; and

   (3) Rotorcraft for which compliance with 27.1043 is shown in any condition other than the most critical flight condition with respect to cooling.

(c) A fuel pressure indicator, for each pump-fed engine.

(d) A fuel quantity indicator, for each fuel tank.

(e) A manifold pressure indicator, for each altitude engine.

(f) An oil temperature warning device to indicate when the temperature exceeds a safe value in each main rotor drive gearbox (including any gearboxes essential to rotor phasing) having an oil system independent of the engine oil system.

(g) An oil pressure warning device to indicate when the pressure falls below a safe value in each pressure-lubricated main rotor drive gearbox (including any gearboxes essential to rotor phasing) having an oil system independent of the engine oil system.

(h) An oil pressure indicator for each engine.

(i) An oil quantity indicator for each oil tank.

(j) An oil temperature indicator for each engine.

(k) At least one tachometer to indicate the r.p.m. of each engine and, as applicable—

   (1) The r.p.m. of the single main rotor;

   (2) The common r.p.m. of any main rotors whose speeds cannot vary appreciably with respect to each other; or

   (3) The r.p.m. of each main rotor whose speed can vary appreciably with respect to that of another main rotor.

(l) A low fuel warning device for each fuel tank which feeds an engine. This device must—

   (1) Provide a warning to the flightcrew when approximately 10 minutes of usable fuel remains in the tank; and

   (2) Be independent of the normal fuel quantity indicating system.

(m) Means to indicate to the flightcrew the failure of any fuel pump installed to show compliance with 27.955.

(n) A gas temperature indicator for each turbine engine.

(o) Means to enable the pilot to determine the torque of each turboshaft engine, if a torque limitation is established for that engine under 27.1521(e).

(p) For each turbine engine, an indicator to indicate the functioning of the powerplant ice protection system.

(q) An indicator for the fuel filter required by 27.997 to indicate the occurrence of contamination of the filter at the degree established by the applicant in compliance with 27.955.

(r) For each turbine engine, a warning means for the oil strainer or filter required by 27.1019, if it has no bypass, to warn the pilot of the occurrence of contamination of the strainer or filter before it reaches the capacity established in accordance with 27.1019(a)(2).

(s) An indicator to indicate the functioning of any selectable or controllable heater used to prevent ice clogging of fuel system components.

(t) For rotorcraft for which a 30-second/2-minute OEI power rating is requested, a means must be provided to alert the pilot when the engine is at the 30-second and the 2-minute OEI power levels, when the event begins, and when the time interval expires.

(u) For each turbine engine utilizing 30-second/2-minute OEI power, a device or system must be provided for use by ground personnel which—

   (1) Automatically records each usage and duration of power at the 30-second and 2-minute OEI levels;

   (2) Permits retrieval of the recorded data;

   (3) Can be reset only by ground maintenance personnel; and

   (4) Has a means to verify proper operation of the system or device.

(v) Warning or caution devices to signal to the flight crew when ferromagnetic particles are detected by the chip detector required by 27.1337(e).

[Doc. No. 5074, 29 FR 15695, Nov. 24, 1964, as amended by Amdt. 27–9, 39 FR 35462, Oct. 1, 1974; Amdt. 27–23, 53 FR 34214, Sept. 2, 1988; Amdt. 27–29, 59 FR 47767, Sept. 16, 1994; Amdt. 27–37, 64 FR 45095, Aug. 18, 1999; 64 FR 47563, Aug. 31, 1999]

27.1307   Miscellaneous equipment

The following is the required miscellaneous equipment:

(a) An approved seat for each occupant.

(b) An approved safety belt for each occupant.

(c) A master switch arrangement.

(d) An adequate source of electrical energy, where electrical energy is necessary for operation of the rotorcraft.

(e) Electrical protective devices.

27.1309   Equipment, systems, and installations

(a) The equipment, systems, and installations whose functioning is required by this subchapter must be designed and installed to ensure that they perform their intended functions under any foreseeable operating condition.

(b) The equipment, systems, and installations of a multiengine rotorcraft must be designed to prevent hazards to the rotorcraft in the event of a probable malfunction or failure.

(c) The equipment, systems, and installations of single-engine rotorcraft must be designed to minimize hazards to the rotorcraft in the event of a probable malfunction or failure.

[Doc. No. 5074, 29 FR 15695, Nov. 24, 1964, as amended by Amdt. 27–21, 49 FR 44435, Nov. 6, 1984; Amdt. 27–46, 76 FR 33135, June 8, 2011]

27.1316   Electrical and electronic system lightning protection

(a) Each electrical and electronic system that performs a function, for which failure would prevent the continued safe flight and landing of the rotorcraft, must be designed and installed so that—

   (1) The function is not adversely affected during and after the time the rotorcraft is exposed to lightning; and

   (2) The system automatically recovers normal operation of that function in a timely manner after the rotorcraft is exposed to lightning.

(b) For rotorcraft approved for instrument flight rules operation, each electrical and electronic system that performs a function, for which failure would reduce the capability of the rotorcraft or the ability of the flightcrew to respond to an adverse operating condition, must be designed and installed so that the function recovers normal operation in a timely manner after the rotorcraft is exposed to lightning.

[FAA–2010–0224, 76 FR 33135, June 8, 2011]

27.1317   High-intensity Radiated Fields (HIRF) Protection

(a) Except as provided in paragraph (d) of this section, each electrical and electronic system that performs a function whose failure would prevent the continued safe flight and landing of the rotorcraft must be designed and installed so that—

(1) The function is not adversely affected during and after the time the rotorcraft is exposed to HIRF environment I, as described in appendix D to this part;

(2) The system automatically recovers normal operation of that function, in a timely manner, after the rotorcraft is exposed to HIRF environment I, as described in appendix D to this part, unless this conflicts with other operational or functional requirements of that system;

(3) The system is not adversely affected during and after the time the rotorcraft is exposed to HIRF environment II, as described in appendix D to this part; and

(4) Each function required during operation under visual flight rules is not adversely affected during and after the time the rotorcraft is exposed to HIRF environment III, as described in appendix D to this part.

(b) Each electrical and electronic system that performs a function whose failure would significantly reduce the capability of the rotorcraft or the ability of the flightcrew to respond to an adverse operating condition must be designed and installed so the system is not adversely affected when the equipment providing these functions is exposed to equipment HIRF test level 1 or 2, as described in appendix D to this part.

(c) Each electrical and electronic system that performs a function whose failure would reduce the capability of the rotorcraft or the ability of the flightcrew to respond to an adverse operating condition, must be designed and installed so the system is not adversely affected when the equipment providing these functions is exposed to equipment HIRF test level 3, as described in appendix D to this part.

(d) Before December 1, 2012, an electrical or electronic system that performs a function whose failure would prevent the continued safe flight and landing of a rotorcraft may be designed and installed without meeting the provisions of paragraph (a) provided—

(1) The system has previously been shown to comply with special conditions for HIRF, prescribed under 21.16, issued before December 1, 2007;

(2) The HIRF immunity characteristics of the system have not changed since compliance with the special conditions was demonstrated; and

(3) The data used to demonstrate compliance with the special conditions is provided.

[Doc. No. FAA–2006–23657, 72 FR 44026, Aug. 6, 2007]

Instruments: Installation

27.1321   Arrangement and visibility

(a) Each flight, navigation, and powerplant instrument for use by any pilot must be easily visible to him.

(b) For each multiengine rotorcraft, identical powerplant instruments must be located so as to prevent confusion as to which engine each instrument relates.

(c) Instrument panel vibration may not damage, or impair the readability or accuracy of, any instrument.

(d) If a visual indicator is provided to indicate malfunction of an instrument, it must be effective under all probable cockpit lighting conditions.

(Secs. 313(a), 601, 603, 604, and 605 of the Federal Aviation Act of 1958 (49 U.S.C. 1354(a), 1421, 1423, 1424, and 1425); and sec. 6(c) of the Dept. of Transportation Act (49 U.S.C. 1655(c)))

[Doc. No. 5074, 29 FR 15695, Nov. 24, 1964; 29 FR 17885, Dec. 17, 1964, as amended by Amdt. 27–13, 42 FR 36971, July 18, 1977]

27.1322   Warning, caution, and advisory lights

If warning, caution or advisory lights are installed in the cockpit, they must, unless otherwise approved by the Administrator, be—

(a) Red, for warning lights (lights indicating a hazard which may require immediate corrective action):

(b) Amber, for caution lights (lights indicating the possible need for future corrective action);

(c) Green, for safe operation lights; and

(d) Any other color, including white, for lights not described in paragraphs (a) through (c) of this section, provided the color differs sufficiently from the colors prescribed in paragraphs (a) through (c) of this section to avoid possible confusion.

[Amdt. 27–11, 41 FR 55470, Dec. 20, 1976]

27.1323   Airspeed indicating system

(a) Each airspeed indicating instrument must be calibrated to indicate true airspeed (at sea level with a standard atmosphere) with a minimum practicable instrument calibration error when the corresponding pitot and static pressures are applied.

(b) The airspeed indicating system must be calibrated in flight at forward speeds of 20 knots and over.

(c) At each forward speed above 80 percent of the climbout speed, the airspeed indicator must indicate true airspeed, at sea level with a standard atmosphere, to within an allowable installation error of not more than the greater of—

(1) ±3 percent of the calibrated airspeed; or

(2) Five knots.

(Secs. 313(a), 601, 603, 604, and 605 of the Federal Aviation Act of 1958 (49 U.S.C. 1354(a), 1421, 1423, 1424, and 1425); and sec. 6(c) of the Dept. of Transportation Act (49 U.S.C. 1655(c)))

[Doc. No. 5074, 29 FR 15695, Nov. 24, 1964, as amended by Amdt. 27–13, 42 FR 36972, July 18, 1977]

27.1325   Static pressure systems

(a) Each instrument with static air case connections must be vented so that the influence of rotorcraft speed, the opening and closing of windows, airflow variation, and moisture or other foreign matter does not seriously affect its accuracy.

(b) Each static pressure port must be designed and located in such manner that the correlation between air pressure in the static pressure system and true ambient atmospheric static pressure is not altered when the rotorcraft encounters icing conditions. An anti-icing means or an alternate source of static pressure may be used in showing compliance with this requirement. If the reading of the altimeter, when on the alternate static pressure system, differs from the reading of the altimeter when on the primary static system by more than 50 feet, a correction card must be provided for the alternate static system.

(c) Except as provided in paragraph (d) of this section, if the static pressure system incorporates both a primary and an alternate static pressure source, the means for selecting one or the other source must be designed so that—

(1) When either source is selected, the other is blocked off; and

(2) Both sources cannot be blocked off simultaneously.

(d) For unpressurized rotorcraft, paragraph (c)(1) of this section does not apply if it can be demonstrated that the static pressure system calibration, when either static pressure source is selected is not changed by the other static pressure source being open or blocked.

(Secs. 313(a), 601, 603, 604, and 605 of the Federal Aviation Act of 1958 (49 U.S.C. 1354(a), 1421, 1423, 1424, and 1425); and sec. 6(c) of the Dept. of Transportation Act (49 U.S.C. 1655(c)))

[Doc. No. 5074, 29 FR 15695, Nov. 24, 1964, as amended by Amdt. 27–13, 42 FR 36972, July 18, 1977]

27.1327   Magnetic direction indicator

(a) Except as provided in paragraph (b) of this section—

(1) Each magnetic direction indicator must be installed so that its accuracy is not excessively affected by the rotorcraft's vibration or magnetic fields; and

(2) The compensated installation may not have a deviation, in level flight, greater than 10 degrees on any heading.

(b) A magnetic nonstabilized direction indicator may deviate more than 10 degrees due to the operation of electrically powered systems such as electrically heated windshields if either a magnetic stabilized direction indicator, which does not have a deviation in level flight greater than 10 degrees on any heading, or a gyroscopic direction indicator, is installed. Deviations of a magnetic nonstabilized direction indicator of more than 10 degrees must be placarded in accordance with 27.1547(e).

(Secs. 313(a), 601, 603, 604, and 605 of the Federal Aviation Act of 1958 (49 U.S.C. 1354(a), 1421, 1423, 1424, and 1425); and sec. 6(c) of the Dept. of Transportation Act (49 U.S.C. 1655(c)))

[Amdt. 27–13, 42 FR 36972, July 18, 1977]

27.1329 Automatic pilot system

(a) Each automatic pilot system must be designed so that the automatic pilot can—

  (1) Be sufficiently overpowered by one pilot to allow control of the rotorcraft; and

  (2) Be readily and positively disengaged by each pilot to prevent it from interfering with control of the rotorcraft.

(b) Unless there is automatic synchronization, each system must have a means to readily indicate to the pilot the alignment of the actuating device in relation to the control system it operates.

(c) Each manually operated control for the system's operation must be readily accessible to the pilots.

(d) The system must be designed and adjusted so that, within the range of adjustment available to the pilot, it cannot produce hazardous loads on the rotorcraft or create hazardous deviations in the flight path under any flight condition appropriate to its use, either during normal operation or in the event of a malfunction, assuming that corrective action begins within a reasonable period of time.

(e) If the automatic pilot integrates signals from auxiliary controls or furnishes signals for operation of other equipment, there must be positive interlocks and sequencing of engagement to prevent improper operation.

(f) If the automatic pilot system can be coupled to airborne navigation equipment, means must be provided to indicate to the pilots the current mode of operation. Selector switch position is not acceptable as a means of indication.

[Amdt. 27–21, 49 FR 44435, Nov. 6, 1984, as amended by Amdt. 27–35, 63 FR 43285, Aug. 12, 1998]

27.1335 Flight director systems

If a flight director system is installed, means must be provided to indicate to the flight crew its current mode of operation. Selector switch position is not acceptable as a means of indication.

(Secs. 313(a), 601, 603, 604, and 605 of the Federal Aviation Act of 1958 (49 U.S.C. 1354(a), 1421, 1423, 1424, and 1425); and sec. 6(c) of the Dept. of Transportation Act (49 U.S.C. 1655(c)))

[Amdt. 27–13, 42 FR 36972, July 18, 1977]

27.1337 Powerplant instruments

(a) Instruments and instrument lines.

  (1) Each powerplant instrument line must meet the requirements of 27.-961 and 27.993.

  (2) Each line carrying flammable fluids under pressure must—

    (i) Have restricting orifices or other safety devices at the source of pressure to prevent the escape of excessive fluid if the line fails; and

    (ii) Be installed and located so that the escape of fluids would not create a hazard.

  (3) Each powerplant instrument that utilizes flammable fluids must be installed and located so that the escape of fluid would not create a hazard.

(b) Fuel quantity indicator. Each fuel quantity indicator must be installed to clearly indicate to the flight crew the quantity of fuel in each tank in flight. In addition—

  (1) Each fuel quantity indicator must be calibrated to read "zero" during level flight when the quantity of fuel remaining in the tank is equal to the unusable fuel supply determined under 27.959;

  (2) When two or more tanks are closely interconnected by a gravity feed system and vented, and when it is impossible to feed from each tank separately, at least one fuel quantity indicator must be installed; and

  (3) Each exposed sight gauge used as a fuel quantity indicator must be protected against damage.

(c) Fuel flowmeter system. If a fuel flowmeter system is installed, each metering component must have a means for bypassing the fuel supply if malfunction of that component severely restricts fuel flow.

(d) Oil quantity indicator. There must be means to indicate the quantity of oil in each tank—

  (1) On the ground (including during the filling of each tank); and

  (2) In flight, if there is an oil transfer system or reserve oil supply system.

(e) Rotor drive system transmissions and gearboxes utilizing ferromagnetic materials must be equipped with chip detectors designed to indicate the presence of ferromagnetic particles resulting from damage or excessive wear. Chip detectors must—

  (1) Be designed to provide a signal to the device required by 27.1305(v) and be provided with a means to allow crewmembers to check, in flight, the function of each detector electrical circuit and signal.

  (2) [Reserved]

(Secs. 313(a), 601, and 603, 72 Stat. 752, 775, 49 U.S.C. 1354(a), 1421, and 1423; sec. 6(c) 49 U.S.C. 1655(c))

[Doc. No. 5074, 29 FR 15695, Nov. 24, 1964, as amended by Amdt. 27–12, 42 FR 15046, Mar. 17, 1977; Amdt. 27–23, 53 FR 34214, Sept. 2, 1988; Amdt. 27–37, 64 FR 45095, Aug. 18, 1999]

Electrical Systems and Equipment

27.1351 General

(a) Electrical system capacity. Electrical equipment must be adequate for its intended use. In addition—

  (1) Electric power sources, their transmission cables, and their associated control and protective devices must be able to furnish the required power at the proper voltage to each load circuit essential for safe operation; and

  (2) Compliance with paragraph (a)(1) of this section must be shown by an electrical load analysis, or by electrical measurements that take into account the electrical loads applied to the electrical system, in probable combinations and for probable durations.

(b) Function. For each electrical system, the following apply:

  (1) Each system, when installed, must be—

    (i) Free from hazards in itself, in its method of operation, and in its effects on other parts of the rotorcraft; and

    (ii) Protected from fuel, oil, water, other detrimental substances, and mechanical damage.

  (2) Electric power sources must function properly when connected in combination or independently.

  (3) No failure or malfunction of any source may impair the ability of any remaining source to supply load circuits essential for safe operation.

  (4) Each electric power source control must allow the independent operation of each source.

(c) Generating system. There must be at least one generator if the system supplies power to load circuits essential for safe operation. In addition—

  (1) Each generator must be able to deliver its continuous rated power;

  (2) Generator voltage control equipment must be able to dependably regulate each generator output within rated limits;

(3) Each generator must have a reverse current cutout designed to disconnect the generator from the battery and from the other generators when enough reverse current exists to damage that generator; and

(4) Each generator must have an overvoltage control designed and installed to prevent damage to the electrical system, or to equipment supplied by the electrical system, that could result if that generator were to develop an overvoltage condition.

(d) *Instruments.* There must be means to indicate to appropriate crewmembers the electric power system quantities essential for safe operation of the system. In addition—

(1) For direct current systems, an ammeter that can be switched into each generator feeder may be used; and

(2) If there is only one generator, the ammeter may be in the battery feeder.

(e) *External power.* If provisions are made for connecting external power to the rotorcraft, and that external power can be electrically connected to equipment other than that used for engine starting, means must be provided to ensure that no external power supply having a reverse polarity, or a reverse phase sequence, can supply power to the rotorcraft's electrical system.

(Secs. 313(a), 601, 603, 604, and 605 of the Federal Aviation Act of 1958 (49 U.S.C. 1354(a), 1421, 1423, 1424, and 1425); and sec. 6(c) of the Dept. of Transportation Act (49 U.S.C. 1655(c)))

[Doc. No. 5074, 29 FR 15695, Nov. 24, 1964, as amended by Amdt. 27–11, 41 FR 55470, Dec. 20, 1976; Amdt. 27–13, 42 FR 36972, July 18, 1977]

27.1353 Storage battery design and installation

(a) Each storage battery must be designed and installed as prescribed in this section.

(b) Safe cell temperatures and pressures must be maintained during any probable charging and discharging condition. No uncontrolled increase in cell temperature may result when the battery is recharged (after previous complete discharge)—

(1) At maximum regulated voltage or power;

(2) During a flight of maximum duration; and

(3) Under the most adverse cooling condition likely to occur in service.

(c) Compliance with paragraph (b) of this section must be shown by test unless experience with similar batteries and installations has shown that maintaining safe cell temperatures and pressures presents no problem.

(d) No explosive or toxic gases emitted by any battery in normal operation, or as the result of any probable malfunction in the charging system or battery installation, may accumulate in hazardous quantities within the rotorcraft.

(e) No corrosive fluids or gases that may escape from the battery may damage surrounding structures or adjacent essential equipment.

(f) Each nickel cadmium battery installation capable of being used to start an engine or auxiliary power unit must have provisions to prevent any hazardous effect on structure or essential systems that may be caused by the maximum amount of heat the battery can generate during a short circuit of the battery or of its individual cells.

(g) Nickel cadmium battery installations capable of being used to start an engine or auxiliary power unit must have—

(1) A system to control the charging rate of the battery automatically so as to prevent battery overheating;

(2) A battery temperature sensing and over-temperature warning system with a means for disconnecting the battery from its charging source in the event of an over-temperature condition; or

(3) A battery failure sensing and warning system with a means for disconnecting the battery from its charging source in the event of battery failure.

(Secs. 313(a), 601, 603, 604, and 605 of the Federal Aviation Act of 1958 (49 U.S.C. 1354(a), 1421, 1423, 1424, and 1425); and sec. 6(c) of the Dept. of Transportation Act (49 U.S.C. 1655(c)))

[Doc. No. 5074, 29 FR 15695, Nov. 24, 1964, as amended by Amdt. 27–13, 42 FR 36972, July 18, 1977; Amdt. 27–14, 43 FR 2325, Jan. 16, 1978]

27.1357 Circuit protective devices

(a) Protective devices, such as fuses or circuit breakers, must be installed in each electrical circuit other than—

(1) The main circuits of starter motors; and

(2) Circuits in which no hazard is presented by their omission.

(b) A protective device for a circuit essential to flight safety may not be used to protect any other circuit.

(c) Each resettable circuit protective device ("trip free" device in which the tripping mechanism cannot be overridden by the operating control) must be designed so that—

(1) A manual operation is required to restore service after tripping; and

(2) If an overload or circuit fault exists, the device will open the circuit regardless of the position of the operating control.

(d) If the ability to reset a circuit breaker or replace a fuse is essential to safety in flight, that circuit breaker or fuse must be located and identified so that it can be readily reset or replaced in flight.

(e) If fuses are used, there must be one spare of each rating, or 50 percent spare fuses of each rating, whichever is greater.

(Secs. 313(a), 601, 603, 604, and 605 of the Federal Aviation Act of 1958 (49 U.S.C. 1354(a), 1421, 1423, 1424, and 1425); and sec. 6(c) of the Dept. of Transportation Act (49 U.S.C. 1655(c)))

[Doc. No. 5074, 29 FR 15695, Nov. 24, 1964; 29 FR 17885, Dec. 17, 1964, as amended by Amdt. 27–13, 42 FR 36972, July 18, 1977]

27.1361 Master switch

(a) There must be a master switch arrangement to allow ready disconnection of each electric power source from the main bus. The point of disconnection must be adjacent to the sources controlled by the switch.

(b) Load circuits may be connected so that they remain energized after the switch is opened, if they are protected by circuit protective devices, rated at five amperes or less, adjacent to the electric power source.

(c) The master switch or its controls must be installed so that the switch is easily discernible and accessible to a crewmember in flight.

27.1365 Electric cables

(a) Each electric connecting cable must be of adequate capacity.

(b) Each cable that would overheat in the event of circuit overload or fault must be at least flame resistant and may not emit dangerous quantities of toxic fumes.

(c) Insulation on electrical wire and cable installed in the rotorcraft must be self-extinguishing when tested in accordance with Appendix F, Part I(a)(3), of part 25 of this chapter.

[Doc. No. 5074, 29 FR 15695, Nov. 24, 1964, as amended by Amdt. 27–35, 63 FR 43285, Aug. 12, 1998]

27.1367 Switches

Each switch must be—

(a) Able to carry its rated current;

(b) Accessible to the crew; and

(c) Labeled as to operation and the circuit controlled.

Lights

27.1381 Instrument lights

The instrument lights must—

(a) Make each instrument, switch, and other devices for which they are provided easily readable; and

(b) Be installed so that—

(1) Their direct rays are shielded from the pilot's eyes; and

(2) No objectionable reflections are visible to the pilot.

27.1383 Landing lights

(a) Each required landing or hovering light must be approved.

(b) Each landing light must be installed so that—

(1) No objectionable glare is visible to the pilot;

(2) The pilot is not adversely affected by halation; and

(3) It provides enough light for night operation, including hovering and landing.

(c) At least one separate switch must be provided, as applicable—

(1) For each separately installed landing light; and

(2) For each group of landing lights installed at a common location.

27.1385 Position light system installation

(a) General. Each part of each position light system must meet the applicable requirements of this section, and each system as a whole must meet the requirements of 27.1387 through 27.1397.

(b) Forward position lights. Forward position lights must consist of a red and a green light spaced laterally as far apart as practicable and installed forward on the rotorcraft so that, with the rotorcraft in the normal flying position, the red light is on the left side and the green light is on the right side. Each light must be approved.

(c) Rear position light. The rear position light must be a white light mounted as far aft as practicable, and must be approved.

(d) Circuit. The two forward position lights and the rear position light must make a single circuit.

(e) Light covers and color filters. Each light cover or color filter must be at least flame resistant and may not change color or shape or lose any appreciable light transmission during normal use.

27.1387 Position light system dihedral angles

(a) Except as provided in paragraph (e) of this section, each forward and rear position light must, as installed, show unbroken light within the dihedral angles described in this section.

(b) Dihedral angle L (left) is formed by two intersecting vertical planes, the first parallel to the longitudinal axis of the rotorcraft, and the other at 110 degrees to the left of the first, as viewed when looking forward along the longitudinal axis.

(c) Dihedral angle R (right) is formed by two intersecting vertical planes, the first parallel to the longitudinal axis of the rotorcraft, and the other at 110 degrees to the right of the first, as viewed when looking forward along the longitudinal axis.

(d) Dihedral angle A (aft) is formed by two intersecting vertical planes making angles of 70 degrees to the right and to the left, respectively, to a vertical plane passing through the longitudinal axis, as viewed when looking aft along the longitudinal axis.

(e) If the rear position light, when mounted as far aft as practicable in accordance with 25.1385(c), cannot show unbroken light within dihedral angle A (as defined in paragraph (d) of this section), a solid angle or angles of obstructed visibility totaling not more than 0.04 steradians is allowable within that dihedral angle, if such solid angle is within a cone whose apex is at the rear position light and whose elements make an angle of 30° with a vertical line passing through the rear position light.

(49 U.S.C. 1655(c))

[Doc. No. 5074, 29 FR 15695, Nov. 24, 1964, as amended by Amdt. 27–7, 36 FR 21278, Nov. 5, 1971]

27.1389 Position light distribution and intensities

(a) General. the intensities prescribed in this section must be provided by new equipment with light covers and color filters in place. Intensities must be determined with the light source operating at a steady value equal to the average luminous output of the source at the normal operating voltage of the rotorcraft. The light distribution and intensity of each position light must meet the requirements of paragraph (b) of this section.

(b) Forward and rear position lights. The light distribution and intensities of forward and rear position lights must be expressed in terms of minimum intensities in the horizontal plane, minimum intensities in any vertical plane, and maximum intensities in overlapping beams, within dihedral angles L, R, and A, and must meet the following requirements:

(1) Intensities in the horizontal plane. Each intensity in the horizontal plane (the plane containing the longitudinal axis of the rotorcraft and perpendicular to the plane of symmetry of the rotorcraft) must equal or exceed the values in 27.1391.

(2) Intensities in any vertical plane. Each intensity in any vertical plane (the plane perpendicular to the horizontal plane) must equal or exceed the appropriate value in 27.1393, where I is the minimum intensity prescribed in 27.1391 for the corresponding angles in the horizontal plane.

(3) Intensities in overlaps between adjacent signals. No intensity in any overlap between adjacent signals may exceed the values in 27.1395, except that higher intensities in overlaps may be used with main beam intensities substantially greater than the minima specified in 27.1391 and 27.1393, if the overlap intensities in relation to the main beam intensities do not adversely affect signal clarity. When the peak intensity of the forward position lights is greater than 100 candles, the maximum overlap intensities between them may exceed the values in 27.1395 if the overlap intensity in Area A is not more than 10 percent of peak position light intensity and the overlap intensity in Area B is not more than 2.5 percent of peak position light intensity.

27.1391 Minimum intensities in the horizontal plane of forward and rear position lights

Each position light intensity must equal or exceed the applicable values in the following table:

DIHEDRAL ANGLE (LIGHT INCLUDED)	ANGLE FROM RIGHT OR LEFT OF LONGITUDINAL AXIS, MEASURED FROM DEAD AHEAD	INTENSITY (CANDLES)
L and R (forward red and green)	10° to 10°	40
	10° to 20°	30
	20° to 110°	5
A (rear white)	110° to 180°	20

27.1393 Minimum intensities in any vertical plane of forward and rear position lights

Each position light intensity must equal or exceed the applicable values in the following table:

ANGLE ABOVE OR BELOW THE HORIZONTAL PLANE	INTENSITY, L
0°	1.00
0° to 5°	0.90
5° to 10°	0.80
10° to 15°	0.70
15° to 20°	0.50
20° to 30°	0.30
30° to 40°	0.10
40° to 90°	0.05

27.1395 Maximum intensities in overlapping beams of forward and rear position lights

No position light intensity may exceed the applicable values in the following table, except as provided in 27.1389(b)(3).

OVERLAPS	MAXIMUM INTENSITY	
	AREA A (CANDLES)	AREA B (CANDLES)
Green in dihedral angle L	10	1
Red in dihedral angle R	10	1
Green in dihedral angle A	5	1
Red in dihedral angle A	5	1
Rear white in dihedral angle L	5	1
Rear white in dihedral angle R	5	1

Where—

(a) Area A includes all directions in the adjacent dihedral angle that pass through the light source and intersect the common boundary plane at more than 10 degrees but less than 20 degrees, and

(b) Area B includes all directions in the adjacent dihedral angle that pass through the light source and intersect the common boundary plane at more than 20 degrees.

27.1397 Color specifications

Each position light color must have the applicable International Commission on Illumination chromaticity coordinates as follows:

(a) Aviation red—

   y is not greater than 0.335; and

   z is not greater than 0.002.

(b) Aviation green—

   x is not greater than 0.440–0.320 y ;

   x is not greater than y –0.170; and

   y is not less than 0.390–0.170 x .

(c) Aviation white—

   x is not less than 0.300 and not greater than 0.540;

   y is not less than x –0.040" or y c–0.010, whichever is the smaller; and

   y is not greater than x +0.020 nor 0.636–0.400 x ;

Where y_c is the y coordinate of the Planckian radiator for the value of x considered.

[Doc. No. 5074, 29 FR 15695, Nov. 24, 1964, as amended by Amdt. 27–6, 36 FR 12972, July 10, 1971]

27.1399 Riding light

(a) Each riding light required for water operation must be installed so that it can—

   (1) Show a white light for at least two nautical miles at night under clear atmospheric conditions; and

   (2) Show a maximum practicable unbroken light with the rotorcraft on the water.

(b) Externally hung lights may be used.

[Doc. No. 5074, 29 FR 15695, Nov. 24, 1964, as amended by Amdt. 27–2, 33 FR 964, Jan. 26, 1968]

27.1401 Anticollision light system

(a) General. If certification for night operation is requested, the rotorcraft must have an anticollision light system that—

   (1) Consists of one or more approved anticollision lights located so that their emitted light will not impair the crew's vision or detract from the conspicuity of the position lights; and

   (2) Meets the requirements of paragraphs (b) through (f) of this section.

(b) Field of coverage. The system must consist of enough lights to illuminate the vital areas around the rotorcraft, considering the physical configuration and flight characteristics of the rotorcraft. The field of coverage must extend in each direction within at least 30 degrees below the horizontal plane of the rotorcraft, except that there may be solid angles of obstructed visibility totaling not more than 0.5 steradians.

(c) Flashing characteristics. The arrangement of the system, that is, the number of light sources, beam width, speed of rotation, and other characteristics, must give an effective flash frequency of not less than 40, nor more than 100, cycles per minute. The effective flash frequency is the frequency at which the rotorcraft's complete anticollision light system is observed from a distance, and applies to each sector of light including any overlaps that exist when the system consists of more than one light source. In overlaps, flash frequencies may exceed 100, but not 180, cycles per minute.

(d) Color. Each anticollision light must be aviation red and must meet the applicable requirements of 27.1397.

(e) Light intensity. The minimum light intensities in any vertical plane, measured with the red filter (if used) and expressed in terms of "effective" intensities, must meet the requirements of paragraph (f) of this section. The following relation must be assumed:

$$I_e = \frac{\int_{t_1}^{t_2} I(t)dt}{0.2 + (t_2 - t_1)}$$

where:

   I_e = effective intensity (candles).

   $I(t)$ = instantaneous intensity as a function of time.

   $t_2 - t_1$ = flash time interval (seconds).

Normally, the maximum value of effective intensity is obtained when t_2 and t_1 are chosen so that the effective intensity is equal to the instantaneous intensity at t_2 and t_1.

(f) Minimum effective intensities for anticollision light. Each anticollision light effective intensity must equal or exceed the applicable values in the following table:

ANGLE ABOVE OR BELOW THE HORIZONTAL PLANE	EFFECTIVE INTENSITY (CANDLES)
0° TO 5°	150
5° to 10°	90
10° to 20°	30
20° to 30°	15

[Doc. No. 5074, 29 FR 15695, Nov. 24, 1964, as amended by Amdt. 27–6, 36 FR 12972, July 10, 1971; Amdt. 27–10, 41 FR 5290, Feb. 5, 1976]

Safety Equipment
27.1411 General

(a) Required safety equipment to be used by the crew in an emergency, such as flares and automatic liferaft releases, must be readily accessible.

(b) Stowage provisions for required safety equipment must be furnished and must—

   (1) Be arranged so that the equipment is directly accessible and its location is obvious; and

   (2) Protect the safety equipment from damage caused by being subjected to the inertia loads specified in 27.561.

[Doc. No. 5074, 29 FR 15695, Nov. 24, 1964, as amended by Amdt. 27–11, 41 FR 55470, Dec. 20, 1976]

27.1413 Safety belts

Each safety belt must be equipped with a metal to metal latching device.

(Secs. 313, 314, and 601 through 610 of the Federal Aviation Act of 1958 (49 U.S.C. 1354, 1355, and 1421 through 1430) and sec. 6(c), Dept. of Transportation Act (49 U.S.C. 1655(c)))

[Doc. No. 5074, 29 FR 15695, Nov. 24, 1964, as amended by Amdt. 27–15, 43 FR 46233, Oct. 5, 1978; Amdt. 27–21, 49 FR 44435, Nov. 6, 1984]

27.1415   Ditching equipment

(a) Emergency flotation and signaling equipment required by any operating rule in this chapter must meet the requirements of this section.

(b) Each raft and each life preserver must be approved and must be installed so that it is readily available to the crew and passengers. The storage provisions for life preservers must accommodate one life preserver for each occupant for which certification for ditching is requested.

(c) Each raft released automatically or by the pilot must be attached to the rotorcraft by a line to keep it alongside the rotorcraft. This line must be weak enough to break before submerging the empty raft to which it is attached.

(d) Each signaling device must be free from hazard in its operation and must be installed in an accessible location.

[Doc. No. 5074, 29 FR 15695, Nov. 24, 1964, as amended by Amdt. 27–11, 41 FR 55470, Dec. 20, 1976]

27.1419   Ice protection

(a) To obtain certification for flight into icing conditions, compliance with this section must be shown.

(b) It must be demonstrated that the rotorcraft can be safely operated in the continuous maximum and intermittent maximum icing conditions determined under appendix C of Part 29 of this chapter within the rotorcraft altitude envelope. An analysis must be performed to establish, on the basis of the rotorcraft's operational needs, the adequacy of the ice protection system for the various components of the rotorcraft.

(c) In addition to the analysis and physical evaluation prescribed in paragraph (b) of this section, the effectiveness of the ice protection system and its components must be shown by flight tests of the rotorcraft or its components in measured natural atmospheric icing conditions and by one or more of the following tests as found necessary to determine the adequacy of the ice protection system:

  (1) Laboratory dry air or simulated icing tests, or a combination of both, of the components or models of the components.

  (2) Flight dry air tests of the ice protection system as a whole, or its individual components.

  (3) Flight tests of the rotorcraft or its components in measured simulated icing conditions.

(d) The ice protection provisions of this section are considered to be applicable primarily to the airframe. Powerplant installation requirements are contained in Subpart E of this part.

(e) A means must be indentified or provided for determining the formation of ice on critical parts of the rotorcraft. Unless otherwise restricted, the means must be available for nighttime as well as daytime operation. The rotorcraft flight manual must describe the means of determining ice formation and must contain information necessary for safe operation of the rotorcraft in icing conditions.

[Amdt. 27–19, 48 FR 4389, Jan. 31, 1983]

27.1435   Hydraulic systems

(a) Design. Each hydraulic system and its elements must withstand, without yielding, any structural loads expected in addition to hydraulic loads.

(b) Tests. Each system must be substantiated by proof pressure tests. When proof tested, no part of any system may fail, malfunction, or experience a permanent set. The proof load of each system must be at least 1.5 times the maximum operating pressure of that system.

(c) Accumulators. No hydraulic accumulator or pressurized reservoir may be installed on the engine side of any firewall unless it is an integral part of an engine.

27.1457   Cockpit voice recorders

(a) Each cockpit voice recorder required by the operating rules of

this chapter must be approved, and must be installed so that it will record the following:

  (1) Voice communications transmitted from or received in the rotorcraft by radio.

  (2) Voice communications of flight crewmembers on the flight deck.

  (3) Voice communications of flight crewmembers on the flight deck, using the rotorcraft's interphone system.

  (4) Voice or audio signals identifying navigation or approach aids introduced into a headset or speaker.

  (5) Voice communications of flight crewmembers using the passenger loudspeaker system, if there is such a system, and if the fourth channel is available in accordance with the requirements of paragraph (c)(4)(ii) of this section.

  (6) If datalink communication equipment is installed, all datalink communications, using an approved data message set. Datalink messages must be recorded as the output signal from the communications unit that translates the signal into usable data.

(b) The recording requirements of paragraph (a)(2) of this section may be met:

  (1) By installing a cockpit-mounted area microphone located in the best position for recording voice communications originating at the first and second pilot stations and voice communications of other crewmembers on the flight deck when directed to those stations; or

  (2) By installing a continually energized or voice-actuated lip microphone at the first and second pilot stations.

The microphone specified in this paragraph must be so located and, if necessary, the preamplifiers and filters of the recorder must be adjusted or supplemented so that the recorded communications are intelligible when recorded under flight cockpit noise conditions and played back. The level of intelligibility must be approved by the Administrator. Repeated aural or visual playback of the record may be used in evaluating intelligibility.

(c) Each cockpit voice recorder must be installed so that the part of the communication or audio signals specified in paragraph (a) of this section obtained from each of the following sources is recorded on a separate channel:

  (1) For the first channel, from each microphone, headset, or speaker used at the first pilot station.

  (2) For the second channel, from each microphone, headset, or speaker used at the second pilot station.

  (3) For the third channel, from the cockpit-mounted area microphone, or the continually energized or voice-actuated lip microphone at the first and second pilot stations.

  (4) For the fourth channel, from:

     (i)   Each microphone, headset, or speaker used at the stations for the third and fourth crewmembers; or

     (ii) If the stations specified in paragraph (c)(4)(i) of this section are not required or if the signal at such a station is picked up by another channel, each microphone on the flight deck that is used with the passenger loudspeaker system if its signals are not picked up by another channel.

     (iii) Each microphone on the flight deck that is used with the rotorcraft's loudspeaker system if its signals are not picked up by another channel.

(d) Each cockpit voice recorder must be installed so that:

  (1)

     (i)   It receives its electrical power from the bus that provides the maximum reliability for operation of the flight data recorder without jeopardizing service to essential or emergency loads.

     (ii) It remains powered for as long as possible without jeopardizing emergency operation of the rotorcraft.

(2) There is an automatic means to simultaneously stop the recorder and prevent each erasure feature from functioning, within 10 minutes after crash impact;

(3) There is an aural or visual means for preflight checking of the recorder for proper operation;

(4) Whether the cockpit voice recorder and digital flight data recorder are installed in separate boxes or in a combination unit, no single electrical failure external to the recorder may disable both the cockpit voice recorder and the digital flight data recorder; and

(5) It has an independent power source—

    (i) That provides 10 ± 1 minutes of electrical power to operate both the cockpit voice recorder and cockpit-mounted area microphone;

    (ii) That is located as close as practicable to the cockpit voice recorder; and

    (iii) To which the cockpit voice recorder and cockpit-mounted area microphone are switched automatically in the event that all other power to the cockpit voice recorder is interrupted either by normal shutdown or by any other loss of power to the electrical power bus.

(e) The record container must be located and mounted to minimize the probability of rupture of the container as a result of crash impact and consequent heat damage to the record from fire.

(f) If the cockpit voice recorder has a bulk erasure device, the installation must be designed to minimize the probability of inadvertent operation and actuation of the device during crash impact.

(g) Each recorder container must be either bright orange or bright yellow.

(h) When both a cockpit voice recorder and a flight data recorder are required by the operating rules, one combination unit may be installed, provided that all other requirements of this section and the requirements for flight data recorders under this part are met.

[Amdt. 27–22, 53 FR 26144, July 11, 1988, as amended by Amdt. No. 27–43, 73 FR 12563, Mar. 7, 2008; Amdt. 27–43, 74 FR 32800, July 9, 2009; Amdt. 27-45, 75 FR 17045, April 5, 2010]

27.1459   Flight data recorders

(a) Each flight recorder required by the operating rules of Subchapter G of this chapter must be installed so that:

(1) It is supplied with airspeed, altitude, and directional data obtained from sources that meet the accuracy requirements of 27.1323, 27.1325, and 27.1327 of this part, as applicable;

(2) The vertical acceleration sensor is rigidly attached, and located longitudinally within the approved center of gravity limits of the rotorcraft;

(3)

    (i) It receives its electrical power from the bus that provides the maximum reliability for operation of the flight data recorder without jeopardizing service to essential or emergency loads.

    (ii) It remains powered for as long as possible without jeopardizing emergency operation of the rotorcraft.

(4) There is an aural or visual means for preflight checking of the recorder for proper recording of data in the storage medium;

(5) Except for recorders powered solely by the engine-driven electrical generator system, there is an automatic means to simultaneously stop a recorder that has a data erasure feature and prevent each erasure feature from functioning, within 10 minutes after any crash impact; and

(6) Whether the cockpit voice recorder and digital flight data recorder are installed in separate boxes or in a combination unit, no single electrical failure external to the recorder may disable both the cockpit voice recorder and the digital flight data recorder.

(b) Each nonejectable recorder container must be located and mounted so as to minimize the probability of container rupture resulting from crash impact and subsequent damage to the record from fire.

(c) A correlation must be established between the flight recorder readings of airspeed, altitude, and heading and the corresponding readings (taking into account correction factors) of the first pilot's instruments. This correlation must cover the airspeed range over which the aircraft is to be operated, the range of altitude to which the aircraft is limited, and 360 degrees of heading. Correlation may be established on the ground as appropriate.

(d) Each recorder container must:

(1) Be either bright orange or bright yellow;

(2) Have a reflective tape affixed to its external surface to facilitate its location under water; and

(3) Have an underwater locating device, when required by the operating rules of this chapter, on or adjacent to the container which is secured in such a manner that they are not likely to be separated during crash impact.

(e) When both a cockpit voice recorder and a flight data recorder are required by the operating rules, one combination unit may be installed, provided that all other requirements of this section and the requirements for cockpit voice recorders under this part are met.

[Amdt. 27–22, 53 FR 26144, July 11, 1988, as amended by Amdt. 27–43, 73 FR 12564, Mar. 7, 2008; Amdt. 27–43, 74 FR 32800, July 9, 2009; Amdt. 27-45, 75 FR 17045, April 5, 2010]

27.1461   Equipment containing high energy rotors

(a) Equipment containing high energy rotors must meet paragraph (b), (c), or (d) of this section.

(b) High energy rotors contained in equipment must be able to withstand damage caused by malfunctions, vibration, abnormal speeds, and abnormal temperatures. In addition—

(1) Auxiliary rotor cases must be able to contain damage caused by the failure of high energy rotor blades; and

(2) Equipment control devices, systems, and instrumentation must reasonably ensure that no operating limitations affecting the integrity of high energy rotors will be exceeded in service.

(c) It must be shown by test that equipment containing high energy rotors can contain any failure of a high energy rotor that occurs at the highest speed obtainable with the normal speed control devices inoperative.

(d) Equipment containing high energy rotors must be located where rotor failure will neither endanger the occupants nor adversely affect continued safe flight.

[Amdt. 27–2, 33 FR 964, Jan. 26, 1968]

Subpart G — Operating Limitations and Information
27.1501   General

(a) Each operating limitation specified in 27.1503 through 27.1525 and other limitations and information necessary for safe operation must be established.

(b) The operating limitations and other information necessary for safe operation must be made available to the crewmembers as prescribed in 27.1541 through 27.1589.

(Secs. 313(a), 601, 603, 604, and 605 of the Federal Aviation Act of 1958 (49 U.S.C. 1354(a), 1421, 1423, 1424, and 1425); and sec. 6(c) of the Dept. of Transportation Act (49 U.S.C. 1655(c)))

[Amdt. 27–14, 43 FR 2325, Jan. 16, 1978]

Operating Limitations

27.1503   Airspeed limitations: general

(a) An operating speed range must be established.

(b) When airspeed limitations are a function of weight, weight distribution, altitude, rotor speed, power, or other factors, airspeed limitations corresponding with the critical combinations of these factors must be established.

27.1505   Never-exceed speed

(a) The never-exceed speed, V_{NE}, must be established so that it is—

(1) Not less than 40 knots (CAS); and

(2) Not more than the lesser of—

    (i)   0.9 times the maximum forward speeds established under 27.309;

    (ii) 0.9 times the maximum speed shown under 27.251 and 27.629; or

    (iii) 0.9 times the maximum speed substantiated for advancing blade tip mach number effects.

(b) V_{NE} may vary with altitude, r.p.m., temperature, and weight, if—

  (1) No more than two of these variables (or no more than two instruments integrating more than one of these variables) are used at one time; and

  (2) The ranges of these variables (or of the indications on instruments integrating more than one of these variables) are large enough to allow an operationally practical and safe variation of V_{NE}.

(c) For helicopters, a stabilized power-off V_{NE} denoted as V_{NE} (power-off) may be established at a speed less than V_{NE} established pursuant to paragraph (a) of this section, if the following conditions are met:

  (1) V_{NE} (power-off) is not less than a speed midway between the power-on V_{NE} and the speed used in meeting the requirements of—

    (i)   27.65(b) for single engine helicopters; and

    (ii) 27.67 for multiengine helicopters.

  (2) V_{NE} (power-off) is—

    (i)   A constant airspeed;

    (ii) A constant amount less than power-on V_{NE}; or

    (iii) A constant airspeed for a portion of the altitude range for which certification is requested, and a constant amount less than power-on V_{NE} for the remainder of the altitude range.

(Secs. 313(a), 601, 603, 604, and 605 of the Federal Aviation Act of 1958 (49 U.S.C. 1354(a), 1421, 1423, 1424, and 1425); and sec. 6(c) of the Dept. of Transportation Act (49 U.S.C. 1655(c)))

[Amdt. 27–2, 33 FR 964, Jan. 26, 1968, and Amdt. 27–14, 43 FR 2325, Jan. 16, 1978; Amdt. 27–21, 49 FR 44435, Nov. 6, 1984]

27.1509   Rotor speed

(a) Maximum power-off (autorotation). The maximum power-off rotor speed must be established so that it does not exceed 95 percent of the lesser of—

  (1) The maximum design r.p.m. determined under 27.309(b); and

  (2) The maximum r.p.m. shown during the type tests.

(b) Minimum power off. The minimum power-off rotor speed must be established so that it is not less than 105 percent of the greater of—

  (1) The minimum shown during the type tests; and

  (2) The minimum determined by design substantiation.

(c) Minimum power on. The minimum power-on rotor speed must be established so that it is—

  (1) Not less than the greater of—

    (i)   The minimum shown during the type tests; and

    (ii) The minimum determined by design substantiation; and

  (2) Not more than a value determined under 27.33(a)(1) and (b)(1).

27.1519   Weight and center of gravity

The weight and center of gravity limitations determined under 27.25 and 27.27, respectively, must be established as operating limitations.

[Amdt. 27–2, 33 FR 965, Jan. 26, 1968, as amended by Amdt. 27–21, 49 FR 44435, Nov. 6, 1984]

27.1521   Powerplant limitations

(a) General. The powerplant limitations prescribed in this section must be established so that they do not exceed the corresponding limits for which the engines are type certificated.

(b) Takeoff operation. The powerplant takeoff operation must be limited by—

  (1) The maximum rotational speed, which may not be greater than—

    (i)   The maximum value determined by the rotor design; or

    (ii) The maximum value shown during the type tests;

  (2) The maximum allowable manifold pressure (for reciprocating engines);

  (3) The time limit for the use of the power corresponding to the limitations established in paragraphs (b)(1) and (2) of this section;

  (4) If the time limit in paragraph (b)(3) of this section exceeds two minutes, the maximum allowable cylinder head, coolant outlet, or oil temperatures;

  (5) The gas temperature limits for turbine engines over the range of operating and atmospheric conditions for which certification is requested.

(c) Continuous operation. The continuous operation must be limited by—

  (1) The maximum rotational speed which may not be greater than—

    (i)   The maximum value determined by the rotor design; or

    (ii) The maximum value shown during the type tests;

  (2) The minimum rotational speed shown under the rotor speed requirements in 27.1509(c); and

  (3) The gas temperature limits for turbine engines over the range of operating and atmospheric conditions for which certification is requested.

(d) Fuel grade or designation. The minimum fuel grade (for reciprocating engines), or fuel designation (for turbine engines), must be established so that it is not less than that required for the operation of the engines within the limitations in paragraphs (b) and (c) of this section.

(e) Turboshaft engine torque. For rotorcraft with main rotors driven by turboshaft engines, and that do not have a torque limiting device in the transmission system, the following apply:

  (1) A limit engine torque must be established if the maximum torque that the engine can exert is greater than—

    (i)   The torque that the rotor drive system is designed to transmit; or

    (ii) The torque that the main rotor assembly is designed to withstand in showing compliance with 27.547(e).

  (2) The limit engine torque established under paragraph (e)(1) of this section may not exceed either torque specified in paragraph (e)(1)(i) or (ii) of this section.

(f) Ambient temperature. For turbine engines, ambient temperature limitations (including limitations for winterization installations, if applicable) must be established as the maximum ambient atmospheric temperature at which compliance with the cooling provisions of 27.1041 through 27.1045 is shown.

(g) Two and one-half-minute OEI power operation. Unless otherwise authorized, the use of $2^1/_2$-minute OEI power must be limited to engine failure operation of multiengine, turbine-powered rotorcraft for not longer than $2^1/_2$minutes after failure of an engine. The use of $2^1/_2$-minute OEI power must also be limited by—

  (1) The maximum rotational speed, which may not be greater than—

    (i)   The maximum value determined by the rotor design; or

    (ii) The maximum demonstrated during the type tests;

  (2) The maximum allowable gas temperature; and

  (3) The maximum allowable torque.

(h) Thirty-minute OEI power operation. Unless otherwise authorized, the use of 30-minute OEI power must be limited to multiengine, turbine-powered rotorcraft for not longer than 30 minutes after failure of an engine. The use of 30-minute OEI power must also be limited by—

(1) The maximum rotational speed, which may not be greater than—

    (i) The maximum value determined by the rotor design; or

    (ii) The maximum value demonstrated during the type tests;

(2) The maximum allowable gas temperature; and

(3) The maximum allowable torque.

(i) *Continuous OEI power operation.* Unless otherwise authorized, the use of continuous OEI power must be limited to multiengine, turbine-powered rotorcraft for continued flight after failure of an engine. The use of continuous OEI power must also be limited by—

(1) The maximum rotational speed, which may not be greater than—

    (i) The maximum value determined by the rotor design; or

    (ii) The maximum value demonstrated during the type tests;

(2) The maximum allowable gas temperature; and

(3) The maximum allowable torque.

(j) *Rated 30-second OEI power operation.* Rated 30-second OEI power is permitted only on multiengine, turbine-powered rotorcraft, also certificated for the use of rated 2-minute OEI power, and can only be used for continued operation of the remaining engine(s) after a failure or precautionary shutdown of an engine. It must be shown that following application of 30-second OEI power, any damage will be readily detectable by the applicable inspections and other related procedures furnished in accordance with Section A27.4 of appendix A of this part and Section A33.4 of appendix A of part 33. The use of 30-second OEI power must be limited to not more than 30 seconds for any period in which that power is used, and by—

(1) The maximum rotational speed, which may not be greater than—

    (i) The maximum value determined by the rotor design; or

    (ii) The maximum value demonstrated during the type tests;

(2) The maximum allowable gas temperature; and

(3) The maximum allowable torque.

(k) *Rated 2-minute OEI power operation.* Rated 2-minute OEI power is permitted only on multiengine, turbine-powered rotorcraft, also certificated for the use of rated 30-second OEI power, and can only be used for continued operation of the remaining engine(s) after a failure or precautionary shutdown of an engine. It must be shown that following application of 2-minute OEI power, any damage will be readily detectable by the applicable inspections and other related procedures furnished in accordance with Section A27.4 of appendix A of this part and Section A33.4 of appendix A of part 33. The use of 2-minute OEI power must be limited to not more than 2 minutes for any period in which that power is used, and by—

(1) The maximum rotational speed, which may not be greater than—

    (i) The maximum value determined by the rotor design; or

    (ii) The maximum value demonstrated during the type tests;

(2) The maximum allowable gas temperature; and

(3) The maximum allowable torque.

(Secs. 313(a), 601, 603, 604, and 605 of the Federal Aviation Act of 1958 (49 U.S.C. 1354(a), 1421, 1423, 1424, and 1425); and sec. 6(c) of the Dept. of Transportation Act (49 U.S.C. 1655(c)))

[Doc. No. 5074, 29 FR 15695, Nov. 24, 1964, as amended by Amdt. 27–14, 43 FR 2325, Jan. 16, 1978; Amdt. 27–23, 53 FR 34214, Sept. 2, 1988; Amdt. 27–29, 59 FR 47767, Sept. 16, 1994]

27.1523 Minimum flight crew

The minimum flight crew must be established so that it is sufficient for safe operation, considering—

(a) The workload on individual crewmembers;

(b) The accessibility and ease of operation of necessary controls by the appropriate crewmember; and

(c) The kinds of operation authorized under 27.1525.

27.1525 Kinds of operations

The kinds of operations (such as VFR, IFR, day, night, or icing) for which the rotorcraft is approved are established by demonstrated compliance with the applicable certification requirements and by the installed equipment.

[Amdt. 27–21, 49 FR 44435, Nov. 6, 1984]

27.1527 Maximum operating altitude

The maximum altitude up to which operation is allowed, as limited by flight, structural, powerplant, functional, or equipment characteristics, must be established.

(Secs. 313(a), 601, 603, 604, and 605 of the Federal Aviation Act of 1958 (49 U.S.C. 1354(a), 1421, 1423, 1424, and 1425); and sec. 6(c) of the Dept. of Transportation Act (49 U.S.C. 1655(c)))

[Amdt. 27–14, 43 FR 2325, Jan. 16, 1978]

27.1529 Instructions for Continued Airworthiness

The applicant must prepare Instructions for Continued Airworthiness in accordance with appendix A to this part that are acceptable to the Administrator. The instructions may be incomplete at type certification if a program exists to ensure their completion prior to delivery of the first rotorcraft or issuance of a standard certificate of airworthiness, whichever occurs later.

[Amdt. 27–18, 45 FR 60177, Sept. 11, 1980]

Markings and Placards

27.1541 General

(a) The rotorcraft must contain—

    (1) The markings and placards specified in 27.1545 through 27.1565, and

    (2) Any additional information, instrument markings, and placards required for the safe operation of rotorcraft with unusual design, operating or handling characteristics.

(b) Each marking and placard prescribed in paragraph (a) of this section—

    (1) Must be displayed in a conspicuous place; and

    (2) May not be easily erased, disfigured, or obscured.

27.1543 Instrument markings: general

For each instrument—

(a) When markings are on the cover glass of the instrument, there must be means to maintain the correct alignment of the glass cover with the face of the dial; and

(b) Each arc and line must be wide enough, and located, to be clearly visible to the pilot.

27.1545 Airspeed indicator

(a) Each airspeed indicator must be marked as specified in paragraph (b) of this section, with the marks located at the corresponding indicated airspeeds.

(b) The following markings must be made:

    (1) A red radial line—

        (i) For rotorcraft other than helicopters, at V_{NE}; and

        (ii) For helicopters at V_{NE} (power-on).

    (2) A red cross-hatched radial line at V_{NE} (power-off) for helicopters, if V_{NE} (power-off) is less than V_{NE} (power-on).

    (3) For the caution range, a yellow arc.

FAR 27

(4) For the safe operating range, a green arc.

(Secs. 313(a), 601, 603, 604, and 605 of the Federal Aviation Act of 1958 (49 U.S.C. 1354(a), 1421, 1423, 1424, and 1425); and sec. 6(c) of the Dept. of Transportation Act (49 U.S.C. 1655(c)))

[Doc. No. 5074, 29 FR 15695, Nov. 24, 1964, as amended by Amdt. 27–14, 43 FR 2325, Jan. 16, 1978; 43 FR 3900, Jan. 30, 1978; Amdt. 27–16, 43 FR 50599, Oct. 30, 1978]

27.1547 Magnetic direction indicator

(a) A placard meeting the requirements of this section must be installed on or near the magnetic direction indicator.

(b) The placard must show the calibration of the instrument in level flight with the engines operating.

(c) The placard must state whether the calibration was made with radio receivers on or off.

(d) Each calibration reading must be in terms of magnetic heading in not more than 45 degree increments.

(e) If a magnetic nonstabilized direction indicator can have a deviation of more than 10 degrees caused by the operation of electrical equipment, the placard must state which electrical loads, or combination of loads, would cause a deviation of more than 10 degrees when turned on.

(Secs. 313(a), 601, 603, 604, and 605 of the Federal Aviation Act of 1958 (49 U.S.C. 1354(a), 1421, 1423, 1424, and 1425); and sec. 6(c) of the Dept. of Transportation Act (49 U.S.C. 1655(c)))

[Doc. No. 5074, 29 FR 15695, Nov. 24, 1964, as amended by Amdt. 27–13, 42 FR 36972, July 18, 1977]

27.1549 Powerplant instruments

For each required powerplant instrument, as appropriate to the type of instrument—

(a) Each maximum and, if applicable, minimum safe operating limit must be marked with a red radial or a red line;

(b) Each normal operating range must be marked with a green arc or green line, not extending beyond the maximum and minimum safe limits;

(c) Each takeoff and precautionary range must be marked with a yellow arc or yellow line;

(d) Each engine or propeller range that is restricted because of excessive vibration stresses must be marked with red arcs or red lines; and

(e) Each OEI limit or approved operating range must be marked to be clearly differentiated from the markings of paragraphs (a) through (d) of this section except that no marking is normally required for the 30-second OEI limit.

[Amdt. 27–11, 41 FR 55470, Dec. 20, 1976, as amended by Amdt. 27–23, 53 FR 34215, Sept. 2, 1988; Amdt. 27–29, 59 FR 47768, Sept. 16, 1994]

27.1551 Oil quantity indicator

Each oil quantity indicator must be marked with enough increments to indicate readily and accurately the quantity of oil.

27.1553 Fuel quantity indicator

If the unusable fuel supply for any tank exceeds one gallon, or five percent of the tank capacity, whichever is greater, a red arc must be marked on its indicator extending from the calibrated zero reading to the lowest reading obtainable in level flight.

27.1555 Control markings

(a) Each cockpit control, other than primary flight controls or control whose function is obvious, must be plainly marked as to its function and method of operation.

(b) For powerplant fuel controls—

(1) Each fuel tank selector control must be marked to indicate the position corresponding to each tank and to each existing cross feed position;

(2) If safe operation requires the use of any tanks in a specific sequence, that sequence must be marked on, or adjacent to, the selector for those tanks; and

(3) Each valve control for any engine of a multiengine rotorcraft must be marked to indicate the position corresponding to each engine controlled.

(c) Usable fuel capacity must be marked as follows:

(1) For fuel systems having no selector controls, the usable fuel capacity of the system must be indicated at the fuel quantity indicator.

(2) For fuel systems having selector controls, the usable fuel capacity available at each selector control position must be indicated near the selector control.

(d) For accessory, auxiliary, and emergency controls—

(1) Each essential visual position indicator, such as those showing rotor pitch or landing gear position, must be marked so that each crewmember can determine at any time the position of the unit to which it relates; and

(2) Each emergency control must be red and must be marked as to method of operation.

(e) For rotorcraft incorporating retractable landing gear, the maximum landing gear operating speed must be displayed in clear view of the pilot.

[Doc. No. 5074, 29 FR 15695, Nov. 24, 1964, as amended by Amdt. 27–11, 41 FR 55470, Dec. 20, 1976; Amdt. 27–21, 49 FR 44435, Nov. 6, 1984]

27.1557 Miscellaneous markings and placards

(a) Baggage and cargo compartments, and ballast location. Each baggage and cargo compartment, and each ballast location must have a placard stating any limitations on contents, including weight, that are necessary under the loading requirements.

(b) Seats. If the maximum allowable weight to be carried in a seat is less than 170 pounds, a placard stating the lesser weight must be permanently attached to the seat structure.

(c) Fuel and oil filler openings. The following apply:

(1) Fuel filler openings must be marked at or near the filler cover with—

(i)   The word "fuel";

(ii) For reciprocating engine powered rotorcraft, the minimum fuel grade;

(iii) For turbine engine powered rotorcraft, the permissible fuel designations; and

(iv) For pressure fueling systems, the maximum permissible fueling supply pressure and the maximum permissible defueling pressure.

(2) Oil filler openings must be marked at or near the filler cover with the word "oil".

(d) Emergency exit placards. Each placard and operating control for each emergency exit must be red. A placard must be near each emergency exit control and must clearly indicate the location of that exit and its method of operation.

[Doc. No. 5074, 29 FR 15695, Nov. 24, 1964, as amended by Amdt. 27–11, 41 FR 55471, Dec. 20, 1976]

27.1559 Limitations placard

There must be a placard in clear view of the pilot that specifies the kinds of operations (such as VFR, IFR, day, night, or icing) for which the rotorcraft is approved.

[Amdt. 27–21, 49 FR 44435, Nov. 6, 1984]

27.1561 Safety equipment

(a) Each safety equipment control to be operated by the crew in emergency, such as controls for automatic liferaft releases, must be plainly marked as to its method of operation.

(b) Each location, such as a locker or compartment, that carries any fire extinguishing, signaling, or other life saving equipment, must be so marked.

27.1565   Tail rotor

Each tail rotor must be marked so that its disc is conspicuous under normal daylight ground conditions.

[Amdt. 27–2, 33 FR 965, Jan. 26, 1968]

Rotorcraft Flight Manual and Approved Manual Material

27.1581   General

(a) Furnishing information. A Rotorcraft Flight Manual must be furnished with each rotorcraft, and it must contain the following:

  (1) Information required by 27.1583 through 27.1589.

  (2) Other information that is necessary for safe operation because of design, operating, or handling characteristics.

(b) Approved information. Each part of the manual listed in 27.1583 through 27.1589, that is appropriate to the rotorcraft, must be furnished, verified, and approved, and must be segregated, identified, and clearly distinguished from each unapproved part of that manual.

(c) [Reserved]

(d) Table of contents. Each Rotorcraft Flight Manual must include a table of contents if the complexity of the manual indicates a need for it.

(Secs. 313(a), 601, 603, 604, and 605 of the Federal Aviation Act of 1958 (49 U.S.C. 1354(a), 1421, 1423, 1424, and 1425); and sec. 6(c) of the Dept. of Transportation Act (49 U.S.C. 1655(c)))

[Amdt. 27–14, 43 FR 2325, Jan. 16, 1978]

27.1583   Operating limitations

(a) Airspeed and rotor limitations. Information necessary for the marking of airspeed and rotor limitations on, or near, their respective indicators must be furnished. The significance of each limitation and of the color coding must be explained.

(b) Powerplant limitations. The following information must be furnished:

  (1) Limitations required by 27.1521.

  (2) Explanation of the limitations, when appropriate.

  (3) Information necessary for marking the instruments required by 27.1549 through 27.1553.

(c) Weight and loading distribution. The weight and center of gravity limits required by 27.25 and 27.27, respectively, must be furnished. If the variety of possible loading conditions warrants, instructions must be included to allow ready observance of the limitations.

(d) Flight crew. When a flight crew of more than one is required, the number and functions of the minimum flight crew determined under 27.1523 must be furnished.

(e) Kinds of operation. Each kind of operation for which the rotorcraft and its equipment installations are approved must be listed.

(f) [Reserved]

(g) Altitude. The altitude established under 27.1527 and an explanation of the limiting factors must be furnished.

(Secs. 313(a), 601, 603, 604, and 605 of the Federal Aviation Act of 1958 (49 U.S.C. 1354(a), 1421, 1423, 1424, and 1425); and sec. 6(c) of the Dept. of Transportation Act (49 U.S.C. 1655(c)))

[Doc. No. 5074, 29 FR 15695, Nov. 24, 1964, as amended by Amdt. 27–2, 33 FR 965, Jan. 26, 1968; Amdt. 27–14, 43 FR 2325, Jan. 16, 1978; Amdt. 27–16, 43 FR 50599, Oct. 30, 1978]

27.1585   Operating procedures

(a) Parts of the manual containing operating procedures must have information concerning any normal and emergency procedures and other information necessary for safe operation, including takeoff and landing procedures and associated airspeeds. The manual must contain any pertinent information including—

  (1) The kind of takeoff surface used in the tests and each appropriate climbout speed; and

  (2) The kind of landing surface used in the tests and appropriate approach and glide airspeeds.

(b) For multiengine rotorcraft, information identifying each operating condition in which the fuel system independence prescribed in 27.953 is necessary for safety must be furnished, together with instructions for placing the fuel system in a configuration used to show compliance with that section.

(c) For helicopters for which a V_{NE} (power-off) is established under 27.1505(c), information must be furnished to explain the V_{NE} (power-off) and the procedures for reducing airspeed to not more than the V_{NE} (power-off) following failure of all engines.

(d) For each rotorcraft showing compliance with 27.1353 (g)(2) or (g)(3), the operating procedures for disconnecting the battery from its charging source must be furnished.

(e) If the unusable fuel supply in any tank exceeds five percent of the tank capacity, or one gallon, whichever is greater, information must be furnished which indicates that when the fuel quantity indicator reads "zero" in level flight, any fuel remaining in the fuel tank cannot be used safely in flight.

(f) Information on the total quantity of usable fuel for each fuel tank must be furnished.

(g) The airspeeds and rotor speeds for minimum rate of descent and best glide angle as prescribed in 27.71 must be provided.

(Secs. 313(a), 601, 603, 604, and 605 of the Federal Aviation Act of 1958 (49 U.S.C. 1354(a), 1421, 1423, 1424, and 1425); and sec. 6(c) of the Dept. of Transportation Act (49 U.S.C. 1655(c)))

[Amdt. 27–1, 32 FR 6914, May 5, 1967, as amended by Amdt. 27–14, 43 FR 2326, Jan. 16, 1978; Amdt. 27–16, 43 FR 50599, Oct. 30, 1978; Amdt. 27–21, 49 FR 44435, Nov. 6, 1984]

27.1587   Performance information

(a) The Rotorcraft Flight Manual must contain the following information, determined in accordance with 27.49 through 27.87 and 27.143(c) and (d):

  (1) Enough information to determine the limiting height-speed envelope.

  (2) Information relative to—

    (i) The steady rates of climb and descent, in-ground effect and out-of-ground effect hovering ceilings, together with the corresponding airspeeds and other pertinent information including the calculated effects of altitude and temperatures;

    (ii) The maximum weight for each altitude and temperature condition at which the rotorcraft can safely hover in-ground effect and out-of-ground effect in winds of not less than 17 knots from all azimuths. These data must be clearly referenced to the appropriate hover charts. In addition, if there are other combinations of weight, altitude and temperature for which performance information is provided and at which the rotorcraft cannot land and take off safely with the maximum wind value, those portions of the operating envelope and the appropriate safe wind conditions must be stated in the Rotorcraft Flight Manual;

    (iii) For reciprocating engine-powered rotorcraft, the maximum atmospheric temperature at which compliance with the cooling provisions of 27.1041 through 27.1045 is shown; and

    (iv) Glide distance as a function of altitude when autorotating at the speeds and conditions for minimum rate of descent and best glide as determined in 27.71.

(b) The Rotorcraft Flight Manual must contain—

  (1) In its performance information section any pertinent information concerning the takeoff weights and altitudes used in compliance with 27.51; and

(2) The horizontal takeoff distance determined in accordance with 27.65(a)(2)(i).

(Secs. 313(a), 601, 603, 604, and 605 of the Federal Aviation Act of 1958 (49 U.S.C. 1354(a), 1421, 1423, 1424, and 1425); and sec. 6(c) of the Dept. of Transportation Act (49 U.S.C. 1655(c)))

[Doc. No. 5074, 29 FR 15695, Nov. 24, 1964, as amended by Amdt. 27–14, 43 FR 2326, Jan. 16, 1978; Amdt. 27–21, 49 FR 44435, Nov. 6, 1984; Amdt. No. 27–44, 73 FR 11000, Feb. 29, 2008; 73 FR 33876, June 16, 2008]

27.1589   Loading information

There must be loading instructions for each possible loading condition between the maximum and minimum weights determined under 27.25 that can result in a center of gravity beyond any extreme prescribed in 27.27, assuming any probable occupant weights.

Appendix A to Part 27 — Instructions for Continued Airworthiness

A27.1   General

(a) This appendix specifies requirements for the preparation of Instructions for Continued Airworthiness as required by 27.1529.

(b) The Instructions for Continued Airworthiness for each rotorcraft must include the Instructions for Continued Airworthiness for each engine and rotor (hereinafter designated 'products'), for each appliance required by this chapter, and any required information relating to the interface of those appliances and products with the rotorcraft. If Instructions for Continued Airworthiness are not supplied by the manufacturer of an appliance or product installed in the rotorcraft, the Instructions for Continued Airworthiness for the rotorcraft must include the information essential to the continued airworthiness of the rotorcraft.

(c) The applicant must submit to the FAA a program to show how changes to the Instructions for Continued Airworthiness made by the applicant or by the manufacturers of products and appliances installed in the rotorcraft will be distributed.

A27.2   Format

(a) The Instructions for Continued Airworthiness must be in the form of a manual or manuals as appropriate for the quantity of data to be provided.

(b) The format of the manual or manuals must provide for a practical arrangement.

A27.3   Content

The contents of the manual or manuals must be prepared in the English language. The Instructions for Continued Airworthiness must contain the following manuals or sections, as appropriate, and information:

(a) Rotorcraft maintenance manual or section.

   (1) Introduction information that includes an explanation of the rotorcraft's features and data to the extent necessary for maintenance or preventive maintenance.

   (2) A description of the rotorcraft and its systems and installations including its engines, rotors, and appliances.

   (3) Basic control and operation information describing how the rotorcraft components and systems are controlled and how they operate, including any special procedures and limitations that apply.

   (4) Servicing information that covers details regarding servicing points, capacities of tanks, reservoirs, types of fluids to be used, pressures applicable to the various systems, location of access panels for inspection and servicing, locations of lubrication points, the lubricants to be used, equipment required for servicing, tow instructions and limitations, mooring, jacking, and leveling information.

(b) Maintenance instructions.

   (1) Scheduling information for each part of the rotorcraft and its engines, auxiliary power units, rotors, accessories, instruments and equipment that provides the recommended periods at which they should be cleaned, inspected, adjusted, tested, and lubricated, and the degree of inspection, the applicable wear tolerances, and work recommended at these periods. However, the applicant may refer to an accessory, instrument, or equipment manufacturer as the source of this information if the applicant shows the item has an exceptionally high degree of complexity requiring specialized maintenance techniques, test equipment, or expertise. The recommended overhaul periods and necessary cross references to the Airworthiness Limitations section of the manual must also be included. In addition, the applicant must include an inspection program that includes the frequency and extent of the inspections necessary to provide for the continued airworthiness of the rotorcraft.

   (2) Troubleshooting information describing problem malfunctions, how to recognize those malfunctions, and the remedial action for those malfunctions.

   (3) Information describing the order and method of removing and replacing products and parts with any necessary precautions to be taken.

   (4) Other general procedural instructions including procedures for system testing during ground running, symmetry checks, weighing and determining the center of gravity, lifting and shoring, and storage limitations.

(c) Diagrams of structural access plates and information needed to gain access for inspections when access plates are not provided.

(d) Details for the application of special inspection techniques including radiographic and ultrasonic testing where such processes are specified.

(e) Information needed to apply protective treatments to the structure after inspection.

(f) All data relative to structural fasteners such as identification, discarded recommendations, and torque values.

(g) A list of special tools needed.

A27.4   Airworthiness Limitations section

The Instructions for Continued Airworthiness must contain a section, titled Airworthiness Limitations that is segregated and clearly distinguishable from the rest of the document. This section must set forth each mandatory replacement time, structural inspection interval, and related structural inspection procedure required for type certification. If the Instructions for Continued Airworthiness consist of multiple documents, the section required by this paragraph must be included in the principal manual. This section must contain a legible statement in a prominent location that reads: "The Airworthiness Limitations section is FAA approved and specifies inspections and other maintenance required under 43.16 and 91.403 of the Federal Aviation Regulations unless an alternative program has been FAA approved."

[Amdt. 27–17, 45 FR 60178, Sept. 11, 1980, as amended by Amdt. 27–24, 54 FR 34329, Aug. 18, 1989]

Appendix B to Part 27—Airworthiness Criteria for Helicopter Instrument Flight

I. General. A normal category helicopter may not be type certificated for operation under the instrument flight rules (IFR) of this chapter unless it meets the design and installation requirements contained in this appendix.

II. Definitions.

(a) V_{YI} means instrument climb speed, utilized instead of V_Y for compliance with the climb requirements for instrument flight.

(b) V_{NEI} means instrument flight never exceed speed, utilized instead of V_{NE} for compliance with maximum limit speed requirements for instrument flight.

(c) V_{MINI} means instrument flight minimum speed, utilized in complying with minimum limit speed requirements for instrument flight.

III. Trim. It must be possible to trim the cyclic, collective, and directional control forces to zero at all approved IFR airspeeds, power settings, and configurations appropriate to the type.

IV. Static longitudinal stability.

(a) General. The helicopter must possess positive static longitudinal control force stability at critical combinations of weight and center of gravity at the conditions specified in paragraph IV (b) or (c) of this appendix, as appropriate. The stick force must vary with speed so that any substantial speed change results in a stick force clearly perceptible to the pilot. For single-pilot approval, the airspeed must return to within 10 percent of the trim speed when the control force is slowly released for each trim condition specified in paragraph IV(b) of the this appendix.

(b) For single-pilot approval:

(1) Climb. Stability must be shown in climb throughout the speed range 20 knots either side of trim with—

   (i) The helicopter trimmed at V_{YI};

   (ii) Landing gear retracted (if retractable); and

   (iii) Power required for limit climb rate (at least 1,000 fpm) at V_{YI} or maximum continuous power, whichever is less.

(2) Cruise. Stability must be shown throughout the speed range from 0.7 to 1.1 V_H or V_{NEI}, whichever is lower, not to exceed ±20 knots from trim with—

   (i) The helicopter trimmed and power adjusted for level flight at 0.9 V_H or 0.9 V_{NEI}, whichever is lower; and

   (ii) Landing gear retracted (if retractable).

(3) Slow cruise. Stability must be shown throughout the speed range from 0.9 V_{MINI} to 1.3 V_{MINI} or 20 knots above trim speed, whichever is greater, with—

   (i) The helicopter trimmed and power adjusted for level flight at 1.1 V_{MINI}; and

   (ii) Landing gear retracted (if retractable).

(4) Descent. Stability must be shown throughout the speed range 20 knots either side of trim with—

   (i) The helicopter trimmed at 0.8 V_H or 0.8 V_{NEI} (or 0.8 V_{LE} for the landing gear extended case), whichever is lower;

   (ii) Power required for 1,000 fpm descent at trim speed; and

   (iii) Landing gear extended and retracted, if applicable.

(5) Approach. Stability must be shown throughout the speed range from 0.7 times the minimum recommended approach speed to 20 knots above the maximum recommended approach speed with—

   (i) The helicopter trimmed at the recommended approach speed or speeds;

   (ii) Landing gear extended and retracted, if applicable; and

   (iii) Power required to maintain a 3° glide path and power required to maintain the steepest approach gradient for which approval is requested.

(c) Helicopters approved for a minimum crew of two pilots must comply with the provisions of paragraphs IV(b)(2) and IV(b)(5) of this appendix.

V. Static Lateral Directional Stability.

(a) Static directional stability must be positive throughout the approved ranges of airspeed, power, and vertical speed. In straight and steady sideslips up to ±10° from trim, directional control position must increase without discontinuity with the angle of sideslip, except for a small range of sideslip angles around trim. At greater angles up to the maximum sideslip angle appropriate to the type, increased directional control position must produce an increased angle of sideslip. It must be possible to maintain balanced flight without exceptional pilot skill or alertness.

(b) During sideslips up to ±10° from trim throughout the approved ranges of airspeed, power, and vertical speed, there must be no negative dihedral stability perceptible to the pilot through lateral control motion or force. Longitudinal cyclic movement with sideslip must not be excessive.

VI. Dynamic stability.

(a) For single-pilot approval—

(1) Any oscillation having a period of less than 5 seconds must damp to 1/2 amplitude in not more than one cycle.

(2) Any oscillation having a period of 5 seconds or more but less than 10 seconds must damp to 1/2 amplitude in not more than two cycles.

(3) Any oscillation having a period of 10 seconds or more but less than 20 seconds must be damped.

(4) Any oscillation having a period of 20 seconds or more may not achieve double amplitude in less than 20 seconds.

(5) Any aperiodic response may not achieve double amplitude in less than 6 seconds.

(b) For helicopters approved with a minimum crew of two pilots—

(1) Any oscillation having a period of less than 5 seconds must damp to 1/2 amplitude in not more than two cycles.

(2) Any oscillation having a period of 5 seconds or more but less than 10 seconds must be damped.

(3) Any oscillation having a period of 10 seconds or more may not achieve double amplitude in less than 10 seconds.

VII. Stability Augmentation System (SAS).

(a) If a SAS is used, the reliability of the SAS must be related to the effects of its failure. Any SAS failure condition that would prevent continued safe flight and landing must be extremely improbable. It must be shown that, for any failure condition of the SAS that is not shown to be extremely improbable—

(1) The helicopter is safely controllable when the failure or malfunction occurs at any speed or altitude within the approved IFR operating limitations; and

(2) The overall flight characteristics of the helicopter allow for prolonged instrument flight without undue pilot effort. Additional unrelated probable failures affecting the control system must be considered. In addition—

   (i) The controllability and maneuverability requirements in Subpart B of this part must be met throughout a practical flight envelope;

   (ii) The flight control, trim, and dynamic stability characteristics must not be impaired below a level needed to allow continued safe flight and landing; and

   (iii) The static longitudinal and static directional stability requirements of Subpart B must be met throughout a practical flight envelope.

(b) The SAS must be designed so that it cannot create a hazardous deviation in flight path or produce hazardous loads on the helicopter during normal operation or in the event of malfunction or failure, assuming corrective action begins within an appropriate period of time. Where multiple systems are installed, subsequent malfunction conditions must be considered in sequence unless their occurrence is shown to be improbable.

VIII. Equipment, systems, and installation. The basic equipment and installation must comply with 29.1303, 29.1431, and 29.1433 through Amendment 29–14, with the following exceptions and additions:

(a) Flight and Navigation Instruments.

(1) A magnetic gyro-stablized direction indicator instead of a gyroscopic direction indicator required by 29.1303(h); and

(2) A standby attitude indicator which meets the requirements of 29.1303(g)(1) through (7) instead of a rate-of-turn indicator required by 29.1303(g). For two-pilot configurations, one pi-

FAR 27

lot's primary indicator may be designated for this purpose. If standby batteries are provided, they may be charged from the aircraft electrical system if adequate isolation is incorporated.

(b) Miscellaneous requirements.

(1) Instrument systems and other systems essential for IFR flight that could be adversely affected by icing must be adequately protected when exposed to the continuous and intermittent maximum icing conditions defined in appendix C of Part 29 of this chapter, whether or not the rotorcraft is certificated for operation in icing conditions.

(2) There must be means in the generating system to automatically de-energize and disconnect from the main bus any power source developing hazardous overvoltage.

(3) Each required flight instrument using a power supply (electric, vacuum, etc.) must have a visual means integral with the instrument to indicate the adequacy of the power being supplied.

(4) When multiple systems performing like functions are required, each system must be grouped, routed, and spaced so that physical separation between systems is provided to ensure that a single malfunction will not adversely affect more than one system.

(5) For systems that operate the required flight instruments at each pilot's station—

(i) Only the required flight instruments for the first pilot may be connected to that operating system;

(ii) Additional instruments, systems, or equipment may not be connected to an operating system for a second pilot unless provisions are made to ensure the continued normal functioning of the required instruments in the event of any malfunction of the additional instruments, systems, or equipment which is not shown to be extremely improbable;

(iii) The equipment, systems, and installations must be designed so that one display of the information essential to the safety of flight which is provided by the instruments will remain available to a pilot, without additional crewmember action, after any single failure or combination of failures that is not shown to be extremely improbable; and

(iv) For single-pilot configurations, instruments which require a static source must be provided with a means of selecting an alternate source and that source must be calibrated.

IX. Rotorcraft Flight Manual. A Rotorcraft Flight Manual or Rotorcraft Flight Manual IFR Supplement must be provided and must contain—

(a) Limitations. The approved IFR flight envelope, the IFR flightcrew composition, the revised kinds of operation, and the steepest IFR precision approach gradient for which the helicopter is approved;

(b) Procedures. Required information for proper operation of IFR systems and the recommended procedures in the event of stability augmentation or electrical system failures; and

(c) Performance. If V_{YI} differs from V_Y, climb performance at V_{YI} and with maximum continuous power throughout the ranges of weight, altitude, and temperature for which approval is requested.

X. Electrical and electronic system lightning protection. For regulations concerning lightning protection for electrical and electronic systems, see 27.1316.

[Amdt. 27–19, 48 FR 4389, Jan. 31, 1983, as amended by Amdt. 27–44, 73 FR 11000, Feb. 29, 2008; Amdt. 27–46, 76 FR 33135, June 8, 2011]

Appendix C to Part 27— Criteria for Category A

C27.1   General

A small multiengine rotorcraft may not be type certificated for Category A operation unless it meets the design installation and performance requirements contained in this appendix in addition to the requirements of this part.

C27.2   Applicable part 29 sections. The following sections of part 29 of this chapter must be met in addition to the requirements of this part:

29.45(a) and (b)(2)—General.
29.49(a)—Performance at minimum operating speed.
29.51—Takeoff data: General.
29.53—Takeoff: Category A.
29.55—Takeoff decision point: Category A.
29.59—Takeoff Path: Category A.
29.60—Elevated heliport takeoff path: Category A.
29.61—Takeoff distance: Category A.
29.62—Rejected takeoff: Category A.
29.64—Climb: General.
29.65(a)—Climb: AEO.
29.67(a)—Climb: OEI.
29.75—Landing: General.
29.77—Landing decision point: Category A.
29.79—Landing: Category A.
29.81—Landing distance (Ground level sites): Category A.
29.85—Balked landing: Category A.
29.87(a)—Height-velocity envelope.
29.547(a) and (b)—Main and tail rotor structure.
29.861(a)—Fire protection of structure, controls, and other parts.
29.901(c)—Powerplant: Installation.
29.903(b) (c) and (e)—Engines.
29.908(a)—Cooling fans.
29.917(b) and (c)(1)—Rotor drive system: Design.
29.927(c)(1)—Additional tests.
29.953(a)—Fuel system independence.
29.1027(a)—Transmission and gearboxes: General.
29.1045(a)(1), (b), (c), (d), and (f)—Climb cooling test procedures.
29.1047(a)—Takeoff cooling test procedures.
29.1181(a)—Designated fire zones: Regions included.
29.1187(e)—Drainage and ventilation of fire zones.
29.1189(c)—Shutoff means.
29.1191(a)(1)—Firewalls.
29.1193(e)—Cowling and engine compartment covering.
29.1195(a) and (d)—Fire extinguishing systems (one shot).
29.1197—Fire extinguishing agents.
29.1199—Extinguishing agent containers.
29.1201—Fire extinguishing system materials.
29.1305(a) (6) and (b)—Powerplant instruments.
29.1309(b)(2) (i) and (d)—Equipment, systems, and installations.
29.1323(c)(1)—Airspeed indicating system.
29.1331(b)—Instruments using a power supply.
29.1351(d)(2)—Electrical systems and equipment: General (operation without normal electrical power).
29.1587(a)—Performance information.

NOTE: *In complying with the paragraphs listed in paragraph C27.2 above, relevant material in the AC "Certification of Transport Category Rotorcraft" should be used.*

[Doc. No. 28008, 61 FR 21907, May 10, 1996]

Appendix D to Part 27 — HIRF Environments and Equipment HIRF Test Levels

This appendix specifies the HIRF environments and equipment HIRF test levels for electrical and electronic systems under 27.1317. The field strength values for the HIRF environments and laboratory equipment HIRF test levels are expressed in root-mean-square units measured during the peak of the modulation cycle.

(a) HIRF environment I is specified in the following table:

TABLE I.—HIRF ENVIRONMENT I		
FREQUENCY	FIELD STRENGTH (VOLTS/METER)	
	PEAK	AVERAGE
10 kHz–2 MHz	50	50
2 MHz–30 MHz	100	100
30 MHz–100 MHz	50	50
100 MHz–400 MHz	100	100
400 MHz–700 MHz	700	50
700 MHz–1 GHz	700	100
1 GHz–2 GHz	2,000	200
2 GHz–6 GHz	3,000	200
6 GHz–8 GHz	1,000	200
8 GHz–12 GHz	3,000	300
12 GHz–18 GHz	2,000	200
18 GHz–40 GHz	600	200

In this table, the higher field strength applies at the frequency band edges.

(b) HIRF environment II is specified in the following table:

TABLE II.—HIRF ENVIRONMENT II		
FREQUENCY	FIELD STRENGTH (VOLTS/METER)	
	PEAK	AVERAGE
10 kHz–500 kHz	20	20
500 kHz–2 MHz	30	30
2 MHz–30 MHz	100	100
30 MHz–100 MHz	10	10
100 MHz–200 MHz	30	10
200 MHz–400 MHz	10	10
400 MHz–1 GHz	700	40
1 GHz–2 GHz	1,300	160
2 GHz–4 GHz	3,000	120
4 GHz–6 GHz	3,000	160
6 GHz–8 GHz	400	170
8 GHz–12 GHz	1,230	230
12 GHz–18 GHz	730	190
18 GHz–40 GHz	600	150

In this table, the higher field strength applies at the frequency band edges.

In this table, the higher field strength applies at the frequency band edges.

(c) HIRF environment III is specified in the following table:

TABLE III.—HIRF ENVIRONMENT III		
FREQUENCY	FIELD STRENGTH (VOLTS/METER)	
	PEAK	AVERAGE
10 kHz–100 kHz	150	150
100 kHz–400 MHz	200	200
400 MHz–700 MHz	730	200
700 MHz–1 GHz	1,400	240
1 GHz–2 GHz	5,000	250
2 GHz–4 GHz	6,000	490
4 GHz–6 GHz	7,200	400
6 GHz–8 GHz	1,100	170
8 GHz–12 GHz	5,000	330
12 GHz–18 GHz	2,000	330
18 GHz–40 GHz	1,000	420

In this table, the higher field strength applies at the frequency band edges.

FAR 27

(d) Equipment HIRF Test Level 1.

(1) From 10 kilohertz (kHz) to 400 megahertz (MHz), use conducted susceptibility tests with continuous wave (CW) and 1 kHz square wave modulation with 90 percent depth or greater. The conducted susceptibility current must start at a minimum of 0.6 milliamperes (mA) at 10 kHz, increasing 20 decibels (dB) per frequency decade to a minimum of 30 mA at 500 kHz.

(2) From 500 kHz to 40 MHz, the conducted susceptibility current must be at least 30 mA.

(3) From 40 MHz to 400 MHz, use conducted susceptibility tests, starting at a minimum of 30 mA at 40 MHz, decreasing 20 dB per frequency decade to a minimum of 3 mA at 400 MHz.

(4) From 100 MHz to 400 MHz, use radiated susceptibility tests at a minimum of 20 volts per meter (V/m) peak with CW and 1 kHz square wave modulation with 90 percent depth or greater.

(5) From 400 MHz to 8 gigahertz (GHz), use radiated susceptibility tests at a minimum of 150 V/m peak with pulse modulation of 4 percent duty cycle with a 1 kHz pulse repetition frequency. This signal must be switched on and off at a rate of 1 Hz with a duty cycle of 50 percent.

(e) Equipment HIRF Test Level 2. Equipment HIRF test level 2 is HIRF environment II in table II of this appendix reduced by acceptable aircraft transfer function and attenuation curves. Testing must cover the frequency band of 10 kHz to 8 GHz.

(f) Equipment HIRF Test Level 3.

(1) From 10 kHz to 400 MHz, use conducted susceptibility tests, starting at a minimum of 0.15 mA at 10 kHz, increasing 20 dB per frequency decade to a minimum of 7.5 mA at 500 kHz.

(2) From 500 kHz to 40 MHz, use conducted susceptibility tests at a minimum of 7.5 mA.

(3) From 40 MHz to 400 MHz, use conducted susceptibility tests, starting at a minimum of 7.5 mA at 40 MHz, decreasing 20 dB per frequency decade to a minimum of 0.75 mA at 400 MHz.

(4) From 100 MHz to 8 GHz, use radiated susceptibility tests at a minimum of 5 V/m.

[Doc. No. FAA–2006–23657, 72 FR 44027, Aug. 6, 2007]

PART 33 — AIRWORTHINESS STANDARDS: AIRCRAFT ENGINES

Authority: 49 U.S.C. 106(g), 40113, 44701, 44702, 44704.

Source: Docket No. 3025, 29 FR 7453, June 10, 1964, unless otherwise noted.

> **NOTE:** *For miscellaneous amendments to cross references in this Part 33, see Amdt. 33–2, 31 FR 9211, July 6, 1966.*

Subpart A — General

33.1   Applicability

(a) This part prescribes airworthiness standards for the issue of type certificates and changes to those certificates, for aircraft engines.

(b) Each person who applies under part 21 for such a certificate or change must show compliance with the applicable requirements of this part and the applicable requirements of part 34 of this chapter.

[Amdt. 33–7, 41 FR 55474, Dec. 20, 1976, as amended by Amdt. 33–14, 55 FR 32861, Aug. 10, 1990]

33.3   General

Each applicant must show that the aircraft engine concerned meets the applicable requirements of this part.

33.4   Instructions for Continued Airworthiness

The applicant must prepare Instructions for Continued Airworthiness in accordance with appendix A to this part that are acceptable to the Administrator. The instructions may be incomplete at type certification if a program exists to ensure their completion prior to delivery of the first aircraft with the engine installed, or upon issuance of a standard certificate of airworthiness for the aircraft with the engine installed, whichever occurs later.

[Amdt. 33–9, 45 FR 60181, Sept. 11, 1980]

33.5   Instruction manual for installing and operating the engine

Each applicant must prepare and make available to the Administrator prior to the issuance of the type certificate, and to the owner at the time of

FAR
33

delivery of the engine, approved instructions for installing and operating the engine. The instructions must include at least the following:

(a) Installation instructions.

    (1) The location of engine mounting attachments, the method of attaching the engine to the aircraft, and the maximum allowable load for the mounting attachments and related structure.

    (2) The location and description of engine connections to be attached to accessories, pipes, wires, cables, ducts, and cowling.

    (3) An outline drawing of the engine including overall dimensions.

    (4) A definition of the physical and functional interfaces with the aircraft and aircraft equipment, including the propeller when applicable.

    (5) Where an engine system relies on components that are not part of the engine type design, the interface conditions and reliability requirements for those components upon which engine type certification is based must be specified in the engine installation instructions directly or by reference to appropriate documentation.

    (6) A list of the instruments necessary for control of the engine, including the overall limits of accuracy and transient response required of such instruments for control of the operation of the engine, must also be stated so that the suitability of the instruments as installed may be assessed.

(b) Operation instructions.

    (1) The operating limitations established by the Administrator.

    (2) The power or thrust ratings and procedures for correcting for nonstandard atmosphere.

    (3) The recommended procedures, under normal and extreme ambient conditions for—

        (i) Starting;

        (ii) Operating on the ground; and

        (iii) Operating during flight.

    (4) For rotorcraft engines having one or more OEI ratings, applicants must provide data on engine performance characteristics and variability to enable the aircraft manufacturer to establish aircraft power assurance procedures.

    (5) A description of the primary and all alternate modes, and any back-up system, together with any associated limitations, of the engine control system and its interface with the aircraft systems, including the propeller when applicable.

(c) Safety analysis assumptions. The assumptions of the safety analysis as described in 33.75(d) with respect to the reliability of safety devices, instrumentation, early warning devices, maintenance checks, and similar equipment or procedures that are outside the control of the engine manufacturer.

[Amdt. 33–6, 39 FR 35463, Oct. 1, 1974, as amended by Amdt. 33–9, 45 FR 60181, Sept. 11, 1980; Amdt. 33–24, 47 FR 50867, Sept. 4, 2007; Amdt. 33–25, 73 FR 48123, Aug. 18, 2008; Amdt. 33–26, 73 FR 48284, Aug. 19, 2008]

33.7   Engine ratings and operating limitations

(a) Engine ratings and operating limitations are established by the Administrator and included in the engine certificate data sheet specified in 21.41 of this chapter, including ratings and limitations based on the operating conditions and information specified in this section, as applicable, and any other information found necessary for safe operation of the engine.

(b) For reciprocating engines, ratings and operating limitations are established relating to the following:

    (1) Horsepower or torque, r.p.m., manifold pressure, and time at critical pressure altitude and sea level pressure altitude for—

        (i) Rated maximum continuous power (relating to unsupercharged operation or to operation in each supercharger mode as applicable); and

        (ii) Rated takeoff power (relating to unsupercharged operation or to operation in each supercharger mode as applicable).

    (2) Fuel grade or specification.

    (3) Oil grade or specification.

    (4) Temperature of the—

        (i) Cylinder;

        (ii) Oil at the oil inlet; and

        (iii) Turbosupercharger turbine wheel inlet gas.

    (5) Pressure of—

        (i) Fuel at the fuel inlet; and

        (ii) Oil at the main oil gallery.

    (6) Accessory drive torque and overhang moment.

    (7) Component life.

    (8) Turbosupercharger turbine wheel r.p.m.

(c) For turbine engines, ratings and operating limitations are established relating to the following:

    (1) Horsepower, torque, or thrust, r.p.m., gas temperature, and time for—

        (i) Rated maximum continuous power or thrust (augmented);

        (ii) Rated maximum continuous power or thrust (unaugmented);

        (iii) Rated takeoff power or thrust (augmented);

        (iv) Rated takeoff power or thrust (unaugmented);

        (v) Rated 30-minute OEI power;

        (vi) Rated 21/2-minute OEI power;

        (vii) Rated continuous OEI power; and

        (viii) Rated 2-minute OEI Power;

        (ix) Rated 30-second OEI power; and

        (x) Auxiliary power unit (APU) mode of operation.

    (2) Fuel designation or specification.

    (3) Oil grade or specification.

    (4) Hydraulic fluid specification.

    (5) Temperature of—

        (i) Oil at a location specified by the applicant;

        (ii) Induction air at the inlet face of a supersonic engine, including steady state operation and transient overtemperature and time allowed;

        (iii) Hydraulic fluid of a supersonic engine;

        (iv) Fuel at a location specified by the applicant; and

        (v) External surfaces of the engine, if specified by the applicant.

    (6) Pressure of—

        (i) Fuel at the fuel inlet;

        (ii) Oil at a location specified by the applicant;

        (iii) Induction air at the inlet face of a supersonic engine, including steady state operation and transient overpressure and time allowed; and

        (iv) Hydraulic fluid.

    (7) Accessory drive torque and overhang moment.

    (8) Component life.

    (9) Fuel filtration.

    (10) Oil filtration.

    (11) Bleed air.

    (12) The number of start-stop stress cycles approved for each rotor disc and spacer.

    (13) Inlet air distortion at the engine inlet.

    (14) Transient rotor shaft overspeed r.p.m., and number of overspeed occurrences.

(15) Transient gas overtemperature, and number of overtemperature occurrences.

(16) Transient engine overtorque, and number of overtorque occurences.

(17) Maximum engine overtorque for turbopropeller and turboshaft engines incorporating free power turbines.

(18) For engines to be used in supersonic aircraft, engine rotor windmilling rotational r.p.m.

(d) In determining the engine performance and operating limitations, the overall limits of accuracy of the engine control system and of the necessary instrumentation as defined in 33.5(a)(6) must be taken into account.

[Amdt. 33–6, 39 FR 35463, Oct. 1, 1974, as amended by Amdt. 33–10, 49 FR 6850, Feb. 23, 1984; Amdt. 33–11, 51 FR 10346, Mar. 25, 1986; Amdt. 33–12, 53 FR 34220, Sept. 2, 1988; Amdt. 33–18, 61 FR 31328, June 19, 1996; Amdt. No. 33–26, 73 FR 48284, Aug. 19, 2008; Amdt. No. 33–30, 74 FR 45310, Sept. 2, 2009]

33.8 Selection of engine power and thrust ratings

(a) Requested engine power and thrust ratings must be selected by the applicant.

(b) Each selected rating must be for the lowest power or thrust that all engines of the same type may be expected to produce under the conditions used to determine that rating.

[Amdt. 33–3, 32 FR 3736, Mar. 4, 1967]

Subpart B — Design and Construction; General

33.11 Applicability

This subpart prescribes the general design and construction requirements for reciprocating and turbine aircraft engines.

33.13 [Reserved]

33.15 Materials

The suitability and durability of materials used in the engine must—

(a) Be established on the basis of experience or tests; and

(b) Conform to approved specifications (such as industry or military specifications) that ensure their having the strength and other properties assumed in the design data.

Secs. 313(a), 601, and 603, 72 Stat. 759, 775, 49 U.S.C. 1354(a), 1421, and 1423; sec. 6(c), 49 U.S.C. 1655(c))

[Amdt. 33–8, 42 FR 15047, Mar. 17, 1977, as amended by Amdt. 33–10, 49 FR 6850, Feb. 23, 1984]

33.17 Fire prevention

(a) The design and construction of the engine and the materials used must minimize the probability of the occurrence and spread of fire during normal operation and failure conditions, and must minimize the effect of such a fire. In addition, the design and construction of turbine engines must minimize the probability of the occurrence of an internal fire that could result in structural failure or other hazardous effects.

(b) Except as provided in paragraph (c) of this section, each external line, fitting, and other component, which contains or conveys flammable fluid during normal engine operation, must be fire resistant or fireproof, as determined by the Administrator. Components must be shielded or located to safeguard against the ignition of leaking flammable fluid.

(c) A tank, which contains flammable fluids and any associated shut-off means and supports, which are part of and attached to the engine, must be fireproof either by construction or by protection unless damage by fire will not cause leakage or spillage of a hazardous quantity of flammable fluid. For a reciprocating engine having an integral oil sump of less than 23.7 liters capacity, the oil sump need not be fireproof or enclosed by a fireproof shield.

(d) An engine component designed, constructed, and installed to act as a firewall must be:

(1) Fireproof;

(2) Constructed so that no hazardous quantity of air, fluid or flame can pass around or through the firewall; and,

(3) Protected against corrosion;

(e) In addition to the requirements of paragraphs (a) and (b) of this section, engine control system components that are located in a designated fire zone must be fire resistant or fireproof, as determined by the Administrator.

(f) Unintentional accumulation of hazardous quantities of flammable fluid within the engine must be prevented by draining and venting.

(g) Any components, modules, or equipment, which are susceptible to or are potential sources of static discharges or electrical fault currents must be designed and constructed to be properly grounded to the engine reference, to minimize the risk of ignition in external areas where flammable fluids or vapors could be present.

[Amdt. 33–29, 74 FR 37930, July 30, 2009]

33.19 Durability

(a) Engine design and construction must minimize the development of an unsafe condition of the engine between overhaul periods. The design of the compressor and turbine rotor cases must provide for the containment of damage from rotor blade failure. Energy levels and trajectories of fragments resulting from rotor blade failure that lie outside the compressor and turbine rotor cases must be defined.

(b) Each component of the propeller blade pitch control system which is a part of the engine type design must meet the requirements of 35.21, 35.23, 35.42 and 35.43 of this chapter.

[Doc. No. 3025, 29 FR 7453, June 10, 1964, as amended by Amdt. 33–9, 45 FR 60181, Sept. 11, 1980; Amdt. 33–10, 49 FR 6851, Feb. 23, 1984; Amdt. 33–28, 73 FR 63346, Oct. 24, 2008]

33.21 Engine cooling

Engine design and construction must provide the necessary cooling under conditions in which the airplane is expected to operate.

33.23 Engine mounting attachments and structure

(a) The maximum allowable limit and ultimate loads for engine mounting attachments and related engine structure must be specified.

(b) The engine mounting attachments and related engine structure must be able to withstand—

(1) The specified limit loads without permanent deformation; and

(2) The specified ultimate loads without failure, but may exhibit permanent deformation.

[Amdt. 33–10, 49 FR 6851, Feb. 23, 1984]

33.25 Accessory attachments

The engine must operate properly with the accessory drive and mounting attachments loaded. Each engine accessory drive and mounting attachment must include provisions for sealing to prevent contamination of, or unacceptable leakage from, the engine interior. A drive and mounting attachment requiring lubrication for external drive splines, or coupling by engine oil, must include provisions for sealing to prevent unacceptable loss of oil and to prevent contamination from sources outside the chamber enclosing the drive connection. The design of the engine must allow for the examination, adjustment, or removal of each accessory required for engine operation.

[Amdt. 33–10, 49 FR 6851, Feb. 23, 1984]

33.27 Turbine, compressor, fan, and turbosupercharger rotor overspeed

(a) For each fan, compressor, turbine, and turbosupercharger rotor, the applicant must establish by test, analysis, or a combination of both, that each rotor will not burst when operated in the engine for 5 minutes at whichever of the conditions defined in paragraph (b) of this section is the most critical with respect to the integrity of such a rotor.

(1) Test rotors used to demonstrate compliance with this section that do not have the most adverse combination of material properties and dimensional tolerances must be tested at conditions which have been adjusted to ensure the minimum specification rotor possesses the required overspeed capability. This can be accomplished by increasing test speed, temperature, and/or loads.

(2) When an engine test is being used to demonstrate compliance with the overspeed conditions listed in paragraph (b)(3) or (b)(4) of this section and the failure of a component or system is sudden and transient, it may not be possible to operate the engine for 5 minutes after the failure. Under these circumstances, the actual overspeed duration is acceptable if the required maximum overspeed is achieved.

(b) When determining the maximum overspeed condition applicable to each rotor in order to comply with paragraphs (a) and (c) of this section, the applicant must evaluate the following rotor speeds taking into consideration the part's operating temperatures and temperature gradients throughout the engine's operating envelope:

(1) 120 percent of the maximum permissible rotor speed associated with any of the engine ratings except one-engine-inoperative (OEI) ratings of less than 2½ minutes.

(2) 115 percent of the maximum permissible rotor speed associated with any OEI ratings of less than 2½ minutes.

(3) 105 percent of the highest rotor speed that would result from either:

(i) The failure of the component or system which, in a representative installation of the engine, is the most critical with respect to overspeed when operating at any rating condition except OEI ratings of less than 2½ minutes, or

(ii) The failure of any component or system in a representative installation of the engine, in combination with any other failure of a component or system that would not normally be detected during a routine preflight check or during normal flight operation, that is the most critical with respect to overspeed, except as provided by paragraph (c) of this section, when operating at any rating condition except OEI ratings of less than 2½ minutes.

(4) 100 percent of the highest rotor speed that would result from the failure of the component or system which, in a representative installation of the engine, is the most critical with respect to overspeed when operating at any OEI rating of less than 2½ minutes.

(c) The highest overspeed that results from a complete loss of load on a turbine rotor, except as provided by paragraph (f) of this section, must be included in the overspeed conditions considered by paragraphs (b)(3)(i), (b)(3)(ii), and (b)(4) of this section, regardless of whether that overspeed results from a failure within the engine or external to the engine. The overspeed resulting from any other single failure must be considered when selecting the most limiting overspeed conditions applicable to each rotor. Overspeeds resulting from combinations of failures must also be considered unless the applicant can show that the probability of occurrence is not greater than extremely remote (probability range of 10^{-7} to 10^{-9} per engine flight hour).

(d) In addition, the applicant must demonstrate that each fan, compressor, turbine, and turbosupercharger rotor complies with paragraphs (d)(1) and (d)(2) of this section for the maximum overspeed achieved when subjected to the conditions specified in paragraphs (b)(3) and (b)(4) of this section. The applicant must use the approach in paragraph (a) of this section which specifies the required test conditions.

(1) Rotor Growth must not cause the engine to:

(i) Catch fire,

(ii) Release high-energy debris through the engine casing or result in a hazardous failure of the engine casing,

(iii) Generate loads greater than those ultimate loads specified in 33.23(a), or

(iv) Lose the capability of being shut down.

(2) Following an overspeed event and after continued operation the rotor may not exhibit conditions such as cracking or distortion which preclude continued safe operation.

(e) The design and functioning of engine control systems, instruments, and other methods not covered under 33.28 must ensure that the engine operating limitations that affect turbine, compressor, fan, and turbosupercharger rotor structural integrity will not be exceeded in service.

(f) Failure of a shaft section may be excluded from consideration in determining the highest overspeed that would result from a complete loss of load on a turbine rotor if the applicant:

(1) Identifies the shaft as an engine life-limited-part and complies with 33.70.

(2) Uses material and design features that are well understood and that can be analyzed by well-established and validated stress analysis techniques.

(3) Determines, based on an assessment of the environment surrounding the shaft section, that environmental influences are unlikely to cause a shaft failure. This assessment must include complexity of design, corrosion, wear, vibration, fire, contact with adjacent components or structure, overheating, and secondary effects from other failures or combination of failures.

(4) Identifies and declares, in accordance with 33.5, any assumptions regarding the engine installation in making the assessment described above in paragraph (f)(3) of this section.

(5) Assesses, and considers as appropriate, experience with shaft sections of similar design.

(6) Does not exclude the entire shaft.

(g) If analysis is used to meet the overspeed requirements, then the analytical tool must be validated to prior overspeed test results of a similar rotor. The tool must be validated for each material. The rotor being certified must not exceed the boundaries of the rotors being used to validate the analytical tool in terms of geometric shape, operating stress, and temperature. Validation includes the ability to accurately predict rotor dimensional growth and the burst speed. The predictions must also show that the rotor being certified does not have lower burst and growth margins than rotors used to validate the tool.

[Amdt. 33–31, 76 FR 42023, July 18, 2011]

33.28   Engine control systems

(a) Applicability. These requirements are applicable to any system or device that is part of engine type design, that controls, limits, or monitors engine operation, and is necessary for the continued airworthiness of the engine.

(b) Validation —

(1) Functional aspects. The applicant must substantiate by tests, analysis, or a combination thereof, that the engine control system performs the intended functions in a manner which:

(i) Enables selected values of relevant control parameters to be maintained and the engine kept within the approved operating limits over changing atmospheric conditions in the declared flight envelope;

(ii) Complies with the operability requirements of 33.51, 33.65 and 33.73, as appropriate, under all likely system inputs and allowable engine power or thrust demands unless it can be demonstrated that failure of the control function results in a non-dispatchable condition in the intended application;

(iii) Allows modulation of engine power or thrust with adequate sensitivity over the declared range of engine operating conditions; and

(iv) Does not create unacceptable power or thrust oscillations.

(2) Environmental limits. The applicant must demonstrate, when complying with 33.53 or 33.91, that the engine control system functionality will not be adversely affected by declared environmental conditions, including electromagnetic interference (EMI), High Intensity Radiated Fields (HIRF), and lightning. The limits to which the system has been qualified must be documented in the engine installation instructions.

(c) Control transitions.

(1) The applicant must demonstrate that, when fault or failure results in a change from one control mode to another, from one channel to another, or from the primary system to the back-up system, the change occurs so that:

(i) The engine does not exceed any of its operating limitations;

(ii) The engine does not surge, stall, or experience unacceptable thrust or power changes or oscillations or other unacceptable characteristics; and

(iii) There is a means to alert the flight crew if the crew is required to initiate, respond to, or be aware of the control mode change. The means to alert the crew must be described in the engine installation instructions, and the crew action must be described in the engine operating instructions;

(2) The magnitude of any change in thrust or power and the associated transition time must be identified and described in the engine installation instructions and the engine operating instructions.

(d) Engine control system failures. The applicant must design and construct the engine control system so that:

(1) The rate for Loss of Thrust (or Power) Control (LOTC/LOPC) events, consistent with the safety objective associated with the intended application can be achieved;

(2) In the full-up configuration, the system is single fault tolerant, as determined by the Administrator, for electrical or electronic failures with respect to LOTC/LOPC events;

(3) Single failures of engine control system components do not result in a hazardous engine effect; and

(4) Foreseeable failures or malfunctions leading to local events in the intended aircraft installation, such as fire, overheat, or failures leading to damage to engine control system components, do not result in a hazardous engine effect due to engine control system failures or malfunctions.

(e) System safety assessment. When complying with this section and 33.75, the applicant must complete a System Safety Assessment for the engine control system. This assessment must identify faults or failures that result in a change in thrust or power, transmission of erroneous data, or an effect on engine operability producing a surge or stall together with the predicted frequency of occurrence of these faults or failures.

(f) Protection systems.

(1) The design and functioning of engine control devices and systems, together with engine instruments and operating and maintenance instructions, must provide reasonable assurance that those engine operating limitations that affect turbine, compressor, fan, and turbosupercharger rotor structural integrity will not be exceeded in service.

(2) When electronic overspeed protection systems are provided, the design must include a means for testing, at least once per engine start/stop cycle, to establish the availability of the protection function. The means must be such that a complete test of the system can be achieved in the minimum number of cycles. If the test is not fully automatic, the requirement for a manual test must be contained in the engine instructions for operation.

(3) When overspeed protection is provided through hydromechanical or mechanical means, the applicant must demonstrate by test or other acceptable means that the overspeed function remains available between inspection and maintenance periods.

(g) Software. The applicant must design, implement, and verify all associated software to minimize the existence of errors by using a method, approved by the FAA, consistent with the criticality of the performed functions.

(h) Aircraft-supplied data. Single failures leading to loss, interruption or corruption of aircraft-supplied data (other than thrust or power command signals from the aircraft), or data shared between engines must:

(1) Not result in a hazardous engine effect for any engine; and

(2) Be detected and accommodated. The accommodation strategy must not result in an unacceptable change in thrust or power or an unacceptable change in engine operating and starting characteristics. The applicant must evaluate and document in the engine installation instructions the effects of these failures on engine power or thrust, engine operability, and starting characteristics throughout the flight envelope.

(i) Aircraft-supplied electrical power.

(1) The applicant must design the engine control system so that the loss, malfunction, or interruption of electrical power supplied from the aircraft to the engine control system will not result in any of the following:

(i) A hazardous engine effect, or

(ii) The unacceptable transmission of erroneous data.

(2) When an engine dedicated power source is required for compliance with paragraph (i)(1) of this section, its capacity should provide sufficient margin to account for engine operation below idle where the engine control system is designed and expected to recover engine operation automatically.

(3) The applicant must identify and declare the need for, and the characteristics of, any electrical power supplied from the aircraft to the engine control system for starting and operating the engine, including transient and steady state voltage limits, in the engine instructions for installation.

(4) Low voltage transients outside the power supply voltage limitations declared in paragraph (i)(3) of this section must meet the requirements of paragraph (i)(1) of this section. The engine control system must be capable of resuming normal operation when aircraft-supplied power returns to within the declared limits.

(j) Air pressure signal. The applicant must consider the effects of blockage or leakage of the signal lines on the engine control system as part of the System Safety Assessment of paragraph (e) of this section and must adopt the appropriate design precautions.

(k) Automatic availability and control of engine power for 30-second OEI rating. Rotorcraft engines having a 30-second OEI rating must incorporate a means, or a provision for a means, for automatic availability and automatic control of the 30-second OEI power within its operating limitations.

(l) Engine shut down means. Means must be provided for shutting down the engine rapidly.

(m) Programmable logic devices. The development of programmable logic devices using digital logic or other complex design technologies must provide a level of assurance for the encoded logic commensurate with the hazard associated with the failure or malfunction of the systems in which the devices are located. The applicant must provide evidence that the development of these devices has been done by using a method, approved by the FAA, that is consistent with the criticality of the performed function.

[Doc. No. 24466, 58 FR 29095, May 18, 1993, Amdt. 33–5, 73 FR 48284, August 18, 2008.]

33.29 Instrument connection

(a) Unless it is constructed to prevent its connection to an incorrect instrument, each connection provided for powerplant instruments required by aircraft airworthiness regulations or necessary to insure operation of the engine in compliance with any engine limitation must be marked to identify it with its corresponding instrument.

(b) A connection must be provided on each turbojet engine for an indicator system to indicate rotor system unbalance.

(c) Each rotorcraft turbine engine having a 30-second OEI rating and a 2-minute OEI rating must have a means or a provision for a means to:

(1) Alert the pilot when the engine is at the 30-second OEI and the 2-minute OEI power levels, when the event begins, and when the time interval expires;

(2) Automatically record each usage and duration of power at the 30-second OEI and 2-minute OEI levels;

(3) Alert maintenance personnel in a positive manner that the engine has been operated at either or both of the 30-second and 2-minute OEI power levels, and permit retrieval of the recorded data; and

(4) Enable routine verification of the proper operation of the above means.

(d) The means, or the provision for a means, of paragraphs (c)(2) and (c)(3) of this section must not be capable of being reset in flight.

(e) The applicant must make provision for the installation of instrumentation necessary to ensure operation in compliance with engine operating limitations. Where, in presenting the safety analysis, or complying with any other requirement, dependence is placed on instrumentation that is not otherwise mandatory in the assumed aircraft installation, then the applicant must specify this instrumentation in the engine installation instructions and declare it mandatory in the engine approval documentation.

(f) As part of the System Safety Assessment of 33.28(e), the applicant must assess the possibility and subsequent effect of incorrect fit of instruments, sensors, or connectors. Where necessary, the applicant must take design precautions to prevent incorrect configuration of the system.

(g) The sensors, together with associated wiring and signal conditioning, must be segregated, electrically and physically, to the extent necessary to ensure that the probability of a fault propagating from instrumentation and monitoring functions to control functions, or vice versa, is consistent with the failure effect of the fault.

(h) The applicant must provide instrumentation enabling the flight crew to monitor the functioning of the turbine cooling system unless appropriate inspections are published in the relevant manuals and evidence shows that:

(1) Other existing instrumentation provides adequate warning of failure or impending failure;

(2) Failure of the cooling system would not lead to hazardous engine effects before detection; or

(3) The probability of failure of the cooling system is extremely remote.

[Amdt. 33–5, 39 FR 1831, Jan. 15, 1974, as amended by Amdt. 33–6, 39 FR 35465, Oct. 1, 1974; Amdt. 33–18, 61 FR 31328, June 19, 1996, Amdt. 33–6 73, FR 48285, Aug. 19, 2008, Amdt. 33–5, 73 FR 48123, Oct. 17, 2008]

Subpart C — Design and Construction; Reciprocating Aircraft Engines

33.31 Applicability

This subpart prescribes additional design and construction requirements for reciprocating aircraft engines.

33.33 Vibration

The engine must be designed and constructed to function throughout its normal operating range of crankshaft rotational speeds and engine powers without inducing excessive stress in any of the engine parts because of vibration and without imparting excessive vibration forces to the aircraft structure.

33.34 Turbocharger rotors

Each turbocharger case must be designed and constructed to be able to contain fragments of a compressor or turbine that fails at the highest speed that is obtainable with normal speed control devices inoperative.

[Amdt. 33–22, 72 FR 50860, Sept. 4, 2007]

33.35 Fuel and induction system

(a) The fuel system of the engine must be designed and constructed to supply an appropriate mixture of fuel to the cylinders throughout the complete operating range of the engine under all flight and atmospheric conditions.

(b) The intake passages of the engine through which air or fuel in combination with air passes for combustion purposes must be designed and constructed to minimize the danger of ice accretion in those passages. The engine must be designed and constructed to permit the use of a means for ice prevention.

(c) The type and degree of fuel filtering necessary for protection of the engine fuel system against foreign particles in the fuel must be specified. The applicant must show that foreign particles passing through the prescribed filtering means will not critically impair engine fuel system functioning.

(d) Each passage in the induction system that conducts a mixture of fuel and air must be self-draining, to prevent a liquid lock in the cylinders, in all attitudes that the applicant establishes as those the engine can have when the aircraft in which it is installed is in the static ground attitude.

(e) If provided as part of the engine, the applicant must show for each fluid injection (other than fuel) system and its controls that the flow of the injected fluid is adequately controlled.

[Doc. No. 3025, 29 FR 7453, June 10, 1964, as amended by Amdt. 33–10, 49 FR 6851, Feb. 23, 1984]

33.37 Ignition system

Each spark ignition engine must have a dual ignition system with at least two spark plugs for each cylinder and two separate electric circuits with separate sources of electrical energy, or have an ignition system of equivalent in-flight reliability.

33.39 Lubrication system

(a) The lubrication system of the engine must be designed and constructed so that it will function properly in all flight attitudes and atmospheric conditions in which the airplane is expected to operate. In wet sump engines, this requirement must be met when only one-half of the maximum lubricant supply is in the engine.

(b) The lubrication system of the engine must be designed and constructed to allow installing a means of cooling the lubricant.

(c) The crankcase must be vented to the atmosphere to preclude leakage of oil from excessive pressure in the crankcase.

Subpart D — Block Tests; Reciprocating Aircraft Engines

33.41 Applicability

This subpart prescribes the block tests and inspections for reciprocating aircraft engines.

33.42 General

Before each endurance test required by this subpart, the adjustment setting and functioning characteristic of each component having an adjustment setting and a functioning characteristic that can be established independent of installation on the engine must be established and recorded.

[Amdt. 33–6, 39 FR 35465, Oct. 1, 1974]

33.43 Vibration test

(a) Each engine must undergo a vibration survey to establish the torsional and bending vibration characteristics of the crankshaft and the propeller shaft or other output shaft, over the range of crankshaft speed and engine power, under steady state and transient conditions, from idling speed to either 110 percent of the desired maximum continuous speed rating or 103 percent of the maximum desired takeoff speed rating, whichever is higher. The survey must be conducted using, for airplane engines, the same configuration of the propeller type which is used for the endurance test, and using, for other engines, the same configuration of the loading device type which is used for the endurance test.

(b) The torsional and bending vibration stresses of the crankshaft and the propeller shaft or other output shaft may not exceed the endurance limit stress of the material from which the shaft is made. If the maximum stress in the shaft cannot be shown to be below the endurance limit by measurement, the vibration frequency and amplitude must be measured. The peak amplitude must be shown to produce a stress below the endurance limit; if not, the engine must be run at the condition producing the peak amplitude until, for steel shafts, 10 million stress reversals have been sustained without fatigue failure and, for other shafts, until it is shown that fatigue will not occur within the endurance limit stress of the material.

(c) Each accessory drive and mounting attachment must be loaded, with the loads imposed by each accessory used only for an aircraft service being the limit load specified by the applicant for the drive or attachment point.

(d) The vibration survey described in paragraph (a) of this section must be repeated with that cylinder not firing which has the most adverse vibration effect, in order to establish the conditions under which the engine can be operated safely in that abnormal state. However, for this vibration survey, the engine speed range need only extend from idle to the maximum desired takeoff speed, and compliance with paragraph (b) of this section need not be shown.

[Amdt. 33–6, 39 FR 35465, Oct. 1, 1974, as amended by Amdt. 33–10, 49 FR 6851, Feb. 23, 1984]

33.45 Calibration tests

(a) Each engine must be subjected to the calibration tests necessary to establish its power characteristics and the conditions for the endurance test specified in 33.49. The results of the power characteristics calibration tests form the basis for establishing the characteristics of the engine over its entire operating range of crankshaft rotational speeds, manifold pressures, fuel/air mixture settings, and altitudes. Power ratings are based upon standard atmospheric conditions with only those accessories installed which are essential for engine functioning.

(b) A power check at sea level conditions must be accomplished on the endurance test engine after the endurance test. Any change in power characteristics which occurs during the endurance test must be determined. Measurements taken during the final portion of the endurance test may be used in showing compliance with the requirements of this paragraph.

[Doc. No. 3025, 29 FR 7453, June 10, 1964, as amended by Amdt. 33–6, 39 FR 35465, Oct. 1, 1974]

33.47 Detonation test

Each engine must be tested to establish that the engine can function without detonation throughout its range of intended conditions of operation.

33.49 Endurance test

(a) *General.* Each engine must be subjected to an endurance test that includes a total of 150 hours of operation (except as provided in paragraph (e)(1)(iii) of this section) and, depending upon the type and contemplated use of the engine, consists of one of the series of runs specified in paragraphs (b) through (e) of this section, as applicable. The runs must be made in the order found appropriate by the Administrator for the particular engine being tested. During the endurance test the engine power and the crankshaft rotational speed must be kept within ±3 percent of the rated values. During the runs at rated takeoff power and for at least 35 hours at rated maximum continuous power, one cylinder must be operated at not less than the limiting temperature, the other cylinders

must be operated at a temperature not lower than 50 degrees F. below the limiting temperature, and the oil inlet temperature must be maintained within ±10 degrees F. of the limiting temperature. An engine that is equipped with a propeller shaft must be fitted for the endurance test with a propeller that thrust-loads the engine to the maximum thrust which the engine is designed to resist at each applicable operating condition specified in this section. Each accessory drive and mounting attachment must be loaded. During operation at rated takeoff power and rated maximum continuous power, the load imposed by each accessory used only for an aircraft service must be the limit load specified by the applicant for the engine drive or attachment point.

(b) *Unsupercharged engines and engines incorporating a gear-driven single-speed supercharger.* For engines not incorporating a supercharger and for engines incorporating a gear-driven single-speed supercharger the applicant must conduct the following runs:

(1) A 30-hour run consisting of alternate periods of 5 minutes at rated takeoff power with takeoff speed, and 5 minutes at maximum best economy cruising power or maximum recommended cruising power.

(2) A 20-hour run consisting of alternate periods of 1-1/2 hours at rated maximum continuous power with maximum continuous speed, and 1/2 hour at 75 percent rated maximum continuous power and 91 percent maximum continuous speed.

(3) A 20-hour run consisting of alternate periods of 1-1/2 hours at rated maximum continuous power with maximum continuous speed, and 1/2 hour at 70 percent rated maximum continuous power and 89 percent maximum continuous speed.

(4) A 20-hour run consisting of alternate periods of 1-1/2 hours at rated maximum continuous power with maximum continuous speed, and 1/2 hour at 65 percent rated maximum continuous power and 87 percent maximum continuous speed.

(5) A 20-hour run consisting of alternate periods of 1-1/2 hours at rated maximum continuous power with maximum continuous speed, and 1/2 hour at 60 percent rated maximum continuous power and 84.5 percent maximum continuous speed.

(6) A 20-hour run consisting of alternate periods of 1-1/2 hours at rated maximum continuous power with maximum continuous speed, and 1/2 hour at 50 percent rated maximum continuous power and 79.5 percent maximum continuous speed.

(7) A 20-hour run consisting of alternate periods of 2-1/2 hours at rated maximum continuous power with maximum continuous speed, and 2-1/2 hours at maximum best economy cruising power or at maximum recommended cruising power.

(c) Engines incorporating a gear-driven two-speed supercharger. For engines incorporating a gear-driven two-speed supercharger the applicant must conduct the following runs:

(1) A 30-hour run consisting of alternate periods in the lower gear ratio of 5 minutes at rated takeoff power with takeoff speed, and 5 minutes at maximum best economy cruising power or at maximum recommended cruising power. If a takeoff power rating is desired in the higher gear ratio, 15 hours of the 30-hour run must be made in the higher gear ratio in alternate periods of 5 minutes at the observed horsepower obtainable with the takeoff critical altitude manifold pressure and takeoff speed, and 5 minutes at 70 percent high ratio rated maximum continuous power and 89 percent high ratio maximum continuous speed.

(2) A 15-hour run consisting of alternate periods in the lower gear ratio of 1 hour at rated maximum continuous power with maximum continuous speed, and 1/2 hour at 75 percent rated maximum continuous power and 91 percent maximum continuous speed.

(3) A 15-hour run consisting of alternate periods in the lower gear ratio of 1 hour at rated maximum continuous power with maximum continuous speed, and 1/2 hour at 70 percent rated maximum continuous power and 89 percent maximum continuous speed.

FAR 33

(4) A 30-hour run in the higher gear ratio at rated maximum continuous power with maximum continuous speed.

(5) A 5-hour run consisting of alternate periods of 5 minutes in each of the supercharger gear ratios. The first 5 minutes of the test must be made at maximum continuous speed in the higher gear ratio and the observed horsepower obtainable with 90 percent of maximum continuous manifold pressure in the higher gear ratio under sea level conditions. The condition for operation for the alternate 5 minutes in the lower gear ratio must be that obtained by shifting to the lower gear ratio at constant speed.

(6) A 10-hour run consisting of alternate periods in the lower gear ratio of 1 hour at rated maximum continuous power with maximum continuous speed, and 1 hour at 65 percent rated maximum continuous power and 87 percent maximum continuous speed.

(7) A 10-hour run consisting of alternate periods in the lower gear ratio of 1 hour at rated maximum continuous power with maximum continuous speed, and 1 hour at 60 percent rated maximum continuous power and 84.5 percent maximum continuous speed.

(8) A 10-hour run consisting of alternate periods in the lower gear ratio of 1 hour at rated maximum continuous power with maximum continuous speed, and 1 hour at 50 percent rated maximum continuous power and 79.5 percent maximum continuous speed.

(9) A 20-hour run consisting of alternate periods in the lower gear ratio of 2 hours at rated maximum continuous power with maximum continuous speed, and 2 hours at maximum best economy cruising power and speed or at maximum recommended cruising power.

(10) A 5-hour run in the lower gear ratio at maximum best economy cruising power and speed or at maximum recommended cruising power and speed.

Where simulated altitude test equipment is not available when operating in the higher gear ratio, the runs may be made at the observed horsepower obtained with the critical altitude manifold pressure or specified percentages thereof, and the fuel-air mixtures may be adjusted to be rich enough to suppress detonation.

(d) Helicopter engines. To be eligible for use on a helicopter each engine must either comply with paragraphs (a) through (j) of 29.923 of this chapter, or must undergo the following series of runs:

(1) A 35-hour run consisting of alternate periods of 30 minutes each at rated takeoff power with takeoff speed, and at rated maximum continuous power with maximum continuous speed.

(2) A 25-hour run consisting of alternate periods of 2 1/2 hours each at rated maximum continuous power with maximum continuous speed, and at 70 percent rated maximum continuous power with maximum continuous speed.

(3) A 25-hour run consisting of alternate periods of 2 1/2 hours each at rated maximum continuous power with maximum continuous speed, and at 70 percent rated maximum continuous power with 80 to 90 percent maximum continuous speed.

(4) A 25-hour run consisting of alternate periods of 2 1/2 hours each at 30 percent rated maximum continuous power with takeoff speed, and at 30 percent rated maximum continuous power with 80 to 90 percent maximum continuous speed.

(5) A 25-hour run consisting of alternate periods of 2 1/2 hours each at 80 percent rated maximum continuous power with takeoff speed, and at either rated maximum continuous power with 110 percent maximum continuous speed or at rated takeoff power with 103 percent takeoff speed, whichever results in the greater speed.

(6) A 15-hour run at 105 percent rated maximum continuous power with 105 percent maximum continuous speed or at full throttle and corresponding speed at standard sea level carbure-tor entrance pressure, if 105 percent of the rated maximum continuous power is not exceeded.

(e) Turbosupercharged engines. For engines incorporating a turbosupercharger the following apply except that altitude testing may be simulated provided the applicant shows that the engine and supercharger are being subjected to mechanical loads and operating temperatures no less severe than if run at actual altitude conditions:

(1) For engines used in airplanes the applicant must conduct the runs specified in paragraph (b) of this section, except—

(i) The entire run specified in paragraph (b)(1) of this section must be made at sea level altitude pressure;

(ii) The portions of the runs specified in paragraphs (b)(2) through (7) of this section at rated maximum continuous power must be made at critical altitude pressure, and the portions of the runs at other power must be made at 8,000 feet altitude pressure; and

(iii) The turbosupercharger used during the 150-hour endurance test must be run on the bench for an additional 50 hours at the limiting turbine wheel inlet gas temperature and rotational speed for rated maximum continuous power operation unless the limiting temperature and speed are maintained during 50 hours of the rated maximum continuous power operation.

(2) For engines used in helicopters the applicant must conduct the runs specified in paragraph (d) of this section, except—

(i) The entire run specified in paragraph (d)(1) of this section must be made at critical altitude pressure;

(ii) The portions of the runs specified in paragraphs (d)(2) and (3) of this section at rated maximum continuous power must be made at critical altitude pressure and the portions of the runs at other power must be made at 8,000 feet altitude pressure;

(iii) The entire run specified in paragraph (d)(4) of this section must be made at 8,000 feet altitude pressure;

(iv) The portion of the runs specified in paragraph (d)(5) of this section at 80 percent of rated maximum continuous power must be made at 8,000 feet altitude pressure and the portions of the runs at other power must be made at critical altitude pressure;

(v) The entire run specified in paragraph (d)(6) of this section must be made at critical altitude pressure; and

(vi) The turbosupercharger used during the endurance test must be run on the bench for 50 hours at the limiting turbine wheel inlet gas temperature and rotational speed for rated maximum continuous power operation unless the limiting temperature and speed are maintained during 50 hours of the rated maximum continuous power operation.

[Amdt. 33–3, 32 FR 3736, Mar. 4, 1967, as amended by Amdt. 33–6, 39 FR 35465, Oct. 1, 1974; Amdt. 33–10, 49 FR 6851, Feb. 23, 1984]

33.51 Operation test

The operation test must include the testing found necessary by the Administrator to demonstrate backfire characteristics, starting, idling, acceleration, overspeeding, functioning of propeller and ignition, and any other operational characteristic of the engine. If the engine incorporates a multispeed supercharger drive, the design and construction must allow the supercharger to be shifted from operation at the lower speed ratio to the higher and the power appropriate to the manifold pressure and speed settings for rated maximum continuous power at the higher supercharger speed ratio must be obtainable within five seconds.

[Doc. No. 3025, 29 FR 7453, June 10, 1964, as amended by Amdt. 33–3, 32 FR 3737, Mar. 4, 1967]

33.53 Engine system and component tests

(a) For those systems and components that cannot be adequately substantiated in accordance with endurance testing of 33.49, the applicant must conduct additional tests to demonstrate that systems or components are able to perform the intended functions in all declared environmental and operating conditions.

(b) Temperature limits must be established for each component that requires temperature controlling provisions in the aircraft installation to assure satisfactory functioning, reliability, and durability.

[Amdt. 33-7, 73 FR 48285, August 19, 2008]

33.55 Teardown inspection

After completing the endurance test—

(a) Each engine must be completely disassembled;

(b) Each component having an adjustment setting and a functioning characteristic that can be established independent of installation on the engine must retain each setting and functioning characteristic within the limits that were established and recorded at the beginning of the test; and

(c) Each engine component must conform to the type design and be eligible for incorporation into an engine for continued operation, in accordance with information submitted in compliance with 33.4.

[Amdt. 33–6, 39 FR 35466, Oct. 1, 1974, as amended by Amdt. 33–9, 45 FR 60181, Sept. 11, 1980]

33.57 General conduct of block tests

(a) The applicant may, in conducting the block tests, use separate engines of identical design and construction in the vibration, calibration, detonation, endurance, and operation tests, except that, if a separate engine is used for the endurance test it must be subjected to a calibration check before starting the endurance test.

(b) The applicant may service and make minor repairs to the engine during the block tests in accordance with the service and maintenance instructions submitted in compliance with 33.4. If the frequency of the service is excessive, or the number of stops due to engine malfunction is excessive, or a major repair, or replacement of a part is found necessary during the block tests or as the result of findings from the teardown inspection, the engine or its parts may be subjected to any additional test the Administrator finds necessary.

(c) Each applicant must furnish all testing facilities, including equipment and competent personnel, to conduct the block tests.

[Doc. No. 3025, 29 FR 7453, June 10, 1964, as amended by Amdt. 33–6, 39 FR 35466, Oct. 1, 1974; Amdt. 33–9, 45 FR 60181, Sept. 11, 1980]

Subpart E — Design and Construction; Turbine Aircraft Engines

33.61 Applicability

This subpart prescribes additional design and construction requirements for turbine aircraft engines.

33.62 Stress analysis

A stress analysis must be performed on each turbine engine showing the design safety margin of each turbine engine rotor, spacer, and rotor shaft.

[Amdt. 33–6, 39 FR 35466, Oct. 1, 1974]

33.63 Vibration

Each engine must be designed and constructed to function throughout its declared flight envelope and operating range of rotational speeds and power/thrust, without inducing excessive stress in any engine part because of vibration and without imparting excessive vibration forces to the aircraft structure.

[Doc. No. 28107, 61 FR 28433, June 4, 1996]

33.64 Pressurized engine static parts

(a) Strength. The applicant must establish by test, validated analysis, or a combination of both, that all static parts subject to significant gas or liquid pressure loads for a stabilized period of one minute will not:

   (1) Exhibit permanent distortion beyond serviceable limits or exhibit leakage that could create a hazardous condition when subjected to the greater of the following pressures:

      (i) 1.1 times the maximum working pressure;

      (ii) 1.33 times the normal working pressure; or

      (iii) 35 kPa (5 p.s.i.) above the normal working pressure.

   (2) Exhibit fracture or burst when subjected to the greater of the following pressures:

      (i) 1.15 times the maximum possible pressure;

      (ii) 1.5 times the maximum working pressure; or

      (iii) 35 kPa (5 p.s.i.) above the maximum possible pressure.

(b) Compliance with this section must take into account:

   (1) The operating temperature of the part;

   (2) Any other significant static loads in addition to pressure loads;

   (3) Minimum properties representative of both the material and the processes used in the construction of the part; and

   (4) Any adverse geometry conditions allowed by the type design.

[Amdt. 33–27; 73 FR 55437, Sept. 25, 2008; Amdt. 33–27, 73 FR 57235, Oct. 2, 2008]

33.65 Surge and stall characteristics

When the engine is operated in accordance with operating instructions required by 33.5(b), starting, a change of power or thrust, power or thrust augmentation, limiting inlet air distortion, or inlet air temperature may not cause surge or stall to the extent that flameout, structural failure, overtemperature, or failure of the engine to recover power or thrust will occur at any point in the operating envelope.

[Amdt. 33–6, 39 FR 35466, Oct. 1, 1974]

33.66 Bleed air system

The engine must supply bleed air without adverse effect on the engine, excluding reduced thrust or power output, at all conditions up to the discharge flow conditions established as a limitation under 33.7(c)(11). If bleed air used for engine anti-icing can be controlled, provision must be made for a means to indicate the functioning of the engine ice protection system.

[Amdt. 33–10, 49 FR 6851, Feb. 23, 1984]

33.67 Fuel system

(a) With fuel supplied to the engine at the flow and pressure specified by the applicant, the engine must function properly under each operating condition required by this part. Each fuel control adjusting means that may not be manipulated while the fuel control device is mounted on the engine must be secured by a locking device and sealed, or otherwise be inaccessible. All other fuel control adjusting means must be accessible and marked to indicate the function of the adjustment unless the function is obvious.

(b) There must be a fuel strainer or filter between the engine fuel inlet opening and the inlet of either the fuel metering device or the engine-driven positive displacement pump whichever is nearer the engine fuel inlet. In addition, the following provisions apply to each strainer or filter required by this paragraph (b):

   (1) It must be accessible for draining and cleaning and must incorporate a screen or element that is easily removable.

   (2) It must have a sediment trap and drain except that it need not have a drain if the strainer or filter is easily removable for drain purposes.

   (3) It must be mounted so that its weight is not supported by the connecting lines or by the inlet or outlet connections of the

FAR 33

strainer or filter, unless adequate strength margins under all loading conditions are provided in the lines and connections.

(4) It must have the type and degree of fuel filtering specified as necessary for protection of the engine fuel system against foreign particles in the fuel. The applicant must show:

    (i) That foreign particles passing through the specified filtering means do not impair the engine fuel system functioning; and

    (ii) That the fuel system is capable of sustained operation throughout its flow and pressure range with the fuel initially saturated with water at 80 °F (27 °C) and having 0.025 fluid ounces per gallon (0.20 milliliters per liter) of free water added and cooled to the most critical condition for icing likely to be encountered in operation. However, this requirement may be met by demonstrating the effectiveness of specified approved fuel anti-icing additives, or that the fuel system incorporates a fuel heater which maintains the fuel temperature at the fuel strainer or fuel inlet above 32 °F (0 °C) under the most critical conditions.

(5) The applicant must demonstrate that the filtering means has the capacity (with respect to engine operating limitations) to ensure that the engine will continue to operate within approved limits, with fuel contaminated to the maximum degree of particle size and density likely to be encountered in service. Operation under these conditions must be demonstrated for a period acceptable to the Administrator, beginning when indication of impending filter blockage is first given by either:

    (i) Existing engine instrumentation; or

    (ii) Additional means incorporated into the engine fuel system.

(6) Any strainer or filter bypass must be designed and constructed so that the release of collected contaminants is minimized by appropriate location of the bypass to ensure that collected contaminants are not in the bypass flow path.

(c) If provided as part of the engine, the applicant must show for each fluid injection (other than fuel) system and its controls that the flow of the injected fluid is adequately controlled.

[Amdt. 33–6, 39 FR 35466, Oct. 1, 1974, as amended by Amdt. 33–10, 49 FR 6851, Feb. 23, 1984; Amdt. 33–18, 61 FR 31328, June 19, 1996, Amdt. 33–6, 73 FR 48123, Aug. 18, 2008, Amdt. 33–8, 73 FR 48285, Aug. 19, 2008]

33.68 Induction system icing

Each engine, with all icing protection systems operating, must:

(a) Operate throughout its flight power range, including the minimum descent idle rotor speeds achievable in flight, in the icing conditions defined for turbojet, turbofan, and turboprop engines in Appendices C and O of part 25 of this chapter, and Appendix D of this part, and for turboshaft engines in Appendix C of part 29 of this chapter, without the accumulation of ice on the engine components that:

    (1) Adversely affects engine operation or that causes an unacceptable permanent loss of power or thrust or unacceptable increase in engine operating temperature; or

    (2) Results in unacceptable temporary power loss or engine damage; or

    (3) Causes a stall, surge, or flameout or loss of engine controllability. The applicant must account for in-flight ram effects in any critical point analysis or test demonstration of these flight conditions.

(b) Operate throughout its flight power range, including minimum descent idle rotor speeds achievable in flight, in the icing conditions defined for turbojet, turbofan, and turboprop engines in Appendices C and O of part 25 of this chapter, and for turboshaft engines in Appendix C of part 29 of this chapter. In addition:

    (1) It must be shown through Critical Point Analysis (CPA) that the complete ice envelope has been analyzed, and that the most critical points must be demonstrated by engine test, analysis, or a combination of the two to operate acceptably. Extended flight in critical flight conditions such as hold, descent, ap-

TABLE 1—CONDITIONS THAT MUST BE DEMONSTRATED BY AN ENGINE TEST				
Condition	Total Air Temperature	Supercooled Water Concentrations (minimum)	Median Volume Drop Diameter	Duration
1. Glaze ice conditions	21 to 25 °F (-6 to -4 °C)	2 g/m^3	25 to 35 microns	(a) 10-minutes for power below sustainable level flight (idle descent).
				(b) Must show repetitive, stabilized operation for higher powers (50%, 75%, 100%MC).
2. Rime ice conditions	-10 to 0 °F (-23 to -18 °C)	1 g/m^3	15 to 25 microns	(a) 10-minutes for power below sustainable level flight (idle descent).
				(b) Must show repetitive, stabilized operation for higher powers (50%, 75%, 100%MC).
3. Glaze ice holding conditions (Turbojet, turbofan, and turboprop only)	Turbojet and Turbofan, only: 10 to 18 °F (-12 to -8 °C)	Alternating cycle: First 1.7 g/m3 (1 minute), Then 0.3 g/m3 (6 minute)	20 to 30 microns	Must show repetitive, stabilized operation (or 45 minutes max).
	Turboprop, only: 2 to 10 °F (-17 to -12 °C)			
4. Rime ice holding conditions (Turbojet, turbofan, and turboprop only)	Turbojet and Turbofan, only: -10 to 0 °F (-23 to -18 °C)	0.25 g/m^3	20 to 30 microns	Must show repetitive, stabilized operation (or 45 minutes max).
	Turboprop, only: 2 to 10 °F (-17 to -12 °C)			

TABLE 2—DEMONSTRATION METHODS FOR SPECIFIC ICING CONDITIONS				
CONDITION	TOTAL AIR TEMPERATURE	SUPERCOOLED WATER CONCENTRATIONS (MINIMUM)	MEAN EFFECTIVE PARTICLE DIAMETER	DEMONSTRATION
1. Rime ice condition	0 to 15 °F (-18 to -9 °C)	Liquid—0.3 g/m³	15-25 microns	By engine test.
2. Glaze ice condition	20 to 30 °F (-7 to -1 °C)	Liquid—0.3 g/m³	15-25 microns	By engine test.
3. Snow ice condition	26 to 32 °F (-3 to 0 °C)	Ice—0.9 g/m³	100 microns (minimum)	By test, analysis or combination of the two.
4. Large drop glaze ice condition (Turbojet, turbofan, and turboprop only)	15 to 30 °F (-9 to -1 °C)	Liquid—0.3 g/m³	100 microns (minimum)	By test, analysis or combination of the two.

proach, climb, and cruise, must be addressed, for the ice conditions defined in these appendices.

(2) It must be shown by engine test, analysis, or a combination of the two that the engine can operate acceptably for the following durations:

(i) At engine powers that can sustain level flight: A duration that achieves repetitive, stabilized operation for turbojet, turbofan, and turboprop engines in the icing conditions defined in Appendices C and O of part 25 of this chapter, and for turboshaft engines in the icing conditions defined in Appendix C of part 29 of this chapter.

(ii) At engine power below that which can sustain level flight:

(A) Demonstration in altitude flight simulation test facility: A duration of 10 minutes consistent with a simulated flight descent of 10,000 ft (3 km) in altitude while operating in Continuous Maximum icing conditions defined in Appendix C of part 25 of this chapter for turbojet, turbofan, and turboprop engines, and for turboshaft engines in the icing conditions defined in Appendix C of part 29 of this chapter, plus 40 percent liquid water content margin, at the critical level of airspeed and air temperature; or

(B) Demonstration in ground test facility: A duration of 3 cycles of alternating icing exposure corresponding to the liquid water content levels and standard cloud lengths starting in Intermittent Maximum and then in Continuous Maximum icing conditions defined in Appendix C of part 25 of this chapter for turbojet, turbofan, and turboprop engines, and for turboshaft engines in the icing conditions defined in Appendix C of part 29 of this chapter, at the critical level of air temperature.

(c) In addition to complying with paragraph (b) of this section, the following conditions shown in Table 1 of this section unless replaced by similar CPA test conditions that are more critical or produce an equivalent level of severity, must be demonstrated by an engine test:

(d) Operate at ground idle speed for a minimum of 30 minutes at each of the following icing conditions shown in Table 2 of this section with the available air bleed for icing protection at its critical condition, without adverse effect, followed by acceleration to takeoff power or thrust. During the idle operation, the engine may be run up periodically to a moderate power or thrust setting in a manner acceptable to the Administrator. Analysis may be used to show ambient temperatures below the tested temperature are less critical. The applicant must document any demonstrated run ups and minimum ambient temperature capability in the engine operating manual as mandatory in icing conditions. The applicant must demonstrate, with consideration of expected airport elevations, the following:

(e) Demonstrate by test, analysis, or combination of the two, acceptable operation for turbojet, turbofan, and turboprop engines in mixed phase and ice crystal icing conditions throughout Appendix D of this part, icing envelope throughout its flight power range, including minimum descent idling speeds.

[Amdt. 33-34, 79 FR 66536, Nov. 4, 2014]

33.69   Ignitions system

Each engine must be equipped with an ignition system for starting the engine on the ground and in flight. An electric ignition system must have at least two igniters and two separate secondary electric circuits, except that only one igniter is required for fuel burning augmentation systems.

[Amdt. 33–6, 39 FR 35466, Oct. 1, 1974]

33.70   Engine life-limited parts

By a procedure approved by the FAA, operating limitations must be established which specify the maximum allowable number of flight cycles for each engine life-limited part. Engine life-limited parts are rotor and major static structural parts whose primary failure is likely to result in a hazardous engine effect. Typically, engine life-limited parts include, but are not limited to disks, spacers, hubs, shafts, high-pressure casings, and non-redundant mount components. For the purposes of this section, a hazardous engine effect is any of the conditions listed in 33.75 of this part. The applicant will establish the integrity of each engine life-limited part by:

(a) An engineering plan that contains the steps required to ensure each engine life-limited part is withdrawn from service at an approved life before hazardous engine effects can occur. These steps include validated analysis, test, or service experience which ensures that the combination of loads, material properties, environmental influences and operating conditions, including the effects of other engine parts influencing these parameters, are sufficiently well known and predictable so that the operating limitations can be established and maintained for each engine life-limited part. Applicants must perform appropriate damage tolerance assessments to address the potential for failure from material, manufacturing, and service induced anomalies within the approved life of the part. Applicants must publish a list of the life-limited engine parts and the approved life for each part in the Airworthiness Limitations Section of the Instructions for Continued Airworthiness as required by 33.4 of this part.

(b) A manufacturing plan that identifies the specific manufacturing constraints necessary to consistently produce each engine life-limited part with the attributes required by the engineering plan.

(c) A service management plan that defines in-service processes for maintenance and the limitations to repair for each engine life-limited part that will maintain attributes consistent with those required by the engineering plan. These processes and limitations will become part of the Instructions for Continued Airworthiness.

[Amdt. 33–22, 72 FR 50860, Sept. 4, 2007]

FAR 33

33.71 Lubrication system

(a) General. Each lubrication system must function properly in the flight attitudes and atmospheric conditions in which an aircraft is expected to operate.

(b) Oil strainer or filter. There must be an oil strainer or filter through which all of the engine oil flows. In addition:

(1) Each strainer or filter required by this paragraph that has a by-pass must be constructed and installed so that oil will flow at the normal rate through the rest of the system with the strainer or filter element completely blocked.

(2) The type and degree of filtering necessary for protection of the engine oil system against foreign particles in the oil must be specified. The applicant must demonstrate that foreign particles passing through the specified filtering means do not impair engine oil system functioning.

(3) Each strainer or filter required by this paragraph must have the capacity (with respect to operating limitations established for the engine) to ensure that engine oil system functioning is not impaired with the oil contaminated to a degree (with respect to particle size and density) that is greater than that established for the engine in paragraph (b)(2) of this section.

(4) For each strainer or filter required by this paragraph, except the strainer or filter at the oil tank outlet, there must be means to indicate contamination before it reaches the capacity established in accordance with paragraph (b)(3) of this section.

(5) Any filter bypass must be designed and constructed so that the release of collected contaminants is minimized by appropriate location of the bypass to ensure that the collected contaminants are not in the bypass flow path.

(6) Each strainer or filter required by this paragraph that has no bypass, except the strainer or filter at an oil tank outlet or for a scavenge pump, must have provisions for connection with a warning means to warn the pilot of the occurence of contamination of the screen before it reaches the capacity established in accordance with paragraph (b)(3) of this section.

(7) Each strainer or filter required by this paragraph must be accessible for draining and cleaning.

(c) Oil tanks.

(1) Each oil tank must have an expansion space of not less than 10 percent of the tank capacity.

(2) It must be impossible to inadvertently fill the oil tank expansion space.

(3) Each recessed oil tank filler connection that can retain any appreciable quantity of oil must have provision for fitting a drain.

(4) Each oil tank cap must provide an oil-tight seal. For an applicant seeking eligibility for an engine to be installed on an airplane approved for ETOPS, the oil tank must be designed to prevent a hazardous loss of oil due to an incorrectly installed oil tank cap.

(5) Each oil tank filler must be marked with the word "oil."

(6) Each oil tank must be vented from the top part of the expansion space, with the vent so arranged that condensed water vapor that might freeze and obstruct the line cannot accumulate at any point.

(7) There must be means to prevent entrance into the oil tank or into any oil tank outlet, of any object that might obstruct the flow of oil through the system.

(8) There must be a shutoff valve at the outlet of each oil tank, unless the external portion of the oil system (including oil tank supports) is fireproof.

(9) Each unpressurized oil tank may not leak when subjected to a maximum operating temperature and an internal pressure of 5 p.s.i., and each pressurized oil tank must meet the requirements of 33.64.

(10) Leaked or spilled oil may not accumulate between the tank and the remainder of the engine.

(11) Each oil tank must have an oil quantity indicator or provisions for one.

(12) If the propeller feathering system depends on engine oil—

(i) There must be means to trap an amount of oil in the tank if the supply becomes depleted due to failure of any part of the lubricating system other than the tank itself;

(ii) The amount of trapped oil must be enough to accomplish the feathering opeation and must be available only to the feathering pump; and

(iii) Provision must be made to prevent sludge or other foreign matter from affecting the safe operation of the propeller feathering system.

(d) Oil drains. A drain (or drains) must be provided to allow safe drainage of the oil system. Each drain must—

(1) Be accessible; and

(2) Have manual or automatic means for positive locking in the closed position.

(e) Oil radiators. Each oil radiator must withstand, without failure, any vibration, inertia, and oil pressure load to which it is subjected during the block tests.

[Amdt. 33–6, 39 FR 35466, Oct. 1, 1974, as amended by Amdt. 33–10, 49 FR 6852, Feb. 23, 1984; Amdt. 33–21, 72 FR 1877, Jan. 16, 2007; Amdt. 33–27, 73 FR 55437, Sept. 25, 2008; Amdt. 33–27, 73 FR 57235, Oct. 2, 2008]

33.72 Hydraulic actuating systems

Each hydraulic actuating system must function properly under all conditions in which the engine is expected to operate. Each filter or screen must be accessible for servicing and each tank must meet the design criteria of 33.71.

[Amdt. 33–6, 39 FR 35467, Oct. 1, 1974]

33.73 Power or thrust response

The design and construction of the engine must enable an increase—

(a) From minimum to rated takeoff power or thrust with the maximum bleed air and power extraction to be permitted in an aircraft, without overtemperature, surge, stall, or other detrimental factors occurring to the engine whenever the power control lever is moved from the minimum to the maximum position in not more than 1 second, except that the Administrator may allow additional time increments for different regimes of control operation requiring control scheduling; and

(b) From the fixed minimum flight idle power lever position when provided, or if not provided, from not more than 15 percent of the rated takeoff power or thrust available to 95 percent rated takeoff power or thrust in not over 5 seconds. The 5-second power or thrust response must occur from a stabilized static condition using only the bleed air and accessories loads necessary to run the engine. This takeoff rating is specified by the applicant and need not include thrust augmentation.

[Amdt. 33–1, 36 FR 5493, Mar. 24, 1971]

33.74 Continued rotation

If any of the engine main rotating systems continue to rotate after the engine is shutdown for any reason while in flight, and if means to prevent that continued rotation are not provided, then any continued rotation during the maximum period of flight, and in the flight conditions expected to occur with that engine inoperative, may not result in any condition described in 33.75(g)(2)(i) through (vi) of this part.

[Amdt. 33–24, 72 FR 50867, Sept. 4, 2007]

33.75 Safety analysis

(a)

(1) The applicant must analyze the engine, including the control system, to assess the likely consequences of all failures that

can reasonably be expected to occur. This analysis will take into account, if applicable:

   (i)   Aircraft-level devices and procedures assumed to be associated with a typical installation. Such assumptions must be stated in the analysis.

   (ii) Consequential secondary failures and latent failures.

   (iii) Multiple failures referred to in paragraph (d) of this section or that result in the hazardous engine effects defined in paragraph (g)(2) of this section.

(2) The applicant must summarize those failures that could result in major engine effects or hazardous engine effects, as defined in paragraph (g) of this section, and estimate the probability of occurrence of those effects. Any engine part the failure of which could reasonably result in a hazardous engine effect must be clearly identified in this summary.

(3) The applicant must show that hazardous engine effects are predicted to occur at a rate not in excess of that defined as extremely remote (probability range of 10^{-7} to 10^{-9} per engine flight hour). Since the estimated probability for individual failures may be insufficiently precise to enable the applicant to assess the total rate for hazardous engine effects, compliance may be shown by demonstrating that the probability of a hazardous engine effect arising from an individual failure can be predicted to be not greater than 10^{-8} per engine flight hour. In dealing with probabilities of this low order of magnitude, absolute proof is not possible, and compliance may be shown by reliance on engineering judgment and previous experience combined with sound design and test philosophies.

(4) The applicant must show that major engine effects are predicted to occur at a rate not in excess of that defined as remote (probability range of 10^{-5} to 10^{-7} per engine flight hour).

(b) The FAA may require that any assumption as to the effects of failures and likely combination of failures be verified by test.

(c) The primary failure of certain single elements cannot be sensibly estimated in numerical terms. If the failure of such elements is likely to result in hazardous engine effects, then compliance may be shown by reliance on the prescribed integrity requirements of 33.15, 33.27, and 33.70 as applicable. These instances must be stated in the safety analysis.

(d) If reliance is placed on a safety system to prevent a failure from progressing to hazardous engine effects, the possibility of a safety system failure in combination with a basic engine failure must be included in the analysis. Such a safety system may include safety devices, instrumentation, early warning devices, maintenance checks, and other similar equipment or procedures. If items of a safety system are outside the control of the engine manufacturer, the assumptions of the safety analysis with respect to the reliability of these parts must be clearly stated in the analysis and identified in the installation instructions under 33.5 of this part.

(e) If the safety analysis depends on one or more of the following items, those items must be identified in the analysis and appropriately substantiated.

(1) Maintenance actions being carried out at stated intervals. This includes the verification of the serviceability of items that could fail in a latent manner. When necessary to prevent hazardous engine effects, these maintenance actions and intervals must be published in the instructions for continued airworthiness required under 33.4 of this part. Additionally, if errors in maintenance of the engine, including the control system, could lead to hazardous engine effects, the appropriate procedures must be included in the relevant engine manuals.

(2) Verification of the satisfactory functioning of safety or other devices at pre-flight or other stated periods. The details of this satisfactory functioning must be published in the appropriate manual.

(3) The provisions of specific instrumentation not otherwise required.

(4) Flight crew actions to be specified in the operating instructions established under 33.5.

(f) If applicable, the safety analysis must also include, but not be limited to, investigation of the following:

   (1) Indicating equipment;

   (2) Manual and automatic controls;

   (3) Compressor bleed systems;

   (4) Refrigerant injection systems;

   (5) Gas temperature control systems;

   (6) Engine speed, power, or thrust governors and fuel control systems;

   (7) Engine overspeed, overtemperature, or topping limiters;

   (8) Propeller control systems; and

   (9) Engine or propeller thrust reversal systems.

(g) Unless otherwise approved by the FAA and stated in the safety analysis, for compliance with part 33, the following failure definitions apply to the engine:

   (1) An engine failure in which the only consequence is partial or complete loss of thrust or power (and associated engine services) from the engine will be regarded as a minor engine effect.

   (2) The following effects will be regarded as hazardous engine effects:

      (i)   Non-containment of high-energy debris;

      (ii) Concentration of toxic products in the engine bleed air intended for the cabin sufficient to incapacitate crew or passengers;

      (iii) Significant thrust in the opposite direction to that commanded by the pilot;

      (iv) Uncontrolled fire;

      (v)   Failure of the engine mount system leading to inadvertent engine separation;

      (vi) Release of the propeller by the engine, if applicable; and

      (vii) Complete inability to shut the engine down.

   (3) An effect whose severity falls between those effects covered in paragraphs (g)(1) and (g)(2) of this section will be regarded as a major engine effect.

[Amdt. No. 33–24, 72 FR 50867, Sept. 4, 2007]

33.76   Bird ingestion

(a) General. Compliance with paragraphs (b), (c), and (d) of this section shall be in accordance with the following:

   (1) Except as specified in paragraph (d) of this section, all ingestion tests must be conducted with the engine stabilized at no less than 100-percent takeoff power or thrust, for test day ambient conditions prior to the ingestion. In addition, the demonstration of compliance must account for engine operation at sea level takeoff conditions on the hottest day that a minimum engine can achieve maximum rated takeoff thrust or power.

   (2) The engine inlet throat area as used in this section to determine the bird quantity and weights will be established by the applicant and identified as a limitation in the installation instructions required under 33.5.

   (3) The impact to the front of the engine from the large single bird, the single largest medium bird which can enter the inlet, and the large flocking bird must be evaluated. Applicants must show that the associated components when struck under the conditions prescribed in paragraphs (b), (c) or (d) of this section, as applicable, will not affect the engine to the extent that the engine cannot comply with the requirements of paragraphs (b)(3), (c)(6) and (d)(4) of this section.

   (4) For an engine that incorporates an inlet protection device, compliance with this section shall be established with the

device functioning. The engine approval will be endorsed to show that compliance with the requirements has been established with the device functioning.

(5) Objects that are accepted by the Administrator may be substituted for birds when conducting the bird ingestion tests required by paragraphs (b), (c) and (d) of this section.

(6) If compliance with the requirements of this section is not established, the engine type certification documentation will show that the engine shall be limited to aircraft installations in which it is shown that a bird cannot strike the engine, or be ingested into the engine, or adversely restrict airflow into the engine.

(b) *Large single bird.* Compliance with the large bird ingestion requirements shall be in accordance with the following:

(1) The large bird ingestion test shall be conducted using one bird of a weight determined from Table 1 aimed at the most critical exposed location on the first stage rotor blades and ingested at a bird speed of 200-knots for engines to be installed on airplanes, or the maximum airspeed for normal rotorcraft flight operations for engines to be installed on rotorcraft.

(2) Power lever movement is not permitted within 15 seconds following ingestion of the large bird.

(3) Ingestion of a single large bird tested under the conditions prescribed in this section may not result in any condition described in 33.75(g)(2) of this part.

(4) Compliance with the large bird ingestion requirements of this paragraph may be shown by demonstrating that the requirements of 33.94(a) constitute a more severe demonstration of blade containment and rotor unbalance than the requirements of this paragraph.

TABLE 1 TO 33.76—LARGE BIRD WEIGHT REQUIREMENTS	
ENGINE INLET THROAT AREA (A)— SQUARE-METERS (SQUARE-INCHES)	BIRD WEIGHT KG. (LB.)
1.35 (2,092)> A	1.85 (4.07) minimum, unless a smaller bird is determined to be a more severe demonstration.
1.35 (2,092)≤ A< 3.90 (6,045)	2.75 (6.05)
3.90 (6,045)≤ A	3.65 (8.03)

(c) *Small and medium flocking bird.* Compliance with the small and medium bird ingestion requirements shall be in accordance with the following:

(1) Analysis or component test, or both, acceptable to the Administrator, shall be conducted to determine the critical ingestion parameters affecting power loss and damage. Critical ingestion parameters shall include, but are not limited to, the effects of bird speed, critical target location, and first stage rotor speed. The critical bird ingestion speed should reflect the most critical condition within the range of airspeeds used for normal flight operations up to 1,500 feet above ground level, but not less than V1 minimum for airplanes.

(2) Medium bird engine tests shall be conducted so as to simulate a flock encounter, and will use the bird weights and quantities specified in Table 2. When only one bird is specified, that bird will be aimed at the engine core primary flow path; the other critical locations on the engine face area must be addressed, as necessary, by appropriate tests or analysis, or both. When two or more birds are specified in Table 2, the largest of those birds must be aimed at the engine core primary flow path, and a second bird must be aimed at the most critical exposed location on the first stage rotor blades. Any remaining birds must be evenly distributed over the engine face area.

(3) In addition, except for rotorcraft engines, it must also be substantiated by appropriate tests or analysis or both, that when the full fan assembly is subjected to the ingestion of the quan-

tity and weights of bird from Table 3, aimed at the fan assembly's most critical location outboard of the primary core flowpath, and in accordance with the applicable test conditions of this paragraph, that the engine can comply with the acceptance criteria of this paragraph.

(4) A small bird ingestion test is not required if the prescribed number of medium birds pass into the engine rotor blades during the medium bird test.

(5) Small bird ingestion tests shall be conducted so as to simulate a flock encounter using one 85 gram (0.187 lb.) bird for each 0.032 square-meter (49.6 square-inches) of inlet area, or fraction thereof, up to a maximum of 16 birds. The birds will be aimed so as to account for any critical exposed locations on the first stage rotor blades, with any remaining birds evenly distributed over the engine face area.

(6) Ingestion of small and medium birds tested under the conditions prescribed in this paragraph may not cause any of the following:

(i)   More than a sustained 25-percent power or thrust loss;

(ii) The engine to be shut down during the required run-on demonstration prescribed in paragraphs (c)(7) or (c)(8) of this section;

(iii) The conditions defined in paragraph (b)(3) of this section.

(iv) Unacceptable deterioration of engine handling characteristics.

(7) Except for rotorcraft engines, the following test schedule shall be used:

(i)   Ingestion so as to simulate a flock encounter, with approximately 1 second elapsed time from the moment of the first bird ingestion to the last.

(ii)   Followed by 2 minutes without power lever movement after the ingestion.

(iii) Followed by 3 minutes at 75-percent of the test condition.

(iv)   Followed by 6 minutes at 60-percent of the test condition.

(v)   Followed by 6 minutes at 40-percent of the test condition.

(vi)   Followed by 1 minute at approach idle.

(vii) Followed by 2 minutes at 75-percent of the test condition.

(viii) Followed by stabilizing at idle and engine shut down.

(ix)   The durations specified are times at the defined conditions with the power being changed between each condition in less than 10 seconds.

(8) For rotorcraft engines, the following test schedule shall be used:

(i)   Ingestion so as to simulate a flock encounter within approximately 1 second elapsed time between the first ingestion and the last.

(ii) Followed by 3 minutes at 75-percent of the test condition.

(iii) Followed by 90 seconds at descent flight idle.

(iv) Followed by 30 seconds at 75-percent of the test condition.

(v)   Followed by stabilizing at idle and engine shut down.

(vi) The durations specified are times at the defined conditions with the power being changed between each condition in less than 10 seconds.

(9) Engines intended for use in multi-engine rotorcraft are not required to comply with the medium bird ingestion portion of this section, providing that the appropriate type certificate documentation is so endorsed.

(10) If any engine operating limit(s) is exceeded during the initial 2 minutes without power lever movement, as provided by paragraph (c)(7)(ii) of this section, then it shall be established that the limit exceedence will not result in an unsafe condition.

TABLE 2 TO 33.76—MEDIUM FLOCKING BIRD WEIGHT AND QUANTITY REQUIREMENTS

Engine Inlet Throat Area (A)— Square-meters (square-inches)	Bird Quantity	Bird Weight kg. (lb.)
0.05 (77.5)> A	none	
0.05 (77.5)≤ A <0.10 (155)	1	0.35 (0.77)
0.10 (155)≤ A <0.20 (310)	1	0.45 (0.99)
0.20 (310)≤ A <0.40 (620)	2	0.45 (0.99)
0.40 (620)≤ A <0.60 (930)	2	0.70 (1.54)
0.60 (930)≤ A <1.00 (1,550)	3	0.70 (1.54)
1.00 (1,550)≤ A <1.35 (2,092)	4	0.70 (1.54)
1.35 (2,092)≤ A <1.70 (2,635)	1 plus 3	1.15 (2.53) 0.70 (1.54)
1.70 (2,635)≤ A <2.10 (3,255)	1 plus 4	1.15 (2.53) 0.70 (1.54)
2.10 (3,255)≤ A <2.50 (3,875)	1 plus 5	1.15 (2.53) 0.70 (1.54)
2.50 (3,875)≤ A <3.90 (6045)	1 plus 6	1.15 (2.53) 0.70 (1.54)
3.90 (6045)≤ A <4.50 (6975)	3	1.15 (2.53)
4.50 (6975)≤ A	4	1.15 (2.53)

TABLE 3 TO 33.76—ADDITIONAL INTEGRITY ASSESSMENT

Engine Inlet Throat Area (A)— square-meters (square-inches)	Bird Quantity	Bird Weight kg. (lb.)
1.35 (2,092)> A	none	
1.35 (2,092)≤ A <2.90 (4,495)	1	1.15 (2.53)
2.90 (4,495)≤ A <3.90 (6,045)	2	1.15 (2.53)
3.90 (6,045)≤ A	1 plus 6	1.15 (2.53) 0.70 (1.54)

(d) *Large flocking bird.* An engine test will be performed as follows:

(1) Large flocking bird engine tests will be performed using the bird mass and weights in Table 4, and ingested at a bird speed of 200 knots.

(2) Prior to the ingestion, the engine must be stabilized at no less than the mechanical rotor speed of the first exposed stage or stages that, on a standard day, would produce 90 percent of the sea level static maximum rated takeoff power or thrust.

(3) The bird must be targeted on the first exposed rotating stage or stages at a blade airfoil height of not less than 50 percent measured at the leading edge.

(4) Ingestion of a large flocking bird under the conditions prescribed in this paragraph must not cause any of the following:

(i) A sustained reduction of power or thrust to less than 50 percent of maximum rated takeoff power or thrust during the run-on segment specified under paragraph (d)(5)(i) of this section.

(ii) Engine shutdown during the required run-on demonstration specified in paragraph (d)(5) of this section.

(iii) The conditions specified in paragraph (b)(3) of this section.

(5) The following test schedule must be used:

(i) Ingestion followed by 1 minute without power lever movement.

(ii) Followed by 13 minutes at not less than 50 percent of maximum rated takeoff power or thrust.

(iii) Followed by 2 minutes between 30 and 35 percent of maximum rated takeoff power or thrust.

(iv) Followed by 1 minute with power or thrust increased from that set in paragraph (d)(5)(iii) of this section, by between 5 and 10 percent of maximum rated takeoff power or thrust.

(v) Followed by 2 minutes with power or thrust reduced from that set in paragraph (d)(5)(iv) of this section, by between 5 and 10 percent of maximum rated takeoff power or thrust.

(vi) Followed by a minimum of 1 minute at ground idle then engine shutdown. The durations specified are times at the defined conditions. Power lever movement between each condition will be 10 seconds or less, except that power lever movements allowed within paragraph (d)(5)(ii) of this section are not limited, and for setting power under paragraph (d)(5)(iii) of this section will be 30 seconds or less.

(6) Compliance with the large flocking bird ingestion requirements of this paragraph (d) may also be demonstrated by:

(i) Incorporating the requirements of paragraph (d)(4) and (d)(5) of this section, into the large single bird test demonstration specified in paragraph (b)(1) of this section; or

(ii) Use of an engine subassembly test at the ingestion conditions specified in paragraph (b)(1) of this section if:

(A) All components critical to complying with the requirements of paragraph (d) of this section are included in the subassembly test;

(B) The components of paragraph (d)(6)(ii)(A) of this section are installed in a representative engine for a run-on demonstration in accordance with paragraphs (d)(4) and (d)(5) of this section; except that section (d)(5)(i) is deleted and section (d)(5)(ii) must be 14 minutes in duration after the engine is started and stabilized; and

(C) The dynamic effects that would have been experienced during a full engine ingestion test can be shown to be negligible with respect to meeting the requirements of paragraphs (d)(4) and (d)(5) of this section.

(7) Applicants must show that an unsafe condition will not result if any engine operating limit is exceeded during the run-on period.

TABLE 4 TO 33.76 — LARGE FLOCKING BIRD MASS AND WEIGHT

Engine inlet throat area (square meters/square inches)	Bird Quantity	Bird mass and weight (kg (lbs))
A < 2.50 (3875)	none	—
2.50 (3875) ≤ A < 3.50 (5425)	1	1.85 (4.08)
3.50 (5425) ≤ A < 3.90 (6045)	1	2.10 (4.63)
3.90 (6045) ≤ A	1	2.50 (5.51)

[Doc. No. FAA–1998–4815, 65 FR 55854, Sept. 14, 2000, as amended by Amdt. 33–20, 68 FR 75391, Dec. 31, 2003; Amdt. 33–24, 72 FR 50868, Sept. 4, 2007; Amdt. 33–23, 72 FR 58974, Oct. 17, 2007]

33.77 Foreign object ingestion—ice

(a) Compliance with the requirements of this section must be demonstrated by engine ice ingestion test or by validated analysis showing equivalence of other means for demonstrating soft body damage tolerance.

(b) [Reserved]

(c) Ingestion of ice under the conditions of this section may not—

(1) Cause an immediate or ultimate unacceptable sustained power or thrust loss; or

(2) Require the engine to be shutdown.

(d) For an engine that incorporates a protection device, compliance with this section need not be demonstrated with respect to ice formed forward of the protection device if it is shown that—

(1) Such ice is of a size that will not pass through the protective device;

(2) The protective device will withstand the impact of the ice; and

(3) The ice stopped by the protective device will not obstruct the flow of induction air into the engine with a resultant sustained reduction in power or thrust greater than those values defined by paragraph (c) of this section.

(e) Compliance with the requirements of this section must be demonstrated by engine ice ingestion test under the following ingestion conditions or by validated analysis showing equivalence of other means for demonstrating soft body damage tolerance.

(1) The minimum ice quantity and dimensions will be established by the engine size as defined in Table 1 of this section.

(2) The ingested ice dimensions are determined by linear interpolation between table values, and are based on the actual engine's inlet hilite area.

(3) The ingestion velocity will simulate ice from the inlet being sucked into the engine.

(4) Engine operation will be at the maximum cruise power or thrust unless lower power is more critical.

TABLE 1—MINIMUM ICE SLAB DIMENSIONS BASED ON ENGINE INLET SIZE			
ENGINE INLET HILITE AREA (SQ. INCH)	THICKNESS (INCH)	WIDTH (INCH)	LENGTH (INCH)
0	0.25	0	3.6
80	0.25	6	3.6
300	0.25	12	3.6
700	0.25	12	4.8
2800	0.35	12	8.5
5000	0.43	12	11.0
7000	0.50	12	12.7
7900	0.50	12	13.4
9500	0.50	12	14.6
11300	0.50	12	15.9
13300	0.50	12	17.1
16500	0.50	12	18.9
20000	0.50	12	20.0

[Doc. No. 16919, 49 FR 6852, Feb. 23, 1984, as amended by Amdt. 33-19, 63 FR 14798, Mar. 26, 1998; 63 FR 53278, Oct. 5, 1998; Amdt. 33-20, 65 FR 55856, Sept. 14, 2000; Amdt. 33-34, 79 FR 65537, Nov. 4, 2014]

33.78 Rain and hail ingestion

(a) All engines

(1) The ingestion of large hailstones (0.8 to 0.9 specific gravity) at the maximum true air speed, up to 15,000 feet (4,500 meters), associated with a representative aircraft operating in rough air, with the engine at maximum continuous power, may not cause unacceptable mechanical damage or unacceptable power or thrust loss after the ingestion, or require the engine to be shut down. One-half the number of hailstones shall be aimed randomly over the inlet face area and the other half aimed at the critical inlet face area. The hailstones shall be ingested in a rapid sequence to simulate a hailstone encounter and the number and size of the hailstones shall be determined as follows:

(i) One 1-inch (25 millimeters) diameter hailstone for engines with inlet areas of not more than 100 square inches (0.0645 square meters).

(ii) One 1-inch (25 millimeters) diameter and one 2-inch (50 millimeters) diameter hailstone for each 150 square inches (0.0968 square meters) of inlet area, or fraction thereof, for engines with inlet areas of more than 100 square inches (0.0645 square meters).

(2) In addition to complying with paragraph (a)(1) of this section and except as provided in paragraph (b) of this section, it must be shown that each engine is capable of acceptable operation throughout its specified operating envelope when subjected to sudden encounters with the certification standard concentrations of rain and hail, as defined in appendix B to this part. Acceptable engine operation precludes flameout, run down, continued or non-recoverable surge or stall, or loss of acceleration and deceleration capability, during any three minute continuous period in rain and during any 30 second continuous period in hail. It must also be shown after the ingestion that there is no unacceptable mechanical damage, unacceptable power or thrust loss, or other adverse engine anomalies.

(b) Engines for rotorcraft. As an alternative to the requirements specified in paragraph (a)(2) of this section, for rotorcraft turbine engines only, it must be shown that each engine is capable of acceptable operation during and after the ingestion of rain with an overall ratio of water droplet flow to airflow, by weight, with a uniform distribution at the inlet plane, of at least four percent. Acceptable engine operation precludes flameout, run down, continued or non-recoverable surge or stall, or loss of acceleration and deceleration capability. It must also be shown after the ingestion that there is no unacceptable mechanical damage, unacceptable power loss, or other adverse engine anomalies. The rain ingestion must occur under the following static ground level conditions:

(1) A normal stabilization period at take-off power without rain ingestion, followed immediately by the suddenly commencing ingestion of rain for three minutes at takeoff power, then

(2) Continuation of the rain ingestion during subsequent rapid deceleration to minimum idle, then

(3) Continuation of the rain ingestion during three minutes at minimum idle power to be certified for flight operation, then

(4) Continuation of the rain ingestion during subsequent rapid acceleration to takeoff power.

(c) Engines for supersonic airplanes. In addition to complying with paragraphs (a)(1) and (a)(2) of this section, a separate test for supersonic airplane engines only, shall be conducted with three hailstones ingested at supersonic cruise velocity. These hailstones shall be aimed at the engine's critical face area, and their ingestion must not cause unacceptable mechanical damage or unacceptable power or thrust loss after the ingestion or require the engine to be shut down. The size of these hailstones shall be determined from the linear variation in diameter from 1-inch (25 millimeters) at 35,000 feet (10,500 meters) to 1/4-inch (6 millimeters) at 60,000 feet (18,000 meters) using the diameter corresponding to the lowest expected supersonic cruise altitude. Alternatively, three larger hailstones may be ingested at subsonic velocities such that the kinetic energy of these larger hailstones is equivalent to the applicable supersonic ingestion conditions.

(d) For an engine that incorporates or requires the use of a protection device, demonstration of the rain and hail ingestion capabilities of the engine, as required in paragraphs (a), (b), and (c) of this section, may be waived wholly or in part by the Administrator if the applicant shows that:

(1) The subject rain and hail constituents are of a size that will not pass through the protection device;

(2) The protection device will withstand the impact of the subject rain and hail constituents; and

(3) The subject of rain and hail constituents, stopped by the protection device, will not obstruct the flow of induction air into the engine, resulting in damage, power or thrust loss, or other adverse engine anomalies in excess of what would be accepted in paragraphs (a), (b), and (c) of this section.

[Doc. No. 28652, 63 FR 14799, Mar. 26, 1998]

33.79   Fuel burning thrust augmentor

Each fuel burning thrust augmentor, including the nozzle, must—

(a) Provide cutoff of the fuel burning thrust augmentor;

(b) Permit on-off cycling;

(c) Be controllable within the intended range of operation;

(d) Upon a failure or malfunction of augmentor combustion, not cause the engine to lose thrust other than that provided by the augmentor; and

(e) Have controls that function compatibly with the other engine controls and automatically shut off augmentor fuel flow if the engine rotor speed drops below the minimum rotational speed at which the augmentor is intended to function.

[Amdt. 33–6, 39 FR 35468, Oct. 1, 1974]

Subpart F — Block Tests; Turbine Aircraft Engines

33.81   Applicability

This subpart prescribes the block tests and inspections for turbine engines.

[Doc. 3025, 29 FR 7453, June 10, 1964, as amended by Amdt. 33–6, 39 FR 35468, Oct. 1, 1974]

33.82   General

Before each endurance test required by this subpart, the adjustment setting and functioning characteristic of each component having an adjustment setting and a functioning characteristic that can be established independent of installation on the engine must be established and recorded.

[Amdt. 36–6, 39 FR 35468, Oct. 1, 1974]

33.83   Vibration test

(a) Each engine must undergo vibration surveys to establish that the vibration characteristics of those components that may be subject to mechanically or aerodynamically induced vibratory excitations are acceptable throughout the declared flight envelope. The engine surveys shall be based upon an appropriate combination of experience, analysis, and component test and shall address, as a minimum, blades, vanes, rotor discs, spacers, and rotor shafts.

(b) The surveys shall cover the ranges of power or thrust, and both the physical and corrected rotational speeds for each rotor system, corresponding to operations throughout the range of ambient conditions in the declared flight envelope, from the minimum rotational speed up to 103 percent of the maximum physical and corrected rotational speed permitted for rating periods of two minutes or longer, and up to 100 percent of all other permitted physical and corrected rotational speeds, including those that are overspeeds. If there is any indication of a stress peak arising at the highest of those required physical or corrected rotational speeds, the surveys shall be extended sufficiently to reveal the maximum stress values present, except that the extension need not cover more than a further 2 percentage points increase beyond those speeds.

(c) Evaluations shall be made of the following:

(1) The effects on vibration characteristics of operating with scheduled changes (including tolerances) to variable vane angles, compressor bleeds, accessory loading, the most adverse inlet air flow distortion pattern declared by the manufacturer, and the most adverse conditions in the exhaust duct(s); and

(2) The aerodynamic and aeromechanical factors which might induce or influence flutter in those systems susceptible to that form of vibration.

(d) Except as provided by paragraph (e) of this section, the vibration stresses associated with the vibration characteristics determined un-

der this section, when combined with the appropriate steady stresses, must be less than the endurance limits of the materials concerned, after making due allowances for operating conditions for the permitted variations in properties of the materials. The suitability of these stress margins must be justified for each part evaluated. If it is determined that certain operating conditions, or ranges, need to be limited, operating and installation limitations shall be established.

(e) The effects on vibration characteristics of excitation forces caused by fault conditions (such as, but not limited to, out-of-balance, local blockage or enlargement of stator vane passages, fuel nozzle blockage, incorrectly schedule compressor variables, etc.) shall be evaluated by test or analysis, or by reference to previous experience and shall be shown not to create a hazardous condition.

(f) Compliance with this section shall be substantiated for each specific installation configuration that can affect the vibration characteristics of the engine. If these vibration effects cannot be fully investigated during engine certification, the methods by which they can be evaluated and methods by which compliance can be shown shall be substantiated and defined in the installation instructions required by 33.5.

[Doc. No. 28107, 61 FR 28433, June 4, 1996, as amended by Amdt. 33-33, 77 FR 39624, July 5, 2012; 77 FR 58301, Sept. 20, 2012]

33.84   Engine overtorque test

(a) If approval of a maximum engine overtorque is sought for an engine incorporating a free power turbine, compliance with this section must be demonstrated by testing.

(1) The test may be run as part of the endurance test requirement of 33.87. Alternatively, tests may be performed on a complete engine or equivalent testing on individual groups of components.

(2) Upon conclusion of tests conducted to show compliance with this section, each engine part or individual groups of components must meet the requirements of 33.93(a)(1) and (a)(2).

(b) The test conditions must be as follows:

(1) A total of 15 minutes run at the maximum engine overtorque to be approved. This may be done in separate runs, each being of at least 2 1/2 minutes duration.

(2) A power turbine rotational speed equal to the highest speed at which the maximum overtorque can occur in service. The test speed may not be more than the limit speed of take-off or OEI ratings longer than 2 minutes.

(3) For engines incorporating a reduction gearbox, a gearbox oil temperature equal to the maximum temperature when the maximum engine overtorque could occur in service; and for all other engines, an oil temperature within the normal operating range.

(4) A turbine entry gas temperature equal to the maximum steady state temperature approved for use during periods longer than 20 seconds when operating at conditions not associated with 30-second or 2 minutes OEI ratings. The requirement to run the test at the maximum approved steady state temperature may be waived by the FAA if the applicant can demonstrate that other testing provides substantiation of the temperature effects when considered in combination with the other parameters identified in paragraphs (b)(1), (b)(2) and (b)(3) of this section.

[Amdt. 33-30, 74 FR 45310, Sept. 2, 2009]

33.85   Calibration tests

(a) Each engine must be subjected to those calibration tests necessary to establish its power characteristics and the conditions for the endurance test specified 33.87. The results of the power characteristics calibration tests form the basis for establishing the characteristics of the engine over its entire operating range of speeds, pressures, temperatures, and altitudes. Power ratings are based upon standard atmospheric conditions with no airbleed for aircraft services and with only those accessories installed which are essential for engine functioning.

(b) A power check at sea level conditions must be accomplished on the endurance test engine after the endurance test and any change in power characteristics which occurs during the endurance test must be determined. Measurements taken during the final portion of the endurance test may be used in showing compliance with the requirements of this paragraph.

(c) In showing compliance with this section, each condition must stabilize before measurements are taken, except as permitted by paragraph (d) of this section.

(d) In the case of engines having 30-second OEI, and 2-minute OEI ratings, measurements taken during the applicable endurance test prescribed in 33.87(f) (1) through (8) may be used in showing compliance with the requirements of this section for these OEI ratings.

[Doc. No. 3025, 29 FR 7453, June 10, 1964, as amended by Amdt. 33–6, 39 FR 35468, Oct. 1, 1974; Amdt. 33–18, 61 FR 31328, June 19, 1996]

33.87   Endurance test

(a) *General.* Each engine must be subjected to an endurance test that includes a total of at least 150 hours of operation and, depending upon the type and contemplated use of the engine, consists of one of the series of runs specified in paragraphs (b) through (g) of this section, as applicable. For engines tested under paragraphs (b), (c), (d), (e) or (g) of this section, the prescribed 6-hour test sequence must be conducted 25 times to complete the required 150 hours of operation. Engines for which the 30-second OEI and 2-minute OEI ratings are desired must be further tested under paragraph (f) of this section. The following test requirements apply:

(1) The runs must be made in the order found appropriate by the FAA for the particular engine being tested.

(2) Any automatic engine control that is part of the engine must control the engine during the endurance test except for operations where automatic control is normally overridden by manual control or where manual control is otherwise specified for a particular test run.

(3) Except as provided in paragraph (a)(5) of this section, power or thrust, gas temperature, rotor shaft rotational speed, and, if limited, temperature of external surfaces of the engine must be at least 100 percent of the value associated with the particular engine operation being tested. More than one test may be run if all parameters cannot be held at the 100 percent level simultaneously.

(4) The runs must be made using fuel, lubricants and hydraulic fluid which conform to the specifications specified in complying with 33.7(c).

(5) Maximum air bleed for engine and aircraft services must be used during at least one-fifth of the runs, except for the test required under paragraph (f) of this section, provided the validity of the test is not compromised. However, for these runs, the power or thrust or the rotor shaft rotational speed may be less than 100 percent of the value associated with the particular operation being tested if the FAA finds that the validity of the endurance test is not compromised.

(6) Each accessory drive and mounting attachment must be loaded in accordance with paragraphs (a)(6)(i) and (ii) of this section, except as permitted by paragraph (a)(6)(iii) of this section for the test required under paragraph (f) of this section.

   (i)   The load imposed by each accessory used only for aircraft service must be the limit load specified by the applicant for the engine drive and attachment point during rated maximum continuous power or thrust and higher output.

   (ii) The endurance test of any accessory drive and mounting attachment under load may be accomplished on a separate rig if the validity of the test is confirmed by an approved analysis.

   (iii) The applicant is not required to load the accessory drives and mounting attachments when running the tests under paragraphs (f)(1) through (f)(8) of this section if the applicant can substantiate that there is no significant effect on the durability of any accessory drive or engine component. However, the applicant must add the equivalent engine output power extraction from the power turbine rotor assembly to the engine shaft output.

(7) During the runs at any rated power or thrust the gas temperature and the oil inlet temperature must be maintained at the limiting temperature except where the test periods are not longer than 5 minutes and do not allow stabilization. At least one run must be made with fuel, oil, and hydraulic fluid at the minimum pressure limit and at least one run must be made with fuel, oil, and hydraulic fluid at the maximum pressure limit with fluid temperature reduced as necessary to allow maximum pressure to be attained.

(8) If the number of occurrences of either transient rotor shaft overspeed, transient gas overtemperature or transient engine overtorque is limited, that number of the accelerations required by paragraphs (b) through (g) of this section must be made at the limiting overspeed, overtemperature or overtorque. If the number of occurrences is not limited, half the required accelerations must be made at the limiting overspeed, overtemperature or overtorque.

(9) For each engine type certificated for use on supersonic aircraft the following additional test requirements apply:

   (i)   To change the thrust setting, the power control lever must be moved from the initial position to the final position in not more than one second except for movements into the fuel burning thrust augmentor augmentation position if additional time to confirm ignition is necessary.

   (ii) During the runs at any rated augmented thrust the hydraulic fluid temperature must be maintained at the limiting temperature except where the test periods are not long enough to allow stabilization.

   (iii) During the simulated supersonic runs the fuel temperature and induction air temperature may not be less than the limiting temperature.

   (iv) The endurance test must be conducted with the fuel burning thrust augmentor installed, with the primary and secondary exhaust nozzles installed, and with the variable area exhaust nozzles operated during each run according to the methods specified in complying with 33.5(b).

   (v)   During the runs at thrust settings for maximum continuous thrust and percentages thereof, the engine must be operated with the inlet air distortion at the limit for those thrust settings.

(b) *Engines other than certain rotorcraft engines.* For each engine except a rotorcraft engine for which a rating is desired under paragraph (c), (d), or (e) of this section, the applicant must conduct the following runs:

(1) *Takeoff and idling.* One hour of alternate five-minute periods at rated takeoff power or thrust and at idling power or thrust. The developed powers and thrusts at takeoff and idling conditions and their corresponding rotor speed and gas temperature conditions must be as established by the power control in accordance with the schedule established by the applicant. The applicant may, during any one period, manually control the rotor speed and power or thrust while taking data to check performance. For engines with augmented takeoff power ratings that involve increases in turbine inlet temperature, rotor speed, or shaft power, this period of running at takeoff must be at the augmented rating. For engines with augmented takeoff power ratings that do not materially increase operating severity, the amount of running conducted at the augmented rating is determined by the FAA. In changing the power setting after each period, the power-control lever must be moved in the manner prescribed in paragraph (b) (5) of this section.

(2) *Rated maximum continuous and takeoff power or thrust.* Thirty minutes at—

   (i)   Rated maximum continuous power or thrust during fifteen of the twenty-five 6-hour endurance test cycles; and

   (ii) Rated takeoff power or thrust during ten of the twenty-five 6-hour endurance test cycles.

(3) Rated maximum continuous power or thrust. One hour and 30 minutes at rated maximum continuous power or thrust.

(4) Incremental cruise power or thrust. Two hours and 30 minutes at the successive power lever positions corresponding to at least 15 approximately equal speed and time increments between maximum continuous engine rotational speed and ground or minimum idle rotational speed. For engines operating at constant speed, the thrust and power may be varied in place of speed. If there is significant peak vibration anywhere between ground idle and maximum continuous conditions, the number of increments chosen may be changed to increase the amount of running made while subject to the peak vibrations up to not more than 50 percent of the total time spent in incremental running.

(5) Acceleration and deceleration runs. 30 minutes of accelerations and decelerations, consisting of six cycles from idling power or thrust to rated takeoff power or thrust and maintained at the takeoff power lever position for 30 seconds and at the idling power lever position for approximately four and one-half minutes. In complying with this paragraph, the power-control lever must be moved from one extreme position to the other in not more than one second, except that, if different regimes of control operations are incorporated necessitating scheduling of the power-control lever motion in going from one extreme position to the other, a longer period of time is acceptable, but not more than two seconds.

(6) Starts. One hundred starts must be made, of which 25 starts must be preceded by at least a two-hour engine shutdown. There must be at least 10 false engine starts, pausing for the applicant's specified minimum fuel drainage time, before attempting a normal start. There must be at least 10 normal restarts with not longer than 15 minutes since engine shutdown. The remaining starts may be made after completing the 150 hours of endurance testing.

(c) Rotorcraft engines for which a 30-minute OEI power rating is desired. For each rotorcraft engine for which a 30-minute OEI power rating is desired, the applicant must conduct the following series of tests:

(1) Takeoff and idling. One hour of alternate 5-minute periods at rated takeoff power and at idling power. The developed powers at takeoff and idling conditions and their corresponding rotor speed and gas temperature conditions must be as established by the power control in accordance with the schedule established by the applicant. During any one period, the rotor speed and power may be controlled manually while taking data to check performance. For engines with augmented takeoff power ratings that involve increases in turbine inlet temperature, rotor speed, or shaft power, this period of running at rated takeoff power must be at the augmented power rating. In changing the power setting after each period, the power control lever must be moved in the manner prescribed in paragraph (c)(6) of this section.

(2) Rated maximum continuous and takeoff power. Thirty minutes at—

   (i) Rated maximum continuous power during fifteen of the twenty-five 6-hour endurance test cycles; and

   (ii) Rated takeoff power during ten of the twenty-five 6-hour endurance test cycles.

(3) Rated maximum continuous power . One hour at rated maximum continuous power.

(4) Rated 30-minute OEI power . Thirty minutes at rated 30-minute OEI power.

(5) Incremental cruise power . Two hours and 30 minutes at the successive power lever positions corresponding with not less than 15 approximately equal speed and time increments between maximum continuous engine rotational speed and ground or minimum idle rotational speed. For engines operating at constant speed, power may be varied in place of speed. If there are significant peak vibrations anywhere between ground idle and

maximum continuous conditions, the number of increments chosen must be changed to increase the amount of running conducted while subject to peak vibrations up to not more than 50 percent of the total time spent in incremental running.

(6) Acceleration and deceleration runs . Thirty minutes of accelerations and decelerations, consisting of six cycles from idling power to rated takeoff power and maintained at the takeoff power lever position for 30 seconds and at the idling power lever position for approximately 4½ minutes. In complying with this paragraph, the power control lever must be moved from one extreme position to the other in not more than one second. If, however, different regimes of control operations are incorporated that necessitate scheduling of the power control lever motion from one extreme position to the other, then a longer period of time is acceptable, but not more than two seconds.

(7) Starts . One hundred starts, of which 25 starts must be preceded by at least a two-hour engine shutdown. There must be at least 10 false engine starts, pausing for the applicant's specified minimum fuel drainage time, before attempting a normal start. There must be at least 10 normal restarts not more than 15 minutes after engine shutdown. The remaining starts may be made after completing the 150 hours of endurance testing.

(d) Rotorcraft engines for which a continuous OEI rating is desired. For each rotorcraft engine for which a continuous OEI power rating is desired, the applicant must conduct the following series of tests:

(1) Takeoff and idling. One hour of alternate 5-minute periods at rated takeoff power and at idling power. The developed powers at takeoff and idling conditions and their corresponding rotor speed and gas temperature conditions must be as established by the power control in accordance with the schedule established by the applicant. During any one period the rotor speed and power may be controlled manually while taking data to check performance. For engines with augmented takeoff power ratings that involve increases in turbine inlet temperature, rotor speed, or shaft power, this period of running at rated takeoff power must be at the augmented power rating. In changing the power setting after each period, the power control lever must be moved in the manner prescribed in paragraph (c)(6) of this section.

(2) Rated maximum continuous and takeoff power. Thirty minutes at—

   (i) Rated maximum continuous power during fifteen of the twenty-five 6-hour endurance test cycles; and

   (ii) Rated takeoff power during ten of the twenty-five 6-hour endurance test cycles.

(3) Rated continuous OEI power. One hour at rated continuous OEI power.

(4) Rated maximum continuous power. One hour at rated maximum continuous power.

(5) Incremental cruise power. Two hours at the successive power lever positions corresponding with not less than 12 approximately equal speed and time increments between maximum continuous engine rotational speed and ground or minimum idle rotational speed. For engines operating at constant speed, power may be varied in place of speed. If there are significant peak vibrations anywhere between ground idle and maximum continuous conditions, the number of increments chosen must be changed to increase the amount of running conducted while being subjected to the peak vibrations up to not more than 50 percent of the total time spent in incremental running.

(6) Acceleration and deceleration runs. Thirty minutes of accelerations and decelerations, consisting of six cycles from idling power to rated takeoff power and maintained at the takeoff power lever position for 30 seconds and at the idling power lever position for approximately 4½ minutes. In complying with this paragraph, the power control lever must be moved from one extreme position to the other in not more than 1 second, except that if different regimes of control operations are incorporated

FAR 33

necessitating scheduling of the power control lever motion in going from one extreme position to the other, a longer period of time is acceptable, but not more than 2 seconds.

(7) Starts. One hundred starts, of which 25 starts must be preceded by at least a 2-hour engine shutdown. There must be at least 10 false engine starts, pausing for the applicant's specified minimum fuel drainage time, before attempting a normal start. There must be at least 10 normal restarts with not longer than 15 minutes since engine shutdown. The remaining starts may be made after completing the 150 hours of endurance testing.

(e) Rotorcraft engines for which a 2-1/2-minute OEI power rating is desired. For each rotorcraft engine for which a 2-1/2-minute OEI power rating is desired, the applicant must conduct the following series of tests:

(1) Takeoff, 2-1/2-minute OEI, and idling. One hour of alternate 5-minute periods at rated takeoff power and at idling power except that, during the third and sixth takeoff power periods, only 2-1/2minutes need be conducted at rated takeoff power, and the remaining 2-1/2minutes must be conducted at rated 2-1/2-minute OEI power. The developed powers at takeoff, 2-1/2-minute OEI, and idling conditions and their corresponding rotor speed and gas temperature conditions must be as established by the power control in accordance with the schedule established by the applicant. The applicant may, during any one period, control manually the rotor speed and power while taking data to check performance. For engines with augmented takeoff power ratings that involve increases in turbine inlet temperature, rotor speed, or shaft power, this period of running at rated takeoff power must be at the augmented rating. In changing the power setting after or during each period, the power control lever must be moved in the manner prescribed in paragraph (b)(5), (c)(6), or (d)(6) of this section, as applicable.

(2) The tests required in paragraphs (b)(2) through (b)(6), or (c)(2) through (c)(7), or (d)(2) through (d)(7) of this section, as applicable, except that in one of the 6-hour test sequences, the last 5 minutes of the 30 minutes at takeoff power test period of paragraph (b)(2) of this section, or of the 30 minutes at 30-minute OEI power test period of paragraph (c)(4) of this section, or of the 1 hour at continuous OEI power test period of paragraph (d)(3) of this section, must be run at 21/2-minute OEI power.

(f) Rotorcraft Engines for which 30-second OEI and 2-minute OEI ratings are desired . For each rotorcraft engine for which 30-second OEI and 2-minute OEI power ratings are desired, and following completion of the tests under paragraphs (b), (c), (d), or (e) of this section, the applicant may disassemble the tested engine to the extent necessary to show compliance with the requirements of 33.93(a). The tested engine must then be reassembled using the same parts used during the test runs of paragraphs (b), (c), (d), or (e) of this section, except those parts described as consumables in the Instructions for Continued Airworthiness. Additionally, the tests required in paragraphs (f)(1) through (f)(8) of this section must be run continuously. If a stop occurs during these tests, the interrupted sequence must be repeated unless the applicant shows that the severity of the test would not be reduced if it were continued. The applicant must conduct the following test sequence four times, for a total time of not less than 120 minutes:

(1) Takeoff power. 3 minutes at rated takeoff power.

(2) 30-second OEI power. 30 seconds at rated 30-second OEI power.

(3) 2-minute OEI power. 2 minutes at rated 2-minute OEI power.

(4) 30-minute OEI power, continuous OEI power, or maximum continuous power . Five minutes at whichever is the greatest of rated 30-minute OEI power, rated continuous OEI power, or rated maximum continuous power, except that, during the first test sequence, this period shall be 65 minutes. However, where the greatest rated power is 30-minute OEI power, that sixty-five minute period shall consist of 30 minutes at 30-minute OEI power followed by 35 minutes at whichever is the greater of continuous OEI power or maximum continuous power.

(5) 50 percent takeoff power. One minute at 50 percent takeoff power.

(6) 30-second OEI power. 30 seconds at rated 30-second OEI power.

(7) 2-minute OEI power. 2 minutes at rated 2-minute OEI power.

(8) Idle . One minute at flight idle.

(g) Supersonic aircraft engines. For each engine type certificated for use on supersonic aircraft the applicant must conduct the following:

(1) Subsonic test under sea level ambient atmospheric conditions. Thirty runs of one hour each must be made, consisting of—

   (i) Two periods of 5 minutes at rated takeoff augmented thrust each followed by 5 minutes at idle thrust;

   (ii) One period of 5 minutes at rated takeoff thrust followed by 5 minutes at not more than 15 percent of rated takeoff thrust;

   (iii) One period of 10 minutes at rated takeoff augmented thrust followed by 2 minutes at idle thrust, except that if rated maximum continuous augmented thrust is lower than rated takeoff augmented thrust, 5 of the 10-minute periods must be at rated maximum continuous augmented thrust; and

   (iv) Six periods of 1 minute at rated takeoff augmented thrust each followed by 2 minutes, including acceleration and deceleration time, at idle thrust.

(2) Simulated supersonic test. Each run of the simulated supersonic test must be preceded by changing the inlet air temperature and pressure from that attained at subsonic condition to the temperature and pressure attained at supersonic velocity, and must be followed by a return to the temperature attained at subsonic condition. Thirty runs of 4 hours each must be made, consisting of—

   (i) One period of 30 minutes at the thrust obtained with the power control lever set at the position for rated maximum continuous augmented thrust followed by 10 minutes at the thrust obtained with the power control lever set at the position for 90 percent of rated maximum continuous augmented thrust. The end of this period in the first five runs must be made with the induction air temperature at the limiting condition of transient overtemperature, but need not be repeated during the periods specified in paragraphs (g)(2)(ii) through (iv) of this section;

   (ii) One period repeating the run specified in paragraph (g)(2)(i) of this section, except that it must be followed by 10 minutes at the thrust obtained with the power control lever set at the position for 80 percent of rated maximum continuous augmented thrust;

   (iii) One period repeating the run specified in paragraph (g)(2)(i) of this section, except that it must be followed by 10 minutes at the thrust obtained with the power control lever set at the position for 60 percent of rated maximum continuous augmented thrust and then 10 minutes at not more than 15 percent of rated takeoff thrust;

   (iv) One period repeating the runs specified in paragraphs (g)(2)(i) and (ii) of this section; and

   (v) One period of 30 minutes with 25 of the runs made at the thrust obtained with the power control lever set at the position for rated maximum continuous augmented thrust, each followed by idle thrust and with the remaining 5 runs at the thrust obtained with the power control lever set at the position for rated maximum continuous augmented thrust for 25 minutes each, followed by subsonic operation at not more than 15 percent or rated takeoff thrust and accelerated to rated takeoff thrust for 5 minutes using hot fuel.

(3) Starts. One hundred starts must be made, of which 25 starts must be preceded by an engine shutdown of at least 2 hours. There must be at least 10 false engine starts, pausing for the applicant's specified minimum fuel drainage time before at-

tempting a normal start. At least 10 starts must be normal re-starts, each made no later than 15 minutes after engine shut-down. The starts may be made at any time, including the period of endurance testing.

[Doc. No. 3025, 29 FR 7453, June 10, 1964, as amended by Amdt. 33-3, 32 FR 3737, Mar. 4, 1967; Amdt. 33-6, 39 FR 35468, Oct. 1, 1974; Amdt. 33-10, 49 FR 6853, Feb. 23, 1984; Amdt. 33-12, 53 FR 34220, Sept. 2, 1988; Amdt. 33-18, 61 FR 31328, June 19, 1996; Amdt. 33-25, 73 FR 48123, Aug. 18, 2008; Amdt. 33-30, 74 FR 45311, Sept. 2, 2009; Amdt. 33-32, 77 FR 22187, Apr. 13, 2012]

33.88 Engine overtemperature test

(a) Each engine must run for 5 minutes at maximum permissible rpm with the gas temperature at least 75 °F (42 °C) higher than the maximum rating's steady-state operating limit, excluding maximum values of rpm and gas temperature associated with the 30-second OEI and 2-minute OEI ratings. Following this run, the turbine assembly must be within serviceable limits.

(b) In addition to the test requirements in paragraph (a) of this section, each engine for which 30-second OEI and 2-minute OEI ratings are desired, that incorporates a means for automatic temperature control within its operating limitations in accordance with 33.28(k), must run for a period of 4 minutes at the maximum power-on rpm with the gas temperature at least 35 °F (19 °C) higher than the maximum operating limit at 30-second OEI rating. Following this run, the turbine assembly may exhibit distress beyond the limits for an overtemperature condition provided the engine is shown by analysis or test, as found necessary by the FAA, to maintain the integrity of the turbine assembly.

(c) A separate test vehicle may be used for each test condition.

[Doc. No. 26019, 61 FR 31329, June 19, 1996]

[Amdt. 33–8, 73 FR 48124, August 18, 2008; Amdt. 33–9, 73 FR 48285, August 19, 2008]

33.89 Operation test

(a) The operation test must include testing found necessary by the Administrator to demonstrate—

(1) Starting, idling, acceleration, overspeeding, ignition, functioning of the propeller (if the engine is designated to operate with a propeller);

(2) Compliance with the engine response requirements of 33.73; and

(3) The minimum power or thrust response time to 95 percent rated takeoff power or thrust, from power lever positions representative of minimum idle and of minimum flight idle, starting from stabilized idle operation, under the following engine load conditions:

   (i) No bleed air and power extraction for aircraft use.

   (ii) Maximum allowable bleed air and power extraction for aircraft use.

   (iii) An intermediate value for bleed air and power extraction representative of that which might be used as a maximum for aircraft during approach to a landing.

(4) If testing facilities are not available, the determination of power extraction required in paragraph (a)(3)(ii) and (iii) of this section may be accomplished through appropriate analytical means.

(b) The operation test must include all testing found necessary by the Administrator to demonstrate that the engine has safe operating characteristics throughout its specified operating envelope.

[Amdt. 33–4, 36 FR 5493, Mar. 24, 1971, as amended by Amdt. 33–6, 39 FR 35469, Oct. 1, 1974; Amdt. 33–10, 49 FR 6853, Feb. 23, 1984]

33.90 Initial maintenance inspection test

Each applicant, except an applicant for an engine being type certificated through amendment of an existing type certificate or through supplemental type certification procedures, must complete one of the following tests on an engine that substantially conforms to the type design to establish when the initial maintenance inspection is required:

(a) An approved engine test that simulates the conditions in which the engine is expected to operate in service, including typical start-stop cycles.

(b) An approved engine test conducted in accordance with 33.201 (c) through (f).

[Doc. No. FAA–2002–6717, 72 FR 1877, Jan. 16, 2007]

33.91 Engine system and component tests

(a) For those systems or components that cannot be adequately substantiated in accordance with endurance testing of 33.87, the applicant must conduct additional tests to demonstrate that the systems or components are able to perform the intended functions in all declared environmental and operating conditions.

(b) Temperature limits must be established for those components that require temperature controlling provisions in the aircraft installation to assure satisfactory functioning, reliability, and durability.

(c) Each unpressurized hydraulic fluid tank may not fail or leak when subjected to maximum operating temperature and an internal pressure of 5 p.s.i., and each pressurized hydraulic fluid tank may not fail or leak when subjected to maximum operating temperature and an internal pressure not less than 5 p.s.i. plus the maximum operating pressure of the tank.

(d) For an engine type certificated for use in supersonic aircraft, the systems, safety devices, and external components that may fail because of operation at maximum and minimum operating temperatures must be identified and tested at maximum and minimum operating temperatures and while temperature and other operating conditions are cycled between maximum and minimum operating values.

[Doc. No. 3025, 29 FR 7453, June 10, 1964, as amended by Amdt. 33–6, 39 FR 35469, Oct. 1, 1974; Amdt. 33–10, 73 FR 48285, August 19, 2008]

33.92 Rotor locking tests

If continued rotation is prevented by a means to lock the rotor(s), the engine must be subjected to a test that includes 25 operations of this means under the following conditions:

(a) The engine must be shut down from rated maximum continuous thrust or power; and

(b) The means for stopping and locking the rotor(s) must be operated as specified in the engine operating instructions while being subjected to the maximum torque that could result from continued flight in this condition; and

(c) Following rotor locking, the rotor(s) must be held stationary under these conditions for five minutes for each of the 25 operations.

[Doc. No. 28107, 61 FR 28433, June 4, 1996]

33.93 Teardown inspection

(a) After completing the endurance testing of 33.87 (b), (c), (d), (e), or (g) of this part, each engine must be completely disassembled, and

(1) Each component having an adjustment setting and a functioning characteristic that can be established independent of installation on the engine must retain each setting and functioning characteristic within the limits that were established and recorded at the beginning of the test; and

(2) Each engine part must conform to the type design and be eligible for incorporation into an engine for continued operation, in accordance with information submitted in compliance with 33.4.

(b) After completing the endurance testing of 33.87(f), each engine must be completely disassembled, and

(1) Each component having an adjustment setting and a functioning characteristic that can be established independent of installation on the engine must retain each setting and functioning characteristic within the limits that were established and recorded at the beginning of the test; and

(2) Each engine may exhibit deterioration in excess of that permitted in paragraph (a)(2) of this section, including some engine parts or components that may be unsuitable for further use. The applicant must show by inspection, analysis, test, or by any combination thereof as found necessary by the FAA, that structural integrity of the engine is maintained; or

(c) In lieu of compliance with paragraph (b) of this section, each engine for which the 30-second OEI and 2-minute OEI ratings are desired, may be subjected to the endurance testing of 33.87 (b), (c), (d), or (e) of this part, and followed by the testing of 33.87(f) without intervening disassembly and inspection. However, the engine must comply with paragraph (a) of this section after completing the endurance testing of 33.87(f).

[Doc. No. 26019, 61 FR 31329, June 19, 1996; as amended by Amdt. No. 33–25, 73 FR 48124, Aug. 18, 2008]]

33.94   Blade containment and rotor unbalance tests

(a) Except as provided in paragraph (b) of this section, it must be demonstrated by engine tests that the engine is capable of containing damage without catching fire and without failure of its mounting attachments when operated for at least 15 seconds, unless the resulting engine damage induces a self shutdown, after each of the following events:

(1) Failure of the most critical compressor or fan blade while operating at maximum permissible r.p.m. The blade failure must occur at the outermost retention groove or, for integrally-bladed rotor discs, at least 80 percent of the blade must fail.

(2) Failure of the most critical turbine blade while operating at maximum permissible r.p.m. The blade failure must occur at the outermost retention groove or, for integrally-bladed rotor discs, at least 80 percent of the blade must fail. The most critical turbine blade must be determined by considering turbine blade weight and the strength of the adjacent turbine case at case temperatures and pressures associated with operation at maximum permissible r.p.m.

(b) Analysis based on rig testing, component testing, or service experience may be substitute for one of the engine tests prescribed in paragraphs (a)(1) and (a)(2) of this section if—

(1) That test, of the two prescribed, produces the least rotor unbalance; and

(2) The analysis is shown to be equivalent to the test.

Secs. 313(a), 601, and 603, Federal Aviation Act of 1958 (49 U.S.C. 1354(a), 1421, and 1423); and 49 U.S.C. 106(g) Revised, Pub. L. 97–449, Jan. 12, 1983)

[Amdt. 33–10, 49 FR 6854, Feb. 23, 1984]

33.95   Engine-propeller systems tests

If the engine is designed to operate with a propeller, the following tests must be made with a representative propeller installed by either including the tests in the endurance run or otherwise performing them in a manner acceptable to the Administrator:

(a) Feathering operation: 25 cycles.

(b) Negative torque and thrust system operation: 25 cycles from rated maximum continuous power.

(c) Automatic decoupler operation: 25 cycles from rated maximum continuous power (if repeated decoupling and recoupling in service is the intended function of the device).

(d) Reverse thrust operation: 175 cycles from the flight-idle position to full reverse and 25 cycles at rated maximum continuous power from full forward to full reverse thrust. At the end of each cycle the propeller must be operated in reverse pitch for a period of 30 seconds at the maximum rotational speed and power specified by the applicant for reverse pitch operation.

[Doc. No. 3025, 29 FR 7453, June 10, 1964, as amended by Amdt. 33–3, 32 FR 3737, Mar. 4, 1967]

33.96   Engine tests in auxiliary power unit (APU) mode

If the engine is designed with a propeller brake which will allow the propeller to be brought to a stop while the gas generator portion of the engine remains in operation, and remain stopped during operation of the engine as an auxiliary power unit ("APU mode"), in addition to the requirements of 33.87, the applicant must conduct the following tests:

(a) Ground locking: A total of 45 hours with the propeller brake engaged in a manner which clearly demonstrates its ability to function without adverse effects on the complete engine while the engine is operating in the APU mode under the maximum conditions of engine speed, torque, temperature, air bleed, and power extraction as specified by the applicant.

(b) Dynamic braking: A total of 400 application-release cycles of brake engagements must be made in a manner which clearly demonstrates its ability to function without adverse effects on the complete engine under the maximum conditions of engine acceleration/deceleration rate, speed, torque, and temperature as specified by the applicant. The propeller must be stopped prior to brake release.

(c) One hundred engine starts and stops with the propeller brake engaged.

(d) The tests required by paragraphs (a), (b), and (c) of this section must be performed on the same engine, but this engine need not be the same engine used for the tests required by 33.87.

(e) The tests required by paragraphs (a), (b), and (c) of this section must be followed by engine disassembly to the extent necessary to show compliance with the requirements of 33.93(a) and 33.93(b).

[Amdt. 33–11, 51 FR 10346, Mar. 25, 1986]

33.97   Thrust reversers

(a) If the engine incorporates a reverser, the endurance calibration, operation, and vibration tests prescribed in this subpart must be run with the reverser installed. In complying with this section, the power control lever must be moved from one extreme position to the other in not more than one second except, if regimes of control operations are incorporated necessitating scheduling of the power-control lever motion in going from one extreme position to the other, a longer period of time is acceptable but not more than three seconds. In addition, the test prescribed in paragraph (b) of this section must be made. This test may be scheduled as part of the endurance run.

(b) 175 reversals must be made from flight-idle forward thrust to maximum reverse thrust and 25 reversals must be made from rated takeoff thrust to maximum reverse thrust. After each reversal the reverser must be operated at full reverse thrust for a period of one minute, except that, in the case of a reverser intended for use only as a braking means on the ground, the reverser need only be operated at full reverse thrust for 30 seconds.

[Doc. No. 3025, 29 FR 7453, June 10, 1964, as amended by Amdt. 33–3, 32 FR 3737, Mar. 4, 1967]

33.99   General conduct of block tests

(a) Each applicant may, in making a block test, use separate engines of identical design and construction in the vibration, calibration, endurance, and operation tests, except that, if a separate engine is used for the endurance test it must be subjected to a calibration check before starting the endurance test.

(b) Each applicant may service and make minor repairs to the engine during the block tests in accordance with the service and maintenance instructions submitted in compliance with 33.4. If the frequency of the service is excessive, or the number of stops due to engine malfunction is excessive, or a major repair, or replacement of a part is found necessary during the block tests or as the result of findings from the teardown inspection, the engine or its parts must be subjected to any additional tests the Administrator finds necessary.

(c) Each applicant must furnish all testing facilities, including equipment and competent personnel, to conduct the block tests.

[Doc. No. 3025, 29 FR 7453, June 10, 1964, as amended by Amdt. 33–6, 39 FR 35470, Oct. 1, 1974; Amdt. 33–9, 45 FR 60181, Sept. 11, 1980]

Subpart G — Special Requirements: Turbine Aircraft Engines

Source: Docket No. FAA–2002–6717, 72 FR 1877, Jan. 16, 2007, unless otherwise noted.

33.201 Design and test requirements for Early ETOPS eligibility

An applicant seeking type design approval for an engine to be installed on a two-engine airplane approved for ETOPS without the service experience specified in part 25, Appendix K, K25.2.1 of this chapter, must comply with the following:

(a) The engine must be designed using a design quality process acceptable to the FAA, that ensures the design features of the engine minimize the occurrence of failures, malfunctions, defects, and maintenance errors that could result in an IFSD, loss of thrust control, or other power loss.

(b) The design features of the engine must address problems shown to result in an IFSD, loss of thrust control, or other power loss in the applicant's other relevant type designs approved within the past 10 years, to the extent that adequate service data is available within that 10-year period. An applicant without adequate service data must show experience with and knowledge of problem mitigating design practices equivalent to that gained from actual service experience in a manner acceptable to the FAA.

(c) Except as specified in paragraph (f) of this section, the applicant must conduct a simulated ETOPS mission cyclic endurance test in accordance with an approved test plan on an engine that substantially conforms to the type design. The test must:

(1) Include a minimum of 3,000 representative service start-stop mission cycles and three simulated diversion cycles at maximum continuous thrust or power for the maximum diversion time for which ETOPS eligibility is sought. Each start-stop mission cycle must include the use of take-off, climb, cruise, descent, approach, and landing thrust or power and the use of thrust reverse (if applicable). The diversions must be evenly distributed over the duration of the test. The last diversion must be conducted within 100 cycles of the completion of the test.

(2) Be performed with the high speed and low speed main engine rotors independently unbalanced to obtain a minimum of 90 percent of the recommended field service maintenance vibration levels. For engines with three main engine rotors, the intermediate speed rotor must be independently unbalanced to obtain a minimum of 90 percent of the recommended production acceptance vibration level. The required peak vibration levels must be verified during a slow acceleration and deceleration run of the test engine covering the main engine rotor operating speed ranges.

(3) Include a minimum of three million vibration cycles for each 60 rpm incremental step of the typical high-speed rotor start-stop mission cycle. The test may be conducted using any rotor speed step increment from 60 to 200 rpm provided the test encompasses the typical service start-stop cycle speed range. For incremental steps greater than 60 rpm, the minimum number of vibration cycles must be linearly increased up to ten million cycles for a 200 rpm incremental step.

(4) Include a minimum of 300,000 vibration cycles for each 60 rpm incremental step of the high-speed rotor approved operational speed range between minimum flight idle and cruise power not covered by paragraph (c)(3) of this section. The test may be conducted using any rotor speed step increment from 60 to 200 rpm provided the test encompasses the applicable speed range. For incremental steps greater than 60 rpm the minimum number of vibration cycles must be linearly increased up to 1 million for a 200 rpm incremental step.

(5) Include vibration surveys at periodic intervals throughout the test. The equivalent value of the peak vibration level observed during the surveys must meet the minimum vibration requirement of 33.201(c)(2).

(d) Prior to the test required by paragraph (c) of this section, the engine must be subjected to a calibration test to document power and thrust characteristics.

(e) At the conclusion of the testing required by paragraph (c) of this section, the engine must:

(1) Be subjected to a calibration test at sea-level conditions. Any change in power or thrust characteristics must be within approved limits.

(2) Be visually inspected in accordance with the on-wing inspection recommendations and limits contained in the Instructions for Continued Airworthiness submitted in compliance with 33.4.

(3) Be completely disassembled and inspected—

  (i) In accordance with the applicable inspection recommendations and limits contained in the Instructions for Continued Airworthiness submitted in compliance with 33.4;

  (ii) With consideration of the causes of IFSD, loss of thrust control, or other power loss identified by paragraph (b) of this section; and

  (iii) In a manner to identify wear or distress conditions that could result in an IFSD, loss of thrust control, or other power loss not specifically identified by paragraph (b) of this section or addressed within the Instructions for Continued Airworthiness.

(4) Not show wear or distress to the extent that could result in an IFSD, loss of thrust control, or other power loss within a period of operation before the component, assembly, or system would likely have been inspected or functionally tested for integrity while in service. Such wear or distress must have corrective action implemented through a design change, a change to maintenance instructions, or operational procedures before ETOPS eligibility is granted. The type and frequency of wear and distress that occurs during the engine test must be consistent with the type and frequency of wear and distress that would be expected to occur on ETOPS eligible engines.

(f) An alternative mission cycle endurance test that provides an equivalent demonstration of the unbalance and vibration specified in paragraph (c) of this section may be used when approved by the FAA.

(g) For an applicant using the simulated ETOPS mission cyclic endurance test to comply with 33.90, the test may be interrupted so that the engine may be inspected by an on-wing or other method, using criteria acceptable to the FAA, after completion of the test cycles required to comply with 33.90(a). Following the inspection, the ETOPS test must be resumed to complete the requirements of this section.

Appendix A to Part 33 — Instructions for Continued Airworthiness

A33.1 General

(a) This appendix specifies requirements for the preparation of Instructions for Continued Airworthiness as required by 33.4.

(b) The Instructions for Continued Airworthiness for each engine must include the Instructions for Continued Airworthiness for all engine parts. If Instructions for Continued Airworthiness are not supplied by the engine part manufacturer for an engine part, the Instructions for Continued Airworthiness for the engine must include the information essential to the continued airworthiness of the engine.

(c) The applicant must submit to the FAA a program to show how changes to the Instructions for Continued Airworthiness made by the applicant or by the manufacturers of engine parts will be distributed.

FAR 33

A33.2 Format

(a) The Instructions for Continued Airworthiness must be in the form of a manual or manuals as appropriate for the quantity of data to be provided.

(b) The format of the manual or manuals must provide for a practical arrangement.

A33.3 Content

The contents of the manual or manuals must be prepared in the English language. The Instructions for Continued Airworthiness must contain the following manuals or sections, as appropriate, and information:

(a) Engine Maintenance Manual or Section.

(1) Introduction information that includes an explanation of the engine's features and data to the extent necessary for maintenance or preventive maintenance.

(2) A detailed description of the engine and its components, systems, and installations.

(3) Installation instructions, including proper procedures for uncrating, deinhibiting, acceptance checking, lifting, and attaching accessories, with any necessary checks.

(4) Basic control and operating information describing how the engine components, systems, and installations operate, and information describing the methods of starting, running, testing, and stopping the engine and its parts including any special procedures and limitations that apply.

(5) Servicing information that covers details regarding servicing points, capacities of tanks, reservoirs, types of fluids to be used, pressures applicable to the various systems, locations of lubrication points, lubricants to be used, and equipment required for servicing.

(6) Scheduling information for each part of the engine that provides the recommended periods at which it should be cleaned, inspected, adjusted, tested, and lubricated, and the degree of inspection the applicable wear tolerances, and work recommended at these periods. However, the applicant may refer to an accessory, instrument, or equipment manufacturer as the source of this information if the applicant shows that the item has an exceptionally high degree of complexity requiring specialized maintenance techniques, test equipment, or expertise. The recommended overhaul periods and necessary cross references to the Airworthiness Limitations section of the manual must also be included. In addition, the applicant must include an inspection program that includes the frequency and extent of the inspections necessary to provide for the continued airworthiness of the engine.

(7) Troubleshooting information describing probable malfunctions, how to recognize those malfunctions, and the remedial action for those malfunctions.

(8) Information describing the order and method of removing the engine and its parts and replacing parts, with any necessary precautions to be taken. Instructions for proper ground handling, crating, and shipping must also be included.

(9) A list of the tools and equipment necessary for maintenance and directions as to their method of use.

(b) Engine Overhaul Manual or Section.

(1) Disassembly information including the order and method of disassembly for overhaul.

(2) Cleaning and inspection instructions that cover the materials and apparatus to be used and methods and precautions to be taken during overhaul. Methods of overhaul inspection must also be included.

(3) Details of all fits and clearances relevant to overhaul.

(4) Details of repair methods for worn or otherwise substandard parts and components along with the information necessary to determine when replacement is necessary.

(5) The order and method of assembly at overhaul.

(6) Instructions for testing after overhaul.

(7) Instructions for storage preparation, including any storage limits.

(8) A list of tools needed for overhaul.

(c) ETOPS Requirements. For an applicant seeking eligibility for an engine to be installed on an airplane approved for ETOPS, the Instructions for Continued Airworthiness must include procedures for engine condition monitoring. The engine condition monitoring procedures must be able to determine prior to flight, whether an engine is capable of providing, within approved engine operating limits, maximum continuous power or thrust, bleed air, and power extraction required for a relevant engine inoperative diversion. For an engine to be installed on a two-engine airplane approved for ETOPS, the engine condition monitoring procedures must be validated before ETOPS eligibility is granted.

A33.4 Airworthiness limitations section

The Instructions for Continued Airworthiness must contain a section titled Airworthiness Limitations that is segregated and clearly distinguishable from the rest of the manual.

(a) For all engines:

(1) The Airworthiness Limitations section must set forth each mandatory replacement time, inspection interval, and related procedure required for type certification. If the Instructions for Continued Airworthiness consist of multiple documents, the section required under this paragraph must be included in the principal manual.

(2) This section must contain a legible statement in a prominent location that reads: "The Airworthiness Limitations section is FAA approved and specifies maintenance required under 43.16 and 91.403 of Title 14 of the Code of Federal Regulations unless an alternative program has been FAA approved."

(b) For rotorcraft engines having 30-second OEI and 2-minute OEI ratings:

(1) The Airworthiness Limitations section must also prescribe the mandatory post-flight inspections and maintenance actions associated with any use of either 30-second OEI or 2-minute OEI ratings.

(2) The applicant must validate the adequacy of the inspections and maintenance actions required under paragraph (b)(1) of this section A33.4.

(3) The applicant must establish an in-service engine evaluation program to ensure the continued adequacy of the instructions for mandatory post-flight inspections and maintenance actions prescribed under paragraph (b)(1) of this section A33.4 and of the data for 33.5(b)(4) pertaining to power availability. The program must include service engine tests or equivalent service engine test experience on engines of similar design and evaluations of service usage of the 30-second OEI or 2-minute OEI ratings.

[Amdt. 33–9, 45 FR 60181, Sept. 11, 1980, as amended by Amdt. 33–13, 54 FR 34330, Aug. 18, 1989; Amdt. 33–21, 72 FR 1878, Jan. 16, 2007; Amdt. 33–10, 73 FR 48124, August 18, 2008]

Appendix B to Part 33 — Certification Standard Atmospheric Concentrations of Rain and Hail

Figure B1, Table B1, Table B2, Table B3, and Table B4 specify the atmospheric concentrations and size distributions of rain and hail for establishing certification, in accordance with the requirements of 33.78(a)(2). In conducting tests, normally by spraying liquid water to simulate rain conditions and by delivering hail fabricated from ice to simulate hail conditions, the use of water droplets and hail having shapes, sizes and distributions of sizes other than those defined in this appendix B, or the use of a single size or shape for each water droplet or hail, can be accepted, provided that applicant shows that the substitution does not reduce the severity of the test.

[Doc. No. 28652, 63 FR 14799, Mar. 26, 1998]

FIGURE B1–ILLUSTRATION OF RAIN AND HAIL THREATS. CERTIFICATION CONCENTRATIONS ARE OBTAINED USING TABLES B1 AND B2

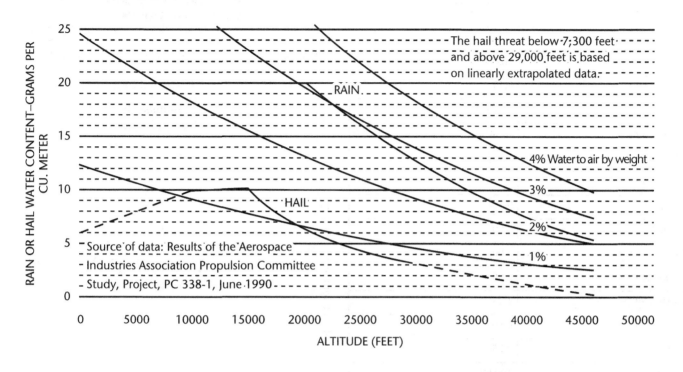

TABLE B1 CERTIFICATION STANDARD ATMOSPHERIC RAIN CONCENTRATIONS	
ALTITUDE (FEET)	RAIN WATER CONTENT (RWC) GRAMS WATER/METER^3 AIR)
0	20.0
20,0000	20.0
26.3000	15.2
32,700	10.8
39,300	7.7
46,000	5.2

RWC values at other altitudes may be determined by linear interpolation.
NOTE: Source of data — Results of the Aerospace Industries Association (AIA) Propulsion Committee Study, Project PC 338-1, June 1990.

TABLE B2 CERTIFICATION STANDARD ATMOSPHERIC HAIL CONCENTRATIONS	
ALTITUDE (FEET)	HAIL WATER CONTENT (HWC) GRAMS WATER/METER^3 AIR)
0	6.0
7,300	8.9
8,500	9.4
10,000	9.9
12,000	10.0
15,000	10.0
16,000	8.9
17,700	7.8
19,300	6.6
21,500	5.6
24,300	4.4
29,000	3.3
46,000	0.2

HWC values at other altitudes may be determined by linear interpolation. The hail threat below 7,300 feet and above 29,000 feet is based on linearly extrapolated data.
NOTE: Source of data — Results of the Aerospace Industries Association (AIA) Propulsion Committee (PC) Study, Project PC 338-1, June 1990.

FAR 33

TABLE B3 CERTIFICATION STANDARD ATMOSPHERIC RAIN DROPLET SIZEDISTRIBUTION	
RAIN DROPLET DIAMETER (MM)	CONTRIBUTION TOTAL RWC (%)
0-0.49	0
0.50-0.99	2.25
1.00-1.49	8.75
1.50-1.99	16.25
2.00-2.49	19.00
2.50-2.99	17.75
3.00-3.49	13.50
3.50-3.99	9.50
4.00-4.49	6.00
4.50-4.99	3.00
5.00-5.49	2.00
5.50-5.99	1.25
6.00-6.49	0.50
6.50-7.00	0.25
Total	100.00

Median diameter of rain droplets is 2.66mm
NOTE: Source of data — Results of the Aerospace Industries Association (AIA) Propulsion Committee (PC) Study, Project PC 338-1, June 1990.

TABLE B4 CERTIFICATION STANDARD ATMOSPHERIC HAIL SIZE DISTRIBUTION	
HAIL DIAMETER (MM)	CONTRIBUTION TOTAL HWC (%)
0-4.9	0
5.0-9.9	17.00
10.0-14.9	25.00
15.0-19.9	22.50
20.0-24.9	16.00
25.0-29.9	9.75
30.0-34.9	4.75
35.0-39.9	2.50
40.00-44.9	1.50
45.0-49.9	0.75
50.0-55.0	0.25
Total	100.00

Median diameter of hail is 16mm
NOTE: Source of data — Results of the Aerospace Industries Association (AIA) Propulsion Committee (PC) Study, Project PC 338-1, June 1990.

Appendix C — [Reserved]

Appendix D to Part 33 — Mixed Phase and Ice Crystal Icing Envelope (Deep Convective Clouds)

The ice crystal icing envelope is depicted in Figure D1 of this Appendix.

Within the envelope, total water content (TWC) in g/m3 has been

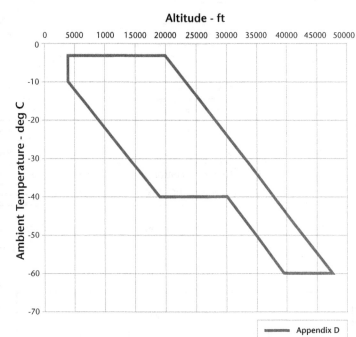

FIGURE D1 — CONVECTIVE CLOUD ICE CRYSTAL ENVELOPE

determined based upon the adiabatic lapse defined by the convective rise of 90% relative humidity air from sea level to higher altitudes and scaled by a factor of 0.65 to a standard cloud length of 17.4 nautical miles. Figure D2 of this Appendix displays TWC for this distance over a range of ambient temperature within the boundaries of the ice crystal envelope specified in Figure D1 of this Appendix.

Ice crystal size median mass dimension (MMD) range is 50-200 microns (equivalent spherical size) based upon measurements near convective storm cores.

The TWC can be treated as completely glaciated (ice crystal) except as noted in the Table 1 of this Appendix.

TABLE 1—SUPERCOOLED LIQUID PORTION OF TWC		
TEMPERATURE RANGE—DEG C	HORIZONTAL CLOUD LENGTH—NAUTICAL MILES	LWC—g/m3
0 to -20	≤50	≤1.0
0 to -20	Indefinite	≤0.5
< -20		0

The TWC levels displayed in Figure D2 of this Appendix represent TWC values for a standard exposure distance (horizontal cloud length) of 17.4 nautical miles that must be adjusted with length of icing exposure.

[Amdt. 33-34, 79 FR 65538, Nov. 4, 2014]

FIGURE D2 — TOTAL WATER CONTENT

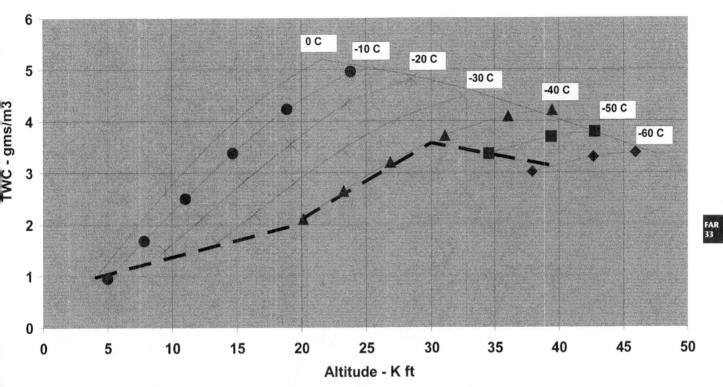

FIGURE D3 — EXPOSURE LENGTH INFLUENCE ON TWC

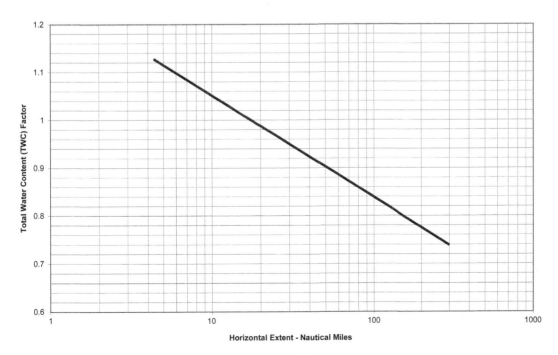

PART 34 — FUEL VENTING AND EXHAUST EMISSION REQUIREMENTS FOR TURBINE ENGINE POWERED AIRPLANES

Subpart A — General Provisions

Subpart B — Engine Fuel Venting Emissions (New and In-Use Aircraft Gas Turbine Engines)

Subpart C — Exhaust Emissions (New Aircraft Gas Turbine Engines)

Subpart D — Exhaust Emissions (In-use Aircraft Gas Turbine Engines)

Subparts E — Certification Provisions

Subpart F [Reserved]

Subpart G — Test Procedures for Engine Exhaust Gaseous Emissions (Aircraft and Aircraft Gas Turbine Engines)

Subpart H — [Reserved]

Authority: 42 U.S.C. 4321 et seq., 7572; 49 U.S.C. 106(g), 40113, 44701–44702, 44704, 44714.

Source: Docket No. 25613, 55 FR 32861, Aug. 10, 1990, unless otherwise noted.

Subpart A — General Provisions

34.1   Definitions

As used in this part, all terms not defined herein shall have the meaning given them in the Clean Air Act, as amended (42 U.S.C. 7401 et. seq.):

Act means the Clean Air Act, as amended (42 U.S.C. 7401 et. seq.).

Administrator means the Administrator of the Federal Aviation Administration or any person to whom he has delegated his authority in the matter concerned.

Administrator of the EPA means the Administrator of the Environmental Protection Agency and any other officer or employee of the Environmental Protection Agency to whom the authority involved may be delegated.

Aircraft as used in this part means any airplane as defined in 14 CFR part 1 for which a U.S. standard airworthiness certificate or equivalent foreign airworthiness certificate is issued.

Aircraft engine means a propulsion engine which is installed in, or which is manufactured for installation in, an aircraft.

Aircraft gas turbine engine means a turboprop, turbofan, or turbojet aircraft engine.

Characteristic level has the meaning given in Appendix 6 of ICAO Annex 16 as of July 2008. The characteristic level is a calculated emission level for each pollutant based on a statistical assessment of measured emissions from multiple tests.[1]

Class TP means all aircraft turboprop engines.

Class TF means all turbofan or turbojet aircraft engines or aircraft engines designed for applications that otherwise would have been fulfilled by turbojet and turbofan engines except engines of class T3, T8, and TSS.

Class T3 means all aircraft gas turbine engines of the JT3D model family.

Class T8 means all aircraft gas turbine engines of the JT8D model family.

Class TSS means all aircraft gas turbine engines employed for propulsion of aircraft designed to operate at supersonic flight speeds.

Commercial aircraft engine means any aircraft engine used or intended for use by an "air carrier" (including those engaged in "intrastate air transportation") or a "commercial operator" (including those engaged in "intrastate air transportation") as these terms are defined in Title 49 of the United States Code and Title 14 of the Code of Federal Regulations.

Commercial aircraft gas turbine engine means a turboprop, turbofan, or turbojet commercial aircraft engine.

Date of manufacture of an engine is the date the inspection acceptance records reflect that the engine is complete and meets the FAA approved type design.

Derivative engine for emissions certification purposes means an engine that has the same or similar emissions characteristics as an engine covered by a U.S. type certificate issued under 14 CFR part 33. These characteristics are specified in 34.48.

Emission measurement system means all of the equipment necessary to transport the emission sample and measure the level of emissions. This includes the sample system and the instrumentation system.

Engine model means all commercial aircraft turbine engines which are of the same general series, displacement, and design characteristics and are approved under the same type certificate.

Excepted, as used in 34.9, means an engine that may be produced and sold that does not meet otherwise applicable standards. Excepted engines must conform to regulatory conditions specified for an exception in 34.9. Excepted engines are subject to the standards of this part even though they are not required to comply with the otherwise applicable requirements. Engines excepted with respect to certain standards must comply with other standards from which they are not specifically excepted.

Exempt means an engine that does not meet certain applicable standards but may be produced and sold under the terms allowed by a grant of exemption issued pursuant to 34.7 of this part and part 11 of this chapter. Exempted engines must conform to regulatory conditions specified in the exemption as well as other applicable regulations. Exempted engines are subject to the standards of this part even though they are not required to comply with the otherwise applicable requirements. Engines exempted with respect to certain standards must comply with other standards as a condition of the exemption.

Exhaust emissions means substances emitted into the atmosphere from the exhaust discharge nozzle of an aircraft or aircraft engine.

Fuel venting emissions means raw fuel, exclusive of hydrocarbons in the exhaust emissions, discharged from aircraft gas turbine engines during all normal ground and flight operations.

Introduction date means the date of manufacture of the first individual production engine of a given engine model or engine type certificate family to be certificated. Neither test engines nor engines not placed into service affect this date.

FAR 34

In-use aircraft gas turbine engine means an aircraft gas turbine engine which is in service.

New aircraft turbine engine means an aircraft gas turbine engine which has never been in service.

Power setting means the power or thrust output of an engine in terms of kilonewtons thrust for turbojet and turbofan engines or shaft power in terms of kilowatts for turboprop engines.

Rated output (rO) means the maximum power/thrust available for takeoff at standard day conditions as approved for the engine by the Federal Aviation Administration, including reheat contribution where applicable, but excluding any contribution due to water injection, expressed in kilowatts or kilonewtons (as applicable), rounded to at least three significant figures.

Rated pressure ratio (rPR) means the ratio between the combustor inlet pressure and the engine inlet pressure achieved by an engine operation at rated output, rounded to at least three significant figures.

Reference day conditions means the reference ambient conditions to which the gaseous emissions (HC and smoke) are to be corrected. The reference day conditions are as follows: Temperature=15°C, specific humidity=0.00629 kg H_2O/kg of dry air, and pressure=101325 Pa.

Sample system means the system which provides for the transportation of the gaseous emission sample from the sample probe to the inlet of the instrumentation system.

Shaft power means only the measured shaft power output of a turboprop engine.

Smoke means the matter in exhaust emissions which obscures the transmission of light.

Smoke number (SN) means the dimensionless term quantifying smoke emissions.

Standard day conditions Standard day conditions means the following ambient conditions: temperature = 15°C, specific humidity = 0.00634 kg H_2O/kg dry air, and pressure = 101.325 kPa.

Taxi/idle (in) means those aircraft operations involving taxi and idle between the time of landing roll-out and final shutdown of all propulsion engines.

Taxi/idle (out) means those aircraft operations involving taxi and idle between the time of initial starting of the propulsion engine(s) used for the taxi and the turn onto the duty runway.

Tier, as used in this part, is a designation related to the NOX emission standard for the engine as specified in 34.21 or 34.23 of this part (e.g., Tier 0).

[1] This incorporation by reference was approved by the Director of the Federal Register in accordance with 5 U.S.C. 552(a) and 1 CFR part 51. This document can be obtained from the ICAO, Document Sales Unit, 999 University Street, Montreal, Quebec H3C 5H7, Canada, phone +1 514-954-8022, or www.icao.int or sales14icao.int. Copies can be reviewed at the FAA New England Regional Office, 12 New England Executive Park, Burlington, Massachusetts, 781-238-7101, or at the National Archives and Records Administration (NARA). For information on the availability of this material at NARA, call 202-741-6030, or go to: http://www.archives.gov/federal_register/code_of_federal_regulations/ibr_locations.html.

[Doc. No. 25613, 55 FR 32861, Aug. 10, 1990; 55 FR 37287, Sept. 10, 1990, as amended by Amdt. 34-3, 64 FR 5558, Feb. 3, 1999; Amdt. 34-5, 77 FR 76849, Dec. 31, 2012; Amdt. 34-5A, 78 FR 63016, Oct. 23, 2013]

34.2 Abbreviations

The abbreviations used in this part have the following meanings in both upper and lower case:

CO_2	Carbon dioxide
CO	Carbon monoxide
EPA	United States Environmental Protection Agency
FAA	Federal Aviation Administration, United States Department of Transportation
g	Gram(s)
HC	Hydrocarbon(s)
HP	Horsepower
hr	Hour(s)
H_2O	water
kg	Kilogram(s)
kJ	Kilojoule(s)
kN	Kilonewton(s)
kW	Kilowatt(s)
lb	Pound(s)
LTO	Landing and takeoff
min	Minute(s)
NO_x	Oxides of nitrogen
Pa	Pascal(s)
rO	Rated output
rPR	Rated pressure ratio
sec	Second(s)
SP	Shaft power
SN	Smoke number
T	Temperature, degrees Kelvin
TIM	Time in mode
W	Watt(s)
°C	Degrees Celsius
%	Percent

[Doc. No. 25613, 55 FR 32861, Aug. 10, 1990, as amended by Amdt. 34-3, 64 FR 5559, Feb. 3, 1999; Amdt. 34-5, 77 FR 76850, Dec. 31, 2012]

34.3 General requirements

(a) This part provides for the approval or acceptance by the Administrator or the Administrator of the EPA of testing and sampling methods, analytical techniques, and related equipment not identical to those specified in this part. Before either approves or accepts any such alternate, equivalent, or otherwise nonidentical procedures or equipment, the Administrator or the Administrator of the EPA shall consult with the other in determining whether or not the action requires rulemaking under sections 231 and 232 of the Clean Air Act, as amended, consistent with the responsibilities of the Administrator of the EPA and the Secretary of Transportation under sections 231 and 232 of the Clean Air Act.

(b) Under section 232 of the Act, the Secretary of Transportation issues regulations to ensure compliance with 40 CFR part 87. This authority has been delegated to the Administrator of the FAA (49 CFR 1.47).

(c) U.S. airplanes. This part applies to civil airplanes that are powered by aircraft gas turbine engines of the classes specified herein and that have U.S. standard airworthiness certificates.

(d) Foreign airplanes. Pursuant to the definition of "aircraft" in 40 CFR 87.1, this regulation applies to civil airplanes that are powered by aircraft gas turbine engines of the classes specified herein and that have foreign airworthiness certificates that are equivalent to U.S. standard airworthiness certificates. This regulation applies only to those foreign civil airplanes that, if registered in the United States, would be required by applicable regulations to have a U.S. standard airworthiness certificate in order to conduct the operations intended for the airplane. Pursuant to 40 CFR 87.3(c), this regulation does not apply where it would be inconsistent with an obligation assumed by the United States to a foreign country in a treaty, convention, or agreement.

(e) Reference in this regulation to 40 CFR part 87 refers to title 40 of the Code of Federal Regulations, chapter I—Environmental Protection Agency, part 87, Control of Air Pollution from Aircraft and Aircraft Engines (40 CFR part 87).

(f) This part contains regulations to ensure compliance with certain standards contained in 40 CFR part 87. If EPA takes any action, including the issuance of an exemption or issuance of a revised or alternate procedure, test method, or other regulation, the effect of which is to relax or delay the effective date of any provision of 40 CFR part 87 that is made applicable to an aircraft under this FAR, the Administrator of FAA will grant a general administrative waiver of its more stringent requirements until this FAR is amended to reflect the more relaxed requirements prescribed by EPA.

(g) Unless otherwise stated, all terminology and abbreviations in this FAR that are defined in 40 CFR part 87 have the meaning specified in that part, and all terms in 40 CFR part 87 that are not defined in that part but that are used in this FAR have the meaning given them in the Clean Air Act, as amended by Public Law 91–604.

(h) All interpretations of 40 CFR part 87 that are rendered by the EPA also apply to this FAR.

(i) If the EPA, under 40 CFR 87.3(a), approves or accepts any testing and sampling procedures or methods, analytical techniques, or related equipment not identical to those specified in that part, this FAR requires an applicant to show that such alternate, equivalent, or otherwise nonidentical procedures have been complied with, and that such alternate equipment was used to show compliance, unless the applicant elects to comply with those procedures, methods, techniques, and equipment specified in 40 CFR part 87.

(j) If the EPA, under 40 CFR 87.5, prescribes special test procedures for any aircraft or aircraft engine that is not susceptible to satisfactory testing by the procedures in 40 CFR part 87, the applicant must show the Administrator that those special test procedures have been complied with.

(k) Wherever 40 CFR part 87 requires agreement, acceptance, or approval by the Administrator of the EPA, this FAR requires a showing that such agreement or approval has been obtained.

(l) Pursuant to 42 U.S.C. 7573, no state or political subdivision thereof may adopt or attempt to enforce any standard respecting emissions of any air pollutant from any aircraft or engine thereof unless that standard is identical to a standard made applicable to the aircraft by the terms of this FAR.

(m) If EPA, by regulation or exemption, relaxes a provision of 40 CFR part 87 that is implemented in this FAR, no state or political subdivision thereof may adopt or attempt to enforce the terms of this FAR that are superseded by the relaxed requirement.

(n) If any provision of this FAR is rendered inapplicable to a foreign aircraft as provided in 40 CFR 87.3(c) (international agreements), and 34.3(d) of this FAR, that provision may not be adopted or enforced against that foreign aircraft by a state or political subdivision thereof.

(o) For exhaust emissions requirements of this FAR that apply beginning February 1, 1974, January 1, 1976, January 1, 1978, January 1, 1984, and August 9, 1985, continued compliance with those requirements is shown for engines for which the type design has been shown to meet those requirements, if the engine is maintained in accordance with applicable maintenance requirements for 14 CFR chapter I. All methods of demonstrating compliance and all model designations previously found acceptable to the Administrator shall be deemed to continue to be an acceptable demonstration of compliance with the specific standards for which they were approved.

(p) Each applicant must allow the Administrator to make, or witness, any test necessary to determine compliance with the applicable provisions of this FAR.

[Doc. No. 25613, 55 FR 32861, Aug. 10, 1990; 55 FR 37287, Sept. 10, 1990]

34.4 [Reserved]

34.5 Special test procedures

The Administrator or the Administrator of the EPA may, upon written application by a manufacturer or operator of aircraft or aircraft engines, approve test procedures for any aircraft or aircraft engine that is not susceptible to satisfactory testing by the procedures set forth herein. Prior to taking action on any such application, the Administrator or the Administrator of the EPA shall consult with the other.

34.6 Aircraft safety

(a) The provisions of this part will be revised if at any time the Administrator determines that an emission standard cannot be met within the specified time without creating a safety hazard.

(b) Consistent with 40 CFR 87.6, if the FAA Administrator determines that any emission control regulation in this part cannot be safely applied to an aircraft, that provision may not be adopted or enforced against that aircraft by any state or political subdivision thereof.

34.7 Exemptions

Notwithstanding part 11 of the Federal Aviation Regulations (14 CFR part 11), all petitions for rulemaking involving either the substance of an emission standard or test procedure prescribed by the EPA that is incorporated in this FAR, or the compliance date for such standard or procedure, must be submitted to the EPA. Information copies of such petitions are invited by the FAA. Petitions for rulemaking or exemption involving provisions of this FAR that do not affect the substance or the compliance date of an emission standard or test procedure that is prescribed by the EPA, and petitions for exemptions under the provisions for which the EPA has specifically granted exemption authority to the Secretary of Transportation are subject to part 11 of the Federal Aviation Regulations (14 CFR part 11). Petitions for rulemaking or exemptions involving these FARs must be submitted to the FAA.

(a) Exemptions based on flights for short durations at infrequent intervals. The emission standards of this part do not apply to engines which power aircraft operated in the United States for short durations at infrequent intervals. Such operations are limited to:

   (1) Flights of an aircraft for the purpose of export to a foreign country, including any flights essential to demonstrate the integrity of an aircraft prior to a flight to a point outside the United States.

   (2) Flights to a base where repairs, alterations or maintenance are to be performed, or to a point of storage, or for the purpose of returning an aircraft to service.

   (3) Official visits by representatives of foreign governments.

   (4) Other flights the Administrator determines, after consultation with the Administrator of the EPA, to be for short durations at infrequent intervals. A request for such a determination shall be made before the flight takes place.

(b) Exemptions for very low production engine models. The emissions standards of this part do not apply to engines of very low production after the date of applicability. For the purpose of this part, "very low production" is limited to a maximum total production for United States civil aviation applications of no more than 200 units covered by the same type certificate after January 1, 1984. Engines manufactured under this provision must be reported to the FAA by serial number on or before the date of manufacture and exemptions granted under this provision are not transferable to any other engine. This exemption is limited to the requirements of 34.21 only.

(c) Exemptions for new engines in other categories. The emissions standards of this part do not apply to engines for which the Administrator determines, with the concurrence of the Administrator of the EPA, that application of any standard under 34.21 is not justified, based upon consideration of—

   (1) Adverse economic impact on the manufacturer;

   (2) Adverse economic impact on the aircraft and airline industries at large;

   (3) Equity in administering the standards among all economically competing parties;

   (4) Public health and welfare effects; and

   (5) Other factors which the Administrator, after consultation with the Administrator of the EPA, may deem relevant to the case in question.

FAR 34

(d) Applicants seeking exemption from other emissions standards of this part and 40 CFR part 87. Applicants must request exemption from both the FAA and the EPA, even where the underlying regulatory requirements are the same. The FAA and EPA will jointly consider such exemption requests, and will assure consistency in the respective agency determinations.

(e) Applications for exemption from this part shall be submitted in duplicate to the Administrator in accordance with the procedures established by the Administrator in part 11.

(f) The Administrator shall publish in the Federal Register the name of the organization to whom exemptions are granted and the period of such exemptions.

(g) No state or political subdivision thereof may attempt to enforce a standard respecting emissions from an aircraft or engine if such aircraft or engine has been exempted from such standard under this part.

[Doc. No. 25613, 55 FR 32861, Aug. 10, 1990, as amended by Amdt. 34-5, 77 FR 76850, Dec. 31, 2012]

34.9   Exceptions

(a) Spare engines. Certain engines that meet the following description are excepted:

(1) This exception allows production of an engine for installation on an in-service aircraft. A spare engine may not be installed on a new aircraft.

(2) Each spare engine must be identical to a sub-model previously certificated to meet all applicable requirements.

(3) A spare engine may be used only when the emissions of the spare do not exceed the certification requirements of the original engine, for all regulated pollutants.

(4) No separate approval is required to produce spare engines.

(5) The record for each engine excepted under this paragraph (c) must indicate that the engine was produced as an excepted spare engine.

(6) Engines produced under this exception must be labeled "EXCEPTED SPARE" in accordance with 45.13 of this chapter.

(b) On and after July 18, 2012, and before August 31, 2013, a manufacturer may produce up to six Tier 4 compliant engines that meet the NOX standards of paragraph (d)(1)(vi) of this section rather than 34.23(a)(2). No separate approval is required to produce these engines. Engines produced under this exception are to be labeled "COMPLY" in accordance with 45.13 of this chapter.

[Doc. No. FAA-2012-1333, 77 FR 76850, Dec. 31, 2012]

Subpart B — Engine Fuel Venting Emissions (New and In-Use Aircraft Gas Turbine Engines)

34.10   Applicability

(a) The provisions of this subpart are applicable to all new aircraft gas turbine engines of classes T3, T8, TSS, and TF equal to or greater than 36 kN (8,090 lb) rated output, manufactured on or after January 1, 1974, and to all in-use aircraft gas turbine engines of classes T3, T8, TSS, and TF equal to or greater than 36 kN (8,090 lb) rated output manufactured after February 1, 1974.

(b) The provisions of this subpart are also applicable to all new aircraft gas turbine engines of class TF less than 36 kN (8,090 lb) rated output and class TP manufactured on or after January 1, 1975, and to all in-use aircraft gas turbine engines of class TF less than 36 kN (8,090 lb) rated output and class TP manufactured after January 1, 1975.

[Doc. No. FAA-2012-1333, 77 FR 76850, Dec. 31, 2012]

34.11   Standard for fuel venting emissions

(a) No fuel venting emissions shall be discharged into the atmosphere from any new or in-use aircraft gas turbine engine subject to the subpart. This paragraph is directed at the elimination of intentional discharge to the atmosphere of fuel drained from fuel nozzle manifolds after engines are shut down and does not apply to normal fuel seepage from shaft seals, joints, and fittings.

(b) Conformity with the standard set forth in paragraph (a) of this section shall be determined by inspection of the method designed to eliminate these emissions.

(c) As applied to an airframe or an engine, any manufacturer or operator may show compliance with the fuel venting and emissions requirements of this section that were effective beginning February 1, 1974 or January 1, 1975, by any means that prevents the intentional discharge of fuel from fuel nozzle manifolds after the engines are shut down. Acceptable means of compliance include one of the following:

(1) Incorporation of an FAA-approved system that recirculates the fuel back into the fuel system.

(2) Capping or securing the pressurization and drain valve.

(3) Manually draining the fuel from a holding tank into a container.

Subpart C — Exhaust Emissions (New Aircraft Gas Turbine Engines)

34.20   Applicability

The provisions of this subpart are applicable to all aircraft gas turbine engines of the classes specified beginning on the dates specified in 34.21.

34.21   Standards for exhaust emissions

(a) Exhaust emissions of smoke from each new aircraft gas turbine engine of class T8 manufactured on or after February 1, 1974, shall not exceed a smoke number (SN) of 30.

(b) Exhaust emissions of smoke from each new aircraft gas turbine engine of class TF and of rated output of 129 kN (29,000 lb) thrust or greater, manufactured on or after January 1, 1976, shall not exceed SN = 83.6 (rO) −0.274 (rO is in kN).

(c) Exhaust emission of smoke from each new aircraft gas turbine engine of class T3 manufactured on or after January 1, 1978, shall not exceed a smoke number (SN) of 25.

(d) Gaseous exhaust emissions from each new aircraft gas turbine engine shall not exceed:

(1) For Classes TF, T3, T8 engines greater than 26.7 kN (6,000 lb) rated output:

(i) Engines manufactured on or after January 1, 1984: Hydrocarbons: 19.6 g/kN rO.

(ii) Engines manufactured on or after July 7, 1997: Carbon Monoxide: 118 g/kN rO.

(iii) Engines of a type or model of which the date of manufacture of the first individual production model was on or before December 31, 1995, and for which the date of manufacture of the individual engine was on or before December 31, 1999 (Tier 2): Oxides of Nitrogen: (40+2(rPR)) g/kN rO.

(iv) Engines of a type or model of which the date of manufacture of the first individual production model was after December 31, 1995, or for which the date of manufacture of the individual engine was after December 31, 1999 (Tier 2): Oxides of Nitrogen: (32+1.6(rPR)) g/kN rO.

(v) The emission standards prescribed in paragraphs (d)(1)(iii) and (iv) of this section apply as prescribed beginning July 7, 1997.

(vi) The emission standards of this paragraph apply as prescribed after December 18, 2005. For engines of a type or model of which the first individual production model was manufactured after December 31, 2003 (Tier 4):

(A) That have a rated pressure ratio of 30 or less and a maximum rated output greater than 89 kN:Oxides of Nitrogen: (19 + 1.6(rPR)) g/kN rO.

(B) That have a rated pressure ratio of 30 or less and a maximum rated output greater than 26.7 kN but not greater than 89 kN: Oxides of Nitrogen: (37.572 + 1.6(rPR) − 0.2087(rO)) g/kN rO.

(C) That have a rated pressure ratio greater than 30 but less than 62.5, and a maximum rated output greater than 89 kN: Oxides of Nitrogen: (7 + 2(rPR)) g/kN rO.

(D) That have a rated pressure ratio greater than 30 but less than 62.5, and a maximum rated output greater than 26.7 kN but not greater than 89 kN: Oxides of Nitrogen: (42.71 + 1.4286(rPR) − 0.4013(rO) + 0.00642(rPR × rO)) g/kN rO.

(E) That have a rated pressure ratio of 62.5 or more: Oxides of Nitrogen: (32 + 1.6(rPR)) g/kN rO.

(2) For Class TSS Engines manufactured on or after January 1, 1984: Hydrocarbons: 140 (0.92)rPR g/kN rO.

(e) Smoke exhaust emissions from each gas turbine engine of the classes specified below shall not exceed:

(1) For Class TF of rated output less than 26.7 kN (6,000 lb) manufactured on or after August 9, 1985: SN = 83.6(rO) −0.274 (rO is in kN) not to exceed a maximum of SN = 50.

(2) For Classes T3, T8, TSS, and TF of rated output equal to or greater than 26.7 kN (6,000 lb) manufactured on or after January 1, 1984: SN = 83.6(rO) −0.274 (rO is in kN) not to exceed a maximum of SN = 50.

(3) For Class TP of rated output equal to or greater than 1,000 kW manufactured on or after January 1, 1984: SN = 187(rO) −0.168 (rO is in kW).

(f) The standards set forth in paragraphs (a), (b), (c), (d), and (e) of this section refer to a composite gaseous emission sample representing the operation cycles and exhaust smoke emission emitted during operation of the engine as specified in the applicable sections of subpart G of this part, and measured and calculated in accordance with the procedures set forth in subpart G.

(g) Where a gaseous emission standard is specified by a formula, calculate and round the standard to three significant figures or to the nearest 0.1 g/kN (for standards at or above 100 g/kN). Where a smoke standard is specified by a formula, calculate and round the standard to the nearest 0.1 SN. Engines comply with an applicable standard if the testing results show that the engine type certificate family's characteristic level does not exceed the numerical level of that standard, as described in 34.60.

[Doc. No. 25613, 55 FR 32861, Aug. 10, 1990; 55 FR 37287, Sept. 10, 1990, as amended by Amdt. 34-3, 64 FR 5559, Feb. 3, 1999; Amdt. 34-4, 74 FR 19127, Apr. 28, 2009; Amdt. 34-5, 77 FR 76851, Dec. 31, 2012]

34.23 Exhaust Emission Standards for Engines Manufactured on and after July 18, 2012

The standards of this section apply to aircraft engines manufactured on and after July 18, 2012, unless otherwise exempted or excepted. Where a gaseous emission standard is specified by a formula, calculate and round the standard to three significant figures or to the nearest 0.1 g/kN (for standards at or above 100 g/kN). Where a smoke standard is specified by a formula, calculate and round the standard to the nearest 0.1 SN. Engines comply with an applicable standard if the testing results show that the engine type certificate family's characteristic level does not exceed the numerical level of that standard, as described in 34.60.

(a) Gaseous exhaust emissions from each new aircraft gas turbine engine shall not exceed:

(1) For Classes TF, T3 and T8 of rated output less than 26.7 kN (6,000 lb) manufactured on and after July 18, 2012: SN = 83.6(rO) −0.274 or 50.0, whichever is smaller

(2) Except as provided in 34.9(b) and 34.21(c), for Classes TF, T3 and T8 engines manufactured on and after July 18, 2012, and for which the first individual production model was manufactured on or before December 31, 2013 (Tier 6):

TIER 6 OXIDES OF NITROGEN EMISSION STANDARDS FOR SUBSONIC ENGINES			
CLASS	RATED PRESSURE RATIO - rPR	RATED OUTPUT rO (kN)	NO$_x$(g/kN)
TF, T3, T8	rPR ≤ 30	26.7 < rO ≤ 89.0	38.5486 + 1.6823 (rPR) - 0.2453 (rO) - (0.00308 (rPR) (rO))
		rO > 89.0	16.72 + 1.4080 (rPR)
	30 < rPR < 82.6	26.7 < rO ≤ 89.0	46.1600 + 1.4286 (rPR) - 0.5303 (rO) + (0.00642 (rPR) (rO))
		rO > 89.0	-1.04 + 2.0 (rPR)
	rPR ≥ 82.6	rO ≥ 26.7	32 + 1.6 (rPR)

(3) Engines exempted from paragraph (a)(2) of this section produced on or before December 31, 2016 must be labeled "EXEMPT NEW" in accordance with 45.13 of this chapter. No exemptions to the requirements of paragraph (a)(2) of this section will be granted after December 31, 2016.

(4) For Class TSS Engines manufactured on and after July 18, 2012:

GASEOUS EMISSION STANDARDS FOR SUPERSONIC ENGINES			
CLASS	RATED OUTPUT rO[1](kN)	NO$_x$ (g/kN)	CO (g/kN)
TSS	All	36 + 2.42 (rPR)	4,550 (rPR)$^{-1.03}$

SPECIFICATION FOR FUEL TO BE USED IN AIRCRAFT TURBINE ENGINE EMISSION TESTING	
PROPERTY	ALLOWABLE RANGE OF VALUES
Density at 15° C	780-820
Distillation Temperature, Degrees C 10% Boiling Point	155-201
Final Boiling Point	235-285
Net Heat of Combustion, MJ/Kg	42.86-43.50
Aromatics, Volume %	15-23
Naphthalenes, Volume %	1.0-3.5
Smoke Point, mm	20-28
Hydrogen, Mass %	13.4-14.1
Sulfur, Mass %	Less than 0.3%
Kinematic Viscosity at -20 degrees C, mm^2/sec.	2.5-6.5

FAR 34

¹rO is the rated output with afterburning applied.

(b) Gaseous exhaust emissions from each new aircraft gas turbine engine shall not exceed:

(1) For Classes TF, T3 and T8 engines of a type or model of which the first individual production model was manufactured after December 31, 2013 (Tier 8):

TIER 8 OXIDES OF NITROGEN EMISSION STANDARDS FOR SUBSONIC ENGINES			
CLASS	RATED PRESSURE RATIO - rPR	RATED OUTPUT rO (kN)	NO_x(g/kN)
TF, T3, T8	rPR ≤ 30	26.7 < rO ≤ 89.0	40.052 + 1.5681 (rPR) - 0.3615 (rO) - (0.0018 (rPR) (rO))
		rO > 89.0	7.88 + 1.4080 (rPR)
	30 < rPR < 104.7	26.7 < rO ≤ 89.0	41.9435 + 1.505 (rPR) - 0.5823 (rO) + (0.005562 (rPR) (rO))
		rO > 89.0	-9.88 + 2.0 (rPR)
	rPR ≥ 104.7	rO ≥ 26.7	32 + 1.6 (rPR)

(c) Engines (including engines that are determined to be derivative engines for the purposes of emission certification) type certificated with characteristic levels at or below the NOX standards of 34.21(d)(1)(vi) of this part (as applicable based on rated output and rated pressure ratio) and introduced before July 18, 2012, may be produced through December 31, 2012, without meeting the NOX standard of paragraph (a)(2) of this section.

[Doc. No. 34-5, 77 FR 76851, Dec. 31, 2012]

Subpart D — Exhaust Emissions (In-use Aircraft Gas Turbine Engines)

34.30   Applicability

The provisions of this subpart are applicable to all in-use aircraft gas turbine engines certificated for operation within the United States of the classes specified, beginning on the dates specified in 34.31.

34.31   Standards for exhaust emissions

(a) Exhaust emissions of smoke from each in-use aircraft gas turbine engine of Class T8, beginning February 1, 1974, shall not exceed a smoke number (SN) of 30.

(b) Exhaust emissions of smoke from each in-use aircraft gas turbine engine of Class TF and of rated output of 129 kN (29,000 lb) thrust or greater, beginning January 1, 1976, shall not exceed: SN=83.6(rO) −0.274 (rO is in kN).

(c) The standards set forth in paragraphs (a) and (b) of this section refer to exhaust smoke emission emitted during operation of the engine as specified in the applicable sections of subpart G of this part, and measured and calculated in accordance with the procedures set forth in subpart G.

[Doc. No. FAA-2012-1333, 77 FR 76852, Dec. 31, 2012].

Subparts E — Certification Provisions

34.48   Derivative engines for emissions certification purposes

(a) General. A derivative engine for emissions certification purposes is an engine configuration that is determined to be similar in design to a previously certificated (original) engine for purposes of compliance with exhaust emissions standards (gaseous and smoke). A type certificate holder may request from the FAA a determination that an engine configuration is considered a derivative engine for emissions certification purposes. To be considered a derivative engine for emission purposes under this part, the configuration must have been derived from the original engine that was certificated to the requirements of part 33 of this chapter and one of the following:

(1) The FAA has determined that a safety issue exists that requires an engine modification.

(2) Emissions from the derivative engines are determined to be similar. In general, this means the emissions must meet the criteria specified in paragraph (b) of this section. The FAA may amend the criteria of paragraph (b) in unusual circumstances, for individual cases, consistent with good engineering judgment.

(3) All of the regulated emissions from the derivative engine are lower than the original engine.

(b) Emissions similarity.

(1) The type certificate holder must demonstrate that the proposed derivative engine model's emissions meet the applicable standards and differ from the original model's emission rates only within the following ranges:

(i) ±3.0 g/kN for NOX .

(ii) ±1.0 g/kN for HC.

(iii) ±5.0 g/kN for CO.

(iv) ±2.0 SN for smoke.

(2) If the characteristic level of the original certificated engine model (or any other sub-models within the emission type certificate family tested for certification) before modification is at or above 95% of the applicable standard for any pollutant, an applicant must measure the proposed derivative engine model's emissions for all pollutants to demonstrate that the derivative engine's resulting characteristic levels will not exceed the applicable emission standards. If the characteristic levels of the originally certificated engine model (and all other sub-models within the emission type certificate family tested for certification) are below 95% of the applicable standard for each pollutant, the applicant may use engineering analysis consistent with good engineering judgment to demonstrate that the derivative engine will not exceed the applicable emission standards. The engineering analysis must address all modifications from the original engine, including those approved for previous derivative engines.

(c) Continued production allowance. Derivative engines for emissions certification purposes may continue to be produced after the applicability date for new emissions standards when the engines conform to the specifications of this section.

(d) Non-derivative engines. If the FAA determines that an engine model does not meet the requirements for a derivative engine for emissions certification purposes, the type certificate holder is required to demonstrate that the engine complies with the emissions standards applicable to a new engine type.

[Doc. No. 34-5, 77 FR 76852, Dec. 31, 2012]

Subpart F [Reserved]

Subpart G — Test Procedures for Engine Exhaust Gaseous Emissions (Aircraft and Aircraft Gas Turbine Engines)

34.60   Introduction

(a) Use the equipment and procedures specified in Appendix 3, Appendix 5, and Appendix 6 of ICAO Annex 16, as applicable, to demonstrate whether engines meet the applicable gaseous emission standards specified in subpart C of this part. Measure the emissions of all regulated gaseous pollutants. Use the equipment and procedures specified in Appendix 2 and Appendix 6 of ICAO Annex 16 to determine whether engines meet the applicable smoke standard specified in subpart C of this part. The compliance demonstration consists of establishing a mean value from testing the specified number of engines, then calculating a "characteristic level" by applying a set of statistical factors that take into account the number of engines tested. Round each characteristic level to the same number of decimal places as the corresponding emission standard. For turboprop engines, use the procedures specified for turbofan engines, consistent with good engineering judgment.

(b) Use a test fuel that meets the specifications described in Appendix 4 of ICAO Annex 16. The test fuel must not have additives whose purpose is to suppress smoke, such as organometallic compounds.

(c) Prepare test engines by including accessories that are available with production engines if they can reasonably be expected to influence emissions. The test engine may not extract shaft power or bleed service air to provide power to auxiliary gearbox-mounted components required to drive aircraft systems.

(d) Test engines must reach a steady operating temperature before the start of emission measurements.

(e) In consultation with the EPA, the FAA may approve alternative procedures for measuring emissions, including testing and sampling methods, analytical techniques, and equipment specifications that differ from those specified in this part. Manufacturers and operators may request approval of alternative procedures by written request with supporting justification to the FAA and to the Designated EPA Program Officer. To be approved, one of the following conditions must be met:

(1) The engine cannot be tested using the specified procedures; or

(2) The alternative procedure is shown to be equivalent to, or more accurate or precise than, the specified procedure.

(f) The following landing and takeoff (LTO) cycles apply for emissions testing and for calculating weighted LTO values:

LTO TEST CYCLES AND TIME IN MODE						
	Class					
Mode	TP		TF, T3, T8		TSS	
	TIM (min)	% of rO	TIM (min)	% of rO	TIM (min)	% of rO
Taxi/Idle	26.0	7	26.0	7	26.0	5.8
Takeoff	0.5	100	0.7	100	1.2	100
Climbout	2.5	90	2.2	85	2.0	65
Descent	N/A	N/A	N/A	N/A	1.2	15
Approach	4.5	30	4.0	30	2.3	34

(g) Engines comply with an applicable standard if the testing results show that the engine type certificate family's characteristic level does not exceed the numerical level of that standard, as described in the applicable appendix of Annex 16.

(h) The system and procedure for sampling and measurement of gaseous emissions shall be as specified by in Appendices 2, 3, 4, 5 and 6 to the International Civil Aviation Organization (ICAO) Annex 16, Environmental Protection, Volume II, Aircraft Engine Emissions, Third Edition, July 2008. This incorporation by reference was approved by the Director of the Federal Register in accordance with 5 U.S.C. 552(a) and 1 CFR part 51. This document can be obtained from the ICAO, Document Sales Unit, 999 University Street, Montreal, Quebec H3C 5H7, Canada, phone +1 514-954-8022, or www.icao.int or sales25icao.int. Copies can be reviewed at the FAA New England Regional Office, 12 New England Executive Park, Burlington, Massachusetts, 781-238-7101, or at the National Archives and Records Administration (NARA). For information on the availability of this material at NARA, call 202-741-6030, or go to: http://www.archives.gov/federal_register/code_of_federal_regulations/ibr_locations.html.

[Doc. No. FAA-2012-1333, 77 FR 76853, Dec. 31, 2012, as amended by Doc. No. FAA-2018-0119, Amdt. 34-6, 83 FR 9170, Mar. 5, 2018]

34.61-34.64 **[Reserved]**

34.65-34.70 **[Reserved]**

34.71 **[Reserved]**

Subpart H — [Reserved]

34.80-34.89 **[Reserved]**

PART 35 — AIRWORTHINESS STANDARDS: PROPELLERS

Subpart A — General

Subpart B — Design and Construction

Subpart C — Tests and Inspections

Appendix A to Part 35 — Instructions for Continued Airworthiness

Authority: 49 U.S.C. 106(f), 106(g), 40113, 44701-44702, 44704.

Source: Docket No. 2095, 29 FR 7458, June 10, 1964, unless otherwise noted.

Subpart A — General

35.1 Applicability

(a) This part prescribes airworthiness standards for the issue of type certificates and changes to those certificates, for propellers.

(b) Each person who applies under Part 21 for such a certificate or change must show compliance with the applicable requirements of this part.

(c) An applicant is eligible for a propeller type certificate and changes to those certificates after demonstrating compliance with subparts A, B, and C of this part. However, the propeller may not be installed on an airplane unless the applicant has shown compliance with either 23.2400(c) or 25.907 of this chapter, as applicable, or compliance is not required for installation on that airplane.

(d) For the purposes of this part, the propeller consists of those components listed in the propeller type design, and the propeller system consists of the propeller and all the components necessary for its functioning, but not necessarily included in the propeller type design.

[Amdt. 35-3, 41 FR 55475, Dec. 20, 1976, as amended by Amdt. 35-8, 73 FR 63346, Oct. 24, 2008; Doc. FAA-2015-1621, Amdt. 35-10, 81 FR 96700, Dec. 30, 2016]

35.2 Propeller configuration

The applicant must provide a list of all the components, including references to the relevant drawings and software design data, that define the type design of the propeller to be approved under 21.31 of this chapter.

[Amdt. 35–8, 73 FR 63346, Oct. 24, 2008]

35.3 Instructions for propeller installation and operation

The applicant must provide instructions that are approved by the Administrator. Those approved instructions must contain:

(a) Instructions for installing the propeller, which:

    (1) Include a description of the operational modes of the propeller control system and functional interface of the control system with the airplane and engine systems;

    (2) Specify the physical and functional interfaces with the airplane, airplane equipment and engine;

    (3) Define the limiting conditions on the interfaces from paragraph (a)(2) of this section;

    (4) List the limitations established under 35.5;

    (5) Define the hydraulic fluids approved for use with the propeller, including grade and specification, related operating pressure, and filtration levels; and

    (6) State the assumptions made to comply with the requirements of this part.

(b) Instructions for operating the propeller which must specify all procedures necessary for operating the propeller within the limitations of the propeller type design.

[Amdt. 35–8, 73 FR 63346, Oct. 24, 2008]

35.4 Instructions for Continued Airworthiness

The applicant must prepare Instructions for Continued Airworthiness in accordance with appendix A to this part that are acceptable to the Administrator. The instructions may be incomplete at type certification if a program exists to ensure their completion prior to delivery of the first aircraft with the propeller installed, or upon issuance of a standard certificate of airworthiness for an aircraft with the propeller installed, whichever occurs later.

[Amdt. 35–5, 45 FR 60181, Sept. 11, 1980]

35.5 Propeller ratings and operating limitations

(a) Propeller ratings and operating limitations must:

    (1) Be established by the applicant and approved by the Administrator.

    (2) Be included directly or by reference in the propeller type certificate data sheet, as specified in 21.41 of this chapter.

    (3) Be based on the operating conditions demonstrated during the tests required by this part as well as any other information the Administrator requires as necessary for the safe operation of the propeller.

(b) Propeller ratings and operating limitations must be established for the following, as applicable:

    (1) Power and rotational speed:

        (i)   For takeoff.

        (ii) For maximum continuous.

        (iii) If requested by the applicant, other ratings may also be established.

    (2) Overspeed and overtorque limits.

[Amdt. 35–8, 73 FR 63346, Oct. 24, 2008]

35.7 Features and characteristics

(a) The propeller may not have features or characteristics, revealed by any test or analysis or known to the applicant, that make it unsafe for the uses for which certification is requested.

(b) If a failure occurs during a certification test, the applicant must determine the cause and assess the effect on the airworthiness of the propeller. The applicant must make changes to the design and conduct additional tests that the Administrator finds necessary to establish the airworthiness of the propeller.

[Amdt. 35–8, 73 FR 63346, Oct. 24, 2008]

FAR 35

Subpart B — Design and Construction

35.11   [Reserved]

35.13   [Reserved]

35.15   Safety analysis

(a)

(1) The applicant must analyze the propeller system to assess the likely consequences of all failures that can reasonably be expected to occur. This analysis will take into account, if applicable:

   (i) The propeller system in a typical installation. When the analysis depends on representative components, assumed interfaces, or assumed installed conditions, the assumptions must be stated in the analysis.

   (ii) Consequential secondary failures and dormant failures.

   (iii) Multiple failures referred to in paragraph (d) of this section, or that result in the hazardous propeller effects defined in paragraph (g)(1) of this section.

(2) The applicant must summarize those failures that could result in major propeller effects or hazardous propeller effects defined in paragraph (g) of this section, and estimate the probability of occurrence of those effects.

(3) The applicant must show that hazardous propeller effects are not predicted to occur at a rate in excess of that defined as extremely remote (probability of 10^{-7} or less per propeller flight hour). Since the estimated probability for individual failures may be insufficiently precise to enable the applicant to assess the total rate for hazardous propeller effects, compliance may be shown by demonstrating that the probability of a hazardous propeller effect arising from an individual failure can be predicted to be not greater than 10^{-8} per propeller flight hour. In dealing with probabilities of this low order of magnitude, absolute proof is not possible and reliance must be placed on engineering judgment and previous experience combined with sound design and test philosophies.

(b) If significant doubt exists as to the effects of failures or likely combination of failures, the Administrator may require assumptions used in the analysis to be verified by test.

(c) The primary failures of certain single propeller elements (for example, blades) cannot be sensibly estimated in numerical terms. If the failure of such elements is likely to result in hazardous propeller effects, those elements must be identified as propeller critical parts. For propeller critical parts, applicants must meet the prescribed integrity specifications of 35.16. These instances must be stated in the safety analysis.

(d) If reliance is placed on a safety system to prevent a failure progressing to hazardous propeller effects, the possibility of a safety system failure in combination with a basic propeller failure must be included in the analysis. Such a safety system may include safety devices, instrumentation, early warning devices, maintenance checks, and other similar equipment or procedures. If items of the safety system are outside the control of the propeller manufacturer, the assumptions of the safety analysis with respect to the reliability of these parts must be clearly stated in the analysis and identified in the propeller installation and operation instructions required under 35.3.

(e) If the safety analysis depends on one or more of the following items, those items must be identified in the analysis and appropriately substantiated.

   (1) Maintenance actions being carried out at stated intervals. This includes verifying that items that could fail in a latent manner are functioning properly. When necessary to prevent hazardous propeller effects, these maintenance actions and intervals must be published in the instructions for continued airworthiness required under 35.4. Additionally, if errors in maintenance of the propeller system could lead to hazardous propeller effects, the appropriate maintenance procedures must be included in the relevant propeller manuals.

   (2) Verification of the satisfactory functioning of safety or other devices at pre-flight or other stated periods. The details of this satisfactory functioning must be published in the appropriate manual.

   (3) The provision of specific instrumentation not otherwise required. Such instrumentation must be published in the appropriate documentation.

   (4) A fatigue assessment.

(f) If applicable, the safety analysis must include, but not be limited to, assessment of indicating equipment, manual and automatic controls, governors and propeller control systems, synchrophasers, synchronizers, and propeller thrust reversal systems.

(g) Unless otherwise approved by the Administrator and stated in the safety analysis, the following failure definitions apply to compliance with this part.

   (1) The following are regarded as hazardous propeller effects:

      (i) The development of excessive drag.

      (ii) A significant thrust in the opposite direction to that commanded by the pilot.

      (iii) The release of the propeller or any major portion of the propeller.

      (iv) A failure that results in excessive unbalance.

   (2) The following are regarded as major propeller effects for variable pitch propellers:

      (i) An inability to feather the propeller for feathering propellers.

      (ii) An inability to change propeller pitch when commanded.

      (iii) A significant uncommanded change in pitch.

      (iv) A significant uncontrollable torque or speed fluctuation.

[Amdt. 35-8, 73 FR 63346, Oct. 24, 2008, as amended by Amdt. 35-9, 78 FR 4041, Jan. 18, 2013; Amdt. 35-9A, 78 FR 45052, July 26, 2013]

35.16   Propeller critical parts

The integrity of each propeller critical part identified by the safety analysis required by 35.15 must be established by:

(a) A defined engineering process for ensuring the integrity of the propeller critical part throughout its service life,

(b) A defined manufacturing process that identifies the requirements to consistently produce the propeller critical part as required by the engineering process, and

(c) A defined service management process that identifies the continued airworthiness requirements of the propeller critical part as required by the engineering process.

[Amdt. 35-9, 78 FR 4042, Jan. 18, 2013]

35.17   Materials and manufacturing methods

(a) The suitability and durability of materials used in the propeller must:

   (1) Be established on the basis of experience, tests, or both.

   (2) Account for environmental conditions expected in service.

(b) All materials and manufacturing methods must conform to specifications acceptable to the Administrator.

(c) The design values of properties of materials must be suitably related to the most adverse properties stated in the material specification for applicable conditions expected in service.

[Amdt. 35–8, 73 FR 63347, Oct. 24, 2008]

35.19   Durability

Each part of the propeller must be designed and constructed to minimize the development of any unsafe condition of the propeller between overhaul periods.

35.21 Variable and reversible pitch propellers

(a) No single failure or malfunction in the propeller system will result in unintended travel of the propeller blades to a position below the in-flight low-pitch position. The extent of any intended travel below the in-flight low-pitch position must be documented by the applicant in the appropriate manuals. Failure of structural elements need not be considered if the occurrence of such a failure is shown to be extremely remote under 35.15.

(b) For propellers incorporating a method to select blade pitch below the in-flight low pitch position, provisions must be made to sense and indicate to the flight crew that the propeller blades are below that position by an amount defined in the installation manual. The method for sensing and indicating the propeller blade pitch position must be such that its failure does not affect the control of the propeller.

[Amdt. 35–8, 73 FR 63347, Oct. 24, 2008]

35.22 Feathering propellers

(a) Feathering propellers are intended to feather from all flight conditions, taking into account expected wear and leakage. Any feathering and unfeathering limitations must be documented in the appropriate manuals.

(b) Propeller pitch control systems that use engine oil to feather must incorporate a method to allow the propeller to feather if the engine oil system fails.

(c) Feathering propellers must be designed to be capable of unfeathering after the propeller system has stabilized to the minimum declared outside air temperature.

[Amdt. 35–8, 73 FR 63347, Oct. 24, 2008]

35.23 Propeller control system

The requirements of this section apply to any system or component that controls, limits or monitors propeller functions.

(a) The propeller control system must be designed, constructed and validated to show that:

(1) The propeller control system, operating in normal and alternative operating modes and in transition between operating modes, performs the functions defined by the applicant throughout the declared operating conditions and flight envelope.

(2) The propeller control system functionality is not adversely affected by the declared environmental conditions, including temperature, electromagnetic interference (EMI), high intensity radiated fields (HIRF) and lightning. The environmental limits to which the system has been satisfactorily validated must be documented in the appropriate propeller manuals.

(3) A method is provided to indicate that an operating mode change has occurred if flight crew action is required. In such an event, operating instructions must be provided in the appropriate manuals.

(b) The propeller control system must be designed and constructed so that, in addition to compliance with 35.15:

(1) No single failure or malfunction of electrical or electronic components in the control system results in a hazardous propeller effect.

(2) Failures or malfunctions directly affecting the propeller control system in a typical airplane, such as structural failures of attachments to the control, fire, or overheat, do not lead to a hazardous propeller effect.

(3) The loss of normal propeller pitch control does not cause a hazardous propeller effect under the intended operating conditions.

(4) The failure or corruption of data or signals shared across propellers does not cause a hazardous propeller effect.

(c) Electronic propeller control system imbedded software must be designed and implemented by a method approved by the Administrator that is consistent with the criticality of the performed functions and that minimizes the existence of software errors.

(d) The propeller control system must be designed and constructed so that the failure or corruption of airplane-supplied data does not result in hazardous propeller effects.

(e) The propeller control system must be designed and constructed so that the loss, interruption or abnormal characteristic of airplane-supplied electrical power does not result in hazardous propeller effects. The power quality requirements must be described in the appropriate manuals.

[Amdt. 35–8, 73 FR 63347, Oct. 24, 2008]

35.24 Strength

The maximum stresses developed in the propeller may not exceed values acceptable to the Administrator considering the particular form of construction and the most severe operating conditions.

[Amdt. 35–8, 73 FR 63348, Oct. 24, 2008]

Subpart C — Tests and Inspections

35.31 [Reserved]

35.33 General

(a) Each applicant must furnish test article(s) and suitable testing facilities, including equipment and competent personnel, and conduct the required tests in accordance with part 21 of this chapter.

(b) All automatic controls and safety systems must be in operation unless it is accepted by the Administrator as impossible or not required because of the nature of the test. If needed for substantiation, the applicant may test a different propeller configuration if this does not constitute a less severe test.

(c) Any systems or components that cannot be adequately substantiated by the applicant to the requirements of this part are required to undergo additional tests or analysis to demonstrate that the systems or components are able to perform their intended functions in all declared environmental and operating conditions.

[Amdt. 35–8, 73 FR 63348, Oct. 24, 2008]

35.34 Inspections, adjustments and repairs

(a) Before and after conducting the tests prescribed in this part, the test article must be subjected to an inspection, and a record must be made of all the relevant parameters, calibrations and settings.

(b) During all tests, only servicing and minor repairs are permitted. If major repairs or part replacement is required, the Administrator must approve the repair or part replacement prior to implementation and may require additional testing. Any unscheduled repair or action on the test article must be recorded and reported.

[Amdt. 35–8, 73 FR 63348, Oct. 24, 2008]

35.35 Centrifugal load tests

The applicant must demonstrate that a propeller complies with paragraphs (a), (b) and (c) of this section without evidence of failure, malfunction, or permanent deformation that would result in a major or hazardous propeller effect. When the propeller could be sensitive to environmental degradation in service, this must be considered. This section does not apply to fixed-pitch wood or fixed-pitch metal propellers of conventional design.

(a) The hub, blade retention system, and counterweights must be tested for a period of one hour to a load equivalent to twice the maximum centrifugal load to which the propeller would be subjected during operation at the maximum rated rotational speed.

(b) Blade features associated with transitions to the retention system (for example, a composite blade bonded to a metallic retention) must be tested either during the test of paragraph (a) of this section or in a separate component test for a period of one hour to a load equivalent to twice the maximum centrifugal load to which the propeller would be subjected during operation at the maximum rated rotational speed.

(c) Components used with or attached to the propeller (for example, spinners, de-icing equipment, and blade erosion shields) must be subjected to a load equivalent to 159 percent of the maximum centrifugal load to which the component would be subjected during operation at the maximum rated rotational speed. This must be performed by either:

(1) Testing at the required load for a period of 30 minutes; or

(2) Analysis based on test.

[Amdt. 35–8, 73 FR 63348, Oct. 24, 2008]

35.36   Bird impact

The applicant must demonstrate, by tests or analysis based on tests or experience on similar designs, that the propeller can withstand the impact of a 4-pound bird at the critical location(s) and critical flight condition(s) of a typical installation without causing a major or hazardous propeller effect. This section does not apply to fixed-pitch wood propellers of conventional design.

[Amdt. 35–8, 73 FR 63348, Oct. 24, 2008]

35.37   Fatigue limits and evaluation

This section does not apply to fixed-pitch wood propellers of conventional design.

(a) Fatigue limits must be established by tests, or analysis based on tests, for propeller:

(1) Hubs.

(2) Blades.

(3) Blade retention components.

(4) Components which are affected by fatigue loads and which are shown under 35.15 to have a fatigue failure mode leading to hazardous propeller effects.

(b) The fatigue limits must take into account:

(1) All known and reasonably foreseeable vibration and cyclic load patterns that are expected in service; and

(2) Expected service deterioration, variations in material properties, manufacturing variations, and environmental effects.

(c) A fatigue evaluation of the propeller must be conducted to show that hazardous propeller effects due to fatigue will be avoided throughout the intended operational life of the propeller on either:

(1) The intended airplane by complying with 23.2400(c) or 25.907 of this chapter, as applicable; or

(2) A typical airplane.

[Amdt. 35-8, 73 FR 63348, Oct. 24, 2008, as amended by Doc. FAA-2015-1621, Amdt. 35-10, 81 FR 96700, Dec. 30, 2016]

35.38   Lightning strike

The applicant must demonstrate, by tests, analysis based on tests, or experience on similar designs, that the propeller can withstand a lightning strike without causing a major or hazardous propeller effect. The limit to which the propeller has been qualified must be documented in the appropriate manuals. This section does not apply to fixed-pitch wood propellers of conventional design.

[Amdt. 35–8, 73 FR 63348, Oct. 24, 2008]

35.39   Endurance test

Endurance tests on the propeller system must be made on a representative engine in accordance with paragraph (a) or (b) of this section, as applicable, without evidence of failure or malfunction.

(a) Fixed-pitch and ground adjustable-pitch propellers must be subjected to one of the following tests:

(1) A 50-hour flight test in level flight or in climb. The propeller must be operated at takeoff power and rated rotational speed during at least five hours of this flight test, and at not less than 90 percent of the rated rotational speed for the remainder of the 50 hours.

(2) A 50-hour ground test at takeoff power and rated rotational speed.

(b) Variable-pitch propellers must be subjected to one of the following tests:

(1) A 110-hour endurance test that must include the following conditions:

(i) Five hours at takeoff power and rotational speed and thirty 10-minute cycles composed of:

(A) Acceleration from idle,

(B) Five minutes at takeoff power and rotational speed,

(C) Deceleration, and

(D) Five minutes at idle.

(ii) Fifty hours at maximum continuous power and rotational speed,

(iii) Fifty hours, consisting of ten 5-hour cycles composed of:

(A) Five accelerations and decelerations between idle and takeoff power and rotational speed,

(B) Four and one half hours at approximately even incremental conditions from idle up to, but not including, maximum continuous power and rotational speed, and

(C) Thirty minutes at idle.

(2) The operation of the propeller throughout the engine endurance tests prescribed in part 33 of this chapter.

(c) An analysis based on tests of propellers of similar design may be used in place of the tests of paragraphs (a) and (b) of this section.

[Amdt. 35–8, 73 FR 63348, Oct. 24, 2008]

35.40   Functional test

The variable-pitch propeller system must be subjected to the applicable functional tests of this section. The same propeller system used in the endurance test (35.39) must be used in the functional tests and must be driven by a representative engine on a test stand or on an airplane. The propeller must complete these tests without evidence of failure or malfunction. This test may be combined with the endurance test for accumulation of cycles.

(a) Manually-controllable propellers. Five hundred representative flight cycles must be made across the range of pitch and rotational speed.

(b) Governing propellers. Fifteen hundred complete cycles must be made across the range of pitch and rotational speed.

(c) Feathering propellers. Fifty cycles of feather and unfeather operation must be made.

(d) Reversible-pitch propellers. Two hundred complete cycles of control must be made from lowest normal pitch to maximum reverse pitch. During each cycle, the propeller must run for 30 seconds at the maximum power and rotational speed selected by the applicant for maximum reverse pitch.

(e) An analysis based on tests of propellers of similar design may be used in place of the tests of this section.

[Amdt. 35–8, 73 FR 63349, Oct. 24, 2008]

35.41   Overspeed and overtorque

(a) When the applicant seeks approval of a transient maximum propeller overspeed, the applicant must demonstrate that the propeller is capable of further operation without maintenance action at the maximum propeller overspeed condition. This may be accomplished by:

(1) Performance of 20 runs, each of 30 seconds duration, at the maximum propeller overspeed condition; or

(2) Analysis based on test or service experience.

(b) When the applicant seeks approval of a transient maximum propeller overtorque, the applicant must demonstrate that the propeller is capable of further operation without maintenance action at the maximum propeller overtorque condition. This may be accomplished by:

(1) Performance of 20 runs, each of 30 seconds duration, at the maximum propeller overtorque condition; or

(2) Analysis based on test or service experience.

[Amdt. 35–8, 73 FR 63349, Oct. 24, 2008]

35.42 Components of the propeller control system

The applicant must demonstrate by tests, analysis based on tests, or service experience on similar components, that each propeller blade pitch control system component, including governors, pitch change assemblies, pitch locks, mechanical stops, and feathering system components, can withstand cyclic operation that simulates the normal load and pitch change travel to which the component would be subjected during the initially declared overhaul period or during a minimum of 1,000 hours of typical operation in service.

[Amdt. 35–8, 73 FR 63349, Oct. 24, 2008]

35.43 Propeller hydraulic components

Applicants must show by test, validated analysis, or both, that propeller components that contain hydraulic pressure and whose structural failure or leakage from a structural failure could cause a hazardous propeller effect demonstrate structural integrity by:

(a) A proof pressure test to 1.5 times the maximum operating pressure for one minute without permanent deformation or leakage that would prevent performance of the intended function.

(b) A burst pressure test to 2.0 times the maximum operating pressure for one minute without failure. Leakage is permitted and seals may be excluded from the test.

[Amdt. 35–8, 73 FR 63349, Oct. 24, 2008]

35.45 [Reserved]

35.47 [Reserved]

Appendix A to Part 35 — Instructions for Continued Airworthiness

A35.1 General

(a) This appendix specifies requirements for the preparation of Instructions for Continued Airworthiness as required by 35.4.

(b) The Instructions for Continued Airworthiness for each propeller must include the Instructions for Continued Airworthiness for all propeller parts. If Instructions for Continued Airworthiness are not supplied by the propeller part manufacturer for a propeller part, the Instructions for Continued Airworthiness for the propeller must include the information essential to the continued airworthiness of the propeller.

(c) The applicant must submit to the FAA a program to show how changes to the Instructions for Continued Airworthiness made by the applicant or by the manufacturers of propeller parts will be distributed.

A35.2 Format

(a) The Instructions for Continued Airworthiness must be in the form of a manual or manuals as appropriate for the quantity of data to be provided.

(b) The format of the manual or manuals must provide for a practical arrangement.

A35.3 Content

The contents of the manual must be prepared in the English language. The Instructions for Continued Airworthiness must contain the following sections and information:

(a) Propeller Maintenance Section.

(1) Introduction information that includes an explanation of the propeller's features and data to the extent necessary for maintenance or preventive maintenance.

(2) A detailed description of the propeller and its systems and installations.

(3) Basic control and operation information describing how the propeller components and systems are controlled and how they operate, including any special procedures that apply.

(4) Instructions for uncrating, acceptance checking, lifting, and installing the propeller.

(5) Instructions for propeller operational checks.

(6) Scheduling information for each part of the propeller that provides the recommended periods at which it should be cleaned, adjusted, and tested, the applicable wear tolerances, and the degree of work recommended at these periods. However, the applicant may refer to an accessory, instrument, or equipment manufacturer as the source of this information if it shows that the item has an exceptionally high degree of complexity requiring specialized maintenance techniques, test equipment, or expertise. The recommended overhaul periods and necessary cross-references to the Airworthiness Limitations section of the manual must also be included. In addition, the applicant must include an inspection program that includes the frequency and extent of the inspections necessary to provide for the continued airworthiness of the propeller.

(7) Troubleshooting information describing probable malfunctions, how to recognize those malfunctions, and the remedial action for those malfunctions.

(8) Information describing the order and method of removing and replacing propeller parts with any necessary precautions to be taken.

(9) A list of the special tools needed for maintenance other than for overhauls.

(b) Propeller Overhaul Section.

(1) Disassembly information including the order and method of disassembly for overhaul.

(2) Cleaning and inspection instructions that cover the materials and apparatus to be used and methods and precautions to be taken during overhaul. Methods of overhaul inspection must also be included.

(3) Details of all fits and clearances relevant to overhaul.

(4) Details of repair methods for worn or otherwise substandard parts and components along with information necessary to determine when replacement is necessary.

(5) The order and method of assembly at overhaul.

(6) Instructions for testing after overhaul.

(7) Instructions for storage preparation including any storage limits.

(8) A list of tools needed for overhaul.

A35.4 Airworthiness limitations section

The Instructions for Continued Airworthiness must contain a section titled Airworthiness Limitations that is segregated and clearly distinguishable from the rest of the document. This section must set forth each mandatory replacement time, inspection interval, and related procedure required for type certification. This section must contain a legible statement in a prominent location that reads: "The Airworthiness Limitations section is FAA approved and specifies maintenance required under 43.16 and 91.403 of the Federal Aviation Regulations unless an alternative program has been FAA approved."

[Amdt. 35–5, 45 FR 60182, Sept. 11, 1980, as amended by Amdt. 35–6, 54 FR 34330, Aug. 18, 1989]

FAR 35

PART 39 — AIRWORTHINESS DIRECTIVES

Authority: 49 U.S.C. 106(g), 40113, 44701.

Source: Doc. No. FAA–2000–8460, 67 FR 48003, July 22, 2002, unless otherwise noted.

39.1   Purpose of this regulation

The regulations in this part provide a legal framework for FAA's system of Airworthiness Directives.

39.3   Definition of airworthiness directives

FAA's airworthiness directives are legally enforceable rules that apply to the following products: aircraft, aircraft engines, propellers, and appliances.

39.5   When does FAA issue airworthiness directives?

FAA issues an airworthiness directive addressing a product when we find that:

(a) An unsafe condition exists in the product; and

(b) The condition is likely to exist or develop in other products of the same type design.

39.7   What is the legal effect of failing to comply with an airworthiness directive?

Anyone who operates a product that does not meet the requirements of an applicable airworthiness directive is in violation of this section.

39.9   What if I operate an aircraft or use a product that does not meet the requirements of an airworthiness directive?

If the requirements of an airworthiness directive have not been met, you violate 39.7 each time you operate the aircraft or use the product.

39.11   What actions do airworthiness directives require?

Airworthiness directives specify inspections you must carry out, conditions and limitations you must comply with, and any actions you must take to resolve an unsafe condition.

39.13   Are airworthiness directives part of the Code of Federal Regulations?

Yes, airworthiness directives are part of the Code of Federal Regulations, but they are not codified in the annual edition. FAA publishes airworthiness directives in full in the Federal Register as amendments to 39.13.

Editorial Note: For a complete list of citations to airworthiness directives published in the Federal Register, consult the following publications: For airworthiness directives published in the Federal Register since 2001, see the entries for 14 CFR 39.13 in the List of CFR Sections Affected, which appears in the "Finding Aids" section of the printed volume and at www.govinfo.gov. For citations to prior amendments, see the entries for 14 CFR 39.13 in the separate publications List of CFR Sections Affected, 1973-1985, List of CFR Sections Affected, 1964-1972, and List of CFR Sections Affected, 1986-2000, and the entries for 14 CFR 507.10 in the List of Sections Affected, 1949-1963. See also the annual editions of the Federal Register Index for subject matter references and citations to FAA airworthiness directives.

39.15   Does an airworthiness directive apply if the product has been changed?

Yes, an airworthiness directive applies to each product identified in the airworthiness directive, even if an individual product has been changed by modifying, altering, or repairing it in the area addressed by the airworthiness directive.

39.17   What must I do if a change in a product affects my ability to accomplish the actions required in an airworthiness directive?

If a change in a product affects your ability to accomplish the actions required by the airworthiness directive in any way, you must request FAA approval of an alternative method of compliance. Unless you can show the change eliminated the unsafe condition, your request should include the specific actions that you propose to address the unsafe condition. Submit your request in the manner described in 39.19.

39.19   May I address the unsafe condition in a way other than that set out in the airworthiness directive?

Yes, anyone may propose to FAA an alternative method of compliance or a change in the compliance time, if the proposal provides an acceptable level of safety. Unless FAA authorizes otherwise, send your proposal to your principal inspector. Include the specific actions you are proposing to address the unsafe condition. The principal inspector may add comments and will send your request to the manager of the office identified in the airworthiness directive (manager). You may send a copy to the manager at the same time you send it to the principal inspector. If you do not have a principal inspector send your proposal directly to the manager. You may use the alternative you propose only if the manager approves it.

39.21   Where can I get information about FAA-approved alternative methods of compliance?

Each airworthiness directive identifies the office responsible for approving alternative methods of compliance. That office can provide information about alternatives it has already approved.

39.23   May I fly my aircraft to a repair facility to do the work required by an airworthiness directive?

Yes, the operations specifications giving some operators authority to operate include a provision that allow them to fly their aircraft to a repair facility to do the work required by an airworthiness directive. If you do not have this authority, the local Flight Standards District Office of FAA may issue you a special flight permit unless the airworthiness directive states otherwise. To ensure aviation safety, FAA may add special requirements for operating your aircraft to a place where the repairs or modifications can be accomplished. FAA may also decline to issue a special flight permit in particular cases if we determine you cannot move the aircraft safely.

39.25   How do I get a special flight permit?

Apply to FAA for a special flight permit following the procedures in 14 CFR 21.199.

FAR
39

39.27 What do I do if the airworthiness directive conflicts with the service document on which it is based?

In some cases an airworthiness directive incorporates by reference a manufacturer's service document. In these cases, the service document becomes part of the airworthiness directive. In some cases the directions in the service document may be modified by the airworthiness directive. If there is a conflict between the service document and the airworthiness directive, you must follow the requirements of the airworthiness directive.

PART 43 — MAINTENANCE, PREVENTIVE MAINTENANCE, REBUILDING, AND ALTERATION

Authority: 42 U.S.C. 7572; 49 U.S.C. 106(f), 106(g), 40105, 40113, 44701-44702, 44704, 44707, 44709, 44711, 44713, 44715, 45303.

Source: Docket No. 1993, 29 FR 5451, Apr. 23, 1964, unless otherwise noted.

Editorial Note: For miscellaneous technical amendments to this part 43, see Amdt. 43-3, 31 FR 3336, Mar. 3, 1966, and Amdt. 43-6, 31 FR 9211, July 6, 1966.

43.1 Applicability

(a) Except as provided in paragraphs (b) and (d) of this section, this part prescribes rules governing the maintenance, preventive maintenance, rebuilding, and alteration of any—

(1) Aircraft having a U.S. airworthiness certificate;

(2) Foreign-registered civil aircraft used in common carriage or carriage of mail under the provisions of Part 121 or 135 of this chapter; and

(3) Airframe, aircraft engines, propellers, appliances, and component parts of such aircraft.

(b) This part does not apply to—

(1) Any aircraft for which the FAA has issued an experimental certificate, unless the FAA has previously issued a different kind of airworthiness certificate for that aircraft;

(2) Any aircraft for which the FAA has issued an experimental certificate under the provisions of 21.191(i)(3) of this chapter, and the aircraft was previously issued a special airworthiness certificate in the light-sport category under the provisions of 21.190 of this chapter; or

(3) Any aircraft that is operated under part 107 of this chapter, except as described in 107.140(d).

(c) This part applies to all life-limited parts that are removed from a type certificated product, segregated, or controlled as provided in 43.10.

(d) This part applies to any aircraft issued a special airworthiness certificate in the light-sport category except:

(1) The repair or alteration form specified in 43.5(b) and 43.9(d) is not required to be completed for products not produced under an FAA approval;

(2) Major repairs and major alterations for products not produced under an FAA approval are not required to be recorded in accordance with appendix B of this part; and

(3) The listing of major alterations and major repairs specified in paragraphs (a) and (b) of appendix A of this part is not applicable to products not produced under an FAA approval.

[Doc. No. 1993, 29 FR 5451, Apr. 23, 1964, as amended by Amdt. 43-23, 47 FR 41084, Sept. 16, 1982; Amdt. 43-37, 66 FR 21066, Apr. 27, 2001; Amdt. 43-38, 67 FR 2109, Jan. 15, 2002; Amdt. 43-39, 69 FR 44863, July 27, 2004; Amdt. 43-44, 75 FR 5219, Feb. 1, 2010; Docket FAA-2015-0150, Amdt. 43-48, 81 FR 42208, June 28, 2016; Docket FAA-2018-1087, Amdt. 43-51, 86 FR 4381, Jan. 15, 2021]

43.2 Records of overhaul and rebuilding

(a) No person may describe in any required maintenance entry or form an aircraft, airframe, aircraft engine, propeller, appliance, or component part as being overhauled unless—

(1) Using methods, techniques, and practices acceptable to the Administrator, it has been disassembled, cleaned, inspected, repaired as necessary, and reassembled; and

(2) It has been tested in accordance with approved standards and technical data, or in accordance with current standards and technical data acceptable to the Administrator, which have been developed and documented by the holder of the type certificate, supplemental type certificate, or a material, part, process, or appliance approval under part 21 of this chapter.

(b) No person may describe in any required maintenance entry or form an aircraft, airframe, aircraft engine, propeller, appliance, or component part as being rebuilt unless it has been disassembled, cleaned, inspected, repaired as necessary, reassembled, and tested to the same tolerances and limits as a new item, using either new parts or used parts that either conform to new part tolerances and limits or to approved oversized or undersized dimensions.

[Amdt. 43–23, 47 FR 41084, Sept. 16, 1982, as amended by Amdt. 43–43, 74 FR 53394, Oct. 16, 2009]

43.3 Persons authorized to perform maintenance, preventive maintenance, rebuilding, and alterations

(a) Except as provided in this section and 43.17, no person may maintain, rebuild, alter, or perform preventive maintenance on an aircraft, airframe, aircraft engine, propeller, appliance, or component part to which this part applies. Those items, the performance of which is a major alteration, a major repair, or preventive maintenance, are listed in appendix A.

(b) The holder of a mechanic certificate may perform maintenance, preventive maintenance, and alterations as provided in Part 65 of this chapter.

(c) The holder of a repairman certificate may perform maintenance, preventive maintenance, and alterations as provided in part 65 of this chapter.

(d) A person working under the supervision of a holder of a mechanic or repairman certificate may perform the maintenance, preventive maintenance, and alterations that his supervisor is authorized to perform, if the supervisor personally observes the work being done to the extent necessary to ensure that it is being done properly and if the supervisor is readily available, in person, for consultation. However, this paragraph does not authorize the performance of any inspection required by Part 91 or Part 125 of this chapter or any inspection performed after a major repair or alteration.

(e) The holder of a repair station certificate may perform maintenance, preventive maintenance, and alterations as provided in Part 145 of this chapter.

(f) The holder of an air carrier operating certificate or an operating certificate issued under Part 121 or 135, may perform maintenance, preventive maintenance, and alterations as provided in Part 121 or 135.

(g) Except for holders of a sport pilot certificate, the holder of a pilot certificate issued under part 61 may perform preventive maintenance on any aircraft owned or operated by that pilot which is not used under part 121, 129, or 135 of this chapter. The holder of a sport pilot certificate may perform preventive maintenance on an aircraft owned or operated by that pilot and issued a special airworthiness certificate in the light-sport category.

(h) Notwithstanding the provisions of paragraph (g) of this section, the Administrator may approve a certificate holder under Part 135 of this chapter, operating rotorcraft in a remote area, to allow a pilot to perform specific preventive maintenance items provided—

  (1) The items of preventive maintenance are a result of a known or suspected mechanical difficulty or malfunction that occurred en route to or in a remote area;

  (2) The pilot has satisfactorily completed an approved training program and is authorized in writing by the certificate holder for each item of preventive maintenance that the pilot is authorized to perform;

  (3) There is no certificated mechanic available to perform preventive maintenance;

  (4) The certificate holder has procedures to evaluate the accomplishment of a preventive maintenance item that requires a decision concerning the airworthiness of the rotorcraft; and

  (5) The items of preventive maintenance authorized by this section are those listed in paragraph (c) of appendix A of this part.

(i) Notwithstanding the provisions of paragraph (g) of this section, in accordance with an approval issued to the holder of a certificate issued under part 135 of this chapter, a pilot of an aircraft type-certificated for 9 or fewer passenger seats, excluding any pilot seat, may perform the removal and reinstallation of approved aircraft cabin seats, approved cabin-mounted stretchers, and when no tools are required, approved cabin-mounted medical oxygen bottles, provided—

  (1) The pilot has satisfactorily completed an approved training program and is authorized in writing by the certificate holder to perform each task; and

  (2) The certificate holder has written procedures available to the pilot to evaluate the accomplishment of the task.

(j) A manufacturer may—

  (1) Rebuild or alter any aircraft, aircraft engine, propeller, or appliance manufactured by him under a type or production certificate;

  (2) Rebuild or alter any appliance or part of aircraft, aircraft engines, propellers, or appliances manufactured by him under a Technical Standard Order Authorization, an FAA-Parts Manufacturer Approval, or Product and Process Specification issued by the Administrator; and

  (3) Perform any inspection required by part 91 or part 125 of this chapter on aircraft it manufactured under a type certificate, or currently manufactures under a production certificate.

(k) Updates of databases in installed avionics meeting the conditions of this paragraph are not considered maintenance and may be performed by pilots provided:

  (1) The database upload is:

    (i) Initiated from the flight deck;

    (ii) Performed without disassembling the avionics unit; and

    (iii) Performed without the use of tools and/or special equipment.

  (2) The pilot must comply with the certificate holder's procedures or the manufacturer's instructions.

  (3) The holder of operating certificates must make available written procedures consistent with manufacturer's instructions to the pilot that describe how to:

    (i) Perform the database update; and

    (ii) Determine the status of the data upload.

[Doc. No. 1993, 29 FR 5451, Apr. 23, 1964, as amended by Amdt. 43-4, 31 FR 5249, Apr. 1, 1966; Amdt. 43-23, 47 FR 41084, Sept. 16, 1982; Amdt. 43-25, 51 FR 40702, Nov. 7, 1986; Amdt. 43-36, 61 FR 19501, May 1, 1996; Amdt. 43-37, 66 FR 21066, Apr. 27, 2001; Amdt. 43-39, 69 FR 44863, July 27, 2004; Amdt. 43-43, 74 FR 53394, Oct. 16, 2009; Amdt. 43-45, 77 FR 71096, Nov. 29, 2012]

43.5 Approval for return to service after maintenance, preventive maintenance, rebuilding, or alteration

No person may approve for return to service any aircraft, airframe, aircraft engine, propeller, or appliance, that has undergone maintenance, preventive maintenance, rebuilding, or alteration unless—

(a) The maintenance record entry required by 43.9 or 43.11, as appropriate, has been made;

(b) The repair or alteration form authorized by or furnished by the Administrator has been executed in a manner prescribed by the Administrator; and

(c) If a repair or an alteration results in any change in the aircraft operating limitations or flight data contained in the approved aircraft flight manual, those operating limitations or flight data are appropriately revised and set forth as prescribed in 91.9 of this chapter.

[Doc. No. 1993, 29 FR 5451, Apr. 23, 1964, as amended by Amdt. 43–23, 47 FR 41084, Sept. 16, 1982; Amdt. 43–31, 54 FR 34330, Aug. 18, 1989]

43.7 Persons authorized to approve aircraft, airframes, aircraft engines, propellers, appliances, or component parts for return to service after maintenance, preventive maintenance, rebuilding, or alteration

(a) Except as provided in this section and 43.17, no person, other than the Administrator, may approve an aircraft, airframe, aircraft engine, propeller, appliance, or component part for return to service after it has undergone maintenance, preventive maintenance, rebuilding, or alteration.

(b) The holder of a mechanic certificate or an inspection authorization may approve an aircraft, airframe, aircraft engine, propeller, appliance, or component part for return to service as provided in Part 65 of this chapter.

(c) The holder of a repair station certificate may approve an aircraft, airframe, aircraft engine, propeller, appliance, or component part for return to service as provided in Part 145 of this chapter.

(d) A manufacturer may approve for return to service any aircraft, airframe, aircraft engine, propeller, appliance, or component part which that manufacturer has worked on under 43.3(j). However except for minor alterations, the work must have been done in accordance with technical data approved by the Administrator.

(e) The holder of an air carrier operating certificate or an operating certificate issued under Part 121 or 135, may approve an aircraft, airframe, aircraft engine, propeller, appliance, or component part for return to service as provided in Part 121 or 135 of this chapter, as applicable.

(f) A person holding at least a private pilot certificate may approve an aircraft for return to service after performing preventive maintenance under the provisions of 43.3(g).

(g) The holder of a repairman certificate (light-sport aircraft) with a maintenance rating may approve an aircraft issued a special airworthiness certificate in light-sport category for return to service, as provided in part 65 of this chapter.

(h) The holder of at least a sport pilot certificate may approve an aircraft owned or operated by that pilot and issued a special airworthiness certificate in the light-sport category for return to service after performing preventive maintenance under the provisions of 43.3(g).

[Amdt. 43–23, 47 FR 41084, Sept. 16, 1982, as amended by Amdt. 43–36, 61 FR 19501, May 1, 1996; Amdt. 43–37, 66 FR 21066, Apr. 27, 2001; Amdt. 43–39, 69 FR 44863, July 27, 2004]

43.9 Content, form, and disposition of maintenance, preventive maintenance, rebuilding, and alteration records (except inspections performed in accordance with part 91, part 125, 135.411(a)(1), and 135.419 of this chapter)

(a) *Maintenance record entries.* Except as provided in paragraphs (b) and (c) of this section, each person who maintains, performs preventive maintenance, rebuilds, or alters an aircraft, airframe, aircraft engine, propeller, appliance, or component part shall make an entry in the maintenance record of that equipment containing the following information:

(1) A description (or reference to data acceptable to the Administrator) of work performed.

(2) The date of completion of the work performed.

(3) The name of the person performing the work if other than the person specified in paragraph (a)(4) of this section.

(4) If the work performed on the aircraft, airframe, aircraft engine, propeller, appliance, or component part has been performed satisfactorily, the signature, certificate number, and kind of certificate held by the person approving the work. The signature constitutes the approval for return to service only for the work performed.

(b) Each holder of an air carrier operating certificate or an operating certificate issued under Part 121 or 135, that is required by its approved operations specifications to provide for a continuous airworthiness maintenance program, shall make a record of the maintenance, preventive maintenance, rebuilding, and alteration, on aircraft, airframes, aircraft engines, propellers, appliances, or component parts which it operates in accordance with the applicable provisions of Part 121 or 135 of this chapter, as appropriate.

(c) This section does not apply to persons performing inspections in accordance with Part 91, 125, 135.411(a)(1), or 135.419 of this chapter.

(d) In addition to the entry required by paragraph (a) of this section, major repairs and major alterations shall be entered on a form, and the form disposed of, in the manner prescribed in appendix B, by the person performing the work.

[Amdt. 43–23, 47 FR 41085, Sept. 16, 1982, as amended by Amdt. 43–37, 66 FR 21066, Apr. 27, 2001; Amdt. 43–39, 69 FR 44863, July 27, 2004]

43.10 Disposition of life-limited aircraft parts

(a) *Definitions used in this section.* For the purposes of this section the following definitions apply.

Life-limited part means any part for which a mandatory replacement limit is specified in the type design, the Instructions for Continued Airworthiness, or the maintenance manual.

Life status means the accumulated cycles, hours, or any other mandatory replacement limit of a life-limited part.

(b) *Temporary removal of parts from type-certificated products.* When a life-limited part is temporarily removed and reinstalled for the purpose of performing maintenance, no disposition under paragraph (c) of this section is required if—

(1) The life status of the part has not changed;

(2) The removal and reinstallation is performed on the same serial numbered product; and

(3) That product does not accumulate time in service while the part is removed.

(c) *Disposition of parts removed from type-certificated products.* Except as provided in paragraph (b) of this section, after April 15, 2002 each person who removes a life-limited part from a type-certificated product must ensure that the part is controlled using one of the methods in this paragraph. The method must deter the installation of the part after it has reached its life limit. Acceptable methods include:

(1) *Record keeping system.* The part may be controlled using a record keeping system that substantiates the part number, serial number, and current life status of the part. Each time the part is removed from a type certificated product, the record must be updated with the current life status. This system may include electronic, paper, or other means of record keeping.

(2) *Tag or record attached to part.* A tag or other record may be attached to the part. The tag or record must include the part number, serial number, and current life status of the part. Each time the part is removed from a type certificated product, either a new tag or record must be created, or the existing tag or record must be updated with the current life status.

(3) *Non-permanent marking.* The part may be legibly marked using a non-permanent method showing its current life status. The life status must be updated each time the part is removed from a type certificated product, or if the mark is removed, another method in this section may be used. The mark must be accomplished in accordance with the instructions under 45.16 of this chapter in order to maintain the integrity of the part.

(4) *Permanent marking.* The part may be legibly marked using a permanent method showing its current life status. The life status must be updated each time the part is removed from a type certificated product. Unless the part is permanently removed from use on type certificated products, this permanent mark must be accomplished in accordance with the instructions under 45.16 of this chapter in order to maintain the integrity of the part.

(5) *Segregation.* The part may be segregated using methods that deter its installation on a type-certificated product. These methods must include, at least—

(i) Maintaining a record of the part number, serial number, and current life status, and

(ii) Ensuring the part is physically stored separately from parts that are currently eligible for installation.

(6) *Mutilation.* The part may be mutilated to deter its installation in a type certificated product. The mutilation must render the part beyond repair and incapable of being reworked to appear to be airworthy.

(7) *Other methods.* Any other method approved or accepted by the FAA.

(d) *Transfer of life-limited parts.* Each person who removes a life-limited part from a type certificated product and later sells or otherwise transfers that part must transfer with the part the mark, tag, or other record used to comply with this section, unless the part is mutilated before it is sold or transferred.

[Doc. No. FAA-2000-8017, 67 FR 2110, Jan. 15, 2002, as amended by Amdt. 43-38A, 79 FR 67055, Nov. 12, 2014]

43.11 Content, form, and disposition of records for inspections conducted under parts 91 and 125 and 135.411(a)(1) and 135.419 of this chapter

(a) *Maintenance record entries.* The person approving or disapproving for return to service an aircraft, airframe, aircraft engine, propeller, appliance, or component part after any inspection performed in accordance with part 91, 125, 135.411(a)(1), or 135.419 shall make an entry in the maintenance record of that equipment containing the following information:

(1) The type of inspection and a brief description of the extent of the inspection.

(2) The date of the inspection and aircraft total time in service.

(3) The signature, the certificate number, and kind of certificate held by the person approving or disapproving for return to service the aircraft, airframe, aircraft engine, propeller, appliance, component part, or portions thereof.

(4) Except for progressive inspections, if the aircraft is found to be airworthy and approved for return to service, the following or a similarly worded statement—"I certify that this aircraft has been inspected in accordance with (insert type) inspection and was determined to be in airworthy condition."

(5) Except for progressive inspections, if the aircraft is not approved for return to service because of needed maintenance, noncompliance with applicable specifications, airworthiness directives, or other approved data, the following or a similarly worded statement—"I certify that this aircraft has been inspected in accordance with (insert type) inspection and a list of discrepancies and unairworthy items dated (date) has been provided for the aircraft owner or operator."

(6) For progressive inspections, the following or a similarly worded statement—"I certify that in accordance with a progressive inspection program, a routine inspection of (identify whether aircraft or components) and a detailed inspection of (identify components) were performed and the (aircraft or components) are (approved or disapproved) for return to service." If disapproved, the entry will further state "and a list of discrepancies and unairworthy items dated (date) has been provided to the aircraft owner or operator."

(7) If an inspection is conducted under an inspection program provided for in part 91, 125, or 135.411(a)(1), the entry must identify the inspection program, that part of the inspection program accomplished, and contain a statement that the inspection was performed in accordance with the inspections and procedures for that particular program.

(b) Listing of discrepancies and placards. If the person performing any inspection required by part 91 or 125 or 135.411(a)(1) of this chapter finds that the aircraft is unairworthy or does not meet the applicable type certificate data, airworthiness directives, or other approved data upon which its airworthiness depends, that persons must give the owner or lessee a signed and dated list of those discrepancies. For those items permitted to be inoperative under 91.213(d)(2) of this chapter, that person shall place a placard, that meets the aircraft's airworthiness certification regulations, on each inoperative instrument and the cockpit control of each item of inoperative equipment, marking it "Inoperative," and shall add the items to the signed and dated list of discrepancies given to the owner or lessee.

[Amdt. 43–23, 47 FR 41085, Sept. 16, 1982, as amended by Amdt. 43–30, 53 FR 50195, Dec. 13, 1988; Amdt. 43–36, 61 FR 19501, May 1, 1996; 71 FR 44188, Aug. 4, 2006]

43.12 Maintenance records: Falsification, reproduction, or alteration

(a) No person may make or cause to be made:

(1) Any fraudulent or intentionally false entry in any record or report that is required to be made, kept, or used to show compliance with any requirement under this part;

(2) Any reproduction, for fraudulent purpose, of any record or report under this part; or

(3) Any alteration, for fraudulent purpose, of any record or report under this part.

(b) The commission by any person of an act prohibited under paragraph (a) of this section is a basis for suspending or revoking the applicable airman, operator, or production certificate, Technical Standard Order Authorization, FAA-Parts Manufacturer Approval, or Product and Process Specification issued by the Administrator and held by that person.

[Amdt. 43–19, 43 FR 22639, May 25, 1978, as amended by Amdt. 43–23, 47 FR 41085, Sept. 16, 1982]

43.13 Performance rules (general)

(a) Each person performing maintenance, alteration, or preventive maintenance on an aircraft, engine, propeller, or appliance shall use the methods, techniques, and practices prescribed in the current manufacturer's maintenance manual or Instructions for Continued Airworthiness prepared by its manufacturer, or other methods, techniques, and practices acceptable to the Administrator, except as noted in 43.16. He shall use the tools, equipment, and test apparatus necessary to assure completion of the work in accordance with accepted industry practices. If special equipment or test apparatus is recommended by the manufacturer involved, he must use that equipment or apparatus or its equivalent acceptable to the Administrator.

(b) Each person maintaining or altering, or performing preventive maintenance, shall do that work in such a manner and use materials of such a quality, that the condition of the aircraft, airframe, aircraft engine, propeller, or appliance worked on will be at least equal to its original or properly altered condition (with regard to aerodynamic function, structural strength, resistance to vibration and deterioration, and other qualities affecting airworthiness).

(c) Special provisions for holders of air carrier operating certificates and operating certificates issued under the provisions of Part 121 or 135 and Part 129 operators holding operations specifications. Unless otherwise notified by the administrator, the methods, techniques, and practices contained in the maintenance manual or the maintenance part of the manual of the holder of an air carrier operating certificate or an operating certificate under Part 121 or 135 and Part 129 operators holding operations specifications (that is required by its operating specifications to provide a continuous airworthiness maintenance and inspection program) constitute acceptable means of compliance with this section.

[Doc. No. 1993, 29 FR 5451, Apr. 23, 1964, as amended by Amdt. 43–20, 45 FR 60182, Sept. 11, 1980; Amdt. 43–23, 47 FR 41085, Sept. 16, 1982; Amdt. 43–28, 52 FR 20028, June 16, 1987; Amdt. 43–37, 66 FR 21066, Apr. 27, 2001]

43.15 Additional performance rules for inspections

(a) General. Each person performing an inspection required by part 91, 125, or 135 of this chapter, shall—

(1) Perform the inspection so as to determine whether the aircraft, or portion(s) thereof under inspection, meets all applicable airworthiness requirements; and

(2) If the inspection is one provided for in part 125, 135, or 91.409(e) of this chapter, perform the inspection in accordance with the instructions and procedures set forth in the inspection program for the aircraft being inspected.

(b) Rotorcraft. Each person performing an inspection required by Part 91 on a rotorcraft shall inspect the following systems in accordance with the maintenance manual or Instructions for Continued Airworthiness of the manufacturer concerned:

(1) The drive shafts or similar systems.

(2) The main rotor transmission gear box for obvious defects.

(3) The main rotor and center section (or the equivalent area).

(4) The auxiliary rotor on helicopters.

(c) Annual and 100-hour inspections.

(1) Each person performing an annual or 100-hour inspection shall use a checklist while performing the inspection. The checklist may be of the person's own design, one provided by the manufacturer of the equipment being inspected or one obtained from another source. This checklist must include the scope and detail of the items contained in appendix D to this part and paragraph (b) of this section.

(2) Each person approving a reciprocating-engine-powered aircraft for return to service after an annual or 100-hour inspection shall, before that approval, run the aircraft engine or engines to determine satisfactory performance in accordance with the manufacturer's recommendations of—

(i) Power output (static and idle r.p.m.);

(ii) Magnetos;

(iii) Fuel and oil pressure; and

(iv) Cylinder and oil temperature.

(3) Each person approving a turbine-engine-powered aircraft for return to service after an annual, 100-hour, or progressive inspection shall, before that approval, run the aircraft engine or engines to determine satisfactory performance in accordance with the manufacturer's recommendations.

(d) Progressive inspection.

(1) Each person performing a progressive inspection shall, at the start of a progressive inspection system, inspect the aircraft completely. After this initial inspection, routine and detailed inspections must be conducted as prescribed in the progressive inspection schedule. Routine inspections consist of visual examination or check of the appliances, the aircraft, and its components and systems, insofar as practicable without disassembly. Detailed inspections consist of a thorough examination of the appliances, the aircraft, and its components and systems, with such disassembly as is necessary. For the purposes of this subparagraph, the overhaul of a component or system is considered to be a detailed inspection.

(2) If the aircraft is away from the station where inspections are normally conducted, an appropriately rated mechanic, a certificated repair station, or the manufacturer of the aircraft may perform inspections in accordance with the procedures and using the forms of the person who would otherwise perform the inspection.

[Doc. No. 1993, 29 FR 5451, Apr. 23, 1964, as amended by Amdt. 43–23, 47 FR 41086, Sept. 16, 1982; Amdt. 43–25, 51 FR 40702, Nov. 7, 1986; Amdt. 43–31, 54 FR 34330, Aug. 18, 1989; 71 FR 44188, Aug. 4, 2006]

43.16 Airworthiness limitations

Each person performing an inspection or other maintenance specified in an Airworthiness Limitations section of a manufacturer's maintenance manual or Instructions for Continued Airworthiness shall perform the inspection or other maintenance in accordance with that section, or in accordance with operations specifications approved by the Administrator under part 121 or 135, or an inspection program approved under 91.409(e).

[71 FR 44188, Aug. 4, 2006]

43.17 Maintenance, preventive maintenance, and alterations performed on U.S. aeronautical products by certain Canadian persons

(a) Definitions . For purposes of this section:

Aeronautical product means any civil aircraft or airframe, aircraft engine, propeller, appliance, component, or part to be installed thereon.

Canadian aeronautical product means any aeronautical product under airworthiness regulation by Transport Canada Civil Aviation.

U.S. aeronautical product means any aeronautical product under airworthiness regulation by the FAA.

(b) Applicability. This section does not apply to any U.S. aeronautical products maintained or altered under any bilateral agreement made between Canada and any country other than the United States.

(c) Authorized persons.

(1) A person holding a valid Transport Canada Civil Aviation Maintenance Engineer license and appropriate ratings may, with respect to a U.S.-registered aircraft located in Canada, perform maintenance, preventive maintenance, and alterations in accordance with the requirements of paragraph (d) of this section and approve the affected aircraft for return to service in accordance with the requirements of paragraph (e) of this section.

(2) A Transport Canada Civil Aviation Approved Maintenance Organization (AMO) holding appropriate ratings may, with respect to a U.S.-registered aircraft or other U.S. aeronautical products located in Canada, perform maintenance, preventive maintenance, and alterations in accordance with the requirements of paragraph (d) of this section and approve the affected products for return to service in accordance with the requirements of paragraph (e) of this section.

(d) Performance requirements . A person authorized in paragraph (c) of this section may perform maintenance (including any inspection required by Sec. 91.409 of this chapter, except an annual inspection), preventive maintenance, and alterations, provided—

(1) The person performing the work is authorized by Transport Canada Civil Aviation to perform the same type of work with respect to Canadian aeronautical products;

(2) The maintenance, preventive maintenance, or alteration is performed in accordance with a Bilateral Aviation Safety Agreement between the United States and Canada and associated Maintenance Implementation Procedures that provide a level of safety equivalent to that provided by the provisions of this chapter;

(3) The maintenance, preventive maintenance, or alteration is performed such that the affected product complies with the applicable requirements of part 36 of this chapter; and

(4) The maintenance, preventive maintenance, or alteration is recorded in accordance with a Bilateral Aviation Safety Agreement between the United States and Canada and associated Maintenance Implementation Procedures that provide a level of safety equivalent to that provided by the provisions of this chapter.

(e) Approval requirements.

(1) To return an affected product to service, a person authorized in paragraph (c) of this section must approve (certify) maintenance, preventive maintenance, and alterations performed under this section, except that an Aircraft Maintenance Engineer may not approve a major repair or major alteration.

(2) An AMO whose system of quality control for the maintenance, preventive maintenance, alteration, and inspection of aeronautical products has been approved by Transport Canada Civil Aviation, or an authorized employee performing work for such an AMO, may approve (certify) a major repair or major alteration performed under this section if the work was performed in accordance with technical data approved by the FAA.

(f) No person may operate in air commerce an aircraft, airframe, aircraft engine, propeller, or appliance on which maintenance, preventive maintenance, or alteration has been performed under this section unless it has been approved for return to service by a person authorized in this section.

[Amdt. 43–33, 56 FR 57571, Nov. 12, 1991, as amended by Amdt. 43–40, 71 FR 40877, July 14, 2005]

Appendix A to Part 43 — Major Alterations, Major Repairs, and Preventive Maintenance

(a) Major alterations —

(1) Airframe major alterations. Alterations of the following parts and alterations of the following types, when not listed in the aircraft specifications issued by the FAA, are airframe major alterations:

(i) Wings.

(ii) Tail surfaces.

(iii) Fuselage.

(iv) Engine mounts.

(v) Control system.

(vi) Landing gear.

(vii) Hull or floats.

(viii) Elements of an airframe including spars, ribs, fittings, shock absorbers, bracing, cowling, fairings, and balance weights.

(ix) Hydraulic and electrical actuating system of components.

FAR 43

    (x)   Rotor blades.

    (xi)   Changes to the empty weight or empty balance which result in an increase in the maximum certificated weight or center of gravity limits of the aircraft.

    (xii)   Changes to the basic design of the fuel, oil, cooling, heating, cabin pressurization, electrical, hydraulic, de-icing, or exhaust systems.

    (xiii) Changes to the wing or to fixed or movable control surfaces which affect flutter and vibration characteristics.

(2) Powerplant major alterations. The following alterations of a powerplant when not listed in the engine specifications issued by the FAA, are powerplant major alterations.

    (i)   Conversion of an aircraft engine from one approved model to another, involving any changes in compression ratio, propeller reduction gear, impeller gear ratios or the substitution of major engine parts which requires extensive rework and testing of the engine.

    (ii)   Changes to the engine by replacing aircraft engine structural parts with parts not supplied by the original manufacturer or parts not specifically approved by the Administrator.

    (iii)   Installation of an accessory which is not approved for the engine.

    (iv)   Removal of accessories that are listed as required equipment on the aircraft or engine specification.

    (v)   Installation of structural parts other than the type of parts approved for the installation.

    (vi)   Conversions of any sort for the purpose of using fuel of a rating or grade other than that listed in the engine specifications.

(3) Propeller major alterations. The following alterations of a propeller when not authorized in the propeller specifications issued by the FAA are propeller major alterations:

    (i)   Changes in blade design.

    (ii)   Changes in hub design.

    (iii)   Changes in the governor or control design.

    (iv)   Installation of a propeller governor or feathering system.

    (v)   Installation of propeller de-icing system.

    (vi)   Installation of parts not approved for the propeller.

(4) Appliance major alterations. Alterations of the basic design not made in accordance with recommendations of the appliance manufacturer or in accordance with an FAA Airworthiness Directive are appliance major alterations. In addition, changes in the basic design of radio communication and navigation equipment approved under type certification or a Technical Standard Order that have an effect on frequency stability, noise level, sensitivity, selectivity, distortion, spurious radiation, AVC characteristics, or ability to meet environmental test conditions and other changes that have an effect on the performance of the equipment are also major alterations.

(b) Major repairs —

(1) Airframe major repairs. Repairs to the following parts of an airframe and repairs of the following types, involving the strengthening, reinforcing, splicing, and manufacturing of primary structural members or their replacement, when replacement is by fabrication such as riveting or welding, are airframe major repairs.

    (i)   Box beams.

    (ii)   Monocoque or semimonocoque wings or control surfaces.

    (iii)   Wing stringers or chord members.

    (iv)   Spars.

    (v)   Spar flanges.

    (vi)   Members of truss-type beams.

    (vii)   Thin sheet webs of beams.

    (viii) Keel and chine members of boat hulls or floats.

    (ix)   Corrugated sheet compression members which act as flange material of wings or tail surfaces.

    (x)   Wing main ribs and compression members.

    (xi)   Wing or tail surface brace struts.

    (xii)   Engine mounts.

    (xiii) Fuselage longerons.

    (xiv) Members of the side truss, horizontal truss, or bulkheads.

    (xv)   Main seat support braces and brackets.

    (xvi) Landing gear brace struts.

    (xvii) Axles.

    (xviii)   Wheels.

    (xix) Skis, and ski pedestals.

    (xx)   Parts of the control system such as control columns, pedals, shafts, brackets, or horns.

    (xxi) Repairs involving the substitution of material.

    (xxii) The repair of damaged areas in metal or plywood stressed covering exceeding six inches in any direction.

    (xxiii)   The repair of portions of skin sheets by making additional seams.

    (xxiv)   The splicing of skin sheets.

    (xxv) The repair of three or more adjacent wing or control surface ribs or the leading edge of wings and control surfaces, between such adjacent ribs.

    (xxvi)   Repair of fabric covering involving an area greater than that required to repair two adjacent ribs.

    (xxvii)   Replacement of fabric on fabric covered parts such as wings, fuselages, stabilizers, and control surfaces.

    (xxviii)   Repairing, including rebottoming, of removable or integral fuel tanks and oil tanks.

(2) Powerplant major repairs. Repairs of the following parts of an engine and repairs of the following types, are powerplant major repairs:

    (i)   Separation or disassembly of a crankcase or crankshaft of a reciprocating engine equipped with an integral supercharger.

    (ii)   Separation or disassembly of a crankcase or crankshaft of a reciprocating engine equipped with other than spur-type propeller reduction gearing.

    (iii)   Special repairs to structural engine parts by welding, plating, metalizing, or other methods.

(3) Propeller major repairs. Repairs of the following types to a propeller are propeller major repairs:

    (i)   Any repairs to, or straightening of steel blades.

    (ii)   Repairing or machining of steel hubs.

    (iii)   Shortening of blades.

    (iv)   Retipping of wood propellers.

    (v)   Replacement of outer laminations on fixed pitch wood propellers.

    (vi)   Repairing elongated bolt holes in the hub of fixed pitch wood propellers.

    (vii) Inlay work on wood blades.

    (viii) Repairs to composition blades.

    (ix)   Replacement of tip fabric.

    (x)   Replacement of plastic covering.

    (xi)   Repair of propeller governors.

    (xii)   Overhaul of controllable pitch propellers.

    (xiii) Repairs to deep dents, cuts, scars, nicks, etc., and straightening of aluminum blades.

(xiv) The repair or replacement of internal elements of blades.

(4) Appliance major repairs. Repairs of the following types to appliances are appliance major repairs:

    (i) Calibration and repair of instruments.

    (ii) Calibration of radio equipment.

    (iii) Rewinding the field coil of an electrical accessory.

    (iv) Complete disassembly of complex hydraulic power valves.

    (v) Overhaul of pressure type carburetors, and pressure type fuel, oil and hydraulic pumps.

(c) Preventive maintenance. Preventive maintenance is limited to the following work, provided it does not involve complex assembly operations:

(1) Removal, installation, and repair of landing gear tires.

(2) Replacing elastic shock absorber cords on landing gear.

(3) Servicing landing gear shock struts by adding oil, air, or both.

(4) Servicing landing gear wheel bearings, such as cleaning and greasing.

(5) Replacing defective safety wiring or cotter keys.

(6) Lubrication not requiring disassembly other than removal of nonstructural items such as cover plates, cowlings, and fairings.

(7) Making simple fabric patches not requiring rib stitching or the removal of structural parts or control surfaces. In the case of balloons, the making of small fabric repairs to envelopes (as defined in, and in accordance with, the balloon manufacturers' instructions) not requiring load tape repair or replacement.

(8) Replenishing hydraulic fluid in the hydraulic reservoir.

(9) Refinishing decorative coating of fuselage, balloon baskets, wings tail group surfaces (excluding balanced control surfaces), fairings, cowlings, landing gear, cabin, or cockpit interior when removal or disassembly of any primary structure or operating system is not required.

(10) Applying preservative or protective material to components where no disassembly of any primary structure or operating system is involved and where such coating is not prohibited or is not contrary to good practices.

(11) Repairing upholstery and decorative furnishings of the cabin, cockpit, or balloon basket interior when the repairing does not require disassembly of any primary structure or operating system or interfere with an operating system or affect the primary structure of the aircraft.

(12) Making small simple repairs to fairings, nonstructural cover plates, cowlings, and small patches and reinforcements not changing the contour so as to interfere with proper air flow.

(13) Replacing side windows where that work does not interfere with the structure or any operating system such as controls, electrical equipment, etc.

(14) Replacing safety belts.

(15) Replacing seats or seat parts with replacement parts approved for the aircraft, not involving disassembly of any primary structure or operating system.

(16) Trouble shooting and repairing broken circuits in landing light wiring circuits.

(17) Replacing bulbs, reflectors, and lenses of position and landing lights.

(18) Replacing wheels and skis where no weight and balance computation is involved.

(19) Replacing any cowling not requiring removal of the propeller or disconnection of flight controls.

(20) Replacing or cleaning spark plugs and setting of spark plug gap clearance.

(21) Replacing any hose connection except hydraulic connections.

(22) Replacing prefabricated fuel lines.

(23) Cleaning or replacing fuel and oil strainers or filter elements.

(24) Replacing and servicing batteries.

(25) Cleaning of balloon burner pilot and main nozzles in accordance with the balloon manufacturer's instructions.

(26) Replacement or adjustment of nonstructural standard fasteners incidental to operations.

(27) The interchange of balloon baskets and burners on envelopes when the basket or burner is designated as interchangeable in the balloon type certificate data and the baskets and burners are specifically designed for quick removal and installation.

(28) The installations of anti-misfueling devices to reduce the diameter of fuel tank filler openings provided the specific device has been made a part of the aircraft type certificate data by the aircraft manufacturer, the aircraft manufacturer has provided FAA-approved instructions for installation of the specific device, and installation does not involve the disassembly of the existing tank filler opening.

(29) Removing, checking, and replacing magnetic chip detectors.

(30) The inspection and maintenance tasks prescribed and specifically identified as preventive maintenance in a primary category aircraft type certificate or supplemental type certificate holder's approved special inspection and preventive maintenance program when accomplished on a primary category aircraft provided:

    (i) They are performed by the holder of at least a private pilot certificate issued under part 61 of this chapter who is the registered owner (including co-owners) of the affected aircraft and who holds a certificate of competency for the affected aircraft (1) issued by the holder of the production certificate for that primary category aircraft that has a special training program approved under 21.24 of this subchapter; or (2) issued by another entity that has a course approved by the Administrator; and

    (ii) The inspections and maintenance tasks are performed in accordance with instructions contained by the special inspection and preventive maintenance program approved as part of the aircraft's type design or supplemental type design.

(31) Removing and replacing self-contained, front instrument panel-mounted navigation and communication devices that employ tray-mounted connectors that connect the unit when the unit is installed into the instrument panel, (excluding automatic flight control systems, transponders, and microwave frequency distance measuring equipment (DME)). The approved unit must be designed to be readily and repeatedly removed and replaced, and pertinent instructions must be provided. Prior to the unit's intended use, and operational check must be performed in accordance with the applicable sections of part 91 of this chapter.

(32) Updating self-contained, front instrument panel-mounted Air Traffic Control (ATC) navigational software data bases (excluding those of automatic flight control systems, transponders, and microwave frequency distance measuring equipment (DME)) provided no disassembly of the unit is required and pertinent instructions are provided. Prior to the unit's intended use, an operational check must be performed in accordance with applicable sections of part 91 of this chapter.

(Secs. 313, 601 through 610, and 1102, Federal Aviation Act of 1958 as amended (49 U.S.C. 1354, 1421 through 1430 and 1502); (49 U.S.C. 106(g) (Revised Pub. L. 97–449, Jan. 21, 1983); and 14 CFR 11.45)

[Doc. No. 1993, 29 FR 5451, Apr. 23, 1964, as amended by Amdt. 43–14, 37 FR 14291, June 19, 1972; Amdt. 43–23, 47 FR 41086, Sept. 16, 1982; Amdt. 43–24, 49 FR 44602, Nov. 7, 1984; Amdt. 43–25, 51 FR 40703, Nov. 7, 1986; Amdt. 43–27, 52 FR 17277, May 6, 1987; Amdt. 43–34, 57 FR 41369, Sept. 9, 1992; Amdt. 43–36, 61 FR 19501, May 1, 1996, Amdt. 43-45, 77 FR 71096, Nov. 29, 2012; Docket No. FAA-2021-0237; Amdt. No. 43-52, 87 FR 31414, May 24, 2022)]

FAR 43

Appendix B to Part 43 — Recording of Major Repairs and Major Alterations

(a) Except as provided in paragraphs (b), (c), and (d) of this appendix, each person performing a major repair or major alteration shall—

(1) Execute FAA Form 337 at least in duplicate;

(2) Give a signed copy of that form to the aircraft owner; and

(3) Forward a copy of that form to the FAA Aircraft Registration Branch in Oklahoma City, Oklahoma, within 48 hours after the aircraft, airframe, aircraft engine, propeller, or appliance is approved for return to service.

(b) For major repairs made in accordance with a manual or specifications acceptable to the Administrator, a certificated repair station may, in place of the requirements of paragraph (a)—

(1) Use the customer's work order upon which the repair is recorded;

(2) Give the aircraft owner a signed copy of the work order and retain a duplicate copy for at least two years from the date of approval for return to service of the aircraft, airframe, aircraft engine, propeller, or appliance;

(3) Give the aircraft owner a maintenance release signed by an authorized representative of the repair station and incorporating the following information:

(i) Identity of the aircraft, airframe, aircraft engine, propeller or appliance.

(ii) If an aircraft, the make, model, serial number, nationality and registration marks, and location of the repaired area.

(iii) If an airframe, aircraft engine, propeller, or appliance, give the manufacturer's name, name of the part, model, and serial numbers (if any); and

(4) Include the following or a similarly worded statement—

"The aircraft, airframe, aircraft engine, propeller, or appliance identified above was repaired and inspected in accordance with current Regulations of the Federal Aviation Agency and is approved for return to service.

Pertinent details of the repair are on file at this repair station under Order No. _____

Date _____

Signed _____

For signature of authorized representative)

Repair station name)

(Certificate No.) _____ ."

(Address)

(c) Except as provided in paragraph (d) of this appendix, for a major repair or major alteration made by a person authorized in 43.17, the person who performs the major repair or major alteration and the person authorized by 43.17 to approve that work shall execute an FAA Form 337 at least in duplicate. A completed copy of that form shall be—

(1) Given to the aircraft owner; and

(2) Forwarded to the Federal Aviation Administration, Aircraft Registration Branch, Post Office Box 25504, Oklahoma City, OK 73125, within 48 hours after the work is inspected.

(d) For extended-range fuel tanks installed within the passenger compartment or a baggage compartment, the person who performs the work and the person authorized to approve the work by 43.7 shall execute an FAA Form 337 in at least triplicate. A completed copy of that form shall be—

(1) Placed on board the aircraft as specified in 91.417 of this chapter;

(2) Given to the aircraft owner; and

(3) Forwarded to the Federal Aviation Administration, Aircra Registration Branch, , Post Office Box 25724, Oklahoma Cit OK 73125, within 48 hours after the work is inspected.

(Secs. 101, 610, 72 Stat. 737, 780, 49 U.S.C. 1301, 1430)

[Doc. No. 1993, 29 FR 5451, Apr. 23, 1964, as amended by Amd 43-10, 33 FR 15989, Oct. 31, 1968; Amdt. 43-29, 52 FR 34101, Sep 9, 1987; Amdt. 43-31, 54 FR 34330, Aug. 18, 1989; 71 FR 5849 Oct. 4, 2006; Amdt. 43-41, 72 FR 53680, Sept. 20, 2007; Doc. N FAA-2018-0119, Amdt. 43-50, 83 FR 9170, Mar. 5, 2018]

Appendix C to Part 43 [Reserved]

Appendix D to Part 43 — Scope and Detail of Items (as Applicable to the Particular Aircraft) To Be Included in Annual and 100-Hour Inspections

(a) Each person performing an annual or 100-hour inspection shal before that inspection, remove or open all necessary inspectio plates, access doors, fairing, and cowling. He shall thoroughl clean the aircraft and aircraft engine.

(b) Each person performing an annual or 100-hour inspection shall in spect (where applicable) the following components of the fuselag and hull group:

(1) Fabric and skin—for deterioration, distortion, other evidenc of failure, and defective or insecure attachment of fittings.

(2) Systems and components—for improper installation, apparer defects, and unsatisfactory operation.

(3) Envelope, gas bags, ballast tanks, and related parts—for poo condition.

(c) Each person performing an annual or 100-hour inspection shal inspect (where applicable) the following components of the cabi and cockpit group:

(1) Generally—for uncleanliness and loose equipment that migh foul the controls.

(2) Seats and safety belts—for poor condition and apparent defects

(3) Windows and windshields—for deterioration and breakage.

(4) Instruments—for poor condition, mounting, marking, an (where practicable) improper operation.

(5) Flight and engine controls—for improper installation and im proper operation.

(6) Batteries—for improper installation and improper charge.

(7) All systems—for improper installation, poor general condi tion, apparent and obvious defects, and insecurity of attach ment.

(d) Each person performing an annual or 100-hour inspection shal inspect (where applicable) components of the engine and nacell group as follows:

(1) Engine section—for visual evidence of excessive oil, fuel, o hydraulic leaks, and sources of such leaks.

(2) Studs and nuts—for improper torquing and obvious defects.

(3) Internal engine—for cylinder compression and for metal parti cles or foreign matter on screens and sump drain plugs. If ther is weak cylinder compression, for improper internal conditio and improper internal tolerances.

(4) Engine mount—for cracks, looseness of mounting, and loose ness of engine to mount.

(5) Flexible vibration dampeners—for poor condition and dete rioration.

(6) Engine controls—for defects, improper travel, and imprope safetying.

(7) Lines, hoses, and clamps—for leaks, improper condition an looseness.

(8) Exhaust stacks—for cracks, defects, and improper attachment

(9) Accessories—for apparent defects in security of mounting.

(10) All systems—for improper installation, poor general condition, defects, and insecure attachment.

(11) Cowling—for cracks, and defects.

(e) Each person performing an annual or 100-hour inspection shall inspect (where applicable) the following components of the landing gear group:

(1) All units—for poor condition and insecurity of attachment.

(2) Shock absorbing devices—for improper oleo fluid level.

(3) Linkages, trusses, and members—for undue or excessive wear fatigue, and distortion.

(4) Retracting and locking mechanism—for improper operation.

(5) Hydraulic lines—for leakage.

(6) Electrical system—for chafing and improper operation of switches.

(7) Wheels—for cracks, defects, and condition of bearings.

(8) Tires—for wear and cuts.

(9) Brakes—for improper adjustment.

(10) Floats and skis—for insecure attachment and obvious or apparent defects.

(f) Each person performing an annual or 100-hour inspection shall inspect (where applicable) all components of the wing and center section assembly for poor general condition, fabric or skin deterioration, distortion, evidence of failure, and insecurity of attachment.

(g) Each person performing an annual or 100-hour inspection shall inspect (where applicable) all components and systems that make up the complete empennage assembly for poor general condition, fabric or skin deterioration, distortion, evidence of failure, insecure attachment, improper component installation, and improper component operation.

(h) Each person performing an annual or 100-hour inspection shall inspect (where applicable) the following components of the propeller group:

(1) Propeller assembly—for cracks, nicks, binds, and oil leakage.

(2) Bolts—for improper torquing and lack of safetying.

(3) Anti-icing devices—for improper operations and obvious defects.

(4) Control mechanisms—for improper operation, insecure mounting, and restricted travel.

(i) Each person performing an annual or 100-hour inspection shall inspect (where applicable) the following components of the radio group:

(1) Radio and electronic equipment—for improper installation and insecure mounting.

(2) Wiring and conduits—for improper routing, insecure mounting, and obvious defects.

(3) Bonding and shielding—for improper installation and poor condition.

(4) Antenna including trailing antenna—for poor condition, insecure mounting, and improper operation.

(j) Each person performing an annual or 100-hour inspection shall inspect (where applicable) each installed miscellaneous item that is not otherwise covered by this listing for improper installation and improper operation.

Appendix E to Part 43 — Altimeter System Test and Inspection

Each person performing the altimeter system tests and inspections required by 91.411 of this chapter must comply with the following:

(a) Static pressure system:

(1) Ensure freedom from entrapped moisture and restrictions.

(2) Perform a proof test to demonstrate the integrity of the static pressure system in a manner acceptable to the Administrator. For airplanes certificated under part 25 of this chapter, determine that leakage is within the tolerances established by 25.1325.

(3) Determine that the static port heater, if installed, is operative.

(4) Ensure that no alterations or deformations of the airframe surface have been made that would affect the relationship between air pressure in the static pressure system and true ambient static air pressure for any flight condition.

(b) Altimeter:

(1) Test by an appropriately rated repair facility in accordance with the following subparagraphs. Unless otherwise specified, each test for performance may be conducted with the instrument subjected to vibration. When tests are conducted with the temperature substantially different from ambient temperature of approximately 25 degrees C., allowance shall be made for the variation from the specified condition.

(i) Scale error. With the barometric pressure scale at 29.92 inches of mercury, the altimeter shall be subjected successively to pressures corresponding to the altitude specified in Table I up to the maximum normally expected operating altitude of the airplane in which the altimeter is to be installed. The reduction in pressure shall be made at a rate not in excess of 20,000 feet per minute to within approximately 2,000 feet of the test point. The test point shall be approached at a rate compatible with the test equipment. The altimeter shall be kept at the pressure corresponding to each test point for at least 1 minute, but not more than 10 minutes, before a reading is taken. The error at all test points must not exceed the tolerances specified in Table I.

TABLE 1		
ALTITUDE	EQUIVALENT PRESSURE (INCHES OF MERCURY)	TOLERANCE +/- (FEET)
-1,000	31.018	20
0	29.921	20
500	29.385	20
1,000	28.856	20
1,500	28.335	25
2,000	27.821	30
3,000	26.817	30
4,000	25.842	35
6,000	23.978	40
8,000	22.225	60
10,000	20.577	80
12,000	19.029	90
14,000	17.577	100
16,000	16.216	110
18,000	14.942	120
20,000	13.750	130
22,000	12.636	140
25,000	11.104	155
30,000	8.885	180
35,000	7.041	205
40,000	5.538	230
45,000	4.335	255
50,000	3.425	280

FAR 43

(ii) Hysteresis. The hysteresis test shall begin not more than 15 minutes after the altimeter's initial exposure to the pressure corresponding to the upper limit of the scale error test prescribed in subparagraph (i); and while the altimeter is at this pressure, the hysteresis test shall commence. Pressure shall be increased at a rate simulating a descent in altitude at the rate of 5,000 to 20,000 feet per minute until within 3,000 feet of the first test point (50 percent of maximum altitude). The test point shall then be approached at a rate of approximately 3,000 feet per minute. The altimeter shall be kept at this pressure for at least 5 minutes, but not more than 15 minutes, before the test reading is taken. After the reading has been taken, the pressure shall be increased further, in the same manner as before, until the pressure corresponding to the second test point (40 percent of maximum altitude) is reached. The altimeter shall be kept at this pressure for at least 1 minute, but not more than 10 minutes, before the test reading is taken. After the reading has been taken, the pressure shall be increased further, in the same manner as before, until atmospheric pressure is reached. The reading of the altimeter at either of the two test points shall not differ by more than the tolerance specified in Table II from the reading of the altimeter for the corresponding altitude recorded during the scale error test prescribed in paragraph (b)(i).

(iii) After effect. Not more than 5 minutes after the completion of the hysteresis test prescribed in paragraph (b)(ii), the reading of the altimeter (corrected for any change in atmospheric pressure) shall not differ from the original atmospheric pressure reading by more than the tolerance specified in Table II.

TABLE II—TEST TOLERANCES	
Test	Tolerance (Feet)
Case Leak Test	+/- 100
Hysteresis Test:	
First Test point (50 percent of maximum altitude)	75
Second Test point (40 percent of maximum altitude)	75
After Effect Test	30

(iv) Friction. The altimeter shall be subjected to a steady rate of decrease of pressure approximating 750 feet per minute. At each altitude listed in Table III, the change in reading of the pointers after vibration shall not exceed the corresponding tolerance listed in Table III.

TABLE III—FRICTION	
Altitude (Feet)	Tolerance (Feet)
1,000	+/-70
2,000	70
3,000	70
5,000	70
10,000	80
15,000	90
20,000	100
25,000	120
30,000	140
35,000	160
40,000	180
50,000	250

(v) Case leak. The leakage of the altimeter case, when the pressure within it corresponds to an altitude of 18,000 feet, shall not change the altimeter reading by more than the tolerance shown in Table II during an interval of 1 minute.

(vi) Barometric scale error. At constant atmospheric pressure, the barometric pressure scale shall be set at each of the pressures (falling within its range of adjustment) that are listed in Table IV, and shall cause the pointer to indicate the equivalent altitude difference shown in Table IV with a tolerance of 25 feet.

TABLE IV—PRESSURE-ALTITUDE DIFFERENCE	
Pressure (inches of Hg)	Altitude difference (feet)
28.10	-1,727
28.50	-1,340
29.00	-863
29.50	-392
29.92	0
30.50	+531
30.90	+893
30.99	+974

(2) Altimeters which are the air data computer type with associated computing systems, or which incorporate air data correction internally, may be tested in a manner and to specifications developed by the manufacturer which are acceptable to the Administrator.

(c) Automatic Pressure Altitude Reporting Equipment and ATC Transponder System Integration Test. The test must be conducted by an appropriately rated person under the conditions specified in paragraph (a). Measure the automatic pressure altitude at the output of the installed ATC transponder when interrogated on Mode C at a sufficient number of test points to ensure that the altitude reporting equipment, altimeters, and ATC transponders perform their intended functions as installed in the aircraft. The difference between the automatic reporting output and the altitude displayed at the altimeter shall not exceed 125 feet.

(d) Records: Comply with the provisions of 43.9 of this chapter as to content, form, and disposition of the records. The person performing the altimeter tests shall record on the altimeter the date and maximum altitude to which the altimeter has been tested and the persons approving the airplane for return to service shall enter that data in the airplane log or other permanent record.

(Secs. 313, 314, and 601 through 610 of the Federal Aviation Act of 1958 (49 U.S.C. 1354, 1355, and 1421 through 1430) and sec. 6(c), Dept. of Transportation Act (49 U.S.C. 1655(c)))

[Amdt. 43-2, 30 FR 8262, June 29, 1965, as amended by Amdt. 43-7, 32 FR 7587, May 24, 1967; Amdt. 43-19, 43 FR 22639, May 25, 1978; Amdt. 43-23, 47 FR 41086, Sept. 16, 1982; Amdt. 43-31, 54 FR 34330, Aug. 18, 1989; Doc. No. FAA-2015-1621, Amdt. 43-49, 81 FR 96700, Dec. 30, 2016]

Appendix F to Part 43 — ATC Transponder Tests and Inspections

The ATC transponder tests required by 91.413 of this chapter may be conducted using a bench check or portable test equipment and must meet the requirements prescribed in paragraphs (a) through (j) of this appendix. If portable test equipment with appropriate coupling to the aircraft antenna system is used, operate the test equipment for ATCRBS transponders at a nominal rate of 235 interrogations per second to avoid possible ATCRBS interference. Operate the test equipment at a nominal rate of 50 Mode S interrogations per second for Mode S. An additional 3 dB loss is allowed to compensate for antenna coupling errors during receiver sensitivity measurements conducted in accordance with paragraph (c)(1) when using portable test equipment.

(a) Radio Reply Frequency:

    (1) For all classes of ATCRBS transponders, interrogate the transponder and verify that the reply frequency is 1090 ±3 Megahertz (MHz).

    (2) For classes 1B, 2B, and 3B Mode S transponders, interrogate the transponder and verify that the reply frequency is 1090 ±3 MHz.

    (3) For classes 1B, 2B, and 3B Mode S transponders that incorporate the optional 1090 ±1 MHz reply frequency, interrogate the transponder and verify that the reply frequency is correct.

    (4) For classes 1A, 2A, 3A, and 4 Mode S transponders, interrogate the transponder and verify that the reply frequency is 1090 ±1 MHz.

(b) Suppression: When Classes 1B and 2B ATCRBS Transponders, or Classes 1B, 2B, and 3B Mode S transponders are interrogated Mode 3/A at an interrogation rate between 230 and 1,000 interrogations per second; or when Classes 1A and 2A ATCRBS Transponders, or Classes 1B, 2A, 3A, and 4 Mode S transponders are interrogated at a rate between 230 and 1,200 Mode 3/A interrogations per second:

    (1) Verify that the transponder does not respond to more than 1 percent of ATCRBS interrogations when the amplitude of P2pulse is equal to the P1pulse.

    (2) Verify that the transponder replies to at least 90 percent of ATCRBS interrogations when the amplitude of the P2pulse is 9 dB less than the P1pulse. If the test is conducted with a radiated test signal, the interrogation rate shall be 235 ±5 interrogations per second unless a higher rate has been approved for the test equipment used at that location.

(c) Receiver Sensitivity:

    (1) Verify that for any class of ATCRBS Transponder, the receiver minimum triggering level (MTL) of the system is −73 ±4 dbm, or that for any class of Mode S transponder the receiver MTL for Mode S format (P6 type) interrogations is −74 ±3 dbm by use of a test set either:

        (i) Connected to the antenna end of the transmission line;

        (ii) Connected to the antenna terminal of the transponder with a correction for transmission line loss; or

        (iii) Utilized radiated signal.

    (2) Verify that the difference in Mode 3/A and Mode C receiver sensitivity does not exceed 1 db for either any class of ATCRBS transponder or any class of Mode S transponder.

(d) Radio Frequency (RF) Peak Output Power:

    (1) Verify that the transponder RF output power is within specifications for the class of transponder. Use the same conditions as described in (c)(1)(i), (ii), and (iii) above.

        (i) For Class 1A and 2A ATCRBS transponders, verify that the minimum RF peak output power is at least 21.0 dbw (125 watts).

        (ii) For Class 1B and 2B ATCRBS Transponders, verify that the minimum RF peak output power is at least 18.5 dbw (70 watts).

        (iii) For Class 1A, 2A, 3A, and 4 and those Class 1B, 2B, and 3B Mode S transponders that include the optional high RF peak output power, verify that the minimum RF peak output power is at least 21.0 dbw (125 watts).

        (iv) For Classes 1B, 2B, and 3B Mode S transponders, verify that the minimum RF peak output power is at least 18.5 dbw (70 watts).

        (v) For any class of ATCRBS or any class of Mode S transponders, verify that the maximum RF peak output power does not exceed 27.0 dbw (500 watts).

NOTE: *The tests in (e) through (j) apply only to Mode S transponders.*

(e) Mode S Diversity Transmission Channel Isolation: For any class of Mode S transponder that incorporates diversity operation, verify that the RF peak output power transmitted from the selected antenna exceeds the power transmitted from the nonselected antenna by at least 20 db.

(f) Mode S Address: Interrogate the Mode S transponder and verify that it replies only to its assigned address. Use the correct address and at least two incorrect addresses. The interrogations should be made at a nominal rate of 50 interrogations per second.

(g) Mode S Formats: Interrogate the Mode S transponder with uplink formats (UF) for which it is equipped and verify that the replies are made in the correct format. Use the surveillance formats UF=4 and 5. Verify that the altitude reported in the replies to UF=4 are the same as that reported in a valid ATCRBS Mode C reply. Verify that the identity reported in the replies to UF=5 are the same as that reported in a valid ATCRBS Mode 3/A reply. If the transponder is so equipped, use the communication formats UF=20, 21, and 24.

(h) Mode S All-Call Interrogations: Interrogate the Mode S transponder with the Mode S-only all-call format UF=11, and the ATCRBS/Mode S all-call formats (1.6 microsecond P4pulse) and verify that the correct address and capability are reported in the replies (downlink format DF=11).

(i) ATCRBS-Only All-Call Interrogation: Interrogate the Mode S transponder with the ATCRBS-only all-call interrogation (0.8 microsecond P4pulse) and verify that no reply is generated.

(j) Squitter: Verify that the Mode S transponder generates a correct squitter approximately once per second.

(k) Records: Comply with the provisions of 43.9 of this chapter as to content, form, and disposition of the records.

[Amdt. 43–26, 52 FR 3390, Feb. 3, 1987; 52 FR 6651, Mar. 4, 1987; as amended by Amdt. 43–31, 54 FR 34330, Aug. 18, 1989]

FAR 43

PART 45 — IDENTIFICATION AND REGISTRATION MARKING

Subpart A — General

Subpart B — Marking of Products and Articles

Subpart C — Nationality and Registration Marks

Authority: 49 U.S.C. 106(f), 106(g), 40103, 40113-40114, 44101-44105, 44107-44111, 44504, 44701, 44708-44709, 44711-44713, 44725, 45302-45303, 46104, 46304, 46306, 47122.

Source: Docket No. 2047, 29 FR 3223, Mar. 11, 1964, unless otherwise noted.

Editorial Note: Nomenclature changes to part 45 appear at 74 FR 53394, Oct. 16, 2009.

Subpart A — General

45.1   Applicability

This part prescribes the requirements for—

(a) Marking products and articles manufactured under—

(1) A type certificate;

(2) A production approval as defined under part 21 of this chapter; and

(3) The provisions of an agreement between the United States and another country or jurisdiction for the acceptance of products and articles; and

(b) Nationality and registration marking of aircraft registered in the United States in accordance with part 47.

[Doc. No. 2047, 29 FR 3223, Mar. 11, 1964, as amended by Amdt. 45-3, 32 FR 188, Jan. 10, 1967; Amdt. 45-26, 74 FR 53394, Oct. 16, 2009; Doc. No. FAA-2015-7396, Amdt. 45-30, 80 FR 78645, Dec. 16, 2015]

Subpart B — Identification of Aircraft and Related Products

45.10   Marking

No person may mark a product or article in accordance with this subpart unless—

(a) That person produced the product or article —

(1) Under part 21, subpart F, G, K, or O of this chapter; or

(2) For export to the United States under the provisions of an agreement between the United States and another country or jurisdiction for the acceptance of products and articles; and

(b) That product or article conforms to its approved design, and is in a condition for safe operation; and, for a TSO article; that TSO article meets the applicable performance standards.

[Doc. No. FAA-2006-25877, 74 FR 53394, Oct. 16, 2009, as amended at 75 FR 9095, Mar. 1, 2010]

45.11   Marking of products

(a) **Aircraft.** A manufacturer of aircraft covered under 21.182 of this chapter must mark each aircraft by attaching a fireproof identification plate that—

(1) Includes the information specified in 45.13 using an approved method of fireproof marking;

(2) Must be secured in such a manner that it will not likely be defaced or removed during normal service, or lost or destroyed in an accident; and

(3) Except as provided in paragraphs (d) through (h) of this section, must be secured to the aircraft fuselage exterior so that it is legible to a person on the ground, and must be either adjacent to and aft of the rear-most entrance door or on the fuselage surface near the tail surfaces.

(b) **Aircraft engines.** A manufacturer of an aircraft engine produced under a type certificate or production certificate must mark each engine by attaching a fireproof identification plate. Such plate—

(1) Must include information specified in 45.13 using an approved method of fireproof marking;

(2) Must be affixed to the engine at an accessible location; and

(3) Must be secured in such a matter that it will not likely be defaced or removed during normal service, or lost or destroyed in an accident.

(c) **Propellers and propeller blades and hubs.** Each person who produces a propeller, propeller blade, or propeller hub under a type certificate or production certificate must mark each product or part. Except for a fixed-pitch wooden propeller, the marking must be accomplished using an approved fireproof method. The marking must—

(1) Be placed on a non-critical surface;

(2) Contain the information specified in 45.13

(3) Not likely be defaced or removed during normal service; and

(4) Not likely be lost or destroyed in an accident.

(d) **Manned free balloons.** A manufacturer of manned free balloons must mark each balloon by attaching the identification plate described in paragraph (a) of this section. The plate must be secured to the balloon envelope and must be located, if practicable, where it is legible to the operator when the balloon is inflated. In addition, the basket and heater assembly must be permanently and legibly marked with the manufacturer's name, part number (or equivalent), and serial number (or equivalent).

(e) **Aircraft manufactured before March 7, 1988.** The owner or operator of an aircraft manufactured before March 7, 1988 must mark the aircraft by attaching the identification plate required by paragraph (a) of this section. The plate must be secured at an accessible exterior or interior location near an entrance, if the model designation and builder's serial number are also displayed on the exterior of the aircraft fuselage. The model designation and builder's serial number must be—

(1) Legible to a person on the ground,

(2) Located either adjacent to and aft of the rear-most entrance door or on the fuselage near the tail surfaces, and

(3) Displayed in such a manner that they are not likely to be defaced or removed during normal service.

(f) For powered parachutes and weight-shift-control aircraft, the identification plate required by paragraph (a) of this section must be secured to the exterior of the aircraft fuselage so that it is legible to a person on the ground.

(g) The identification plate described in paragraph (a) of this section may be secured to the aircraft at an accessible location near an entrance for—

(1) Aircraft produced for—

(i)   Operations under part 121 of this chapter,

(ii)   Commuter operations (as defined in 110.2 of this chapter), or

(iii) Export.

FAR 45

(2) Aircraft operating under part 121 of this chapter and under an FAA-approved continuous airworthiness maintenance program; or

(3) Aircraft operating in commuter air carrier operations (as defined in 110.2 of this chapter) under an FAA-approved continuous airworthiness maintenance program.

(h) Gliders. Paragraphs (a)(3) and (e) of this section do not apply to gliders.

[Amdt. 45-26, 74 FR 53394, Oct. 16, 2009, as amended by Amdt. 45-27, 76 FR 7486, Feb. 10, 2011; Doc. No. FAA-2013-0933, Amdt. 21-98, 80 FR 59031, Oct. 1, 2015, as amended by Amdt. 21-98A, 80 FR 59031, Dec. 17, 2015]

45.13 Identification data

(a) The identification required by 45.11 (a) through (c) shall include the following information:

(1) Builder's name.

(2) Model designation.

(3) Builder's serial number.

(4) Type certificate number, if any.

(5) Production certificate number, if any.

(6) For aircraft engines, the established rating.

(7) On or after January 1, 1984, for aircraft engines specified in part 34 of this chapter, the date of manufacture as defined in 34.1 of this chapter, and a designation, approved by the FAA, that indicates compliance with the applicable exhaust emission provisions of part 34 of this chapter and 40 CFR part 87. Approved designations include COMPLY, EXEMPT, and NON-US, as appropriate. After December 31, 2012, approved designations also include EXEMPT NEW, and EXCEPTED SPARE, as appropriate.

　(i) The designation COMPLY indicates that the engine is in compliance with all of the applicable exhaust emissions provisions of part 34. For any engine with a rated thrust in excess of 26.7 kilonewtons (6000 pounds) which is not used or intended for use in commercial operations and which is in compliance with the applicable provisions of part 34, but does not comply with the hydrocarbon emissions standard of 34.21(d), the statement "May not be used as a commercial aircraft engine" must be noted in the permanent powerplant record that accompanies the engine at the time of manufacture of the engine.

　(ii) The designation EXEMPT indicates that the engine has been granted an exemption pursuant to the applicable provision of 34.7 (a)(1), (a)(4), (b), (c), or (d), and an indication of the type of exemption and the reason for the grant must be noted in the permanent powerplant record that accompanies the engine from the time of manufacture of the engine.

　(iii) The designation NON-US indicates that the engine has been granted an exemption pursuant to 34.7(a)(1), and the notation "This aircraft may not be operated within the United States", or an equivalent notation approved by the Administrator of the FAA, must be inserted in the aircraft logbook, or alternate equivalent document, at the time of installation of the engine.

　(iv) The designation EXEMPT NEW indicates that the engine has been granted an exemption pursuant to the applicable provision of 34.7(h) of this chapter; the designation must be noted in the permanent powerplant record that accompanies the engine from the time of its manufacture.

　(v) The designation EXCEPTED SPARE indicates that the engine has been excepted pursuant to the applicable provision of 34.9(b) of this chapter; the designation must be noted in the permanent powerplant record that accompanies the engine from the time of its manufacture.

(8) Any other information the Administrator finds appropriate.

(b) Except as provided in paragraph (d)(1) of this section, no person may remove, change, or place identification information required by paragraph (a) of this section, on any aircraft, aircraft engine, propeller, propeller blade, or propeller hub, without the approval of the Administrator.

(c) Except as provided in paragraph (d)(2) of this section, no person may remove or install any identification plate required by 45.11 without the approval of the Administrator.

(d) Persons performing work under the provisions of Part 43 of this chapter may, in accordance with methods, techniques, and practices acceptable to the Administrator—

(1) Remove, change, or place the identification information required by paragraph (a) of this section on any aircraft, aircraft engine, propeller, propeller blade, or propeller hub; or

(2) Remove an identification plate required by 45.11 when necessary during maintenance operations.

(e) No person may install an identification plate removed in accordance with paragraph (d)(2) of this section on any aircraft, aircraft engine, propeller, propeller blade, or propeller hub other than the one from which it was removed.

[Amdt. 45-3, 32 FR 188, Jan. 10, 1967, as amended by Amdt. 45-10, 44 FR 45379, Aug. 2, 1979; Amdt. 45-12, 45 FR 60183, Sept. 11, 1980; Amdt. 45-20, 55 FR 32861, Aug. 10, 1990; 55 FR 37287, Sept. 10, 1990; Amdt. 45-26, 74 FR 53395, Oct. 16, 2009; Amdt. 45-28, 77 FR 76854, Dec. 31, 2012]

45.15 Marking requirements for PMA articles, TSO articles, and Critical parts.

(a) PMA articles . The manufacturer of a PMA article must permanently and legibly mark—

(1) Each PMA article, with the PMA holder's name, trademark, symbol, or other FAA approved identification and part number; and

(2) The letters "FAA–PMA".

(b) TSO articles . The manufacturer of a TSO article must permanently and legibly mark —

(1) Each TSO article with the TSO holder's name, trademark, symbol, or other FAA approved identification and part number; and

(2) Each TSO article, unless otherwise specified in the applicable TSO, with the TSO number and letter of designation, all markings specifically required by the applicable TSO, and the serial number or the date of manufacture of the article or both.

(c) Critical parts . Each person who manufactures a part for which a replacement time, inspection interval, or related procedure is specified in the Airworthiness Limitations section of a manufacturer's maintenance manual or Instructions for Continued Airworthiness must permanently and legibly mark that part with a serial number (or equivalent) unique to that part in addition to the other applicable requirements of this section.

(d) If the FAA finds a part or article is too small or otherwise impractical to mark with any of the information required by this part, the manufacturer must attach that information to the part or its container.

[Doc. No. FAA–2006–25877, 74 FR 53395, Oct. 16, 2009, as amended at 75 FR 9095, Mar. 1, 2010]

45.16 Marking of life-limited parts

When requested by a person required to comply with 43.10 of this chapter, the holder of a type certificate or design approval for a life-limited part must provide marking instructions, or must state that the part cannot be practically marked without compromising its integrity.

[Doc. No. FAA–200–8017, 67 FR 2110, Jan. 15, 2002, as amended by Amdt. 45–26, 74 FR 53395, Oct. 16, 2009; 75 FR 9095, Mar. 1, 2010]

Subpart C — Nationality and Registration Marks

45.21 General

(a) Except as provided in 45.22, no person may operate a U.S.-registered aircraft unless that aircraft displays nationality and registration marks in accordance with the requirements of this section and 45.23 through 45.33.

(b) Unless otherwise authorized by the Administrator, no person may place on any aircraft a design, mark, or symbol that modifies or confuses the nationality and registration marks.

(c) Aircraft nationality and registration marks must—

(1) Except as provided in paragraph (d) of this section, be painted on the aircraft or affixed by any other means insuring a similar degree of permanence;

(2) Have no ornamentation;

(3) Contrast in color with the background; and

(4) Be legible.

(d) The aircraft nationality and registration marks may be affixed to an aircraft with readily removable material if—

(1) It is intended for immediate delivery to a foreign purchaser;

(2) It is bearing a temporary registration number; or

(3) It is marked temporarily to meet the requirements of 45.22(c)(1) or 45.29(h) of this part, or both.

[Doc. No. 8093, Amdt. 45–5, 33 FR 450, Jan 12, 1968, as amended by Amdt. 45–17, 52 FR 34102, Sept. 9, 1987]

45.22 Exhibition, antique, and other aircraft: Special rules

(a) When display of aircraft nationality and registration marks in accordance with 45.21 and 45.23 through 45.33 would be inconsistent with exhibition of that aircraft, a U.S.-registered aircraft may be operated without displaying those marks anywhere on the aircraft if:

(1) It is operated for the purpose of exhibition, including a motion picture or television production, or an airshow;

(2) Except for practice and test fights necessary for exhibition purposes, it is operated only at the location of the exhibition, between the exhibition locations, and between those locations and the base of operations of the aircraft; and

(3) For each flight in the United States:

(i) It is operated with the prior approval of the responsible Flight Standards office, in the case of a flight within the lateral boundaries of the surface areas of Class B, Class C, Class D, or Class E airspace designated for the takeoff airport, or within 4.4 nautical miles of that airport if it is within Class G airspace; or

(ii) It is operated under a flight plan filed under either 91.153 or 91.169 of this chapter describing the marks it displays, in the case of any other flight.

(b) A small U.S.-registered aircraft built at least 30 years ago or a U.S.-registered aircraft for which an experimental certificate has been issued under 21.191(d) or 21.191(g) for operation as an exhibition aircraft or as an amateur-built aircraft and which has the same external configuration as an aircraft built at least 30 years ago may be operated without displaying marks in accordance with 45.21 and 45.23 through 45.33 if:

(1) It displays in accordance with 45.21(c) marks at least 2 inches high on each side of the fuselage or vertical tail surface consisting of the Roman capital letter "N" followed by:

(i) The U.S. registration number of the aircraft; or

(ii) The symbol appropriate to the airworthiness certificate of the aircraft ("C", standard; "R", restricted; "L", limited; or "X", experimental) followed by the U.S. registration number of the aircraft; and

(2) It displays no other mark that begins with the letter "N" anywhere on the aircraft, unless it is the same mark that is displayed under paragraph (b)(1) of this section.

(c) No person may operate an aircraft under paragraph (a) or (b) of this section—

(1) In an ADIZ or DEWIZ described in Part 99 of this chapter unless it temporarily bears marks in accordance with 45.21 and 45.23 through 45.33;

(2) In a foreign country unless that country consents to that operation; or

(3) In any operation conducted under Part 121, 133, 135, or 137 of this chapter.

(d) If, due to the configuration of an aircraft, it is impossible for a person to mark it in accordance with 45.21 and 45.23 through 45.33, he may apply to the Administrator for a different marking procedure.

[Doc. No. 8093, Amdt. 45-5, 33 FR 450, Jan. 12, 1968, as amended by Amdt. 45-13, 46 FR 48603, Oct. 1, 1981; Amdt. 45-19, 54 FR 39291, Sept. 25, 1989; Amdt. 45-18, 54 FR 34330, Aug. 18, 1989; Amdt. 45-21, 56 FR 65653, Dec. 17, 1991; Amdt. 45-22, 66 FR 21066, Apr. 27, 2001; Doc. No. FAA-2018-0119, Amdt. 45-31, 83 FR 9170, Mar. 5, 2018]

45.23 Display of marks; general

(a) Each operator of an aircraft shall display on that aircraft marks consisting of the Roman capital letter "N" (denoting United States registration) followed by the registration number of the aircraft. Each suffix letter used in the marks displayed must also be a Roman capital letter.

(b) When marks include only the Roman capital letter "N" and the registration number is displayed on limited, restricted or light-sport category aircraft or experimental or provisionally certificated aircraft, the operator must also display on that aircraft near each entrance to the cabin, cockpit, or pilot station, in letters not less than 2 inches nor more than 6 inches high, the words "limited," "restricted," "light-sport," "experimental," or "provisional," as applicable.

[Doc. No. 8093, Amdt. 45–5, 33 FR 450, Jan. 12, 1968, as amended by Amdt. 45–9, 42 FR 41102, Aug. 15, 1977; Amdt. 45–24, 69 FR 44863, July 27, 2004]

45.25 Location of marks on fixed-wing aircraft

(a) The operator of a fixed-wing aircraft shall display the required marks on either the vertical tail surfaces or the sides of the fuselage, except as provided in 45.29(f).

(b) The marks required by paragraph (a) of this section shall be displayed as follows:

(1) If displayed on the vertical tail surfaces, horizontally on both surfaces, horizontally on both surfaces of a single vertical tail or on the outer surfaces of a multivertical tail. However, on aircraft on which marks at least 3 inches high may be displayed in accordance with 45.29(b)(1), the marks may be displayed vertically on the vertical tail surfaces.

(2) If displayed on the fuselage surfaces, horizontally on both sides of the fuselage between the trailing edge of the wing and the leading edge of the horizontal stabilizer. However, if engine pods or other appurtenances are located in this area and are an integral part of the fuselage side surfaces, the operator may place the marks on those pods or appurtenances.

[Amdt. 45–9, 42 FR 41102, Aug. 15, 1977]

45.27 Location of marks; nonfixed-wing aircraft

(a) Rotorcraft. Each operator of a rotorcraft shall display on that rotorcraft horizontally on both surfaces of the cabin, fuselage, boom, or tail the marks required by 45.23.

(b) Airships. Each operator of an airship shall display on that airship the marks required by 45.23, horizontally on—

(1) The upper surface of the right horizontal stabilizer and on the under surface of the left horizontal stabilizer with the top of the marks toward the leading edge of each stabilizer; and

(2) Each side of the bottom half of the vertical stabilizer.

(c) Spherical balloons. Each operator of a spherical balloon shall display the marks required by 45.23 in two places diametrically opposite and near the maximum horizontal circumference of that balloon.

(d) Nonspherical balloons. Each operator of a nonspherical balloon shall display the marks required by 45.23 on each side of the balloon near its maximum cross section and immediately above either the rigging band or the points of attachment of the basket or cabin suspension cables.

(e) Powered parachutes and weight-shift-control aircraft. Each operator of a powered parachute or a weight-shift-control aircraft must display the marks required by 45.23 and 45.29(b)(2) of this part. The marks must be displayed in two diametrically opposite positions on the fuselage, a structural member, or a component of the aircraft and must be visible from the side of the aircraft.

[Doc. No. 2047, 29 FR 3223, Mar. 11, 1964, as amended by Amdt. 45–15, 48 FR 11392, Mar. 17, 1983; Amdt. 45–24, 69 FR 44863, July 27, 2004; Amdt. 45–25, 72 FR 52469, Sept. 14, 2007]

45.29   Size of marks

(a) Except as provided in paragraph (f) of this section, each operator of an aircraft shall display marks on the aircraft meeting the size requirements of this section.

(b) Height. Except as provided in paragraph (h) of this part, the nationality and registration marks must be of equal height and on—

(1) Fixed-wing aircraft, must be at least 12 inches high, except that:

(i) An aircraft displaying marks at least 2 inches high before November 1, 1981 and an aircraft manufactured after November 2, 1981, but before January 1, 1983, may display those marks until the aircraft is repainted or the marks are repainted, restored, or changed;

(ii) Marks at least 3 inches high may be displayed on a glider;

(iii) Marks at least 3 inches high may be displayed on an aircraft for which the FAA has issued an experimental certificate under 21.191 (d), 21.191 (g), or 21.191 (i) of this chapter to operate as an exhibition aircraft, an amateur-built aircraft, or a light-sport aircraft when the maximum cruising speed of the aircraft does not exceed 180 knots CAS; and

(iv) Marks may be displayed on an exhibition, antique, or other aircraft in accordance with 45.22.

(2) Airships, spherical balloons, nonspherical balloons, powered parachutes, and weight-shift-control aircraft must be at least 3 inches high; and

(3) Rotorcraft, must be at least 12 inches high, except that rotorcraft displaying before April 18, 1983, marks required by 45.29(b)(3) in effect on April 17, 1983, and rotorcraft manufactured on or after April 18, 1983, but before December 31, 1983, may display those marks until the aircraft is repainted or the marks are repainted, restored, or changed.

(c) Width. Characters must be two-thirds as wide as they are high, except the number "1", which must be one-sixth as wide as it is high, and the letters "M" and "W" which may be as wide as they are high.

(d) Thickness. Characters must be formed by solid lines one-sixth as thick as the character is high.

(e) Spacing. The space between each character may not be less than one-fourth of the character width.

(f) If either one of the surfaces authorized for displaying required marks under 45.25 is large enough for display of marks meeting the size requirements of this section and the other is not, full size marks shall be placed on the larger surface. If neither surface is large enough for full-size marks, marks as large as practicable shall be displayed on the larger of the two surfaces. If no surface authorized to be marked by 45.27 is large enough for full-size marks, marks as large as practicable shall be placed on the largest of the authorized surfaces. However, powered parachutes and weight-shift-control aircraft must display marks at least 3 inches high.

(g) Uniformity. The marks required by this part for fixed-wing aircraft must have the same height, width, thickness, and spacing on both sides of the aircraft.

(h) After March 7, 1988, each operator of an aircraft penetrating an ADIZ or DEWIZ shall display on that aircraft temporary or permanent nationality and registration marks at least 12 inches high.

[Doc. No. 2047, 29 FR 3223, Mar. 11, 1964, as amended by Amdt. 45–2, 31 FR 9863, July 21, 1966; Amdt. 45–9, 42 FR 41102, Aug. 15, 1977; Amdt. 45–13, 46 FR 48604, Oct. 1, 1981; Amdt. 45–15, 48 FR 11392, Mar. 17, 1983; Amdt. 45–17, 52 FR 34102, Sept. 9, 1987; 52 FR 36566, Sept. 30, 1987; Amdt. 45–24, 69 FR 44863, July 27, 2004; Amdt. No. 45–25, 72 FR 52469, Sept. 14, 2007]

45.31   Marking of export aircraft

A person who manufactures an aircraft in the United States for delivery outside thereof may display on that aircraft any marks required by the State of registry of the aircraft. However, no person may operate an aircraft so marked within the United States, except for test and demonstration flights for a limited period of time, or while in necessary transit to the purchaser.

45.33   Sale of aircraft; removal of marks

When an aircraft that is registered in the United States is sold, the holder of the Certificate of Aircraft Registration shall remove, before its delivery to the purchaser, all United States marks from the aircraft, unless the purchaser is—

(a) A citizen of the United States;

(b) An individual citizen of a foreign country who is lawfully admitted for permanent residence in the United States; or

(c) When the aircraft is to be based and primarily used in the United States, a corporation (other than a corporation which is a citizen of the United States) lawfully organized and doing business under the laws of the United States or any State thereof.

[Amdt. 45–11, 44 FR 61938, Oct. 29, 1979]

PART 47 — AIRCRAFT REGISTRATION

Subpart A — General

Subpart B — Certificates of Aircraft Registration

Subpart C — Dealers' Aircraft Registration Certificate

Authority: 4 U.S.T. 1830; Pub. L. 108-297, 118 Stat. 1095 (49 U.S.C. 40101 note, 49 U.S.C. 44101 note); 49 U.S.C. 106(f), 106(g), 40113-40114, 44101-44108, 44110-44113, 44703-44704, 44713, 44809(f), 45302, 45305, 46104, 46301.

Source: Docket No. 7190, 31 FR 4495, Mar. 17, 1966, unless otherwise noted.

Editorial Note: Nomenclature changes to part 47 appear at 75 FR 41979, July 20, 2010.

Subpart A — General

47.1 Applicability

This part prescribes the requirements for registering aircraft under 49 U.S.C. 44101–44104. Subpart B applies to each applicant for, and holder of, a Certificate of Aircraft Registration, AC Form 8050–3. Subpart C applies to each applicant for, and holder of, a Dealer's Aircraft Registration Certificate, AC Form 8050–6.

[Amdt. 47–29, 75 FR 41979, July 20, 2010]

47.2 Definitions

The following are definitions of terms used in this part:

Citizen of the United States or U.S. citizen means one of the following:

(1) An individual who is a citizen of the United States or one of its possessions.

(2) A partnership each of whose partners is an individual who is a citizen of the United States.

(3) A corporation or association organized under the laws of the United States or a State, the District of Columbia, or a territory or possession of the United States, of which the president and at least two-thirds of the board of directors and other managing officers are citizens of the United States, which is under the actual control of citizens of the United States, and in which at least 75 percent of the voting interest is owned or controlled by persons that are citizens of the United States.

Registry means the FAA, Civil Aviation Registry, Aircraft Registration Branch.

Resident alien means an individual citizen of a foreign country lawfully admitted for permanent residence in the United States as an immigrant in conformity with the regulations of the Department of Homeland Security (8 CFR Chapter 1).

[Doc. No. FAA-2015-7396; Amdt. 47-30, 80 FR 78645, Dec. 16, 2015]

47.3 Registration required

(a) An aircraft may be registered under 49 U.S.C. 44103 only when the aircraft is not registered under the laws of a foreign country and is—

  (1) Owned by a citizen of the United States;

  (2) Owned by an individual citizen of a foreign country lawfully admitted for permanent residence in the United States;

  (3) Owned by a corporation not a citizen of the United States when the corporation is organized and doing business under the laws of the United States or a State within the United States, and the aircraft is based and primarily used in the United States; or

  (4) An aircraft of—

    (i) The United States Government; or

    (ii) A State, the District of Columbia, a territory or possession of the United States, or a political subdivision of a State, territory, or possession.

(b) No person may operate an aircraft that is eligible for registration under 49 U.S.C. 44101–44104, unless the aircraft—

  (1) Has been registered by its owner;

  (2) Is carrying aboard the temporary authorization required by 47.31(c); or

  (3) Is an aircraft of the Armed Forces of the United States.

(c) Governmental units are those named in paragraph (a) of this section and Puerto Rico.

[Doc. No. 7190, 31 FR 4495, Mar. 17, 1966, as amended by Amdt. 47–20, 44 FR 61939, Oct. 29, 1979; Amdt. 47–27, 70 FR 244, Jan. 3, 2005; Amdt. 47–29, 75 FR 41979, July 20, 2010]

47.5 Applicants

(a) A person who wishes to register an aircraft in the United States must submit an Aircraft Registration Application, AC Form 8050–1 under this part.

(b) An aircraft may be registered only by and in the legal name of its owner.

(c) 49 U.S.C. 44103(c), provides that registration is not evidence of ownership of aircraft in any proceeding in which ownership by a particular person is in issue. The FAA does not issue any certificate of ownership or endorse any information with respect to ownership on a Certificate of Aircraft Registration, AC Form 8050–3. The FAA issues a Certificate of Aircraft Registration, AC Form 8050–3 to the person who appears to be the owner on the basis of the evidence of ownership submitted pursuant to 47.11 with the Aircraft Registration Application, or recorded at the Registry.

(d) In this part, "owner" includes a buyer in possession, a bailee, or a lessee of an aircraft under a contract of conditional sale, and the assignee of that person.

[Amdt. 47–20, 44 FR 61939, Oct. 29, 1979, as amended by Amdt. 47–27, 70 FR 244, Jan. 3, 2005; Amdt. 47–29, 75 FR 41979, July 20, 2010]

47.7 United States citizens and resident aliens

(a) U.S. citizens. An applicant for aircraft registration under this part who is a U.S. citizen must certify to this in the Aircraft Registration Application, AC Form 8050–1.

(b) Resident aliens. An applicant for aircraft registration under 49 U.S.C. 44102 who is a resident alien must furnish a representation of permanent residence and the applicant's alien registration number issued by the Department of Homeland Security.

(c) Trustees. An applicant for aircraft registration under 49 U.S.C. 44102 that holds legal title to an aircraft in trust must comply with the following requirements:

(1) Each trustee must be either a U.S. citizen or a resident alien.

(2) The applicant must submit with the Aircraft Registration Application—

(i) A copy of each document legally affecting a relationship under the trust;

(ii) If each beneficiary under the trust, including each person whose security interest in the aircraft is incorporated in the trust, is either a U.S. citizen or a resident alien, an affidavit by the applicant to that effect; and

(iii) If any beneficiary under the trust, including any person whose security interest in the aircraft is incorporated in the trust, is not a U.S. citizen or resident alien, an affidavit from each trustee stating that the trustee is not aware of any reason, situation, or relationship (involving beneficiaries or other persons who are not U.S. citizens or resident aliens) as a result of which those persons together would have more than 25 percent of the aggregate power to influence or limit the exercise of the trustee's authority.

(3) If persons who are neither U.S. citizens nor resident aliens have the power to direct or remove a trustee, either directly or indirectly through the control of another person, the trust instrument must provide that those persons together may not have more than 25 percent of the aggregate power to direct or remove a trustee. Nothing in this paragraph prevents those persons from having more than 25 percent of the beneficial interest in the trust.

(d) Partnerships. A partnership may apply for a Certificate of Aircraft Registration, AC Form 8050–3, under 49 U.S.C. 44102 only if each partner, whether a general or limited partner, is an individual who is a citizen of the United States. Nothing in this section makes ineligible for registration an aircraft which is not owned as a partnership asset but is co-owned by—

(1) Resident aliens; or

(2) One or more resident aliens and one or more U.S. citizens.

[Amdt. 47–20, 44 FR 61939, Oct. 29, 1979, as amended by Amdt. 47–27, 70 FR 244, Jan. 3, 2005; Amdt. 47–29, 75 FR 41980, July 20, 2010]

47.8 Voting trusts

(a) If a voting trust is used to qualify a domestic corporation as a U.S. citizen, the corporate applicant must submit to the Registry—

(1) A true copy of the fully executed voting trust agreement, which must identify each voting interest of the applicant, and which must be binding upon each voting trustee, the applicant corporation, all foreign stockholders, and each other party to the transaction; and

(2) An affidavit executed by each person designated as voting trustee in the voting trust agreement, in which each affiant represents—

(i) That each voting trustee is a citizen of the United States within the meaning of 49 U.S.C. 40102(a)(15).

(ii) That each voting trustee is not a past, present, or prospective director, officer, employee, attorney, or agent of any other party to the trust agreement;

(iii) That each voting trustee is not a present or prospective beneficiary, creditor, debtor, supplier or contractor of any other party to the trust agreement;

(iv) That each voting trustee is not aware of any reason, situation, or relationship under which any other party to the agreement might influence the exercise of the voting trustee's totally independent judgment under the voting trust agreement.

(b) Each voting trust agreement submitted under paragraph (a)(1) of this section must provide for the succession of a voting trustee in the event of death, disability, resignation, termination of citizenship, or any other event leading to the replacement of any voting trustee. Upon succession, the replacement voting trustee shall immediately submit to the Registry the affidavit required by paragraph (a)(2) of this section.

(c) If the voting trust terminates or is modified, and the result is less than 75 percent control of the voting interest in the corporation by citizens of the United States, a loss of citizenship of the holder of the Certificate of Aircraft Registration, AC Form 8050–3 occurs, and 47.41(a)(3) of this part applies.

(d) A voting trust agreement may not empower a trustee to act through a proxy.

[Amdt. 47–20, 44 FR 61939, Oct. 29, 1979, as amended by Amdt. 47–27, 70 FR 245, Jan. 3, 2005; Amdt. 47–29, 75 FR 41980, July 20, 2010]

47.9 Corporations not U.S. citizens

(a) Each corporation applying for registration of an aircraft under 49 U.S.C. 44102 must submit to the Registry with the Aircraft Registration Application, AC Form 8050–1—

(1) A certified copy of its certificate of incorporation;

(2) A certification that it is lawfully qualified to do business in one or more States;

(3) A certification that the aircraft will be based and primarily used in the United States; and

(4) The location where the records required by paragraph (e) of this section will be maintained.

(b) For the purposes of registration, an aircraft is based and primarily used in the United States if the flight hours accumulated within the United States amount to at least 60 percent of the total flight hours of the aircraft during—

(1) For aircraft registered on or before January 1, 1980, the 6-calendar month period beginning on January 1, 1980, and each 6-calendar month period thereafter; and

(2) For aircraft registered after January 1, 1980, the period consisting in the remainder of the registration month and the succeeding 6 calendar months and each 6-calendar month period thereafter.

(c) For the purpose of this section, only those flight hours accumulated during non-stop (except for stops in emergencies or for purposes of refueling) flight between two points in the United States, even if the aircraft is outside of the United States during part of the flight, are considered flight hours accumulated within the United States.

(d) In determining compliance with this section, any periods during which the aircraft is not validly registered in the United States are disregarded.

(e) The corporation that registers an aircraft pursuant to 49 U.S.C. 44102 shall maintain, and make available for inspection by the FAA upon request, records containing the total flight hours in the United States of the aircraft for three calendar years after the year in which the flight hours were accumulated.

(f) The corporation that registers an aircraft pursuant to 49 U.S.C. 44102 shall send to the Registry, at the end of each period of time described in paragraphs (b)(1) and (2) of this section, either—

(1) A signed report containing—

(i) The total time in service of the airframe as provided in 91.417(a)(2)(i), accumulated during that period; and

(ii) The total flight hours in the United States of the aircraft accumulated during that period; or

(2) A signed statement that the total flight hours of the aircraft, while registered in the United States during that period, have been exclusively within the United States.

[Amdt. 47–20, 44 FR 61940, Oct. 29, 1979, as amended by Amdt. 47–24, 54 FR 34330, Aug. 18, 1989; Amdt. 47–27, 70 FR 245, Jan. 3, 2005]

47.11 Evidence of ownership

Except as provided in 47.33 and 47.35, each person that submits an Aircraft Registration Application, AC Form 8050–1 under this part must also submit the required evidence of ownership, recordable under 49.13 and 49.17 of this chapter, as follows:

(a) The buyer in possession, the bailee, or the lessee of an aircraft under a contract of conditional sale must submit the contract. The assignee under a contract of conditional sale must submit both the contract (unless it is already recorded at the Registry), and his assignment from the original buyer, bailee, lessee, or prior assignee.

(b) The repossessor of an aircraft must submit—

(1) A Certificate of Repossession of Encumbered Aircraft, FAA Form 8050–4, or its equivalent, signed by the applicant and stating that the aircraft was repossessed or otherwise seized under the security agreement involved and applicable local law;

(2) The security agreement (unless it is already recorded at the Registry), or a copy thereof certified as true under 49.21 of this chapter; and

(3) When repossession was through foreclosure proceedings resulting in sale, a bill of sale signed by the sheriff, auctioneer, or other authorized person who conducted the sale, and stating that the sale was made under applicable local law.

(c) The buyer of an aircraft at a judicial sale, or at a sale to satisfy a lien or charge, must submit a bill of sale signed by the sheriff, auctioneer, or other authorized person who conducted the sale, and stating that the sale was made under applicable local law.

(d) The owner of an aircraft, the title to which has been in controversy and has been determined by a court, must submit a certified copy of the decision of the court.

(e) The executor or administrator of the estate of the deceased former owner of an aircraft must submit a certified copy of the letters testimentary or letters of administration appointing him executor or administrator. The Certificate of Aircraft Registration, AC Form 8050–3 is issued to the applicant as executor or administrator.

(f) The buyer of an aircraft from the estate of a deceased former owner must submit both a bill of sale, signed for the estate by the executor or administrator, and a certified copy of the letters testimentary or letters of administration. When no executor or administrator has been or is to be appointed, the applicant must submit both a bill of sale, signed by the heir-at-law of the deceased former owner, and an affidavit of the heir-at-law stating that no application for appointment of an executor or administrator has been made, that so far as he can determine none will be made, and that he is the person entitled to, or having the right to dispose of, the aircraft under applicable local law.

(g) The guardian of another person's property that includes an aircraft must submit a certified copy of the order of the court appointing him guardian. The Certificate of Aircraft Registration is issued to the applicant as guardian.

(h) The trustee of property that includes an aircraft, as described in 47.7(c), must submit either a certified copy of the order of the court appointing the trustee, or a complete and true copy of the instrument creating the trust. If there is more than one trustee, each trustee must sign the Aircraft Registration Application. The Certificate of Aircraft Registration is issued to a single applicant as trustee, or to several trustees jointly as co-trustees.

[Doc. No. 7190, 31 FR 4495, Mar. 17, 1966, as amended by Amdt. 47–20, 44 FR 61940, Oct. 29, 1979; Amdt. 47–23, 53 FR 1915, Jan. 25, 1988; Amdt. 47–29, 75 FR 41980, July 20, 2010]

47.13 Signatures and instruments made by representatives

(a) Each person signing an Aircraft Registration Application, AC Form 8050–1, or a document submitted as supporting evidence under this part, must sign in ink or by other means acceptable to the FAA. If signed in ink, the Aircraft Registration Application must also have the typed or legibly printed name of each signer in the signature block.

(b) When one or more persons doing business under a trade name submits an Aircraft Registration Application, a document submitted as supporting evidence under this part, or a request for cancellation of a Certificate of Aircraft Registration, AC Form 8050–3, the application, document, or request must be signed by, or on behalf of, each person who shares title to the aircraft.

(c) When an agent submits an Aircraft Registration Application, a document submitted as supporting evidence under this part, or a request for cancellation of a Certificate of Aircraft Registration, on behalf of the owner, that agent must—

(1) State the name of the owner on the application, document, or request;

(2) Sign as agent or attorney-in-fact on the application, document, or request; and

(3) Submit a signed power of attorney, or a true copy thereof certified under 49.21 of this chapter, with the application, document, or request.

(d) When a corporation submits an Aircraft Registration Application, a document submitted as supporting evidence under this part, or a request for cancellation of a Certificate of Aircraft Registration, it must—

(1) Have an authorized person sign, by means acceptable to the FAA, the application, document, or request;

(2) Show the title of the signer's office on the application, document, or request; and

(3) Submit a copy of the authorization from the board of directors to sign for the corporation, certified as true under 49.21 of this chapter by a corporate officer or other person in a managerial position therein, with the application, document, or request, unless—

(i) The signer of the application, document, or request is a corporate officer or other person in a managerial position in the corporation and the title of his office is stated in connection with his signature; or

(ii) A valid authorization to sign is on file at the Registry.

(4) The provisions of paragraph (d)(3) of this section do not apply to an irrevocable deregistration and export request authorization when an irrevocable deregistration and export request authorization under the Cape Town Treaty is signed by a corporate officer and is filed with the Registry.

(e) When a partnership submits an Aircraft Registration Application, a document submitted as supporting evidence under this part, or a request for cancellation of a Certificate of Aircraft Registration, it must—

(1) State the full name of the partnership on the application, document, or request;

(2) State the name of each general partner on the application, document, or request; and

(3) Have a general partner sign the application, document, or request.

(f) When co-owners, who are not engaged in business as partners, submit an Aircraft Registration Application, a document submitted as supporting evidence under this part, or a request for cancellation of a Certificate of Aircraft Registration, each person who shares title to the aircraft under the arrangement must sign the application, document, or request.

(g) A power of attorney or other evidence of a person's authority to sign for another, submitted under this part, is valid for the purposes of this section, unless sooner revoked, until—

FAR 47

(1) Its expiration date stated therein; or

(2) If an expiration date is not stated therein, for not more than 3 years after the date—

    (i) It is signed; or

    (ii) The grantor (a corporate officer or other person in a managerial position therein, where the grantor is a corporation) certifies in writing that the authority to sign shown by the power of attorney or other evidence is still in effect.

[Doc. No. 7190, 31 FR 4495, Mar. 17, 1966, as amended by Amdt. 47–2, 31 FR 15349, Dec. 8, 1966; Amdt. 47–3, 32 FR 6554, Apr. 28, 1967; Amdt. 47–12, 36 FR 8661, May 11, 1971; Amdt. 47–27, 70 FR 245, Jan. 3, 2005; Amdt. 47–29, 75 FR 41979, July 20, 2010]

47.14 Serial numbers for unmanned aircraft

(a) The unmanned aircraft serial number provided as part of any application for aircraft registration of any standard remote identification unmanned aircraft must be the serial number issued by the manufacturer of the unmanned aircraft in accordance with the design and production requirements of part 89 of this chapter. The serial number provided in this application must not be listed on more than one Certificate of Aircraft Registration at the same time.

(b) The unmanned aircraft serial number provided as part of any application for registration of any unmanned aircraft with a remote identification broadcast module must be the serial number issued by the manufacturer of the remote identification broadcast module in accordance with the design and production requirements of part 89 of this chapter. The serial number provided in this application must not be listed on more than one Certificate of Aircraft Registration at the same time.

[Docket No. FAA-2019-1100, Amdt. 47-31, 86 FR 4503, Jan. 15, 2021]

47.15 Registration number

(a) *Number required.* An applicant for aircraft registration must place a U.S. registration number (registration mark) on the Aircraft Registration Application, AC Form 8050–1, and on any evidence submitted with the application. There is no charge for the assignment of numbers provided in this paragraph. This paragraph does not apply to an aircraft manufacturer who applies for a group of U.S. registration numbers under paragraph (c) of this section; a person who applies for a special registration number under paragraphs (d) through (f) of this section; or a holder of a Dealer's Aircraft Registration Certificate, AC Form 8050–6, who applies for a temporary registration number under 47.16.

(1) *Aircraft not previously registered anywhere.* The applicant must obtain the U.S. registration number from the Registry by request in writing describing the aircraft by make, type, model, and serial number (or, if it is amateur-built, as provided in 47.33(b)) and stating that the aircraft has not previously been registered anywhere. If the aircraft was brought into the United States from a foreign country, the applicant must submit evidence that the aircraft has never been registered in a foreign country.

(2) *Aircraft last previously registered in the United States.* Unless the applicant applies for a different number under paragraphs (d) through (f) of this section, the applicant must place the U.S. registration number that is already assigned to the aircraft on the Aircraft Registration Application, and the supporting evidence. If there is no number assigned, the applicant must obtain a U.S. registration number from the Registry by making a written request that describes the aircraft by make, model, and serial number.

(3) *Aircraft last previously registered in a foreign country.* Whether or not the foreign registration has ended, the applicant must obtain a U.S. registration number from the Registry for an aircraft last previously registered in a foreign country, by request in writing describing the aircraft by make, model, and serial number, accompanied by—

    (i) Evidence of termination of foreign registration in accordance with 47.37(b) or the applicant's affidavit showing that foreign registration has ended; or

    (ii) If foreign registration has not ended, the applicant's affidavit stating that the number will not be placed on the aircraft until foreign registration has ended.

(4) *Duration of a U.S. registration number assignment.* Authority to use the registration number obtained under paragraph (a) (1), (2), or (3) of this section expires 90 days after the date it is issued unless the applicant submits an Aircraft Registration Application and complies with 47.33 or 47.37, as applicable, within that period of time. However, the applicant may obtain an extension of this 90-day period from the Registry if the applicant shows that the delay in complying with that section is due to circumstances beyond the applicant's control.

(b) A U.S. registration number may not exceed five symbols in addition to the prefix letter "N". These symbols may be all numbers (N10000), one to four numbers and one suffix letter (N 1000A), or one to three numbers and two suffix letters (N 100AB). The letters "I" and "O" may not be used. The first zero in a number must always be preceded by at least one of the numbers 1 through 9.

(c) An aircraft manufacturer may apply to the Registry for enough U.S. registration numbers to supply estimated production for the next 18 months. There is no charge for this allocation of numbers.

(d) Any available, unassigned U.S. registration number may be assigned as a special registration number. An applicant who wants a special registration number or wants to change the registration number of his aircraft may apply for it to the Registry. The fee required by 47.17 must accompany the application.

(e) [Reserved]

(f) The Registry authorizes a special registration number change on the Assignment of Special Registration Numbers, AC Form 8050–64. The authorization expires one year from the date the Registry issues an Assignment of Special Registration Numbers unless the special registration number is permanently placed on the aircraft. Within five days after the special registration number is placed on the aircraft, the owner must complete and sign the Assignment of Special Registration Numbers, state the date the number was placed on the aircraft, and return the original form to the Registry. The duplicate of the Assignment of Special Registration Numbers and the present Certificate of Aircraft Registration, AC Form 8050–3, must be carried in the aircraft as temporary authority to operate it. This temporary authority is valid until the date the owner receives the revised Certificate of Aircraft Registration showing the new registration number, but in no case is it valid for more than 120 days from the date the number is placed on the aircraft.

(g) [Reserved]

(h) A special registration number may be reserved for no more than 1 year. If a person wishes to renew his reservation from year to year, he must apply to the Registry for renewal and submit the fee required by 47.17 for a special registration number.

(i) When aircraft registration has ended, as described in 47.41(a), the assignment of a registration number to an aircraft is no longer authorized for use except as provided in 47.31(c) and will be cancelled:

(1) Following the date established in 47.40(a)(1) for any aircraft that has not been re-registered under 47.40(a);

(2) Following the expiration date shown on the Certificate of Aircraft Registration for any aircraft whose registration has not been renewed under 47.40(c);

(3) Following the expiration date shown on the Dealer's Aircraft Registration Certificate, AC Form 8050–6, for any aircraft registered under Subpart C of this part, when the certificate has not been renewed, and the owner has not applied for registration in accordance with 47.31; or

(4) When ownership has transferred—

    (i) Six months after first receipt of notice of aircraft sale or evidence of ownership from the last registered owner or successive owners, and an Aircraft Registration Application has not been received.

    (ii) Six months after evidence of ownership authorized under 47.67 has been submitted, and the applicant has not met the requirements of this part.

    (iii) Twelve months after a new owner has submitted evidence of ownership and an Aircraft Registration Application under 47.31, and the applicant or a successive applicant has not met the requirements of this part.

(j) At the time an assignment of registration number is cancelled, the number may be reserved for one year in the name of the last owner of record if a request has been submitted with the fee required by 47.17. If the request for reservation and fee are not submitted prior to cancellation, the registration number is unavailable for assignment for a period of five years.

[Doc. No. 7190, 31 FR 4495, Mar. 17, 1966, as amended by Amdt. 47–1, 31 FR 13314, Oct. 14, 1966; Amdt. 47–5, 32 FR 13505, Sept. 27, 1967; Amdt. 47–7, 34 FR 2480, Feb. 21, 1969; Amdt. 47–13, 36 FR 16187, Aug. 20, 1971; Amdt. 47–15, 37 FR 21528, Oct. 12, 1972; Amdt. 47–16, 37 FR 25487, Dec. 1, 1972; Amdt. 47–17, 39 FR 1353, Jan. 8, 1974; Amdt. 47–22, 47 FR 12153, Mar. 22, 1982; Amdt. 47–29, 75 FR 41980, July 20, 2010]

47.16 Temporary registration numbers

(a) Temporary registration numbers are issued by the FAA to manufacturers, distributors, and dealers who are holders of Dealer's Aircraft Registration Certificates, AC Form 8050–6, for temporary display on aircraft during flight allowed under Subpart C of this part.

(b) The holder of a Dealer's Aircraft Registration Certificate may apply to the Registry for as many temporary registration numbers as are necessary for his business. The application must be in writing and include—

    (1) Sufficient information to justify the need for the temporary registration numbers requested; and

    (2) The number of each Dealer's Aircraft Registration Certificate held by the applicant.

There is no charge for these numbers.

(c) The use of temporary registration numbers is subject to the following conditions:

    (1) The numbers may be used and reused—

        (i) Only in connection with the holder's Dealer's Aircraft Registration Certificate;

        (ii) Within the limitations of 47.69 where applicable, including the requirements of 47.67; and

        (iii) On aircraft not registered under Subpart B of this part or in a foreign country, and not displaying any other identification markings.

    (2) A temporary registration number may not be used on more than one aircraft in flight at the same time.

    (3) Temporary registration numbers may not be used to fly aircraft into the United States for the purpose of importation.

(d) The assignment of any temporary registration number to any person lapses upon the expiration of all of his Dealer's Aircraft Registration Certificates. When a temporary registration number is used on a flight outside the United States for delivery purposes, the holder shall record the assignment of that number to the aircraft and shall keep that record for at least 1 year after the removal of the number from that aircraft. Whenever the owner of an aircraft bearing a temporary registration number applies for an airworthiness certificate under Part 21 of this chapter he shall furnish that number in the application. The temporary registration number must be removed from the aircraft not later than the date on which either title or possession passes to another person.

[Amdt. 47–4, 32 FR 12556, Aug. 30, 1967, as amended by Amdt. 47–29, 75 FR 41981, July 20, 2010]

47.17 Fees

(a) The fees for applications under this part are as follows:

(1)	Certificate of Aircraft Registration (each aircraft)	$5.00
(2)	Dealer's Aircraft Registration Certificate	10.00
(3)	Additional Dealer's aircraft Registration Certificate (issued to same dealer)	2.00
(4)	Special registration number (each number)	10.00
(5)	To change, reassign, or reserve a registration number	10.00
(6)	Replacement Certificate of Aircraft Registration	2.00
(7)	Reregistation or Renewal Certificate of Aircraft Registration	5.00

(b) Each application must be accompanied by the proper fee, that may be paid by check or money order to the Federal Aviation Administration.

[Doc. No. 7190, 31 FR 4495, Mar. 17, 1966; 31 FR 5483, Apr. 7, 1966, as amended by Doc. No. 8084, 32 FR 5769, Apr. 11, 1967; Amdt. 47–29, 75 FR 41981, July 20, 2010]

47.19 Registry

Each application, request, notification, or other communication sent to the FAA under this Part must be mailed to the Registry, Department of Transportation, Post Office Box 25504, Oklahoma City, Oklahoma 73125–0504, or delivered to the Registry at 6425 S. Denning Ave., Oklahoma City, Oklahoma 73169.

[Amdt. 47–27, 70 FR 245, Jan. 3, 2005]

Subpart B — Certificates of Aircraft Registration

47.31 Application

(a) Each applicant for a Certificate of Aircraft Registration, AC Form 8050–3 must submit the following to the Registry—

    (1) An Aircraft Registration Application, AC Form 8050–1, signed by the applicant in the manner prescribed by 47.13;

    (2) The original Aircraft Bill of Sale, AC Form 8050–2, or other evidence of ownership authorized by 47.33, 47.35, or 47.37 (unless already recorded at the Registry); and

    (3) The fee required by 47.17.

(b) The FAA rejects an application when

    (1) Any form is not completed;

    (2) The name and signature of the applicant are not the same throughout; or

    (3) The applicant does not provide a legibly printed or typed name with the signature in the signature block.

(c) After compliance with paragraph (a) of this section, the applicant for registration of an aircraft last previously registered in the United States must carry the second copy of the Aircraft Registration Application in the aircraft as temporary authority to operate without registration.

    (1) This temporary authority is valid for operation within the United States until the date the applicant receives the Certificate of Aircraft Registration or until the date the FAA denies the application, but in no case for more than 90 days after the date the applicant signs the application. If by 90 days after the date the applicant signs the Aircraft Registration Application, the FAA has neither issued the Certificate of Aircraft Registration nor denied the application, the Registry will issue a letter of extension that serves as authority to continue to operate the aircraft without registration while it is carried in the aircraft.

    (2) This temporary authority is not available in connection with any Aircraft Registration Application received when 12 months have passed since the receipt of the first application following transfer of ownership by the last registered owner.

    (3) If there is no registration number assigned at the time application for registration is made, the second copy of the Air-

craft Registration Application may not be used as temporary authority to operate the aircraft.

[Doc. No. 7190, 31 FR 4495, Mar. 17, 1966; 31 FR 5483, Apr. 7, 1966, as amended by Amdt. 47–6, 33 FR 11, Jan. 3, 1968; Amdt. 47–15, 37 FR 21528, Oct. 12, 1972; Amdt. 47–16, 37 FR 25487, Dec. 1, 1972; Amdt. 47–28, 73 FR 10667, Feb. 28, 2008; Amdt. 47–29, 75 FR 41981, July 20, 2010]

47.33 Aircraft not previously registered anywhere

(a) A person who is the owner of an aircraft that has not been registered under 49 U.S.C. 44101–44104, under other law of the United States, or under foreign law, may register it under this part if he—

    (1) Complies with 47.3, 47.7, 47.8, 47.9, 47.11, 47.13, 47.15, and 47.17, as applicable; and

    (2) Submits with his Aircraft Registration Application, AC Form 8050–1, an Aircraft Bill of Sale, AC Form 8050–2, signed by the seller, an equivalent bill of sale, or other evidence of ownership authorized by 47.11.

(b) If, for good reason, the applicant cannot produce the evidence of ownership required by paragraph (a) of this section, he must submit other evidence that is satisfactory to the FAA. This other evidence may be an affidavit stating why he cannot produce the required evidence, accompanied by whatever further evidence is available to prove the transaction.

(c) The owner of an amateur-built aircraft who applies for registration under paragraphs (a) and (b) of this section must describe the aircraft by class (airplane, rotorcraft, glider, or balloon), serial number, number of seats, type of engine installed, (reciprocating, turbopropeller, turbojet, or other), number of engines installed, and make, model, and serial number of each engine installed; and must state whether the aircraft is built for land or water operation. Also, he must submit as evidence of ownership an affidavit giving the U.S. registration number, and stating that the aircraft was built from parts and that he is the owner. If he built the aircraft from a kit, the applicant must also submit a bill of sale from the manufacturer of the kit.

(d) The owner, other than the holder of the type certificate, of an aircraft that he assembles from parts to conform to the approved type design, must describe the aircraft and engine in the manner required by paragraph (c) of this section, and also submit evidence of ownership satisfactory to the FAA, such as bills of sale, for all major components of the aircraft.

[Doc. No. 7190, 31 FR 4495, Mar. 17, 1966; 31 FR 5483, Apr. 7, 1966, as amended by Amdt. 47–16, 37 FR 25487, Dec. 1, 1972; Amdt. 47–20, 44 FR 61940, Oct. 29, 1979; Amdt. 47–27, 70 FR 245, Jan. 3, 2005; Amdt. 47–29, 75 FR 41979, July 20, 2010]

47.35 Aircraft last previously registered in the United States

(a) A person who is the owner of an aircraft last previously registered under 49 U.S.C. Sections 44101–44104, or under other law of the United States, may register it under this part if he complies with 47.3, 47.7, 47.8, 47.9, 47.11, 47.13, 47.15, and 47.17, as applicable and submits with his Aircraft Registration Application, AC Form 8050–1 an Aircraft Bill of Sale, AC Form 8050–2, signed by the seller or an equivalent conveyance, or other evidence of ownership authorized by 47.11.

    (1) If the applicant bought the aircraft from the last registered owner, the conveyance must be from that owner to the applicant.

    (2) If the applicant did not buy the aircraft from the last registered owner, he must submit conveyances or other instruments showing consecutive transactions from the last registered owner through each intervening owner to the applicant.

(b) If, for good reason, the applicant cannot produce the evidence of ownership required by paragraph (a) of this section, he must submit other evidence that is satisfactory to the FAA. This other evidence may be an affidavit stating why he cannot produce the

required evidence, accompanied by whatever further evidence is available to prove the transaction.

[Doc. No. 7190, 31 FR 4495, Mar. 17, 1966, as amended by Amdt. 47–16, 37 FR 25487, Dec. 1, 1972; Amdt. 47–20, 44 FR 61940, Oct. 29, 1979; Amdt. 47–27, 70 FR 245, Jan. 3, 2005; 73 FR 55722, Sept. 26, 2008; Amdt. 47–29, 75 FR 41979, July 20, 2010]

47.37 Aircraft last previously registered in a foreign country

(a) A person who is the owner of an aircraft last previously registered under the law of a foreign country may register it under this part if the owner—

    (1) Complies with 47.3, 47.7, 47.8, 47.9, 47.11, 47.13, 47.15, and 47.17, as applicable;

    (2) Submits with his Aircraft Registration Application, AC Form 8050–1 a bill of sale from the foreign seller or other evidence satisfactory to the FAA that he owns the aircraft; and

    (3) Submits evidence satisfactory to the FAA that—

        (i) If the country in which the aircraft was registered has not ratified the Convention on the International Recognition of Rights in Aircraft (4 U.S.T. 1830), (the Geneva Convention), or the Convention on International Interests in Mobile Equipment, as modified by the Protocol to the Convention on International Interests in Mobile Equipment on Matters Specific to Aircraft Equipment (the Cape Town Treaty), the foreign registration has ended or is invalid; or

        (ii) If that country has ratified the Geneva Convention, but has not ratified the Cape Town Treaty, the foreign registration has ended or is invalid, and each holder of a recorded right against the aircraft has been satisfied or has consented to the transfer, or ownership in the country of export has been ended by a sale in execution under the terms of the Geneva Convention; or

        (iii) If that country has ratified the Cape Town Treaty and the aircraft is subject to the Treaty, that the foreign registration has ended or is invalid, and that all interests ranking in priority have been discharged or that the holders of such interests have consented to the deregistration and export of the aircraft.

        (iv) Nothing under (a)(3)(iii) affects rights established prior to the Treaty entering into force with respect to the country in which the aircraft was registered.

(b) For the purposes of paragraph (a)(3) of this section, satisfactory evidence of termination of the foreign registration may be—

    (1) A statement, by the official having jurisdiction over the national aircraft registry of the foreign country, that the registration has ended or is invalid, and showing the official's name and title and describing the aircraft by make, model, and serial number; or

    (2) A final judgment or decree of a court of competent jurisdiction of the foreign country, determining that, under the laws of that country, the registration has become invalid.

[Doc. No. 7190, 31 FR 4495, Mar. 17, 1966, as amended by Amdt. 47–20, 44 FR 61940, Oct. 29, 1979; Amdt. 47–26, 68 FR 10317, Mar. 4, 2003; Amdt. 47–27, 70 FR 245, Jan. 3, 2005]

47.39 Effective date of registration

An aircraft is registered on the date the Registry determines that the submissions meet the requirements of this part. The effective date of registration is shown by a date stamp on the Aircraft Registration Application, AC Form 8050–1, and as the date of issue on the Certificate of Aircraft Registration, AC Form 8050–3.

[Amdt. 47–29, 75 FR 41981, July 20, 2010]

47.40 Registration expiration and renewal

(a) Re-registration. Each aircraft registered under this part before October 1, 2010, must be re-registered in accordance with this paragraph (a).

  (1) A Certificate of Aircraft Registration issued before October 1, 2010, expires on the expiration date identified in the following schedule that corresponds with the month in which the certificate was issued.

IF THE CERTIFICATE WAS ISSUED IN:	THE CERTIFICATE EXPIRES ON:	THE OWNER MUST APPLY FOR REREGISTRATION BETWEEN THESE DATES— *to allow delivery of the new certificate before expiration*
March of any year	March 31, 2011	November 1, 2010 and January 31, 2011
April of any year	June 30, 2011	February 1, 2011 and April 30, 2011
May of any year	September 30, 2011	May 1, and July 31, 2011
June of any year	December 31, 2011	August 1, 2011 and October 31, 2011
July of any year	March 31, 2012	November 1, 2011 and January 31, 2012
August of any year	June 30, 2012	February 1, 2012 and April 30, 2012
September of any year	September 30, 2012	May 1, 2012 and July 31, 2012
October of any year	December 31, 2012	August 1, 2012 and October 31, 2012
November of any year	March 31, 2013	November 1, 2012 and January 31, 2013
December of any year	June 30, 2013	February 1, 2013 and April 30, 2013
January of any year	September 30, 2013	May 1, 2013 and July 31, 2013
February of any year	December 31, 2013	August 1, 2013 and October 31, 2013

  (2) Each holder of a Certificate of Aircraft Registration, AC Form 8050–3, issued before October 1, 2010, must submit an Application for Aircraft Re-registration, AC Form 8050–1A, and the fee required by 47.17, between October 1, 2010, and December 31, 2013, according to the schedule in paragraph (a)(1) of this section.

  (3) A Certificate of Aircraft Registration issued under this paragraph expires three years after the last day of the month in which it is issued.

(b) Initial Registration. A Certificate of Aircraft Registration issued in accordance with 47.31 expires three years after the last day of the month in which it is issued.

(c) Renewal. Each holder of a Certificate of Aircraft Registration, AC Form 8050–3, containing an expiration date may apply for renewal by submitting an Application for Aircraft Registration Renewal, AC Form 8050–1B, and the fee required by 47.17 during the six months preceding the expiration date. A certificate issued under this paragraph expires three years from the expiration date of the previous certificate.

[Amdt. 47–29, 75 FR 41981, July 20, 2010]

47.41 Duration and return of Certificate

(a) Each Certificate of Aircraft Registration, AC Form 8050–3, issued by the FAA under this subpart is effective, unless registration has ended by reason of having been revoked, canceled, expired, or the ownership is transferred, until the date upon which one of the following events occurs:

  (1) Subject to the Convention on the International Recognition of Rights in Aircraft when applicable, the aircraft is registered under the laws of a foreign country.

  (2) The aircraft is totally destroyed or scrapped.

  (3) The holder of the certificate loses his U.S. citizenship.

  (4) 30 days have elapsed since the death of the holder of the certificate.

  (5) The owner, if an individual who is not a citizen of the United States, loses status as a resident alien, unless that person becomes a citizen of the United States at the same time.

  (6) If the owner is a corporation other than a corporation which is a citizen of the United States—

    (i) The corporation ceases to be lawfully organized and doing business under the laws of the United States or any State thereof; or

    (ii) A period described in 47.9(b) ends and the aircraft was not based and primarily used in the United States during that period.

  (7) If the trustee in whose name the aircraft is registered—

    (i) Loses U.S. citizenship;

    (ii) Loses status as a resident alien and does not become a citizen of the United States at the same time; or

    (iii) In any manner ceases to act as trustee and is not immediately replaced by another who meets the requirements of 47.7(c).

(b) The Certificate of Aircraft Registration, with the reverse side completed, must be returned to the Registry—

  (1) Within 21 days in the case of registration under the laws of a foreign country, by the person who was the owner of the aircraft before foreign registration;

  (2) Within 60 days after the death of the holder of the certificate, by the administrator or executor of his estate, or by his heir-at-law if no administrator or executor has been or is to be appointed; or

  (3) Within 21 days of the termination of the registration, by the holder of the Certificate of Aircraft Registration in all other cases mentioned in paragraph (a) of this section, except in the case of expired certificates, the holder must destroy the expired certificate.

  (4) If the certificate is not available for return, as directed in paragraph (b) of this section, a statement describing the aircraft and stating the reason the certificate is not available must be submitted to the Registry within the time required by paragraph (b) of this section.

[Doc. No. 7190, 31 FR 4495, Mar. 17, 1966; 31 FR 5483, Apr. 7, 1966, as amended by Amdt. 47–20, 44 FR 61940, Oct. 29, 1979; Amdt. 47–28, 73 FR 10667, Feb. 28, 2008; Amdt. 47–29, 75 FR 41982, July 20, 2010]

47.43 Invalid registration

(a) The registration of an aircraft is invalid if, at the time it is made—

  (1) The aircraft is registered in a foreign country;

  (2) The applicant is not the owner;

  (3) The applicant is not qualified to submit an application under this part; or

  (4) The interest of the applicant in the aircraft was created by a transaction that was not entered into in good faith, but rather was made to avoid (with or without the owner's knowledge) compliance with 49 U.S.C. 44101–44104.

FAR 47

(b) If the registration of an aircraft is invalid under paragraph (a) of this section, the holder of the invalid Certificate of Aircraft Registration, AC Form 8050–3, must return it as soon as possible to the Registry.

[Doc. No. 7190, 31 FR 4495, Mar. 17, 1966; 31 FR 5483, Apr. 7, 1966, as amended by Amdt. 47–20, 44 FR 61940, Oct. 29, 1979; Amdt. 47–27, 70 FR 245, Jan. 3, 2005; Amdt. 47–29, 75 FR 41982, July 20, 2010]

47.45   Change of address

Within 30 days after any change in a registered owner's mailing address, the registered owner must notify the Registry in writing of the change of address. If a post office box or mailing drop is used for mailing purposes, the registered owner also must provide that owner's physical address or location. Upon acceptance, the Registry will issue, without charge, a revised Certificate of Aircraft Registration, AC Form 8050–3, reflecting the new mailing address. When a post office box or mailing drop is used for mailing purposes, and the registered owner's physical address or location changes, the registered owner must notify the Registry in writing of the new address or location within 30 days.

[Amdt. 47–29, 75 FR 41982, July 20, 2010]

47.47   Cancellation of Certificate for export purpose

(a) The holder of a Certificate of Aircraft Registration, AC Form 8050–3, or the holder of an irrevocable deregistration and export request authorization recognized under the Cape Town Treaty and filed with the FAA, who wishes to cancel the Certificate of Aircraft Registration for the purpose of export must submit to the Registry—

   (1) A written request for cancellation of the Certificate of Aircraft Registration describing the aircraft by make, model, and serial number, and stating the U.S. registration number and the country to which the aircraft will be exported;

   (2)

      (i)   For an aircraft not subject to the Cape Town Treaty, evidence satisfactory to the FAA that each holder of a recorded right has been satisfied or has consented to the transfer; or

      (ii) For an aircraft subject to the Cape Town Treaty, evidence satisfactory to the FAA that each holder of a recorded right established prior to the date the Treaty entered into force with respect to the United States has been satisfied or has consented to the transfer; and

   (3) A written certification that all registered interests ranking in priority to that of the requestor have been discharged or that the holders of such interests have consented to the cancellation for export purposes.

(b) If the aircraft is subject to the Cape Town Treaty and an irrevocable deregistration and export request authorization has been filed with the Registry, the Registry will honor a request for cancellation only if an authorized party makes the request.

(c) The Registry notifies the country to which the aircraft is to be exported of the cancellation.

[Amdt. 47–27, 70 FR 245, Jan. 3, 2005, as amended by Amdt. 47–29, 75 FR 41982, July 20, 2010]

47.49   Replacement of Certificate

(a) If the original Certificate of Aircraft Registration, AC Form 8050–3, is lost, stolen, or mutilated, the registered owner may submit to the Registry a written request that states the reason a replacement certificate is needed and the fee required by 47.17. The Registry will send a replacement certificate to the registered owner's mailing address or to another mailing address if requested in writing by the registered owner.

(b) The registered owner may request a temporary Certificate of Aircraft Registration pending receipt of a replacement certificate. The Registry issues a temporary Certificate of Aircraft Registration in the form of a fax that must be carried in the aircraft until receipt of the replacement certificate.

[Amdt. 47–29, 75 FR 41982, July 20, 2010]

47.51   [Reserved]

Subpart C — Dealers' Aircraft Registration Certificate

47.61   Dealer's Aircraft Registration Certificates

(a) The FAA issues a Dealer's Aircraft Registration Certificate, AC Form 8050–6, to U.S. manufacturers and dealers to—

   (1) Allow manufacturers to make any required flight tests of aircraft.

   (2) Facilitate operating, demonstrating, and merchandising aircraft by the manufacturer or dealer without the burden of obtaining a Certificate of Aircraft Registration, AC Form 8050–3, for each aircraft with each transfer of ownership, under Subpart B of this part.

(b) A Dealer's Aircraft Registration Certificate is an alternative for the Certificate of Aircraft Registration issued under Subpart B of this part. A dealer may, under this subpart, obtain one or more Dealer's Aircraft Registration Certificates in addition to his original certificate, and he may use a Dealer's Aircraft Registration Certificate for any aircraft he owns.

(c) If the Dealer's Aircraft Registration Certificate expires under 47.71, and an aircraft is registered under this Subpart, application for registration must be made under 47.31, or the assignment of registration number may be cancelled in accordance with 47.15(i)(3).

[Doc. No. 7190, 31 FR 4495, Mar. 17, 1966; as amended by Amdt. 47–9, 35 FR 802, Jan. 21, 1970; Amdt. 47–16, 37 FR 25487, Dec. 1, 1972; Amdt. 47–29, 75 FR 41982, July 20, 2010]

47.63   Application

A manufacturer or dealer that wishes to obtain a Dealer's Aircraft Registration Certificate, AC Form 8050–6, must submit—

(a) A Dealer's Aircraft Registration Certificate Application, AC Form 8050–5; and

(b) The fee required by 47.17.

[Doc. No. 7190, 31 FR 4495, Mar. 17, 1966, as amended by Amdt. 47–16, 37 FR 25487, Dec. 1, 1972; Amdt. 47–29, 75 FR 41982, July 20, 2010]

47.65   Eligibility

To be eligible for a Dealer's Aircraft Registration Certificate, AC Form 8050–6, the applicant must have an established place of business in the United States, must be substantially engaged in manufacturing or selling aircraft, and must be a citizen of the United States, as defined by 49 U.S.C. 40102 (a)(15).

[Amdt. 47–29, 75 FR 41983, July 20, 2010]

47.67   Evidence of ownership

Before using a Dealer's Aircraft Registration Certificate, AC Form 8050–6, for operating the aircraft, the holder of the certificate (other than a manufacturer) must send to the Registry evidence of ownership under 47.11. An Aircraft Bill of Sale, AC Form 8050–2, or its equivalent, may be used as evidence of ownership. There is no recording fee.

[Amdt. 47–29, 75 FR 41983, July 20, 2010]

47.69   Limitations

A Dealer's Aircraft Registration Certificate, AC Form 8050–6 is valid only in connection with use of aircraft—

(a) By the owner of the aircraft to whom it was issued, his agent or employee, or a prospective buyer, and in the case of a dealer other than a manufacturer, only after he has complied with 47.67;

(b) Within the United States, except when used to deliver to a foreign purchaser an aircraft displaying a temporary registration number and carrying an airworthiness certificate on which that number is written;

(c) While a certificate is carried within the aircraft; and

(d) On a flight that is—

   (1) For required flight testing of aircraft; or

   (2) Necessary for, or incident to, sale of the aircraft.

However, a prospective buyer may operate an aircraft for demonstration purposes only while he is under the direct supervision of the holder of the Dealer's Aircraft Registration Certificate or his agent.

[Doc. No. 7190 31 FR 4495, Mar. 17, 1966; 31 FR 5483, Apr. 7, 1966, as amended by Amdt. 47–4, 32 FR 12556, Aug. 30, 1967; Amdt. 47–29, 75 FR 41983, July 20, 2010]

47.71   Duration of Certificate; change of status

(a) A Dealer's Aircraft Registration Certificate, AC Form 8050–6, expires 1 year after the date it is issued. Each additional certificate expires on the date the original certificate expires.

(b) The holder of a Dealer's Aircraft Registration Certificate must immediately notify the Registry of any of the following—

   (1) A change of name;

   (2) A change of address;

   (3) A change that affects status as a citizen of the United States; or

   (4) The discontinuance of business.

[31 FR 4495, Mar. 17, 1966, as amended by Amdt. 47–29, 75 FR 41983, July 20, 2010]

PART 65 — CERTIFICATION: AIRMEN OTHER THAN FLIGHT CREWMEMBERS

Special Federal Aviation Regulation No. 100-2

Special Federal Aviation Regulation No. 103

Process for Requesting Waiver of Mandatory Separation Age for a Federal Aviation Administration Air Traffic Control Specialist In Flight Service Stations, Enroute or Terminal Facilities, and the David J. Hurley Air Traffic Control System Command Center

Appendix A to Part 65 — Aircraft Dispatcher Courses

Authority: 49 U.S.C. 106(f), 106(g), 40113, 44701-44703, 44707, 44709-44711, 45102-45103, 45301-45302.

Source: Docket No. 1179, 27 FR 7973, Aug. 10, 1962, unless otherwise noted.

Special Federal Aviation Regulation No. 100-2

Editorial Note: For the text of SFAR No. 100–2, see part 61 of this chapter.

Special Federal Aviation Regulation No. 103

Process for Requesting Waiver of Mandatory Separation Age for a Federal Aviation Administration Air Traffic Control Specialist In Flight Service Stations, Enroute or Terminal Facilities, and the David J. Hurley Air Traffic Control System Command Center

1. To whom does this SFAR apply? This Special Federal Aviation Regulation (SFAR) applies to you if you are an air traffic control specialist (ATCS) employed by the FAA in flight service stations, enroute facilities, terminal facilities, or at the David J. Hurley Air Traffic Control System Command Center who wishes to obtain a waiver of the mandatory separation age as provided by 5 U.S.C. section 8335(a).

2. When must I file for a waiver? No earlier than the beginning of the twelfth month before, but no later than the beginning of the sixth month before, the month in which you turn 56, your official chain-of-command must receive your written request asking for a waiver of mandatory separation.

3. What if I do not file a request before six months before the month in which I turn 56? If your official chain-of-command does not receive your written request for a waiver of mandatory separation before the beginning of the sixth month before the month in which you turn 56, your request will be denied.

4. How will the FAA determine if my request meets the filing time requirements of this SFAR?

   a. We consider your request to be filed in a timely manner under this SFAR if your official chain-of-command receives it or it is postmarked:

FAR 65

i. After 12 a.m. on the first day of the twelfth month before the month in which you turn 56; and

    ii. Before 12 a.m. of the first day of the sixth month before the month in which you turn 56.

b. If you file your request by mail and the postmark is not legible, we will consider it to comply with paragraph a.2 of this section if we receive it by 12 p.m. of the fifth day of the sixth month before the month in which you turn 56.

c. If the last day of the time period specified in paragraph a.2 or paragraph b falls on a Saturday, Sunday, or Federal holiday, we will consider the time period to end at 12 p.m. of the next business day.

5. Where must I file my request for waiver and what must it include?

a. You must file your request for waiver of mandatory separation in writing with the Air Traffic Manager in flight service stations, enroute facilities, terminal facilities, or the David J. Hurley Air Traffic Control System Command Center in which you are employed.

b. Your request for waiver must include all of the following:

    i. Your name.

    ii. Your current facility.

    iii. Your starting date at the facility.

    iv. A list of positions at the facility that you are certified in and how many hours it took to achieve certification at the facility.

    v. Your area of specialty at the facility.

    vi. Your shift schedule.

    vii. [Reserved]

    viii. A list of all facilities where you have worked as a certified professional controller (CPC) including facility level and dates at each facility;

    ix. Evidence of your exceptional skills and experience as a controller; and

    x. Your signature.

6. How will my waiver request be reviewed?

a. Upon receipt of your request for waiver, the Air Traffic Manager of your facility will make a written recommendation that the Administrator either approve or deny your request. If the manager recommends approval of your request, he or she will certify in writing the accuracy of the information you provided as evidence of your exceptional skills and experience as a controller.

b. The Air Traffic Manager will then forward the written recommendation with a copy of your request to the senior executive manager in the Air Traffic Manager's regional chain-of-command.

c. The senior executive manager in the regional chain-of-command will make a written recommendation that the Administrator either approve or deny your request. If the senior executive manager recommends approval of your request, he or she will certify in writing the accuracy of the information you have provided as evidence of exceptional skills and experience.

d. The senior executive manager in the regional chain-of-command will then forward his or her recommendation with a copy of your request to the appropriate Vice President at FAA Headquarters. Depending on the facility in which you are employed, the request will be forwarded to either the Vice President for Flight Services, the Vice President for Enroute and Oceanic Services, the Vice President for Terminal Services or the Vice President for Systems Operations. For example, if you work at a flight service station at the time that you request a waiver, the request will be forwarded to the Vice President for Flight Services.

e. The appropriate Vice President will review your request and make a written recommendation that the Administrator either approve or deny your request, which will be forwarded to the Administrator.

f. The Administrator will issue the final decision on your request.

7. If I am granted a waiver, when will it expire?

a. Waivers will be granted for a period of one year.

b. No later than 90-days prior to expiration of a waiver, you may request that the waiver be extended using the same process identified in section 6.

c. If you timely request an extension of the waiver and it is denied, you will receive a 60-day advance notice of your separation date simultaneously with notification of the denial.

d. If you do not request an extension of the waiver granted, you will receive a 60-day advance notice of your separation date.

e. Action to separate you from your covered position becomes effective on the last day of the month in which the 60-day notice expires.

8. Under what circumstances may my waiver be terminated?

a. The FAA/DOT may terminate your waiver under the following circumstances:

    i. The needs of the FAA; or

    ii. If you are identified as a primary contributor to an operational error/deviation or runway incursion.

b. If the waiver is terminated for either of the reasons identified in paragraph 1 of this section, the air traffic control specialist will receive a 60-day advance notice.

c. Action to separate you from your covered position becomes effective on the last day of the month in which the 60-day notice expires.

9. Appeal of denial or termination of waiver request: The denial or termination of a waiver of mandatory separation request is neither appealable nor grievable.

[Doc. No. FAA–2004–17334, 70 FR 1636, Jan. 7, 2005, as amended by Amdt. 65–55, 76 FR 12, Jan. 3, 2011]

Subpart A — General

65.1   Applicability

This part prescribes the requirements for issuing the following certificates and associated ratings and the general operating rules for the holders of those certificates and ratings:

(a) Air-traffic control-tower operators.

(b) Aircraft dispatchers.

(c) Mechanics.

(d) Repairmen.

(e) Parachute riggers.

65.3   Certification of foreign airmen other than flight crewmembers

A person who is neither a U.S. citizen nor a resident alien is issued a certificate under subpart D of this part, outside the United States, only when the Administrator finds that the certificate is needed for the operation or continued airworthiness of a U.S.-registered civil aircraft.

[Doc. 65–28, 47 FR 35693, Aug. 16, 1982]

65.11   Application and issue

(a) Application for a certificate and appropriate class rating, or for an additional rating, under this part must be made on a form and in a manner prescribed by the Administrator. Each person who applies for airmen certification services to be administered outside the United States or for any certificate or rating issued under this part must show evidence that the fee prescribed in appendix A of part 187 of this chapter has been paid.

(b) Except for FAA Credential holders with tower ratings, an applicant who meets the requirements of this part is entitled to an appropriate certificate and rating.

(c) Unless authorized by the Administrator, a person whose air traffic control tower operator, mechanic, or parachute rigger certificate is suspended may not apply for any rating to be added to that certificate during the period of suspension.

(d) Unless the order of revocation provides otherwise—

(1) A person whose air traffic control tower operator, aircraft dispatcher, or parachute rigger certificate is revoked may not apply for the same kind of certificate for 1 year after the date of revocation; and

(2) A person whose mechanic or repairman certificate is revoked may not apply for either of those kinds of certificates for 1 year after the date of revocation.

[Doc. No. 1179, 27 FR 7973, Aug. 10, 1962, as amended by Amdt. 65-9, 31 FR 13524, Oct. 20, 1966; Amdt. 65-28, 47 FR 35693, Aug. 16, 1982; Amdt. 65-49, 72 FR 18559, Apr. 12, 2007; Amdt. 65-56, 79 FR 74611, Dec. 16, 2014]

65.12 Offenses involving alcohol or drugs

(a) A conviction for the violation of any Federal or state statute relating to the growing, processing, manufacture, sale, disposition, possession, transportation, or importation of narcotic drugs, marihuana, or depressant or stimulant drugs or substances is grounds for—

(1) Denial of an application for any certificate or rating issued under this part for a period of up to 1 year after the date of final conviction; or

(2) Suspension or revocation of any certificate or rating issued under this part.

(b) The commission of an act prohibited by 91.19(a) of this chapter is grounds for—

(1) Denial of an application for a certificate or rating issued under this part for a period of up to 1 year after the date of that act; or

(2) Suspension or revocation of any certificate or rating issued under this part.

[Doc. No. 21956, 50 FR 15379, Apr. 17, 1985, as amended by Amdt. 65-34, 54 FR 34330, Aug. 18, 1989]

65.13 Temporary certificate

A certificate and ratings effective for a period of not more than 120 days may be issued to a qualified applicant, pending review of his application and supplementary documents and the issue of the certificate and ratings for which he applied.

[Doc. No. 1179, 27 FR 7973, Aug. 10, 1962, as amended by Amdt. 65-23, 43 FR 22640, May 25, 1978]

65.14 [Reserved]

65.15 Duration of certificates

(a) Except for repairman certificates, a certificate or rating issued under this part is effective until it is surrendered, suspended, or revoked.

(b) Unless it is sooner surrendered, suspended, or revoked, a repairman certificate is effective until the holder is relieved from the duties for which the holder was employed and certificated.

(c) The holder of a certificate issued under this part that is suspended, revoked, or no longer effective shall return it to the Administrator.

(d) Except for temporary certificates issued under 65.13, the holder of a paper certificate issued under this part may not exercise the privileges of that certificate after March 31, 2013.

[Doc. No. 22052, 47 FR 35693, Aug. 16, 1982, as amended by Amdt. 65-51, 73 FR 10668, Feb. 28, 2008]

65.16 Change of name: replacement of lost or destroyed certificate

(a) An application for a change of name on a certificate issued under this part must be accompanied by the applicant's current certificate and the marriage license, court order, or other document verifying the change. The documents are returned to the applicant after inspection.

(b) An application for a replacement of a lost or destroyed certificate is made by letter to the Department of Transportation, Federal Aviation Administration, Airman Certification Branch, Post Office Box 25082, Oklahoma City, OK 73125. The letter must—

(1) Contain the name in which the certificate was issued, the permanent mailing address (including zip code), social security number (if any), and date and place of birth of the certificate holder, and any available information regarding the grade, number, and date of issue of the certificate, and the ratings on it; and

(2) Be accompanied by a check or money order for $2, payable to the Federal Aviation Administration.

(c) An application for a replacement of a lost or destroyed medical certificate is made by letter to the Department of Transportation, Federal Aviation Administration, Aerospace Medical Certification Division, Post Office Box 26200, Oklahoma City, OK 73125, accompanied by a check or money order for $2.00.

(d) A person whose certificate issued under this part or medical certificate, or both, has been lost may obtain a telegram from the FAA confirming that it was issued. The telegram may be carried as a certificate for a period not to exceed 60 days pending his receiving a duplicate certificate under paragraph (b) or (c) of this section, unless he has been notified that the certificate has been suspended or revoked. The request for such a telegram may be made by prepaid telegram, stating the date upon which a duplicate certificate was requested, or including the request for a duplicate and a money order for the necessary amount. The request for a telegraphic certificate should be sent to the office prescribed in paragraph (b) or (c) of this section, as appropriate. However, a request for both at the same time should be sent to the office prescribed in paragraph (b) of this section.

[Doc. No. 7258, 31 FR 13524, Oct. 20, 1966, as amended by Doc. No. 8084, 32 FR 5769, Apr. 11, 1967; Amdt. 65–16, 35 FR 14075, Sept. 4, 1970; Amdt. 65–17, 36 FR 2865, Feb. 11, 1971; Amdt. 65–52, 73 FR 43065, July 24, 2008]

65.17 Tests: general procedure

(a) Tests prescribed by or under this part are given at times and places, and by persons, designated by the Administrator.

(b) The minimum passing grade for each test is 70 percent.

65.18 Written tests: cheating or other unauthorized conduct

(a) Except as authorized by the Administrator, no person may—

(1) Copy, or intentionally remove, a written test under this part;

(2) Give to another, or receive from another, any part or copy of that test;

(3) Give help on that test to, or receive help on that test from, any person during the period that test is being given;

(4) Take any part of that test in behalf of another person;

(5) Use any material or aid during the period that test is being given; or

(6) Intentionally cause, assist, or participate in any act prohibited by this paragraph.

(b) No person who commits an act prohibited by paragraph (a) of this section is eligible for any airman or ground instructor certificate or rating under this chapter for a period of 1 year after the date of that act. In addition, the commission of that act is a basis for suspending or revoking any airman or ground instructor certificate or rating held by that person.

[Doc. No. 4086, 30 FR 2196, Feb. 18, 1965]

65.19 Retesting after failure

An applicant for a written, oral, or practical test for a certificate and rating, or for an additional rating under this part, may apply for retesting—

(a) After 30 days after the date the applicant failed the test; or

(b) Before the 30 days have expired if the applicant presents a signed statement from an airman holding the certificate and rating sought by the applicant, certifying that the airman has given the applicant additional instruction in each of the subjects failed and that the airman considers the applicant ready for retesting.

[Doc. No. 16383, 43 FR 22640, May 25, 1978]

65.20   Applications, certificates, logbooks, reports, and records: falsification, reproduction, or alteration

(a) No person may make or cause to be made—

    (1) Any fraudulent or intentionally false statement on any application for a certificate or rating under this part;

    (2) Any fraudulent or intentionally false entry in any logbook, record, or report that is required to be kept, made, or used, to show compliance with any requirement for any certificate or rating under this part;

    (3) Any reproduction, for fraudulent purpose, of any certificate or rating under this part; or

    (4) Any alteration of any certificate or rating under this part.

(b) The commission by any person of an act prohibited under paragraph (a) of this section is a basis for suspending or revoking any airman or ground instructor certificate or rating held by that person.

[Doc. No. 4086, 30 FR 2196, Feb. 18, 1965]

65.21   Change of address

Within 30 days after any change in his permanent mailing address, the holder of a certificate issued under this part shall notify the Department of Transportation, Federal Aviation Administration, Airman Certification Branch, Post Office Box 25082, Oklahoma City, OK 73125, in writing, of his new address.

[Doc. No. 10536, 35 FR 14075, Sept. 4, 1970]

65.23   Incorporation by reference

Certain material is incorporated by reference into this part with the approval of the Director of the Federal Register under 5 U.S.C. 552(a) and 1 CFR part 51. This material is available for inspection at the Federal Aviation Administration (FAA) and at the National Archives and Records Administration (NARA). Contact FAA, Airman Testing Standards Branch/Regulatory Support Division, 405-954-4151, AFS630Comments@faa.gov. For information on the availability of this material at NARA, email fr.inspection@nara.gov, or go to www.archives.gov/federal-register/cfr/ibr-locations.html. The material may be obtained from the source in the following paragraph of this section.

(a) Federal Aviation Administration, 800 Independence Avenue SW, Washington, DC 20591, 866-835-5322, www.faa.gov/training_testing.

    (1) FAA-S-8081-26B, Aviation Mechanic General, Airframe, and Powerplant Practical Test Standards, November 1, 2021; IBR approved for 65.75 and 65.79.

    (2) FAA-S-ACS-1, Aviation Mechanic General, Airframe, and Powerplant Airman Certification Standards, November 1, 2021; IBR approved for 65.75 and 65.79.

(b) [Reserved]

[Docket No.: FAA-2021-0237; Amdt. No. 65-63, 87 FR 31414, May 24, 2022]

Subpart B — Air Traffic Control Tower Operators

Source: Docket No. 10193, 35 FR 12326, Aug. 1, 1970, unless otherwise noted.

65.31   Required credentials, certificates, and ratings or qualifications.

No person may act as an air traffic control tower operator at an air traffic control tower in connection with civil aircraft unless he or she—

(a) Holds an FAA Credential with a tower rating or an air traffic control tower operator certificate issued under this subpart;

(b) Holds a facility rating for that control tower issued under this subpart, or has qualified for the operating position at which he or she acts and is under the supervision of the holder of a facility rating for that control tower; and

For the purpose of this subpart, operating position means an air traffic control function performed within or directly associated with the control tower;

(c) Except for a person employed by the FAA or employed by, or on active duty with, the Department of the Air Force, Army, or Navy or the Coast Guard, holds at least a second-class medical certificate issued under part 67 of this chapter.

[Doc. No. 10193, 35 FR 12326, Aug. 1, 1970, as amended by Amdt. 65-25, 45 FR 18911, Mar. 24, 1980; Amdt. 65-31, 52 FR 17518, May 8, 1987; Amdt. 65-56, 79 FR 74611, Dec. 16, 2014]

65.33   Eligibility requirements: general

To be eligible for an air traffic control tower operator certificate a person must—

(a) Be at least 18 years of age;

(b) Be of good moral character;

(c) Be able to read, write, and understand the English language and speak it without accent or impediment of speech that would interfere with two-way radio conversation;

(d) Except for a person employed by the FAA or employed by, or on active duty with, the Department of the Air Force, Army, or Navy or the Coast Guard, hold at least a second-class medical certificate issued under part 67 of this chapter within the 12 months before the date application is made; and

(e) Comply with 65.35.

[Doc. No. 10193, 35 FR 12326, Aug. 1, 1970, as amended by Amdt. 65–25, 45 FR 18911, Mar. 24, 1980; Amdt. 65–31, 52 FR 17518, May 8, 1987]

65.35   Knowledge requirements

Each applicant for an air traffic control tower operator certificate must pass a written test on—

(a) The flight rules in part 91 of this chapter;

(b) Airport traffic control procedures, and this subpart;

(c) En route traffic control procedures;

(d) Communications operating procedures;

(e) Flight assistance service;

(f) Air navigation, and aids to air navigation; and

(g) Aviation weather.

65.37   Skill requirements: operating positions

No person may act as an air traffic control tower operator at any operating position unless he has passed a practical test on—

(a) Control tower equipment and its use;

(b) Weather reporting procedures and use of reports;

(c) Notices to Airmen, and use of the Airman's Information Manual;

(d) Use of operational forms;

(e) Performance of noncontrol operational duties; and

(f) Each of the following procedures that is applicable to that operating position and is required by the person performing the examination:

    (1) The airport, including rules, equipment, runways, taxiways, and obstructions.

    (2) The terrain features, visual checkpoints, and obstructions within the lateral boundaries of the surface areas of Class B, Class C, Class D, or Class E airspace designated for the airport.

    (3) Traffic patterns and associated procedures for use of preferential runways and noise abatement.

    (4) Operational agreements.

    (5) The center, alternate airports, and those airways, routes, reporting points, and air navigation aids used for terminal air traffic control.

    (6) Search and rescue procedures.

    (7) Terminal air traffic control procedures and phraseology.

    (8) Holding procedures, prescribed instrument approach, and departure procedures.

    (9) Radar alignment and technical operation.

    (10) The application of the prescribed radar and nonradar separation standard, as appropriate.

Doc. No. 10193, 35 FR 12326, Aug. 1, 1991, as amended by Amdt. 65–36, 56 FR 65653, Dec. 17, 1991]

65.39 Practical experience requirements: facility rating

Each applicant for a facility rating at any air traffic control tower must have satisfactorily served—

(a) As an air traffic control tower operator at that control tower without a facility rating for at least 6 months; or

(b) As an air traffic control tower operator with a facility rating at a different control tower for at least 6 months before the date he applies for the rating.

However, an applicant who is a member of an Armed Force of the United States meets the requirements of this section if he has satisfactorily served as an air traffic control tower operator for at least 6 months.

Doc. No. 1179, 27 FR 7973, Aug. 10, 1962, as amended by Amdt. 65–19, 36 FR 21280, Nov. 5, 1971]

65.41 Skill requirements: facility ratings

Each applicant for a facility rating at an air traffic control tower must have passed a practical test on each item listed in 65.37 of this part that is applicable to each operating position at the control tower at which the rating is sought.

65.43 [Reserved]

65.45 Performance of duties

(a) An air traffic control tower operator shall perform his duties in accordance with the limitations on his certificate and the procedures and practices prescribed in air traffic control manuals of the FAA, to provide for the safe, orderly, and expeditious flow of air traffic.

(b) An operator with a facility rating may control traffic at any operating position at the control tower at which he holds a facility rating. However, he may not issue an air traffic clearance for IFR flight without authorization from the appropriate facility exercising IFR control at that location.

(c) An operator who does not hold a facility rating for a particular control tower may act at each operating position for which he has qualified, under the supervision of an operator holding a facility rating for that control tower.

Doc. No. 10193, 35 FR 12326, Aug. 1, 1970, as amended by Amdt. 65–16, 35 FR 14075, Sept. 4, 1970]

65.46 [Reserved]

65.46a [Reserved]

65.46b [Reserved]

65.47 Maximum hours

Except in an emergency, a certificated air traffic control tower operator must be relieved of all duties for at least 24 consecutive hours at least once during each 7 consecutive days. Such an operator may not serve or be required to serve—

(a) For more than 10 consecutive hours; or

(b) For more than 10 hours during a period of 24 consecutive hours, unless he has had a rest period of at least 8 hours at or before the end of the 10 hours of duty.

65.49 General operating rules

(a) Except for a person employed by the FAA or employed by, or on active duty with, the Department of the Air Force, Army, or Navy, or the Coast Guard, no person may act as an air traffic control tower operator under a certificate issued to him or her under this part unless he or she has in his or her personal possession an appropriate current medical certificate issued under part 67 of this chapter.

(b) Each person holding an air traffic control tower operator certificate shall keep it readily available when performing duties in an air traffic control tower, and shall present that certificate or his medical certificate or both for inspection upon the request of the Administrator or an authorized representative of the National Transportation Safety Board, or of any Federal, State, or local law enforcement officer.

(c) A certificated air traffic control tower operator who does not hold a facility rating for a particular control tower may not act at any operating position at the control tower concerned unless there is maintained at that control tower, readily available to persons named in paragraph (b) of this section, a current record of the operating positions at which he has qualified.

(d) An air traffic control tower operator may not perform duties under his certificate during any period of known physical deficiency that would make him unable to meet the physical requirements for his current medical certificate. However, if the deficiency is temporary, he may perform duties that are not affected by it whenever another certificated and qualified operator is present and on duty.

(e) A certificated air traffic control tower operator may not control air traffic with equipment that the Administrator has found to be inadequate.

(f) The holder of an air traffic control tower operator certificate, or an applicant for one, shall, upon the reasonable request of the Administrator, cooperate fully in any test that is made of him.

[Doc. No. 1179, 27 FR 7973, Aug. 10, 1962, as amended by Amdt. 65–31, 52 FR 17519, May 8, 1987]

65.50 Currency requirements

The holder of an air traffic control tower operator certificate may not perform any duties under that certificate unless—

(a) He has served for at least three of the preceding 6 months as an air traffic control tower operator at the control tower to which his facility rating applies, or at the operating positions for which he has qualified; or

(b) He has shown that he meets the requirements for his certificate and facility rating at the control tower concerned, or for operating at positions for which he has previously qualified.

Subpart C — Aircraft Dispatchers

Source: Docket No. FAA–1998–4553, 64 FR 68923, Dec. 8, 1999, unless otherwise noted.

65.51 Certificate required

(a) No person may act as an aircraft dispatcher (exercising responsibility with the pilot in command in the operational control of a flight) in connection with any civil aircraft in air commerce unless that person has in his or her personal possession an aircraft dispatcher certificate issued under this subpart.

(b) Each person who holds an aircraft dispatcher certificate must present it for inspection upon the request of the Administrator or an authorized representative of the National Transportation Safety Board, or of any Federal, State, or local law enforcement officer.

65.53 Eligibility requirements: general

(a) To be eligible to take the aircraft dispatcher knowledge test, a person must be at least 21 years of age.

(b) To be eligible for an aircraft dispatcher certificate, a person must—

(1) Be at least 23 years of age;

(2) Be able to read, speak, write, and understand the English language;

(3) Pass the required knowledge test prescribed by 65.55 of this part;

(4) Pass the required practical test prescribed by 65.59 of this part; and

(5) Comply with the requirements of 65.57 of this part.

65.55 Knowledge requirements

(a) A person who applies for an aircraft dispatcher certificate must pass a knowledge test on the following aeronautical knowledge areas:

FAR 65

(1) Applicable Federal Aviation Regulations of this chapter that relate to airline transport pilot privileges, limitations, and flight operations;

(2) Meteorology, including knowledge of and effects of fronts, frontal characteristics, cloud formations, icing, and upper-air data;

(3) General system of weather and NOTAM collection, dissemination, interpretation, and use;

(4) Interpretation and use of weather charts, maps, forecasts, sequence reports, abbreviations, and symbols;

(5) National Weather Service functions as they pertain to operations in the National Airspace System;

(6) Windshear and microburst awareness, identification, and avoidance;

(7) Principles of air navigation under instrument meteorological conditions in the National Airspace System;

(8) Air traffic control procedures and pilot responsibilities as they relate to enroute operations, terminal area and radar operations, and instrument departure and approach procedures;

(9) Aircraft loading, weight and balance, use of charts, graphs, tables, formulas, and computations, and their effect on aircraft performance;

(10) Aerodynamics relating to an aircraft's flight characteristics and performance in normal and abnormal flight regimes;

(11) Human factors;

(12) Aeronautical decision making and judgment; and

(13) Crew resource management, including crew communication and coordination.

(b) The applicant must present documentary evidence satisfactory to the administrator of having passed an aircraft dispatcher knowledge test within the preceding 24 calendar months.

65.57   Experience or training requirements

An applicant for an aircraft dispatcher certificate must present documentary evidence satisfactory to the Administrator that he or she has the experience prescribed in paragraph (a) of this section or has accomplished the training described in paragraph (b) of this section as follows:

(a) A total of at least 2 years experience in the 3 years before the date of application, in any one or in any combination of the following areas:

(1) In military aircraft operations as a—

(i) Pilot;

(ii) Flight navigator; or

(iii) Meteorologist.

(2) In aircraft operations conducted under part 121 of this chapter as—

(i) An assistant in dispatching air carrier aircraft, under the direct supervision of a dispatcher certificated under this subpart;

(ii) A pilot;

(iii) A flight engineer; or

(iv) A meteorologist.

(3) In aircraft operations as—

(i) An Air Traffic Controller; or

(ii) A Flight Service Specialist.

(4) In aircraft operations, performing other duties that the Administrator finds provide equivalent experience.

(b) A statement of graduation issued or revalidated in accordance with 65.70(b) of this part, showing that the person has successfully completed an approved aircraft dispatcher course.

65.59   Skill requirements

An applicant for an aircraft dispatcher certificate must pass a practical test given by the Administrator, with respect to any one type of large aircraft used in air carrier operations. To pass the practical test for an aircraft dispatcher certificate, the applicant must demonstrate skill in applying the areas of knowledge and topics specified in appendix A of this part to preflight and all phases of flight, including abnormal and emergency procedures.

[Docket FAA-2016-6142, Amdt. 65-58, 83 FR 30281, June 27, 2018]

65.61   Aircraft dispatcher certification courses: content and minimum hours

(a) An approved aircraft dispatcher certification course must:

(1) Provide instruction in the areas of knowledge and topics listed in appendix A of this part;

(2) Include a minimum of 200 hours of instruction.

(b) An applicant for approval of an aircraft dispatcher course must submit an outline that describes the major topics and subtopics to be covered and the number of hours proposed for each.

(c) Additional subject headings for an aircraft dispatcher certification course may also be included, however the hours proposed for any subjects not listed in appendix A of this part must be in addition to the minimum 200 course hours required in paragraph (a) of this section.

(d) For the purpose of completing an approved course, a student may substitute previous experience or training for a portion of the minimum 200 hours of training. The course operator determines the number of hours of credit based on an evaluation of the experience or training to determine if it is comparable to portions of the approved course curriculum. The credit allowed, including the total hours and the basis for it, must be placed in the student's record required by 65.70(a) of this part.

65.63   Aircraft dispatcher certification courses: application, duration, and other general requirements

(a) Application. Application for original approval of an aircraft dispatcher certification course or the renewal of approval of an aircraft dispatcher certification course under this part must be:

(1) Made in writing to the Administrator;

(2) Accompanied by two copies of the course outline required under 65.61(b) of this part, for which approval is sought;

(3) Accompanied by a description of the equipment and facilities to be used; and

(4) Accompanied by a list of the instructors and their qualifications.

(b) Duration. Unless withdrawn or canceled, an approval of an aircraft dispatcher certification course of study expires:

(1) On the last day of the 24th month from the month the approval was issued; or

(2) Except as provided in paragraph (f) of this section, on the date that any change in ownership of the school occurs.

(c) Renewal. Application for renewal of an approved aircraft dispatcher certification course must be made within 30 days preceding the month the approval expires, provided the course operator meets the following requirements:

(1) At least 80 percent of the graduates from that aircraft dispatcher certification course, who applied for the practical test required by 65.59 of this part, passed the practical test on their first attempt; and

(2) The aircraft dispatcher certification course continues to meet the requirements of this subpart for course approval.

(d) Course revisions. Requests for approval of a revision of the course outline, facilities, or equipment must be in accordance with paragraph (a) of this section. Proposed revisions of the course outline or the description of facilities and equipment must be submitted in a format that will allow an entire page or pages of the approved outline or description to be removed and replaced by any approved revision. The list of instructors may be revised at any time without request for approval, provided the minimum requirements of 65.67 of this part are maintained and the Administrator is notified in writing.

(e) Withdrawal or cancellation of approval. Failure to continue to meet the requirements of this subpart for the approval or operation of an approved aircraft dispatcher certification course is grounds for withdrawal of approval of the course. A course operator may request cancellation of course approval by a letter to the Administrator. The operator must forward any records to the FAA as requested by the Administrator.

(f) Change in ownership. A change in ownership of a part 65, appendix A-approved course does not terminate that aircraft dispatcher certification course approval if, within 10 days after the date that any change in ownership of the school occurs:

(1) Application is made for an appropriate amendment to the approval; and

(2) No change in the facilities, personnel, or approved aircraft dispatcher certification course is involved.

(g) Change in name or location. A change in name or location of an approved aircraft dispatcher certification course does not invalidate the approval if, within 10 days after the date that any change in name or location occurs, the course operator of the part 65, appendix A-approved course notifies the Administrator, in writing, of the change.

65.65 Aircraft dispatcher certification courses: training facilities

An applicant for approval of authority to operate an aircraft dispatcher course of study must have facilities, equipment, and materials adequate to provide each student the theoretical and practical aspects of aircraft dispatching. Each room, training booth, or other space used for instructional purposes must be temperature controlled, lighted, and ventilated to conform to local building, sanitation, and health codes. In addition, the training facility must be so located that the students in that facility are not distracted by the instruction conducted in other rooms.

65.67 Aircraft dispatcher certification courses: personnel

(a) Each applicant for an aircraft dispatcher certification course must meet the following personnel requirements:

(1) Each applicant must have adequate personnel, including one instructor who holds an aircraft dispatcher certificate and is available to coordinate all training course instruction.

(2) Each applicant must not exceed a ratio of 25 students for one instructor.

(b) The instructor who teaches the practical dispatch applications area of the appendix A course must hold an aircraft dispatchers certificate

65.70 Aircraft dispatcher certification courses: records

(a) The operator of an aircraft dispatcher course must maintain a record for each student, including a chronological log of all instructors, subjects covered, and course examinations and results. The record must be retained for at least 3 years after graduation. The course operator also must prepare, for its records, and transmit to the Administrator not later than January 31 of each year, a report containing the following information for the previous year:

(1) The names of all students who graduated, together with the results of their aircraft dispatcher certification courses.

(2) The names of all the students who failed or withdrew, together with the results of their aircraft dispatcher certification courses or the reasons for their withdrawal.

(b) Each student who successfully completes the approved aircraft dispatcher certification course must be given a written statement of graduation, which is valid for 90 days. After 90 days, the course operator may revalidate the graduation certificate for an additional 90 days if the course operator determines that the student remains proficient in the subject areas listed in appendix A of this part.

Subpart D — Mechanics

65.71 Eligibility requirements: General

(a) To be eligible for a mechanic certificate and associated ratings, a person must—

(1) Be at least 18 years of age;

(2) Be able to read, write, speak, and understand the English language, or in the case of an applicant who does not meet this requirement and who is employed outside of the United States by a U.S. air carrier, have his certificate endorsed "Valid only outside the United States";

(3) Have passed all of the prescribed tests within a period of 24 months; and

(4) Comply with the sections of this subpart that apply to the rating he seeks.

(b) A certificated mechanic who applies for an additional rating must meet the requirements of 65.77 and, within a period of 24 months, pass the tests prescribed by 65.75 and 65.79 for the additional rating sought.

[Doc. No. 1179, 27 FR 7973, Aug. 10, 1962, as amended by Amdt. 65–6, 31 FR 5950, Apr. 19, 1966]

65.73 Ratings

(a) The following ratings are issued under this subpart:

(1) Airframe.

(2) Powerplant.

(b) A mechanic certificate with an aircraft or aircraft engine rating, or both, that was issued before, and was valid on, June 15, 1952, is equal to a mechanic certificate with an airframe or powerplant rating, or both, as the case may be, and may be exchanged for such a corresponding certificate and rating or ratings.

65.75 Knowledge requirements

(a) Except as specified in paragraph (c) of this section, each applicant for a mechanic certificate or rating must, after meeting the applicable experience requirements of 65.77, pass a written test, appropriate to the rating sought, which includes:

(1) Until July 31, 2023, the subject areas contained in the Aviation Mechanic General, Airframe, and Powerplant Practical Test Standards (incorporated by reference, see 65.23), as appropriate to the rating sought.

(2) After July 31, 2023, the aeronautical knowledge subject areas contained in the Aviation Mechanic General, Airframe, and Powerplant Airman Certification Standards (incorporated by reference, see 65.23), as appropriate to the rating sought.

(b) The applicant must pass each section of the test before applying for the oral and practical tests prescribed by 65.79. A report of the written test is sent to the applicant.

(c) An applicant for a mechanic certificate or rating may take the mechanic general written test prior to meeting the applicable experience requirements of 65.77, provided the applicant presents an authenticated document from a certificated aviation maintenance technician school that demonstrates satisfactory completion of the general portion of the school's curriculum and specifies the completion date.

[Doc. No. 1179, 27 FR 7973, Aug. 10, 1962, as amended by Amdt. 65–1, 27 FR 10410, Oct. 25, 1962; Amdt. 65–6, 31 FR 5950, Apr. 19, 1966; Amdt. No. 65-63, 87 FR 31414, May 24, 2022)]

65.77 Experience requirements

Each applicant for a mechanic certificate or rating must present either—

(a) An authenticated document from a certificated aviation maintenance technician school in accordance with 147.21 of this chapter; or

(b) Documentary evidence, satisfactory to the Administrator, of—

(1) At least 18 months of practical experience with the procedures, practices, materials, tools, machine tools, and equipment generally used in constructing, maintaining, or altering airframes or powerplants, appropriate to the rating sought; or

(2) At least 30 months of practical experience concurrently performing the duties appropriate to both the airframe and powerplant ratings.

[Doc. No.: FAA-2021-0237; Amdt. No. 65-63, 87 FR 31415, May 24, 2022)]

FAR 65

65.79 Skill requirements

Each applicant for a mechanic certificate or rating must pass an oral test and a practical test, as appropriate to the rating sought, by demonstrating:

(a) Until July 31, 2023, the prescribed proficiency in the assigned objectives for the subject areas contained in the Aviation Mechanic General, Airframe, and Powerplant Practical Test Standard (incorporated by reference, see 65.23), as appropriate to the rating sought.

(b) After July 31, 2023, satisfactory understanding of the knowledge, risk management, and skill elements for each subject contained in the Aviation Mechanic General, Airframe, and Powerplant Airman Certification Standards (incorporated by reference, see 65.23), as appropriate to the rating sought.

[Doc. No.: FAA-2121-0237; Amdt. No. 65-63, 87 FR 31415, May 23, 2022)]

65.80 Certificated aviation maintenance technician school students

Whenever an aviation maintenance technician school certificated under part 147 of this chapter shows to the Administrator that any of its students has made satisfactory progress at the school and is prepared to take the oral and practical tests prescribed by 65.79, that student may take those tests during the final subjects of the student's training in the curriculum required under part 147, before the student meets the applicable experience requirements of 65.77 and before the student passes each section of the written test prescribed by 65.75.

[Doc. No.: FAA-2121-0237; Amdt. No. 65-63, 87 FR 31415, May 24, 2022)]

65.81 General privileges and limitations

(a) A certificated mechanic may perform or supervise the maintenance, preventive maintenance or alteration of an aircraft or appliance, or a part thereof, for which he is rated (but excluding major repairs to, and major alterations of, propellers, and any repair to, or alteration of, instruments), and may perform additional duties in accordance with 65.85, 65.87, and 65.95. However, he may not supervise the maintenance, preventive maintenance, or alteration of, or approve and return to service, any aircraft or appliance, or part thereof, for which he is rated unless he has satisfactorily performed the work concerned at an earlier date. If he has not so performed that work at an earlier date, he may show his ability to do it by performing it to the satisfaction of the Administrator or under the direct supervision of a certificated and appropriately rated mechanic, or a certificated repairman, who has had previous experience in the specific operation concerned.

(b) A certificated mechanic may not exercise the privileges of his certificate and rating unless he understands the current instructions of the manufacturer, and the maintenance manuals, for the specific operation concerned.

[Doc. No. 1179, 27 FR 7973, Aug. 10, 1962, as amended by Amdt. 65–2, 29 FR 5451, Apr. 23, 1964; Amdt. 65–26, 45 FR 46737, July 10, 1980]

65.83 Recent experience requirements

A certificated mechanic may not exercise the privileges of his certificate and rating unless, within the preceding 24 months—

(a) The Administrator has found that he is able to do that work; or

(b) He has, for at least 6 months—

(1) Served as a mechanic under his certificate and rating;

(2) Technically supervised other mechanics;

(3) Supervised, in an executive capacity, the maintenance or alteration of aircraft; or

(4) Been engaged in any combination of paragraph (b) (1), (2), or (3) of this section.

65.85 Airframe rating; additional privileges

(a) Except as provided in paragraph (b) of this section, a certificated mechanic with an airframe rating may approve and return to service an airframe, or any related part or appliance, after he has performed, supervised, or inspected its maintenance or alteration (excluding major repairs and major alterations). In addition, he may perform the 100-hour inspection required by part 91 of this chapter on an airframe, or any related part or appliance, and approve and return it to service.

(b) A certificated mechanic with an airframe rating can approve and return to service an airframe, or any related part or appliance, of an aircraft with a special airworthiness certificate in the light-sport category after performing and inspecting a major repair or major alteration for products that are not produced under an FAA approval, provided the work was performed in accordance with instructions developed by the manufacturer or a person acceptable to the FAA.

[Doc. No. 1179, 27 FR 7973, Aug. 10, 1962, as amended by Amdt 65–10, 32 FR 5770, Apr. 11, 1967; Amdt. 65–45, 69 FR 44879, July 27, 2004]

65.87 Powerplant rating; additional privileges

(a) Except as provided in paragraph (b) of this section, a certificated mechanic with a powerplant rating may approve and return to service a powerplant or propeller or any related part or appliance after he has performed, supervised, or inspected its maintenance or alteration (excluding major repairs and major alterations). In addition, he may perform the 100-hour inspection required by part 91 of this chapter on a powerplant or propeller, or any part thereof and approve and return it to service.

(b) A certificated mechanic with a powerplant rating can approve and return to service a powerplant or propeller, or any related part or appliance, of an aircraft with a special airworthiness certificate in the light-sport category after performing and inspecting a major repair or major alteration for products that are not produced under an FAA approval, provided the work was performed in accordance with instructions developed by the manufacturer or a person acceptable to the FAA.

[Doc. No. 1179, 27 FR 7973, Aug. 10, 1962, as amended by Amdt 65–10, 32 FR 5770, Apr. 11, 1967; Amdt. 65–45, 69 FR 44879, July 27, 2004]

65.89 Display of certificate

Each person who holds a mechanic certificate shall keep it within the immediate area where he normally exercises the privileges of the certificate and shall present it for inspection upon the request of the Administrator or an authorized representative of the National Transportation Safety Board, or of any Federal, State, or local law enforcement officer.

[Doc. No. 7258, 31 FR 13524, Oct. 20, 1966, as amended by Doc. No. 8084, 32 FR 5769, Apr. 11, 1967]

65.91 Inspection authorization

(a) An application for an inspection authorization is made on a form and in a manner prescribed by the Administrator.

(b) An applicant who meets the requirements of this section is entitled to an inspection authorization.

(c) To be eligible for an inspection authorization, an applicant must—

(1) Hold a currently effective mechanic certificate with both an airframe rating and a powerplant rating, each of which is currently effective and has been in effect for a total of at least 3 years;

(2) Have been actively engaged, for at least the 2-year period before the date he applies, in maintaining aircraft certificated and maintained in accordance with this chapter;

(3) Have a fixed base of operations at which he may be located in person or by telephone during a normal working week but it need not be the place where he will exercise his inspection authority;

(4) Have available to him the equipment, facilities, and inspection data necessary to properly inspect airframes, powerplants, propellers, or any related part or appliance; and

(5) Pass a written test on his ability to inspect according to safety standards for returning aircraft to service after major repairs and major alterations and annual and progressive inspections performed under part 43 of this chapter.

An applicant who fails the test prescribed in paragraph (c)(5) of this section may not apply for retesting until at least 90 days after the date he failed the test.

[Doc. No. 1179, 27 FR 7973, Aug. 10, 1962, as amended by Amdt. 65–5, 31 FR 3337, Mar. 3, 1966; Amdt. 65–22, 42 FR 46279, Sept. 15, 1977; Amdt. 65–30, 50 FR 15700, Apr. 19, 1985]

65.92 Inspection authorization: duration

(a) Each inspection authorization expires on March 31 of each odd-numbered year. However, the holder may exercise the privileges of that authorization only while he holds a currently effective mechanic certificate with both a currently effective airframe rating and a currently effective powerplant rating.

(b) An inspection authorization ceases to be effective whenever any of the following occurs:

(1) The authorization is surrendered, suspended, or revoked.

(2) The holder no longer has a fixed base of operation.

(3) The holder no longer has the equipment, facilities, and inspection data required by 65.91(c) (3) and (4) for issuance of his authorization.

(c) The holder of an inspection authorization that is suspended or revoked shall, upon the Administrator's request, return it to the Administrator.

[Doc. No. 12537, 42 FR 46279, Sept. 15, 1977, as amended by Amdt. 65–50, 72 FR 4404, Jan. 30, 2007]

65.93 Inspection authorization: renewal

(a) To be eligible for renewal of an inspection authorization for a 2-year period an applicant must present evidence during the month of March of each odd-numbered year, at the responsible Flight Standards office, that the applicant still meets the requirements of 65.91(c) (1) through (4). In addition, during the time the applicant held the inspection authorization, the applicant must show completion of one of the activities in 65.93(a) (1) through (5) below by March 31 of the first year of the 2-year inspection authorization period, and completion of one of the five activities during the second year of the 2-year period:

(1) Performed at least one annual inspection for each 90 days that the applicant held the current authority; or

(2) Performed at least two major repairs or major alterations for each 90 days that the applicant held the current authority; or

(3) Performed or supervised and approved at least one progressive inspection in accordance with standards prescribed by the Administrator; or

(4) Attended and successfully completed a refresher course, acceptable to the Administrator, of not less than 8 hours of instruction; or

(5) Passed an oral test by an FAA inspector to determine that the applicant's knowledge of applicable regulations and standards is current.

(b) The holder of an inspection authorization that has been in effect:

(1) for less than 90 days before the expiration date need not comply with paragraphs (a)(1) through (5) of this section.

(2) for less than 90 days before March 31 of an even-numbered year need not comply with paragraphs (a)(1) through (5) of this section for the first year of the 2-year inspection authorization period.

(c) An inspection authorization holder who does not complete one of the activities set forth in 65.93(a) (1) through (5) of this section by March 31 of the first year of the 2-year inspection authorization period may not exercise inspection authorization privileges after March 31 of the first year. The inspection authorization holder may resume exercising inspection authoriza-tion privileges after passing an oral test from an FAA inspector to determine that the applicant's knowledge of the applicable regulations and standards is current. An inspection authorization holder who passes this oral test is deemed to have completed the requirements of 65.93(a) (1) through (5) by March 31 of the first year.

[Doc. No. FAA-2007-27108, 72 FR 4404, Jan. 30, 2007, as amended by Docket FAA-2018-0119, Amdt. 65-57A, 83 FR 9171, Mar. 5, 2018]

65.95 Inspection authorization: privileges and limitations

(a) The holder of an inspection authorization may—

(1) Inspect and approve for return to service any aircraft or related part or appliance (except any aircraft maintained in accordance with a continuous airworthiness program under part 121 of this chapter) after a major repair or major alteration to it in accordance with part 43 [New] of this chapter, if the work was done in accordance with technical data approved by the Administrator; and

(2) Perform an annual, or perform or supervise a progressive inspection according to 43.13 and 43.15 of this chapter.

(b) When he exercises the privileges of an inspection authorization the holder shall keep it available for inspection by the aircraft owner, the mechanic submitting the aircraft, repair, or alteration for approval (if any), and shall present it upon the request of the Administrator or an authorized representative of the National Transportation Safety Board, or of any Federal, State, or local law enforcement officer.

(c) An inspection authorization holder who does not complete one of the activities set forth in 65.93(a) (1) through (5) of this section by March 31 of the first year of the 2-year inspection authorization period may not exercise inspection authorization privileges after March 31 of the first year. The inspection authorization holder may resume exercising inspection authorization privileges after passing an oral test from an FAA inspector to determine that the applicant's knowledge of the applicable regulations and standards is current. An inspection authorization holder who passes this oral test is deemed to have completed the requirements of 65.93(a) (1) through (5) by March 31 of the first year.

[Doc. No. FAA-2007-27108, 72 FR 4404, Jan. 30, 2007, as amended by Docket FAA-2018-0119, Amdt. 65-57A, 83 FR 9171, Mar. 5, 2018]

Subpart E — Repairmen

65.101 Eligibility requirements: General

(a) To be eligible for a repairman certificate a person must—

(1) Be at least 18 years of age;

(2) Be specially qualified to perform maintenance on aircraft or components thereof, appropriate to the job for which he is employed;

(3) Be employed for a specific job requiring those special qualifications by a certificated repair station, or by a certificated commercial operator or certificated air carrier, that is required by its operating certificate or approved operations specifications to provide a continuous airworthiness maintenance program according to its maintenance manuals;

(4) Be recommended for certification by his employer, to the satisfaction of the Administrator, as able to satisfactorily maintain aircraft or components, appropriate to the job for which he is employed;

(5) Have either—

(i) At least 18 months of practical experience in the procedures, practices, inspection methods, materials, tools, machine tools, and equipment generally used in the maintenance duties of the specific job for which the person is to be employed and certificated; or

FAR 65

(ii) Completed formal training that is acceptable to the Administrator and is specifically designed to qualify the applicant for the job on which the applicant is to be employed; and

(6) Be able to read, write, speak, and understand the English language, or, in the case of an applicant who does not meet this requirement and who is employed outside the United States by a certificated repair station, a certificated U.S. commercial operator, or a certificated U.S. air carrier, described in paragraph (a)(3) of this section, have this certificate endorsed "Valid only outside the United States."

(b) This section does not apply to the issuance of a repairman certificate (experimental aircraft builder) under 65.104 or to a repairman certificate (light-sport aircraft) under 65.107.

[Doc. No. 1179, 27 FR 7973, Aug. 10, 1962, as amended by Amdt. 65–11, 32 FR 13506, Sept. 27, 1967; Amdt. 65–24, 44 FR 46781, Aug. 9, 1979; Amdt. 65–27, 47 FR 13316, Mar. 29, 1982; Amdt. 65–45, 69 FR 44879, July 27, 2004; 72 FR 7739, Feb. 20, 2007]

65.103 Repairman certificate: privileges and limitations

(a) A certificated repairman may perform or supervise the maintenance, preventive maintenance, or alteration of aircraft or aircraft components appropriate to the job for which the repairman was employed and certificated, but only in connection with duties for the certificate holder by whom the repairman was employed and recommended.

(b) A certificated repairman may not perform or supervise duties under the repairman certificate unless the repairman understands the current instructions of the certificate holder by whom the repairman is employed and the manufacturer's instructions for continued airworthiness relating to the specific operations concerned.

(c) This section does not apply to the holder of a repairman certificate (light-sport aircraft) while that repairman is performing work under that certificate.

[Doc. No. 18241, 45 FR 46738, July 10, 1980, as amended by Amdt. 65–45, 69 FR 44879, July 27, 2004]

65.104 Repairman certificate—experimental aircraft builder—Eligibility, privileges and limitations

(a) To be eligible for a repairman certificate (experimental aircraft builder), an individual must—

(1) Be at least 18 years of age;

(2) Be the primary builder of the aircraft to which the privileges of the certificate are applicable;

(3) Show to the satisfaction of the Administrator that the individual has the requisite skill to determine whether the aircraft is in a condition for safe operations; and

(4) Be a citizen of the United States or an individual citizen of a foreign country who has lawfully been admitted for permanent residence in the United States.

(b) The holder of a repairman certificate (experimental aircraft builder) may perform condition inspections on the aircraft constructed by the holder in accordace with the operating limitations of that aircraft.

(c) Section 65.103 does not apply to the holder of a repairman certificate (experimental aircraft builder) while performing under that certificate.

[Doc. No. 18739, 44 FR 46781, Aug. 9, 1979]

65.105 Display of certificate

Each person who holds a repairman certificate shall keep it within the immediate area where he normally exercises the privileges of the certificate and shall present it for inspection upon the request of the Administrator or an authorized representative of the National Transportation Safety Board, or of any Federal, State, or local law enforcement officer.

[Doc. No. 7258, 31 FR 13524, Oct. 20, 1966, as amended by Doc. No. 8084, 32 FR 5769, Apr. 11, 1967]

65.107 Repairman certificate (light-sport aircraft): eligibility, privileges, and limits

(a) Use the following table to determine your eligibility for a repairman certificate (light-sport aircraft) and appropriate rating:

TO BE ELIGIBLE FOR	YOU MUST
(1) A repairman certificate (light-sport aircraft).	(i) Be at least 18 years aircraft old, (ii) Be able to read, speak,write, and understand English. If for medical reasons you cannot meet one of these requirements, the FAA may place limits on your repairman certificate necessary to safely perform the actions authorized by the certificate and rating, (iii) Demonstrate the requisite skill to determine whether a light-sport aircraft is in a condition for safe operation, and (iv) Be a citizen of the United States, or a citizen of a foreign country who has been lawfully admitted for permanent residence in the United States.
(2) A repairman certificate (light-sport aircraft) with an inspection rating.	(i) Meet the requirements of aircraft) with an inspection rating. paragraph (a)(1) of this section, and (ii) Complete a 16-hour training course acceptable to the FAA on inspecting the particular class of experimental light-sport aircraft for which you intend to exercise the privileges of this rating.
(3) A repairman certificate (light-sport aircraft) with a maintenance rating	(i) Meet the requirements of aircraft) with a maintenance rating paragraph (a)(1) of this section, and (ii) Complete a training course acceptable to the FAA on maintaining the particular class of light-sport aircraft for which you intend to exercise the privileges of this rating. The training course must, at a minimum, provide the following number of hours of instruction: (A) For airplane class privileges_120-hours, (B) For weight-shift control aircraft class privileges_104 hours, (C) For powered parachute class privileges_104 hours, (D) For lighter than air class privileges_80 hours, (E) For glider class privileges_80 hours.

(b) The holder of a repairman certificate (light-sport aircraft) with an inspection rating may perform the annual condition inspection on a light-sport aircraft:

(1) That is owned by the holder;

(2) That has been issued an experimental certificate for operating a light-sport aircraft under 21.191(i) of this chapter; and

(3) That is in the same class of light-sport-aircraft for which the holder has completed the training specified in paragraph (a)(2)(ii) of this section.

(c) The holder of a repairman certificate (light-sport aircraft) with a maintenance rating may—

(1) Approve and return to service an aircraft that has been issued a special airworthiness certificate in the light-sport category under 21.190 of this chapter, or any part thereof, after performing or inspecting maintenance (to include the annual condition inspection and the 100-hour inspection required by 91.327 of this chapter), preventive maintenance, or an altera-

tion (excluding a major repair or a major alteration on a product produced under an FAA approval);

(2) Perform the annual condition inspection on a light-sport aircraft that has been issued an experimental certificate for operating a light-sport aircraft under 21.191(i) of this chapter; and

(3) Only perform maintenance, preventive maintenance, and an alteration on a light-sport aircraft that is in the same class of light-sport aircraft for which the holder has completed the training specified in paragraph (a)(3)(ii) of this section. Before performing a major repair, the holder must complete additional training acceptable to the FAA and appropriate to the repair performed.

(d) The holder of a repairman certificate (light-sport aircraft) with a maintenance rating may not approve for return to service any aircraft or part thereof unless that person has previously performed the work concerned satisfactorily. If that person has not previously performed that work, the person may show the ability to do the work by performing it to the satisfaction of the FAA, or by performing it under the direct supervision of a certificated and appropriately rated mechanic, or a certificated repairman, who has had previous experience in the specific operation concerned. The repairman may not exercise the privileges of the certificate unless the repairman understands the current instructions of the manufacturer and the maintenance manuals for the specific operation concerned.

[Doc. No. FAA–2001–11133, 69 FR 44879, July 27, 2004]

Subpart F — Parachute Riggers

65.111   Certificate required

(a) No person may pack, maintain, or alter any personnel-carrying parachute intended for emergency use in connection with civil aircraft of the United States (including the reserve parachute of a dual parachute system to be used for intentional parachute jumping) unless that person holds an appropriate current certificate and type rating issued under this subpart and complies with 65.127 through 65.133.

(b) No person may pack any main parachute of a dual-parachute system to be used for intentional parachute jumping in connection with civil aircraft of the United States unless that person—

(1) Has an appropriate current certificate issued under this subpart;

(2) Is under the supervision of a current certificated parachute rigger;

(3) Is the person making the next parachute jump with that parachute in accordance with 105.43(a) of this chapter; or

(4) Is the parachutist in command making the next parachute jump with that parachute in a tandem parachute operation conducted under 105.45(b)(1) of this chapter.

(c) No person may maintain or alter any main parachute of a dual-parachute system to be used for intentional parachute jumping in connection with civil aircraft of the United States unless that person—

(1) Has an appropriate current certificate issued under this subpart; or

(2) Is under the supervision of a current certificated parachute rigger;

(d) Each person who holds a parachute rigger certificate shall present it for inspection upon the request of the Administrator or an authorized representative of the National Transportation Safety Board, or of any Federal, State, or local law enforcement officer.

(e) The following parachute rigger certificates are issued under this part:

(1) Senior parachute rigger.

(2) Master parachute rigger.

(f) Sections 65.127 through 65.133 do not apply to parachutes packed, maintained, or altered for the use of the armed forces.

[Doc. No. 1179, 27 FR 7973, Aug. 10, 1962, as amended by Amdt. 65–9, 31 FR 13524, Oct. 20, 1966; 32 FR 5769, Apr. 11, 1967; Amdt. 65–42, 66 FR 23553, May 9, 2001; Amdt. 65–54, 75 FR 31285, June 3, 2010]

65.113   Eligibility requirements: general

(a) To be eligible for a parachute rigger certificate, a person must—

(1) Be at least 18 years of age;

(2) Be able to read, write, speak, and understand the English language, or, in the case of a citizen of Puerto Rico, or a person who is employed outside of the United States by a U.S. air carrier, and who does not meet this requirement, be issued a certificate that is valid only in Puerto Rico or while he is employed outside of the United States by that air carrier, as the case may be; and

(3) Comply with the sections of this subpart that apply to the certificate and type rating he seeks.

(b) Except for a master parachute rigger certificate, a parachute rigger certificate that was issued before, and was valid on, October 31, 1962, is equal to a senior parachute rigger certificate, and may be exchanged for such a corresponding certificate.

65.115   Senior parachute rigger certificate: experience, knowledge, and skill requirements

Except as provided in 65.117, an applicant for a senior parachute rigger certificate must—

(a) Present evidence satisfactory to the Administrator that he has packed at least 20 parachutes of each type for which he seeks a rating, in accordance with the manufacturer's instructions and under the supervision of a certificated parachute rigger holding a rating for that type or a person holding an appropriate military rating;

(b) Pass a written test, with respect to parachutes in common use, on—

(1) Their construction, packing, and maintenance;

(2) The manufacturer's instructions;

(3) The regulations of this subpart; and

(c) Pass an oral and practical test showing his ability to pack and maintain at least one type of parachute in common use, appropriate to the type rating he seeks.

[Doc. No. 10468, 37 FR 13251, July 6, 1972]

65.117   Military riggers or former military riggers: special certification rule

In place of the procedure in 65.115, an applicant for a senior parachute rigger certificate is entitled to it if he passes a written test on the regulations of this subpart and presents satisfactory documentary evidence that he—

(a) Is a member or civilian employee of an Armed Force of the United States, is a civilian employee of a regular armed force of a foreign country, or has, within the 12 months before he applies, been honorably discharged or released from any status covered by this paragraph;

(b) Is serving, or has served within the 12 months before he applies, as a parachute rigger for such an Armed Force; and

(c) Has the experience required by 65.115(a).

65.119   Master parachute rigger certificate: experience, knowledge, and skill requirements

An applicant for a master parachute rigger certificate must meet the following requirements:

(a) Present evidence satisfactory to the Administrator that he has had at least 3 years of experience as a parachute rigger and has satisfactorily packed at least 100 parachutes of each of two types in common use, in accordance with the manufacturer's instructions—

(1) While a certificated and appropriately rated senior parachute rigger; or

(2) While under the supervision of a certificated and appropriately rated parachute rigger or a person holding appropriate military ratings.

An applicant may combine experience specified in paragraphs (a) (1) and (2) of this section to meet the requirements of this paragraph.

(b) If the applicant is not the holder of a senior parachute rigger certificate, pass a written test, with respect to parachutes in common use, on—

  (1) Their construction, packing, and maintenance;

  (2) The manufacturer's instructions; and

  (3) The regulations of this subpart.

(c) Pass an oral and practical test showing his ability to pack and maintain two types of parachutes in common use, appropriate to the type ratings he seeks.

[Doc. No. 10468, 37 FR 13252, July 6, 1972]

65.121 Type ratings

(a) The following type ratings are issued under this subpart:

  (1) Seat.

  (2) Back.

  (3) Chest.

  (4) Lap.

(b) The holder of a senior parachute rigger certificate who qualifies for a master parachute rigger certificate is entitled to have placed on his master parachute rigger certificate the ratings that were on his senior parachute rigger certificate.

65.123 Additional type ratings: requirements

A certificated parachute rigger who applies for an additional type rating must—

(a) Present evidence satisfactory to the Administrator that he has packed at least 20 parachutes of the type for which he seeks a rating, in accordance with the manufacturer's instructions and under the supervision of a certificated parachute rigger holding a rating for that type or a person holding an appropriate military rating; and

(b) Pass a practical test, to the satisfaction of the Administrator, showing his ability to pack and maintain the type of parachute for which he seeks a rating.

[Doc. No. 1179, 27 FR 7973, Aug. 10, 1962, as amended by Amdt. 65–20, 37 FR 13251, July 6, 1972]

65.125 Certificates: privileges

(a) A certificated senior parachute rigger may—

  (1) Pack or maintain (except for major repair) any type of parachute for which he is rated; and

  (2) Supervise other persons in packing any type of parachute for which that person is rated in accordance with 105.43(a) or 105.45(b)(1) of this chapter.

(b) A certificated master parachute rigger may—

  (1) Pack, maintain, or alter any type of parachute for which he is rated; and

  (2) Supervise other persons in packing, maintaining, or altering any type of parachute for which the certificated parachute rigger is rated in accordance with 105.43(a) or 105.45(b)(1) of this chapter.

(c) A certificated parachute rigger need not comply with 65.127 through 65.133 (relating to facilities, equipment, performance standards, records, recent experience, and seal) in packing, maintaining, or altering (if authorized) the main parachute of a dual parachute pack to be used for intentional jumping.

[Doc. No. 1179, 27 FR 7973, Aug. 10, 1962, as amended by Amdt. 65–20, 37 FR 13252, July 6, 1972; Amdt. 65–42, 66 FR 23553, May 9, 2001]

65.127 Facilities and equipment

No certificated parachute rigger may exercise the privileges of his certificate unless he has at least the following facilities and equipment available to him:

(a) A smooth top table at least three feet wide by 40 feet long.

(b) Suitable housing that is adequately heated, lighted, and ventilated for drying and airing parachutes.

(c) Enough packing tools and other equipment to pack and maintain the types of parachutes that he services.

(d) Adequate housing facilities to perform his duties and to protect his tools and equipment.

[Doc. No. 1179, 27 FR 7973, Aug. 10, 1962, as amended by Amdt. 65–27, 47 FR 13316, Mar. 29, 1982]

65.129 Performance standards

No certificated parachute rigger may—

(a) Pack, maintain, or alter any parachute unless he is rated for that type;

(b) Pack a parachute that is not safe for emergency use;

(c) Pack a parachute that has not been thoroughly dried and aired;

(d) Alter a parachute in a manner that is not specifically authorized by the Administrator or the manufacturer;

(e) Pack, maintain, or alter a parachute in any manner that deviates from procedures approved by the Administrator or the manufacturer of the parachute; or

(f) Exercise the privileges of his certificate and type rating unless he understands the current manufacturer's instructions for the operation involved and has—

  (1) Performed duties under his certificate for at least 90 days within the preceding 12 months; or

  (2) Shown the Administrator that he is able to perform those duties.

65.131 Records

(a) Each certificated parachute rigger shall keep a record of the packing, maintenance, and alteration of parachutes performed or supervised by him. He shall keep in that record, with respect to each parachute worked on, a statement of—

  (1) Its type and make;

  (2) Its serial number;

  (3) The name and address of its owner;

  (4) The kind and extent of the work performed;

  (5) The date when and place where the work was performed; and

  (6) The results of any drop tests made with it.

(b) Each person who makes a record under paragraph (a) of this section shall keep it for at least 2 years after the date it is made.

(c) Each certificated parachute rigger who packs a parachute shall write, on the parachute packing record attached to the parachute, the date and place of the packing and a notation of any defects he finds on inspection. He shall sign that record with his name and the number of his certificate.

65.133 Seal

Each certificated parachute rigger must have a seal with an identifying mark prescribed by the Administrator, and a seal press. After packing a parachute he shall seal the pack with his seal in accordance with the manufacturer's recommendation for that type of parachute.

Appendix A to Part 65 — Aircraft Dispatcher Courses

Overview

This appendix sets forth the areas of knowledge necessary to perform dispatcher functions. The items listed below indicate the minimum set of topics that must be covered in a training course for aircraft dispatcher certification. The order of coverage is at the discretion of the approved school.

I. Regulations
  A. Subpart C of this part;
  B. Parts 1, 25, 61, 71, 91, 121, 139, and 175, of this chapter;
  C. 49 CFR part 830;
  D. General Operating Manual.
II. Meteorology
  A. Basic Weather Studies
    (1) The earth's motion and its effects on weather.
    (2) Analysis of the following regional weather types, characteristics, and structures, or combinations thereof:
      (a) Maritime.
      (b) Continental.
      (c) Polar.
      (d) Tropical.
    (3) Analysis of the following local weather types, characteristics, and structures or combinations thereof:
      (a) Coastal.
      (b) Mountainous.
      (c) Island.
      (d) Plains.
    (4) The following characteristics of the atmosphere:
      (a) Layers.
      (b) Composition.
      (c) Global Wind Patterns.
      (d) Ozone.
    (5) Pressure:
      (a) Units of Measure.
      (b) Weather Systems Characteristics.
      (c) Temperature Effects on Pressure.
      (d) Altimeters.
      (e) Pressure Gradient Force.
      (f) Pressure Pattern Flying Weather.
    (6) Wind:
      (a) Major Wind Systems and Coriolis Force.
      (b) Jetstreams and their Characteristics.
      (c) Local Wind and Related Terms.
    (7) States of Matter:
      (a) Solids, Liquid, and Gases.
      (b) Causes of change of state.
    (8) Clouds:
      (a) Composition, Formation, and Dissipation.
      (b) Types and Associated Precipitation.
      (c) Use of Cloud Knowledge in Forecasting.
    (9) Fog:
      (a) Causes, Formation, and Dissipation.
      (b) Types.
    (10) Ice:
      (a) Causes, Formation, and Dissipation.
      (b) Types.
    (11) Stability/Instability:
      (a) Temperature Lapse Rate, Convection.
      (b) Adiabatic Processes.
      (c) Lifting Processes.
      (d) Divergence.
      (e) Convergence.
    (12) Turbulence:
      (a) Jetstream Associated.
      (b) Pressure Pattern Recognition.
      (c) Low Level Windshear.
      (d) Mountain Waves.
      (e) Thunderstorms.
      (f) Clear Air Turbulence.
    (13) Airmasses:
      (a) Classification and Characteristics.
      (b) Source Regions.
      (c) Use of Airmass Knowledge in Forecasting.
    (14) Fronts:
      (a) Structure and Characteristics, Both Vertical and Horizontal.
      (b) Frontal Types.
      (c) Frontal Weather Flying.
    (15) Theory of Storm Systems:
      (a) Thunderstorms.
      (b) Tornadoes.
      (c) Hurricanes and Typhoons.
      (d) Microbursts.
      (e) Causes, Formation, and Dissipation.
  B. Weather, Analysis, and Forecasts
    (1) Observations:
      (a) Surface Observations.
        (i) Observations made by certified weather observer.
        (ii) Automated Weather Observations.
      (b) Terminal Forecasts.
      (c) Significant En route Reports and Forecasts.
        (i)   Pilot Reports.
        (ii) Area Forecasts.
        (iii) Sigmets, Airmets.
        (iv) Center Weather Advisories.
      (d) Weather Imagery.
        (i)   Surface Analysis.
        (ii)   Weather Depiction.
        (iii) Significant Weather Prognosis.
        (iv)   Winds and Temperature Aloft.
        (v)   Tropopause Chart.
        (vi)   Composite Moisture Stability Chart.
        (vii) Surface Weather Prognostic Chart.
        (viii) Radar Meteorology.
        (ix)   Satellite Meteorology.
        (x)   Other charts as applicable.
      (e) Meteorological Information Data Collection Systems.
    (2) Data Collection, Analysis, and Forecast Facilities.
    (3) Service Outlets Providing Aviation Weather Products.
  C. Weather Related Aircraft Hazards
    (1) Crosswinds and Gusts.
    (2) Contaminated Runways.
    (3) Restrictions to Surface Visibility.
    (4) Turbulence and Windshear.
    (5) Icing.
    (6) Thunderstorms and Microburst.
    (7) Volcanic Ash.
III. Navigation
  A. Study of the Earth
    (1) Time reference and location (0 Longitude, UTC).
    (2) Definitions.
    (3) Projections.
    (4) Charts.
  B. Chart Reading, Application, and Use.
  C. National Airspace Plan.
  D. Navigation Systems.
  E. Airborne Navigation Instruments.
  F. Instrument Approach Procedures.
    (1) Transition Procedures.
    (2) Precision Approach Procedures.
    (3) Non-precision Approach Procedures.
    (4) Minimums and the relationship to weather.
  G. Special Navigation and Operations.
    (1) North Atlantic.
    (2) Pacific.
    (3) Global Differences.

FAR 65

IV. Aircraft
   A. Aircraft Flight Manual.
   B. Systems Overview.
     (1) Flight controls.
     (2) Hydraulics.
     (3) Electrical.
     (4) Air Conditioning and Pressurization.
     (5) Ice and Rain protection.
     (6) Avionics, Communication, and Navigation.
     (7) Powerplants and Auxiliary Power Units.
     (8) Emergency and Abnormal Procedures.
     (9) Fuel Systems and Sources.
   C. Minimum Equipment List/Configuration Deviation List (MEL/CDL) and Applications.
   D. Performance.
     (1) Aircraft in general.
     (2) Principles of flight:
       (a) Group one aircraft.
       (b) Group two aircraft.
     (3) Aircraft Limitations.
     (4) Weight and Balance.
     (5) Flight instrument errors.
     (6) Aircraft performance:
       (a) Take-off performance.
       (b) En route performance.
       (c) Landing performance.

V. Communications
   A. Regulatory requirements.
   B. Communication Protocol.
   C. Voice and Data Communications.
   D. Notice to Airmen (NOTAMS).
   E. Aeronautical Publications.
   F. Abnormal Procedures.

VI. Air Traffic Control
   A. Responsibilities.
   B. Facilities and Equipment.
   C. Airspace classification and route structure.
   D. Flight Plans.
     (1) Domestic.
     (2) International.
   E. Separation Minimums.
   F. Priority Handling.
   G. Holding Procedures.
   H. Traffic Management.

VII. Emergency and Abnormal Procedures
   A. Security measures on the ground.
   B. Security measures in the air.
   C. FAA responsibility and services.
   D. Collection and dissemination of information on overdue or missing aircraft.
   E. Means of declaring an emergency.
   F. Responsibility for declaring an emergency.
   G. Required reporting of an emergency.
   H. NTSB reporting requirements.

VIII. Practical Dispatch Applications
   A. Human Factors.
     (1) Decisionmaking:
       (a) Situation Assessment.
       (b) Generation and Evaluation of Alternatives.
         (i) Tradeoffs and Prioritization.
         (ii) Contingency Planning.
       (c) Support Tools and Technologies.
     (2) Human Error:
       (a) Causes.
         (i) Individual and Organizational Factors.
         (ii) Technology-Induced Error.

       (b) Prevention.
       (c) Detection and Recovery.
     (3) Teamwork:
       (a) Communication and Information Exchange.
       (b) Cooperative and Distributed Problem-Solving.
       (c) Resource Management.
         (i) Air Traffic Control (ATC) activities and workload.
         (ii) Flightcrew activities and workload.
         (iii) Maintenance activities and workload.
         (iv) Operations Control Staff activities and workload.
   B. Applied Dispatching.
     (1) Briefing techniques, Dispatcher, Pilot.
     (2) Preflight:
       (a) Safety.
       (b) Weather Analysis.
         (i) Satellite imagery.
         (ii) Upper and lower altitude charts.
         (iii) Significant en route reports and forecasts.
         (iv) Surface charts.
         (v) Surface observations.
         (vi) Terminal forecasts and orientation to Enhanced Weather Information System (EWINS).
       (c) NOTAMS and airport conditions.
       (d) Crew.
         (i) Qualifications.
         (ii) Limitations.
       (e) Aircraft.
         (i) Systems.
         (ii) Navigation instruments and avionics systems.
         (iii) Flight instruments.
         (iv) Operations manuals and MEL/CDL.
         (v) Performance and limitations.
       (f) Flight Planning.
         (i) Route of flight.
           1. Standard Instrument Departures and Standard Terminal Arrival Routes.
           2. En route charts.
           3. Operational altitude.
           4. Departure and arrival charts.
         (ii) Minimum departure fuel.
           1. Climb.
           2. Cruise.
           3. Descent.
       (g) Weight and balance.
       (h) Economics of flight overview (Performance, Fuel Tankering).
       (i) Decision to operate the flight.
       (j) ATC flight plan filing.
       (k) Flight documentation.
         (i) Flight plan.
         (ii) Dispatch release.
     (3) Authorize flight departure with concurrence of pilot in command.
     (4) In-flight operational control:
       (a) Current situational awareness.
       (b) Information exchange.
       (c) Amend original flight release as required.
     (5) Post-Flight:
       (a) Arrival verification.
       (b) Weather debrief.
       (c) Flight irregularity reports as required.

[Doc. No. FAA–1998–4553, 64 FR 68925, Dec. 8, 1999]

PART 91 — GENERAL OPERATING AND FLIGHT RULES

FAR
91

Subpart J — Waivers

Subpart K — Fractional Ownership Operations

Operational Control

Program Management

Subpart L — Continued Airworthiness and Safety Improvements

Subpart M — Special Federal Aviation Regulations

FAR
91

Subpart N — Mitsubishi MU-2B Series Special Training, Experience, and Operating Requirements

Appendix A to Part 91 — Category II Operations: Manual, Instruments, Equipment, and Maintenance

Appendix B to Part 91 — [Reserved]

Appendix C to Part 91 — [Reserved]

Appendix D to Part 91 — Airports/Locations: Special Operating Restrictions

Appendix E to Part 91 — Airplane Flight Recorder Specifications

Appendix F to Part 91 — Helicopter Flight Recorder Specifications

Appendix G to Part 91 — Operations in Reduced Vertical Separation Minimum (RVSM) Airspace

Authority: 49 U.S.C. 106(f), 106(g), 40101, 40103, 40105, 40113, 40120, 44101, 44111, 44701, 44704, 44709, 44711, 44712, 44715, 44716, 44717, 44722, 46306, 46315, 46316, 46504, 46506-46507, 47122, 47508, 47528-47531, 47534, Pub. L. 114-190, 130 Stat. 615 (49 U.S.C. 44703 note); articles 12 and 29 of the Convention on International Civil Aviation (61 Stat. 1180), (126 Stat. 11).

Special Federal Aviation Regulation No. 50–2 — Special Flight Rules in the Vicinity of the Grand Canyon National Park, AZ

Section 1. Applicability.

This rule prescribes special operating rules for all persons operating aircraft in the following airspace, designated as the Grand Canyon National Park Special Flight Rules Area:

That airspace extending upward from the surface up to but not including 14,500 feet MSL within an area bounded by a line beginning at lat. 36°09'30" N., long. 114°03'00" W.; northeast to lat. 36°14'00" N., long. 113°09'50" W.; thence northeast along the boundary of the Grand Canyon National Park to lat. 36°24'47" N., long. 112°52'00" W.; to lat. 36°30'30" N., long. 112°36'15" W. to lat. 36°21'30" N., long. 112°00'00" W. to lat. 36°35'30" N., long. 111°53'10" W., to lat. 36°53'00" N., long. 111°36'45" W. to lat. 36°53'00" N., long. 111°33'00" W.; to lat. 36°19'00" N., long. 111°50'50" W.; to lat. 36°17'00" N., long. 111°42'00" W.; to lat. 35°59'30" N., long. 111°42'00" W.; to lat. 35°57'30" N., long. 112°03'55" W.; thence counterclockwise via the 5 statute mile radius of the Grand Canyon Airport airport reference point (lat. 35°57'09" N., long. 112°08'47" W.) to lat. 35°57'30" N., long. 112°14'00" W.; to lat. 35°57'30" N., long. 113°11'00" W.; to lat. 35°42'30" N., long. 113°11'00" W.; to 35°38'30" N.; long. 113°27'30" W.; thence counterclockwise via the 5 statute mile radius of the Peach Springs VORTAC to lat. 35°41'20" N., long. 113°36'00" W.; to lat. 35°55'25" N., long. 113°49'10" W.; to lat. 35°57'45" N., 113°45'20" W.; thence northwest along the park bound-

ary to lat. 36°02'20" N., long. 113°50'15" W.; to 36°00'10" N., long. 113°53'45" W.; thence to the point of beginning.

Section 3. Aircraft operations: general

Except in an emergency, no person may operate an aircraft in the Special Flight Rules, Area under VFR on or after September 22, 1988, or under IFR on or after April 6, 1989, unless the operation—

(a) Is conducted in accordance with the following procedures:

NOTE: *The following procedures do not relieve the pilot from see-and-avoid responsibility or compliance with FAR 91.119.*

(1) Unless necessary to maintain a safe distance from other aircraft or terrain—

    (i)   Remain clear of the areas described in Section 4; and

    (ii) Remain at or above the following altitudes in each sector of the canyon:

Eastern section from Lees Ferry to North Canyon and North Canyon to Boundary Ridge: as prescribed in Section 5.

Boundary Ridge to Supai Point (Yumtheska Point): 10,000 feet MSL.

Western section from Diamond Creek to the Grant Wash Cliffs: 8,000 feet MSL.

(2) Proceed through the four flight corridors describe in Section 4 at the following altitudes unless otherwise authorized in writing by the responsible Flight Standards office:

Northbound

11,500 or

13,500 feet MSL

Southbound

>10,500 or

>12,500 feet MSL

(b) Is authorized in writing by the responsible Flight Standards office and is conducted in compliance with the conditions contained in that authorization. Normally authorization will be granted for operation in the areas described in Section 4 or below the altitudes listed in Section 5 only for operations of aircraft necessary for law enforcement, firefighting, emergency medical treatment/evacuation of persons in the vicinity of the Park; for support of Park maintenance or activities; or for aerial access to and maintenance of other property located within the Special Flight Rules Area. Authorization may be issued on a continuing basis.

(c)

(1) Prior to November 1, 1988, is conducted in accordance with a specific authorization to operate in that airspace incorporated in the operator's part 135 operations specifications in accordance with the provisions of SFAR 50–1, notwithstanding the provisions of Sections 4 and 5; and

(2) On or after November 1, 1988, is conducted in accordance with a specific authorization to operate in that airspace incorporated in the operated in the operator's operations specifications and approved by the responsible Flight Standards office in accordance with the provisions of SFAR 50-2.

(d) Is a search and rescue mission directed by the U.S. Air Force Rescue Coordination Center.

(e) Is conducted within 3 nautical miles of Whitmore Airstrip, Pearce Ferry Airstrip, North Rim Airstrip, Cliff Dwellers Airstrip, or Marble Canyon Airstrip at an altitudes less than 3,000 feet above airport elevation, for the purpose of landing at or taking off from that facility. Or

(f) Is conducted under an IFR clearance and the pilot is acting in accordance with ATC instructions. An IFR flight plan may not be filed on a route or at an altitude that would require operation in an area described in Section 4.

Section 4. Flight-free zones

Except in an emergency or if otherwise necessary for safety of flight, or unless otherwise authorized by the responsible Flight Standards office for a purpose listed in Section 3(b), no person may operate an aircraft in the Special Flight Rules Area within the following areas:

(a) Desert View Flight-Free Zone. Within an area bounded by a line beginning at Lat. 35°59'30" N., Long. 111°46'20" W. to 35°59'30" N., Long. 111°52'45" W.; to Lat. 36°04'50" N., Long. 111°52'00" W.; to Lat. 36°06'00" N., Long. 111°46'20" W.; to the point of origin; but not including the airspace at and above 10,500 feet MSL within 1 mile of the western boundary of the zone. The area between the Desert View and Bright Angel Flight-Free Zones is designated the "Zuni Point Corridor."

(b) Bright Angel Flight-Free Zone. Within an area bounded by a line beginning at Lat. 35°59'30" N., Long. 111°55'30" W.; to Lat. 35°59'30" N., Long. 112°04'00" W.; thence counterclockwise via the 5 statute mile radius of the Grand Canyon Airport point (Lat. 35°57'09" N., Long. 112°08'47" W.) to Lat. 36°01'30" N., Long. 112°11'00" W.; to Lat. 36°06'15" N., Long. 112°12'50" W.; to Lat. 36°14'40" N., Long. 112°08'50" W.; to Lat. 36°14'40" N., Long. 111°57'30" W.; to Lat. 36°12'30" N., Long. 111°53'50" W.; to the point of origin; but not including the airspace at and above 10,500 feet MSL within 1 mile of the eastern boundary between the southern boundary and Lat. 36°04'50" N. or the airspace at and above 10,500 feet MSL within 2 miles of the northwest boundary. The area bounded by the Bright Angel and Shinumo Flight-Free Zones is designated the "Dragon Corridor."

(c) Shinumo Flight-Free Zone. Within an area bounded by a line beginning at Lat. 36°04'00" N., Long. 112°16'40" W.; northwest along the park boundary to a point at Lat. 36°12'47" N., Long. 112°30'53" W.; to Lat. 36°21'15" N., Long. 112°20'20" W.; east along the park boundary to Lat. 36°21'15" N., Long. 112°13'55" W.; to Lat. 36°14'40" N., Long. 112°11'25" W.; to the point of origin. The area between the Thunder River/Toroweap and Shinumo Flight Free Zones is designated the "Fossil Canyon Corridor."

(d) Toroweap/Thunder River Flight-Free Zone. Within an area bounded by a line beginning at Lat. 36°22'45" N., Long. 112°20'35" W.; thence northwest along the boundary of the Grand Canyon National Park to Lat. 36°17'48" N., Long. 113°03'15" W.; to Lat. 36°15'00" N., Long. 113°07'10" W.; to Lat. 36°10'30" N., Long. 113°07'10" W.; thence east along the Colorado River to the confluence of Havasu Canyon (Lat. 36°18'40" N., Long. 112°45'45" W.;) including that area within a 1.5 nautical mile radius of Toroweap Overlook (Lat. 36°12'45" N., Long. 113°03'30" W.); to the point of origin; but not including the following airspace designated as the "Tuckup Corridor": at or above 10,500 feet MSL within 2 nautical miles either side of a line extending between Lat. 36°24'47" N., Long. 112°48'50" W. and Lat. 36°17'10" N., Long. 112°48'50" W.; to the point of origin.

Section 5. Minimum flight altitudes

Except in an emergency or if otherwise necessary for safety of flight, or unless otherwise authorized by the responsible Flight Standards office for a purpose listed in Section 3(b), no person may operate an aircraft in the Special Flight Rules Area at an altitude lower than the following:

(a) Eastern section from Lees Ferry to North Canyon: 5,000 feet MSL.

(b) Eastern section from North Canyon to Boundary Ridge: 6,000 feet MSL.

(c) Boundary Ridge to Supai (Yumtheska) Point: 7,500 feet MSL.

(d) Supai Point to Diamond Creek: 6,500 feet MSL.

(e) Western section from Diamond Creek to the Grand Wash Cliffs: 5,000 feet MSL.

Section 9. Termination date.

Section 1. Applicability, Section 4, Flight-free zones, and Section 5. Minimum flight altitudes, expire on April 19, 2001.

NOTE: *[Removed]*

[66 FR 1003, Jan. 4, 2001, as amended at 66 FR 16584, Mar. 26, 2001; 72 FR 9846, Mar. 6, 2007; Docket FAA-2018-0119, Amdt. 91-350, 83 FR 9171, Mar. 5, 2018]

Special Federal Aviation Regulation No. 60 — Air Traffic Control System Emergency Operation

1. Each person shall, before conducting any operation under the Feeral Aviation Regulations (14 CFR chapter I), be familiar with all available information concerning that operation, including Notices to Airmen issued under 91.139 and, when activated, the provisions of the National Air Traffic Reduced Complement Operations Plan available for inspection at operating air traffic facilities and Regional air traffic division offices, and the General Aviation Reservation Program. No operator may change the designated airport of intended operation for any flight contained in the October 1, 1990, OAG.

2. Notwithstanding any provision of the Federal Aviation Regulations to the contrary, no person may operate an aircraft in the Air Traffic Control System:

   a. Contrary to any restriction, prohibition, procedure or other action taken by the Director of the Office of Air Traffic Systems Management (Director) pursuant to paragraph 3 of this regulation and announced in a Notice to Airmen pursuant to 91.139 of the Federal Aviation Regulations.

   b. When the National Air Traffic Reduced Complement Operations Plan is activated pursuant to paragraph 4 of this regulation, except in accordance with the pertinent provisions of the National Air Traffic Reduced Complement Operations Plan.

3. Prior to or in connection with the implementation of the RCOP, and as conditions warrant, the Director is authorized to:

   a. Restrict, prohibit, or permit VFR and/or IFR operations at any airport, Class B airspace area, Class C airspace area, or other class of controlled airspace.

   b. Give priority at any airport to flights that are of military necessity, or are medical emergency flights, Presidential flights, and flights transporting critical Government employees.

   c. Implement, at any airport, traffic management procedures, that may include reduction of flight operations. Reduction of flight operations will be accomplished, to the extent practical, on a pro rata basis among and between air carrier, commercial operator, and general aviation operations. Flights cancelled under this SFAR at a high density traffic airport will be considered to have been operated for purposes of part 93 of the Federal Aviation Regulations.

4. The Director may activate the National Air Traffic Reduced Complement Operations Plan at any time he finds that it is necessary for the safety and efficiency of the National Airspace System. Upon activation of the RCOP and notwithstanding any provision of the FAR to the contrary, the Director is authorized to suspend or modify any airspace designation.

5. Notice of restrictions, prohibitions, procedures and other actions taken by the Director under this regulation with respect to the operation of the Air Traffic Control system will be announced in Notices to Airmen issued pursuant to 91.139 of the Federal Aviation Regulations.

6. The Director may delegate his authority under this regulation to the extent he considers necessary for the safe and efficient operation of the National Air Traffic Control System.

Authority: 49 U.S.C. app. 1301(7), 1303, 1344, 1348, 1352 through 1355, 1401, 1421 through 1431, 1471, 1472, 1502, 1510, 1522, and 2121 through 2125; articles 12, 29, 31, and 32(a) of the Convention on International Civil Aviation (61 stat. 1180); 42 U.S.C. 4321 et seq.; E.O. 11514, 35 FR 4247, 3 CFR, 1966–1970 Comp., p. 902; 49 U.S.C. 106(g).

[Doc. No. 26351, 55 FR 40760, Oct. 4, 1990, as amended by Amdt. 91–227, 56 FR 65652, Dec. 17, 1991]

Special Federal Aviation Regulation No. 97— Special Operating Rules for the Conduct of Instrument Flight Rules (IFR) Area Navigation (RNAV) Operations using Global Positioning Systems (GPS) in Alaska

Those persons identified in Section 1 may conduct IFR en route RNAV operations in the State of Alaska and its airspace on published air traffic routes using TSO C145a/C146a navigation systems as the only means of IFR navigation. Despite contrary provisions of parts 71, 91, 95, 121, 125, and 135 of this chapter, a person may operate aircraft in accordance with this SFAR if the following requirements are met.

Section 1. Purpose, use, and limitations

(a) This SFAR permits TSO C145a/C146a GPS (RNAV) systems to be used for IFR en route operations in the United States airspace over and near Alaska (as set forth in paragraph c of this section) at Special Minimum En Route Altitudes (MEA) that are outside the operational service volume of ground-based navigation aids, if the aircraft operation also meets the requirements of sections 3 and 4 of this SFAR.

(b) Certificate holders and part 91 operators may operate aircraft under this SFAR provided that they comply with the requirements of this SFAR.

(c) Operations conducted under this SFAR are limited to United States Airspace within and near the State of Alaska as defined in the following area description:

From 62°00'00.000"N, Long. 141°00'00.00"W.;

to Lat. 59°47'54.11"N., Long. 135°28'38.34"W.;

to Lat. 56°00'04.11"N., Long. 130°00'07.80"W.;

to Lat. 54°43'00.00"N., Long. 130°37'00.00"W.;

to Lat. 51°24'00.00"N., Long. 167°49'00.00"W.;

to Lat. 50°08'00.00"N., Long. 176°34'00.00"W.;

to Lat. 45°42'00.00"N., Long. −162°55'00.00"E.;

to Lat. 50°05'00.00"N., Long. −159°00'00.00"E.;

to Lat. 54°00'00.00"N., Long. −169°00'00.00"E.;

to Lat. 60°00 00.00"N., Long. −180°00' 00.00"E;

to Lat. 65°00'00.00"N., Long. 168°58'23.00"W.;

to Lat. 90°00'00.00"N., Long. 00°00'0.00"W.;

to Lat. 62°00'00.000"N, Long. 141°00'00.00"W.

(d) No person may operate an aircraft under IFR during the en route portion of flight below the standard MEA or at the special MEA unless the operation is conducted in accordance with sections 3 and 4 of this SFAR.

Section 2. Definitions and abbreviations

For the purposes of this SFAR, the following definitions and abbreviations apply.

Area navigation (RNAV). RNAV is a method of navigation that permits aircraft operations on any desired flight path.

Area navigation (RNAV) route. RNAV route is a published route based on RNAV that can be used by suitably equipped aircraft.

Certificate holder. A certificate holder means a person holding a certificate issued under part 119 or part 125 of this chapter or holding operations specifications issued under part 129 of this chapter.

Global Navigation Satellite System (GNSS). GNSS is a world-wide position and time determination system that uses satellite ranging signals to determine user location. It encompasses all satellite ranging technologies, including GPS and additional satellites. Components of the GNSS include GPS, the Global Orbiting Navigation Satellite System, and WAAS satellites.

Global Positioning System (GPS). GPS is a satellite-based radio navigational, positioning, and time transfer system. The system provides highly accurate position and velocity information and precise time on a continuous global basis to properly equipped users.

Minimum crossing altitude (MCA). The minimum crossing altitude (MCA) applies to the operation of an aircraft proceeding to a higher minimum en route altitude when crossing specified fixes.

Required navigation system. Required navigation system means navigation equipment that meets the performance requirements of TSO C145a/C146a navigation systems certified for IFR en route operations.

Route segment. Route segment is a portion of a route bounded on each end by a fix or NAVAID.

Special MEA. Special MEA refers to the minimum en route altitudes, using required navigation systems, on published routes outside the operational service volume of ground-based navigation aids and are depicted on the published Low Altitude and High Altitude En Route Charts using the color blue and with the suffix "G." For example, a GPS MEA of 4000 feet MSL would be depicted using the color blue, as 4000G.

Standard MEA. Standard MEA refers to the minimum en route IFR altitude on published routes that uses ground-based navigation aids and are depicted on the published Low Altitude and High Altitude En Route Charts using the color black.

Station referenced. Station referenced refers to radio navigational aids or fixes that are referenced by ground based navigation facilities such as VOR facilities.

Wide Area Augmentation System (WAAS). WAAS is an augmentation to GPS that calculates GPS integrity and correction data on the ground and uses geo-stationary satellites to broadcast GPS integrity and correction data to GPS/WAAS users and to provide ranging signals. It is a safety critical system consisting of a ground network of reference and integrity monitor data processing sites to assess current GPS performance, as well as a space segment that broadcasts that assessment to GNSS users to support en route through precision approach navigation. Users of the system include all aircraft applying the WAAS data and ranging signal.

Section 3. Operational Requirements

To operate an aircraft under this SFAR, the following requirements must be met:

(a) Training and qualification for operations and maintenance personnel on required navigation equipment used under this SFAR.

(b) Use authorized procedures for normal, abnormal, and emergency situations unique to these operations, including degraded navigation capabilities, and satellite system outages.

(c) For certificate holders, training of flight crewmembers and other personnel authorized to exercise operational control on the use of those procedures specified in paragraph b of this section.

(d) Part 129 operators must have approval from the State of the operator to conduct operations in accordance with this SFAR.

(e) In order to operate under this SFAR, a certificate holder must be authorized in operations specifications.

Section 4. Equipment Requirements

(a) The certificate holder must have properly installed, certificated, and functional dual required navigation systems as defined in section 2 of this SFAR for the en route operations covered under this SFAR.

(b) When the aircraft is being operated under part 91, the aircraft must be equipped with at least one properly installed, certificated, and functional required navigation system as defined in section 2 of this SFAR for the en route operations covered under this SFAR.

Section 5. Expiration date

This Special Federal Aviation Regulation will remain in effect until rescinded.

[Doc. No. FAA–2003–14305, 68 FR 14077, Mar. 21, 2003]

Special Federal Aviation Regulation No. 104— Prohibition Against Certain Flights by Syrian Air Carriers to the United States

1. Applicability. This Special Federal Aviation Regulation (SFAR) No. 104 applies to any air carrier owned or controlled by Syria that is engaged in scheduled international air services.

2. Special flight restrictions. Except as provided in paragraphs 3 and 4 of this SFAR No. 104, no air carrier described in paragraph 1 may take off from or land in the territory of the United States.

3. Permitted operations. This SFAR does not prohibit overflights of the territory of the United States by any air carrier described in paragraph 1.

4. Emergency situations. In an emergency that requires immediate decision and action for the safety of the flight, the pilot in com-

mand of an aircraft of any air carrier described in paragraph 1 may deviate from this SFAR to the extent required by that emergency. Each person who deviates from this rule must, within 10 days of the deviation, excluding Saturdays, Sundays, and Federal holidays, submit to the responsible Flight Standards office a complete report of the operations or the aircraft involved in the deviation, including a description of the deviation and the reasons therefor.

5. Duration. This SFAR No. 104 will remain in effect until further notice.

[Doc. No. FAA-2004-17763, 69 FR 31719, June 4, 2004, as amended by Docket FAA-2018-0119, Amdt. 91-350, 83 FR 9171, Mar. 5, 2018]

Subpart A—General

Source: Docket No. 18334, 54 FR 34292, Aug. 18, 1989, unless otherwise noted.

91.1   Applicability

(a) Except as provided in paragraphs (b), (c), (e), and (f) of this section and 91.701 and 91.703, this part prescribes rules governing the operation of aircraft within the United States, including the waters within 3 nautical miles of the U.S. coast.

(b) Each person operating an aircraft in the airspace overlying the waters between 3 and 12 nautical miles from the coast of the United States must comply with 91.1 through 91.21; 91.101 through 91.143; 91.151 through 91.159; 91.167 through 91.193; 91.203; 91.205; 91.209 through 91.217; 91.221; 91.225; 91.303 through 91.319; 91.323 through 91.327; 91.605; 91.609; 91.703 through 91.715; and 91.903.

(c) This part applies to each person on board an aircraft being operated under this part, unless otherwise specified.

(d) This part also establishes requirements for operators to take actions to support the continued airworthiness of each airplane.

(e) This part does not apply to any aircraft or vehicle governed by part 103 of this chapter, or subparts B, C, or D of part 101 of this chapter.

(f) Except as provided in 107.13, 107.27, 107.47, 107.57, and 107.59 of this chapter, this part does not apply to any aircraft governed by part 107 of this chapter.

[Doc. No. 18334, 54 FR 34292, Aug. 18, 1989, as amended by Amdt. 91-257, 64 FR 1079, Jan. 7, 1999; Amdt. 91-282, 69 FR 44880, July 27, 2004; Amdt. 91-297, 72 FR 63410, Nov. 8, 2007; Amdt. 91-314, 75 FR 30193, May 28, 2010; Docket FAA-2015-0150, Amdt. 91-343, 81 FR 42208, June 28, 2016]

91.3   Responsibility and authority of the pilot in command

(a) The pilot in command of an aircraft is directly responsible for, and is the final authority as to, the operation of that aircraft.

(b) In an in-flight emergency requiring immediate action, the pilot in command may deviate from any rule of this part to the extent required to meet that emergency.

(c) Each pilot in command who deviates from a rule under paragraph (b) of this section shall, upon the request of the Administrator, send a written report of that deviation to the Administrator.

(Approved by the Office of Management and Budget under control number 2120-0005)

91.5   Pilot in command of aircraft requiring more than one required pilot

No person may operate an aircraft that is type certificated for more than one required pilot flight crewmember unless the pilot in command meets the requirements of 61.58 of this chapter.

91.7   Civil aircraft airworthiness

(a) No person may operate a civil aircraft unless it is in an airworthy condition.

(b) The pilot in command of a civil aircraft is responsible for determining whether that aircraft is in condition for safe flight. The pilot in command shall discontinue the flight when unairworthy mechanical, electrical, or structural conditions occur.

91.9   Civil aircraft flight manual, marking, and placard requirements

(a) Except as provided in paragraph (d) of this section, no person may operate a civil aircraft without complying with the operating limitations specified in the approved Airplane or Rotorcraft Flight Manual, markings, and placards, or as otherwise prescribed by the certificating authority of the country of registry.

(b) No person may operate a U.S.-registered civil aircraft—

(1) For which an Airplane or Rotorcraft Flight Manual is required by 21.5 of this chapter unless there is available in the aircraft a current, approved Airplane or Rotorcraft Flight Manual or the manual provided for in 121.141(b); and

(2) For which an Airplane or Rotorcraft Flight Manual is not required by 21.5 of this chapter, unless there is available in the aircraft a current approved Airplane or Rotorcraft Flight Manual, approved manual material, markings, and placards, or any combination thereof.

(c) No person may operate a U.S.-registered civil aircraft unless that aircraft is identified in accordance with part 45 of this chapter.

(d) Any person taking off or landing a helicopter certificated under part 29 of this chapter at a heliport constructed over water may make such momentary flight as is necessary for takeoff or landing through the prohibited range of the limiting height-speed envelope established for the helicopter if that flight through the prohibited range takes place over water on which a safe ditching can be accomplished and if the helicopter is amphibious or is equipped with floats or other emergency flotation gear adequate to accomplish a safe emergency ditching on open water.

91.11   Prohibition on interference with crewmembers

No person may assault, threaten, intimidate, or interfere with a crewmember in the performance of the crewmember's duties aboard an aircraft being operated.

91.13   Careless or reckless operation

(a) Aircraft operations for the purpose of air navigation. No person may operate an aircraft in a careless or reckless manner so as to endanger the life or property of another.

(b) Aircraft operations other than for the purpose of air navigation. No person may operate an aircraft, other than for the purpose of air navigation, on any part of the surface of an airport used by aircraft for air commerce (including areas used by those aircraft for receiving or discharging persons or cargo), in a careless or reckless manner so as to endanger the life or property of another.

91.15   Dropping objects

No pilot in command of a civil aircraft may allow any object to be dropped from that aircraft in flight that creates a hazard to persons or property. However, this section does not prohibit the dropping of any object if reasonable precautions are taken to avoid injury or damage to persons or property.

91.17   Alcohol or drugs

(a) No person may act or attempt to act as a crewmember of a civil aircraft—

(1) Within 8 hours after the consumption of any alcoholic beverage;

(2) While under the influence of alcohol;

(3) While using any drug that affects the person's faculties in any way contrary to safety; or

(4) While having an alcohol concentration of 0.04 or greater in a blood or breath specimen. Alcohol concentration means grams of alcohol per deciliter of blood or grams of alcohol per 210 liters of breath.

(b) Except in an emergency, no pilot of a civil aircraft may allow a person who appears to be intoxicated or who demonstrates by manner or physical indications that the individual is under the influence of drugs (except a medical patient under proper care) to be carried in that aircraft.

FAR 91

(c) A crewmember shall do the following:

(1) On request of a law enforcement officer, submit to a test to indicate the alcohol concentration in the blood or breath, when—

(i) The law enforcement officer is authorized under State or local law to conduct the test or to have the test conducted; and

(ii) The law enforcement officer is requesting submission to the test to investigate a suspected violation of State or local law governing the same or substantially similar conduct prohibited by paragraph (a)(1), (a)(2), or (a)(4) of this section.

(2) Whenever the FAA has a reasonable basis to believe that a person may have violated paragraph (a)(1), (a)(2), or (a)(4) of this section, on request of the FAA, that person must furnish to the FAA the results, or authorize any clinic, hospital, or doctor, or other person to release to the FAA, the results of each test taken within 4 hours after acting or attempting to act as a crewmember that indicates an alcohol concentration in the blood or breath specimen.

(d) Whenever the Administrator has a reasonable basis to believe that a person may have violated paragraph (a)(3) of this section, that person shall, upon request by the Administrator, furnish the Administrator, or authorize any clinic, hospital, doctor, or other person to release to the Administrator, the results of each test taken within 4 hours after acting or attempting to act as a crewmember that indicates the presence of any drugs in the body.

(e) Any test information obtained by the Administrator under paragraph (c) or (d) of this section may be evaluated in determining a person's qualifications for any airman certificate or possible violations of this chapter and may be used as evidence in any legal proceeding under section 602, 609, or 901 of the Federal Aviation Act of 1958.

[Doc. No. 18334, 54 FR 34292, Aug. 18, 1989, as amended by Amdt. 91–291, June 21, 2006]

91.19 Carriage of narcotic drugs, marijuana, and depressant or stimulant drugs or substances

(a) Except as provided in paragraph (b) of this section, no person may operate a civil aircraft within the United States with knowledge that narcotic drugs, marijuana, and depressant or stimulant drugs or substances as defined in Federal or State statutes are carried in the aircraft.

(b) Paragraph (a) of this section does not apply to any carriage of narcotic drugs, marijuana, and depressant or stimulant drugs or substances authorized by or under any Federal or State statute or by any Federal or State agency.

91.21 Portable electronic devices

(a) Except as provided in paragraph (b) of this section, no person may operate, nor may any operator or pilot in command of an aircraft allow the operation of, any portable electronic device on any of the following U.S.-registered civil aircraft:

(1) Aircraft operated by a holder of an air carrier operating certificate or an operating certificate; or

(2) Any other aircraft while it is operated under IFR.

(b) Paragraph (a) of this section does not apply to—

(1) Portable voice recorders;

(2) Hearing aids;

(3) Heart pacemakers;

(4) Electric shavers; or

(5) Any other portable electronic device that the operator of the aircraft has determined will not cause interference with the navigation or communication system of the aircraft on which it is to be used.

(c) In the case of an aircraft operated by a holder of an air carrier operating certificate or an operating certificate, the determination required by paragraph (b)(5) of this section shall be made by that operator of the aircraft on which the particular device is to be used. In the case of other aircraft, the determination may be made by the pilot in command or other operator of the aircraft.

91.23 Truth-in-leasing clause requirement in leases and conditional sales contracts

(a) Except as provided in paragraph (b) of this section, the parties to a lease or contract of conditional sale involving a U.S.-registered large civil aircraft and entered into after January 2, 1973, shall execute a written lease or contract and include therein a written truth-in-leasing clause as a concluding paragraph in large print, immediately preceding the space for the signature of the parties, which contains the following with respect to each such aircraft:

(1) Identification of the Federal Aviation Regulations under which the aircraft has been maintained and inspected during the 12 months preceding the execution of the lease or contract of conditional sale, and certification by the parties thereto regarding the aircraft's status of compliance with applicable maintenance and inspection requirements in this part for the operation to be conducted under the lease or contract of conditional sale.

(2) The name and address (printed or typed) and the signature of the person responsible for operational control of the aircraft under the lease or contract of conditional sale, and certification that each person understands that person's responsibilities for compliance with applicable Federal Aviation Regulations.

(3) A statement that an explanation of factors bearing on operational control and pertinent Federal Aviation Regulations can be obtained from the responsible Flight Standards office.

(b) The requirements of paragraph (a) of this section do not apply—

(1) To a lease or contract of conditional sale when—

(i) The party to whom the aircraft is furnished is a foreign air carrier or certificate holder under part 121, 125, 135, or 141 of this chapter, or

(ii) The party furnishing the aircraft is a foreign air carrier or a person operating under part 121, 125, and 141 of this chapter, or a person operating under part 135 of this chapter having authority to engage in on-demand operations with large aircraft.

(2) To a contract of conditional sale, when the aircraft involved has not been registered anywhere prior to the execution of the contract, except as a new aircraft under a dealer's aircraft registration certificate issued in accordance with 47.61 of this chapter.

(c) No person may operate a large civil aircraft of U.S. registry that is subject to a lease or contract of conditional sale to which paragraph (a) of this section applies, unless—

(1) The lessee or conditional buyer, or the registered owner if the lessee is not a citizen of the United States, has mailed a copy of the lease or contract that complies with the requirements of paragraph (a) of this section, within 24 hours of its execution to the Aircraft Registration Branch, Attn: Technical Section P.O. Box 25724, Oklahoma City, OK 73125;

(2) A copy of the lease or contract that complies with the requirements of paragraph (a) of this section is carried in the aircraft. The copy of the lease or contract shall be made available for review upon request by the Administrator, and

(3) The lessee or conditional buyer, or the registered owner if the lessee is not a citizen of the United States, has notified by telephone or in person the responsible Flight Standards office. Unless otherwise authorized by that office, the notification shall be given at least 48 hours before takeoff in the case of the first flight of that aircraft under that lease or contract and inform the FAA of—

(i) The location of the airport of departure;

(ii) The departure time; and

(iii) The registration number of the aircraft involved.

(d) The copy of the lease or contract furnished to the FAA under paragraph (c) of this section is commercial or financial information obtained from a person. It is, therefore, privileged and confidential and will not be made available by the FAA for public inspection or copying under 5 U.S.C. 552(b)(4) unless recorded with the FAA under part 49 of this chapter.

(e) For the purpose of this section, a lease means any agreement by a person to furnish an aircraft to another person for compensation or hire, whether with or without flight crewmembers, other than an agreement for the sale of an aircraft and a contract of conditional sale under section 101 of the Federal Aviation Act of 1958. The person furnishing the aircraft is referred to as the lessor, and the person to whom it is furnished the lessee.

(Approved by the Office of Management and Budget under control number 2120–0005)

[Doc. No. 18334, 54 FR 34292, Aug. 18, 1989, as amended by Amdt. 91-212, 54 FR 39293, Sept. 25, 1989; Amdt. 91-253, 62 FR 13253, Mar. 19, 1997; Amdt. 91-267, 66 FR 21066, Apr. 27, 2001; Docket FAA-2018-0119, Amdt. 91-350, 83 FR 9171, Mar. 5, 2018]

91.25 Aviation Safety Reporting Program: prohibition against use of reports for enforcement purposes

The Administrator of the FAA will not use reports submitted to the National Aeronautics and Space Administration under the Aviation Safety Reporting Program (or information derived therefrom) in any enforcement action except information concerning accidents or criminal offenses which are wholly excluded from the Program.

91.27-91.99   [Reserved]

Subpart B — Flight Rules

Source: Docket No. 18334, 54 FR 34294, Aug. 18, 1989, unless otherwise noted.

General

91.101   Applicability

This subpart prescribes flight rules governing the operation of aircraft within the United States and within 12 nautical miles from the coast of the United States.

91.103   Preflight action

Each pilot in command shall, before beginning a flight, become familiar with all available information concerning that flight. This information must include—

(a) For a flight under IFR or a flight not in the vicinity of an airport, weather reports and forecasts, fuel requirements, alternatives available if the planned flight cannot be completed, and any known traffic delays of which the pilot in command has been advised by ATC;

(b) For any flight, runway lengths at airports of intended use, and the following takeoff and landing distance information:

(1) For civil aircraft for which an approved Airplane or Rotorcraft Flight Manual containing takeoff and landing distance data is required, the takeoff and landing distance data contained therein; and

(2) For civil aircraft other than those specified in paragraph (b)(1) of this section, other reliable information appropriate to the aircraft, relating to aircraft performance under expected values of airport elevation and runway slope, aircraft gross weight, and wind and temperature.

91.105   Flight crewmembers at stations

(a) During takeoff and landing, and while en route, each required flight crewmember shall—

(1) Be at the crewmember station unless the absence is necessary to perform duties in connection with the operation of the aircraft or in connection with physiological needs; and

(2) Keep the safety belt fastened while at the crewmember station.

(b) Each required flight crewmember of a U.S.-registered civil aircraft shall, during takeoff and landing, keep his or her shoulder harness fastened while at his or her assigned duty station. This paragraph does not apply if—

(1) The seat at the crewmember's station is not equipped with a shoulder harness; or

(2) The crewmember would be unable to perform required duties with the shoulder harness fastened.

[Doc. No. 18334, 54 FR 34294, Aug. 18, 1989, as amended by Amdt. 91–231, 57 FR 42671, Sept. 15, 1992]

91.107   Use of safety belts, shoulder harnesses, and child restraint systems

(a) Unless otherwise authorized by the Administrator—

(1) No pilot may take off a U.S.-registered civil aircraft (except a free balloon that incorporates a basket or gondola, or an airship type certificated before November 2, 1987) unless the pilot in command of that aircraft ensures that each person on board is briefed on how to fasten and unfasten that person's safety belt and, if installed, shoulder harness.

(2) No pilot may cause to be moved on the surface, take off, or land a U.S.-registered civil aircraft (except a free balloon that incorporates a basket or gondola, or an airship type certificated before November 2, 1987) unless the pilot in command of that aircraft ensures that each person on board has been notified to fasten his or her safety belt and, if installed, his or her shoulder harness.

(3) Except as provided in this paragraph, each person on board a U.S.-registered civil aircraft (except a free balloon that incorporates a basket or gondola or an airship type certificated before November 2, 1987) must occupy an approved seat or berth with a safety belt and, if installed, shoulder harness, properly secured about him or her during movement on the surface, takeoff, and landing. For seaplane and float equipped rotorcraft operations during movement on the surface, the person pushing off the seaplane or rotorcraft from the dock and the person mooring the seaplane or rotorcraft at the dock are excepted from the preceding seating and safety belt requirements. Notwithstanding the preceding requirements of this paragraph, a person may:

(i)   Be held by an adult who is occupying an approved seat or berth, provided that the person being held has not reached his or her second birthday and does not occupy or use any restraining device;

(ii) Use the floor of the aircraft as a seat, provided that the person is on board for the purpose of engaging in sport parachuting; or

(iii) Notwithstanding any other requirement of this chapter, occupy an approved child restraint system furnished by the operator or one of the persons described in paragraph (a)(3)(iii)(A) of this section provided that:

(A) The child is accompanied by a parent, guardian, or attendant designated by the child's parent or guardian to attend to the safety of the child during the flight;

(B) Except as provided in paragraph (a)(3)(iii)(B)(4) of this action, the approved child restraint system bears one or more labels as follows:

(1) Seats manufactured to U.S. standards between January 1, 1981, and February 25, 1985, must bear the label: "This child restraint system conforms to all applicable Federal motor vehicle safety standards";

(2) Seats manufactured to U.S. standards on or after February 26, 1985, must bear two labels:

(i) "This child restraint system conforms to all applicable Federal motor vehicle safety standards"; and

(ii) "THIS RESTRAINT IS CERTIFIED FOR USE IN MOTOR VEHICLES AND AIRCRAFT" in red lettering;

(3) Seats that do not qualify under paragraphs (a)(3)(iii)(B)(1) and (a)(3)(iii)(B)(2) of this section must bear a label or markings showing:

(i) That the seat was approved by a foreign government;

(ii) That the seat was manufactured under the standards of the United Nations;

(iii) That the seat or child restraint device furnished by the operator was approved by the FAA through Type Certificate or Supplemental Type Certificate; or

(iv) That the seat or child restraint device furnished by the operator, or one of the persons described in paragraph (a)(3)(iii)(A) of this section, was approved by the FAA in accordance with 21.8(d) of this chapter or Technical Standard Order C-100b or a later version. The child restraint device manufactured by AmSafe, Inc. (CARES, Part No. 4082) and approved by the FAA in accordance with 21.305(d) (2010 ed.) of this chapter may continue to bear a label or markings showing FAA approval in accordance with 21.305(d) (2010 ed.) of this chapter.

(4) Except as provided in 91.107(a)(3)(iii)(B)(3)(iii) and 91.107(a)(3)(iii)(B)(3)(iv), booster-type child restraint systems (as defined in Federal Motor Vehicle Safety Standard No. 213 (49 CFR 571.213)), vest- and harness-type child restraint systems, and lap held child restraints are not approved for use in aircraft; and

(C) The operator complies with the following requirements:

(1) The restraint system must be properly secured to an approved forward-facing seat or berth;

(2) The child must be properly secured in the restraint system and must not exceed the specified weight limit for the restraint system; and

(3) The restraint system must bear the appropriate label(s).

(b) Unless otherwise stated, this section does not apply to operations conducted under part 121, 125, or 135 of this chapter. Paragraph (a)(3) of this section does not apply to persons subject to 91.105.

[Doc. No. 26142, 57 FR 42671, Sept. 15, 1992, as amended by Amdt. 91-250, 61 FR 28421, June 4, 1996; Amdt. 91-289, 70 FR 50906, Aug. 26, 2005; Amdt. 91-292, 71 FR 40009, July 14, 2006; Amdt. 91-317, 75 FR 48857, Aug. 12, 2010; Amdt. 91-332, 79 FR 28812, May 20, 2014]

91.109 Flight instruction; Simulated instrument flight and certain flight tests

(a) No person may operate a civil aircraft (except a manned free balloon) that is being used for flight instruction unless that aircraft has fully functioning dual controls. However, instrument flight instruction may be given in an airplane that is equipped with a single, functioning throwover control wheel that controls the elevator and ailerons, in place of fixed, dual controls, when—

(1) The instructor has determined that the flight can be conducted safely; and

(2) The person manipulating the controls has at least a private pilot certificate with appropriate category and class ratings.

(b) An airplane equipped with a single, functioning throwover control wheel that controls the elevator and ailerons, in place of fixed, dual controls may be used for flight instruction to conduct a flight review required by 61.56 of this chapter, or to obtain recent flight experience or an instrument proficiency check required by 61.57 when—

(1) The airplane is equipped with operable rudder pedals at both pilot stations;

(2) The pilot manipulating the controls is qualified to serve and serves as pilot in command during the entire flight;

(3) The instructor is current and qualified to serve as pilot in command of the airplane, meets the requirements of 61.195(b) and has logged at least 25 hours of pilot-in-command flight time in the make and model of airplane; and

(4) The pilot in command and the instructor have determined the flight can be conducted safely.

(c) No person may operate a civil aircraft in simulated instrument flight unless—

(1) The other control seat is occupied by a safety pilot who possesses at least:

(i) A private pilot certificate with category and class ratings appropriate to the aircraft being flown; or

(ii) For purposes of providing training for a solo cross-country endorsement under 61.93 of this chapter, a flight instructor certificate with an appropriate sport pilot rating and meets the requirements of 61.412 of this chapter.

(2) The safety pilot has adequate vision forward and to each side of the aircraft, or a competent observer in the aircraft adequately supplements the vision of the safety pilot; and

(3) Except in the case of lighter-than-air aircraft, that aircraft is equipped with fully functioning dual controls. However, simulated instrument flight may be conducted in a single-engine airplane, equipped with a single, functioning, throwover control wheel, in place of fixed, dual controls of the elevator and ailerons, when—

(i) The safety pilot has determined that the flight can be conducted safely; and

(ii) The person manipulating the controls has at least a private pilot certificate with appropriate category and class ratings.

(d) No person may operate a civil aircraft that is being used for a flight test for an airline transport pilot certificate or a class or type rating on that certificate, or for a part 121 proficiency flight test, unless the pilot seated at the controls, other than the pilot being checked is fully qualified to act as pilot in command of the aircraft.

[Doc. No. 18334, 54 FR 34294, Aug. 18, 1989, as amended by Amdt. 91-324, 76 FR 54107, Aug. 31, 2011; Amdt. 61-142, 83 FR 30281 June 27, 2018]

91.111 Operating near other aircraft

(a) No person may operate an aircraft so close to another aircraft as to create a collision hazard.

(b) No person may operate an aircraft in formation flight except by arrangement with the pilot in command of each aircraft in the formation.

(c) No person may operate an aircraft, carrying passengers for hire, in formation flight.

91.113 Right-of-way rules: except water operations

(a) Inapplicability. This section does not apply to the operation of an aircraft on water.

(b) General. When weather conditions permit, regardless of whether an operation is conducted under instrument flight rules or visual flight rules, vigilance shall be maintained by each person operating an aircraft so as to see and avoid other aircraft. When a rule of this section gives another aircraft the right-of-way, the pilot shall give way to that aircraft and may not pass over, under, or ahead of it unless well clear.

(c) In distress. An aircraft in distress has the right-of-way over all other air traffic.

(d) Converging. When aircraft of the same category are converging at approximately the same altitude (except head-on, or nearly so) the aircraft to the other's right has the right-of-way. If the aircraft are of different categories—

(1) A balloon has the right-of-way over any other category of aircraft;

(2) A glider has the right-of-way over an airship, powered parachute, weight-shift-control aircraft, airplane, or rotorcraft.

(3) An airship has the right-of-way over a powered parachute, weight-shift-control aircraft, airplane, or rotorcraft. However, an aircraft towing or refueling other aircraft has the right-of-way over all other engine-driven aircraft.

(e) Approaching head-on. When aircraft are approaching each other head-on, or nearly so, each pilot of each aircraft shall alter course to the right.

(f) Overtaking. Each aircraft that is being overtaken has the right-of-way and each pilot of an overtaking aircraft shall alter course to the right to pass well clear.

(g) Landing. Aircraft, while on final approach to land or while landing, have the right-of-way over other aircraft in flight or operating on the surface, except that they shall not take advantage of this rule to force an aircraft off the runway surface which has already landed and is attempting to make way for an aircraft on final approach. When two or more aircraft are approaching an airport for the purpose of landing, the aircraft at the lower altitude has the right-of-way, but it shall not take advantage of this rule to cut in front of another which is on final approach to land or to overtake that aircraft.

[Doc. No. 18334, 54 FR 34294, Aug. 18, 1989, as amended by Amdt. 91-282, 69 FR 44880, July 27, 2004]

91.115 Right-of-way rules: water operations

(a) General. Each person operating an aircraft on the water shall, insofar as possible, keep clear of all vessels and avoid impeding their navigation, and shall give way to any vessel or other aircraft that is given the right-of-way by any rule of this section.

(b) Crossing. When aircraft, or an aircraft and a vessel, are on crossing courses, the aircraft or vessel to the other's right has the right-of-way.

(c) Approaching head-on. When aircraft, or an aircraft and a vessel, are approaching head-on, or nearly so, each shall alter its course to the right to keep well clear.

(d) Overtaking. Each aircraft or vessel that is being overtaken has the right-of-way, and the one overtaking shall alter course to keep well clear.

(e) Special circumstances. When aircraft, or an aircraft and a vessel, approach so as to involve risk of collision, each aircraft or vessel shall proceed with careful regard to existing circumstances, including the limitations of the respective craft.

91.117 Aircraft speed

(a) Unless otherwise authorized by the Administrator, no person may operate an aircraft below 10,000 feet MSL at an indicated airspeed of more than 250 knots (288 m.p.h.).

(b) Unless otherwise authorized or required by ATC, no person may operate an aircraft at or below 2,500 feet above the surface within 4 nautical miles of the primary airport of a Class C or Class D airspace area at an indicated airspeed of more than 200 knots (230 mph.). This paragraph (b) does not apply to any operations within a Class B airspace area. Such operations shall comply with paragraph (a) of this section.

(c) No person may operate an aircraft in the airspace underlying a Class B airspace area designated for an airport or in a VFR corridor designated through such a Class B airspace area, at an indicated airspeed of more than 200 knots (230 mph).

(d) If the minimum safe airspeed for any particular operation is greater than the maximum speed prescribed in this section, the aircraft may be operated at that minimum speed.

[Doc. No. 18334, 54 FR 34292, Aug. 18, 1989, as amended by Amdt. 91–219, 55 FR 34708, Aug. 24, 1990; Amdt. 91–227, 56 FR 65657, Dec. 17, 1991; Amdt. 91–233, 58 FR 43554, Aug. 17, 1993]

91.119 Minimum safe altitudes: general

Except when necessary for takeoff or landing, no person may operate an aircraft below the following altitudes:

(a) Anywhere. An altitude allowing, if a power unit fails, an emergency landing without undue hazard to persons or property on the surface.

(b) Over congested areas. Over any congested area of a city, town, or settlement, or over any open air assembly of persons, an altitude of 1,000 feet above the highest obstacle within a horizontal radius of 2,000 feet of the aircraft.

(c) Over other than congested areas. An altitude of 500 feet above the surface, except over open water or sparsely populated areas. In those cases, the aircraft may not be operated closer than 500 feet to any person, vessel, vehicle, or structure.

(d) Helicopters, powered parachutes, and weight-shift-control aircraft. If the operation is conducted without hazard to persons or property on the surface—

(1) A helicopter may be operated at less than the minimums prescribed in paragraph (b) or (c) of this section, provided each person operating the helicopter complies with any routes or altitudes specifically prescribed for helicopters by the FAA; and

(2) A powered parachute or weight-shift-control aircraft may be operated at less than the minimums prescribed in paragraph (c) of this section.

[Docket No. 18334, 54 FR 34294; Aug. 18, 1989, as amended by Amdt. 91-311, 75 FR 5223, Feb. 1, 2010]

91.121 Altimeter settings

(a) Each person operating an aircraft shall maintain the cruising altitude or flight level of that aircraft, as the case may be, by reference to an altimeter that is set, when operating—

(1) Below 18,000 feet MSL, to—

(i) The current reported altimeter setting of a station along the route and within 100 nautical miles of the aircraft;

(ii) If there is no station within the area prescribed in paragraph (a)(1)(i) of this section, the current reported altimeter setting of an appropriate available station; or

(iii) In the case of an aircraft not equipped with a radio, the elevation of the departure airport or an appropriate altimeter setting available before departure; or

(2) At or above 18,000 feet MSL, to 29.92" Hg.

(b) The lowest usable flight level is determined by the atmospheric pressure in the area of operation as shown in the following table:

(c) To convert minimum altitude prescribed under 91.119 and 91.177 to the minimum flight level, the pilot shall take the flight level equivalent of the minimum altitude in feet and add the appropriate number of feet specified below, according to the current reported altimeter setting:

FAR 91

CURRENT ALTIMETER SETTING	ADJUSTABLE FACTOR
29.92 (or higher)	None
29.91 through 29.42	500
29.41 through 28.92	1,000
28.91 through 28.42	1,500
28.41 through 27.92	2,000
27.91 through 27.42	2,500
27.41 through 26.92	3,000

CURRENT ALTIMETER SETTING	LOWEST USABLE FLIGHT LEVEL
29.92 (or higher)	180
29.91 through 29.42	185
29.41 through 28.92	190
28.91 through 28.42	195
28.41 through 27.92	200
27.91 through 27.42	205
27.41 through 26.92	210

91.123 Compliance with ATC clearances and instructions

(a) When an ATC clearance has been obtained, no pilot in command may deviate from that clearance unless an amended clearance is obtained, an emergency exists, or the deviation is in response to a traffic alert and collision avoidance system resolution advisory. However, except in Class A airspace, a pilot may cancel an IFR flight plan if the operation is being conducted in VFR weather conditions. When a pilot is uncertain of an ATC clearance, that pilot shall immediately request clarification from ATC.

(b) Except in an emergency, no person may operate an aircraft contrary to an ATC instruction in an area in which air traffic control is exercised.

(c) Each pilot in command who, in an emergency, or in response to a traffic alert and collision avoidance system resolution advisory, deviates from an ATC clearance or instruction shall notify ATC of that deviation as soon as possible.

(d) Each pilot in command who (though not deviating from a rule of this subpart) is given priority by ATC in an emergency, shall submit a detailed report of that emergency within 48 hours to the manager of that ATC facility, if requested by ATC.

(e) Unless otherwise authorized by ATC, no person operating an aircraft may operate that aircraft according to any clearance or instruction that has been issued to the pilot of another aircraft for radar air traffic control purposes.

(Approved by the Office of Management and Budget under control number 2120–0005)

[Doc. No. 18834, 54 FR 34294, Aug. 18, 1989, as amended by Amdt. 91–227, 56 FR 65658, Dec. 17, 1991; Amdt. 91–244, 60 FR 50679, Sept. 29, 1995]

91.125 ATC light signals

ATC light signals have the meaning shown in the following table:

COLOR AND TYPE OF SIGNAL	MEANING WITH RESPECT TO AIRCRAFT ON THE SURFACE	MEANING WITH RESPECT TO AIRCRAFT IN FLIGHT
Steady green	Cleared for takeoff	Cleared to land
Flashing green	Cleared to taxi	Return for landing (to be followed by steady green at proper time)
Steady red	Stop	Give way to other aircraft and continue circling
Flashing red	Taxi clear of runway in use.	Airport unsafe—do not land
Flashing white	Return to starting point on airport.	Not applicable
Alternating red and green.	Exercise extreme caution.	Exercise extreme caution

91.126 Operating on or in the vicinity of an airport in Class G airspace

(a) *General.* Unless otherwise authorized or required, each person operating an aircraft on or in the vicinity of an airport in a Class G airspace area must comply with the requirements of this section.

(b) *Direction of turns.* When approaching to land at an airport without an operating control tower in Class G airspace—

(1) Each pilot of an airplane must make all turns of that airplane to the left unless the airport displays approved light signals or visual markings indicating that turns should be made to the right, in which case the pilot must make all turns to the right; and

(2) Each pilot of a helicopter or a powered parachute must avoid the flow of fixed-wing aircraft.

(c) *Flap settings.* Except when necessary for training or certification, the pilot in command of a civil turbojet-powered aircraft must use, as a final flap setting, the minimum certificated landing flap setting set forth in the approved performance information in the Airplane Flight Manual for the applicable conditions. However, each pilot in command has the final authority and responsibility for the safe operation of the pilot's airplane, and may use a different flap setting for that airplane if the pilot determines that it is necessary in the interest of safety.

(d) *Communications with control towers.* Unless otherwise authorized or required by ATC, no person may operate an aircraft to, from, through, or on an airport having an operational control tower unless two-way radio communications are maintained between that aircraft and the control tower. Communications must be established prior to 4 nautical miles from the airport, up to and including 2,500 feet AGL. However, if the aircraft radio fails in flight, the pilot in command may operate that aircraft and land if weather conditions are at or above basic VFR weather minimums, visual contact with the tower is maintained, and a clearance to land is received. If the aircraft radio fails while in flight under IFR, the pilot must comply with 91.185.

[Doc. No. 24458, 56 FR 65658, Dec. 17, 1991, as amended by Amdt. 91–239, 59 FR 11693, Mar. 11, 1994; Amdt. 91–282, 69 FR 44880, July 27, 2004]

91.127 Operating on or in the vicinity of an airport in Class E airspace

(a) Unless otherwise required by part 93 of this chapter or unless otherwise authorized or required by the ATC facility having jurisdiction over the Class E airspace area, each person operating an aircraft on or in the vicinity of an airport in a Class E airspace area must comply with the requirements of 91.126.

(b) *Departures.* Each pilot of an aircraft must comply with any traffic patterns established for that airport in part 93 of this chapter.

(c) *Communications with control towers.* Unless otherwise authorized or required by ATC, no person may operate an aircraft to, from, through, or on an airport having an operational control tower unless two-way radio communications are maintained between that aircraft and the control tower. Communications must be established prior to 4 nautical miles from the airport, up to and including 2,500 feet AGL. However, if the aircraft radio fails in flight, the pilot in command may operate that aircraft and land if weather conditions are at or above basic VFR weather minimums, visual contact with the tower is maintained, and a clearance to land is received. If the aircraft radio fails while in flight under IFR, the pilot must comply with 91.185.

[Doc. No. 24458, 56 FR 65658, Dec. 17, 1991, as amended by Amdt. 91–239, 59 FR 11693, Mar. 11, 1994]

91.129 Operations in Class D airspace

(a) *General.* Unless otherwise authorized or required by the ATC facility having jurisdiction over the Class D airspace area, each person operating an aircraft in Class D airspace must comply with the applicable provisions of this section. In addition, each person must comply with 91.126 and 91.127. For the purpose of this section, the primary airport is the airport for which the Class D airspace area is designated. A satellite airport is any other airport within the Class D airspace area.

(b) Deviations. An operator may deviate from any provision of this section under the provisions of an ATC authorization issued by the ATC facility having jurisdiction over the airspace concerned. ATC may authorize a deviation on a continuing basis or for an individual flight, as appropriate.

(c) Communications. Each person operating an aircraft in Class D airspace must meet the following two-way radio communications requirements:

(1) Arrival or through flight. Each person must establish two-way radio communications with the ATC facility (including foreign ATC in the case of foreign airspace designated in the United States) providing air traffic services prior to entering that airspace and thereafter maintain those communications while within that airspace.

(2) Departing flight. Each person—

(i) From the primary airport or satellite airport with an operating control tower must establish and maintain two-way radio communications with the control tower, and thereafter as instructed by ATC while operating in the Class D airspace area; or

(ii) From a satellite airport without an operating control tower, must establish and maintain two-way radio communications with the ATC facility having jurisdiction over the Class D airspace area as soon as practicable after departing.

(d) Communications failure. Each person who operates an aircraft in a Class D airspace area must maintain two-way radio communications with the ATC facility having jurisdiction over that area.

(1) If the aircraft radio fails in flight under IFR, the pilot must comply with 91.185 of the part.

(2) If the aircraft radio fails in flight under VFR, the pilot in command may operate that aircraft and land if—

(i) Weather conditions are at or above basic VFR weather minimums;

(ii) Visual contact with the tower is maintained; and

(iii) A clearance to land is received.

(e) Minimum altitudes when operating to an airport in Class D airspace.

(1) Unless required by the applicable distance-from-cloud criteria, each pilot operating a large or turbine-powered airplane must enter the traffic pattern at an altitude of at least 1,500 feet above the elevation of the airport and maintain at least 1,500 feet until further descent is required for a safe landing.

(2) Each pilot operating a large or turbine-powered airplane approaching to land on a runway served by an instrument approach procedure with vertical guidance, if the airplane is so equipped, must:

(i) Operate that airplane at an altitude at or above the glide path between the published final approach fix and the decision altitude (DA), or decision height (DH), as applicable; or

(ii) If compliance with the applicable distance-from-cloud criteria requires glide path interception closer in, operate that airplane at or above the glide path, between the point of interception of glide path and the DA or the DH.

(3) Each pilot operating an airplane approaching to land on a runway served by a visual approach slope indicator must maintain an altitude at or above the glide path until a lower altitude is necessary for a safe landing.

(4) Paragraphs (e)(2) and (e)(3) of this section do not prohibit normal bracketing maneuvers above or below the glide path that are conducted for the purpose of remaining on the glide path.

(f) Approaches. Except when conducting a circling approach under part 97 of this chapter or unless otherwise required by ATC, each pilot must—

(1) Circle the airport to the left, if operating an airplane; or

(2) Avoid the flow of fixed-wing aircraft, if operating a helicopter.

(g) Departures. No person may operate an aircraft departing from an airport except in compliance with the following:

(1) Each pilot must comply with any departure procedures established for that airport by the FAA.

(2) Unless otherwise required by the prescribed departure procedure for that airport or the applicable distance from clouds criteria, each pilot of a turbine-powered airplane and each pilot of a large airplane must climb to an altitude of 1,500 feet above the surface as rapidly as practicable.

(h) Noise abatement. Where a formal runway use program has been established by the FAA, each pilot of a large or turbine-powered airplane assigned a noise abatement runway by ATC must use that runway. However, consistent with the final authority of the pilot in command concerning the safe operation of the aircraft as prescribed in 91.3(a), ATC may assign a different runway if requested by the pilot in the interest of safety.

(i) Takeoff, landing, taxi clearance. No person may, at any airport with an operating control tower, operate an aircraft on a runway or taxiway, or take off or land an aircraft, unless an appropriate clearance is received from ATC.

[Doc. No. 24458, 56 FR 65658, Dec. 17, 1991, as amended by Amdt. 91–234, 58 FR 48793, Sept. 20, 1993; Amdt. 91–296, 72 FR 31678, June 7, 2007; 77 FR 28250, May 14, 2012]

91.130 Operations in Class C airspace

(a) General. Unless otherwise authorized by ATC, each aircraft operation in Class C airspace must be conducted in compliance with this section and 91.129. For the purpose of this section, the primary airport is the airport for which the Class C airspace area is designated. A satellite airport is any other airport within the Class C airspace area.

(b) Traffic patterns. No person may take off or land an aircraft at a satellite airport within a Class C airspace area except in compliance with FAA arrival and departure traffic patterns.

(c) Communications. Each person operating an aircraft in Class C airspace must meet the following two-way radio communications requirements:

(1) Arrival or through flight. Each person must establish two-way radio communications with the ATC facility (including foreign ATC in the case of foreign airspace designated in the United States) providing air traffic services prior to entering that airspace and thereafter maintain those communications while within that airspace.

(2) Departing flight. Each person—

(i) From the primary airport or satellite airport with an operating control tower must establish and maintain two-way radio communications with the control tower, and thereafter as instructed by ATC while operating in the Class C airspace area; or

(ii) From a satellite airport without an operating control tower, must establish and maintain two-way radio communications with the ATC facility having jurisdiction over the Class C airspace area as soon as practicable after departing.

(d) Equipment requirements. Unless otherwise authorized by the ATC having jurisdiction over the Class C airspace area, no person may operate an aircraft within a Class C airspace area designated for an airport unless that aircraft is equipped with the applicable equipment specified in 91.215 and after January 1, 2020, 91.225.

(e) Deviations. An operator may deviate from any provision of this section under the provisions of an ATC authorization issued by the ATC facility having jurisdiction over the airspace concerned. ATC may authorize a deviation on a continuing basis or for an individual flight, as appropriate.

[Doc. No. 24458, 56 FR 65659, Dec. 17, 1991, as amended by Amdt. 91–232, 58 FR 40736, July 30, 1993; Amdt. 91–239, 59 FR 11693, Mar. 11, 1994; Amdt. 91-314, 75 FR 30193, May 28, 2010]

FAR 91

91.131 Operations in Class B airspace

(a) Operating rules. No person may operate an aircraft within a Class B airspace area except in compliance with 91.129 and the following rules:

(1) The operator must receive an ATC clearance from the ATC facility having jurisdiction for that area before operating an aircraft in that area.

(2) Unless otherwise authorized by ATC, each person operating a large turbine engine-powered airplane to or from a primary airport for which a Class B airspace area is designated must operate at or above the designated floors of the Class B airspace area while within the lateral limits of that area.

(3) Any person conducting pilot training operations at an airport within a Class B airspace area must comply with any procedures established by ATC for such operations in that area.

(b) Pilot requirements.

(1) No person may take off or land a civil aircraft at an airport within a Class B airspace area or operate a civil aircraft within a Class B airspace area unless—

(i) The pilot in command holds at least a private pilot certificate;

(ii) The pilot in command holds a recreational pilot certificate and has met—

(A) The requirements of 61.101(d) of this chapter; or

(B) The requirements for a student pilot seeking a recreational pilot certificate in 61.94 of this chapter;

(iii) The pilot in command holds a sport pilot certificate and has met—

(A) The requirements of 61.325 of this chapter; or

(B) The requirements for a student pilot seeking a recreational pilot certificate in 61.94 of this chapter; or

(iv) The aircraft is operated by a student pilot who has met the requirements of 61.94 or 61.95 of this chapter, as applicable.

(2) Notwithstanding the provisions of paragraphs (b)(1)(ii), (b)(1)(iii) and (b)(1)(iv) of this section, no person may take off or land a civil aircraft at those airports listed in section 4 of appendix D to this part unless the pilot in command holds at least a private pilot certificate.

(c) Communications and navigation equipment requirements. Unless otherwise authorized by ATC, no person may operate an aircraft within a Class B airspace area unless that aircraft is equipped with—

(1) For IFR operation. An operable VOR or TACAN receiver or an operable and suitable RNAV system; and

(2) For all operations. An operable two-way radio capable of communications with ATC on appropriate frequencies for that Class B airspace area.

(d) Other equipment requirements. No person may operate an aircraft in a Class B airspace area unless the aircraft is equipped with—

(1) The applicable operating transponder and automatic altitude reporting equipment specified in 91.215 (a), except as provided in 91.215 (e), and

(2) After January 1, 2020, the applicable Automatic Dependent Surveillance-Broadcast Out equipment specified in 91.225.

[Doc. No. 24458, 56 FR 65658, Dec. 17, 1991, as amended by Amdt. 91–282, 69 FR 44880, July 27, 2004; Amdt. 91–296, 72 FR 31678, June 7, 2007; Amdt. 91-314, 75 FR 30193, May 28, 2010]

91.133 Restricted and prohibited areas

(a) No person may operate an aircraft within a restricted area (designated in part 73) contrary to the restrictions imposed, or within a prohibited area, unless that person has the permission of the using or controlling agency, as appropriate.

(b) Each person conducting, within a restricted area, an aircraft operation (approved by the using agency) that creates the same hazards as the operations for which the restricted area was designated may deviate from the rules of this subpart that are not compatible with the operation of the aircraft.

91.135 Operations in Class A airspace

Except as provided in paragraph (d) of this section, each person operating an aircraft in Class A airspace must conduct that operation under instrument flight rules (IFR) and in compliance with the following:

(a) Clearance. Operations may be conducted only under an ATC clearance received prior to entering the airspace.

(b) Communications. Unless otherwise authorized by ATC, each aircraft operating in Class A airspace must be equipped with a two-way radio capable of communicating with ATC on a frequency assigned by ATC. Each pilot must maintain two-way radio communications with ATC while operating in Class A airspace.

(c) Equipment requirements. Unless otherwise authorized by ATC, no person may operate an aircraft within Class A airspace unless that aircraft is equipped with the applicable equipment specified in 91.215, and after January 1, 2020, 91.225.

(d) ATC authorizations. An operator may deviate from any provision of this section under the provisions of an ATC authorization issued by the ATC facility having jurisdiction of the airspace concerned. In the case of an inoperative transponder, ATC may immediately approve an operation within a Class A airspace area allowing flight to continue, if desired, to the airport of ultimate destination, including any intermediate stops, or to proceed to a place where suitable repairs can be made, or both. Requests for deviation from any provision of this section must be submitted in writing, at least 4 days before the proposed operation. ATC may authorize a deviation on a continuing basis or for an individual flight.

[Doc. No. 24458, 56 FR 65659, Dec. 17, 1991; as amended by ; Amdt. 91-314, 75 FR 30193, May 28, 2010]

91.137 Temporary flight restrictions in the vicinity of disaster/hazard areas

(a) The Administrator will issue a Notice to Airmen (NOTAM) designating an area within which temporary flight restrictions apply and specifying the hazard or condition requiring their imposition, whenever he determines it is necessary in order to—

(1) Protect persons and property on the surface or in the air from a hazard associated with an incident on the surface;

(2) Provide a safe environment for the operation of disaster relief aircraft; or

(3) Prevent an unsafe congestion of sightseeing and other aircraft above an incident or event which may generate a high degree of public interest.

The Notice to Airmen will specify the hazard or condition that requires the imposition of temporary flight restrictions.

(b) When a NOTAM has been issued under paragraph (a)(1) of this section, no person may operate an aircraft within the designated area unless that aircraft is participating in the hazard relief activities and is being operated under the direction of the official in charge of on scene emergency response activities.

(c) When a NOTAM has been issued under paragraph (a)(2) of this section, no person may operate an aircraft within the designated area unless at least one of the following conditions are met:

(1) The aircraft is participating in hazard relief activities and is being operated under the direction of the official in charge of on scene emergency response activities.

(2) The aircraft is carrying law enforcement officials.

(3) The aircraft is operating under the ATC approved IFR flight plan.

(4) The operation is conducted directly to or from an airport within the area, or is necessitated by the impracticability of VFR flight above or around the area due to weather, or terrain; notification is given to the Flight Service Station (FSS)

or ATC facility specified in the NOTAM to receive advisories concerning disaster relief aircraft operations; and the operation does not hamper or endanger relief activities and is not conducted for the purpose of observing the disaster.

(5) The aircraft is carrying properly accredited news representatives, and, prior to entering the area, a flight plan is filed with the appropriate FAA or ATC facility specified in the Notice to Airmen and the operation is conducted above the altitude used by the disaster relief aircraft, unless otherwise authorized by the official in charge of on scene emergency response activities.

(d) When a NOTAM has been issued under paragraph (a)(3) of this section, no person may operate an aircraft within the designated area unless at least one of the following conditions is met:

(1) The operation is conducted directly to or from an airport within the area, or is necessitated by the impracticability of VFR flight above or around the area due to weather or terrain, and the operation is not conducted for the purpose of observing the incident or event.

(2) The aircraft is operating under an ATC approved IFR flight plan.

(3) The aircraft is carrying incident or event personnel, or law enforcement officials.

(4) The aircraft is carrying properly accredited news representatives and, prior to entering that area, a flight plan is filed with the appropriate FSS or ATC facility specified in the NOTAM.

(e) Flight plans filed and notifications made with an FSS or ATC facility under this section shall include the following information:

(1) Aircraft identification, type and color.

(2) Radio communications frequencies to be used.

(3) Proposed times of entry of, and exit from, the designated area.

(4) Name of news media or organization and purpose of flight.

(5) Any other information requested by ATC.

91.138 Temporary flight restrictions in national disaster areas in the State of Hawaii

(a) When the Administrator has determined, pursuant to a request and justification provided by the Governor of the State of Hawaii, or the Governor's designee, that an inhabited area within a declared national disaster area in the State of Hawaii is in need of protection for humanitarian reasons, the Administrator will issue a Notice to Airmen (NOTAM) designating an area within which temporary flight restrictions apply. The Administrator will designate the extent and duration of the temporary flight restrictions necessary to provide for the protection of persons and property on the surface.

(b) When a NOTAM has been issued in accordance with this section, no person may operate an aircraft within the designated area unless at least one of the following conditions is met:

(1) That person has obtained authorization from the official in charge of associated emergency or disaster relief response activities, and is operating the aircraft under the conditions of that authorization.

(2) The aircraft is carrying law enforcement officials.

(3) The aircraft is carrying persons involved in an emergency or a legitimate scientific purpose.

(4) The aircraft is carrying properly accredited newspersons, and that prior to entering the area, a flight plan is filed with the appropriate FAA or ATC facility specified in the NOTAM and the operation is conducted in compliance with the conditions and restrictions established by the official in charge of on-scene emergency response activities.

(5) The aircraft is operating in accordance with an ATC clearance or instruction.

(c) A NOTAM issued under this section is effective for 90 days or until the national disaster area designation is terminated, whichever comes first, unless terminated by notice or extended by the Ad-

ministrator at the request of the Governor of the State of Hawaii or the Governor's designee.

[Doc. No. 26476, 56 FR 23178, May 20, 1991, as amended by Amdt. 91–270, 66 FR 47377, Sept. 11, 2001]

91.139 Emergency air traffic rules

(a) This section prescribes a process for utilizing Notices to Airmen (NOTAMs) to advise of the issuance and operations under emergency air traffic rules and regulations and designates the official who is authorized to issue NOTAMs on behalf of the Administrator in certain matters under this section.

(b) Whenever the Administrator determines that an emergency condition exists, or will exist, relating to the FAA's ability to operate the air traffic control system and during which normal flight operations under this chapter cannot be conducted consistent with the required levels of safety and efficiency—

(1) The Administrator issues an immediately effective air traffic rule or regulation in response to that emergency condition; and

(2) The Administrator or the Associate Administrator for Air Traffic may utilize the NOTAM system to provide notification of the issuance of the rule or regulation.

Those NOTAMs communicate information concerning the rules and regulations that govern flight operations, the use of navigation facilities, and designation of that airspace in which the rules and regulations apply.

(c) When a NOTAM has been issued under this section, no person may operate an aircraft, or other device governed by the regulation concerned, within the designated airspace except in accordance with the authorizations, terms, and conditions prescribed in the regulation covered by the NOTAM.

91.141 Flight restrictions in the proximity of the Presidential and other parties

No person may operate an aircraft over or in the vicinity of any area to be visited or traveled by the President, the Vice President, or other public figures contrary to the restrictions established by the Administrator and published in a Notice to Airmen (NOTAM).

91.143 Flight limitation in the proximity of space flight operations

When a Notice to Airmen (NOTAM) is issued in accordance with this section, no person may operate any aircraft of U.S. registry, or pilot any aircraft under the authority of an airman certificate issued by the Federal Aviation Administration, within areas designated in a NOTAM for space flight operation except when authorized by ATC.

[Doc. No. FAA–2004–19246, 69 FR 59753, Oct. 5, 2004]

91.144 Temporary restriction on flight operations during abnormally high barometric pressure conditions

(a) Special flight restrictions. When any information indicates that barometric pressure on the route of flight currently exceeds or will exceed 31 inches of mercury, no person may operate an aircraft or initiate a flight contrary to the requirements established by the Administrator and published in a Notice to Airmen issued under this section.

(b) Waivers. The Administrator is authorized to waive any restriction issued under paragraph (a) of this section to permit emergency supply, transport, or medical services to be delivered to isolated communities, where the operation can be conducted with an acceptable level of safety.

[Amdt. 91–240, 59 FR 17452, Apr. 12, 1994; 59 FR 37669, July 25, 1994]

91.145 Management of aircraft operations in the vicinity of aerial demonstrations and major sporting events

(a) The FAA will issue a Notice to Airmen (NOTAM) designating an area of airspace in which a temporary flight restriction applies when it determines that a temporary flight restriction is necessary to protect persons or property on the surface or in the air, to maintain air safety and efficiency, or to prevent the unsafe congestion

FAR 91

of aircraft in the vicinity of an aerial demonstration or major sporting event. These demonstrations and events may include:

(1) United States Naval Flight Demonstration Team (Blue Angels);

(2) United States Air Force Air Demonstration Squadron (Thunderbirds);

(3) United States Army Parachute Team (Golden Knights);

(4) Summer/Winter Olympic Games;

(5) Annual Tournament of Roses Football Game;

(6) World Cup Soccer;

(7) Major League Baseball All-Star Game;

(8) World Series;

(9) Kodak Albuquerque International Balloon Fiesta;

(10) Sandia Classic Hang Gliding Competition;

(11) Indianapolis 500 Mile Race;

(12) Any other aerial demonstration or sporting event the FAA determines to need a temporary flight restriction in accordance with paragraph (b) of this section.

(b) In deciding whether a temporary flight restriction is necessary for an aerial demonstration or major sporting event not listed in paragraph (a) of this section, the FAA considers the following factors:

(1) Area where the event will be held.

(2) Effect flight restrictions will have on known aircraft operations.

(3) Any existing ATC airspace traffic management restrictions.

(4) Estimated duration of the event.

(5) Degree of public interest.

(6) Number of spectators.

(7) Provisions for spectator safety.

(8) Number and types of participating aircraft.

(9) Use of mixed high and low performance aircraft.

(10) Impact on non-participating aircraft.

(11) Weather minimums.

(12) Emergency procedures that will be in effect.

(c) A NOTAM issued under this section will state the name of the aerial demonstration or sporting event and specify the effective dates and times, the geographic features or coordinates, and any other restrictions or procedures governing flight operations in the designated airspace.

(d) When a NOTAM has been issued in accordance with this section, no person may operate an aircraft or device, or engage in any activity within the designated airspace area, except in accordance with the authorizations, terms, and conditions of the temporary flight restriction published in the NOTAM, unless otherwise authorized by:

(1) Air traffic control; or

(2) A Flight Standards Certificate of Waiver or Authorization issued for the demonstration or event.

(e) For the purpose of this section:

(1) Flight restricted airspace area for an aerial demonstration— The amount of airspace needed to protect persons and property on the surface or in the air, to maintain air safety and efficiency, or to prevent the unsafe congestion of aircraft will vary depending on the aerial demonstration and the factors listed in paragraph (b) of this section. The restricted airspace area will normally be limited to a 5 nautical mile radius from the center of the demonstration and an altitude 17000 mean sea level (for high performance aircraft) or 13000 feet above the surface (for certain parachute operations), but will be no greater than the minimum airspace necessary for the management of aircraft operations in the vicinity of the specified area.

(2) Flight restricted area for a major sporting event— The amount of airspace needed to protect persons and property on the surface or in the air, to maintain air safety and efficiency, or to prevent the unsafe congestion of aircraft will vary depending

on the size of the event and the factors listed in paragraph (b) this section. The restricted airspace will normally be limited a 3 nautical mile radius from the center of the event and 250 feet above the surface but will not be greater than the minimu airspace necessary for the management of aircraft operations the vicinity of the specified area.

(f) A NOTAM issued under this section will be issued at least 30 day in advance of an aerial demonstration or a major sporting event, u less the FAA finds good cause for a shorter period and explains th in the NOTAM.

(g) When warranted, the FAA Administrator may exclude the follow ing flights from the provisions of this section:

(1) Essential military.

(2) Medical and rescue.

(3) Presidential and Vice Presidential.

(4) Visiting heads of state.

(5) Law enforcement and security.

(6) Public health and welfare.

[Doc. No. FAA–2000–8274, 66 FR 47378, Sept. 11, 2001]

91.146 Passenger-carrying flights for the benefit of a char itable, nonprofit, or community event

(a) Definitions. For purposes of this section, the following definition apply:

Charitable event means an event that raises funds for the benef of a charitable organization recognized by the Department of th Treasury whose donors may deduct contributions under section 17 of the Internal Revenue Code (26 U.S.C. Section 170).

Community event means an event that raises funds for the benef of any local or community cause that is not a charitable event c non-profit event.

Non-profit event means an event that raises funds for the benef of a non-profit organization recognized under State or Federal law as long as one of the organization's purposes is the promotion o aviation safety.

(b) Passenger carrying flights for the benefit of a charitable, nonprofi or community event identified in paragraph (c) of this section ar not subject to the certification requirements of part 119 or the dru and alcohol testing requirements in part 120 of this chapter, pro vided the following conditions are satisfied and the limitations i paragraphs (c) and (d) are not exceeded:

(1) The flight is nonstop and begins and ends at the same airport an is conducted within a 25-statute mile radius of that airport;

(2) The flight is conducted from a public airport that is adequat for the airplane or helicopter used, or from another location th FAA approves for the operation;

(3) The airplane or helicopter has a maximum of 30 seats, exclud ing each crewmember seat, and a maximum payload capacity o 7,500 pounds;

(4) The flight is not an aerobatic or a formation flight;

(5) Each airplane or helicopter holds a standard airworthiness cer tificate, is airworthy, and is operated in compliance with the ap plicable requirements of subpart E of this part;

(6) Each flight is made during day VFR conditions;

(7) Reimbursement of the operator of the airplane or helicopter i limited to that portion of the passenger payment for the fligh that does not exceed the pro rata cost of owning, operating, an maintaining the aircraft for that flight, which may include fuel oil, airport expenditures, and rental fees;

(8) The beneficiary of the funds raised is not in the business o transportation by air;

(9) A private pilot acting as pilot in command has at least 500 hour of flight time;

(10) Each flight is conducted in accordance with the safety provi sions of part 136, subpart A of this chapter; and

(11) Flights are not conducted over a national park, unit of a national park, or abutting tribal lands, unless the operator has secured a letter of agreement from the FAA, as specified under subpart B of part 136 of this chapter, and is operating in accordance with that agreement during the flights.

(c)

(1) Passenger-carrying flights or series of flights are limited to a total of four charitable events or non-profit events per year, with no event lasting more than three consecutive days.

(2) Passenger-carrying flights or series of flights are limited to one community event per year, with no event lasting more than three consecutive days.

(d) Pilots and sponsors of events described in this section are limited to no more than 4 events per calendar year.

(e) At least seven days before the event, each sponsor of an event described in this section must furnish to the responsible Flight Standards office for the area where the event is scheduled:

(1) A signed letter detailing the name of the sponsor, the purpose of the event, the date and time of the event, the location of the event, all prior events under this section participated in by the sponsor in the current calendar year;

(2) A photocopy of each pilot in command's pilot certificate, medical certificate, and logbook entries that show the pilot is current in accordance with 61.56 and 61.57 of this chapter and that any private pilot has at least 500 hours of flight time; and

(3) A signed statement from each pilot that lists all prior events under this section in which the pilot has participated during the current calendar year.

[Doc. No. FAA-1998-4521, 72 FR 6910, Feb. 13, 2007, as amended by Amdt. 91-308, 74 FR 32804, July 9, 2009; Docket FAA-2018-0119, Amdt. 91-350, 83 FR 9171, Mar. 5, 2018]

91.147   Passenger carrying flights for compensation or hire

Each Operator conducting passenger-carrying flights for compensation or hire must meet the following requirements unless all flights are conducted under 91.146.

(a) For the purposes of this section and for drug and alcohol testing, Operator means any person conducting nonstop passenger-carrying flights in an airplane or helicopter for compensation or hire in accordance with 119.1(e)(2), 135.1(a)(5), or 121.1(d), of this chapter that begin and end at the same airport and are conducted within a 25-statute mile radius of that airport.

(b) An Operator must comply with the safety provisions of part 136, subpart A of this chapter, and apply for and receive a Letter of Authorization from the responsible Flight Standards office.

(c) Each application for a Letter of Authorization must include the following information:

(1) Name of Operator, agent, and any d/b/a (doing-business-as) under which that Operator does business;

(2) Principal business address and mailing address;

(3) Principal place of business (if different from business address);

(4) Name of person responsible for management of the business;

(5) Name of person responsible for aircraft maintenance;

(6) Type of aircraft, registration number(s), and make/model/series; and

(7) An Antidrug and Alcohol Misuse Prevention Program registration.

(d) The Operator must register and implement its drug and alcohol testing programs in accordance with part 120 of this chapter.

(e) The Operator must comply with the provisions of the Letter of Authorization received.

[Doc. No. FAA-1998-4521, 72 FR 6911, Feb. 13, 2007, as amended by Amdt. 91-307, 74 FR 22652, May 14, 2009; Amdt. 91-320, 76 FR 8893, Feb. 16, 2011; Docket FAA-2018-0119, Amdt. 91-350, 83 FR 9171, Mar. 5, 2018]

91.148-91.149   [Reserved]

Visual Flight Rules

91.151   Fuel requirements for flight in VFR conditions.

(a) No person may begin a flight in an airplane under VFR conditions unless (considering wind and forecast weather conditions) there is enough fuel to fly to the first point of intended landing and, assuming normal cruising speed—

(1) During the day, to fly after that for at least 30 minutes; or

(2) At night, to fly after that for at least 45 minutes.

(b) No person may begin a flight in a rotorcraft under VFR conditions unless (considering wind and forecast weather conditions) there is enough fuel to fly to the first point of intended landing and, assuming normal cruising speed, to fly after that for at least 20 minutes.

91.153   VFR flight plan: information required

(a) Information required. Unless otherwise authorized by ATC, each person filing a VFR flight plan shall include in it the following information:

(1) The aircraft identification number and, if necessary, its radio call sign.

(2) The type of the aircraft or, in the case of a formation flight, the type of each aircraft and the number of aircraft in the formation.

(3) The full name and address of the pilot in command or, in the case of a formation flight, the formation commander.

(4) The point and proposed time of departure.

(5) The proposed route, cruising altitude (or flight level), and true airspeed at that altitude.

(6) The point of first intended landing and the estimated elapsed time until over that point.

(7) The amount of fuel on board (in hours).

(8) The number of persons in the aircraft, except where that information is otherwise readily available to the FAA.

(9) Any other information the pilot in command or ATC believes is necessary for ATC purposes.

(b) Cancellation. When a flight plan has been activated, the pilot in command, upon canceling or completing the flight under the flight plan, shall notify an FAA Flight Service Station or ATC facility.

91.155   Basic VFR weather minimums

(a) Except as provided in paragraph (b) of this section and 91.157, no person may operate an aircraft under VFR when the flight visibility is less, or at a distance from clouds that is less, than that prescribed for the corresponding altitude and class of airspace in the following table:

AIRSPACE	FLIGHT VISIBILITY	DISTANCE FROM CLOUDS
Class A	Not Applicable	Not Applicable
Class B	3 statute miles	Clear of Clouds
Class C	3 statute miles	500 feet below 1,000 feet above 2,000 feet horizontal
Class D	3 statute miles	500 feet below 1,000 feet above 2,000 feet horizontal
Class E		
Less than 10,000 feet MSL	3 statute miles	500 feet below 1,000 feet above 2,000 feet horizontal
At or above 10,000 feet MSL	5 statute miles	1,000 feet below 1,000 feet above 1 statute mile horizontal

AIRSPACE	FLIGHT VISIBILITY	DISTANCE FROM CLOUDS
Class G		
1,200 feet or less above the surface (regardless of MSL altitude)		
For aircraft other than helicopters		
Day except as provided in 91.155(b)	1 statute mile	Clear of Clouds
Night except as provided in 91.155(b)	3 statute miles	500 feet below 1,000 feet above 2,000 feet horizontal
For helicopters		
Day	1/2 statute mile	Clear of Clouds
Night except as provided in 91.155(b)	1 statute mile	Clear of Clouds
More than 1,000 feet above the surface but less than 10,000 feet MSL		
Day	1 statute mile	500 feet below 1,000 feet above 2,000 feet horizontal
Night	3 statute miles	500 feet below 1,000 feet above 2,000 feet horizontal
More than 1,200 feet above the surface and at or above 10,000 MSL	5 statute miles	1,000 feet below 1,000 feet above 1 statute mile horizontal

(b) Class G Airspace. Notwithstanding the provisions of paragraph (a) of this section, the following operations may be conducted in Class G airspace below 1,200 feet above the surface:

(1) Helicopter. A helicopter may be operated clear of clouds in an airport traffic pattern within 1/2 mile of the runway or helipad of intended landing if the flight visibility is not less than 1/2 statute mile.

(2) Airplane, powered parachute, or weight-shift-control aircraft. If the visibility is less than 3 statute miles but not less than 1 statute mile during night hours and you are operating in an airport traffic pattern within 1/2 mile of the runway, you may operate an airplane, powered parachute, or weight-shift-control aircraft clear of clouds.

(c) Except as provided in 91.157, no person may operate an aircraft beneath the ceiling under VFR within the lateral boundaries of controlled airspace designated to the surface for an airport when the ceiling is less than 1,000 feet.

(d) Except as provided in 91.157 of this part, no person may take off or land an aircraft, or enter the traffic pattern of an airport, under VFR, within the lateral boundaries of the surface areas of Class B, Class C, Class D, or Class E airspace designated for an airport—

(1) Unless ground visibility at that airport is at least 3 statute miles; or

(2) If ground visibility is not reported at that airport, unless flight visibility during landing or takeoff, or while operating in the traffic pattern is at least 3 statute miles.

(e) For the purpose of this section, an aircraft operating at the base altitude of a Class E airspace area is considered to be within the airspace directly below that area.

[Doc. No. 24458, 56 FR 65660, Dec. 17, 1991, as amended by Amdt. 91-235, 58 FR 51968, Oct. 5, 1993; Amdt. 91-282, 69 FR 44880, July 27, 2004; Amdt. 91-330, 79 FR 9972, Feb. 21, 2014; Amdt. 91-330A, 79 FR 41125, July 15, 2014]

91.157   Special VFR weather minimums

(a) Except as provided in appendix D, section 3, of this part, special VFR operations may be conducted under the weather minimums and requirements of this section, instead of those contained in 91.155, below 10,000 feet MSL within the airspace contained by the upward extension of the lateral boundaries of the controlled airspace designated to the surface for an airport.

(b) Special VFR operations may only be conducted—

(1) With an ATC clearance;

(2) Clear of clouds;

(3) Except for helicopters, when flight visibility is at least 1 statute mile; and

(4) Except for helicopters, between sunrise and sunset (or in Alaska when the sun is 6 degrees or more below the horizon) unless—

(i)   The person being granted the ATC clearance meets the applicable requirements for instrument flight under part 61 of this chapter; and

(ii)   The aircraft is equipped as required in 91.205(d).

(c) No person may take off or land an aircraft (other than a helicopter under special VFR—

(1) Unless ground visibility is at least 1 statute mile; or

(2) If ground visibility is not reported, unless flight visibility is at least 1 statute mile. For the purposes of this paragraph, the term flight visibility includes the visibility from the cockpit of an aircraft in takeoff position if:

(i)   The flight is conducted under this part 91; and

(ii)   The airport at which the aircraft is located is a satellite airport that does not have weather reporting capabilities.

(d) The determination of visibility by a pilot in accordance with paragraph (c)(2) of this section is not an official weather report or an official ground visibility report.

[Amdt. 91-235, 58 FR 51968, Oct. 5, 1993, as amended by Amdt. 91-247, 60 FR 66874, Dec. 27, 1995; Amdt. 91-262, 65 FR 16116, Mar. 24, 2000]

91.159   VFR cruising altitude or flight level

Except while holding in a holding pattern of 2 minutes or less, or while turning, each person operating an aircraft under VFR in level cruising flight more than 3,000 feet above the surface shall maintain the appropriate altitude or flight level prescribed below, unless otherwise authorized by ATC:

(a) When operating below 18,000 feet MSL and—

(1) On a magnetic course of zero degrees through 179 degrees, any odd thousand foot MSL altitude +500 feet (such as 3,500, 5,500, or 7,500); or

(2) On a magnetic course of 180 degrees through 359 degrees, any even thousand foot MSL altitude +500 feet (such as 4,500, 6,500, or 8,500).

(b) When operating above 18,000 feet MSL, maintain the altitude or flight level assigned by ATC.

[Doc. No. 18334, 54 FR 34294, Aug. 18, 1989, as amended by Amdt. 91-276, 68 FR 61321, Oct. 27, 2003; 68 FR 70133, Dec. 17, 2003]

91.161   Special awareness training required for pilots flying under visual flight rules within a 60-nautical mile radius of the Washington, DC VOR/DME

(a) Operations within a 60-nautical mile radius of the Washington, DC VOR/DME under visual flight rules (VFR). Except as provided under paragraph (e) of this section, no person may serve as a pilot in command or as second in command of an aircraft while flying within a 60-nautical mile radius of the DCA VOR/DME, under VFR, unless that pilot has completed Special Awareness Training and holds a certificate of training completion.

(b) Special Awareness Training. The Special Awareness Training consists of information to educate pilots about the procedures for flying in the Washington, DC area and, more generally, in other types of special use airspace. This free training is available on the FAA's Web site. Upon completion of the training, each person will need to print out a copy of the certificate of training completion.

(c) Inspection of certificate of training completion. Each person who holds a certificate for completing the Special Awareness Training must present it for inspection upon request from:

(1) An authorized representative of the FAA;

(2) An authorized representative of the National Transportation Safety Board;

(3) Any Federal, State, or local law enforcement officer; or

(4) An authorized representative of the Transportation Security Administration.

(d) *Emergency declared.* The failure to complete the Special Awareness Training course on flying in and around the Washington, DC Metropolitan Area is not a violation of this section if an emergency is declared by the pilot, as described under 91.3(b), or there was a failure of two-way radio communications when operating under IFR as described under 91.185.

(e) *Exceptions.* The requirements of this section do not apply if the flight is being performed in an aircraft of an air ambulance operator certificated to conduct part 135 operations under this chapter, the U.S. Armed Forces, or a law enforcement agency.

[Doc. No. FAA–2006–25250, 73 FR 46803, Aug. 12, 2008]

91.162-91.165   [Reserved]

Instrument Flight Rules

91.167   Fuel requirements for flight in IFR conditions

(a) No person may operate a civil aircraft in IFR conditions unless it carries enough fuel (considering weather reports and forecasts and weather conditions) to—

(1) Complete the flight to the first airport of intended landing;

(2) Except as provided in paragraph (b) of this section, fly from that airport to the alternate airport; and

(3) Fly after that for 45 minutes at normal cruising speed or, for helicopters, fly after that for 30 minutes at normal cruising speed.

(b) Paragraph (a)(2) of this section does not apply if:

(1) Part 97 of this chapter prescribes a standard instrument approach procedure to, or a special instrument approach procedure has been issued by the Administrator to the operator for, the first airport of intended landing; and

(2) Appropriate weather reports or weather forecasts, or a combination of them, indicate the following:

(i) For aircraft other than helicopters. For at least 1 hour before and for 1 hour after the estimated time of arrival, the ceiling will be at least 2,000 feet above the airport elevation and the visibility will be at least 3 statute miles.

(ii) For helicopters. At the estimated time of arrival and for 1 hour after the estimated time of arrival, the ceiling will be at least 1,000 feet above the airport elevation, or at least 400 feet above the lowest applicable approach minima, whichever is higher, and the visibility will be at least 2 statute miles.

[Doc. No. 98-4390, 65 FR 3546, Jan. 21, 2000]

91.169 — IFR flight plan: Information required

(a) *Information required.* Unless otherwise authorized by ATC, each person filing an IFR flight plan must include in it the following information:

(1) Information required under 91.153 (a) of this part;

(2) Except as provided in paragraph (b) of this section, an alternate airport.

(b) Paragraph (a)(2) of this section does not apply if :

(1) Part 97 of this chapter prescribes a standard instrument approach procedure to, or a special instrument approach procedure has been issued by the Administrator to the operator for, the first airport of intended landing; and

(2) Appropriate weather reports or weather forecasts, or a combination of them, indicate the following:

(i) For aircraft other than helicopters. For at least 1 hour before and for 1 hour after the estimated time of arrival, the ceiling will be at least 2,000 feet above the airport elevation and the visibility will be at least 3 statute miles.

(ii) For helicopters. At the estimated time of arrival and for 1 hour after the estimated time of arrival, the ceiling will be at least 1,000 feet above the airport elevation, or at least 400 feet above the lowest applicable approach minima, whichever is higher, and the visibility will be at least 2 statute miles.

(c) *IFR alternate airport weather minima.* Unless otherwise authorized by the Administrator, no person may include an alternate airport in an IFR flight plan unless appropriate weather reports or weather forecasts, or a combination of them, indicate that, at the estimated time of arrival at the alternate airport, the ceiling and visibility at that airport will be at or above the following weather minima:

(1) If an instrument approach procedure has been published in part 97 of this chapter, or a special instrument approach procedure has been issued by the Administrator to the operator, for that airport, the following minima:

(i) For aircraft other than helicopters: The alternate airport minima specified in that procedure, or if none are specified the following standard approach minima:

(A) For a precision approach procedure. Ceiling 600 feet and visibility 2 statute miles.

(B) For a nonprecision approach procedure. Ceiling 800 feet and visibility 2 statute miles.

(ii) For helicopters: Ceiling 200 feet above the minimum for the approach to be flown, and visibility at least 1 statute mile but never less than the minimum visibility for the approach to be flown, and

(2) If no instrument approach procedure has been published in part 97 of this chapter and no special instrument approach procedure has been issued by the Administrator to the operator, for the alternate airport, the ceiling and visibility minima are those allowing descent from the MEA, approach, and landing under basic VFR.

(d) *Cancellation.* When a flight plan has been activated, the pilot in command, upon canceling or completing the flight under the flight plan, shall notify an FAA Flight Service Station or ATC facility.

[Doc. No. 18334, 54 FR 34294, Aug. 18, 1989, as amended by Amdt. 91–259, 65 FR 3546, Jan. 21, 2000]

91.171   VOR equipment check for IFR operations

(a) No person may operate a civil aircraft under IFR using the VOR system of radio navigation unless the VOR equipment of that aircraft—

(1) Is maintained, checked, and inspected under an approved procedure; or

(2) Has been operationally checked within the preceding 30 days, and was found to be within the limits of the permissible indicated bearing error set forth in paragraph (b) or (c) of this section.

(b) Except as provided in paragraph (c) of this section, each person conducting a VOR check under paragraph (a)(2) of this section shall—

(1) Use, at the airport of intended departure, an FAA-operated or approved test signal or a test signal radiated by a certificated and appropriately rated radio repair station or, outside the United States, a test signal operated or approved by an appropriate authority to check the VOR equipment (the maximum permissible indicated bearing error is plus or minus 4 degrees); or

(2) Use, at the airport of intended departure, a point on the airport surface designated as a VOR system checkpoint by the Administrator, or, outside the United States, by an appropriate authority (the maximum permissible bearing error is plus or minus 4 degrees);

(3) If neither a test signal nor a designated checkpoint on the surface is available, use an airborne checkpoint designated by the Administrator or, outside the United States, by an appropriate authority (the maximum permissible bearing error is plus or minus 6 degrees); or

(4) If no check signal or point is available, while in flight—

   (i) Select a VOR radial that lies along the centerline of an established VOR airway;

   (ii) Select a prominent ground point along the selected radial preferably more than 20 nautical miles from the VOR ground facility and maneuver the aircraft directly over the point at a reasonably low altitude; and

   (iii) Note the VOR bearing indicated by the receiver when over the ground point (the maximum permissible variation between the published radial and the indicated bearing is 6 degrees).

(c) If dual system VOR (units independent of each other except for the antenna) is installed in the aircraft, the person checking the equipment may check one system against the other in place of the check procedures specified in paragraph (b) of this section. Both systems shall be tuned to the same VOR ground facility and note the indicated bearings to that station. The maximum permissible variation between the two indicated bearings is 4 degrees.

(d) Each person making the VOR operational check, as specified in paragraph (b) or (c) of this section, shall enter the date, place, bearing error, and sign the aircraft log or other record. In addition, if a test signal radiated by a repair station, as specified in paragraph (b) (1) of this section, is used, an entry must be made in the aircraft log or other record by the repair station certificate holder or the certificate holder's representative certifying to the bearing transmitted by the repair station for the check and the date of transmission.

(Approved by the Office of Management and Budget under control number 2120–0005)

91.173   ATC clearance and flight plan required

No person may operate an aircraft in controlled airspace under IFR unless that person has—

(a) Filed an IFR flight plan; and

(b) Received an appropriate ATC clearance.

91.175   Takeoff and landing under IFR

(a) Instrument approaches to civil airports. Unless otherwise authorized by the FAA, when it is necessary to use an instrument approach to a civil airport, each person operating an aircraft must use a standard instrument approach procedure prescribed in part 97 of this chapter for that airport. This paragraph does not apply to United States military aircraft.

(b) Authorized DA/DH or MDA. For the purpose of this section, when the approach procedure being used provides for and requires the use of a DA/DH or MDA, the authorized DA/DH or MDA is the highest of the following:

(1) The DA/DH or MDA prescribed by the approach procedure.

(2) The DA/DH or MDA prescribed for the pilot in command.

(3) The DA/DH or MDA appropriate for the aircraft equipment available and used during the approach.

(c) Operation below DA/DH or MDA. Except as provided in 91.176 of this chapter, where a DA/DH or MDA is applicable, no pilot may operate an aircraft, except a military aircraft of the United States, below the authorized MDA or continue an approach below the authorized DA/DH unless—

(1) The aircraft is continuously in a position from which a descent to a landing on the intended runway can be made at a normal rate of descent using normal maneuvers, and for operations conducted under part 121 or part 135 unless that descent rate will allow touchdown to occur within the touchdown zone of the runway of intended landing;

(2) The flight visibility is not less than the visibility prescribed in the standard instrument approach being used; and

(3) Except for a Category II or Category III approach where any necessary visual reference requirements are specified by the Administrator, at least one of the following visual references for the intended runway is distinctly visible and identifiable to the pilot:

   (i) The approach light system, except that the pilot may not descend below 100 feet above the touchdown zone elevation using the approach lights as a reference unless the red terminating bars or the red side row bars are also distinctly visible and identifiable.

   (ii) The threshold.

   (iii) The threshold markings.

   (iv) The threshold lights.

   (v) The runway end identifier lights.

   (vi) The touchdown zone or touchdown zone markings.

   (vii) The touchdown zone or touchdown zone markings.

   (viii) The touchdown zone lights.

   (ix) The runway or runway markings.

   (x) The runway lights.

(d) Landing. No pilot operating an aircraft, except a military aircraft of the United States, may land that aircraft when—

(1) For operations conducted under 91.176 of this part, the requirements of paragraphs (a)(3)(iii) or (b)(3)(iii), as applicable, of that section are not met; or

(3) For all other operations under this part and parts 121, 125, 129, and 135, the flight visibility is less than the visibility prescribed in the standard instrument approach procedure being used.

(e) Missed approach procedures. Each pilot operating an aircraft, except a military aircraft of the United States, shall immediately execute an appropriate missed approach procedure when either of the following conditions exist:

(1) Whenever operating an aircraft pursuant to paragraph (c) of this section or 91.176 of this part, and the requirements of that paragraph or section are not met at either of the following times:

   (i) When the aircraft is being operated below MDA; or

   (ii) Upon arrival at the missed approach point, including a DA/DH where a DA/DH is specified and its use is required, and at any time after that until touchdown.

(2) Whenever an identifiable part of the airport is not distinctly visible to the pilot during a circling maneuver at or above MDA, unless the inability to see an identifiable part of the airport results only from a normal bank of the aircraft during the circling approach.

(f) Civil airport takeoff minimums. This paragraph applies to persons operating an aircraft under part 121, 125, 129, or 135 of this chapter.

(1) Unless otherwise authorized by the FAA, no pilot may takeoff from a civil airport under IFR unless the weather conditions at time of takeoff are at or above the weather minimums for IFR takeoff prescribed for that airport under part 97 of this chapter.

(2) If takeoff weather minimums are not prescribed under part 97 of this chapter for a particular airport, the following weather minimums apply to takeoffs under IFR:

   (i) For aircraft, other than helicopters, having two engines or less—1 statute mile visibility.

   (ii) For aircraft having more than two engines—1/2 statute mile visibility.

   (iii) For helicopters—1/2 statute mile visibility.

.(4) Notwithstanding the requirements of paragraph (f)(3) of this section, no pilot may takeoff from an airport under IFR unless:

   (i) For part 121 and part 135 operators, the pilot uses a takeoff obstacle clearance or avoidance procedure that ensures compliance with the applicable airplane performance operating limitations requirements under part 121, subpart I or part 135, subpart I for takeoff at that airport; or

   (ii) For part 129 operators, the pilot uses a takeoff obstacle clearance or avoidance procedure that ensures compliance with the airplane performance operating limitations prescribed by the State of the operator for takeoff at that airport.

(g) Military airports. Unless otherwise prescribed by the Administrator, each person operating a civil aircraft under IFR into or out of a military airport shall comply with the instrument approach procedures and the takeoff and landing minimum prescribed by the military authority having jurisdiction of that airport.

(h) Comparable values of RVR and ground visibility.

(1) Except for Category II or Category III minimums, if RVR minimums for takeoff or landing are prescribed in an instrument approach procedure, but RVR is not reported for the runway of intended operation, the RVR minimum shall be converted to ground visibility in accordance with the table in paragraph (h)(2) of this section and shall be the visibility minimum for takeoff or landing on that runway.

(2)

RVR (FEET)	VISIBILITY (STATUTE MILES)
1,600	1/4
2,400	1/2
3,200	5/8
4,000	3/4
4,500	7/8
5,000	1
6,000	1 1/4

(i) Operations on unpublished routes and use of radar in instrument approach procedures. When radar is approved at certain locations for ATC purposes, it may be used not only for surveillance and precision radar approaches, as applicable, but also may be used in conjunction with instrument approach procedures predicated on other types of radio navigational aids. Radar vectors may be authorized to provide course guidance through the segments of an approach to the final course or fix. When operating on an unpublished route or while being radar vectored, the pilot, when an approach clearance is received, shall, in addition to complying with 91.177, maintain the last altitude assigned to that pilot until the aircraft is established on a segment of a published route or instrument approach procedure unless a different altitude is assigned by ATC. After the aircraft is so established, published altitudes apply to descent within each succeeding route or approach segment unless a different altitude is assigned by ATC. Upon reaching the final approach course or fix, the pilot may either complete the instrument approach in accordance with a procedure approved for the facility or continue a surveillance or precision radar approach to a landing.

(j) Limitation on procedure turns. In the case of a radar vector to a final approach course or fix, a timed approach from a holding fix, or an approach for which the procedure specifies "No PT," no pilot may make a procedure turn unless cleared to do so by ATC.

(k) ILS components. The basic components of an ILS are the localizer, glide slope, and outer marker, and, when installed for use with Category II or Category III instrument approach procedures, an inner marker. The following means may be used to substitute for the outer marker: Compass locator; precision approach radar (PAR) or airport surveillance radar (ASR); DME, VOR, or nondirectional beacon fixes authorized in the standard instrument approach procedure; or a suitable RNAV system in conjunction with a fix identified in the standard instrument approach procedure. Applicability of, and substitution for, the inner marker for a Category II or III approach is determined by the appropriate 14 CFR part 97 approach procedure, letter of authorization, or operations specifications issued to an operator.

[Doc. No. 18334, 54 FR 34294, Aug. 18, 1989, as amended by Amdt. 91-267, 66 FR 21066, Apr. 27, 2001; Amdt. 91-281, 69 FR 1640, Jan. 9, 2004; Amdt. 91-296, 72 FR 31678, June 7, 2007; Amdt. 91-306, 74 FR 20205, May 1, 2009; Docket FAA-2013-0485, Amdt. 91-345, 81 FR 90172, Dec. 13, 2016; Amdt. 91-345B, 83 FR 10568, Mar. 12, 2018]

91.176 Straight-in landing operations below DA/DH or MDA using an enhanced flight vision system (EFVS) under IFR

(a) EFVS operations to touchdown and rollout. Unless otherwise authorized by the Administrator to use an MDA as a DA/DH with vertical navigation on an instrument approach procedure, or un-less paragraph (d) of this section applies, no person may conduct an EFVS operation in an aircraft, except a military aircraft of the United States, at any airport below the authorized DA/DH to touchdown and rollout unless the minimums used for the particular approach procedure being flown include a DA or DH, and the following requirements are met:

(1) Equipment.

(i) The aircraft must be equipped with an operable EFVS that meets the applicable airworthiness requirements. The EFVS must:

(A) Have an electronic means to provide a display of the forward external scene topography (the applicable natural or manmade features of a place or region especially in a way to show their relative positions and elevation) through the use of imaging sensors, including but not limited to forward-looking infrared, millimeter wave radiometry, millimeter wave radar, or low-light level image intensification.

(B) Present EFVS sensor imagery, aircraft flight information, and flight symbology on a head up display, or an equivalent display, so that the imagery, information and symbology are clearly visible to the pilot flying in his or her normal position with the line of vision looking forward along the flight path. Aircraft flight information and flight symbology must consist of at least airspeed, vertical speed, aircraft attitude, heading, altitude, height above ground level such as that provided by a radio altimeter or other device capable of providing equivalent performance, command guidance as appropriate for the approach to be flown, path deviation indications, flight path vector, and flight path angle reference cue. Additionally, for aircraft other than rotorcraft, the EFVS must display flare prompt or flare guidance.

(C) Present the displayed EFVS sensor imagery, attitude symbology, flight path vector, and flight path angle reference cue, and other cues, which are referenced to the EFVS sensor imagery and external scene topography, so that they are aligned with, and scaled to, the external view.

(D) Display the flight path angle reference cue with a pitch scale. The flight path angle reference cue must be selectable by the pilot to the desired descent angle for the approach and be sufficient to monitor the vertical flight path of the aircraft.

(E) Display the EFVS sensor imagery, aircraft flight information, and flight symbology such that they do not adversely obscure the pilot's outside view or field of view through the cockpit window.

(F) Have display characteristics, dynamics, and cues that are suitable for manual control of the aircraft to touchdown in the touchdown zone of the runway of intended landing and during rollout.

(ii) When a minimum flightcrew of more than one pilot is required, the aircraft must be equipped with a display that provides the pilot monitoring with EFVS sensor imagery. Any symbology displayed may not adversely obscure the sensor imagery of the runway environment.

(2) Operations.

(i) The pilot conducting the EFVS operation may not use circling minimums.

(ii) Each required pilot flightcrew member must have adequate knowledge of, and familiarity with, the aircraft, the EFVS, and the procedures to be used.

(iii) The aircraft must be equipped with, and the pilot flying must use, an operable EFVS that meets the equipment requirements of paragraph (a)(1) of this section.

FAR 91

(iv) When a minimum flightcrew of more than one pilot is required, the pilot monitoring must use the display specified in paragraph (a)(1)(ii) to monitor and assess the safe conduct of the approach, landing, and rollout.

(v) The aircraft must continuously be in a position from which a descent to a landing on the intended runway can be made at a normal rate of descent using normal maneuvers.

(vi) The descent rate must allow touchdown to occur within the touchdown zone of the runway of intended landing.

(vii) Each required pilot flightcrew member must meet the following requirements—

(A) A person exercising the privileges of a pilot certificate issued under this chapter, any person serving as a required pilot flightcrew member of a U.S.-registered aircraft, or any person serving as a required pilot flightcrew member for a part 121, 125, or 135 operator, must be qualified in accordance with part 61 and, as applicable, the training, testing, and qualification provisions of subpart K of this part, part 121, 125, or 135 of this chapter that apply to the operation; or

(B) Each person acting as a required pilot flightcrew member for a foreign air carrier subject to part 129, or any person serving as a required pilot flightcrew member of a foreign registered aircraft, must be qualified in accordance with the training requirements of the civil aviation authority of the State of the operator for the EFVS operation to be conducted.

(viii) A person conducting operations under this part must conduct the operation in accordance with a letter of authorization for the use of EFVS unless the operation is conducted in an aircraft that has been issued an experimental certificate under §21.191 of this chapter for the purpose of research and development or showing compliance with regulations, or the operation is being conducted by a person otherwise authorized to conduct EFVS operations under paragraphs (a)(2)(ix) through (xii) of this section. A person applying to the FAA for a letter of authorization must submit an application in a form and manner prescribed by the Administrator.

(ix) A person conducting operations under subpart K of this part must conduct the operation in accordance with management specifications authorizing the use of EFVS.

(x) A person conducting operations under part 121, 129, or 135 of this chapter must conduct the operation in accordance with operations specifications authorizing the use of EFVS.

(xi) A person conducting operations under part 125 of this chapter must conduct the operation in accordance with operations specifications authorizing the use of EFVS or, for a holder of a part 125 letter of deviation authority, a letter of authorization for the use of EFVS.

(xii) A person conducting an EFVS operation during an authorized Category II or Category III operation must conduct the operation in accordance with operations specifications, management specifications, or a letter of authorization authorizing EFVS operations during authorized Category II or Category III operations.

(3) *Visibility and visual reference requirements.* No pilot operating under this section or 121.651, 125.381, or 135.225 of this chapter may continue an approach below the authorized DA/DH and land unless:

(i) The pilot determines that the enhanced flight visibility observed by use of an EFVS is not less than the visibility prescribed in the instrument approach procedure being used.

(ii) From the authorized DA/DH to 100 feet above the touchdown zone elevation of the runway of intended landing, any approach light system or both the runway threshold and the touchdown zone are distinctly visible and identifiable to the pilot using an EFVS.

(A) The pilot must identify the runway threshold using at least one of the following visual references—

(1) The beginning of the runway landing surface;

(2) The threshold lights; or

(3) The runway end identifier lights.

(B) The pilot must identify the touchdown zone using at least one of the following visual references—

(1) The runway touchdown zone landing surface;

(2) The touchdown zone lights;

(3) The touchdown zone markings; or

(4) The runway lights.

(iii) At 100 feet above the touchdown zone elevation of the runway of intended landing and below that altitude, the enhanced flight visibility using EFVS must be sufficient for one of the following visual references to be distinctly visible and identifiable to the pilot—

(A) The runway threshold;

(B) The lights or markings of the threshold;

(C) The runway touchdown zone landing surface; or

(D) The lights or markings of the touchdown zone.

(4) *Additional requirements.* The Administrator may prescribe additional equipment, operational, and visibility and visual reference requirements to account for specific equipment characteristics, operational procedures, or approach characteristics. These requirements will be specified in an operator's operations specifications, management specifications, or letter of authorization authorizing the use of EFVS.

(b) *EFVS operations to 100 feet above the touchdown zone elevation.* Except as specified in paragraph (d) of this section, no person may conduct an EFVS operation in an aircraft, except a military aircraft of the United States, at any airport below the authorized DA/DH or MDA to 100 feet above the touchdown zone elevation unless the following requirements are met:

(1) *Equipment.*

(i) The aircraft must be equipped with an operable EFVS that meets the applicable airworthiness requirements.

(ii) The EFVS must meet the requirements of paragraph (a)(1)(i)(A) through (F) of this section, but need not present flare prompt, flare guidance, or height above ground level.

(2) *Operations.*

(i) The pilot conducting the EFVS operation may not use circling minimums.

(ii) Each required pilot flightcrew member must have adequate knowledge of, and familiarity with, the aircraft, the EFVS, and the procedures to be used.

(iii) The aircraft must be equipped with, and the pilot flying must use, an operable EFVS that meets the equipment requirements of paragraph (b)(1) of this section.

(iv) The aircraft must continuously be in a position from which a descent to a landing on the intended runway can be made at a normal rate of descent using normal maneuvers.

(v) For operations conducted under part 121 or part 135 of this chapter, the descent rate must allow touchdown to occur within the touchdown zone of the runway of intended landing.

(vi) Each required pilot flightcrew member must meet the following requirements—

(A) A person exercising the privileges of a pilot certificate issued under this chapter, any person serving as a required pilot flightcrew member of a U.S.-registered aircraft, or any person serving as a required pilot flightcrew member for a part 121, 125, or 135 operator, must be qualified in accordance with part 61 and, as applicable, the training, testing, and qualification provisions of subpart K of this part, part 121, 125, or 135 of this chapter that apply to the operation; or

(B) Each person acting as a required pilot flightcrew member for a foreign air carrier subject to part 129, or any person serving as a required pilot flightcrew member of a foreign registered aircraft, must be qualified in accordance with the training requirements of the civil aviation authority of the State of the operator for the EFVS operation to be conducted.

(vii) A person conducting operations under subpart K of this part must conduct the operation in accordance with management specifications authorizing the use of EFVS.

(viii) A person conducting operations under part 121, 129, or 135 of this chapter must conduct the operation in accordance with operations specifications authorizing the use of EFVS.

(ix) A person conducting operations under part 125 of this chapter must conduct the operation in accordance with operations specifications authorizing the use of EFVS or, for a holder of a part 125 letter of deviation authority, a letter of authorization for the use of EFVS.

(x) A person conducting an EFVS operation during an authorized Category II or Category III operation must conduct the operation in accordance with operations specifications, management specifications, or a letter of authorization authorizing EFVS operations during authorized Category II or Category III operations.

(3) Visibility and Visual Reference Requirements. No pilot operating under this section or §121.651, §125.381, or §135.225 of this chapter may continue an approach below the authorized MDA or continue an approach below the authorized DA/DH and land unless:

(i) The pilot determines that the enhanced flight visibility observed by use of an EFVS is not less than the visibility prescribed in the instrument approach procedure being used.

(ii) From the authorized MDA or DA/DH to 100 feet above the touchdown zone elevation of the runway of intended landing, any approach light system or both the runway threshold and the touchdown zone are distinctly visible and identifiable to the pilot using an EFVS.

(A) The pilot must identify the runway threshold using at least one of the following visual references-

(1) The beginning of the runway landing surface;

(2) The threshold lights; or

(3) The runway end identifier lights.

(B) The pilot must identify the touchdown zone using at least one of the following visual references—

(1) The runway touchdown zone landing surface;

(2) The touchdown zone lights;

(3) The touchdown zone markings; or

(4) The runway lights.

(iii) At 100 feet above the touchdown zone elevation of the runway of intended landing and below that altitude, the flight visibility must be sufficient for one of the following visual references to be distinctly visible and identifiable to the pilot without reliance on the EFVS—

(A) The runway threshold;

(B) The lights or markings of the threshold;

(C) The runway touchdown zone landing surface; or

(D) The lights or markings of the touchdown zone.

(4) Compliance Date. Beginning on March 13, 2018, a person conducting an EFVS operation to 100 feet above the touchdown zone elevation must comply with the requirements of paragraph (b) of this section.

(c) Public aircraft certification and training requirements. A public aircraft operator, other than the U.S. military, may conduct an EFVS operation under paragraph (a) or (b) of this section only if:

(1) The aircraft meets all of the civil certification and airworthiness requirements of paragraph (a)(1) or (b)(1) of this section, as applicable to the EFVS operation to be conducted; and

(2) The pilot flightcrew member, or any other person who manipulates the controls of an aircraft during an EFVS operation, meets the training, recent flight experience and refresher training requirements of §61.66 of this chapter applicable to EFVS operations.

(d) Exception for Experimental Aircraft. The requirement to use an EFVS that meets the applicable airworthiness requirements specified in paragraphs (a)(1)(i), (a)(2)(iii), (b)(1)(i), and (b)(2)(iii) of this section does not apply to operations conducted in an aircraft issued an experimental certificate under §21.191 of this chapter for the purpose of research and development or showing compliance with regulations, provided the Administrator has determined that the operations can be conducted safely in accordance with operating limitations issued for that purpose.

[Docket FAA-2013-0485, Amdt. 91-345, 81 FR 90172, Dec. 13, 2016; 82 FR 2193, Jan. 9, 2017]

91.177 Minimum altitudes for IFR operations

(a) Operation of aircraft at minimum altitudes. Except when necessary for takeoff or landing, or unless otherwise authorized by the FAA, no person may operate an aircraft under IFR below—

(1) The applicable minimum altitudes prescribed in parts 95 and 97 of this chapter. However, if both a MEA and a MOCA are prescribed for a particular route or route segment, a person may operate an aircraft below the MEA down to, but not below, the MOCA, provided the applicable navigation signals are available. For aircraft using VOR for navigation, this applies only when the aircraft is within 22 nautical miles of that VOR (based on the reasonable estimate by the pilot operating the aircraft of that distance); or

(2) If no applicable minimum altitude is prescribed in parts 95 and 97 of this chapter, then—

(i) In the case of operations over an area designated as a mountainous area in part 95 of this chapter, an altitude of 2,000 feet above the highest obstacle within a horizontal distance of 4 nautical miles from the course to be flown; or

(ii) In any other case, an altitude of 1,000 feet above the highest obstacle within a horizontal distance of 4 nautical miles from the course to be flown.

(b) Climb. Climb to a higher minimum IFR altitude shall begin immediately after passing the point beyond which that minimum altitude applies, except that when ground obstructions intervene, the point beyond which that higher minimum altitude applies shall be crossed at or above the applicable MCA.

[Doc. No. 18334, 54 FR 34294, Aug. 18, 1989, as amended by Amdt. 91–296, 72 FR 31678, June 7, 2007; Amdt. 91-315, 75 FR 30690, June 2, 2010]

91.179 IFR cruising altitude or flight level

Unless otherwise authorized by ATC, the following rules apply—

(a) In controlled airspace. Each person operating an aircraft under IFR in level cruising flight in controlled airspace shall maintain the altitude or flight level assigned that aircraft by ATC. However, if the ATC clearance assigns "VFR conditions on-top," that person shall maintain an altitude or flight level as prescribed by 91.159.

FAR 91

(b) In uncontrolled airspace. Except while in a holding pattern of 2 minutes or less or while turning, each person operating an aircraft under IFR in level cruising flight in uncontrolled airspace shall maintain an appropriate altitude as follows:

(1) When operating below 18,000 feet MSL and—

   (i) On a magnetic course of zero degrees through 179 degrees, any odd thousand foot MSL altitude (such as 3,000, 5,000, or 7,000); or

   (ii) On a magnetic course of 180 degrees through 359 degrees, any even thousand foot MSL altitude (such as 2,000, 4,000, or 6,000).

(2) When operating at or above 18,000 feet MSL but below flight level 290, and—

   (i) On a magnetic course of zero degrees through 179 degrees, any odd flight level (such as 190, 210, or 230); or

   (ii) On a magnetic course of 180 degrees through 359 degrees, any even flight level (such as 180, 200, or 220).

(3) When operating at flight level 290 and above in non-RVSM airspace, and—

   (i) On a magnetic course of zero degrees through 179 degrees, any flight level, at 4,000-foot intervals, beginning at and including flight level 290 (such as flight level 290, 330, or 370); or

   (ii) On a magnetic course of 180 degrees through 359 degrees, any flight level, at 4,000-foot intervals, beginning at and including flight level 310 (such as flight level 310, 350, or 390).

(4) When operating at flight level 290 and above in airspace designated as Reduced Vertical Separation Minimum (RVSM) airspace and—

   (i) On a magnetic course of zero degrees through 179 degrees, any odd flight level, at 2,000-foot intervals beginning at and including flight level 290 (such as flight level 290, 310, 330, 350, 370, 390, 410); or

   (ii) On a magnetic course of 180 degrees through 359 degrees, any even flight level, at 2000-foot intervals beginning at and including flight level 300 (such as 300, 320, 340, 360, 380, 400).

[Doc. No. 18334, 54 FR 34294, Aug. 18, 1989, as amended by Amdt. 91–276, 68 FR 61321, Oct. 27, 2003; 68 FR 70133, Dec. 17, 2003; Amdt. 91–296, 72 FR 31679, June 7, 2007]

91.180   Operations within airspace designated as Reduced Vertical Separation Minimum airspace

(a) Except as provided in paragraph (b) of this section, no person may operate a civil aircraft in airspace designated as Reduced Vertical Separation Minimum (RVSM) airspace unless:

(1) The operator and the operator's aircraft comply with the minimum standards of appendix G of this part; and

(2) The operator is authorized by the Administrator or the country of registry to conduct such operations.

(b) The Administrator may authorize a deviation from the requirements of this section.

[Amdt. 91–276, 68 FR 70133, Dec. 17, 2003]

91.181   Course to be flown

Unless otherwise authorized by ATC, no person may operate an aircraft within controlled airspace under IFR except as follows:

(a) On an ATS route, along the centerline of that airway.

(b) On any other route, along the direct course between the navigational aids or fixes defining that route. However, this section does not prohibit maneuvering the aircraft to pass well clear of other air traffic or the maneuvering of the aircraft in VFR conditions to clear the intended flight path both before and during climb or descent.

[Doc. No. 18334, 54 FR 34294, Aug. 18, 1989, as amended by Amdt. 91–296, 72 FR 31679, June 7, 2007]

91.183   IFR communications

Unless otherwise authorized by ATC, the pilot in command of each aircraft operated under IFR in controlled airspace must ensure that a continuous watch is maintained on the appropriate frequency and must report the following as soon as possible—

(a) The time and altitude of passing each designated reporting point, or the reporting points specified by ATC, except that while the aircraft is under radar control, only the passing of those reporting points specifically requested by ATC need be reported;

(b) Any unforecast weather conditions encountered; and

(c) Any other information relating to the safety of flight.

[Doc. No. 18334, 54 FR 34294, Aug. 18, 1989, as amended by Amdt. 91–296, 72 FR 31679, June 7, 2007]

91.185   IFR operations: two-way radio communications failure

(a) *General.* Unless otherwise authorized by ATC, each pilot who has two-way radio communications failure when operating under IFR shall comply with the rules of this section.

(b) *VFR conditions.* If the failure occurs in VFR conditions, or if VFR conditions are encountered after the failure, each pilot shall continue the flight under VFR and land as soon as practicable.

(c) *IFR conditions.* If the failure occurs in IFR conditions, or if paragraph (b) of this section cannot be complied with, each pilot shall continue the flight according to the following:

(1) *Route.*

   (i)   By the route assigned in the last ATC clearance received;

   (ii) If being radar vectored, by the direct route from the point of radio failure to the fix, route, or airway specified in the vector clearance;

   (iii) In the absence of an assigned route, by the route that ATC has advised may be expected in a further clearance; or

   (iv) In the absence of an assigned route or a route that ATC has advised may be expected in a further clearance, by the route filed in the flight plan.

(2) *Altitude.* At the highest of the following altitudes or flight levels for the route segment being flown:

   (i)   The altitude or flight level assigned in the last ATC clearance received;

   (ii) The minimum altitude (converted, if appropriate, to minimum flight level as prescribed in 91.121(c)) for IFR operations; or

   (iii) The altitude or flight level ATC has advised may be expected in a further clearance.

(3) *Leave clearance limit.*

   (i)   When the clearance limit is a fix from which an approach begins, commence descent or descent and approach as close as possible to the expect-further-clearance time if one has been received, or if one has not been received, as close as possible to the estimated time of arrival as calculated from the filed or amended (with ATC) estimated time en route.

   (ii) If the clearance limit is not a fix from which an approach begins, leave the clearance limit at the expect-further-clearance time if one has been received, or if none has been received, upon arrival over the clearance limit, and proceed to a fix from which an approach begins and commence descent or descent and approach as close as possible to the estimated time of arrival as calculated from the filed or amended (with ATC) estimated time en route.

[Doc. No. 18334, 54 FR 34294, Aug. 18, 1989; Amdt. 91–211, 54 FR 41211, Oct. 5, 1989]

91.187 Operation under IFR in controlled airspace: malfunction reports

(a) The pilot in command of each aircraft operated in controlled airspace under IFR shall report as soon as practical to ATC any malfunctions of navigational, approach, or communication equipment occurring in flight.

(b) In each report required by paragraph (a) of this section, the pilot in command shall include the—

(1) Aircraft identification;

(2) Equipment affected;

(3) Degree to which the capability of the pilot to operate under IFR in the ATC system is impaired; and

(4) Nature and extent of assistance desired from ATC.

91.189 Category II and III operations: general operating rules

(a) No person may operate a civil aircraft in a Category II or III operation unless—

(1) The flight crew of the aircraft consists of a pilot in command and a second in command who hold the appropriate authorizations and ratings prescribed in 61.3 of this chapter;

(2) Each flight crewmember has adequate knowledge of, and familiarity with, the aircraft and the procedures to be used; and

(3) The instrument panel in front of the pilot who is controlling the aircraft has appropriate instrumentation for the type of flight control guidance system that is being used.(b) Unless otherwise authorized by the Administrator, no person may operate a civil aircraft in a Category II or Category III operation unless each ground component required for that operation and the related airborne equipment is installed and operating.

(c) Authorized DA/DH. For the purpose of this section, when the approach procedure being used provides for and requires the use of a DA/DH, the authorized DA/DH is the highest of the following:

(1) The DA/DH prescribed by the approach procedure.

(2) The DA/DH prescribed for the pilot in command.

(3) The DA/DH for which the aircraft is equipped.

(d) Except as provided in 91.176 of this part or unless otherwise authorized by the Administrator, no pilot operating an aircraft in a Category II or Category III approach that provides and requires the use of a DA/DH may continue the approach below the authorized decision height unless the following conditions are met:

(1) The aircraft is in a position from which a descent to a landing on the intended runway can be made at a normal rate of descent using normal maneuvers, and where that descent rate will allow touchdown to occur within the touchdown zone of the runway of intended landing.

(2) At least one of the following visual references for the intended runway is distinctly visible and identifiable to the pilot:

(i) The approach light system, except that the pilot may not descend below 100 feet above the touchdown zone elevation using the approach lights as a reference unless the red terminating bars or the red side row bars are also distinctly visible and identifiable.

(ii) The threshold.

(iii) The threshold markings.

(iv) The threshold lights.

(v) The touchdown zone or touchdown zone markings.

(vi) The touchdown zone lights.

(e) Except as provided in 91.176 of this part or unless otherwise authorized by the Administrator, each pilot operating an aircraft shall immediately execute an appropriate missed approach whenever, prior to touchdown, the requirements of paragraph (d) of this section are not met.

(f) No person operating an aircraft using a Category III approach without decision height may land that aircraft except in accordance with the provisions of the letter of authorization issued by the Administrator.

(g) Paragraphs (a) through (f) of this section do not apply to operations conducted by certificate holders operating under part 121, 125, 129, or 135 of this chapter, or holders of management specifications issued in accordance with subpart K of this part. Holders of operations specifications or management specifications may operate a civil aircraft in a Category II or Category III operation only in accordance with their operations specifications or management specifications, as applicable.

[Doc. No. 18334, 54 FR 34294, Aug. 18, 1989, as amended by Amdt. 91–280, 68 FR 54560, Sept. 17, 2003; Amdt. 91–296, 72 FR 31679, June 7, 2007]

91.191 Category II and Category III manual

(a) Except as provided in paragraph (c) of this section, after August 4, 1997, no person may operate a U.S.-registered civil aircraft in a Category II or a Category III operation unless—

(1) There is available in the aircraft a current and approved Category II or Category III manual, as appropriate, for that aircraft;

(2) The operation is conducted in accordance with the procedures, instructions, and limitations in the appropriate manual; and

(3) The instruments and equipment listed in the manual that are required for a particular Category II or Category III operation have been inspected and maintained in accordance with the maintenance program contained in the manual.

(b) Each operator must keep a current copy of each approved manual at its principal base of operations and must make each manual available for inspection upon request by the Administrator.

(c) This section does not apply to operations conducted by a certificate holder operating under part 121 or part 135 of this chapter or a holder of management specifications issued in accordance with subpart K of this part.

[Doc. No. 26933, 61 FR 34560, July 2, 1996, as amended by Amdt. 91–280, 68 FR 54560, Sept. 17, 2003]

91.193 Certificate of authorization for certain Category II operations

The Administrator may issue a certificate of authorization authorizing deviations from the requirements of 91.189, 91.191, and 91.205(f) for the operation of small aircraft identified as Category A aircraft in 97.3 of this chapter in Category II operations if the Administrator finds that the proposed operation can be safely conducted under the terms of the certificate. Such authorization does not permit operation of the aircraft carrying persons or property for compensation or hire.

91.195-91.199—[Reserved]

Subpart C — Equipment, Instrument, and Certificate Requirements

FAR 91

Source: Docket No. 18334, 54 FR 34304, Aug. 18, 1989, unless otherwise noted.

91.201 [Reserved]

91.203 Civil aircraft: certifications required

(a) Except as provided in 91.715, no person may operate a civil aircraft unless it has within it the following:

(1) An appropriate and current airworthiness certificate. Each U.S. airworthiness certificate used to comply with this subparagraph (except a special flight permit, a copy of the applicable operations specifications issued under 21.197(c) of this chapter, appropriate sections of the air carrier manual required by parts 121 and 135 of this chapter containing that portion of the operations specifications issued under 21.197(c), or an authorization under t91.611) must have on it the registration number assigned to the aircraft under part 47 of this chapter. However, the airworthiness certificate need not have on it an assigned special identification number before 10 days after that number is first affixed

to the aircraft. A revised airworthiness certificate having on it an assigned special identification number, that has been affixed to an aircraft, may only be obtained upon application to the responsible Flight Standards office.

(2) An effective U.S. registration certificate issued to its owner or, for operation within the United States, the second copy of the Aircraft registration Application as provided for in §47.31(c), a Certificate of Aircraft registration as provided in part 48, or a registration certification issued under the laws of a foreign country.

(b) No person may operate a civil aircraft unless the airworthiness certificate required by paragraph (a) of this section or a special flight authorization issued under 91.715 is displayed at the cabin or cockpit entrance so that it is legible to passengers or crew.

(c) No person may operate an aircraft with a fuel tank installed within the passenger compartment or a baggage compartment unless the installation was accomplished pursuant to part 43 of this chapter, and a copy of FAA Form 337 authorizing that installation is on board the aircraft.

(d) No person may operate a civil airplane (domestic or foreign) into or out of an airport in the United States unless it complies with the fuel venting and exhaust emissions requirements of part 34 of this chapter.

[Doc. No. 18334, 54 FR 34292, Aug. 18, 1989, as amended by Amdt. 91-218, 55 FR 32861, Aug. 10, 1990; Amdt. 91-318, 75 FR 41983, July 20, 2010; Amdt. 91-338, 80 FR 78648, Dec. 16, 2015; Docket FAA-2018-0119, Amdt. 91-350, 83 FR 9171, Mar. 5, 2018]

91.205 Powered civil aircraft with standard category U.S. airworthiness certificates: instrument and equipment requirements

(a) General. Except as provided in paragraphs (c)(3) and (e) of this section, no person may operate a powered civil aircraft with a standard category U.S. airworthiness certificate in any operation described in paragraphs (b) through (f) of this section unless that aircraft contains the instruments and equipment specified in those paragraphs (or FAA-approved equivalents) for that type of operation, and those instruments and items of equipment are in operable condition.

(b) Visual-flight rules (day). For VFR flight during the day, the following instruments and equipment are required:

(1) Airspeed indicator.

(2) Altimeter.

(3) Magnetic direction indicator.

(4) Tachometer for each engine.

(5) Oil pressure gauge for each engine using pressure system.

(6) Temperature gauge for each liquid-cooled engine.

(7) Oil temperature gauge for each air-cooled engine.

(8) Manifold pressure gauge for each altitude engine.

(9) Fuel gauge indicating the quantity of fuel in each tank.

(10) Landing gear position indicator, if the aircraft has a retractable landing gear.

(11) For small civil airplanes certificated after March 11, 1996, in accordance with part 23 of this chapter, an approved aviation red or aviation white anticollision light system. In the event of failure of any light of the anticollision light system, operation of the aircraft may continue to a location where repairs or replacement can be made.

(12) If the aircraft is operated for hire over water and beyond power-off gliding distance from shore, approved flotation gear readily available to each occupant and, unless the aircraft is operating under part 121 of this subchapter, at least one pyrotechnic signaling device. As used in this section, "shore" means that area of the land adjacent to the water which is above the high water mark and excludes land areas which are intermittently under water.

(13) An approved safety belt with an approved metal-to-metal latching device, or other approved restraint system for each occupant 2 years of age or older.

(14) For small civil airplanes manufactured after July 18, 1978, an approved shoulder harness or restraint system for each front seat. For small civil airplanes manufactured after December 12, 1986, an approved shoulder harness or restraint system for all seats. Shoulder harnesses installed at flightcrew stations must permit the flightcrew member, when seated and with the safety belt and shoulder harness fastened, to perform all functions necessary for flight operations. For purposes of this paragraph—

(i) The date of manufacture of an airplane is the date the inspection acceptance records reflect that the airplane is complete and meets the FAA-approved type design data; and

(ii) A front seat is a seat located at a flightcrew member station or any seat located alongside such a seat.

(15) An emergency locator transmitter, if required by 91.207.

(16) [Reserved]

(17) For rotorcraft manufactured after September 16, 1992, a shoulder harness for each seat that meets the requirements of 27.2 or 29.2 of this chapter in effect on September 16, 1991.

(c) Visual flight rules (night). For VFR flight at night, the following instruments and equipment are required:

(1) Instruments and equipment specified in paragraph (b) of this section.

(2) Approved position lights.

(3) An approved aviation red or aviation white anticollision light system on all U.S.-registered civil aircraft. Anticollision light systems initially installed after August 11, 1971, on aircraft for which a type certificate was issued or applied for before August 11, 1971, must at least meet the anticollision light standards of part 23, 25, 27, or 29 of this chapter, as applicable, that were in effect on August 10, 1971, except that the color may be either aviation red or aviation white. In the event of failure of any light of the anticollision light system, operations with the aircraft may be continued to a stop where repairs or replacement can be made.

(4) If the aircraft is operated for hire, one electric landing light.

(5) An adequate source of electrical energy for all installed electrical and radio equipment.

(6) One spare set of fuses, or three spare fuses of each kind required, that are accessible to the pilot in flight.

(d) Instrument flight rules. For IFR flight, the following instruments and equipment are required:

(1) Instruments and equipment specified in paragraph (b) of this section, and, for night flight, instruments and equipment specified in paragraph (c) of this section.

(2) Two-way radio communication and navigation equipment suitable for the route to be flown.

(3) Gyroscopic rate-of-turn indicator, except on the following aircraft:

(i) Airplanes with a third attitude instrument system usable through flight attitudes of 360 degrees of pitch and roll and installed in accordance with the instrument requirements prescribed in 121.305(j) of this chapter; and

(ii) Rotorcraft with a third attitude instrument system usable through flight attitudes of ±80 degrees of pitch and ±120 degrees of roll and installed in accordance with 29.1303(g) of this chapter.

(4) Slip-skid indicator.

(5) Sensitive altimeter adjustable for barometric pressure.

(6) A clock displaying hours, minutes, and seconds with a sweep-second pointer or digital presentation.

(7) Generator or alternator of adequate capacity.

(8) Gyroscopic pitch and bank indicator (artificial horizon).

(9) Gyroscopic direction indicator (directional gyro or equivalent).

(e) Flight at and above 24,000 feet MSL (FL 240). If VOR navigation equipment is required under paragraph (d)(2) of this section, no person may operate a U.S.-registered civil aircraft within the 50 states and the District of Columbia at or above FL 240 unless that aircraft is equipped with approved DME or a suitable RNAV system. When the DME or RNAV system required by this paragraph fails at and above FL 240, the pilot in command of the aircraft must notify ATC immediately, and then may continue operations at and above FL 240 to the next airport of intended landing where repairs or replacement of the equipment can be made.

(f) Category II operations. The requirements for Category II operations are the instruments and equipment specified in—

(1) Paragraph (d) of this section; and

(2) Appendix A to this part.

(g) Category III operations. The instruments and equipment required for Category III operations are specified in paragraph (d) of this section.

(h) Night vision goggle operations. For night vision goggle operations, the following instruments and equipment must be installed in the aircraft, functioning in a normal manner, and approved for use by the FAA:

(1) Instruments and equipment specified in paragraph (b) of this section, instruments and equipment specified in paragraph (c) of this section;

(2) Night vision goggles;

(3) Interior and exterior aircraft lighting system required for night vision goggle operations;

(4) Two-way radio communications system;

(5) Gyroscopic pitch and bank indicator (artificial horizon);

(6) Generator or alternator of adequate capacity for the required instruments and equipment; and

(7) Radar altimeter.

(i) Exclusions. Paragraphs (f) and (g) of this section do not apply to operations conducted by a holder of a certificate issued under part 121 or part 135 of this chapter.

[Doc. No. 18334, 54 FR 34292, Aug. 18, 1989, as amended by Amdt. 91-220, 55 FR 43310, Oct. 26, 1990; Amdt. 91-223, 56 FR 41052, Aug. 16, 1991; Amdt. 91-231, 57 FR 42672, Sept. 15, 1992; Amdt. 91-248, 61 FR 5171, Feb. 9, 1996; Amdt. 91-251, 61 FR 34560, July 2, 1996; Amdt. 91-285, 69 FR 77599, Dec. 27, 2004; Amdt. 91-296, 72 FR 31679, June 7, 2007; Amdt. 91-309, 74 FR 42563, Aug. 21, 2009; Docket FAA-2015-1621, Amdt. 91-346, 81 FR 96700, Dec. 30, 2016]

91.207   Emergency locator transmitters

(a) Except as provided in paragraphs (e) and (f) of this section, no person may operate a U.S.-registered civil airplane unless—

(1) There is attached to the airplane an approved automatic type emergency locator transmitter that is in operable condition for the following operations, except that after June 21, 1995, an emergency locator transmitter that meets the requirements of TSO-C91 may not be used for new installations:

(i) Those operations governed by the supplemental air carrier and commercial operator rules of parts 121 and 125;

(ii) Charter flights governed by the domestic and flag air carrier rules of part 121 of this chapter; and

(iii) Operations governed by part 135 of this chapter; or

(2) For operations other than those specified in paragraph (a)(1) of this section, there must be attached to the airplane an approved personal type or an approved automatic type emergency locator transmitter that is in operable condition, except that after June 21, 1995, an emergency locator transmitter that meets the requirements of TSO-C91 may not be used for new installations.

(b) Each emergency locator transmitter required by paragraph (a) of this section must be attached to the airplane in such a manner that the probability of damage to the transmitter in the event of crash impact is minimized. Fixed and deployable automatic type transmitters must be attached to the airplane as far aft as practicable.

(c) Batteries used in the emergency locator transmitters required by paragraphs (a) and (b) of this section must be replaced (or recharged, if the batteries are rechargeable)—

(1) When the transmitter has been in use for more than 1 cumulative hour; or

(2) When 50 percent of their useful life (or, for rechargeable batteries, 50 percent of their useful life of charge) has expired, as established by the transmitter manufacturer under its approval.

The new expiration date for replacing (or recharging) the battery must be legibly marked on the outside of the transmitter and entered in the aircraft maintenance record. Paragraph (c)(2) of this section does not apply to batteries (such as water-activated batteries) that are essentially unaffected during probable storage intervals.

(d) Each emergency locator transmitter required by paragraph (a) of this section must be inspected within 12 calendar months after the last inspection for—

(1) Proper installation;

(2) Battery corrosion;

(3) Operation of the controls and crash sensor; and

(4) The presence of a sufficient signal radiated from its antenna.

(e) Notwithstanding paragraph (a) of this section, a person may—

(1) Ferry a newly acquired airplane from the place where possession of it was taken to a place where the emergency locator transmitter is to be installed; and

(2) Ferry an airplane with an inoperative emergency locator transmitter from a place where repairs or replacements cannot be made to a place where they can be made.

No person other than required crewmembers may be carried aboard an airplane being ferried under paragraph (e) of this section.

(f) Paragraph (a) of this section does not apply to—

(1) Before January 1, 2004, turbojet-powered aircraft;

(2) Aircraft while engaged in scheduled flights by scheduled air carriers;

(3) Aircraft while engaged in training operations conducted entirely within a 50-nautical mile radius of the airport from which such local flight operations began;

(4) Aircraft while engaged in flight operations incident to design and testing;

(5) New aircraft while engaged in flight operations incident to their manufacture, preparation, and delivery;

(6) Aircraft while engaged in flight operations incident to the aerial application of chemicals and other substances for agricultural purposes;

(7) Aircraft certificated by the Administrator for research and development purposes;

(8) Aircraft while used for showing compliance with regulations, crew training, exhibition, air racing, or market surveys;

(9) Aircraft equipped to carry not more than one person.

(10) An aircraft during any period for which the transmitter has been temporarily removed for inspection, repair, modification, or replacement, subject to the following:

(i) No person may operate the aircraft unless the aircraft records contain an entry which includes the date of initial removal, the make, model, serial number, and reason for removing the transmitter, and a placard located in view of the pilot to show "ELT not installed."

(ii) No person may operate the aircraft more than 90 days after the ELT is initially removed from the aircraft; and

(11) On and after January 1, 2004, aircraft with a maximum payload capacity of more than 18,000 pounds when used in air transportation.

[Doc. No. 18334, 54 FR 34304, Aug. 18, 1989, as amended by Amdt. 91-242, 59 FR 32057, June 21, 1994; 59 FR 34578, July 6, 1994; Amdt. 91-265, 65 FR 81319, Dec. 22, 2000; 66 FR 16316, Mar. 23, 2001]

FAR 91

91.209   Aircraft lights

No person may:

(a) During the period from sunset to sunrise (or, in Alaska, during the period a prominent unlighted object cannot be seen from a distance of 3 statute miles or the sun is more than 6 degrees below the horizon)—

  (1) Operate an aircraft unless it has lighted position lights;

  (2) Park or move an aircraft in, or in dangerous proximity to, a night flight operations area of an airport unless the aircraft—

    (i)   Is clearly illuminated;

    (ii) Has lighted position lights; or

    (iii) Is in an area that is marked by obstruction lights;

  (3) Anchor an aircraft unless the aircraft—

    (i)   Has lighted anchor lights; or

    (ii) Is in an area where anchor lights are not required on vessels; or

(b) Operate an aircraft that is equipped with an anticollision light system, unless it has lighted anticollision lights. However, the anticollision lights need not be lighted when the pilot-in-command determines that, because of operating conditions, it would be in the interest of safety to turn the lights off.

[Doc. No. 27806, 61 FR 5171, Feb. 9, 1996]

91.211   Supplemental oxygen

(a) *General.* No person may operate a civil aircraft of U.S. registry—

  (1) At cabin pressure altitudes above 12,500 feet (MSL) up to and including 14,000 feet (MSL) unless the required minimum flight crew is provided with and uses supplemental oxygen for that part of the flight at those altitudes that is of more than 30 minutes duration;

  (2) At cabin pressure altitudes above 14,000 feet (MSL) unless the required minimum flight crew is provided with and uses supplemental oxygen during the entire flight time at those altitudes; and

  (3) At cabin pressure altitudes above 15,000 feet (MSL) unless each occupant of the aircraft is provided with supplemental oxygen.

(b) *Pressurized cabin aircraft.*

  (1) No person may operate a civil aircraft of U.S. registry with a pressurized cabin—

    (i)   At flight altitudes above flight level 250 unless at least a 10-minute supply of supplemental oxygen, in addition to any oxygen required to satisfy paragraph (a) of this section, is available for each occupant of the aircraft for use in the event that a descent is necessitated by loss of cabin pressurization; and

    (ii) At flight altitudes above flight level 350 unless one pilot at the controls of the airplane is wearing and using an oxygen mask that is secured and sealed and that either supplies oxygen at all times or automatically supplies oxygen whenever the cabin pressure altitude of the airplane exceeds 14,000 feet (MSL), except that the one pilot need not wear and use an oxygen mask while at or below flight level 410 if there are two pilots at the controls and each pilot has a quick-donning type of oxygen mask that can be placed on the face with one hand from the ready position within 5 seconds, supplying oxygen and properly secured and sealed.

  (2) Notwithstanding paragraph (b)(1)(ii) of this section, if for any reason at any time it is necessary for one pilot to leave the controls of the aircraft when operating at flight altitudes above flight level 350, the remaining pilot at the controls shall put on and use an oxygen mask until the other pilot has returned to that crewmember's station.

91.213   Inoperative instruments and equipment

(a) Except as provided in paragraph (d) of this section, no person may take off an aircraft with inoperative instruments or equipment installed unless the following conditions are met:

  (1) An approved Minimum Equipment List exists for that aircraft.

  (2) The aircraft has within it a letter of authorization, issued by the responsible Flight Standards office, authorizing operation of the aircraft under the Minimum Equipment List. The letter of authorization may be obtained by written request of the airworthiness certificate holder. The Minimum Equipment List and the letter of authorization constitute a supplemental type certificate for the aircraft.

  (3) The approved Minimum Equipment List must—

    (i)   Be prepared in accordance with the limitations specified in paragraph (b) of this section; and

    (ii) Provide for the operation of the aircraft with the instruments and equipment in an inoperable condition.

  (4) The aircraft records available to the pilot must include an entry describing the inoperable instruments and equipment.

  (5) The aircraft is operated under all applicable conditions and limitations contained in the Minimum Equipment List and the letter authorizing the use of the list.

(b) The following instruments and equipment may not be included in a Minimum Equipment List:

  (1) Instruments and equipment that are either specifically or otherwise required by the airworthiness requirements under which the aircraft is type certificated and which are essential for safe operations under all operating conditions.

  (2) Instruments and equipment required by an airworthiness directive to be in operable condition unless the airworthiness directive provides otherwise.

  (3) Instruments and equipment required for specific operations by this part.

(c) A person authorized to use an approved Minimum Equipment List issued for a specific aircraft under subpart K of this part, part 121, 125, or 135 of this chapter must use that Minimum Equipment List to comply with the requirements in this section.

(d) Except for operations conducted in accordance with paragraph (a) or (c) of this section, a person may takeoff an aircraft in operations conducted under this part with inoperative instruments and equipment without an approved Minimum Equipment List provided—

  (1) The flight operation is conducted in a—

    (i)   Rotorcraft, non-turbine-powered airplane, glider, lighter-than-air aircraft, powered parachute, or weight-shift-control aircraft, for which a master minimum equipment list has not been developed; or

    (ii) Small rotorcraft, nonturbine-powered small airplane, glider, or lighter-than-air aircraft for which a Master Minimum Equipment List has been developed; and

  (2) The inoperative instruments and equipment are not—

    (i)   Part of the VFR-day type certification instruments and equipment prescribed in the applicable airworthiness regulations under which the aircraft was type certificated;

    (ii) Indicated as required on the aircraft's equipment list, or on the Kinds of Operations Equipment List for the kind of flight operation being conducted;

    (iii) Required by 91.205 or any other rule of this part for the specific kind of flight operation being conducted; or

    (iv) Required to be operational by an airworthiness directive; and

  (3) The inoperative instruments and equipment are—

    (i)   Removed from the aircraft, the cockpit control placarded, and the maintenance recorded in accordance with 43.9 of this chapter; or

    (ii) Deactivated and placarded "Inoperative." If deactivation of the inoperative instrument or equipment involves maintenance, it must be accomplished and recorded in accordance with part 43 of this chapter; and

(4) A determination is made by a pilot, who is certificated and appropriately rated under part 61 of this chapter, or by a person, who is certificated and appropriately rated to perform maintenance on the aircraft, that the inoperative instrument or equipment does not constitute a hazard to the aircraft.

An aircraft with inoperative instruments or equipment as provided in paragraph (d) of this section is considered to be in a properly altered condition acceptable to the Administrator.

(e) Notwithstanding any other provision of this section, an aircraft with inoperable instruments or equipment may be operated under a special flight permit issued in accordance with 21.197 and 21.199 of this chapter.

[Doc. No. 18334, 54 FR 34304, Aug. 18, 1989, as amended by Amdt. 91-280, 68 FR 54560, Sept. 17, 2003; Amdt. 91-282, 69 FR 44880, July 27, 2004; Docket FAA-2018-0119, Amdt. 91-350, 83 FR 9171, Mar. 5, 2018]

91.215 ATC transponder and altitude reporting equipment and use

(a) All airspace: U.S.-registered civil aircraft. For operations not conducted under part 121 or 135 of this chapter, ATC transponder equipment installed must meet the performance and environmental requirements of any class of TSO-C74b (Mode A) or any class of TSO-C74c (Mode A with altitude reporting capability) as appropriate, or the appropriate class of TSO-C112 (Mode S).

(b) All airspace. Unless otherwise authorized or directed by ATC, and except as provided in paragraph (e)(1) of this section, no person may operate an aircraft in the airspace described in paragraphs (b)(1) through (5) of this section, unless that aircraft is equipped with an operable coded radar beacon transponder having either Mode 3/A 4096 code capability, replying to Mode 3/A interrogations with the code specified by ATC, or a Mode S capability, replying to Mode 3/A interrogations with the code specified by ATC and intermode and Mode S interrogations in accordance with the applicable provisions specified in TSO C-112, and that aircraft is equipped with automatic pressure altitude reporting equipment having a Mode C capability that automatically replies to Mode C interrogations by transmitting pressure altitude information in 100-foot increments. The requirements of this paragraph (b) apply to—

(1) All aircraft. In Class A, Class B, and Class C airspace areas;

(2) All aircraft. In all airspace within 30 nautical miles of an airport listed in appendix D, section 1 of this part from the surface upward to 10,000 feet MSL;

(3) Notwithstanding paragraph (b)(2) of this section, any aircraft which was not originally certificated with an engine-driven electrical system or which has not subsequently been certified with such a system installed, balloon or glider may conduct operations in the airspace within 30 nautical miles of an airport listed in appendix D, section 1 of this part provided such operations are conducted—

　　(i) Outside any Class A, Class B, or Class C airspace area; and

　　(ii) Below the altitude of the ceiling of a Class B or Class C airspace area designated for an airport or 10,000 feet MSL, whichever is lower; and

(4) All aircraft in all airspace above the ceiling and within the lateral boundaries of a Class B or Class C airspace area designated for an airport upward to 10,000 feet MSL; and

(5) All aircraft except any aircraft which was not originally certificated with an engine-driven electrical system or which has not subsequently been certified with such a system installed, balloon, or glider—

　　(i) In all airspace of the 48 contiguous states and the District of Columbia at and above 10,000 feet MSL, excluding the airspace at and below 2,500 feet above the surface; and

　　(ii) In the airspace from the surface to 10,000 feet MSL within a 10-nautical-mile radius of any airport listed in appendix D, section 2 of this part, excluding the airspace below 1,200 feet outside of the lateral boundaries of the surface area of the airspace designated for that airport.

(c) Transponder-on operation. Except as provided in paragraph (e)(2) of this section, while in the airspace as specified in paragraph (b) of this section or in all controlled airspace, each person operating an aircraft equipped with an operable ATC transponder maintained in accordance with 91.413 shall operate the transponder, including Mode C equipment if installed, and shall reply on the appropriate code or as assigned by ATC, unless otherwise directed by ATC when transmitting would jeopardize the safe execution of air traffic control functions.

(d) ATC authorized deviations. Requests for ATC authorized deviations must be made to the ATC facility having jurisdiction over the concerned airspace within the time periods specified as follows:

(1) For operation of an aircraft with an operating transponder but without operating automatic pressure altitude reporting equipment having a Mode C capability, the request may be made at any time.

(2) For operation of an aircraft with an inoperative transponder to the airport of ultimate destination, including any intermediate stops, or to proceed to a place where suitable repairs can be made or both, the request may be made at any time.

(3) For operation of an aircraft that is not equipped with a transponder, the request must be made at least one hour before the proposed operation.

(e) Unmanned aircraft.

(1) The requirements of paragraph (b) of this section do not apply to a person operating an unmanned aircraft under this part unless the operation is conducted under a flight plan and the person operating the unmanned aircraft maintains two-way communication with ATC.

(2) No person may operate an unmanned aircraft under this part with a transponder on unless:

　　(i) The operation is conducted under a flight plan and the person operating the unmanned aircraft maintains two-way communication with ATC; or

　　(ii) The use of a transponder is otherwise authorized by the Administrator.

(Approved by the Office of Management and Budget under control number 2120–0005)

[Doc. No. 18334, 54 FR 34304, Aug. 18, 1989, as amended by Amdt. 91-221, 56 FR 469, Jan. 4, 1991; Amdt. 91-227, 56 FR 65660, Dec. 17, 1991; Amdt. 91-227, 7 FR 328, Jan. 3, 1992; Amdt. 91-229, 57 FR 34618, Aug. 5, 1992; Amdt. 91-267, 66 FR 21066, Apr. 27, 2001; Amdt. 91-355, 84 FR 34287, July 18, 2019; Amdt. No. 91-361, 86 FR 4512, Jan. 15, 2021]

91.217 Data correspondence between automatically reported pressure altitude data and the pilot's altitude reference

(a) No person may operate any automatic pressure altitude reporting equipment associated with a radar beacon transponder—

(1) When deactivation of that equipment is directed by ATC;

(2) Unless, as installed, that equipment was tested and calibrated to transmit altitude data corresponding within 125 feet (on a 95 percent probability basis) of the indicated or calibrated datum of the altimeter normally used to maintain flight altitude, with that altimeter referenced to 29.92 inches of mercury for altitudes from sea level to the maximum operating altitude of the aircraft; or

(3) Unless the altimeters and digitizers in that equipment meet the standards of TSO-C10b and TSO-C88, respectively.

(b) No person may operate any automatic pressure altitude reporting equipment associated with a radar beacon transponder or with ADS-B Out equipment unless the pressure altitude reported for ADS-B Out and Mode C/S is derived from the same source for aircraft equipped with both a transponder and ADS-B Out.

[Docket No. 18334, 54 FR 34304, Aug. 18, 1989, as amended by Admt. 91–314, 75 FR 30193, May 28, 2010]

FAR 91

91.219 Altitude alerting system or device: turbojet-powered civil airplanes

(a) Except as provided in paragraph (d) of this section, no person may operate a turbojet-powered U.S.-registered civil airplane unless that airplane is equipped with an approved altitude alerting system or device that is in operable condition and meets the requirements of paragraph (b) of this section.

(b) Each altitude alerting system or device required by paragraph (a) of this section must be able to—

 (1) Alert the pilot—

  (i) Upon approaching a preselected altitude in either ascent or descent, by a sequence of both aural and visual signals in sufficient time to establish level flight at that preselected altitude; or

  (ii) Upon approaching a preselected altitude in either ascent or descent, by a sequence of visual signals in sufficient time to establish level flight at that preselected altitude, and when deviating above and below that preselected altitude, by an aural signal;

 (2) Provide the required signals from sea level to the highest operating altitude approved for the airplane in which it is installed;

 (3) Preselect altitudes in increments that are commensurate with the altitudes at which the aircraft is operated;

 (4) Be tested without special equipment to determine proper operation of the alerting signals; and

 (5) Accept necessary barometric pressure settings if the system or device operates on barometric pressure. However, for operation below 3,000 feet AGL, the system or device need only provide one signal, either visual or aural, to comply with this paragraph. A radio altimeter may be included to provide the signal if the operator has an approved procedure for its use to determine DA/DH or MDA, as appropriate.

(c) Each operator to which this section applies must establish and assign procedures for the use of the altitude alerting system or device and each flight crewmember must comply with those procedures assigned to him.

(d) Paragraph (a) of this section does not apply to any operation of an airplane that has an experimental certificate or to the operation of any airplane for the following purposes:

 (1) Ferrying a newly acquired airplane from the place where possession of it was taken to a place where the altitude alerting system or device is to be installed.

 (2) Continuing a flight as originally planned, if the altitude alerting system or device becomes inoperative after the airplane has taken off; however, the flight may not depart from a place where repair or replacement can be made.

 (3) Ferrying an airplane with any inoperative altitude alerting system or device from a place where repairs or replacements cannot be made to a place where it can be made.

 (4) Conducting an airworthiness flight test of the airplane.

 (5) Ferrying an airplane to a place outside the United States for the purpose of registering it in a foreign country.

 (6) Conducting a sales demonstration of the operation of the airplane.

 (7) Training foreign flight crews in the operation of the airplane before ferrying it to a place outside the United States for the purpose of registering it in a foreign country.

[Doc. No. 18334, 54 FR 34304, Aug. 18, 1989, as amended by Amdt. 91–296, 72 FR 31679, June 7, 2007]

91.221 Traffic alert and collision avoidance system equipment and use

(a) All airspace: U.S.-registered civil aircraft. Any traffic alert and collision avoidance system installed in a U.S.-registered civil aircraft must be approved by the Administrator.

(b) Traffic alert and collision avoidance system, operation required. Each person operating an aircraft equipped with an operable traffic alert and collision avoidance system shall have that system on and operating.

91.223 Terrain awareness and warning system

(a) Airplanes manufactured after March 29, 2002. Except as provided in paragraph (d) of this section, no person may operate a turbine-powered U.S.-registered airplane configured with six or more passenger seats, excluding any pilot seat, unless that airplane is equipped with an approved terrain awareness and warning system that as a minimum meets the requirements for Class B equipment in Technical Standard Order (TSO)–C151.

(b) Airplanes manufactured on or before March 29, 2002. Except as provided in paragraph (d) of this section, no person may operate a turbine-powered U.S.-registered airplane configured with six or more passenger seats, excluding any pilot seat, after March 29, 2005, unless that airplane is equipped with an approved terrain awareness and warning system that as a minimum meets the requirements for Class B equipment in Technical Standard Order (TSO)–C151.

(Approved by the Office of Management and Budget under control number 2120–0631)

(c) Airplane Flight Manual. The Airplane Flight Manual shall contain appropriate procedures for—

 (1) The use of the terrain awareness and warning system; and

 (2) Proper flight crew reaction in response to the terrain awareness and warning system audio and visual warnings.

(d) Exceptions. Paragraphs (a) and (b) of this section do not apply to—

 (1) Parachuting operations when conducted entirely within a 50 nautical mile radius of the airport from which such local flight operations began.

 (2) Firefighting operations.

 (3) Flight operations when incident to the aerial application of chemicals and other substances.

[Doc. No. 29312, 65 FR 16755, Mar. 29, 2000]

91.225 Automatic Dependent Surveillance-Broadcast (ADS–B) Out equipment and use

(a) After January 1, 2020, unless otherwise authorized by ATC, no person may operate an aircraft in Class A airspace unless the aircraft has equipment installed that —

 (1) Meets the performance requirements in TSO-C166b, Extended Squitter Automatic Dependent Surveillance-Broadcast (ADS-B) and Traffic Information Service-Broadcast (TIS-B) Equipment Operating on the Radio Frequency of 1090 Megahertz (MHz); and

 (2) Meets the requirements of 91.227.

(b) After January 1, 2020, except as prohibited in paragraph (i)(2) of this section or unless otherwise authorized by ATC, no person may operate an aircraft below 18,000 feet MSL and in airspace described in paragraph (d) of this section unless the aircraft has equipment installed that —

 (1) Meets the performance requirements in—

  (i) TSO-C166b; or

  (ii) TSO-C154c, Universal Access Transceiver (UAT) Automatic Dependent Surveillance-Broadcast (ADS-B) Equipment Operating on the Frequency of 978 MHz;

 (2) Meets the requirements of 91.227.

(c) Operators with equipment installed with an approved deviation under 21.618 of this chapter also are in compliance with this section.

(d) After January 1, 2020, except as prohibited in paragraph (i)(2) of this section or unless otherwise authorized by ATC, no person may operate an aircraft in the following airspace unless the aircraft has equipment installed that meets the requirements in paragraph (b) of this section:

 (1) Class B and Class C airspace areas;

(2) Except as provided for in paragraph (e) of this section, within 30 nautical miles of an airport listed in appendix D, section 1 to this part from the surface upward to 10,000 feet MSL;

(3) Above the ceiling and within the lateral boundaries of a Class B or Class C airspace area designated for an airport upward to 10,000 feet MSL;

(4) Except as provided in paragraph (e) of this section, Class E airspace within the 48 contiguous states and the District of Columbia at and above 10,000 feet MSL, excluding the airspace at and below 2,500 feet above the surface; and

(5) Class E airspace at and above 3,000 feet MSL over the Gulf of Mexico from the coastline of the United States out to 12 nautical miles.

(e) The requirements of paragraph (b) of this section do not apply to any aircraft that was not originally certificated with an electrical system, or that has not subsequently been certified with such a system installed, including balloons and gliders. These aircraft may conduct operations without ADS–B Out in the airspace specified in paragraphs (d)(2) and (d)(4) of this section. Operations authorized by this section must be conducted—

(1) Outside any Class B or Class C airspace area; and

(2) Below the altitude of the ceiling of a Class B or Class C airspace area designated for an airport, or 10,000 feet MSL, whichever is lower.

(f) Except as prohibited in paragraph (i)(2) of this section, each person operating an aircraft equipped with ADS-B Out must operate this equipment in the transmit mode at all times unless —

(1) Otherwise authorized by the FAA when the aircraft is performing a sensitive government mission for national defense, homeland security, intelligence or law enforcement purposes and transmitting would compromise the operations security of the mission or pose a safety risk to the aircraft, crew, or people and property in the air or on the ground; or

(2) Otherwise directed by ATC when transmitting would jeopardize the safe execution of air traffic control functions.

(g) Requests for ATC authorized deviations from the requirements of this section must be made to the ATC facility having jurisdiction over the concerned airspace within the time periods specified as follows:

(1) For operation of an aircraft with an inoperative ADS–B Out, to the airport of ultimate destination, including any intermediate stops, or to proceed to a place where suitable repairs can be made or both, the request may be made at any time.

(2) For operation of an aircraft that is not equipped with ADS–B Out, the request must be made at least 1 hour before the proposed operation.

(h) The standards required in this section are incorporated by reference with the approval of the Director of the Office of the Federal Register under 5 U.S.C. 552(a) and 1 CFR part 51. All approved materials are available for inspection at the FAA's Office of Rulemaking (ARM–1), 800 Independence Avenue, SW., Washington, DC 20590 (telephone 202–267–9677), or at the National Archives and Records Administration (NARA). For information on the availability of this material at NARA, call 202–741–6030, or go to http://www.archives.gov/federal_register/code_of_federal_regulations/ibr_locations.html. This material is also available from the sources indicated in paragraphs (h)(1) and (h)(2) of this section.

(1) Copies of Technical Standard Order (TSO)–C166b, Extended Squitter Automatic Dependent Surveillance-Broadcast (ADS–B) and Traffic Information Service-Broadcast (TIS–B) Equipment Operating on the Radio Frequency of 1090 Megahertz (MHz) (December 2, 2009) and TSO–C154c, Universal Access Transceiver (UAT) Automatic Dependent Surveillance-Broadcast (ADS–B) Equipment Operating on the Frequency of 978 MHz (December 2, 2009) may be obtained from the U.S. Department of Transportation, Subsequent Distribution Office, DOT Warehouse M30, Ardmore East Business Center, 3341 Q 75th Avenue, Landover, MD 20785; telephone (301) 322–5377. Copies of TSO –C166B and TSO–C154c are also available on the FAA's Web site, at http://www.faa.gov/aircraft/air_cert/design_approvals/tso/. Select the link "Search Technical Standard Orders."

(2) Copies of Section 2, Equipment Performance Requirements and Test Procedures, of RTCA DO–260B, Minimum Operational Performance Standards for 1090 MHz Extended Squitter Automatic Dependent Surveillance-Broadcast (ADS–B) and Traffic Information Services-Broadcast (TIS–B), December 2, 2009 (referenced in TSO–C166b) and Section 2, Equipment Performance Requirements and Test Procedures, of RTCA DO–282B, Minimum Operational Performance Standards for Universal Access Transceiver (UAT) Automatic Dependent Surveillance-Broadcast (ADS–B), December 2, 2009 (referenced in TSO C–154c) may be obtained from RTCA, Inc., 1828 L Street, NW., Suite 805, Washington, DC 20036–5133, telephone 202–833–9339. Copies of RTCA DO–260B and RTCA DO–282B are also available on RTCA Inc.'s Web site, at http://www.rtca.org/onlinecart/allproducts.cfm.

(i) For unmanned aircraft:

(1) No person may operate an unmanned aircraft under a flight plan and in two way communication with ATC unless:

(i) That aircraft has equipment installed that meets the performance requirements in TSO-C166b or TSO-C154c; and

(ii) The equipment meets the requirements of § 91.227.

(2) No person may operate an unmanned aircraft under this part with Automatic Dependent Surveillance-Broadcast Out equipment in transmit mode unless:

(i) The operation is conducted under a flight plan and the person operating that unmanned aircraft maintains two-way communication with ATC; or

(ii) The use of ADS-B Out is otherwise authorized by the Administrator.

[Doc. No. FAA-2007-29305, 75 FR 30193, May 28, 2010; Amdt. 91-314-A, 75 FR 37712, June 30, 2010; Amdt. 91-316, 75 FR 37712, June 30, 2010; Amdt. 91-336, 80 FR 6900, Feb. 9, 2015; Amdt. 91-336A, 80 FR 11537, Mar. 4, 2015; Amdt. 91-355, 84 FR 34287, July 18, 2019; Amdt. No. 91-361, 86 FR 4513, Jan. 15, 2021]

91.227 Automatic Dependent Surveillance-Broadcast (ADS–B) Out equipment performance requirements

(a) Definitions. For the purposes of this section:

ADS–B Out is a function of an aircraft's onboard avionics that periodically broadcasts the aircraft's state vector (3-dimensional position and 3-dimensional velocity) and other required information as described in this section.

Navigation Accuracy Category for Position (NAC P) specifies the accuracy of a reported aircraft's position, as defined in TSO–C166b and TSO–C154c.

Navigation Accuracy Category for Velocity (NAC V) specifies the accuracy of a reported aircraft's velocity, as defined in TSO–C166b and TSO–C154c.

Navigation Integrity Category (NIC) specifies an integrity containment radius around an aircraft's reported position, as defined in TSO–C166b and TSO–C154c.

Position Source refers to the equipment installed onboard an aircraft used to process and provide aircraft position (for example, latitude, longitude, and velocity) information.

Source Integrity Level (SIL) indicates the probability of the reported horizontal position exceeding the containment radius defined by the NIC on a per sample or per hour basis, as defined in TSO–C166b and TSO–C154c.

System Design Assurance (SDA) indicates the probability of an aircraft malfunction causing false or misleading information to be transmitted, as defined in TSO–C166b and TSO–C154c.

Total latency is the total time between when the position is measured and when the position is transmitted by the aircraft.

Uncompensated latency is the time for which the aircraft does not compensate for latency.

(b) 1090 MHz ES and UAT Broadcast Links and Power Requirements —

(1) Aircraft operating in Class A airspace must have equipment installed that meets the antenna and power output requirements of Class A1, A1S, A2, A3, B1S, or B1 equipment as defined in TSO–C166b, Extended Squitter Automatic Dependent Surveillance-Broadcast (ADS–B) and Traffic Information Service-Broadcast (TIS–B) Equipment Operating on the Radio Frequency of 1090 Megahertz (MHz).

(2) Aircraft operating in airspace designated for ADS–B Out, but outside of Class A airspace, must have equipment installed that meets the antenna and output power requirements of either:

(i) Class A1, A1S, A2, A3, B1S, or B1 as defined in TSO–C166b; or

(ii) Class A1H, A1S, A2, A3, B1S, or B1 equipment as defined in TSO–C154c, Universal Access Transceiver (UAT) Automatic Dependent Surveillance–Broadcast (ADS–B) Equipment Operating on the Frequency of 978 MHz.

(c) ADS–B Out Performance Requirements for NAC P, NAC V, NIC, SDA, and SIL —

(1) For aircraft broadcasting ADS–B Out as required under 91.225 (a) and (b)—

(i) The aircraft's NAC_p must be less than 0.05 nautical miles;

(ii) The aircraft's NAC_V must be less than 10 meters per second;

(iii) The aircraft's NIC must be less than 0.2 nautical miles;

(iv) The aircraft's SDA must be 2; and

(v) The aircraft's SIL must be 3.

(2) Changes in NAC_p, NAC_V, SDA, and SIL must be broadcast within 10 seconds.

(3) Changes in NIC must be broadcast within 12 seconds.

(d) Minimum Broadcast Message Element Set for ADS–B Out. Each aircraft must broadcast the following information, as defined in TSO–C166b or TSO–C154c. The pilot must enter information for message elements listed in paragraphs (d)(7) through (d)(10) of this section during the appropriate phase of flight.

(1) The length and width of the aircraft;

(2) An indication of the aircraft's latitude and longitude;

(3) An indication of the aircraft's barometric pressure altitude;

(4) An indication of the aircraft's velocity;

(5) An indication if TCAS II or ACAS is installed and operating in a mode that can generate resolution advisory alerts;

(6) If an operable TCAS II or ACAS is installed, an indication if a resolution advisory is in effect;

(7) An indication of the Mode 3/A transponder code specified by ATC;

(8) An indication of the aircraft's call sign that is submitted on the flight plan, or the aircraft's registration number, except when the pilot has not filed a flight plan, has not requested ATC services, and is using a TSO–C154c self-assigned temporary 24-bit address;

(9) An indication if the flightcrew has identified an emergency, radio communication failure, or unlawful interference;

(10) An indication of the aircraft's "IDENT" to ATC;

(11) An indication of the aircraft assigned ICAO 24-bit address, except when the pilot has not filed a flight plan, has not requested ATC services, and is using a TSO–C154c self-assigned temporary 24-bit address;

(12) An indication of the aircraft's emitter category;

(13) An indication of whether an ADS–B In capability is installed;

(14) An indication of the aircraft's geometric altitude;

(15) An indication of the Navigation Accuracy Category for Position (NAC_p);

(16) An indication of the Navigation Accuracy Category for Velocity (NAC_V);

(17) An indication of the Navigation Integrity Category (NIC);

(18) An indication of the System Design Assurance (SDA); and

(19) An indication of the Source Integrity Level (SIL).

(e) ADS–B Latency Requirements —

(1) The aircraft must transmit its geometric position no later than 2.0 seconds from the time of measurement of the position to the time of transmission.

(2) Within the 2.0 total latency allocation, a maximum of 0.6 seconds can be uncompensated latency. The aircraft must compensate for any latency above 0.6 seconds up to the maximum 2.0 seconds total by extrapolating the geometric position to the time of message transmission.

(3) The aircraft must transmit its position and velocity at least once per second while airborne or while moving on the airport surface.

(4) The aircraft must transmit its position at least once every 5 seconds while stationary on the airport surface.

(f) Equipment with an approved deviation. Operators with equipment installed with an approved deviation under 21.618 of this chapter also are in compliance with this section.

(g) Incorporation by Reference. The standards required in this section are incorporated by reference with the approval of the Director of the Office of the Federal Register under 5 U.S.C. 552(a) and 1 CFR part 51. All approved materials are available for inspection at the FAA's Office of Rulemaking (ARM–1), 800 Independence Avenue, SW., Washington, DC 20590 (telephone 202–267–9677), or at the National Archives and Records Administration (NARA). For information on the availability of this material at NARA, call 202–741–6030, or go to http://www.archives.gov/federal_register/code_of_federal_regulations/ibr_locations.html. This material is also available from the sources indicated in paragraphs (g)(1) and (g)(2) of this section.

(1) Copies of Technical Standard Order (TSO)–C166b, Extended Squitter Automatic Dependent Surveillance–Broadcast (ADS–B) and Traffic Information Service–Broadcast (TIS–B) Equipment Operating on the Radio Frequency of 1090 Megahertz (MHz) (December 2, 2009) and TSO–C154c, Universal Access Transceiver (UAT) Automatic Dependent Surveillance–Broadcast (ADS–B) Equipment Operating on the Frequency of 978 MHz (December 2, 2009) may be obtained from the U.S. Department of Transportation, Subsequent Distribution Office, DOT Warehouse M30, Ardmore East Business Center, 3341 Q 75th Avenue Landover, MD 20785; telephone (301) 322–5377. Copies of TSO–C166B and TSO–C154c are also available on the FAA's Web site, at http://www.faa.gov/aircraft/air_cert/design_approvals/tso/. Select the link "Search Technical Standard Orders."

(2) Copies of Section 2, Equipment Performance Requirements and Test Procedures, of RTCA DO–260B, Minimum Operational Performance Standards for 1090 MHz Extended Squitter Automatic Dependent Surveillance-Broadcast (ADS–B) and Traffic Information Services-Broadcast (TIS–B), December 2, 2009 (referenced in TSO–C166b) and Section 2, Equipment Performance Requirements and Test Procedures, of RTCA DO–282B, Minimum Operational Performance Standards for Universal Access Transceiver (UAT) Automatic Dependent Surveillance-Broadcast (ADS–B), December 2, 2009 (referenced in TSO C–154c) may be obtained from RTCA Inc., 1828 L Street, NW., Suite 805, Washington, DC 20036-5133, telephone 202–833–9339. Copies of RTCA DO–260B and RTCA DO–282B are also available on RTCA Inc.'s Web site, at http://www.rtca.org/onlinecart/allproducts.cfm.

[Doc. No. FAA–2007–29305, 75 FR 30194, May 28, 2010; Amdt. 91-314–A, 75 FR 37712, June 30, 2010; Amdt. 91–316, 75 FR 37712, June 30, 2010]

91.228-91.299   [Reserved]

Subpart D — Special Flight Operations

Source: Docket No. 18334, 54 FR 34308, Aug. 18, 1989, unless otherwise noted.

91.301   [Reserved]

91.303   Aerobatic flight

No person may operate an aircraft in aerobatic flight—

(a) Over any congested area of a city, town, or settlement;

(b) Over an open air assembly of persons;

(c) Within the lateral boundaries of the surface areas of Class B, Class C, Class D, or Class E airspace designated for an airport;

(d) Within 4 nautical miles of the center line of any Federal airway;

(e) Below an altitude of 1,500 feet above the surface; or

(f) When flight visibility is less than 3 statute miles.

For the purposes of this section, aerobatic flight means an intentional maneuver involving an abrupt change in an aircraft's attitude, an abnormal attitude, or abnormal acceleration, not necessary for normal flight.

[Doc. No. 18834, 54 FR 34308, Aug. 18, 1989, as amended by Amdt. 91–227, 56 FR 65661, Dec. 17, 1991]

91.305   Flight test areas

No person may flight test an aircraft except over open water, or sparsely populated areas, having light air traffic.

91.307   Parachutes and parachuting

(a) No pilot of a civil aircraft may allow a parachute that is available for emergency use to be carried in that aircraft unless it is an approved type and has been packed by a certificated and appropriately rated parachute rigger—

(1) Within the preceding 180 days, if its canopy, shrouds, and harness are composed exclusively of nylon, rayon, or other similar synthetic fiber or materials that are substantially resistant to damage from mold, mildew, or other fungi and other rotting agents propagated in a moist environment; or

(2) Within the preceding 60 days, if any part of the parachute is composed of silk, pongee, or other natural fiber or materials not specified in paragraph (a)(1) of this section.

(b) Except in an emergency, no pilot in command may allow, and no person may conduct, a parachute operation from an aircraft within the United States except in accordance with part 105 of this chapter.

(c) Unless each occupant of the aircraft is wearing an approved parachute, no pilot of a civil aircraft carrying any person (other than a crewmember) may execute any intentional maneuver that exceeds—

(1) A bank of 60 degrees relative to the horizon; or

(2) A nose-up or nose-down attitude of 30 degrees relative to the horizon.

(d) Paragraph (c) of this section does not apply to—

(1) Flight tests for pilot certification or rating; or

(2) Spins and other flight maneuvers required by the regulations for any certificate or rating when given by—

   (i) A certificated flight instructor; or

   (ii) An airline transport pilot instructing in accordance with 61.67 of this chapter.

(e) For the purposes of this section, approved parachute means—

(1) A parachute manufactured under a type certificate or a technical standard order (C–23 series); or

(2) A personnel-carrying military parachute identified by an NAF, AAF, or AN drawing number, an AAF order number, or any other military designation or specification number.

[Doc. No. 18334, 54 FR 34308, Aug. 18, 1989, as amended by Amdt. 91–255, 62 FR 68137, Dec. 30, 1997; Amdt. 91–268, 66 FR 23553, May 9, 2001; Amdt. 91–305, 73 FR 69530, Nov. 19, 2008]

91.309   Towing: gliders and unpowered ultralight vehicles

(a) No person may operate a civil aircraft towing a glider or unpowered ultralight vehicle unless—

(1) The pilot in command of the towing aircraft is qualified under 61.69 of this chapter;

(2) The towing aircraft is equipped with a tow-hitch of a kind, and installed in a manner, that is approved by the Administrator;

(3) The towline used has breaking strength not less than 80 percent of the maximum certificated operating weight of the glider or unpowered ultralight vehicle and not more than twice this operating weight. However, the towline used may have a breaking strength more than twice the maximum certificated operating weight of the glider or unpowered ultralight vehicle if—

   (i) A safety link is installed at the point of attachment of the towline to the glider or unpowered ultralight vehicle with a breaking strength not less than 80 percent of the maximum certificated operating weight of the glider or unpowered ultralight vehicle and not greater than twice this operating weight;

   (ii) A safety link is installed at the point of attachment of the towline to the towing aircraft with a breaking strength greater, but not more than 25 percent greater, than that of the safety link at the towed glider or unpowered ultralight vehicle end of the towline and not greater than twice the maximum certificated operating weight of the glider or unpowered ultralight vehicle;

(4) Before conducting any towing operation within the lateral boundaries of the surface areas of Class B, Class C, Class D, or Class E airspace designated for an airport, or before making each towing flight within such controlled airspace if required by ATC, the pilot in command notifies the control tower. If a control tower does not exist or is not in operation, the pilot in command must notify the FAA flight service station serving that controlled airspace before conducting any towing operations in that airspace; and

(5) The pilots of the towing aircraft and the glider or unpowered ultralight vehicle have agreed upon a general course of action, including takeoff and release signals, airspeeds, and emergency procedures for each pilot.

(b) No pilot of a civil aircraft may intentionally release a towline, after release of a glider or unpowered ultralight vehicle, in a manner that endangers the life or property of another.

[Doc. No. 18834, 54 FR 34308, Aug. 18, 1989, as amended by Amdt. 91–227, 56 FR 65661, Dec. 17, 1991; Amdt. 91–282, 69 FR 44880, July 27, 2004]

91.311   Towing: other than under 91.309

No pilot of a civil aircraft may tow anything with that aircraft (other than under 91.309) except in accordance with the terms of a certificate of waiver issued by the Administrator.

FAR 91

91.313   Restricted category civil aircraft: Operating limitations

(a) No person may operate a restricted category civil aircraft—

(1) For other than the special purpose for which it is certificated; or

(2) In an operation other than one necessary to accomplish the work activity directly associated with that special purpose.

(b) For the purpose of paragraph (a) of this section, the following operations are considered necessary to accomplish the work activity directly associated with a special purpose operation:

(1) Flights conducted for flight crewmember training in a special purpose operation for which the aircraft is certificated.

(2) Flights conducted to satisfy proficiency check and recent flight experience requirements under part 61 of this chapter provided the flight crewmember holds the appropriate category, class, and type ratings and is employed by the operator to perform the appropriate special purpose operation.

(3) Flights conducted to relocate the aircraft for delivery, repositioning, or maintenance.

(c) No person may operate a restricted category civil aircraft carrying persons or property for compensation or hire. For the purposes of this paragraph (c), a special purpose operation involving the carriage of persons or material necessary to accomplish that operation, such as crop dusting, seeding, spraying, and banner towing (including the carrying of required persons or material to the location of that operation), an operation for the purpose of providing flight crewmember training in a special purpose operation, and an operation conducted under the authority provided in paragraph (h) of this section are not considered to be the carriage of persons or property for compensation or hire.

(d) No person may be carried on a restricted category civil aircraft unless that person—

(1) Is a flight crewmember;

(2) Is a flight crewmember trainee;

(3) Performs an essential function in connection with a special purpose operation for which the aircraft is certificated;

(4) Is necessary to accomplish the work activity directly associated with that special purpose; or

(5) Is necessary to accomplish an operation under paragraph (h) of this section.

(e) Except when operating in accordance with the terms and conditions of a certificate of waiver or special operating limitations issued by the Administrator, no person may operate a restricted category civil aircraft within the United States—

(1) Over a densely populated area;

(2) In a congested airway; or

(3) Near a busy airport where passenger transport operations are conducted.

(f) This section does not apply to nonpassenger-carrying civil rotorcraft external-load operations conducted under part 133 of this chapter.

(g) No person may operate a small restricted-category civil airplane manufactured after July 18, 1978, unless an approved shoulder harness is installed for each front seat. The shoulder harness must be designed to protect each occupant from serious head injury when the occupant experiences the ultimate inertia forces specified in 23.561(b)(2) of this chapter. The shoulder harness installation at each flight crewmember station must permit the crewmember, when seated and with the safety belt and shoulder harness fastened, to perform all functions necessary for flight operation. For purposes of this paragraph—

(1) The date of manufacture of an airplane is the date the inspection acceptance records reflect that the airplane is complete and meets the FAA-approved type design data; and

(2) A front seat is a seat located at a flight crewmember station or any seat located alongside such a seat.

(h)

(1) An operator may apply for deviation authority from the provisions of paragraph (a) of this section to conduct operations for the following purposes:

  (i) Flight training and the practical test for issuance of a type rating provided—

   (A) The pilot being trained and tested holds at least a commercial pilot certificate with the appropriate category and class ratings for the aircraft type;

   (B) The pilot receiving flight training is employed by the operator to perform a special purpose operation; and

   (C) The flight training is conducted by the operator who employs the pilot to perform a special purpose operation.

  (ii) Flights to designate an examiner or qualify an FAA inspector in the aircraft type and flights necessary to provide continuing oversight and evaluation of an examiner.

(2) The FAA will issue this deviation authority as a letter of deviation authority.

(3) The FAA may cancel or amend a letter of deviation authority at any time.

(4) An applicant must submit a request for deviation authority in a form and manner acceptable to the Administrator at least 60 days before the date of intended operations. A request for deviation authority must contain a complete description of the proposed operation and justification that establishes a level of safety equivalent to that provided under the regulations for the deviation requested.

91.315   Limited category civil aircraft: operating limitations

No person may operate a limited category civil aircraft carrying persons or property for compensation or hire.

91.317   Provisionally certificated civil aircraft: operating limitations

(a) No person may operate a provisionally certificated civil aircraft unless that person is eligible for a provisional airworthiness certificate under 21.213 of this chapter.

(b) No person may operate a provisionally certificated civil aircraft outside the United States unless that person has specific authority to do so from the Administrator and each foreign country involved.

(c) Unless otherwise authorized by the Executive Director, Flight Standards Service, no person may operate a provisionally certificated civil aircraft in air transportation.

(d) Unless otherwise authorized by the Administrator, no person may operate a provisionally certificated civil aircraft except—

(1) In direct conjunction with the type or supplemental type certification of that aircraft;

(2) For training flight crews, including simulated air carrier operations;

(3) Demonstration flight by the manufacturer for prospective purchasers;

(4) Market surveys by the manufacturer;

(5) Flight checking of instruments, accessories, and equipment that do not affect the basic airworthiness of the aircraft; or

(6) Service testing of the aircraft.

(e) Each person operating a provisionally certificated civil aircraft shall operate within the prescribed limitations displayed in the aircraft or set forth in the provisional aircraft flight manual or other appropriate document. However, when operating in direct conjunction with the type or supplemental type certification of the aircraft, that person shall operate under the experimental aircraft limitations of 21.191 of this chapter and when flight testing, shall operate under the requirements of 91.305 of this part.

(f) Each person operating a provisionally certificated civil aircraft shall establish approved procedures for—

(1) The use and guidance of flight and ground personnel in operating under this section; and

(2) Operating in and out of airports where takeoffs or approaches over populated areas are necessary. No person may operate that aircraft except in compliance with the approved procedures.

(g) No person may operate a small restricted-category civil airplane manufactured after July 18, 1978, unless an approved shoulder harness or restraint system is installed for each front seat. The shoulder harness or restraint system installation at each flightcrew station must permit the flightcrew member, when seated and with the safety belt and shoulder harness fastened or the restraint system engaged, to perform all functions necessary for flight operation. For purposes of this paragraph—

(h) Each person operating a provisionally certificated civil aircraft shall maintain it as required by applicable regulations and as may be specially prescribed by the Administrator.

(i) Whenever the manufacturer, or the Administrator, determines that a change in design, construction, or operation is necessary to ensure safe operation, no person may operate a provisionally certificated civil aircraft until that change has been made and approved. Section 21.99 of this chapter applies to operations under this section.

(j) Each person operating a provisionally certificated civil aircraft—

(1) May carry in that aircraft only persons who have a proper interest in the operations allowed by this section or who are specifically authorized by both the manufacturer and the Administrator; and

(2) Shall advise each person carried that the aircraft is provisionally certificated.

(k) The Administrator may prescribe additional limitations or procedures that the Administrator considers necessary, including limitations on the number of persons who may be carried in the aircraft.

(Approved by the Office of Management and Budget under control number 2120–0005)

[Doc. No. 18334, 54 FR 34308, Aug. 18, 1989, as amended by Amdt. 91-212, 54 FR 39293, Sept. 25, 1989; Docket FAA-2018-0119, Amdt. 91-350, 83 FR 9171, Mar. 5, 2018]]

91.319 Aircraft having experimental certificates: operating limitations

(a) No person may operate an aircraft that has an experimental certificate—

(1) For other than the purpose for which the certificate was issued; or

(2) Carrying persons or property for compensation or hire.

(b) No person may operate an aircraft that has an experimental certificate outside of an area assigned by the Administrator until it is shown that—

(1) The aircraft is controllable throughout its normal range of speeds and throughout all the maneuvers to be executed; and

(2) The aircraft has no hazardous operating characteristics or design features.

(c) Unless otherwise authorized by the Administrator in special operating limitations, no person may operate an aircraft that has an experimental certificate over a densely populated area or in a congested airway. The Administrator may issue special operating limitations for particular aircraft to permit takeoffs and landings to be conducted over a densely populated area or in a congested airway, in accordance with terms and conditions specified in the authorization in the interest of safety in air commerce.

(d) Each person operating an aircraft that has an experimental certificate shall—

(1) Advise each person carried of the experimental nature of the aircraft;

(2) Operate under VFR, day only, unless otherwise specifically authorized by the Administrator; and

(3) Notify the control tower of the experimental nature of the aircraft when operating the aircraft into or out of airports with operating control towers.

(e) No person may operate an aircraft that is issued an experimental certificate under 21.191(i) of this chapter for compensation or hire, except a person may operate an aircraft issued an experimental certificate under 21.191(i)(1) for compensation or hire to—

(1) Tow a glider that is a light-sport aircraft or unpowered ultralight vehicle in accordance with 91.309; or

(2) Conduct flight training in an aircraft which that person provides prior to January 31, 2010.

(f) No person may lease an aircraft that is issued an experimental certificate under 21.191(i) of this chapter, except in accordance with paragraph (e)(1) of this section.

(g) No person may operate an aircraft issued an experimental certificate under 21.191(i)(1) of this chapter to tow a glider that is a light-sport aircraft or unpowered ultralight vehicle for compensation or hire or to conduct flight training for compensation or hire in an aircraft which that persons provides unless within the preceding 100 hours of time in service the aircraft has—

(1) Been inspected by a certificated repairman (light-sport aircraft) with a maintenance rating, an appropriately rated mechanic, or an appropriately rated repair station in accordance with inspection procedures developed by the aircraft manufacturer or a person acceptable to the FAA; or

(2) Received an inspection for the issuance of an airworthiness certificate in accordance with part 21 of this chapter.

(h) The FAA may issue deviation authority providing relief from the provisions of paragraph (a) of this section for the purpose of conducting flight training. The FAA will issue this deviation authority as a letter of deviation authority.

(1) The FAA may cancel or amend a letter of deviation authority at any time.

(2) An applicant must submit a request for deviation authority to the FAA at least 60 days before the date of intended operations. A request for deviation authority must contain a complete description of the proposed operation and justification that establishes a level of safety equivalent to that provided under the regulations for the deviation requested.

(i) The Administrator may prescribe additional limitations that the Administrator considers necessary, including limitations on the persons that may be carried in the aircraft.

(j) No person may operate an aircraft that has an experimental certificate under 61.113(i) of this chapter unless the aircraft is carrying not more than 6 occupants.

(Approved by the Office of Management and Budget under control number 2120-0005)

[Doc. No. 18334, 54 FR 34308, Aug. 18, 1989, as amended by Amdt. 91-282, 69 FR 44881, July 27, 2004; Docket FAA-2016-9157, Amdt. 91-347, 82 FR 3167, Jan. 11, 2017]

91.321 Carriage of candidates in elections

(a) As an aircraft operator, you may receive payment for carrying a candidate, agent of a candidate, or person traveling on behalf of a candidate, running for Federal, State, or local election, without having to comply with the rules in parts 121, 125 or 135 of this chapter, under the following conditions:

(1) Your primary business is not as an air carrier or commercial operator;

(2) You carry the candidate, agent, or person traveling on behalf of a candidate, under the rules of part 91; and

(3) By Federal, state or local law, you are required to receive payment for carrying the candidate, agent, or person traveling on behalf of a candidate. For federal elections, the payment may not exceed the amount required by the Federal Election Commission. For a state or local election, the payment may not exceed the amount required under the applicable state or local law.

(b) For the purposes of this section, for Federal elections, the terms candidate and election have the same meaning as set forth in the regulations of the Federal Election Commission. For State or local elections, the terms candidate and election have the same meaning as provided by the applicable State or local law and those terms relate to candidates for election to public office in State and local government elections.

[Doc. No. FAA–2005–20168, 70 FR 4982, Jan. 31, 2005]

91.323 Increased maximum certificated weights for certain airplanes operated in Alaska

(a) Notwithstanding any other provision of the Federal Aviation Regulations, the Administrator will approve, as provided in this section, an increase in the maximum certificated weight of an airplane type certificated under Aeronautics Bulletin No. 7–A of the U.S. Department of Commerce dated January 1, 1931, as amended, or under the normal category of part 4a of the former Civil Air Regulations (14 CFR part 4a, 1964 ed.) if that airplane is operated in the State of Alaska by—

(1) A certificate holder conducting operations under part 121 or part 135 of this chapter; or

(2) The U.S. Department of Interior in conducting its game and fish law enforcement activities or its management, fire detection, and fire suppression activities concerning public lands.

(b) The maximum certificated weight approved under this section may not exceed—

(1) 12,500 pounds;

(2) 115 percent of the maximum weight listed in the FAA aircraft specifications;

(3) The weight at which the airplane meets the positive maneuvering load factor n, where n=2.1+(24,000/(W+10,000)) and W=design maximum takeoff weight, except that n need not be more than 3.8; or

(4) The weight at which the airplane meets the climb performance requirements under which it was type certificated.

(c) In determining the maximum certificated weight, the Administrator considers the structural soundness of the airplane and the terrain to be traversed.

(d) The maximum certificated weight determined under this section is added to the airplane's operation limitations and is identified as the maximum weight authorized for operations within the State of Alaska.

[Doc. No. 18334, 54 FR 34308, Aug. 18, 1989; Amdt. 91–211, 54 FR 41211, Oct. 5, 1989, as amended by Amdt. 91–253, 62 FR 13253, Mar. 19, 1997]

91.325   Primary category aircraft: operating limitations

(a) No person may operate a primary category aircraft carrying persons or property for compensation or hire.

(b) No person may operate a primary category aircraft that is maintained by the pilot-owner under an approved special inspection and maintenance program except—

(1) The pilot-owner; or

(2) A designee of the pilot-owner, provided that the pilot-owner does not receive compensation for the use of the aircraft.

[Doc. No. 23345, 57 FR 41370, Sept. 9, 1992]

91.327   Aircraft having a special airworthiness certificate in the light-sport category: operating limitations

(a) No person may operate an aircraft that has a special airworthiness certificate in the light-sport category for compensation or hire except—

(1) To tow a glider or an unpowered ultralight vehicle in accordance with 91.309 of this chapter; or

(2) To conduct flight training.

(b) No person may operate an aircraft that has a special airworthiness certificate in the light-sport category unless—

(1) The aircraft is maintained by a certificated repairman with a light-sport aircraft maintenance rating, an appropriately rated mechanic, or an appropriately rated repair station in accordance with the applicable provisions of part 43 of this chapter and maintenance and inspection procedures developed by the aircraft manufacturer or a person acceptable to the FAA;

(2) A condition inspection is performed once every 12 calendar months by a certificated repairman (light-sport aircraft) with a maintenance rating, an appropriately rated mechanic, or an appropriately rated repair station in accordance with inspection procedures developed by the aircraft manufacturer or a person acceptable to the FAA;

(3) The owner or operator complies with all applicable airworthiness directives;

(4) The owner or operator complies with each safety directive applicable to the aircraft that corrects an existing unsafe condition. In lieu of complying with a safety directive an owner or operator may—

(i) Correct the unsafe condition in a manner different from that specified in the safety directive provided the person issuing the directive concurs with the action; or

(ii) Obtain an FAA waiver from the provisions of the safety directive based on a conclusion that the safety directive was issued without adhering to the applicable consensus standard;

(5) Each alteration accomplished after the aircraft's date of manufacture meets the applicable and current consensus standard and has been authorized by either the manufacturer or a person acceptable to the FAA;

(6) Each major alteration to an aircraft product produced under a consensus standard is authorized, performed and inspected in accordance with maintenance and inspection procedures developed by the manufacturer or a person acceptable to the FAA; and

(7) The owner or operator complies with the requirements for the recording of major repairs and major alterations performed on type-certificated products in accordance with 43.9(d) of this chapter, and with the retention requirements in 91.417.

(c) No person may operate an aircraft issued a special airworthiness certificate in the light-sport category to tow a glider or unpowered ultralight vehicle for compensation or hire or conduct flight training for compensation or hire in an aircraft which that persons provides unless within the preceding 100 hours of time in service the aircraft has—

(1) Been inspected by a certificated repairman with a light-sport aircraft maintenance rating, an appropriately rated mechanic, or an appropriately rated repair station in accordance with inspection procedures developed by the aircraft manufacturer or a person acceptable to the FAA and been approved for return to service in accordance with part 43 of this chapter; or

(2) Received an inspection for the issuance of an airworthiness certificate in accordance with part 21 of this chapter.

(d) Each person operating an aircraft issued a special airworthiness certificate in the light-sport category must operate the aircraft in accordance with the aircraft's operating instructions, including any provisions for necessary operating equipment specified in the aircraft's equipment list.

(e) Each person operating an aircraft issued a special airworthiness certificate in the light-sport category must advise each person carried of the special nature of the aircraft and that the aircraft does not meet the airworthiness requirements for an aircraft issued a standard airworthiness certificate.

(f) The FAA may prescribe additional limitations that it considers necessary.

[Doc. No. FAA–2001–11133, 69 FR 44881, July 27, 2004]

91.328-91.399   [Reserved]

Subpart E — Maintenance, Preventive Maintenance, and Alterations

Source: Docket No. 18334, 54 FR 34311, Aug. 18, 1989, unless otherwise noted.

91.401   Applicability

(a) This subpart prescribes rules governing the maintenance, preventive maintenance, and alterations of U.S.-registered civil aircraft operating within or outside of the United States.

(b) Sections 91.405, 91.409, 91.411, 91.417, and 91.419 of this subpart do not apply to an aircraft maintained in accordance with a continuous airworthiness maintenance program as provided in part 121, 129, or 91.1411 or 135.411(a)(2) of this chapter.

(c) Sections 91.405 and 91.409 of this part do not apply to an airplane inspected in accordance with part 125 of this chapter.

[Doc. No. 18334, 54 FR 34311, Aug. 18, 1989, as amended by Amdt. 91–267, 66 FR 21066, Apr. 27, 2001; Amdt. 91–280, 68 FR 54560, Sept. 17, 2003]

91.403 General

(a) The owner or operator of an aircraft is primarily responsible for maintaining that aircraft in an airworthy condition, including compliance with part 39 of this chapter.

(b) No person may perform maintenance, preventive maintenance, or alterations on an aircraft other than as prescribed in this subpart and other applicable regulations, including part 43 of this chapter.

(c) No person may operate an aircraft for which a manufacturer's maintenance manual or instructions for continued airworthiness has been issued that contains an airworthiness limitations section unless the mandatory replacement times, inspection intervals, and related procedures specified in that section or alternative inspection intervals and related procedures set forth in an operations specification approved by the Administrator under part 121 or 135 of this chapter or in accordance with an inspection program approved under 91.409(e) have been complied with.

(d) A person must not alter an aircraft based on a supplemental type certificate unless the owner or operator of the aircraft is the holder of the supplemental type certificate, or has written permission from the holder.

[Doc. No. 18334, 54 FR 34311, Aug. 18, 1989, as amended by Amdt. 91–267, 66 FR 21066, Apr. 27, 2001; Amdt. 91–293, 71 FR 56005, Sept. 26, 2006]

91.405 Maintenance required

Each owner or operator of an aircraft—

(a) Shall have that aircraft inspected as prescribed in subpart E of this part and shall between required inspections, except as provided in paragraph (c) of this section, have discrepancies repaired as prescribed in part 43 of this chapter;

(b) Shall ensure that maintenance personnel make appropriate entries in the aircraft maintenance records indicating the aircraft has been approved for return to service;

(c) Shall have any inoperative instrument or item of equipment, permitted to be inoperative by 91.213(d)(2) of this part, repaired, replaced, removed, or inspected at the next required inspection; and

(d) When listed discrepancies include inoperative instruments or equipment, shall ensure that a placard has been installed as required by 43.11 of this chapter.

91.407 Operation after maintenance, preventive maintenance, rebuilding, or alteration

(a) No person may operate any aircraft that has undergone maintenance, preventive maintenance, rebuilding, or alteration unless—

   (1) It has been approved for return to service by a person authorized under 43.7 of this chapter; and

   (2) The maintenance record entry required by 43.9 or 43.11, as applicable, of this chapter has been made.

(b) No person may carry any person (other than crewmembers) in an aircraft that has been maintained, rebuilt, or altered in a manner that may have appreciably changed its flight characteristics or substantially affected its operation in flight until an appropriately rated pilot with at least a private pilot certificate flies the aircraft, makes an operational check of the maintenance performed or alteration made, and logs the flight in the aircraft records.

(c) The aircraft does not have to be flown as required by paragraph (b) of this section if, prior to flight, ground tests, inspection, or both show conclusively that the maintenance, preventive maintenance, rebuilding, or alteration has not appreciably changed the flight characteristics or substantially affected the flight operation of the aircraft.

(Approved by the Office of Management and Budget under control number 2120–0005)

91.409 Inspections

(a) Except as provided in paragraph (c) of this section, no person may operate an aircraft unless, within the preceding 12 calendar months, it has had—

   (1) An annual inspection in accordance with part 43 of this chapter and has been approved for return to service by a person authorized by 43.7 of this chapter; or

   (2) An inspection for the issuance of an airworthiness certificate in accordance with part 21 of this chapter.

No inspection performed under paragraph (b) of this section may be substituted for any inspection required by this paragraph unless it is performed by a person authorized to perform annual inspections and is entered as an "annual" inspection in the required maintenance records.

(b) Except as provided in paragraph (c) of this section, no person may operate an aircraft carrying any person (other than a crewmember) for hire, and no person may give flight instruction for hire in an aircraft which that person provides, unless within the preceding 100 hours of time in service the aircraft has received an annual or 100-hour inspection and been approved for return to service in accordance with part 43 of this chapter or has received an inspection for the issuance of an airworthiness certificate in accordance with part 21 of this chapter. The 100-hour limitation may be exceeded by not more than 10 hours while en route to reach a place where the inspection can be done. The excess time used to reach a place where the inspection can be done must be included in computing the next 100 hours of time in service.

(c) Paragraphs (a) and (b) of this section do not apply to—

   (1) An aircraft that carries a special flight permit, a current experimental certificate, or a light-sport or provisional airworthiness certificate;

   (2) An aircraft inspected in accordance with an approved aircraft inspection program under part 125 or 135 of this chapter and so identified by the registration number in the operations specifications of the certificate holder having the approved inspection program;

   (3) An aircraft subject to the requirements of paragraph (d) or (e) of this section; or

   (4) Turbine-powered rotorcraft when the operator elects to inspect that rotorcraft in accordance with paragraph (e) of this section.

(d) Progressive inspection. Each registered owner or operator of an aircraft desiring to use a progressive inspection program must submit a written request to the responsible Flight Standards office, and shall provide—

   (1) A certificated mechanic holding an inspection authorization, a certificated airframe repair station, or the manufacturer of the aircraft to supervise or conduct the progressive inspection;

   (2) A current inspection procedures manual available and readily understandable to pilot and maintenance personnel containing, in detail—

      (i) An explanation of the progressive inspection, including the continuity of inspection responsibility, the making of reports, and the keeping of records and technical reference material;

      (ii) An inspection schedule, specifying the intervals in hours or days when routine and detailed inspections will be performed and including instructions for exceeding an inspection interval by not more than 10 hours while en route and for changing an inspection interval because of service experience;

      (iii) Sample routine and detailed inspection forms and instructions for their use; and

      (iv) Sample reports and records and instructions for their use;

   (3) Enough housing and equipment for necessary disassembly and proper inspection of the aircraft; and

   (4) Appropriate current technical information for the aircraft.

The frequency and detail of the progressive inspection shall provide for the complete inspection of the aircraft within each 12 calendar months and be consistent with the manufacturer's recommendations, field service experience, and the kind of operation in which the aircraft is engaged. The progressive inspection schedule must ensure that the aircraft, at all times, will be airworthy and will conform to all applicable FAA aircraft specifications, type certificate data sheets, airworthiness directives, and other approved data. If the progressive inspection is discontinued, the owner or operator shall immediately notify the responsible Flight Standards office, in writing, of the discontinuance. After the discontinuance, the first annual inspection under 91.409(a)(1) is due within 12 calendar months after the last complete inspection of the aircraft under the progressive inspection. The 100-hour inspection under §91.409(b) is due within 100 hours after that complete inspection. A complete inspection of the aircraft, for the purpose of determining when the annual and 100-hour inspections are due, requires a detailed inspection of the aircraft and all its components in accordance with the progressive inspection. A routine inspection of the aircraft and a detailed inspection of several components is not considered to be a complete inspection.

(e) Large airplanes (to which part 125 is not applicable), turbojet multiengine airplanes, turbopropeller-powered multiengine airplanes, and turbine-powered rotorcraft. No person may operate a large airplane, turbojet multiengine airplane, turbopropeller-powered multiengine airplane, or turbine-powered rotorcraft unless the replacement times for life-limited parts specified in the aircraft specifications, type data sheets, or other documents approved by the Administrator are complied with and the airplane or turbine-powered rotorcraft, including the airframe, engines, propellers, rotors, appliances, survival equipment, and emergency equipment, is inspected in accordance with an inspection program selected under the provisions of paragraph (f) of this section, except that, the owner or operator of a turbine-powered rotorcraft may elect to use the inspection provisions of 91.409(a), (b), (c), or (d) in lieu of an inspection option of 91.409(f).

(f) Selection of inspection program under paragraph (e) of this section. The registered owner or operator of each airplane or turbine-powered rotorcraft described in paragraph (e) of this section must select, identify in the aircraft maintenance records, and use one of the following programs for the inspection of the aircraft:

(1) A continuous airworthiness inspection program that is part of a continuous airworthiness maintenance program currently in use by a person holding an air carrier operating certificate or an operating certificate issued under part 121 or 135 of this chapter and operating that make and model aircraft under part 121 of this chapter or operating that make and model under part 135 of this chapter and maintaining it under 135.411(a)(2) of this chapter.

(2) An approved aircraft inspection program approved under 135.419 of this chapter and currently in use by a person holding an operating certificate issued under part 135 of this chapter.

(3) A current inspection program recommended by the manufacturer.

(4) Any other inspection program established by the registered owner or operator of that airplane or turbine-powered rotorcraft and approved by the Administrator under paragraph (g) of this section. However, the Administrator may require revision of this inspection program in accordance with the provisions of 91.415.

Each operator shall include in the selected program the name and address of the person responsible for scheduling the inspections required by the program and make a copy of that program available to the person performing inspections on the aircraft and, upon request, to the Administrator.

(g) Inspection program approved under paragraph (e) of this section. Each operator of an airplane or turbine-powered rotorcraft desiring to establish or change an approved inspection program under paragraph (f)(4) of this section must submit the program for approval to the responsible Flight Standards office. The program must be in writing and include at least the following information:

(1) Instructions and procedures for the conduct of inspections for the particular make and model airplane or turbine-powered rotorcraft, including necessary tests and checks. The instructions and procedures must set forth in detail the parts and areas of the airframe, engines, propellers, rotors, and appliances, including survival and emergency equipment required to be inspected.

(2) A schedule for performing the inspections that must be performed under the program expressed in terms of the time in service, calendar time, number of system operations, or any combination of these.

(h) Changes from one inspection program to another. When an operator changes from one inspection program under paragraph (f) of this section to another, the time in service, calendar times, or cycles of operation accumulated under the previous program must be applied in determining inspection due times under the new program.

(Approved by the Office of Management and Budget under control number 2120–0005)

[Doc. No. 18334, 54 FR 34311, Aug. 18, 1989; Amdt. 91-211, 54 FR 41211, Oct. 5, 1989; Amdt. 91-267, 66 FR 21066, Apr. 27, 2001; Amdt. 91-282, 69 FR 44882, July 27, 2004; Docket FAA-2018-0119, Amdt. 91-350, 83 FR 9171, Mar. 5, 2018]

91.410   [Reserved]

91.411   Altimeter system and altitude reporting equipment tests and inspections

(a) No person may operate an airplane, or helicopter, in controlled airspace under IFR unless—

(1) Within the preceding 24 calendar months, each static pressure system, each altimeter instrument, and each automatic pressure altitude reporting system has been tested and inspected and found to comply with appendices E and F of part 43 of this chapter;

(2) Except for the use of system drain and alternate static pressure valves, following any opening and closing of the static pressure system, that system has been tested and inspected and found to comply with paragraph (a), appendix E, of part 43 of this chapter; and

(3) Following installation or maintenance on the automatic pressure altitude reporting system of the ATC transponder where data correspondence error could be introduced, the integrated system has been tested, inspected, and found to comply with paragraph (c), appendix E, of part 43 of this chapter.

(b) The tests required by paragraph (a) of this section must be conducted by—

(1) The manufacturer of the airplane, or helicopter, on which the tests and inspections are to be performed;

(2) A certificated repair station properly equipped to perform those functions and holding—

   (i)   An instrument rating, Class I;

   (ii) A limited instrument rating appropriate to the make and model of appliance to be tested;

   (iii) A limited rating appropriate to the test to be performed;

   (iv) An airframe rating appropriate to the airplane, or helicopter, to be tested; or

(3) A certificated mechanic with an airframe rating (static pressure system tests and inspections only).

(c) Altimeter and altitude reporting equipment approved under Technical Standard Orders are considered to be tested and inspected as of the date of their manufacture.

(d) No person may operate an airplane, or helicopter, in controlled airspace under IFR at an altitude above the maximum altitude at which all altimeters and the automatic altitude reporting system of that airplane, or helicopter, have been tested.

[Docket No. 18334, 54 FR 34308, Aug. 18, 1989, as amended by Amdt. 91–269, 66 FR 41116, Aug. 6, 2001; 72 FR 7739, Feb. 20, 2007]

91.413   ATC transponder tests and inspections

(a) No persons may use an ATC transponder that is specified in 91.215(a), 121.345(c), or 135.143(c) of this chapter unless, within the preceding 24 calendar months, the ATC transponder has been tested and inspected and found to comply with appendix F of part 43 of this chapter; and

(b) Following any installation or maintenance on an ATC transponder where data correspondence error could be introduced, the integrated system has been tested, inspected, and found to comply with paragraph (c), appendix E, of part 43 of this chapter.

(c) The tests and inspections specified in this section must be conducted by—

(1) A certificated repair station properly equipped to perform those functions and holding—

(i) A radio rating, Class III;

(ii) A limited radio rating appropriate to the make and model transponder to be tested;

(iii) A limited rating appropriate to the test to be performed;

(2) A holder of a continuous airworthiness maintenance program as provided in part 121 or 135.411(a)(2) of this chapter; or

(3) The manufacturer of the aircraft on which the transponder to be tested is installed, if the transponder was installed by that manufacturer.

Doc. No. 18334, 54 FR 34311, Aug. 18, 1989, as amended by Amdt. 91–267, 66 FR 21066, Apr. 27, 2001; Amdt. 91–269, 66 FR 41116, Aug. 5, 2001]

91.415 Changes to aircraft inspection programs

(a) Whenever the Administrator finds that revisions to an approved aircraft inspection program under 91.409(f)(4) or 91.1109 are necessary for the continued adequacy of the program, the owner or operator must, after notification by the Administrator, make any changes in the program found to be necessary by the Administrator.

(b) The owner or operator may petition the Administrator to reconsider the notice to make any changes in a program in accordance with paragraph (a) of this section.

(c) The petition must be filed with the Executive Director, Flight Standards Service within 30 days after the certificate holder or fractional ownership program manager receives the notice.

(d) Except in the case of an emergency requiring immediate action in the interest of safety, the filing of the petition stays the notice pending a decision by the Administrator.

Doc. No. 18334, 54 FR 34311, Aug. 18, 1989, as amended by Amdt. 91–280, 68 FR 54560, Sept. 17, 2003; Docket FAA-2018-0119, Amdt. 91–350, 83 FR 9171, Mar. 5, 2018]

91.417 Maintenance records

(a) Except for work performed in accordance with 91.411 and 91.413, each registered owner or operator shall keep the following records for the periods specified in paragraph (b) of this section:

(1) Records of the maintenance, preventive maintenance, and alteration and records of the 100-hour, annual, progressive, and other required or approved inspections, as appropriate, for each aircraft (including the airframe) and each engine, propeller, rotor, and appliance of an aircraft. The records must include—

(i) A description (or reference to data acceptable to the Administrator) of the work performed; and

(ii) The date of completion of the work performed; and

(iii) The signature, and certificate number of the person approving the aircraft for return to service.

(2) Records containing the following information:

(i) The total time in service of the airframe, each engine, each propeller, and each rotor.

(ii) The current status of life-limited parts of each airframe, engine, propeller, rotor, and appliance.

(iii) The time since last overhaul of all items installed on the aircraft which are required to be overhauled on a specified time basis.

(iv) The current inspection status of the aircraft, including the time since the last inspection required by the inspection program under which the aircraft and its appliances are maintained.

(v) The current status of applicable airworthiness directives (AD) and safety directives including, for each, the method of compliance, the AD or safety directive number and revision date. If the AD or safety directive involves recurring action, the time and date when the next action is required.

(vi) Copies of the forms prescribed by 43.9(d) of this chapter for each major alteration to the airframe and currently installed engines, rotors, propellers, and appliances.

(b) The owner or operator shall retain the following records for the periods prescribed:

(1) The records specified in paragraph (a)(1) of this section shall be retained until the work is repeated or superseded by other work or for 1 year after the work is performed.

(2) The records specified in paragraph (a)(2) of this section shall be retained and transferred with the aircraft at the time the aircraft is sold.

(3) A list of defects furnished to a registered owner or operator under 43.11 of this chapter shall be retained until the defects are repaired and the aircraft is approved for return to service.

(c) The owner or operator shall make all maintenance records required to be kept by this section available for inspection by the Administrator or any authorized representative of the National Transportation Safety Board (NTSB). In addition, the owner or operator shall present Form 337 described in paragraph (d) of this section for inspection upon request of any law enforcement officer.

(d) When a fuel tank is installed within the passenger compartment or a baggage compartment pursuant to part 43 of this chapter, a copy of FAA Form 337 shall be kept on board the modified aircraft by the owner or operator.

(Approved by the Office of Management and Budget under control number 2120–0005)

[Docket No. 18334, 54 FR 34311, Aug. 18, 1989, as amended by Amdt. 91–311, 75 FR 5223, Feb. 1, 2010; Amdt. 91–323, 76 FR 39260, July 6, 2011]

91.419 Transfer of maintenance records

Any owner or operator who sells a U.S.-registered aircraft shall transfer to the purchaser, at the time of sale, the following records of that aircraft, in plain language form or in coded form at the election of the purchaser, if the coded form provides for the preservation and retrieval of information in a manner acceptable to the Administrator:

(a) The records specified in 91.417(a)(2).

(b) The records specified in 91.417(a)(1) which are not included in the records covered by paragraph (a) of this section, except that the purchaser may permit the seller to keep physical custody of such records. However, custody of records by the seller does not relieve the purchaser of the responsibility under 91.417(c) to make the records available for inspection by the Administrator or any authorized representative of the National Transportation Safety Board (NTSB).

91.421 Rebuilt engine maintenance records

(a) The owner or operator may use a new maintenance record, without previous operating history, for an aircraft engine rebuilt by the manufacturer or by an agency approved by the manufacturer.

(b) Each manufacturer or agency that grants zero time to an engine rebuilt by it shall enter in the new record—

(1) A signed statement of the date the engine was rebuilt;

(2) Each change made as required by airworthiness directives; and

(3) Each change made in compliance with manufacturer's service bulletins, if the entry is specifically requested in that bulletin.

(c) For the purposes of this section, a rebuilt engine is a used engine that has been completely disassembled, inspected, repaired as necessary, reassembled, tested, and approved in the same manner and to the same tolerances and limits as a new engine with either new or used parts. However, all parts used in it must conform to the production drawing tolerances and limits for new parts or be of approved oversized or undersized dimensions for a new engine.

91.423-91.499   [Reserved]

Subpart F — Large and Turbine-Powered Multiengine Airplanes and Fractional Ownership Program Aircraft

Source: Docket No. 18334, 54 FR 34314, Aug. 18, 1989, unless otherwise noted.

91.501   Applicability

(a) This subpart prescribes operating rules, in addition to those prescribed in other subparts of this part, governing the operation of large airplanes of U.S. registry, turbojet-powered multiengine civil airplanes of U.S. registry, and fractional ownership program aircraft of U.S. registry that are operating under subpart K of this part in operations not involving common carriage. The operating rules in this subpart do not apply to those aircraft when they are required to be operated under parts 121, 125, 129, 135, and 137 of this chapter. (Section 91.409 prescribes an inspection program for large and for turbine-powered (turbojet and turboprop) multiengine airplanes and turbine-powered rotorcraft of U.S. registry when they are operated under this part or part 129 or 137.)

(b) Operations that may be conducted under the rules in this subpart instead of those in parts 121, 129, 135, and 137 of this chapter when common carriage is not involved, include—

(1) Ferry or training flights;

(2) Aerial work operations such as aerial photography or survey, or pipeline patrol, but not including fire fighting operations;

(3) Flights for the demonstration of an airplane to prospective customers when no charge is made except for those specified in paragraph (d) of this section;

(4) Flights conducted by the operator of an airplane for his personal transportation, or the transportation of his guests when no charge, assessment, or fee is made for the transportation;

(5) Carriage of officials, employees, guests, and property of a company on an airplane operated by that company, or the parent or a subsidiary of the company or a subsidiary of the parent, when the carriage is within the scope of, and incidental to, the business of the company (other than transportation by air) and no charge, assessment or fee is made for the carriage in excess of the cost of owning, operating, and maintaining the airplane, except that no charge of any kind may be made for the carriage of a guest of a company, when the carriage is not within the scope of, and incidental to, the business of that company;

(6) The carriage of company officials, employees, and guests of the company on an airplane operated under a time sharing, interchange, or joint ownership agreement as defined in paragraph (c) of this section;

(7) The carriage of property (other than mail) on an airplane operated by a person in the furtherance of a business or employment (other than transportation by air) when the carriage is within the scope of, and incidental to, that business or employment and no charge, assessment, or fee is made for the carriage other than those specified in paragraph (d) of this section;

(8) The carriage on an airplane of an athletic team, sports group, choral group, or similar group having a common purpose or objective when there is no charge, assessment, or fee of any kind made by any person for that carriage; and

(9) The carriage of persons on an airplane operated by a person in the furtherance of a business other than transportation by air for the purpose of selling them land, goods, or property, including franchises or distributorships, when the carriage is within the scope of, and incidental to, that business and no charge, assessment, or fee is made for that carriage.

(10) Any operation identified in paragraphs (b)(1) through (b)(9) of this section when conducted—

　(i)　By a fractional ownership program manager, or

　(ii)　By a fractional owner in a fractional ownership program aircraft operated under subpart K of this part, except that a flight under a joint ownership arrangement under paragraph (b)(6) of this section may not be conducted. For a flight under an interchange agreement under paragraph (b)(6) of this section, the exchange of equal time for the operation must be properly accounted for as part of the total hours associated with the fractional owner's share of ownership.

(c) As used in this section—

(1) A time sharing agreement means an arrangement whereby a person leases his airplane with flight crew to another person, and no charge is made for the flights conducted under that arrangement other than those specified in paragraph (d) of this section;

(2) An interchange agreement means an arrangement whereby a person leases his airplane to another person in exchange for equal time, when needed, on the other person's airplane, and no charge, assessment, or fee is made, except that a charge may be made not to exceed the difference between the cost of owning, operating, and maintaining the two airplanes;

(3) A joint ownership agreement means an arrangement whereby one of the registered joint owners of an airplane employs and furnishes the flight crew for that airplane and each of the registered joint owners pays a share of the charge specified in the agreement.

(d) The following may be charged, as expenses of a specific flight, for transportation as authorized by paragraphs (b) (3) and (7) and (c) (1) of this section:

(1) Fuel, oil, lubricants, and other additives.

(2) Travel expenses of the crew, including food, lodging, and ground transportation.

(3) Hangar and tie-down costs away from the aircraft's base of operation.

(4) Insurance obtained for the specific flight.

(5) Landing fees, airport taxes, and similar assessments.

(6) Customs, foreign permit, and similar fees directly related to the flight.

(7) In flight food and beverages.

(8) Passenger ground transportation.

(9) Flight planning and weather contract services.

(10) An additional charge equal to 100 percent of the expenses listed in paragraph (d)(1) of this section.

[Doc. No. 18334, 54 FR 34314, Aug. 18, 1989, as amended by Amdt 91–280, 68 FR 54560, Sept. 17, 2003]

91.503   Flying equipment and operating information

(a) The pilot in command of an airplane shall ensure that the following flying equipment and aeronautical charts and data, in current and appropriate form, are accessible for each flight at the pilot station of the airplane:

(1) A flashlight having at least two size "D" cells, or the equivalent, that is in good working order.

(2) A cockpit checklist containing the procedures required by paragraph (b) of this section.

(3) Pertinent aeronautical charts.

(4) For IFR, VFR over-the-top, or night operations, each pertinent navigational en route, terminal area, and approach and letdown chart.

(5) In the case of multiengine airplanes, one-engine inoperative climb performance data.

(b) Each cockpit checklist must contain the following procedures and shall be used by the flight crewmembers when operating the airplane

(1) Before starting engines.

(2) Before takeoff.

(3) Cruise.

(4) Before landing.

(5) After landing.

(6) Stopping engines.

(7) Emergencies.

(c) Each emergency cockpit checklist procedure required by paragraph (b)(7) of this section must contain the following procedures, as appropriate:

(1) Emergency operation of fuel, hydraulic, electrical, and mechanical systems.

(2) Emergency operation of instruments and controls.

(3) Engine inoperative procedures.

(4) Any other procedures necessary for safety.

(d) The equipment, charts, and data prescribed in this section shall be used by the pilot in command and other members of the flight crew, when pertinent.

91.505 Familiarity with operating limitations and emergency equipment

(a) Each pilot in command of an airplane shall, before beginning a flight, become familiar with the Airplane Flight Manual for that airplane, if one is required, and with any placards, listings, instrument markings, or any combination thereof, containing each operating limitation prescribed for that airplane by the Administrator, including those specified in 91.9(b).

(b) Each required member of the crew shall, before beginning a flight, become familiar with the emergency equipment installed on the airplane to which that crewmember is assigned and with the procedures to be followed for the use of that equipment in an emergency situation.

91.507 Equipment requirements: over-the-top or night VFR operations

No person may operate an airplane over-the-top or at night under VFR unless that airplane is equipped with the instruments and equipment required for IFR operations under 91.205(d) and one electric landing light for night operations. Each required instrument and item of equipment must be in operable condition.

91.509 Survival equipment for overwater operations

(a) No person may take off an airplane for a flight over water more than 50 nautical miles from the nearest shore unless that airplane is equipped with a life preserver or an approved flotation means for each occupant of the airplane.

(b) Except as provided in paragraph (c) of this section, no person may take off an airplane for flight over water more than 30 minutes flying time or 100 nautical miles from the nearest shore, whichever is less, unless it has on board the following survival equipment:

(1) A life preserver, equipped with an approved survivor locator light, for each occupant of the airplane.

(2) Enough liferafts (each equipped with an approved survival locator light) of a rated capacity and buoyancy to accommodate the occupants of the airplane.

(3) At least one pyrotechnic signaling device for each liferaft.

(4) One self-buoyant, water-resistant, portable emergency radio signaling device that is capable of transmission on the appropriate emergency frequency or frequencies and not dependent upon the airplane power supply.

(5) A lifeline stored in accordance with 25.1411(g) of this chapter.

(c) A fractional ownership program manager under subpart K of this part may apply for a deviation from paragraphs (b)(2) through (5) of this section for a particular over water operation or the Administrator may amend the management specifications to require the carriage of all or any specific items of the equipment listed in paragraphs (b)(2) through (5) of this section.

(d) The required life rafts, life preservers, and signaling devices must be installed in conspicuously marked locations and easily accessible in the event of a ditching without appreciable time for preparatory procedures.

(e) A survival kit, appropriately equipped for the route to be flown, must be attached to each required life raft.

(f) As used in this section, the term shore means that area of the land adjacent to the water that is above the high water mark and excludes land areas that are intermittently under water.

[Doc. No. 18334, 54 FR 34314, Aug. 18, 1989, as amended by Amdt. 91–280, 68 FR 54561, Sept. 17, 2003]

91.511 Communication and navigation equipment for overwater operations

(a) Except as provided in paragraphs (c), (d), and (f) of this section, no person may take off an airplane for a flight over water more than 30 minutes flying time or 100 nautical miles from the nearest shore unless it has at least the following operable equipment:

(1) Radio communication equipment appropriate to the facilities to be used and able to transmit to, and receive from, at least one communication facility from any place along the route:

(i) Two transmitters.

(ii) Two microphones.

(iii) Two headsets or one headset and one speaker.

(iv) Two independent receivers.

(2) Appropriate electronic navigational equipment consisting of at least two independent electronic navigation units capable of providing the pilot with the information necessary to navigate the airplane within the airspace assigned by air traffic control. However, a receiver that can receive both communications and required navigational signals may be used in place of a separate communications receiver and a separate navigational signal receiver or unit.

(b) For the purposes of paragraphs (a)(1)(iv) and (a)(2) of this section, a receiver or electronic navigation unit is independent if the function of any part of it does not depend on the functioning of any part of another receiver or electronic navigation unit.

(c) Notwithstanding the provisions of paragraph (a) of this section, a person may operate an airplane on which no passengers are carried from a place where repairs or replacement cannot be made to a place where they can be made, if not more than one of each of the dual items of radio communication and navigational equipment specified in paragraphs (a)(1) (i) through (iv) and (a)(2) of this section malfunctions or becomes inoperative.

(d) Notwithstanding the provisions of paragraph (a) of this section, when both VHF and HF communications equipment are required for the route and the airplane has two VHF transmitters and two VHF receivers for communications, only one HF transmitter and one HF receiver is required for communications.

(e) As used in this section, the term shore means that area of the land adjacent to the water which is above the high-water mark and excludes land areas which are intermittently under water.

(f) Notwithstanding the requirements in paragraph (a)(2) of this section, a person may operate in the Gulf of Mexico, the Caribbean Sea, and the Atlantic Ocean west of a line which extends from 44°47'00" N / 67°00'00" W to 39°00'00" N / 67°00'00" W to 38°30'00" N / 60°00'00" W south along the 60°00'00" W longitude line to the point where the line intersects with the northern coast of South America, when:

(1) A single long-range navigation system is installed, operational, and appropriate for the route; and

(2) Flight conditions and the aircraft's capabilities are such that no more than a 30-minute gap in two-way radio very high frequency communications is expected to exist.

[Doc. No. 18334, 54 FR 34314, Aug. 18, 1989, as amended by Amdt. 91–249, 61 FR 7190, Feb. 26, 1996; Amdt. 91–296, 72 FR 31679, June 7, 2007]

91.513 Emergency equipment

(a) No person may operate an airplane unless it is equipped with the emergency equipment listed in this section.

(b) Each item of equipment—

FAR
91

(1) Must be inspected in accordance with 91.409 to ensure its continued serviceability and immediate readiness for its intended purposes;

(2) Must be readily accessible to the crew;

(3) Must clearly indicate its method of operation; and

(4) When carried in a compartment or container, must have that compartment or container marked as to contents and date of last inspection.

(c) Hand fire extinguishers must be provided for use in crew, passenger, and cargo compartments in accordance with the following:

(1) The type and quantity of extinguishing agent must be suitable for the kinds of fires likely to occur in the compartment where the extinguisher is intended to be used.

(2) At least one hand fire extinguisher must be provided and located on or near the flight deck in a place that is readily accessible to the flight crew.

(3) At least one hand fire extinguisher must be conveniently located in the passenger compartment of each airplane accommodating more than six but less than 31 passengers, and at least two hand fire extinguishers must be conveniently located in the passenger compartment of each airplane accommodating more than 30 passengers.

(4) Hand fire extinguishers must be installed and secured in such a manner that they will not interfere with the safe operation of the airplane or adversely affect the safety of the crew and passengers. They must be readily accessible and, unless the locations of the fire extinguishers are obvious, their stowage provisions must be properly identified.

(d) First aid kits for treatment of injuries likely to occur in flight or in minor accidents must be provided.

(e) Each airplane accommodating more than 19 passengers must be equipped with a crash axe.

(f) Each passenger-carrying airplane must have a portable battery-powered megaphone or megaphones readily accessible to the crewmembers assigned to direct emergency evacuation, installed as follows:

(1) One megaphone on each airplane with a seating capacity of more than 60 but less than 100 passengers, at the most rearward location in the passenger cabin where it would be readily accessible to a normal flight attendant seat. However, the Administrator may grant a deviation from the requirements of this subparagraph if the Administrator finds that a different location would be more useful for evacuation of persons during an emergency.

(2) On each airplane with a seating capacity of 100 or more passengers, one megaphone installed at the forward end and one installed at the most rearward location where it would be readily accessible to a normal flight attendant seat.

91.515 Flight altitude rules

(a) Notwithstanding 91.119, and except as provided in paragraph (b) of this section, no person may operate an airplane under VFR at less than—

(1) One thousand feet above the surface, or 1,000 feet from any mountain, hill, or other obstruction to flight, for day operations; and

(2) The altitudes prescribed in 91.177, for night operations.

(b) This section does not apply—

(1) During takeoff or landing;

(2) When a different altitude is authorized by a waiver to this section under subpart J of this part; or

(3) When a flight is conducted under the special VFR weather minimums of 91.157 with an appropriate clearance from ATC.

91.517 Passenger information

(a) Except as provided in paragraph (b) of this section, no person may operate an airplane carrying passengers unless it is equipped with signs that are visible to passengers and flight attendants to notify them when smoking is prohibited and when safety belts must be fastened. The signs must be so constructed that the crew can turn them on and off. They must be turned on during airplane movement on the surface, for each takeoff, for each landing, and when otherwise considered to be necessary by the pilot in command.

(b) The pilot in command of an airplane that is not required, in accordance with applicable aircraft and equipment requirements of this chapter, to be equipped as provided in paragraph (a) of this section shall ensure that the passengers are notified orally each time that it is necessary to fasten their safety belts and when smoking is prohibited.

(c) If passenger information signs are installed, no passenger or crew member may smoke while any "no smoking" sign is lighted nor may any passenger or crewmember smoke in any lavatory.

(d) Each passenger required by 91.107(a)(3) to occupy a seat or berth shall fasten his or her safety belt about him or her and keep it fastened while any "fasten seat belt" sign is lighted.

(e) Each passenger shall comply with instructions given him or her by crewmembers regarding compliance with paragraphs (b), (c), and (d) of this section.

[Doc. No. 26142, 57 FR 42672, Sept. 15, 1992]

91.519 Passenger briefing

(a) Before each takeoff the pilot in command of an airplane carrying passengers shall ensure that all passengers have been orally briefed on—

(1) Smoking. Each passenger shall be briefed on when, where, and under what conditions smoking is prohibited. This briefing shall include a statement, as appropriate, that the Federal Aviation Regulations require passenger compliance with lighted passenger information signs and no smoking placards prohibit smoking in lavatories, and require compliance with crewmember instructions with regard to these items;

(2) Use of safety belts and shoulder harnesses. Each passenger shall be briefed on when, where, and under what conditions it is necessary to have his or her safety belt and, if installed, his or her shoulder harness fastened about him or her. This briefing shall include a statement, as appropriate, that Federal Aviation Regulations require passenger compliance with the lighted passenger sign and/or crewmember instructions with regard to these items.

(3) Location and means for opening the passenger entry door and emergency exits;

(4) Location of survival equipment;

(5) Ditching procedures and the use of flotation equipment required under 91.509 for a flight over water; and

(6) The normal and emergency use of oxygen equipment installed on the airplane.

(b) The oral briefing required by paragraph (a) of this section shall be given by the pilot in command or a member of the crew, but need not be given when the pilot in command determines that the passengers are familiar with the contents of the briefing. It may be supplemented by printed cards for the use of each passenger containing—

(1) A diagram of, and methods of operating, the emergency exits; and

(2) Other instructions necessary for use of emergency equipment.

(c) Each card used under paragraph (b) must be carried in convenient locations on the airplane for the use of each passenger and must contain information that is pertinent only to the type and model airplane on which it is used.

(d) For operations under subpart K of this part, the passenger briefing requirements of 91.1035 apply, instead of the requirements of paragraphs (a) through (c) of this section.

[Doc. No. 18334, 54 FR 34314, Aug. 18, 1989, as amended by Amdt. 91–231, 57 FR 42672, Sept. 15, 1992; Amdt. 91–280, 68 FR 54561, Sept. 17, 2003]

91.521 Shoulder harness

(a) No person may operate a transport category airplane that was type certificated after January 1, 1958, unless it is equipped at each seat at a flight deck station with a combined safety belt and shoulder harness that meets the applicable requirements specified in 25.785 of this chapter, except that—

(1) Shoulder harnesses and combined safety belt and shoulder harnesses that were approved and installed before March 6, 1980, may continue to be used; and

(2) Safety belt and shoulder harness restraint systems may be designed to the inertia load factors established under the certification basis of the airplane.

(b) No person may operate a transport category airplane unless it is equipped at each required flight attendant seat in the passenger compartment with a combined safety belt and shoulder harness that meets the applicable requirements specified in 25.785 of this chapter, except that—

(1) Shoulder harnesses and combined safety belt and shoulder harnesses that were approved and installed before March 6, 1980, may continue to be used; and

(2) Safety belt and shoulder harness restraint systems may be designed to the inertia load factors established under the certification basis of the airplane.

91.523 Carry-on baggage

No pilot in command of an airplane having a seating capacity of more than 19 passengers may permit a passenger to stow baggage aboard that airplane except—

(a) In a suitable baggage or cargo storage compartment, or as provided in 91.525; or

(b) Under a passenger seat in such a way that it will not slide forward under crash impacts severe enough to induce the ultimate inertia forces specified in 25.561(b)(3) of this chapter, or the requirements of the regulations under which the airplane was type certificated. Restraining devices must also limit sideward motion of under-seat baggage and be designed to withstand crash impacts severe enough to induce sideward forces specified in 25.561(b)(3) of this chapter.

91.525 Carriage of cargo

(a) No pilot in command may permit cargo to be carried in any airplane unless—

(1) It is carried in an approved cargo rack, bin, or compartment installed in the airplane;

(2) It is secured by means approved by the Administrator; or

(3) It is carried in accordance with each of the following:

(i) It is properly secured by a safety belt or other tiedown having enough strength to eliminate the possibility of shifting under all normally anticipated flight and ground conditions.

(ii) It is packaged or covered to avoid possible injury to passengers.

(iii) It does not impose any load on seats or on the floor structure that exceeds the load limitation for those components.

(iv) It is not located in a position that restricts the access to or use of any required emergency or regular exit, or the use of the aisle between the crew and the passenger compartment.

(v) It is not carried directly above seated passengers.

(b) When cargo is carried in cargo compartments that are designed to require the physical entry of a crewmember to extinguish any fire that may occur during flight, the cargo must be loaded so as to allow a crewmember to effectively reach all parts of the compartment with the contents of a hand fire extinguisher.

91.527 Operating in icing conditions

(a) No pilot may take off an airplane that has frost, ice or snow adhering to any propeller, windshield, stabilizing or control surface; to a powerplant installation; or to an airspeed altimeter, rate of limb, or flight attitude instrument system or wing, except that takeoffs may be made with frost under the wing in the area of the fuel tanks if authorized by the FAA.

(b) No pilot may fly under IFR into known or forecast light or moderate icing conditions, or under VFR into known light or moderate icing conditions, unless—

(1) The aircraft has functioning deicing or anti-icing equipment protecting each rotor blade, propeller, windshield, wing, stabilizing or control surface, and each airspeed, altimeter, rate of climb, or flight attitude instrument system;

(2) The airplane has ice protection provisions that meet section 34 of Special Federal Aviation Regulation No. 23; or

(3) The airplane meets transport category airplane type certification provisions, including the requirements for certification for flight in icing conditions.

(c) Except for an airplane that has ice protection provisions that meet the requirements in section 34 of Special Federal Aviation Regulation No. 23, or those for transport category airplane type certification, no pilot may fly an airplane into known or forecast severe icing conditions.

(d) If current weather reports and briefing information relied upon by the pilot in command indicate that the forecast icing conditions that would otherwise prohibit the flight will not be encountered during the flight because of changed weather conditions since the forecast, the restrictions in paragraphs (b) and (c) of this section based on forecast conditions do not apply.

[Doc. No. 18334, 54 FR 34314, Aug. 18, 1989, as amended by Amdt. 91-310, 74 FR 62696, Dec. 1, 2009]

91.529 Flight engineer requirements

(a) No person may operate the following airplanes without a flight crewmember holding a current flight engineer certificate:

(1) An airplane for which a type certificate was issued before January 2, 1964, having a maximum certificated takeoff weight of more than 80,000 pounds.

(2) An airplane type certificated after January 1, 1964, for which a flight engineer is required by the type certification requirements.

(b) No person may serve as a required flight engineer on an airplane unless, within the preceding 6 calendar months, that person has had at least 50 hours of flight time as a flight engineer on that type airplane or has been checked by the Administrator on that type airplane and is found to be familiar and competent with all essential current information and operating procedures.

91.531 Second in command requirements

(a) Except as provided in paragraph (b) of this section, no person may operate the following airplanes without a pilot designated as second in command:

(1) Any airplane that is type certificated for more than one required pilot.

(2) Any large airplane.

(3) Any commuter category airplane.

(b) A person may operate the following airplanes without a pilot designated as second in command:

(1) Any airplane certificated for operation with one pilot.

(2) A large airplane or turbojet-powered multiengine airplane that holds a special airworthiness certificate, if:

(i) The airplane was originally designed with only one pilot station; or

(ii) The airplane was originally designed with more than one pilot station, but single pilot operations were permitted by the airplane flight manual or were otherwise permitted by a branch of the United States Armed Forces or the armed forces of a foreign contracting State to the Convention on International Civil Aviation.

FAR 91

(c) No person may designate a pilot to serve as second in command, nor may any pilot serve as second in command, of an airplane required under this section to have two pilots unless that pilot meets the qualifications for second in command prescribed in 61.55 of this chapter.

[Docket FAA-2016-6142, Amdt. 91-351, 83 FR 30282, June 27, 2018]

91.533 Flight attendant requirements

(a) No person may operate an airplane unless at least the following number of flight attendants are on board the airplane:

  (1) For airplanes having more than 19 but less than 51 passengers on board, one flight attendant.

  (2) For airplanes having more than 50 but less than 101 passengers on board, two flight attendants.

  (3) For airplanes having more than 100 passengers on board, two flight attendants plus one additional flight attendant for each unit (or part of a unit) of 50 passengers above 100.

(b) No person may serve as a flight attendant on an airplane when required by paragraph (a) of this section unless that person has demonstrated to the pilot in command familiarity with the necessary functions to be performed in an emergency or a situation requiring emergency evacuation and is capable of using the emergency equipment installed on that airplane.

91.535 Stowage of food, beverage, and passenger service equipment during aircraft movement on the surface, takeoff, and landing

(a) No operator may move an aircraft on the surface, take off, or land when any food, beverage, or tableware furnished by the operator is located at any passenger seat.

(b) No operator may move an aircraft on the surface, take off, or land unless each food and beverage tray and seat back tray table is secured in its stowed position.

(c) No operator may permit an aircraft to move on the surface, take off, or land unless each passenger serving cart is secured in its stowed position.

(d) No operator may permit an aircraft to move on the surface, take off, or land unless each movie screen that extends into the aisle is stowed.

(e) Each passenger shall comply with instructions given by a crewmember with regard to compliance with this section.

[Doc. No. 26142, 57 FR 42672, Sept. 15, 1992]

91.536-91.599 [Reserved]

Subpart G — Additional Equipment and Operating Requirements for Large and Transport Category Aircraft

Source: Docket No. 18334, 54 FR 34318, Aug. 18, 1989, unless otherwise noted.

91.601 Applicability

This subpart applies to operation of large and transport category U.S.-registered civil aircraft.

91.603 Aural speed warning device

No person may operate a transport category airplane in air commerce unless that airplane is equipped with an aural speed warning device that complies with 25.1303(c)(1).

91.605 Transport category civil airplane weight limitations

(a) No person may take off any transport category airplane (other than a turbine-engine-powered airplane certificated after September 30, 1958) unless—

  (1) The takeoff weight does not exceed the authorized maximum takeoff weight for the elevation of the airport of takeoff;

  (2) The elevation of the airport of takeoff is within the altitude range for which maximum takeoff weights have been determined;

  (3) Normal consumption of fuel and oil in flight to the airport of intended landing will leave a weight on arrival not in excess of the authorized maximum landing weight for the elevation of that airport; and

  (4) The elevations of the airport of intended landing and of all specified alternate airports are within the altitude range for which the maximum landing weights have been determined.

(b) No person may operate a turbine-engine-powered transport category airplane certificated after September 30, 1958, contrary to the Airplane Flight Manual, or take off that airplane unless—

  (1) The takeoff weight does not exceed the takeoff weight specified in the Airplane Flight Manual for the elevation of the airport and for the ambient temperature existing at the time of takeoff;

  (2) Normal consumption of fuel and oil in flight to the airport of intended landing and to the alternate airports will leave a weight on arrival not in excess of the landing weight specified in the Airplane Flight Manual for the elevation of each of the airports involved and for the ambient temperatures expected at the time of landing;

  (3) The takeoff weight does not exceed the weight shown in the Airplane Flight Manual to correspond with the minimum distances required for takeoff, considering the elevation of the airport, the runway to be used, the effective runway gradient, the ambient temperature and wind component at the time of takeoff, and, if operating limitations exist for the minimum distances required for takeoff from wet runways, the runway surface condition (dry or wet). Wet runway distances associated with grooved or porous friction course runways, if provided in the Airplane Flight Manual, may be used only for runways that are grooved or treated with a porous friction course (PFC) overlay, and that the operator determines are designed, constructed, and maintained in a manner acceptable to the Administrator.

  (4) Where the takeoff distance includes a clearway, the clearway distance is not greater than one-half of—

    (i)   The takeoff run, in the case of airplanes certificated after September 30, 1958, and before August 30, 1959; or

    (ii) The runway length, in the case of airplanes certificated after August 29, 1959.

(c) No person may take off a turbine-engine-powered transport category airplane certificated after August 29, 1959, unless, in addition to the requirements of paragraph (b) of this section—

  (1) The accelerate-stop distance is no greater than the length of the runway plus the length of the stopway (if present); and

  (2) The takeoff distance is no greater than the length of the runway plus the length of the clearway (if present); and

  (3) The takeoff run is no greater than the length of the runway.

[Doc. No. 18334, 54 FR 34318, Aug. 18, 1989, as amended by Amdt. 91–256, 63 FR 8321, Feb. 18, 1998]

91.607 Emergency exits for airplanes carrying passengers for hire

(a) Notwithstanding any other provision of this chapter, no person may operate a large airplane (type certificated under the Civil Air Regulations effective before April 9, 1957) in passenger-carrying operations for hire, with more than the number of occupants—

  (1) Allowed under Civil Air Regulations 4b.362 (a), (b), and (c) as in effect on December 20, 1951; or

  (2) Approved under Special Civil Air Regulations SR–387, SR–389, SR–389A, or SR–389B, or under this section as in effect.

However, an airplane type listed in the following table may be operated with up to the listed number of occupants (including crewmembers) and the corresponding number of exits (including emergency exits and doors) approved for the emergency exit of passengers or with an occupant-exit configuration approved under paragraph (b) or (c) of this section.

AIRPLANE TYPE	MAXIMUM NUMBER OF OCCUPANTS INCLUDING ALL CREWMEMBERS	CORRESPONDING NUMBER OF EXITS AUTHORIZED FOR PASSENGER USE
B-307	61	4
B-377	96	9
C-46	67	4
CV-240	53	6
CV-340 and CV-440	53	6
DC-3	35	4
DC-3 (Super)	39	5
DC-4	86	5
DC-6	87	7
DC-6B	112	11
L-18	17	3
L-049, L-649, L-749	87	7
L-1049	96	9
M-202	53	6
M-404	53	7
Viscount 700 series	53	7

b) Occupants in addition to those authorized under paragraph (a) of this section may be carried as follows:

   (1) For each additional floor-level exit at least 24 inches wide by 48 inches high, with an unobstructed 20-inch-wide access aisleway between the exit and the main passenger aisle, 12 additional occupants.

   (2) For each additional window exit located over a wing that meets the requirements of the airworthiness standards under which the airplane was type certificated or that is large enough to inscribe an ellipse 19×26 inches, eight additional occupants.

   (3) For each additional window exit that is not located over a wing but that otherwise complies with paragraph (b)(2) of this section, five additional occupants.

   (4) For each airplane having a ratio (as computed from the table in paragraph (a) of this section) of maximum number of occupants to number of exits greater than 14:1, and for each airplane that does not have at least one full-size, door-type exit in the side of the fuselage in the rear part of the cabin, the first additional exit must be a floor-level exit that complies with paragraph (b)(1) of this section and must be located in the rear part of the cabin on the opposite side of the fuselage from the main entrance door. However, no person may operate an airplane under this section carrying more than 115 occupants unless there is such an exit on each side of the fuselage in the rear part of the cabin.

c) No person may eliminate any approved exit except in accordance with the following:

   (1) The previously authorized maximum number of occupants must be reduced by the same number of additional occupants authorized for that exit under this section.

   (2) Exits must be eliminated in accordance with the following priority schedule: First, non-over-wing window exits; second, over-wing window exits; third, floor-level exits located in the forward part of the cabin; and fourth, floor-level exits located in the rear of the cabin.

   (3) At least one exit must be retained on each side of the fuselage regardless of the number of occupants.

   (4) No person may remove any exit that would result in a ratio of maximum number of occupants to approved exits greater than 14:1.

d) This section does not relieve any person operating under part 121 of this chapter from complying with 121.291.

91.609 Flight data recorders and cockpit voice recorders

(a) No holder of an air carrier operating certificate or an operating certificate may conduct any operation under this part with an aircraft listed in the holder's operations specifications or current list of aircraft used in air transportation unless that aircraft complies with any applicable flight recorder and cockpit voice recorder requirements of the part under which its certificate is issued except that the operator may—

   (1) Ferry an aircraft with an inoperative flight recorder or cockpit voice recorder from a place where repair or replacement cannot be made to a place where they can be made;

   (2) Continue a flight as originally planned, if the flight recorder or cockpit voice recorder becomes inoperative after the aircraft has taken off;

   (3) Conduct an airworthiness flight test during which the flight recorder or cockpit voice recorder is turned off to test it or to test any communications or electrical equipment installed in the aircraft; or

   (4) Ferry a newly acquired aircraft from the place where possession of it is taken to a place where the flight recorder or cockpit voice recorder is to be installed.

(b) Notwithstanding paragraphs (c) and (e) of this section, an operator other than the holder of an air carrier or a commercial operator certificate may—

   (1) Ferry an aircraft with an inoperative flight recorder or cockpit voice recorder from a place where repair or replacement cannot be made to a place where they can be made;

   (2) Continue a flight as originally planned if the flight recorder or cockpit voice recorder becomes inoperative after the aircraft has taken off;

   (3) Conduct an airworthiness flight test during which the flight recorder or cockpit voice recorder is turned off to test it or to test any communications or electrical equipment installed in the aircraft;

   (4) Ferry a newly acquired aircraft from a place where possession of it was taken to a place where the flight recorder or cockpit voice recorder is to be installed; or

   (5) Operate an aircraft:

      (i) For not more than 15 days while the flight recorder and/or cockpit voice recorder is inoperative and/or removed for repair provided that the aircraft maintenance records contain an entry that indicates the date of failure, and a placard is located in view of the pilot to show that the flight recorder or cockpit voice recorder is inoperative.

      (ii) For not more than an additional 15 days, provided that the requirements in paragraph (b)(5)(i) are met and that a certificated pilot, or a certificated person authorized to return an aircraft to service under 43.7 of this chapter, certifies in the aircraft maintenance records that additional time is required to complete repairs or obtain a replacement unit.

(c)

   (1) No person may operate a U.S. civil registered, multiengine, turbine-powered airplane or rotorcraft having a passenger seating configuration, excluding any pilot seats of 10 or more that has been manufactured after October 11, 1991, unless it is equipped with one or more approved flight recorders that utilize a digital method of recording and storing data and a method of readily retrieving that data from the storage medium, that are capable of recording the data specified in appendix E to this part, for an airplane, or appendix F to this part, for a rotorcraft, of this part within the range, accuracy, and recording interval specified, and that are capable of retaining no less than 8 hours of aircraft operation.

   (2) All airplanes subject to paragraph (c)(1) of this section that are manufactured before April 7, 2010, by April 7, 2012, must meet the requirements of 23.1459(a)(7) or 25.1459(a)(8) of this chapter, as applicable.

   (3) All airplanes and rotorcraft subject to paragraph (c)(1) of this section that are manufactured on or after April 7, 2010, must meet the flight data recorder requirements of 23.1459, 25.1459, 27.1459, or 29.1459 of this chapter, as applicable,

and retain at least the last 25 hours of recorded information using a recorder that meets the standards of TSO–C124a, or later revision.

(d) Whenever a flight recorder, required by this section, is installed, it must be operated continuously from the instant the airplane begins the takeoff roll or the rotorcraft begins lift-off until the airplane has completed the landing roll or the rotorcraft has landed at its destination.

(e) Unless otherwise authorized by the Administrator, after October 11, 1991, no person may operate a U.S. civil registered multiengine, turbine-powered airplane or rotorcraft having a passenger seating configuration of six passengers or more and for which two pilots are required by type certification or operating rule unless it is equipped with an approved cockpit voice recorder that:

(1) Is installed in compliance with 23.1457 (a)(1) and (2), (b), (c), (d)(1)(i), (2) and (3), (e), (f), and (g); 25.1457 (a)(1) and (2), (b), (c), (d)(1)(i), (2) and (3), (e), (f), and (g); 27.1457 (a)(1) and (2), (b), (c), (d)(1)(i), (2) and (3), (e), (f), and (g); or 29.1457 (a)(1) and (2), (b), (c), (d)(1)(i), (2) and (3), (e), (f) and (g) of this chapter, as applicable; and

(2) Is operated continuously from the use of the checklist before the flight to completion of the final checklist at the end of the flight.

(f) In complying with this section, an approved cockpit voice recorder having an erasure feature may be used, so that at any time during the operation of the recorder, information recorded more than 15 minutes earlier may be erased or otherwise obliterated.

(g) In the event of an accident or occurrence requiring immediate notification to the National Transportation Safety Board under part 830 of its regulations that results in the termination of the flight, any operator who has installed approved flight recorders and approved cockpit voice recorders shall keep the recorded information for at least 60 days or, if requested by the Administrator or the Board, for a longer period. Information obtained from the record is used to assist in determining the cause of accidents or occurrences in connection with the investigation under part 830. The Administrator does not use the cockpit voice recorder record in any civil penalty or certificate action.

(h) All airplanes required by this section to have a cockpit voice recorder and a flight data recorder, that are manufactured before April 7, 2010, must by April 7, 2012, have a cockpit voice recorder that also—

(1) Meets the requirements of 23.1457(d)(6) or 25.1457(d)(6) of this chapter, as applicable; and

(2) If transport category, meets the requirements of 25.1457(a)(3), (a)(4), and (a)(5) of this chapter.

(i) All airplanes or rotorcraft required by this section to have a cockpit voice recorder and flight data recorder, that are manufactured on or after April 7, 2010, must have a cockpit voice recorder installed that also—

(1) Is installed in accordance with the requirements of 23.1457 (except for paragraphs (a)(6) and (d)(5)); 25.1457 (except for paragraphs (a)(6) and (d)(5)); 27.1457 (except for paragraphs (a)(6) and (d)(5)); or 29.1457 (except for paragraphs (a)(6) and (d)(5)) of this chapter, as applicable; and

(2) Retains at least the last 2 hours of recorded information using a recorder that meets the standards of TSO–C123a, or later revision.

(3) For all airplanes or rotorcraft manufactured on or after April 6, 2012, also meets the requirements of 23.1457 (a)(6) and (d)(5); 25.1457 (a)(6) and (d)(5); 27.1457 (a)(6) and (d)(5); or 29.1457 (a)(6) and (d)(5) of this chapter, as applicable.

(j) All airplanes or rotorcraft required by this section to have a cockpit voice recorder and a flight data recorder, that install datalink communication equipment on or after April 6, 2012, must record all datalink messages as required by the certification rule applicable to the aircraft.

[Doc. No. 18334, 54 FR 34318, Aug. 18, 1989, as amended by Amdt. 91–226, 56 FR 51621, Oct. 11, 1991; Amdt. 91–228, 57 FR 19353, May 5, 1992; Amdt. 91–300, 73 FR 12564, Mar. 7, 2008; Amdt. 91-300, 74 FR 32800, July 9, 2009; Amdt. 91-313, 75 FR 17045, Apr. 5, 2010]

91.611 Authorization for ferry flight with one engine inoperative

(a) *General.* The holder of an air carrier operating certificate or an operating certificate issued under part 125 may conduct a ferry flight of a four-engine airplane or a turbine-engine-powered airplane equipped with three engines, with one engine inoperative, to a base for the purpose of repairing that engine subject to the following:

(1) The airplane model has been test flown and found satisfactory for safe flight in accordance with paragraph (b) or (c) of this section, as appropriate. However, each operator who before November 19, 1966, has shown that a model of airplane with an engine inoperative is satisfactory for safe flight by a test flight conducted in accordance with performance data contained in the applicable Airplane Flight Manual under paragraph (a)(2) of this section need not repeat the test flight for that model.

(2) The approved Airplane Flight Manual contains the following performance data and the flight is conducted in accordance with that data:

   (i) Maximum weight.

   (ii) Center of gravity limits.

   (iii) Configuration of the inoperative propeller (if applicable).

   (iv) Runway length for takeoff (including temperature accountability).

   (v) Altitude range.

   (vi) Certificate limitations.

   (vii) Ranges of operational limits.

   (viii) Performance information.

   (ix) Operating procedures.

(3) The operator has FAA approved procedures for the safe operation of the airplane, including specific requirements for—

   (i) Limiting the operating weight on any ferry flight to the minimum necessary for the flight plus the necessary reserve fuel load;

   (ii) A limitation that takeoffs must be made from dry runways unless, based on a showing of actual operating takeoff techniques on wet runways with one engine inoperative, takeoffs with full controllability from wet runways have been approved for the specific model aircraft and included in the Airplane Flight Manual:

   (iii) Operations from airports where the runways may require a takeoff or approach over populated areas; and

   (iv) Inspection procedures for determining the operating condition of the operative engines.

(4) No person may take off an airplane under this section if—

   (i) The initial climb is over thickly populated areas; or

   (ii) Weather conditions at the takeoff or destination airport are less than those required for VFR flight.

(5) Persons other than required flight crewmembers shall not be carried during the flight.

(6) No person may use a flight crewmember for flight under this section unless that crewmember is thoroughly familiar with the operating procedures for one-engine inoperative ferry flight contained in the certificate holder's manual and the limitations and performance information in the Airplane Flight Manual.

(b) *Flight tests: reciprocating-engine-powered airplanes.* The airplane performance of a reciprocating-engine-powered airplane with one engine inoperative must be determined by flight test as follows:

(1) A speed not less than 1.3 V_{S1} must be chosen at which the airplane may be controlled satisfactorily in a climb with the critical engine inoperative (with its propeller removed or in a configuration desired by the operator and with all other engines operating at the maximum power determined in paragraph (b)(3) of this section.

(2) The distance required to accelerate to the speed listed in paragraph (b)(1) of this section and to climb to 50 feet must be determined with—

   (i) The landing gear extended;

   (ii) The critical engine inoperative and its propeller removed or in a configuration desired by the operator; and

   (iii) The other engines operating at not more than maximum power established under paragraph (b)(3) of this section.

(3) The takeoff, flight and landing procedures, such as the approximate trim settings, method of power application, maximum power, and speed must be established.

(4) The performance must be determined at a maximum weight not greater than the weight that allows a rate of climb of at least 400 feet per minute in the en route configuration set forth in 25.67(d) of this chapter in effect on January 31, 1977, at an altitude of 5,000 feet.

(5) The performance must be determined using temperature accountability for the takeoff field length, computed in accordance with 25.61 of this chapter in effect on January 31, 1977.

(c) *Flight tests: Turbine-engine-powered airplanes.* The airplane performance of a turbine-engine-powered airplane with one engine inoperative must be determined by flight tests, including at least three takeoff tests, in accordance with the following:

(1) Takeoff speeds V_R and V_2, not less than the corresponding speeds under which the airplane was type certificated under 25.107 of this chapter, must be chosen at which the airplane may be controlled satisfactorily with the critical engine inoperative (with its propeller removed or in a configuration desired by the operator, if applicable) and with all other engines operating at not more than the power selected for type certification as set forth in 25.101 of this chapter.

(2) The minimum takeoff field length must be the horizontal distance required to accelerate and climb to the 35-foot height at V2speed (including any additional speed increment obtained in the tests) multiplied by 115 percent and determined with—

   (i) The landing gear extended;

   (ii) The critical engine inoperative and its propeller removed or in a configuration desired by the operator (if applicable); and

   (iii) The other engine operating at not more than the power selected for type certification as set forth in 25.101 of this chapter.

(3) The takeoff, flight, and landing procedures such as the approximate trim setting, method of power application, maximum power, and speed must be established. The airplane must be satisfactorily controllable during the entire takeoff run when operated according to these procedures.

(4) The performance must be determined at a maximum weight not greater than the weight determined under 25.121(c) of this chapter but with—

   (i) The actual steady gradient of the final takeoff climb requirement not less than 1.2 percent at the end of the takeoff path with two critical engines inoperative; and

   (ii) The climb speed not less than the two-engine inoperative trim speed for the actual steady gradient of the final takeoff climb prescribed by paragraph (c)(4)(i) of this section.

(5) The airplane must be satisfactorily controllable in a climb with two critical engines inoperative. Climb performance may be shown by calculations based on, and equal in accuracy to, the results of testing.

(6) The performance must be determined using temperature accountability for takeoff distance and final takeoff climb computed in accordance with 25.101 of this chapter.

For the purpose of paragraphs (c)(4) and (5) of this section, two critical engines means two adjacent engines on one side of an airplane with four engines, and the center engine and one outboard engine on an airplane with three engines.

91.613   Materials for compartment interiors

(a) No person may operate an airplane that conforms to an amended or supplemental type certificate issued in accordance with SFAR No. 41 for a maximum certificated takeoff weight in excess of 12,500 pounds unless within 1 year after issuance of the initial airworthiness certificate under that SFAR the airplane meets the compartment interior requirements set forth in 25.853 (a), (b), (b–1), (b–2), and (b–3) of this chapter in effect on September 26, 1978.

(b) *Thermal/acoustic insulation materials.* For transport category airplanes type certificated after January 1, 1958:

(1) For airplanes manufactured before September 2, 2005, when thermal/acoustic insulation is installed in the fuselage as replacements after September 2, 2005, the insulation must meet the flame propagation requirements of 25.856 of this chapter, effective September 2, 2003, if it is:

   (i) Of a blanket construction or

   (ii) Installed around air ducting.

(2) For airplanes manufactured after September 2, 2005, thermal/acoustic insulation materials installed in the fuselage must meet the flame propagation requirements of 25.856 of this chapter, effective September 2, 2003.

[Doc. No. 18334, 54 FR 34318, Aug. 18, 1989, as amended by Amdt. 91–279, 68 FR 45083, July 31, 2003; Amdt. 91–290, 70 FR 77752, Dec. 30, 2005]

91.615-91.699   [Reserved]

Subpart H — Foreign Aircraft Operations and Operations of U.S.-Registered Civil Aircraft Outside of the United States; and Rules Governing Persons on Board Such Aircraft

Source: Docket No. 18334, 54 FR 34320, Aug. 18, 1989, unless otherwise noted.

91.701   Applicability

(a) This subpart applies to the operations of civil aircraft of U.S. registry outside of the United States and the operations of foreign civil aircraft within the United States.

(b) Section 91.702 of this subpart also applies to each person on board an aircraft operated as follows:

(1) A U.S. registered civil aircraft operated outside the United States;

(2) Any aircraft operated outside the United States—

   (i) That has its next scheduled destination or last place of departure in the United States if the aircraft next lands in the United States; or

   (ii) If the aircraft lands in the United States with the individual still on the aircraft regardless of whether it was a scheduled or otherwise planned landing site.

[Doc. No. FAA–1998–4954, 64 FR 1079, Jan. 7, 1999]

91.702   Persons on board

Section 91.11 of this part (Prohibitions on interference with crewmembers) applies to each person on board an aircraft.

[Doc. No. FAA–1998–4954, 64 FR 1079, Jan. 7, 1999]

FAR 91

91.703   Operations of civil aircraft of U.S. registry outside of the United States

(a) Each person operating a civil aircraft of U.S. registry outside of the United States shall—

(1) When over the high seas, comply with Annex 2 (Rules of the Air) to the Convention on International Civil Aviation and with 91.117(c), 91.127, 91.129, and 91.131;

(2) When within a foreign country, comply with the regulations relating to the flight and maneuver of aircraft there in force;

(3) Except for 91.117(a), 91.307(b), 91.309, 91.323, and 91.711, comply with this part so far as it is not inconsistent with applicable regulations of the foreign country where the aircraft is operated or Annex 2 of the Convention on International Civil Aviation; and

(4) When operating within airspace designated as Reduced Vertical Separation Minimum (RVSM) airspace, comply with 91.706.

(5) For aircraft subject to ICAO Annex 16, carry on board the aircraft documents that summarize the noise operating characteristics and certifications of the aircraft that demonstrate compliance with this part and part 36 of this chapter.

(b) Annex 2 to the Convention on International Civil Aviation, Rules of the Air, Tenth Edition—July 2005, with Amendments through Amendment 45, applicable November 10, 2016, is incorporated by reference into this section with the approval of the Director of the Federal Register under 5 U.S.C. 552(a) and 1 CFR part 51. To enforce any edition other than that specified in this section, the FAA must publish a document in the Federal Register and the material must be available to the public. All approved material is available for inspection at U.S. Department of Transportation, Docket Operations, West Building Ground Floor, Room W12-140, 1200 New Jersey Avenue SE., Washington, DC 20590 and is available from the International Civil Aviation Organization (ICAO), Marketing and Customer Relations Unit, 999 Robert Bourassa Boulevard, Montreal, Quebec H3C 5H7, Canada; http://store1.icao.int/; or by contacting the ICAO Marketing and Customer Relations Unit by telephone at 514-954-8022 or by email at sales@icao.int. For questions about ICAO Annex 2, contact the FAA's Office of International Affairs at (202) 267-1000. It is also available for inspection at the National Archives and Records Administration (NARA). For information on the availability of this material at NARA, call 202-741-6030, or go to http://www.archives.gov/federal_register/code_of_federal_regulations/ibr_locations.html.

[Doc. No. 18834, 54 FR 34320, Aug. 18, 1989, as amended by Amdt. 91-227, 56 FR 65661, Dec. 17, 1991; Amdt. 91-254, 62 FR 17487, Apr. 9, 1997; 69 FR 18803, Apr. 9, 2004; Amdt. 91-299, 73 FR 10143, Feb. 26, 2008; Amdt. 91-312, 75 FR 9333, Mar. 2, 2010; Docket FAA-2016-9154, Amdt. 91-348, 82 FR 39664, Aug. 22, 2017]

91.705   [Reserved]

91.706   Operations within airspace designed as Reduced Vertical Separation Minimum Airspace

(a) Except as provided in paragraph (b) of this section, no person may operate a civil aircraft of U.S. registry in airspace designated as Reduced Vertical Separation Minimum (RVSM) airspace unless:

(1) The operator and the operator's aircraft comply with the requirements of appendix G of this part; and

(2) The operator is authorized by the Administrator to conduct such operations.

(b) The Administrator may authorize a deviation from the requirements of this section in accordance with Section 5 of appendix G to this part.

[Doc. No. 28870, 62 FR 17487, Apr. 9, 1997]

91.707   Flights between Mexico or Canada and the United States

Unless otherwise authorized by ATC, no person may operate a civil aircraft between Mexico or Canada and the United States without filing an IFR or VFR flight plan, as appropriate.

91.709   Operations to Cuba

No person may operate a civil aircraft from the United States to Cuba unless—

(a) Departure is from an international airport of entry designated in 6.13 of the Air Commerce Regulations of the Bureau of Customs (19 CFR 6.13); and

(b) In the case of departure from any of the 48 contiguous States or the District of Columbia, the pilot in command of the aircraft has filed—

(1) A DVFR or IFR flight plan as prescribed in 99.11 or 99.13 of this chapter; and

(2) A written statement, within 1 hour before departure, with the Office of Immigration and Naturalization Service at the airport of departure, containing—

(i)   All information in the flight plan;

(ii) The name of each occupant of the aircraft;

(iii) The number of occupants of the aircraft; and

(iv) A description of the cargo, if any.

This section does not apply to the operation of aircraft by a scheduled air carrier over routes authorized in operations specifications issued by the Administrator.

(Approved by the Office of Management and Budget under control number 2120–0005)

91.711   Special rules for foreign civil aircraft

(a) *General.* In addition to the other applicable regulations of this part, each person operating a foreign civil aircraft within the United States shall comply with this section.

(b) *VFR.* No person may conduct VFR operations which require two-way radio communications under this part unless at least one crewmember of that aircraft is able to conduct two-way radio communications in the English language and is on duty during that operation.

(c) *IFR.* No person may operate a foreign civil aircraft under IFR unless—

(1) That aircraft is equipped with—

(i) Radio equipment allowing two-way radio communication with ATC when it is operated in controlled airspace; and

(ii) Navigation equipment suitable for the route to be flown.

(2) Each person piloting the aircraft—

(i) Holds a current United States instrument rating or is authorized by his foreign airman certificate to pilot under IFR; and

(ii) Is thoroughly familiar with the United States en route, holding, and letdown procedures; and

(3) At least one crewmember of that aircraft is able to conduct two-way radiotelephone communications in the English language and that crewmember is on duty while the aircraft is approaching, operating within, or leaving the United States.

(d) *Over water.* Each person operating a foreign civil aircraft over water off the shores of the United States shall give flight notification or file a flight plan in accordance with the Supplementary Procedures for the ICAO region concerned.

(e) *Flight at and above FL 240.* If VOR navigation equipment is required under paragraph (c)(1)(ii) of this section, no person may operate a foreign civil aircraft within the 50 States and the District of Columbia at or above FL 240, unless the aircraft is equipped with approved DME or a suitable RNAV system. When the DME or RNAV system required by this paragraph fails at and above FL 240, the pilot in command of the aircraft must notify ATC immediately and may then continue operations at and above FL 240 to the next airport of intended landing where repairs or replacement of the equipment can be made. A foreign civil aircraft may be operated within the 50 States and the District of Columbia at or above FL 240 without DME or an RNAV system when operated for the following purposes, and ATC is notified before each takeoff:

(1) Ferry flights to and from a place in the United States where repairs or alterations are to be made.

(2) Ferry flights to a new country of registry.

(3) Flight of a new aircraft of U.S. manufacture for the purpose of—

    (i)   Flight testing the aircraft;

    (ii) Training foreign flight crews in the operation of the aircraft; or

    (iii) Ferrying the aircraft for export delivery outside the United States.

(4) Ferry, demonstration, and test flight of an aircraft brought to the United States for the purpose of demonstration or testing the whole or any part thereof.

[Doc. No. 18834, 54 FR 34320, Aug. 18, 1989, as amended by Amdt. 91–227, 56 FR 65661, Dec. 17, 1991; Amdt. 91–296, 72 FR 31679, June 7, 2007]

91.713 Operation of civil aircraft of Cuban registry

No person may operate a civil aircraft of Cuban registry except in controlled airspace and in accordance with air traffic clearance or air traffic control instructions that may require use of specific airways or routes and landings at specific airports.

91.715 Special flight authorizations for foreign civil aircraft

(a) Foreign civil aircraft may be operated without airworthiness certificates required under 91.203 if a special flight authorization for that operation is issued under this section. Application for a special flight authorization must be made to the appropriate Flight Standards Division Manager, or Aircraft Certification Service Division Director. However, in the case of an aircraft to be operated in the U.S. for the purpose of demonstration at an airshow, the application may be made to the appropriate Flight Standards Division Manager or Aircraft Certification Service Division Director responsible for the airshow location.

(b) The Administrator may issue a special flight authorization for a foreign civil aircraft subject to any conditions and limitations that the Administrator considers necessary for safe operation in the U.S. airspace.

(c) No person may operate a foreign civil aircraft under a special flight authorization unless that operation also complies with part 375 of the Special Regulations of the Department of Transportation (14 CFR part 375).

(Approved by the Office of Management and Budget under control number 2120–0005)

[Doc. No. 18334, 54 FR 34320, Aug. 18, 1989, as amended by Amdt. 91-212, 54 FR 39293, Sept. 25, 1989; Docket FAA-2018-0119, Amdt. 91-350, 83 FR 9171, Mar. 5, 2018]

91.717-91.799 [Reserved]

Subpart I — Operating Noise Limits

Source: Docket No. 18334, 54 FR 34321, Aug. 18, 1989, unless otherwise noted.

91.801 Applicability: Relation to part 36

(a) This subpart prescribes operating noise limits and related requirements that apply, as follows, to the operation of civil aircraft in the United States.

(1) Sections 91.803, 91.805, 91.807, 91.809, and 91.811 apply to civil subsonic jet (turbojet) airplanes with maximum weights of more than 75,000 pounds and—

    (i)   If U.S. registered, that have standard airworthiness certificates; or

    (ii) If foreign registered, that would be required by this chapter to have a U.S. standard airworthiness certificate in order to conduct the operations intended for the airplane were it registered in the United States. Those sections apply to operations to or from airports in the United States under this part and parts 121, 125, 129, and 135 of this chapter.

(2) Section 91.813 applies to U.S. operators of civil subsonic jet (turbojet) airplanes covered by this subpart. This section applies to operators operating to or from airports in the United States under this part and parts 121, 125, and 135, but not to those operating under part 129 of this chapter.

(3) Sections 91.803, 91.819, and 91.821 apply to U.S.-registered civil supersonic airplanes having standard airworthiness certificates and to foreign-registered civil supersonic airplanes that, if registered in the United States, would be required by this chapter to have U.S. standard airworthiness certificates in order to conduct the operations intended for the airplane. Those sections apply to operations under this part and under parts 121, 125, 129, and 135 of this chapter.

(b) Unless otherwise specified, as used in this subpart "part 36" refers to 14 CFR part 36, including the noise levels under appendix C of that part, notwithstanding the provisions of that part excepting certain airplanes from the specified noise requirements. For purposes of this subpart, the various stages of noise levels, the terms used to describe airplanes with respect to those levels, and the terms "subsonic airplane" and "supersonic airplane" have the meanings specified under part 36 of this chapter. For purposes of this subpart, for subsonic airplanes operated in foreign air commerce in the United States, the Administrator may accept compliance with the noise requirements under annex 16 of the International Civil Aviation Organization when those requirements have been shown to be substantially compatible with, and achieve results equivalent to those achievable under, part 36 for that airplane. Determinations made under these provisions are subject to the limitations of 36.5 of this chapter as if those noise levels were part 36 noise levels.

(c) Sections 91.851 through 91.877 of this subpart prescribe operating noise limits and related requirements that apply to any civil subsonic jet (turbojet) airplane (for which an airworthiness certificate other than an experimental certificate has been issued by the Administrator) with a maximum certificated takeoff weight of more than 75,000 pounds operating to or from an airport in the 48 contiguous United States and the District of Columbia under this part, parts 121, 125, 129, or 135 of this chapter on and after September 25, 1991.

(d) Section 91.877 prescribes reporting requirements that apply to any civil subsonic jet (turbojet) airplane with a maximum weight of more than 75,000 pounds operated by an air carrier or foreign air carrier between the contiguous United States and the State of Hawaii, between the State of Hawaii and any point outside of the 48 contiguous United States, or between the islands of Hawaii in turnaround service, under part 121 or 129 of this chapter on or after November 5, 1990.

(e) Sections 91.881 through 91.883 of this subpart prescribe operating noise limits and related requirements that apply to any civil subsonic jet airplane with a maximum takeoff weight of 75,000 pounds or less and for which an airworthiness certificate (other than an experimental certificate) has been issued, operating to or from an airport in the contiguous United States under this part, part 121, 125, 129, or 135 of this chapter on and after December 31, 2015.

[Doc. No. 18334, 54 FR 34321, Aug. 18, 1989; Amdt. 91-211, 54 FR 41211, Oct. 5, 1989, as amended by Amdt. 91-225, 56 FR 48658, Sept. 25, 1991; Amdt. 91-252, 61 FR 66185, Dec. 16, 1996; Amdt. 91-275, 67 FR 45237, July 8, 2002; Amdt. 91-276, 67 FR 46571, July 15, 2002; Amdt. 91-328, 78 FR 39583, July 2, 2013]

91.803 Part 125 operators: designation of applicable regulations

For airplanes covered by this subpart and operated under part 125 of this chapter, the following regulations apply as specified:

(a) For each airplane operation to which requirements prescribed under this subpart applied before November 29, 1980, those requirements of this subpart continue to apply.

FAR 91

(b) For each subsonic airplane operation to which requirements prescribed under this subpart did not apply before November 29, 1980, because the airplane was not operated in the United States under this part or part 121, 129, or 135 of this chapter, the requirements prescribed under 91.805 of this subpart apply.

(c) For each supersonic airplane operation to which requirements prescribed under this subpart did not apply before November 29, 1980, because the airplane was not operated in the United States under this part or part 121, 129, or 135 of this chapter, the requirements of 91.819 and 91.821 of this subpart apply.

(d) For each airplane required to operate under part 125 for which a deviation under that part is approved to operate, in whole or in part, under this part or part 121, 129, or 135 of this chapter, notwithstanding the approval, the requirements prescribed under paragraphs (a), (b), and (c) of this section continue to apply.

[Docket No. 18334, 54 FR 34321, Aug. 18, 1989, as amended by Amdt. 91–276, 67 FR 46571, July 15, 2002]

91.805 Final compliance: subsonic airplanes

Except as provided in 91.809 and 91.811, on and after January 1, 1985, no person may operate to or from an airport in the United States any subsonic airplane covered by this subpart unless that airplane has been shown to comply with Stage 2 or Stage 3 noise levels under part 36 of this chapter.

91.807-91.813 [Reserved]

91.815 Agricultural and fire fighting airplanes: noise operating limitations

(a) This section applies to propeller-driven, small airplanes having standard airworthiness certificates that are designed for "agricultural aircraft operations" (as defined in 137.3 of this chapter, as effective on January 1, 1966) or for dispensing fire fighting materials.

(b) If the Airplane Flight Manual, or other approved manual material information, markings, or placards for the airplane indicate that the airplane has not been shown to comply with the noise limits under part 36 of this chapter, no person may operate that airplane, except—

(1) To the extent necessary to accomplish the work activity directly associated with the purpose for which it is designed;

(2) To provide flight crewmember training in the special purpose operation for which the airplane is designed; and

(3) To conduct "nondispensing aerial work operations" in accordance with the requirements under 137.29(c) of this chapter.

91.817 Civil aircraft sonic boom

(a) No person may operate a civil aircraft in the United States at a true flight Mach number greater than 1 except in compliance with conditions and limitations in an authorization to exceed Mach 1 issued to the operator in accordance with 91.818.

(b) In addition, no person may operate a civil aircraft for which the maximum operating limit speed MM0exceeds a Mach number of 1, to or from an airport in the United States, unless—

(1) Information available to the flight crew includes flight limitations that ensure that flights entering or leaving the United States will not cause a sonic boom to reach the surface within the United States; and

(2) The operator complies with the flight limitations prescribed in paragraph (b)(1) of this section or complies with conditions and limitations in an authorization to exceed Mach 1 issued in accordance with 91.818.

(Approved by the Office of Management and Budget under control number 2120–0005)

[Docket No. 18334, 54 FR 34321, Aug. 18, 1989, as amended by Amdt. No. 91-362, 86 FR 3792, Jan. 15, 2021]

91.818 Special flight authorization to exceed Mach 1

For all civil aircraft, any operation that exceeds Mach 1 may be conducted only in accordance with a special flight authorization issued to an operator in accordance with the requirements of this section.

(a) Application. Application for a special flight authorization to exceed Mach 1 must be made to the FAA Office of Environment and Energy for consideration by the Administrator. Each application must include:

(1) The name of the operator;

(2) The number and model(s) of the aircraft to be operated;

(3) The number of proposed flights;

(4) The date range during which the flight(s) would be conducted;

(5) The time of day the flight(s) would be conducted. Proposed night operations may require further justification for their necessity;

(6) A description of the flight area requested by the applicant, including any environmental information required to be submitted pursuant to paragraph (c) of this section;

(7) All conditions and limitations on the flight(s) that will ensure that no measurable sonic boom overpressure will reach the surface outside of the proposed flight area; and

(8) The reason(s) that operation at a speed greater than Mach 1 is necessary. A special flight authorization to exceed Mach 1 may be granted only for operations that are intended to:

(i) Show compliance with airworthiness requirements;

(ii) Determine the sonic boom characteristics of an aircraft;

(iii) Establish a means of reducing or eliminating the effects of sonic boom, including flight profiles and special features of an aircraft;

(iv) Demonstrate the conditions and limitations under which speeds in excess of Mach 1 will not cause a measurable sonic boom overpressure to reach the surface; or

(v) Measure the noise characteristics of an aircraft to demonstrate compliance with noise requirements imposed under this chapter, or to determine the limits for operation in accordance with § 91.817(b).

(9) For any purpose listed in paragraph (a)(8) of this section, each applicant must indicate why its intended operation cannot be safely or properly accomplished over the ocean at a distance ensuring that no sonic boom overpressure reaches any land surface in the United States.

(b) Operation outside a test area. An applicant may apply for an authorization to conduct flights outside a test area under certain conditions and limitations upon a conservative showing that:

(1) Flight(s) within a test area have been conducted in accordance with an authorization issued for the purpose specified in paragraph (a)(8)(iv) of this section;

(2) The results of the flight test(s) required by paragraph (b)(1) of this section demonstrate that a speed in excess of Mach 1 does not cause a measurable sonic boom overpressure to reach the surface; and

(3) The conditions and limitations determined by the test(s) represent all foreseeable operating conditions and are effective on all flights conducted under an authorization.

(c) Environmental findings.

(1) No special flight authorization will be granted if the Administrator finds that such action is necessary to protect or enhance the environment.

(2) The Administrator is required to consider the potential environmental impacts resulting from the issuance of an authorization for a particular flight area pursuant to the National Environmental Policy Act of 1969 (NEPA) (42 U.S.C 4321 et seq.), all applicable regulations implementing NEPA, and related Executive orders and guidance. Accordingly, each applicant must provide information that sufficiently describes the potential environmental impact of any flight in excess of Mach 1, including the effect of a sonic boom reaching the

surface in the proposed flight area, to enable the FAA to determine whether such impacts are significant within the meaning of NEPA.

(d) Issuance. An authorization to operate a civil aircraft in excess of Mach 1 may be issued only after an applicant has submitted the information described in this section and the Administrator has taken the required action regarding the environmental findings described in paragraph (c) of this section.

(e) Duration.

    (1) An authorization to exceed Mach 1 will be granted for the time the Administrator determines necessary to conduct the flights for the described purposes.

    (2) An authorization to exceed Mach 1 is effective until it expires or is surrendered.

    (3) An authorization to exceed Mach 1 may be terminated, suspended, or amended by the Administrator at any time the Administrator finds that such action is necessary to protect the environment.

    (4) The holder of an authorization to exceed Mach 1 may request reconsideration of a termination, amendment, or suspension issued under paragraph (e)(3) of this section within 30 days of notice of the action. Failure to request reconsideration and provide information why the Administrator's action is not appropriate will result in permanent termination of the authorization.

    (5) Findings made by and actions taken by the Administrator under this section do not affect any certificate issued under chapter 447 of Title 49 of the United States Code.

[Docket No. FAA-2019-0451; Amdt. No. 91-362, 86 FR 3792, Jan. 15, 2021]

91.819 Civil supersonic airplanes that do not comply with part 36

    (a) Applicability. This section applies to civil supersonic airplanes that have not been shown to comply with the Stage 2 noise limits of part 36 in effect on October 13, 1977, using applicable trade-off provisions, and that are operated in the United States, after July 31, 1978.

    (b) Airport use. Except in an emergency, the following apply to each person who operates a civil supersonic airplane to or from an airport in the United States:

    (1) Regardless of whether a type design change approval is applied for under part 21 of this chapter, no person may land or take off an airplane covered by this section for which the type design is changed, after July 31, 1978, in a manner constituting an "acoustical change" under 21.93 unless the acoustical change requirements of part 36 are complied with.

    (2) No flight may be scheduled, or otherwise planned, for takeoff or landing after 10 p.m. and before 7 a.m. local time.

91.821 Civil supersonic airplanes: noise limits

Except for Concorde airplanes having flight time before January 1, 1980, no person may operate in the United States, a civil supersonic airplane that does not comply with Stage 2 noise limits of part 36 in effect on October 13, 1977, using applicable trade-off provisions.

91.823-91.849 [Reserved]

91.851 Definitions

For the purposes of 91.851 through 91.877 of this subpart:

Chapter 4 noise level means a noise level at or below the maximum noise level prescribed in Chapter 4, Paragraph 4.4, Maximum Noise Levels, of the International Civil Aviation Organization (ICAO) Annex 16, Volume I, Amendment 7, effective March 21, 2002. The Director of the Federal Register in accordance with 5 U.S.C. 552(a) and 1 CFR part 51 approved the incorporation by reference of this document, which can be obtained from the International Civil Aviation Organization (ICAO), Document Sales Unit, 999 University Street, Montreal, Quebec H3C 5H7, Canada. Also, you may obtain documents on the Internet at http://www.ICAO.int/eshop/index.cfm. Copies may be reviewed at the U.S. Department of Transportation, Docket Operations, West Building Ground Floor, Room W12–140, 1200 New Jersey Avenue, SE., Washington, DC 20590 or at the National Archives and Records Administration (NARA). For information on the availability of this material at NARA, call 202–741–6030, or go to: http://www.archives.gov/federal_register/code_of_federal_regulations/ibr_locations.html

Contiguous United States means the area encompassed by the 48 contiguous United States and the District of Columbia.

Fleet means those civil subsonic jet (turbojet) airplanes with a maximum certificated weight of more than 75,000 pounds that are listed on an operator's operations specifications as eligible for operation in the contiguous United States.

Import means a change in ownership of an airplane from a non-U.S. person to a U.S. person when the airplane is brought into the United States for operation.

Operations specifications means an enumeration of airplanes by type, model, series, and serial number operated by the operator or foreign air carrier on a given day, regardless of how or whether such airplanes are formally listed or designated by the operator.

Owner means any person that has indicia of ownership sufficient to register the airplane in the United States pursuant to part 47 of this chapter.

New entrant means an air carrier or foreign air carrier that, on or before November 5, 1990, did not conduct operations under part 121 or 129 of this chapter using an airplane covered by this subpart to or from any airport in the contiguous United States, but that initiates such operation after that date.

Stage 2 noise levels mean the requirements for Stage 2 noise levels as defined in part 36 of this chapter in effect on November 5, 1990.

Stage 3 noise levels mean the requirements for Stage 3 noise levels as defined in part 36 of this chapter in effect on November 5, 1990.

Stage 4 noise level means a noise level at or below the Stage 4 noise limit prescribed in part 36 of this chapter.

Stage 2 airplane means a civil subsonic jet (turbojet) airplane with a maximum certificated weight of 75,000 pounds or more that complies with Stage 2 noise levels as defined in part 36 of this chapter.

Stage 3 airplane means a civil subsonic jet (turbojet) airplane with a maximum certificated weight of 75,000 pounds or more that complies with Stage 3 noise levels as defined in part 36 of this chapter.

Stage 4 airplane means an airplane that has been shown not to exceed the Stage 4 noise limit prescribed in part 36 of this chapter. A Stage 4 airplane complies with all of the noise operating rules of this part.

Stage 5 airplane means an airplane that has been shown not to exceed the Stage 5 noise limit prescribed in part 36 of this chapter. A Stage 5 airplane complies with all of the noise operating rules of this part.

Stage 5 noise level means a noise level at or below the Stage 5 noise limit prescribed in part 36 of this chapter.

[Doc. No. 26433, 56 FR 48658, Sept. 25, 1991, as amended by Amdt. 91-252, 61 FR 66185, Dec. 16, 1996; Amdt. 91-275, 67 FR 45237, July 8, 2002; Amdt. 91-288, 70 FR 38749, July 5, 2005; 72 FR 68475, Dec. 5, 2007; Docket FAA-2015-3782, Amdt. 91-349, 82 FR 46132, Oct. 4, 2017]

91.853 Final compliance: civil subsonic airplanes

Except as provided in 91.873, after December 31, 1999, no person shall operate to or from any airport in the contiguous United States any airplane subject to 91.801(c), unless that airplane has been shown to comply with Stage 3, Stage 4, or Stage 5 noise levels.

[Docket FAA-2015-3782, Amdt. 91-349, 82 FR 46132, Oct. 4, 2017]

91.855 Entry and nonaddition rule

No person may operate any airplane subject to 91.801(c) of this subpart to or from an airport in the contiguous United States unless one or more of the following apply:

    (a) The airplane complies with Stage 3, Stage 4, or Stage 5 noise levels.

(b) The airplane complies with Stage 2 noise levels and was owned by a U.S. person on and since November 5, 1990. Stage 2 airplanes that meet these criteria and are leased to foreign airlines are also subject to the return provisions of paragraph (e) of this section.

(c) The airplane complies with Stage 2 noise levels, is owned by a non-U.S. person, and is the subject of a binding lease to a U.S. person effective before and on September 25, 1991. Any such airplane may be operated for the term of the lease in effect on that date, and any extensions thereof provided for in that lease.

(d) The airplane complies with Stage 2 noise levels and is operated by a foreign air carrier.

(e) The airplane complies with Stage 2 noise levels and is operated by a foreign operator other than for the purpose of foreign air commerce.

(f) The airplane complies with Stage 2 noise levels and—

(1) On November 5, 1990, was owned by:

(i) A corporation, trust, or partnership organized under the laws of the United States or any State (including individual States, territories, possessions, and the District of Columbia);

(ii) An individual who is a citizen of the United States; or

(iii) An entity owned or controlled by a corporation, trust, partnership, or individual described in paragraph (f)(1) (i) or (ii) of this section; and

(2) Enters into the United States not later than 6 months after the expiration of a lease agreement (including any extensions thereof) between an owner described in paragraph (f)(1) of this section and a foreign airline.

(g) The airplane complies with Stage 2 noise levels and was purchased by the importer under a written contract executed before November 5, 1990.

(h) Any Stage 2 airplane described in this section is eligible for operation in the contiguous United States only as provided under 91.865 or 91.867.

Doc. No. 26433, 56 FR 48658, Sept. 25, 1991; 56 FR 51167, Oct. 10, 1991, as amended by Amdt. 91-288, 70 FR 38750, July 5, 2005; Docket FAA-2015-3782, Amdt. 91-349, 82 FR 46132, Oct. 4, 2017]

91.857 Stage 2 operations outside of the 48 contiguous United States

An operator of a Stage 2 airplane that is operating only between points outside the contiguous United States on or after November 5, 1990, must include in its operations specifications a statement that such airplane may not be used to provide air transportation to or from any airport in the contiguous United States.

[Doc. No. FAA–2002–12771, 67 FR 46571, July 15, 2002]

91.858 Special flight authorizations for non-revenue Stage 2 operations

(a) After December 31, 1999, any operator of a Stage 2 airplane over 75,000 pounds may operate that airplane in nonrevenue service in the contiguous United States only for the following purposes:

(1) Sell, lease, or scrap the airplane;

(2) Obtain modifications to meet Stage 3, Stage 4, or Stage 5 noise levels.

(3) Obtain scheduled heavy maintenance or significant modifications;

(4) Deliver the airplane to a lessee or return it to a lessor;

(5) Park or store the airplane; and

(6) Prepare the airplane for any of the purposes listed in paragraph (a)(1) thru (a)(5) of this section.

(b) An operator of a Stage 2 airplane that needs to operate in the contiguous United States for any of the purposes listed above may apply to FAA's Office of Environment and Energy for a special flight authorization. The applicant must file in advance. Applications are due 30 days in advance of the planned flight and must provide the information necessary for the FAA to determine that the planned flight is within the limits prescribed in the law.

[Doc. No. FAA-2002-12771, 67 FR 46571, July 15, 2002, as amended by Docket FAA-2015-3782, Amdt. 91-349, 82 FR 46132, Oct. 4, 2017]

91.859 Modification to meet Stage 3 or Stage 4 noise levels

For an airplane subject to 91.801(c) of this subpart and otherwise prohibited from operation to or from an airport in the contiguous United States by 91.855, any person may apply for a special flight authorization for that airplane to operate in the contiguous United States for the purpose of obtaining modifications to meet Stage 3, Stage 4, or Stage 5 noise levels.

[Docket FAA-2015-3782, Amdt. 91-349, 82 FR 46132, Oct. 4, 2017]

91.861 Base level

(a) U.S. Operators. The base level of a U.S. operator is equal to the number of owned or leased Stage 2 airplanes subject to 91.801(c) of this subpart that were listed on that operator's operations specifications for operations to or from airports in the contiguous United States on any one day selected by the operator during the period January 1, 1990, through July 1, 1991, plus or minus adjustments made pursuant to paragraphs (a)(1) and (2).

(1) The base level of a U.S. operator shall be increased by a number equal to the total of the following—

(i) The number of Stage 2 airplanes returned to service in the United States pursuant to 91.855(f);

(ii) The number of Stage 2 airplanes purchased pursuant to 91.855(g); and

(iii) Any U.S. operator base level acquired with a Stage 2 airplane transferred from another person under 91.863.

(2) The base level of a U.S. operator shall be decreased by the amount of U.S. operator base level transferred with the corresponding number of Stage 2 airplanes to another person under 91.863.

(b) Foreign air carriers. The base level of a foreign air carrier is equal to the number of owned or leased Stage 2 airplanes that were listed on that carrier's U.S. operations specifications on any one day during the period January 1, 1990, through July 1, 1991, plus or minus any adjustments to the base levels made pursuant to paragraphs (b)(1) and (2).

(1) The base level of a foreign air carrier shall be increased by the amount of foreign air carrier base level acquired with a Stage 2 airplane from another person under 91.863.

(2) The base level of a foreign air carrier shall be decreased by the amount of foreign air carrier base level transferred with a Stage 2 airplane to another person under 91.863.

(c) New entrants do not have a base level.

[Doc. No. 26433, 56 FR 48659, Sept. 25, 1991; 56 FR 51167, Oct. 10, 1991]

91.863 Transfers of Stage 2 airplanes with base level

(a) Stage 2 airplanes may be transferred with or without the corresponding amount of base level. Base level may not be transferred without the corresponding number of Stage 2 airplanes.

(b) No portion of a U.S. operator's base level established under 91.861(a) may be used for operations by a foreign air carrier. No portion of a foreign air carrier's base level established under 91.861(b) may be used for operations by a U.S. operator.

(c) Whenever a transfer of Stage 2 airplanes with base level occurs, the transferring and acquiring parties shall, within 10 days, jointly submit written notification of the transfer to the FAA, Office of Environment and Energy. Such notification shall state:

(1) The names of the transferring and acquiring parties;

(2) The name, address, and telephone number of the individual responsible for submitting the notification on behalf of the transferring and acquiring parties;

(3) The total number of Stage 2 airplanes transferred, listed by airplane type, model, series, and serial number;

(4) The corresponding amount of base level transferred and whether it is U.S. operator or foreign air carrier base level; and

(5) The effective date of the transaction.

(d) If, taken as a whole, a transaction or series of transactions made pursuant to this section does not produce an increase or decrease in the number of Stage 2 airplanes for either the acquiring or transferring operator, such transaction or series of transactions may not be used to establish compliance with the requirements of 91.865.

[Doc. No. 26433, 56 FR 48659, Sept. 25, 1991]

91.865   Phased compliance for operators with base level

Except as provided in paragraph (a) of this section, each operator that operates an airplane under part 91, 121, 125, 129, or 135 of this chapter, regardless of the national registry of the airplane, shall comply with paragraph (b) or (d) of this section at each interim compliance date with regard to its subsonic airplane fleet covered by 91.801(c) of this subpart.

(a) This section does not apply to new entrants covered by 91.867 or to foreign operators not engaged in foreign air commerce.

(b) Each operator that chooses to comply with this paragraph pursuant to any interim compliance requirement shall reduce the number of Stage 2 airplanes it operates that are eligible for operation in the contiguous United States to a maximum of:

(1) After December 31, 1994, 75 percent of the base level held by the operator;

(2) After December 31, 1996, 50 percent of the base level held by the operator;

(3) After December 31, 1998, 25 percent of the base level held by the operator.

(c) Except as provided under 91.871, the number of Stage 2 airplanes that must be reduced at each compliance date contained in paragraph (b) of this section shall be determined by reference to the amount of base level held by the operator on that compliance date, as calculated under 91.861.

(d) Each operator that chooses to comply with this paragraph pursuant to any interim compliance requirement shall operate a fleet that consists of:

(1) After December 31, 1994, not less than 55 percent Stage 3 airplanes;

(2) After December 31, 1996, not less than 65 percent Stage 3 airplanes;

(3) After December 31, 1998, not less than 75 percent Stage 3 airplanes.

(e) Calculations resulting in fractions may be rounded to permit the continued operation of the next whole number of Stage 2 airplanes.

[Doc. No. 26433, 56 FR 48659, Sept. 25, 1991]

91.867   Phased compliance for new entrants

(a) New entrant U.S. air carriers.

(1) A new entrant initiating operations under part 121 of this chapter on or before December 31, 1994, may initiate service without regard to the percentage of its fleet composed of Stage 3 airplanes.

(2) After December 31, 1994, at least 25 percent of the fleet of a new entrant must comply with Stage 3 noise levels.

(3) After December 31, 1996, at least 50 percent of the fleet of a new entrant must comply with Stage 3 noise levels.

(4) After December 31, 1998, at least 75 percent of the fleet of a new entrant must comply with Stage 3 noise levels.

(b) New entrant foreign air carriers.

(1) A new entrant foreign air carrier initiating part 129 operations on or before December 31, 1994, may initiate service without regard to the percentage of its fleet composed of Stage 3 airplanes.

(2) After December 31, 1994, at least 25 percent of the fleet on U.S. operations specifications of a new entrant foreign air carrier must comply with Stage 3 noise levels.

(3) After December 31, 1996, at least 50 percent of the fleet on U.S. operations specifications of a new entrant foreign air carrier must comply with Stage 3 noise levels.

(4) After December 31, 1998, at least 75 percent of the fleet on U.S. operations specifications of a new entrant foreign air carrier must comply with Stage 3 noise levels.

(c) Calculations resulting in fractions may be rounded to permit the continued operation of the next whole number of Stage 2 airplanes.

[Doc. No. 26433, 56 FR 48659, Sept. 25, 1991, as amended by Amdt. 91–252, 61 FR 66185, Dec. 16, 1996]

91.869   Carry-forward compliance

(a) Any operator that exceeds the requirements of paragraph (b) of 91.865 of this part on or before December 31, 1994, or on or before December 31, 1996, may claim a credit that may be applied at a subsequent interim compliance date.

(b) Any operator that eliminates or modifies more Stage 2 airplanes pursuant to 91.865(b) than required as of December 31, 1994, or December 31, 1996, may count the number of additional Stage 2 airplanes reduced as a credit toward—

(1) The number of Stage 2 airplanes it would otherwise be required to reduce following a subsequent interim compliance date specified in 91.865(b); or

(2) The number of Stage 3 airplanes it would otherwise be required to operate in its fleet following a subsequent interim compliance date to meet the percentage requirements specified in 91.865(d).

[Doc. No. 26433, 56 FR 48659, Sept. 25, 1991; 56 FR 65783, Dec. 18, 1991]

91.871   Waivers from interim compliance requirements

(a) Any U.S. operator or foreign air carrier subject to the requirements of 91.865 or 91.867 of this subpart may request a waiver from any individual compliance requirement.

(b) Applications must be filed with the Secretary of Transportation at least 120 days prior to the compliance date from which the waiver is requested.

(c) Applicants must show that a grant of waiver would be in the public interest, and must include in its application its plans and activities for modifying its fleet, including evidence of good faith efforts to comply with the requirements of 91.865 or 91.867. The application should contain all information the applicant considers relevant, including, as appropriate, the following:

(1) The applicant's balance sheet and cash flow positions;

(2) The composition of the applicant's current fleet; and

(3) The applicant's delivery position with respect to new airplanes or noise-abatement equipment.

(d) Waivers will be granted only upon a showing by the applicant that compliance with the requirements of 91.865 or 91.867 at a particular interim compliance date is financially onerous, physically impossible, or technologically infeasible, or that it would have an adverse effect on competition or on service to small communities.

(e) The conditions of any waiver granted under this section shall be determined by the circumstances presented in the application, but in no case may the term extend beyond the next interim compliance date.

(f) A summary of any request for a waiver under this section will be published in the Federal Register, and public comment will be invited. Unless the Secretary finds that circumstances require otherwise, the public comment period will be at least 14 days.

[Doc. No. 26433, 56 FR 48660, Sept. 25, 1991]

91.873   Waivers from final compliance

(a) A U.S. air carrier or a foreign air carrier may apply for a waiver from the prohibition contained in 91.853 of this part for its remaining Stage 2 airplanes, provided that, by July 1, 1999, at least 85 percent of the airplanes used by the carrier to provide service to or from an airport in the contiguous United States will comply with the Stage 3 noise levels.

(b) An application for the waiver described in paragraph (a) of this section must be filed with the Secretary of Transportation no later than January 1, 1999, or, in the case of a foreign air carrier, no later than April 20, 2000. Such application must include a plan with firm orders for replacing or modifying all airplanes to comply with Stage 3 noise levels at the earliest practicable time.

(c) To be eligible to apply for the waiver under this section, a new entrant U.S. air carrier must initiate service no later than January 1, 1999, and must comply fully with all provisions of this section.

(d) The Secretary may grant a waiver under this section if the Secretary finds that granting such waiver is in the public interest. In making such a finding, the Secretary shall include consideration of the effect of granting such waiver on competition in the air carrier industry and the effect on small community air service, and any other information submitted by the applicant that the Secretary considers relevant.

(e) The term of any waiver granted under this section shall be determined by the circumstances presented in the application, but in no case will the waiver permit the operation of any Stage 2 airplane covered by this subchapter in the contiguous United States after December 31, 2003.

(f) A summary of any request for a waiver under this section will be published in theFederal Register,and public comment will be invited. Unless the secretary finds that circumstances require otherwise, the public comment period will be at least 14 days.

[Doc. No. 26433, 56 FR 48660, Sept. 25, 1991; 56 FR 51167 Oct. 10, 1991; Amdt. 91–276, 67 FR 46571, July 15, 2002]

91.875 Annual progress reports

(a) Each operator subject to 91.865 or 91.867 of this chapter shall submit an annual report to the FAA, Office of Environment and Energy, on the progress it has made toward complying with the requirements of that section. Such reports shall be submitted no later than 45 days after the end of a calendar year. All progress reports must provide the information through the end of the calendar year, be certified by the operator as true and complete (under penalty of 18 U.S.C. 1001), and include the following information:

(1) The name and address of the operator;

(2) The name, title, and telephone number of the person designated by the operator to be responsible for ensuring the accuracy of the information in the report;

(3) The operator's progress during the reporting period toward compliance with the requirements of 91.853, 91.865 or 91.867. For airplanes on U.S. operations specifications, each operator shall identify the airplanes by type, model, series, and serial number.

   (i) Each Stage 2 airplane added or removed from operation or U.S. operations specifications (grouped separately by those airplanes acquired with and without base level);

   (ii) Each Stage 2 airplane modified to Stage 3 noise levels (identifying the manufacturer and model of noise abatement retrofit equipment;

   (iii) Each Stage 3 airplane on U.S. operations specifications as of the last day of the reporting period; and

   (iv) For each Stage 2 airplane transferred or acquired, the name and address of the recipient or transferor; and, if base level was transferred, the person to or from whom base level was transferred or acquired pursuant to Section 91.863 along with the effective date of each base level transaction, and the type of base level transferred or acquired.

(b) Each operator subject to 91.865 or 91.867 of this chapter shall submit an initial progress report covering the period from January 1, 1990, through December 31, 1991, and provide:

(1) For each operator subject to 91.865:

   (i) The date used to establish its base level pursuant to 91.861(a); and

   (ii) A list of those Stage 2 airplanes (by type, model, series and serial number) in its base level, including adjustments made pursuant to 91.861 after the date its base level was established.

(2) For each U.S. operator:

   (i) A plan to meet the compliance schedules in 91.865 or 91.867 and the final compliance date of 91.853, including the schedule for delivery of replacement Stage 3 airplanes or the installation of noise abatement retrofit equipment; and

   (ii) A separate list (by type, model, series, and serial number) of those airplanes included in the operator's base level, pursuant to 91.861(a)(1) (i) and (ii), under the categories "returned" or "purchased," along with the date each was added to its operations specifications.

(c) Each operator subject to 91.865 or 91.867 of this chapter shall submit subsequent annual progress reports covering the calendar year preceding the report and including any changes in the information provided in paragraphs (a) and (b) of this section; including the use of any carry-forward credits pursuant to 91.869.

(d) An operator may request, in any report, that specific planning data be considered proprietary.

(e) If an operator's actions during any reporting period cause it to achieve compliance with 91.853, the report should include a statement to that effect. Further progress reports are not required unless there is any change in the information reported pursuant to paragraph (a) of this section.

(f) For each U.S. operator subject to 91.865, progress reports submitted for calendar years 1994, 1996, and 1998, shall also state how the operator achieved compliance with the requirements of that section, i.e.—

(1) By reducing the number of Stage 2 airplanes in its fleet to no more than the maximum permitted percentage of its base level under 91.865(b), or

(2) By operating a fleet that consists of at least the minimum required percentage of Stage 3 airplanes under 91.865(d).

(Approved by the Office of Management and Budget under control number 2120–0553)

[Doc. No. 26433, 56 FR 48660, Sept. 25, 1991; 56 FR 51168, Oct. 10, 1991, as amended by 57 FR 5977, Feb. 19, 1992]

91.877 Annual reporting of Hawaiian operations

(a) Each air carrier or foreign air carrier subject to 91.865 or 91.867 of this part that conducts operations between the contiguous United States and the State of Hawaii, between the State of Hawaii and any point outside of the contiguous United States, or between the islands of Hawaii in turnaround service, on or since November 5, 1990, shall include in its annual report the information described in paragraph (c) of this section.

(b) Each air carrier or foreign air carrier not subject to 91.865 or 91.867 of this part that conducts operations between the contiguous U.S. and the State of Hawaii, between the State of Hawaii and any point outside of the contiguous United States, or between the islands of Hawaii in turnaround service, on or since November 5, 1990, shall submit an annual report to the FAA, Office of Environment and Energy, on its compliance with the Hawaiian operations provisions of 49 U.S.C. 47528. Such reports shall be submitted no later than 45 days after the end of a calendar year. All progress reports must provide the information through the end of the calendar year, be certified by the operator as true and complete (under penalty of 18 U.S.C. 1001), and include the following information—

(1) The name and address of the air carrier or foreign air carrier;

(2) The name, title, and telephone number of the person designated by the air carrier or foreign air carrier to be responsible for ensuring the accuracy of the information in the report; and

(3) The information specified in paragraph (c) of this section.

(c) The following information must be included in reports filed pursuant to this section—

(1) For operations conducted between the contiguous United States and the State of Hawaii—

  (i) The number of Stage 2 airplanes used to conduct such operations as of November 5, 1990;

  (ii) Any change to that number during the calendar year being reported, including the date of such change;

(2) For air carriers that conduct inter-island turnaround service in the State of Hawaii—

  (i) The number of Stage 2 airplanes used to conduct such operations as of November 5, 1990;

  (ii) Any change to that number during the calendar year being reported, including the date of such change;

  (iii) For an air carrier that provided inter-island trunaround service within the state of Hawaii on November 5, 1990, the number reported under paragraph (c)(2)(i) of this section may include all Stage 2 airplanes with a maximum certificated takeoff weight of more than 75,000 pounds that were owned or leased by the air carrier on November 5, 1990, regardless of whether such airplanes were operated by that air carrier or foreign air carrier on that date.

(3) For operations conducted between the State of Hawaii and a point outside the contiguous United States—

  (i) The number of Stage 2 airplanes used to conduct such operations as of November 5, 1990; and

  (ii) Any change to that number during the calendar year being reported, including the date of such change.

(d) Reports or amended reports for years predating this regulation are required to be filed concurrently with the next annual report.

[Doc. No. 28213, 61 FR 66185, Dec. 16, 1996]

91.881   Final compliance: Civil subsonic jet airplanes weighing 75,000 pounds or less.

Except as provided in 91.883, after December 31, 2015, a person may not operate to or from an airport in the contiguous United States a civil subsonic jet airplane subject to 91.801(e) of this subpart that weighs less than 75,000 pounds unless that airplane has been shown to comply with Stage 3, Stage 4, or Stage 5 noise levels.

[Docket FAA-2015-3782, Amdt. 91-349, 82 FR 46132, Oct. 4, 2017]

91.883   Special flight authorizations for jet airplanes weighing 75,000 pounds or less.

(a) After December 31, 2015, an operator of a jet airplane weighing 75,000 pounds or less that does not comply with Stage 3 noise levels may, when granted a special flight authorization by the FAA, operate that airplane in the contiguous United States only for one of the following purposes:

(1) To sell, lease, or use the airplane outside the 48 contiguous States;

(2) To scrap the airplane;

(3) To obtain modifications to the airplane to meet Stage 3, Stage 4, or Stage 5 noise levels.

(4) To perform scheduled heavy maintenance or significant modifications on the airplane at a maintenance facility located in the contiguous 48 States;

(5) To deliver the airplane to an operator leasing the airplane from the owner or return the airplane to the lessor;

(6) To prepare, park, or store the airplane in anticipation of any of the activities described in paragraphs (a)(1) through (a)(5) of this section;

(7) To provide transport of persons and goods in the relief of an emergency situation; or

(8) To divert the airplane to an alternative airport in the 48 contiguous States on account of weather, mechanical, fuel, air traffic control, or other safety reasons while conducting a flight in order to perform any of the activities described in paragraphs (a)(1) through (a)(7) of this section.

(b) An operator of an affected airplane may apply for a special flight authorization for one of the purposes listed in paragraph (a) of this section by filing an application with the FAA's Office of Environment and Energy. Except for emergency relief authorizations sought under paragraph (a)(7) of this section, applications must be filed at least 30 days in advance of the planned flight. All applications must provide the information necessary for the FAA to determine that the planned flight is within the limits prescribed in the law.

[Doc. No. FAA-2013-0503, 78 FR 39583, July 2, 2013, as amended by Docket FAA-2015-3782, Amdt. 91-349, 82 FR 46132, Oct. 4, 2017]

91.884-91.899   [Reserved]

Subpart J — Waivers

91.901   [Reserved]

91.903   Policy and procedures

(a) The Administrator may issue a certificate of waiver authorizing the operation of aircraft in deviation from any rule listed in this subpart if the Administrator finds that the proposed operation can be safely conducted under the terms of that certificate of waiver.

(b) An application for a certificate of waiver under this part is made on a form and in a manner prescribed by the Administrator and may be submitted to any FAA office.

(c) A certificate of waiver is effective as specified in that certificate of waiver.

[Doc. No. 18334, 54 FR 34325, Aug. 18, 1989]

91.905   List of rules subject to waivers

Sec.

Sec.	
91.107	Use of safety belts.
91.111	Operating near other aircraft.
91.113	Right-of-way rules: Except water operations.
91.115	Right-of-way rules: Water operations.
91.117	Aircraft speed.
91.119	Minimum safe altitudes: General.
91.121	Altimeter settings.
91.123	Compliance with ATC clearances and instructions.
91.125	ATC light signals.
91.126	Operating on or in the vicinity of an airport in Class G airspace.
91.127	Operating on or in the vicinity of an airport in Class E airspace.
91.129	Operations in Class D airspace.
91.130	Operations in Class C airspace.
91.131	Operations in Class B airspace.
91.133	Restricted and prohibited areas.
91.135	Operations in Class A airspace.
91.137	Temporary flight restrictions.
91.141	Flight restrictions in the proximity of the Presidential and other parties.
91.143	Flight limitation in the proximity of space flight operations.
91.153	VFR flight plan: Information required.
91.155	Basic VFR weather minimums
91.157	Special VFR weather minimums.
91.159	VFR cruising altitude or flight level.
91.169	IFR flight plan: Information required.
91.173	ATC clearance and flight plan required.
91.175	Takeoff and landing under IFR.
91.176	Operations below DA/DH or MDA using an enhanced flight vision system (EFVS) under IFR.
91.177	Minimum altitudes for IFR operations.
91.179	IFR cruising altitude or flight level.
91.181	Course to be flown.
91.183	IFR radio communications.
91.185	IFR operations: Two-way radio communications failure.

FAR 91

91.187	Operation under IFR in controlled airspace: Malfunction reports.
91.209	Aircraft lights.
91.303	Aerobatic flights.
91.305	Flight test areas.
91.311	Towing: Other than under 91.309.
91.313(e)	Restricted category civil aircraft: Operating limitations.
91.515	Flight altitude rules.
91.707	Flights between Mexico or Canada and the United States.
91.713	Operation of civil aircraft of Cuban registry.

[Doc. No. 18334, 54 FR 34325, Aug. 18, 1989, as amended by Amdt. 91–227, 56 FR 65661, Dec. 17, 1991]

91.907-91.999   [Reserved]

Subpart K — Fractional Ownership Operations

Source: Docket No. FAA–2001–10047, 68 FR 54561, Sept. 17, 2003, unless otherwise noted.

91.1001   Applicability

(a) This subpart prescribes rules, in addition to those prescribed in other subparts of this part, that apply to fractional owners and fractional ownership program managers governing—

(1) The provision of program management services in a fractional ownership program;

(2) The operation of a fractional ownership program aircraft in a fractional ownership program; and

(3) The operation of a program aircraft included in a fractional ownership program managed by an affiliate of the manager of the program to which the owner belongs.

(b) As used in this part—

(1) Affiliate of a program manager means a manager that, directly, or indirectly, through one or more intermediaries, controls, is controlled by, or is under common control with, another program manager. The holding of at least forty percent (40 percent) of the equity and forty percent (40 percent) of the voting power of an entity will be presumed to constitute control for purposes of determining an affiliation under this subpart.

(2) A dry-lease aircraft exchange means an arrangement, documented by the written program agreements, under which the program aircraft are available, on an as needed basis without crew, to each fractional owner.

(3) A fractional owner or owner means an individual or entity that possesses a minimum fractional ownership interest in a program aircraft and that has entered into the applicable program agreements; provided, however, that in the case of the flight operations described in paragraph (b)(6)(ii) of this section, and solely for purposes of requirements pertaining to those flight operations, the fractional owner operating the aircraft will be deemed to be a fractional owner in the program managed by the affiliate.

(4) A fractional ownership interest means the ownership of an interest or holding of a multi-year leasehold interest and/or a multi-year leasehold interest that is convertible into an ownership interest in a program aircraft.

(5) A fractional ownership program or program means any system of aircraft ownership and exchange that consists of all of the following elements:

(i) The provision for fractional ownership program management services by a single fractional ownership program manager on behalf of the fractional owners.

(ii) Two or more airworthy aircraft.

(iii) One or more fractional owners per program aircraft, with at least one program aircraft having more than one owner.

(iv) Possession of at least a minimum fractional ownership interest in one or more program aircraft by each fractional owner.

(v) A dry-lease aircraft exchange arrangement among all of the fractional owners.

(vi) Multi-year program agreements covering the fractional ownership, fractional ownership program management services, and dry-lease aircraft exchange aspects of the program.

(6) A fractional ownership program aircraft or program aircraft means:

(i) An aircraft in which a fractional owner has a minimal fractional ownership interest and that has been included in the dry-lease aircraft exchange pursuant to the program agreements, or

(ii) In the case of a fractional owner from one program operating an aircraft in a different fractional ownership program managed by an affiliate of the operating owner's program manager, the aircraft being operated by the fractional owner, so long as the aircraft is:

(A) Included in the fractional ownership program managed by the affiliate of the operating owner's program manager, and

(B) Included in the operating owner's program's dry-lease aircraft exchange pursuant to the program agreements of the operating owner's program.

(iii) An aircraft owned in whole or in part by the program manager that has been included in the dry-lease aircraft exchange and is used to supplement program operations.

(7) A Fractional Ownership Program Flight or Program Flight means a flight under this subpart when one or more passengers or property designated by a fractional owner are on board the aircraft.

(8) Fractional ownership program management services or program management services mean administrative and aviation support services furnished in accordance with the applicable requirements of this subpart or provided by the program manager on behalf of the fractional owners, including, but not limited to, the—

(i) Establishment and implementation of program safety guidelines;

(ii) Employment, furnishing, or contracting of pilots and other crewmembers;

(iii) Training and qualification of pilots and other crewmembers and personnel;

(iv) Scheduling and coordination of the program aircraft and crews;

(v) Maintenance of program aircraft;

(vi) Satisfaction of recordkeeping requirements;

(vii) Development and use of a program operations manual and procedures; and

(viii) Application for and maintenance of management specifications and other authorizations and approvals.

(9) A fractional ownership program manager or program manager means the entity that offers fractional ownership program management services to fractional owners, and is designated in the multi-year program agreements referenced in paragraph (b)(1)(v) of this section to fulfill the requirements of this chapter applicable to the manager of the program containing the aircraft being flown. When a fractional owner is operating an aircraft in a fractional ownership program managed by an affiliate of the owner's program manager, the references in this subpart to the flight-related responsibilities of the program manager apply, with respect to that particular flight, to the affiliate of the owner's program manager rather than to the owner's program manager.

(10) A minimum fractional ownership interest means—

(i) A fractional ownership interest equal to, or greater

than, one-sixteenth (1/16) of at least one subsonic, fixed-wing or powered-lift program aircraft; or

    (ii) A fractional ownership interest equal to, or greater than, one-thirty-second (1/32) of at least one rotorcraft program aircraft.

(c) The rules in this subpart that refer to a fractional owner or a fractional ownership program manager also apply to any person who engages in an operation governed by this subpart without the management specifications required by this subpart.

91.1002 Compliance date

No person that conducted flights before November 17, 2003 under a program that meets the definition of fractional ownership program in 91.1001 may conduct such flights after February 17, 2005 unless it has obtained management specifications under this subpart.

[Doc. No. FAA–2001–10047, 68 FR 54561, Sept. 17, 2003; 69 FR 74413, Dec. 14, 2004]

91.1003 Management contract between owner and program manager

Each owner must have a contract with the program manager that—

(a) Requires the program manager to ensure that the program conforms to all applicable requirements of this chapter.

(b) Provides the owner the right to inspect and to audit, or have a designee of the owner inspect and audit, the records of the program manager pertaining to the operational safety of the program and those records required to show compliance with the management specifications and all applicable regulations. These records include, but are not limited to, the management specifications, authorizations, approvals, manuals, log books, and maintenance records maintained by the program manager.

(c) Designates the program manager as the owner's agent to receive service of notices pertaining to the program that the FAA seeks to provide to owners and authorizes the FAA to send such notices to the program manager in its capacity as the agent of the owner for such service.

(d) Acknowledges the FAA's right to contact the owner directly if the Administrator determines that direct contact is necessary.

91.1005 Prohibitions and limitations

(a) Except as provided in 91.321 or 91.501, no owner may carry persons or property for compensation or hire on a program flight.

(b) During the term of the multi-year program agreements under which a fractional owner has obtained a minimum fractional ownership interest in a program aircraft, the flight hours used during that term by the owner on program aircraft must not exceed the total hours associated with the fractional owner's share of ownership.

(c) No person may sell or lease an aircraft interest in a fractional ownership program that is smaller than that prescribed in the definition of "minimum fractional ownership interest" in 91.1001(b)(10) unless flights associated with that interest are operated under part 121 or 135 of this chapter and are conducted by an air carrier or commercial operator certificated under part 119 of this chapter.

91.1007 Flights conducted under part 121 or part 135 of this chapter

(a) Except as provided in 91.501(b), when a nonprogram aircraft is used to substitute for a program flight, the flight must be operated in compliance with part 121 or part 135 of this chapter, as applicable.

(b) A program manager who holds a certificate under part 119 of this chapter may conduct a flight for the use of a fractional owner under part 121 or part 135 of this chapter if the aircraft is listed on that certificate holder's operations specifications for part 121 or part 135, as applicable.

(c) The fractional owner must be informed when a flight is being conducted as a program flight or is being conducted under part 121 or part 135 of this chapter.

Operational Control

91.1009 Clarification of operational control

(a) An owner is in operational control of a program flight when the owner—

    (1) Has the rights and is subject to the limitations set forth in 91.1003 through 91.1013;

    (2) Has directed that a program aircraft carry passengers or property designated by that owner; and

    (3) The aircraft is carrying those passengers or property.

(b) An owner is not in operational control of a flight in the following circumstances:

    (1) A program aircraft is used for a flight for administrative purposes such as demonstration, positioning, ferrying, maintenance, or crew training, and no passengers or property designated by such owner are being carried; or

    (2) The aircraft being used for the flight is being operated under part 121 or 135 of this chapter.

91.1011 Operational control responsibilities and delegation

(a) Each owner in operational control of a program flight is ultimately responsible for safe operations and for complying with all applicable requirements of this chapter, including those related to airworthiness and operations in connection with the flight. Each owner may delegate some or all of the performance of the tasks associated with carrying out this responsibility to the program manager, and may rely on the program manager for aviation expertise and program management services. When the owner delegates performance of tasks to the program manager or relies on the program manager's expertise, the owner and the program manager are jointly and individually responsible for compliance.

(b) The management specifications, authorizations, and approvals required by this subpart are issued to, and in the sole name of, the program manager on behalf of the fractional owners collectively. The management specifications, authorizations, and approvals will not be affected by any change in ownership of a program aircraft, as long as the aircraft remains a program aircraft in the identified program.

91.1013 Operational control briefing and acknowledgment

(a) Upon the signing of an initial program management services contract, or a renewal or extension of a program management services contract, the program manager must brief the fractional owner on the owner's operational control responsibilities, and the owner must review and sign an acknowledgment of these operational control responsibilities. The acknowledgment must be included with the program management services contract. The acknowledgment must define when a fractional owner is in operational control and the owner's responsibilities and liabilities under the program. These include:

    (1) Responsibility for compliance with the management specifications and all applicable regulations.

    (2) Enforcement actions for any noncompliance.

    (3) Liability risk in the event of a flight-related occurrence that causes personal injury or property damage.

(b) The fractional owner's signature on the acknowledgment will serve as the owner's affirmation that the owner has read, understands, and accepts the operational control responsibilities described in the acknowledgment.

(c) Each program manager must ensure that the fractional owner or owner's representatives have access to the acknowledgments for such owner's program aircraft. Each program manager must ensure that the FAA has access to the acknowledgments for all program aircraft.

Program Management

91.1014 Issuing or denying management specifications

(a) A person applying to the Administrator for management specifications under this subpart must submit an application—

   (1) In a form and manner prescribed by the Administrator; and

   (2) Containing any information the Administrator requires the applicant to submit.

(b) Management specifications will be issued to the program manager on behalf of the fractional owners if, after investigation, the Administrator finds that the applicant:

   (1) Meets the applicable requirements of this subpart; and

   (2) Is properly and adequately equipped in accordance with the requirements of this chapter and is able to conduct safe operations under appropriate provisions of part 91 of this chapter and management specifications issued under this subpart.

(c) An application for management specifications will be denied if the Administrator finds that the applicant is not properly or adequately equipped or is not able to conduct safe operations under this part.

91.1015 Management specifications

(a) Each person conducting operations under this subpart or furnishing fractional ownership program management services to fractional owners must do so in accordance with management specifications issued by the Administrator to the fractional ownership program manager under this subpart. Management specifications must include:

   (1) The current list of all fractional owners and types of aircraft, registration markings and serial numbers;

   (2) The authorizations, limitations, and certain procedures under which these operations are to be conducted,

   (3) Certain other procedures under which each class and size of aircraft is to be operated;

   (4) Authorization for an inspection program approved under 91.1109, including the type of aircraft, the registration markings and serial numbers of each aircraft to be operated under the program. No person may conduct any program flight using any aircraft not listed.

   (5) Time limitations, or standards for determining time limitations, for overhauls, inspections, and checks for airframes, engines, propellers, rotors, appliances, and emergency equipment of aircraft.

   (6) The specific location of the program manager's principal base of operations and, if different, the address that will serve as the primary point of contact for correspondence between the FAA and the program manager and the name and mailing address of the program manager's agent for service;

   (7) Other business names the program manager may use;

   (8) Authorization for the method of controlling weight and balance of aircraft;

   (9) Any authorized deviation and exemption granted from any requirement of this chapter; and

   (10) Any other information the Administrator determines is necessary.

(b) The program manager may keep the current list of all fractional owners required by paragraph (a)(1) of this section at its principal base of operation or other location approved by the Administrator and referenced in its management specifications. Each program manager shall make this list of owners available for inspection by the Administrator.

(c) Management specifications issued under this subpart are effective unless—

   (1) The management specifications are amended as provided in 91.1017; or

   (2) The Administrator suspends or revokes the management specifications.

(d) At least 30 days before it proposes to establish or change the location of its principal base of operations, its main operations base, or its main maintenance base, a program manager must provide written notification to the Flight Standards office that issued the program manager's management specifications.

(e) Each program manager must maintain a complete and separate set of its management specifications at its principal base of operations, or at a place approved by the Administrator, and must make its management specifications available for inspection by the Administrator and the fractional owner(s) to whom the program manager furnishes its services for review and audit.

(f) Each program manager must insert pertinent excerpts of its management specifications, or references thereto, in its program manual and must—

   (1) Clearly identify each such excerpt as a part of its management specifications; and

   (2) State that compliance with each management specifications requirement is mandatory.

(g) Each program manager must keep each of its employees and other persons who perform duties material to its operations informed of the provisions of its management specifications that apply to that employee's or person's duties and responsibilities.

(h) A program manager may obtain approval to provide a temporary document verifying a flightcrew member's airman certificate and medical certificate privileges under an approved certificate verification plan set forth in the program manager's management specifications. A document provided by the program manager may be carried as an airman certificate or medical certificate on flights within the United States for up to 72 hours.

[Docket No. FAA-2001-10047, 68 FR 54561, Sept. 17, 2003, as amended by Docket FAA-2018-0119, Amdt. 91-350, 83 FR 9171 Mar. 5, 2018]

91.1017 Amending program manager's management specifications

(a) The Administrator may amend any management specifications issued under this subpart if—

   (1) The Administrator determines that safety and the public interest require the amendment of any management specifications; or

   (2) The program manager applies for the amendment of any management specifications, and the Administrator determines that safety and the public interest allows the amendment.

(b) Except as provided in paragraph (e) of this section, when the Administrator initiates an amendment of a program manager's management specifications, the following procedure applies:

   (1) The Flight Standards office that issued the program manager's management specifications will notify the program manager in writing of the proposed amendment.

   (2) The Flight Standards office that issued the program manager's management specifications will set a reasonable period (but not less than 7 days) within which the program manager may submit written information, views, and arguments on the amendment.

   (3) After considering all material presented, the Flight Standards office that issued the program manager's management specifications will notify the program manager of—

      (i) The adoption of the proposed amendment,

      (ii) The partial adoption of the proposed amendment, or

      (iii) The withdrawal of the proposed amendment.

   (4) If the Flight Standards office that issued the program manager's management specifications issues an amendment of the management specifications, it becomes effective not less than 30 days after the program manager receives notice of it unless—

      (i) The Flight Standards office that issued the program manager's management specifications finds under paragraph (e) of this section that there is an emergency requiring immediate action with respect to safety; or

    (ii) The program manager petitions for reconsideration of the amendment under paragraph (d) of this section.

(c) When the program manager applies for an amendment to its management specifications, the following procedure applies:

  (1) The program manager must file an application to amend its management specifications—

    (i) At least 90 days before the date proposed by the applicant for the amendment to become effective, unless a shorter time is approved, in cases such as mergers, acquisitions of operational assets that require an additional showing of safety (for example, proving tests or validation tests), and resumption of operations following a suspension of operations as a result of bankruptcy actions.

    (ii) At least 15 days before the date proposed by the applicant for the amendment to become effective in all other cases.

  (2) The application must be submitted to the Flight Standards office that issued the program manager's management specifications in a form and manner prescribed by the Administrator.

  (3) After considering all material presented, the Flight Standards office that issued the program manager's management specifications will notify the program manager of—

    (i) The adoption of the applied for amendment;

    (ii) The partial adoption of the applied for amendment; or

    (iii) The denial of the applied for amendment. The program manager may petition for reconsideration of a denial under paragraph (d) of this section.

  (4) If the Flight Standards office that issued the program manager's management specifications approves the amendment, following coordination with the program manager regarding its implementation, the amendment is effective on the date the Administrator approves it.

(d) When a program manager seeks reconsideration of a decision of the Flight Standards office that issued the program manager's management specifications concerning the amendment of management specifications, the following procedure applies:

  (1) The program manager must petition for reconsideration of that decision within 30 days of the date that the program manager receives a notice of denial of the amendment of its management specifications, or of the date it receives notice of an FAA-initiated amendment of its management specifications, whichever circumstance applies.

  (2) The program manager must address its petition to the Executive Director, Flight Standards Service.

  (3) A petition for reconsideration, if filed within the 30-day period, suspends the effectiveness of any amendment issued by the Flight Standards office that issued the program manager's management specifications unless that office has found, under paragraph (e) of this section, that an emergency exists requiring immediate action with respect to safety.

  (4) If a petition for reconsideration is not filed within 30 days, the procedures of paragraph (c) of this section apply.

(e) If the Flight Standards office that issued the program manager's management specifications finds that an emergency exists requiring immediate action with respect to safety that makes the procedures set out in this section impracticable or contrary to the public interest—

  (1) The Flight Standards office amends the management specifications and makes the amendment effective on the day the program manager receives notice of it; and

  (2) In the notice to the program manager, the Flight Standards office will articulate the reasons for its finding that an emergency exists requiring immediate action with respect to safe-

ty or that makes it impracticable or contrary to the public interest to stay the effectiveness of the amendment.

[Docket No. FAA-2001-10047, 68 FR 54561, Sept. 17, 2003, as amended by Docket FAA-2018-0119, Amdt. 91-350, 83 FR 9171, Mar. 5, 2018]

91.1019 Conducting tests and inspections

(a) At any time or place, the Administrator may conduct an inspection or test, other than an en route inspection, to determine whether a program manager under this subpart is complying with title 49 of the United States Code, applicable regulations, and the program manager's management specifications.

(b) The program manager must—

  (1) Make available to the Administrator at the program manager's principal base of operations, or at a place approved by the Administrator, the program manager's management specifications; and

  (2) Allow the Administrator to make any test or inspection, other than an en route inspection, to determine compliance respecting any matter stated in paragraph (a) of this section.

(c) Each employee of, or person used by, the program manager who is responsible for maintaining the program manager's records required by or necessary to demonstrate compliance with this subpart must make those records available to the Administrator.

(d) The Administrator may determine a program manager's continued eligibility to hold its management specifications on any grounds listed in paragraph (a) of this section, or any other appropriate grounds.

(e) Failure by any program manager to make available to the Administrator upon request, the management specifications, or any required record, document, or report is grounds for suspension of all or any part of the program manager's management specifications.

91.1021 Internal safety reporting and incident/accident response

(a) Each program manager must establish an internal anonymous safety reporting procedure that fosters an environment of safety without any potential for retribution for filing the report.

(b) Each program manager must establish procedures to respond to an aviation incident/accident.

91.1023 Program operating manual requirements

(a) Each program manager must prepare and keep current a program operating manual setting forth procedures and policies acceptable to the Administrator. The program manager's management, flight, ground, and maintenance personnel must use this manual to conduct operations under this subpart. However, the Administrator may authorize a deviation from this paragraph if the Administrator finds that, because of the limited size of the operation, part of the manual is not necessary for guidance of management, flight, ground, or maintenance personnel.

(b) Each program manager must maintain at least one copy of the manual at its principal base of operations.

(c) No manual may be contrary to any applicable U.S. regulations, foreign regulations applicable to the program flights in foreign countries, or the program manager's management specifications.

(d) The program manager must make a copy of the manual, or appropriate portions of the manual (and changes and additions), available to its maintenance and ground operations personnel and must furnish the manual to—

  (1) Its crewmembers; and

  (2) Representatives of the Administrator assigned to the program manager.

(e) Each employee of the program manager to whom a manual or appropriate portions of it are furnished under paragraph (d)(1) of this section must keep it up-to-date with the changes and additions furnished to them.

(f) Except as provided in paragraph (h) of this section, the appropriate parts of the manual must be carried on each aircraft when away from the principal operations base. The appropriate parts must be available for use by ground or flight personnel.

(g) For the purpose of complying with paragraph (d) of this section, a program manager may furnish the persons listed therein with all or part of its manual in printed form or other form, acceptable to the Administrator, that is retrievable in the English language. If the program manager furnishes all or part of the manual in other than printed form, it must ensure there is a compatible reading device available to those persons that provides a legible image of the maintenance information and instructions, or a system that is able to retrieve the maintenance information and instructions in the English language.

(h) If a program manager conducts aircraft inspections or maintenance at specified facilities where the approved aircraft inspection program is available, the program manager is not required to ensure that the approved aircraft inspection program is carried aboard the aircraft en route to those facilities.

(i) Program managers that are also certificated to operate under part 121 or 135 of this chapter may be authorized to use the operating manual required by those parts to meet the manual requirements of subpart K, provided:

(1) The policies and procedures are consistent for both operations, or

(2) When policies and procedures are different, the applicable policies and procedures are identified and used.

91.1025   Program operating manual contents

Each program operating manual must have the date of the last revision on each revised page. Unless otherwise authorized by the Administrator, the manual must include the following:

(a) Procedures for ensuring compliance with aircraft weight and balance limitations;

(b) Copies of the program manager's management specifications or appropriate extracted information, including area of operations authorized, category and class of aircraft authorized, crew complements, and types of operations authorized;

(c) Procedures for complying with accident notification requirements;

(d) Procedures for ensuring that the pilot in command knows that required airworthiness inspections have been made and that the aircraft has been approved for return to service in compliance with applicable maintenance requirements;

(e) Procedures for reporting and recording mechanical irregularities that come to the attention of the pilot in command before, during, and after completion of a flight;

(f) Procedures to be followed by the pilot in command for determining that mechanical irregularities or defects reported for previous flights have been corrected or that correction of certain mechanical irregularities or defects have been deferred;

(g) Procedures to be followed by the pilot in command to obtain maintenance, preventive maintenance, and servicing of the aircraft at a place where previous arrangements have not been made by the program manager or owner, when the pilot is authorized to so act for the operator;

(h) Procedures under 91.213 for the release of, and continuation of flight if any item of equipment required for the particular type of operation becomes inoperative or unserviceable en route;

(i) Procedures for refueling aircraft, eliminating fuel contamination, protecting from fire (including electrostatic protection), and supervising and protecting passengers during refueling;

(j) Procedures to be followed by the pilot in command in the briefing under 91.1035.

(k) Procedures for ensuring compliance with emergency procedures, including a list of the functions assigned each category of required crewmembers in connection with an emergency and emergency evacuation duties;

(l) The approved aircraft inspection program, when applicable;

(m) Procedures for the evacuation of persons who may need the assistance of another person to move expeditiously to an exit if an emergency occurs;

(n) Procedures for performance planning that take into account take off, landing and en route conditions;

(o) An approved Destination Airport Analysis, when required by 91.1037(c), that includes the following elements, supported by aircraft performance data supplied by the aircraft manufacturer for the appropriate runway conditions—

(1) Pilot qualifications and experience;

(2) Aircraft performance data to include normal, abnormal and emergency procedures as supplied by the aircraft manufacturer;

(3) Airport facilities and topography;

(4) Runway conditions (including contamination);

(5) Airport or area weather reporting;

(6) Appropriate additional runway safety margins, if required;

(7) Airplane inoperative equipment;

(8) Environmental conditions; and

(9) Other criteria that affect aircraft performance.

(p) A suitable system (which may include a coded or electronic system) that provides for preservation and retrieval of maintenance recordkeeping information required by 91.1113 in a manner acceptable to the Administrator that provides—

(1) A description (or reference to date acceptable to the Administrator) of the work performed:

(2) The name of the person performing the work if the work is performed by a person outside the organization of the program manager; and

(3) The name or other positive identification of the individual approving the work.

(q) Flight locating and scheduling procedures; and

(r) Other procedures and policy instructions regarding program operations that are issued by the program manager or required by the Administrator.

91.1027   Record keeping

(a) Each program manager must keep at its principal base of operations or at other places approved by the Administrator, and must make available for inspection by the Administrator all of the following:

(1) The program manager's management specifications.

(2) A current list of the aircraft used or available for use in operations under this subpart, the operations for which each is equipped (for example, RNP5/10, RVSM.).

(3) An individual record of each pilot used in operations under this subpart, including the following information:

(i) The full name of the pilot.

(ii) The pilot certificate (by type and number) and ratings that the pilot holds.

(iii) The pilot's aeronautical experience in sufficient detail to determine the pilot's qualifications to pilot aircraft in operations under this subpart.

(iv) The pilot's current duties and the date of the pilot's assignment to those duties.

(v) The effective date and class of the medical certificate that the pilot holds.

(vi) The date and result of each of the initial and recurrent competency tests and proficiency checks required by this subpart and the type of aircraft flown during that test or check.

(vii) The pilot's flight time in sufficient detail to determine compliance with the flight time limitations of this subpart.

(viii) The pilot's check pilot authorization, if any.

(ix) Any action taken concerning the pilot's release from employ-ment for physical or professional disqualification; and

(x) The date of the satisfactory completion of initial, transition, upgrade, and differences training and each recurrent training phase required by this subpart.

(4) An individual record for each flight attendant used in operations under this subpart, including the following information:

(i) The full name of the flight attendant, and

(ii) The date and result of training required by 91.1063, as applicable.

(5) A current list of all fractional owners and associated aircraft. This list or a reference to its location must be included in the management specifications and should be of sufficient detail to determine the minimum fractional ownership interest of each aircraft.

(b) Each program manager must keep each record required by paragraph (a)(2) of this section for at least 6 months, and must keep each record required by paragraphs (a)(3) and (a)(4) of this section for at least 12 months. When an employee is no longer employed or affiliated with the program manager or fractional owner, each record required by paragraphs (a)(3) and (a)(4) of this section must be retained for at least 12 months.

(c) Each program manager is responsible for the preparation and accuracy of a load manifest in duplicate containing information concerning the loading of the aircraft. The manifest must be prepared before each takeoff and must include—

(1) The number of passengers;

(2) The total weight of the loaded aircraft;

(3) The maximum allowable takeoff weight for that flight;

(4) The center of gravity limits;

(5) The center of gravity of the loaded aircraft, except that the actual center of gravity need not be computed if the aircraft is loaded according to a loading schedule or other approved method that ensures that the center of gravity of the loaded aircraft is within approved limits. In those cases, an entry must be made on the manifest indicating that the center of gravity is within limits according to a loading schedule or other approved method;

(6) The registration number of the aircraft or flight number;

(7) The origin and destination; and

(8) Identification of crewmembers and their crew position assignments.

(d) The pilot in command of the aircraft for which a load manifest must be prepared must carry a copy of the completed load manifest in the aircraft to its destination. The program manager must keep copies of completed load manifest for at least 30 days at its principal operations base, or at another location used by it and approved by the Administrator.

(e) Each program manager is responsible for providing a written document that states the name of the entity having operational control on that flight and the part of this chapter under which the flight is operated. The pilot in command of the aircraft must carry a copy of the document in the aircraft to its destination. The program manager must keep a copy of the document for at least 30 days at its principal operations base, or at another location used by it and approved by the Administrator.

(f) Records may be kept either in paper or other form acceptable to the Administrator.

(g) Program managers that are also certificated to operate under part 121 or 135 of this chapter may satisfy the recordkeeping requirements of this section and of 91.1113 with records maintained to fulfill equivalent obligations under part 121 or 135 of this chapter.

91.1029 Flight scheduling and locating requirements

(a) Each program manager must establish and use an adequate system to schedule and release program aircraft.

(b) Except as provided in paragraph (d) of this section, each program manager must have adequate procedures established for locating each flight, for which a flight plan is not filed, that—

(1) Provide the program manager with at least the information required to be included in a VFR flight plan;

(2) Provide for timely notification of an FAA facility or search and rescue facility, if an aircraft is overdue or missing; and

(3) Provide the program manager with the location, date, and estimated time for reestablishing radio or telephone communications, if the flight will operate in an area where communications cannot be maintained.

(c) Flight locating information must be retained at the program manager's principal base of operations, or at other places designated by the program manager in the flight locating procedures, until the completion of the flight.

(d) The flight locating requirements of paragraph (b) of this section do not apply to a flight for which an FAA flight plan has been filed and the flight plan is canceled within 25 nautical miles of the destination airport.

91.1031 Pilot in command or second in command: designation required

(a) Each program manager must designate a—

(1) Pilot in command for each program flight; and

(2) Second in command for each program flight requiring two pilots.

(b) The pilot in command, as designated by the program manager, must remain the pilot in command at all times during that flight.

91.1033 Operating information required

(a) Each program manager must, for all program operations, provide the following materials, in current and appropriate form, accessible to the pilot at the pilot station, and the pilot must use them—

(1) A cockpit checklist;

(2) For multiengine aircraft or for aircraft with retractable landing gear, an emergency cockpit checklist containing the procedures required by paragraph (c) of this section, as appropriate;

(3) At least one set of pertinent aeronautical charts; and

(4) For IFR operations, at least one set of pertinent navigational en route, terminal area, and instrument approach procedure charts.

(b) Each cockpit checklist required by paragraph (a)(1) of this section must contain the following procedures:

(1) Before starting engines;

(2) Before takeoff;

(3) Cruise;

(4) Before landing;

(5) After landing; and

(6) Stopping engines.

FAR 91

(c) Each emergency cockpit checklist required by paragraph (a)(2) of this section must contain the following procedures, as appropriate:

(1) Emergency operation of fuel, hydraulic, electrical, and mechanical systems.

(2) Emergency operation of instruments and controls.

(3) Engine inoperative procedures.

(4) Any other emergency procedures necessary for safety.

91.1035 Passenger awareness

(a) Prior to each takeoff, the pilot in command of an aircraft carrying passengers on a program flight must ensure that all passengers have been orally briefed on—

288   *Part 91—General Operating and Flight Rules*

(1) Smoking: Each passenger must be briefed on when, where, and under what conditions smoking is prohibited. This briefing must include a statement, as appropriate, that the regulations require passenger compliance with lighted passenger information signs and no smoking placards, prohibit smoking in lavatories, and require compliance with crewmember instructions with regard to these items;

(2) Use of safety belts, shoulder harnesses, and child restraint systems: Each passenger must be briefed on when, where and under what conditions it is necessary to have his or her safety belt and, if installed, his or her shoulder harness fastened about him or her, and if a child is being transported, the appropriate use of child restraint systems, if available. This briefing must include a statement, as appropriate, that the regulations require passenger compliance with the lighted passenger information sign and/or crewmember instructions with regard to these items;

(3) The placement of seat backs in an upright position before takeoff and landing;

(4) Location and means for opening the passenger entry door and emergency exits;

(5) Location of survival equipment;

(6) Ditching procedures and the use of flotation equipment required under 91.509 for a flight over water;

(7) The normal and emergency use of oxygen installed in the aircraft; and

(8) Location and operation of fire extinguishers.

(b) Prior to each takeoff, the pilot in command of an aircraft carrying passengers on a program flight must ensure that each person who may need the assistance of another person to move expeditiously to an exit if an emergency occurs and that person's attendant, if any, has received a briefing as to the procedures to be followed if an evacuation occurs. This paragraph does not apply to a person who has been given a briefing before a previous leg of that flight in the same aircraft.

(c) Prior to each takeoff, the pilot in command must advise the passengers of the name of the entity in operational control of the flight.

(d) The oral briefings required by paragraphs (a), (b), and (c) of this section must be given by the pilot in command or another crewmember.

(e) The oral briefing required by paragraph (a) of this section may be delivered by means of an approved recording playback device that is audible to each passenger under normal noise levels.

(f) The oral briefing required by paragraph (a) of this section must be supplemented by printed cards that must be carried in the aircraft in locations convenient for the use of each passenger. The cards must—

(1) Be appropriate for the aircraft on which they are to be used;

(2) Contain a diagram of, and method of operating, the emergency exits; and

(3) Contain other instructions necessary for the use of emergency equipment on board the aircraft.

91.1037   Large transport category airplanes: turbine engine powered; Limitations; Destination and alternate airports

(a) No program manager or any other person may permit a turbine engine powered large transport category airplane on a program flight to take off that airplane at a weight that (allowing for normal consumption of fuel and oil in flight to the destination or alternate airport) the weight of the airplane on arrival would exceed the landing weight in the Airplane Flight Manual for the elevation of the destination or alternate airport and the ambient temperature expected at the time of landing.

(b) Except as provided in paragraph (c) of this section, no program manager or any other person may permit a turbine engine powered large transport category airplane on a program flight to take off that airplane unless its weight on arrival, allowing for normal consumption of fuel and oil in flight (in accordance with the landing distance in the Airplane Flight Manual for the elevation of the destination airport and the wind conditions expected there at the time of landing), would allow a full stop landing at the intended destination airport within 60 percent of the effective length of each runway described below from a point 50 feet above the intersection of the obstruction clearance plane and the runway. For the purpose of determining the allowable landing weight at the destination airport, the following is assumed:

(1) The airplane is landed on the most favorable runway and in the most favorable direction, in still air.

(2) The airplane is landed on the most suitable runway considering the probable wind velocity and direction and the ground handling characteristics of that airplane, and considering other conditions such as landing aids and terrain.

(c) A program manager or other person flying a turbine engine powered large transport category airplane on a program flight may permit that airplane to take off at a weight in excess of that allowed by paragraph (b) of this section if all of the following conditions exist:

(1) The operation is conducted in accordance with an approved Destination Airport Analysis in that person's program operating manual that contains the elements listed in 91.1025(o).

(2) The airplane's weight on arrival, allowing for normal consumption of fuel and oil in flight (in accordance with the landing distance in the Airplane Flight Manual for the elevation of the destination airport and the wind conditions expected there at the time of landing), would allow a full stop landing at the intended destination airport within 80 percent of the effective length of each runway described below from a point 50 feet above the intersection of the obstruction clearance plane and the runway. For the purpose of determining the allowable landing weight at the destination airport, the following is assumed:

(i) The airplane is landed on the most favorable runway and in the most favorable direction, in still air.

(ii) The airplane is landed on the most suitable runway considering the probable wind velocity and direction and the ground handling characteristics of that airplane, and considering other conditions such as landing aids and terrain.

(3) The operation is authorized by management specifications.

(d) No program manager or other person may select an airport as an alternate airport for a turbine engine powered large transport category airplane unless (based on the assumptions in paragraph (b) of this section) that airplane, at the weight expected at the time of arrival, can be brought to a full stop landing within 80 percent of the effective length of the runway from a point 50 feet above the intersection of the obstruction clearance plane and the runway.

(e) Unless, based on a showing of actual operating landing techniques on wet runways, a shorter landing distance (but never less than that required by paragraph (b) or (c) of this section) has been approved for a specific type and model airplane and included in the Airplane Flight Manual, no person may take off a turbojet airplane when the appropriate weather reports or forecasts, or any combination of them, indicate that the runways at the destination or alternate airport may be wet or slippery at the estimated time of arrival unless the effective runway length at the destination airport is at least 115 percent of the runway length required under paragraph (b) or (c) of this section.

91.1039   IFR takeoff, approach and landing minimums

(a) No pilot on a program aircraft operating a program flight may begin an instrument approach procedure to an airport unless—

(1) Either that airport or the alternate airport has a weather reporting facility operated by the U.S. National Weather Service, a source approved by the U.S. National Weather Service, or a source approved by the Administrator; and

(2) The latest weather report issued by the weather reporting facility includes a current local altimeter setting for the destination airport. If no local altimeter setting is available at the destination airport, the pilot must obtain the current local altimeter setting from a source provided by the facility designated on the approach chart for the destination airport.

(b) For flight planning purposes, if the destination airport does not have a weather reporting facility described in paragraph (a)(1) of this section, the pilot must designate as an alternate an airport that has a weather reporting facility meeting that criteria.

(c) The MDA or Decision Altitude and visibility landing minimums prescribed in part 97 of this chapter or in the program manager's management specifications are increased by 100 feet and 1/2 mile respectively, but not to exceed the ceiling and visibility minimums for that airport when used as an alternate airport, for each pilot in command of a turbine-powered aircraft who has not served at least 100 hours as pilot in command in that type of aircraft.

(d) No person may take off an aircraft under IFR from an airport where weather conditions are at or above takeoff minimums but are below authorized IFR landing minimums unless there is an alternate airport within one hour's flying time (at normal cruising speed, in still air) of the airport of departure.

(e) Except as provided in 91.175(l) or 91.176 of this chapter, each pilot making an IFR takeoff or approach and landing at an airport must comply with applicable instrument approach procedures and takeoff and landing weather minimums prescribed by the authority having jurisdiction over the airport. In addition, no pilot may take off at that airport when the visibility is less than 600 feet, unless otherwise authorized in the program manager's management specifications for EFVS operations.

[Docket No. FAA-2001-10047, 68 FR 54561, Sept. 17, 2003, as amended by Docket FAA-2013-0485, Amdt. 91-345, 81 FR 90175, Dec. 13, 2016]

91.1041 Aircraft proving and validation tests

(a) No program manager may permit the operation of an aircraft, other than a turbojet aircraft, for which two pilots are required by the type certification requirements of this chapter for operations under VFR, if it has not previously proved such an aircraft in operations under this part in at least 25 hours of proving tests acceptable to the Administrator including—

(1) Five hours of night time, if night flights are to be authorized;

(2) Five instrument approach procedures under simulated or actual conditions, if IFR flights are to be authorized; and

(3) Entry into a representative number of en route airports as determined by the Administrator.

(b) No program manager may permit the operation of a turbojet airplane if it has not previously proved a turbojet airplane in operations under this part in at least 25 hours of proving tests acceptable to the Administrator including—

(1) Five hours of night time, if night flights are to be authorized;

(2) Five instrument approach procedures under simulated or actual conditions, if IFR flights are to be authorized; and

(3) Entry into a representative number of en route airports as determined by the Administrator.

(c) No program manager may carry passengers in an aircraft during proving tests, except those needed to make the tests and those designated by the Administrator to observe the tests. However, pilot flight training may be conducted during the proving tests.

(d) Validation testing is required to determine that a program manager is capable of conducting operations safely and in compliance with applicable regulatory standards. Validation tests are required for the following authorizations:

(1) The addition of an aircraft for which two pilots are required for operations under VFR or a turbojet airplane, if that aircraft or an aircraft of the same make or similar design has not been previously proved or validated in operations under this part.

(2) Operations outside U.S. airspace.

(3) Class II navigation authorizations.

(4) Special performance or operational authorizations.

(e) Validation tests must be accomplished by test methods acceptable to the Administrator. Actual flights may not be required when an applicant can demonstrate competence and compliance with appropriate regulations without conducting a flight.

(f) Proving tests and validation tests may be conducted simultaneously when appropriate.

(g) The Administrator may authorize deviations from this section if the Administrator finds that special circumstances make full compliance with this section unnecessary.

91.1043 [Reserved]

91.1045 Additional equipment requirements

No person may operate a program aircraft on a program flight unless the aircraft is equipped with the following—

(a) Airplanes having a passenger-seat configuration of more than 30 seats or a payload capacity of more than 7,500 pounds:

(1) A cockpit voice recorder as required by 121.359 of this chapter as applicable to the aircraft specified in that section.

(2) A flight recorder as required by 121.343 or 121.344 of this chapter as applicable to the aircraft specified in that section.

(3) A terrain awareness and warning system as required by 121.354 of this chapter as applicable to the aircraft specified in that section.

(4) A traffic alert and collision avoidance system as required by 121.356 of this chapter as applicable to the aircraft specified in that section.

(5) Airborne weather radar as required by 121.357 of this chapter, as applicable to the aircraft specified in that section.

(b) Airplanes having a passenger-seat configuration of 30 seats or fewer, excluding each crewmember, and a payload capacity of 7,500 pounds or less, and any rotorcraft (as applicable):

(1) A cockpit voice recorder as required by 135.151 of this chapter as applicable to the aircraft specified in that section.

(2) A flight recorder as required by 135.152 of this chapter as applicable to the aircraft specified in that section.

(3) A terrain awareness and warning system as required by 135.154 of this chapter as applicable to the aircraft specified in that section.

(4) A traffic alert and collision avoidance system as required by 135.180 of this chapter as applicable to the aircraft specified in that section.

(5) As applicable to the aircraft specified in that section, either:

(i) Airborne thunderstorm detection equipment as required by 135.173 of this chapter; or

(ii) Airborne weather radar as required by 135.175 of this chapter.

91.1047 Drug and alcohol misuse education program

(a) Each program manager must provide each direct employee performing flight crewmember, flight attendant, flight instructor, or aircraft maintenance duties with drug and alcohol misuse education.

(b) No program manager may use any contract employee to perform flight crewmember, flight attendant, flight instructor, or aircraft maintenance duties for the program manager unless that contract employee has been provided with drug and alcohol misuse education.

(c) Program managers must disclose to their owners and prospective owners the existence of a company drug and alcohol misuse testing program. If the program manager has implemented a company testing program, the program manager's disclosure must include the following:

(1) Information on the substances that they test for, for example, alcohol and a list of the drugs;

(2) The categories of employees tested, the types of tests, for example, pre-employment, random, reasonable cause/suspicion, post accident, return to duty and follow-up; and

(3) The degree to which the program manager's company testing program is comparable to the federally mandated drug and alcohol testing program required under part 120 of this chapter, regarding the information in paragraphs (c)(1) and (c)(2) of this section.

(d) If a program aircraft is operated on a program flight into an airport at which no maintenance personnel are available that are subject to the requirements of paragraphs (a) or (b) of this section and emergency maintenance is required, the program manager may use persons not meeting the requirements of paragraphs (a) or (b) of this section to provide such emergency maintenance under both of the following conditions:

(1) The program manager must notify the Drug Abatement Program Division, AAM–800, 800 Independence Avenue, SW., Washington, DC 20591 in writing within 10 days after being provided emergency maintenance in accordance with this paragraph. The program manager must retain copies of all such written notifications for two years.

(2) The aircraft must be reinspected by maintenance personnel who meet the requirements of paragraph (a) or (b) of this section when the aircraft is next at an airport where such maintenance personnel are available.

(e) For purposes of this section, emergency maintenance means maintenance that—

(1) Is not scheduled, and

(2) Is made necessary by an aircraft condition not discovered prior to the departure for that location.

(f) Notwithstanding paragraphs (a) and (b) of this section, drug and alcohol misuse education conducted under an FAA-approved drug and alcohol misuse prevention program may be used to satisfy these requirements.

[Docket No. FAA-2001-10047, 68 FR 54561, Sept. 17, 2003, as amended by Amdt. 91-307, 74 FR 22653, May 14, 2009]

91.1049   Personnel

(a) Each program manager and each fractional owner must use in program operations on program aircraft flight crews meeting 91.1053 criteria and qualified under the appropriate regulations. The program manager must provide oversight of those crews.

(b) Each program manager must employ (either directly or by contract) an adequate number of pilots per program aircraft. Flight crew staffing must be determined based on the following factors, at a minimum:

(1) Number of program aircraft.

(2) Program manager flight, duty, and rest time considerations, and in all cases within the limits set forth in 91.1057 through 91.1061.

(3) Vacations.

(4) Operational efficiencies.

(5) Training.

(6) Single pilot operations, if authorized by deviation under paragraph (d) of this section.

(c) Each program manager must publish pilot and flight attendant duty schedules sufficiently in advance to follow the flight, duty, and rest time limits in 91.1057 through 91.1061 in program operations.

(d) Unless otherwise authorized by the Administrator, when any program aircraft is flown in program operations with passengers onboard, the crew must consist of at least two qualified pilots employed or contracted by the program manager or the fractional owner.

(e) The program manager must ensure that trained and qualified scheduling or flight release personnel are on duty to schedule and release program aircraft during all hours that such aircraft are available for program operations.

91.1050   Employment of former FAA employees

(a) Except as specified in paragraph (c) of this section, no fraction owner or fractional ownership program manager may knowingly employ or make a contractual arrangement which permits a individual to act as an agent or representative of the fraction owner or fractional ownership program manager in any matte before the Federal Aviation Administration if the individual, the preceding 2 years—

(1) Served as, or was directly responsible for the oversight of, Flight Standards Service aviation safety inspector; and

(2) Had direct responsibility to inspect, or oversee the inspection of, the operations of the fractional owner or fractiona ownership program manager.

(b) For the purpose of this section, an individual shall be considere to be acting as an agent or representative of a fractional owne or fractional ownership program manager in a matter before th agency if the individual makes any written or oral communica tion on behalf of the fractional owner or fractional ownershi program manager to the agency (or any of its officers or em ployees) in connection with a particular matter, whether or nc involving a specific party and without regard to whether the ind vidual has participated in, or had responsibility for, the particu lar matter while serving as a Flight Standards Service aviatio safety inspector.

(c) The provisions of this section do not prohibit a fractional owne or fractional ownership program manager from knowingly em ploying or making a contractual arrangement which permits a individual to act as an agent or representative of the fractiona owner or fractional ownership program manager in any matte before the Federal Aviation Administration if the individual wa employed by the fractional owner or fractional ownership pro gram manager before October 21, 2011.

[Doc. No. FAA–2008–1154, 76 FR 52235, Aug. 22, 2011]

91.1051   Pilot safety background check

Within 90 days of an individual beginning service as a pilot, th program manager must request the following information:

(a) FAA records pertaining to—

(1) Current pilot certificates and associated type ratings.

(2) Current medical certificates.

(3) Summaries of legal enforcement actions resulting in a find ing by the Administrator of a violation.

(b) Records from all previous employers during the five years preced ing the date of the employment application where the applican worked as a pilot. If any of these firms are in bankruptcy, the re cords must be requested from the trustees in bankruptcy for thos employees. If the previous employer is no longer in business, documented good faith effort must be made to obtain the records Records from previous employers must include, as applicable—

(1) Crew member records.

(2) Drug testing—collection, testing, and rehabilitation record pertaining to the individual.

(3) Alcohol misuse prevention program records pertaining to th individual.

(4) The applicant's individual record that includes certifications ratings, aeronautical experience, effective date and class o the medical certificate.

91.1053   Crewmember experience

(a) No program manager or owner may use any person, nor may any person serve, as a pilot in command or second in command of a program aircraft, or as a flight attendant on a program aircraft, ir program operations under this subpart unless that person has me the applicable requirements of part 61 of this chapter and has th following experience and ratings:

(1) Total flight time for all pilots:

(i)   Pilot in command—A minimum of 1,500 hours.

(ii) Second in command—A minimum of 500 hours.

(2) For multi-engine turbine-powered fixed-wing and powered-lift aircraft, the following FAA certification and ratings requirements:

(i) Pilot in command—Airline transport pilot and applicable type ratings.

(ii) Second in command—Commercial pilot and instrument ratings.

(iii) Flight attendant (if required or used)—Appropriately trained personnel.

(3) For all other aircraft, the following FAA certification and rating requirements:

(i) Pilot in command—Commercial pilot and instrument ratings.

(ii) Second in command—Commercial pilot and instrument ratings.

(iii) Flight attendant (if required or used)—Appropriately trained personnel.

(b) The Administrator may authorize deviations from paragraph (a)(1) of this section if the Flight Standards office that issued the program manager's management specifications finds that the crewmember has comparable experience, and can effectively perform the functions associated with the position in accordance with the requirements of this chapter. Grants of deviation under this paragraph may be granted after consideration of the size and scope of the operation, the qualifications of the intended personnel and the circumstances set forth in §91.1055(b)(1) through (3). The Administrator may, at any time, terminate any grant of deviation authority issued under this paragraph.

[Docket No. FAA-2001-10047, 68 FR 54561, Sept. 17, 2003, as amended by Docket FAA-2018-0119, Amdt. 91-350, 83 FR 9171, Mar. 5, 2018]

91.1055 Pilot operating limitations and pairing requirement

(a) If the second in command of a fixed-wing program aircraft has fewer than 100 hours of flight time as second in command flying in the aircraft make and model and, if a type rating is required, in the type aircraft being flown, and the pilot in command is not an appropriately qualified check pilot, the pilot in command shall make all takeoffs and landings in any of the following situations:

(1) Landings at the destination airport when a Destination Airport Analysis is required by 91.1037(c); and

(2) In any of the following conditions:

(i) The prevailing visibility for the airport is at or below 3/4 mile.

(ii) The runway visual range for the runway to be used is at or below 4,000 feet.

(iii) The runway to be used has water, snow, slush, ice or similar contamination that may adversely affect aircraft performance.

(iv) The braking action on the runway to be used is reported to be less than "good."

(v) The crosswind component for the runway to be used is in excess of 15 knots.

(vi) Windshear is reported in the vicinity of the airport.

(vii) Any other condition in which the pilot in command determines it to be prudent to exercise the pilot in command's authority.

(b) No program manager may release a program flight under this subpart unless, for that aircraft make or model and, if a type rating is required, for that type aircraft, either the pilot in command or the second in command has at least 75 hours of flight time, either as pilot in command or second in command. The Administrator may, upon application by the program manager, authorize deviations from the requirements of this paragraph by an appropriate amendment to the management specifications in any of the following circumstances:

(1) A newly authorized program manager does not employ any pilots who meet the minimum requirements of this paragraph.

(2) An existing program manager adds to its fleet a new category and class aircraft not used before in its operation.

(3) An existing program manager establishes a new base to which it assigns pilots who will be required to become qualified on the aircraft operated from that base.

(c) No person may be assigned in the capacity of pilot in command in a program operation to more than two aircraft types that require a separate type rating.

91.1057 Flight, duty and rest time requirements: all crewmembers

(a) For purposes of this subpart—

Augmented flight crew means at least three pilots.

Calendar day means the period of elapsed time, using Coordinated Universal Time or local time that begins at midnight and ends 24 hours later at the next midnight.

Duty period means the period of elapsed time between reporting for an assignment involving flight time and release from that assignment by the program manager. All time between these two points is part of the duty period, even if flight time is interrupted by nonflight-related duties. The time is calculated using either Coordinated Universal Time or local time to reflect the total elapsed time.

Extension of flight time means an increase in the flight time because of circumstances beyond the control of the program manager or flight crewmember (such as adverse weather) that are not known at the time of departure and that prevent the flightcrew from reaching the destination within the planned flight time.

Flight attendant means an individual, other than a flight crewmember, who is assigned by the program manager, in accordance with the required minimum crew complement under the program manager's management specifications or in addition to that minimum complement, to duty in an aircraft during flight time and whose duties include but are not necessarily limited to cabin-safety-related responsibilities.

Multi-time zone flight means an easterly or westerly flight or multiple flights in one direction in the same duty period that results in a time zone difference of 5 or more hours and is conducted in a geographic area that is south of 60 degrees north latitude and north of 60 degrees south latitude.

Reserve status means that status in which a flight crewmember, by arrangement with the program manager: Holds himself or herself fit to fly to the extent that this is within the control of the flight crewmember; remains within a reasonable response time of the aircraft as agreed between the flight crewmember and the program manager; and maintains a ready means whereby the flight crewmember may be contacted by the program manager. Reserve status is not part of any duty period or rest period.

Rest period means a period of time required pursuant to this subpart that is free of all responsibility for work or duty prior to the commencement of, or following completion of, a duty period, and during which the flight crewmember or flight attendant cannot be required to receive contact from the program manager. A rest period does not include any time during which the program manager imposes on a flight crewmember or flight attendant any duty or restraint, including any actual work or present responsibility for work should the occasion arise.

Standby means that portion of a duty period during which a flight crewmember is subject to the control of the program manager and holds himself or herself in a condition of readiness to undertake a flight. Standby is not part of any rest period.

(b) A program manager may assign a crewmember and a crewmember may accept an assignment for flight time only when the applicable requirements of this section and 91.1059–91.1062 are met.

(c) No program manager may assign any crewmember to any duty during any required rest period.

(d) Time spent in transportation, not local in character, that a program manager requires of a crewmember and provides to transport the crewmember to an airport at which he or she is to serve on a flight

FAR 91

as a crewmember, or from an airport at which he or she was relieved from duty to return to his or her home station, is not considered part of a rest period.

(e) A flight crewmember may continue a flight assignment if the flight to which he or she is assigned would normally terminate within the flight time limitations, but because of circumstances beyond the control of the program manager or flight crewmember (such as adverse weather conditions), is not at the time of departure expected to reach its destination within the planned flight time. The extension of flight time under this paragraph may not exceed the maximum time limits set forth in 91.1059.

(f) Each flight assignment must provide for at least 10 consecutive hours of rest during the 24-hour period that precedes the completion time of the assignment.

(g) The program manager must provide each crewmember at least 13 rest periods of at least 24 consecutive hours each in each calendar quarter.

(h) A flight crewmember may decline a flight assignment if, in the flight crewmember's determination, to do so would not be consistent with the standard of safe operation required under this subpart, this part, and applicable provisions of this title.

(i) Any rest period required by this subpart may occur concurrently with any other rest period.

(j) If authorized by the Administrator, a program manager may use the applicable unscheduled flight time limitations, duty period limitations, and rest requirements of part 121 or part 135 of this chapter instead of the flight time limitations, duty period limitations, and rest requirements of this subpart.

91.1059 Flight time limitations and rest requirements: one or two pilot crews

(a) No program manager may assign any flight crewmember, and no flight crewmember may accept an assignment, for flight time as a member of a one- or two-pilot crew if that crewmember's total flight time in all commercial flying will exceed—

(1) 500 hours in any calendar quarter;

(2) 800 hours in any two consecutive calendar quarters;

(3) 1,400 hours in any calendar year.

(b) Except as provided in paragraph (c)of this section, during any 24 consecutive hours the total flight time of the assigned flight, when added to any commercial flying by that flight crewmember, may not exceed—

(1) 8 hours for a flight crew consisting of one pilot; or

(2) 10 hours for a flight crew consisting of two pilots qualified under this subpart for the operation being conducted.

(c) No program manager may assign any flight crewmember, and no flight crewmember may accept an assignment, if that crewmember's flight time or duty period will exceed, or rest time will be less than—

	NORMAL DUTY	EXTENSION OF FLIGHT TIME
(1) Minimum Rest immediately Before Duty.	10 Hours	10 Hours
(2) Duty Period	Up to 14 Hours	Up to 14 Hours.
(3) Flight Time For 1 Pilot	Up to 8 Hours.	Exceeding 8 Hours up to 9 Hours.
(4) Flight Time For 2 Pilots	Up to 10 Hours.	Exceeding 10 Hours up to 12 Hours.
(5) Minimum After Duty Rest	10 Hours	12 Hours
(6) Minimum After Duty Rest Period for Multi-Time Zone Flights.	14 Hours	18 Hours.

91.1061 Augmented flight crews

(a) No program manager may assign any flight crewmember, and no flight crewmember may accept an assignment, for flight time as a member of an augmented crew if that crewmember's total flight time in all commercial flying will exceed—

(1) 500 hours in any calendar quarter;

(2) 800 hours in any two consecutive calendar quarters;

(3) 1,400 hours in any calendar year.

(b) No program manager may assign any pilot to an augmented crew, unless the program manager ensures:

(1) Adequate sleeping facilities are installed on the aircraft for the pilots.

(2) No more than 8 hours of flight deck duty is accrued in any 24 consecutive hours.

(3) For a three-pilot crew, the crew must consist of at least the following:

(i) A pilot in command (PIC) who meets the applicable flight crewmember requirements of this subpart and 61.57 of this chapter.

(ii) A PIC qualified pilot who meets the applicable flight crewmember requirements of this subpart and 61.57(c) and (d) of this chapter.

(iii) A second in command (SIC) who meets the SIC qualifications of this subpart. For flight under IFR that person must also meet the recent instrument experience requirements of part 61 of this chapter.

(4) For a four-pilot crew, at least three pilots who meet the conditions of paragraph (b)(3) of this section, plus a fourth pilot who meets the SIC qualifications of this subpart. For flight under IFR, that person must also meet the recent instrument experience requirements of part 61 of this chapter.

(c) No program manager may assign any flight crewmember, and no flight crewmember may accept an assignment, if that crewmember's flight time or duty period will exceed, or rest time will be less than—

	3-PILOT CREW	4-PILOT CREW
(1) Minimum Rest Immediately Before Duty.	10 Hours	10 Hours
(2) Duty Period	Up to 16 Hours	Up to 18 Hours
(3) Flight Time	Up to 12 Hours	Up to 16 Hours
(4) Minimum After Duty Rest	12 Hours	18 Hours
(5) Minimum After Duty Rest Period for Multi-Time Zone Flights.	for 18 hours	24 hours

91.1062 Duty periods and rest requirements: flight attendants

(a) Except as provided in paragraph (b) of this section, a program manager may assign a duty period to a flight attendant only when the assignment meets the applicable duty period limitations and rest requirements of this paragraph.

(1) Except as provided in paragraphs (a)(4), (a)(5), and (a)(6) of this section, no program manager may assign a flight attendant to a scheduled duty period of more than 14 hours.

(2) Except as provided in paragraph (a)(3) of this section, a flight attendant scheduled to a duty period of 14 hours or less as provided under paragraph (a)(1) of this section must be given a scheduled rest period of at least 9 consecutive hours. This rest period must occur between the completion of the scheduled duty period and the commencement of the subsequent duty period.

(3) The rest period required under paragraph (a)(2) of this section may be scheduled or reduced to 8 consecutive hours if

the flight attendant is provided a subsequent rest period of at least 10 consecutive hours; this subsequent rest period must be scheduled to begin no later than 24 hours after the beginning of the reduced rest period and must occur between the completion of the scheduled duty period and the commencement of the subsequent duty period.

(4) A program manager may assign a flight attendant to a scheduled duty period of more than 14 hours, but no more than 16 hours, if the program manager has assigned to the flight or flights in that duty period at least one flight attendant in addition to the minimum flight attendant complement required for the flight or flights in that duty period under the program manager's management specifications.

(5) A program manager may assign a flight attendant to a scheduled duty period of more than 16 hours, but no more than 18 hours, if the program manager has assigned to the flight or flights in that duty period at least two flight attendants in addition to the minimum flight attendant complement required for the flight or flights in that duty period under the program manager's management specifications.

(6) A program manager may assign a flight attendant to a scheduled duty period of more than 18 hours, but no more than 20 hours, if the scheduled duty period includes one or more flights that land or take off outside the 48 contiguous states and the District of Columbia, and if the program manager has assigned to the flight or flights in that duty period at least three flight attendants in addition to the minimum flight attendant complement required for the flight or flights in that duty period under the program manager's management specifications.

(7) Except as provided in paragraph (a)(8) of this section, a flight attendant scheduled to a duty period of more than 14 hours but no more than 20 hours, as provided in paragraphs (a)(4), (a)(5), and (a)(6) of this section, must be given a scheduled rest period of at least 12 consecutive hours. This rest period must occur between the completion of the scheduled duty period and the commencement of the subsequent duty period.

(8) The rest period required under paragraph (a)(7) of this section may be scheduled or reduced to 10 consecutive hours if the flight attendant is provided a subsequent rest period of at least 14 consecutive hours; this subsequent rest period must be scheduled to begin no later than 24 hours after the beginning of the reduced rest period and must occur between the completion of the scheduled duty period and the commencement of the subsequent duty period.

(9) Notwithstanding paragraphs (a)(4), (a)(5), and (a)(6) of this section, if a program manager elects to reduce the rest period to 10 hours as authorized by paragraph (a)(8) of this section, the program manager may not schedule a flight attendant for a duty period of more than 14 hours during the 24-hour period commencing after the beginning of the reduced rest period.

(b) Notwithstanding paragraph (a) of this section, a program manager may apply the flight crewmember flight time and duty limitations and rest requirements of this part to flight attendants for all operations conducted under this part provided that the program manager establishes written procedures that—

(1) Apply to all flight attendants used in the program manager's operation;

(2) Include the flight crewmember rest and duty requirements of 91.1057, 91.1059, and 91.1061, as appropriate to the operation being conducted, except that rest facilities on board the aircraft are not required;

(3) Include provisions to add one flight attendant to the minimum flight attendant complement for each flight crewmember who is in excess of the minimum number required in the aircraft type certificate data sheet and who is assigned to the aircraft under the provisions of 91.1061; and

(4) Are approved by the Administrator and described or referenced in the program manager's management specifications.

91.1063 Testing and training: applicability and terms used

(a) Sections 91.1065 through 91.1107:

(1) Prescribe the tests and checks required for pilots and flight attendant crewmembers and for the approval of check pilots in operations under this subpart;

(2) Prescribe the requirements for establishing and maintaining an approved training program for crewmembers, check pilots and instructors, and other operations personnel employed or used by the program manager in program operations;

(3) Prescribe the requirements for the qualification, approval and use of aircraft simulators and flight training devices in the conduct of an approved training program; and

(4) Permits training center personnel authorized under part 142 of this chapter who meet the requirements of 91.1075 to conduct training, testing and checking under contract or other arrangements to those persons subject to the requirements of this subpart.

(b) If authorized by the Administrator, a program manager may comply with the applicable training and testing sections of part 121, subparts N and O of this chapter instead of 91.1065 through 91.1107, provided that the following additional limitations and allowances apply to program managers so authorized:

(1) Operating experience and operations familiarization. Program managers are not required to comply with the operating experience requirements of 121.434 or the operations familiarization requirements of 121.435 of this chapter.

(2) Upgrade training.

(i) Each program manager must include in upgrade ground training for pilots, instruction in at least the subjects identified in 121.419(a) of this chapter, as applicable to their assigned duties; and, for pilots serving in crews of two or more pilots, beginning on April 27, 2022, instruction and facilitated discussion in the subjects identified in 121.419(c) of this chapter.

(ii) Each program manager must include in upgrade flight training for pilots, flight training for the maneuvers and procedures required in 121.424(a), (c), (e), and (f) of this chapter; and, for pilots serving in crews of two or more pilots, beginning on April 27, 2022, the flight training required in 121.424(b) of this chapter.

(3) Initial and recurrent leadership and command and mentoring training. Program managers are not required to include leadership and command training in 121.409(b)(2)(ii)(B)(6), 121.419(c)(1), 121.424(b) and 121.427(d)(1) of this chapter, and mentoring training in 121.419(c)(2) and 121.427(d)(1) of this chapter in initial and recurrent training for pilots in command who serve in operations that use only one pilot.

(4) One-time leadership and command and mentoring training. Section 121.429 of this chapter does not apply to program managers conducting operations under this subpart when those operations use only one pilot.

(c) If authorized by the Administrator, a program manager may comply with the applicable training and testing sections of subparts G and H of part 135 of this chapter instead of 91.1065 through 91.1107, except for the operating experience requirements of 135.244 of this chapter.

(d) For the purposes of this subpart, the following terms and definitions apply:

(1) Initial training. The training required for crewmembers who have not qualified and served in the same capacity on an aircraft.

(2) Transition training. The training required for crewmembers who have qualified and served in the same capacity on another aircraft.

(3) *Upgrade training.* The training required for crewmembers who have qualified and served as second in command on a particular aircraft type, before they serve as pilot in command on that aircraft.

(4) *Differences training.* The training required for crewmembers who have qualified and served on a particular type aircraft, when the Administrator finds differences training is necessary before a crewmember serves in the same capacity on a particular variation of that aircraft.

(5) *Recurrent training.* The training required for crewmembers to remain adequately trained and currently proficient for each aircraft crewmember position, and type of operation in which the crewmember serves.

(6) *In flight.* The maneuvers, procedures, or functions that will be conducted in the aircraft.

(7) *Training center.* An organization governed by the applicable requirements of part 142 of this chapter that conducts training, testing, and checking under contract or other arrangement to program managers subject to the requirements of this subpart.

(8) *Requalification training.* The training required for crewmembers previously trained and qualified, but who have become unqualified because of not having met within the required period any of the following:

 (i) Recurrent crewmember training requirements of 91.1107.

 (ii) Instrument proficiency check requirements of 91.1069.

 (iii) Testing requirements of 91.1065.

 (iv) Recurrent flight attendant testing requirements of 91.1067.

[Docket No. FAA-2001-10047, 68 FR 54561, Sept. 17, 2003, as amended by Amdt. 61-144, 85 FR 10920, Feb. 25, 2020]

91.1065   Initial and recurrent pilot testing requirements

(a) No program manager or owner may use a pilot, nor may any person serve as a pilot, unless, since the beginning of the 12th month before that service, that pilot has passed either a written or oral test (or a combination), given by the Administrator or an authorized check pilot, on that pilot's knowledge in the following areas—

(1) The appropriate provisions of parts 61 and 91 of this chapter and the management specifications and the operating manual of the program manager;

(2) For each type of aircraft to be flown by the pilot, the aircraft powerplant, major components and systems, major appliances, performance and operating limitations, standard and emergency operating procedures, and the contents of the accepted operating manual or equivalent, as applicable;

(3) For each type of aircraft to be flown by the pilot, the method of determining compliance with weight and balance limitations for takeoff, landing and en route operations;

(4) Navigation and use of air navigation aids appropriate to the operation or pilot authorization, including, when applicable, instrument approach facilities and procedures;

(5) Air traffic control procedures, including IFR procedures when applicable;

(6) Meteorology in general, including the principles of frontal systems, icing, fog, thunderstorms, and windshear, and, if appropriate for the operation of the program manager, high altitude weather;

(7) Procedures for—

 (i) Recognizing and avoiding severe weather situations;

 (ii) Escaping from severe weather situations, in case of inadvertent encounters, including low-altitude windshear (except that rotorcraft aircraft pilots are not required to be tested on escaping from low-altitude windshear); and

 (iii) Operating in or near thunderstorms (including best penetration altitudes), turbulent air (including clear air turbulence), icing, hail, and other potentially hazardous meteorological conditions; and

(8) New equipment, procedures, or techniques, as appropriate.

(b) No program manager or owner may use a pilot, nor may any person serve as a pilot, in any aircraft unless, since the beginning of the 12th month before that service, that pilot has passed a competency check given by the Administrator or an authorized check pilot in that class of aircraft, if single-engine aircraft other than turbojet, or that type of aircraft, if rotorcraft, multiengine aircraft, or turbojet airplane, to determine the pilot's competence in practical skills and techniques in that aircraft or class of aircraft. The extent of the competency check will be determined by the Administrator or authorized check pilot conducting the competency check. The competency check may include any of the maneuvers and procedures currently required for the original issuance of the particular pilot certificate required for the operations authorized and appropriate to the category, class and type of aircraft involved. For the purposes of this paragraph, type, as to an airplane, means any one of a group of airplanes determined by the Administrator to have a similar means of propulsion, the same manufacturer, and no significantly different handling or flight characteristics. For the purposes of this paragraph, type, as to a rotorcraft, means a basic make and model.

(c) The instrument proficiency check required by 91.1069 may be substituted for the competency check required by this section for the type of aircraft used in the check.

(d) For the purpose of this subpart, competent performance of a procedure or maneuver by a person to be used as a pilot requires that the pilot be the obvious master of the aircraft, with the successful outcome of the maneuver never in doubt.

(e) The Administrator or authorized check pilot certifies the competency of each pilot who passes the knowledge or flight check in the program manager's pilot records.

(f) All or portions of a required competency check may be given in an aircraft simulator or other appropriate training device, if approved by the Administrator.

(g) If the program manager is authorized to conduct EFVS operations, the competency check in paragraph (b) of this section must include tasks appropriate to the EFVS operations the certificate holder is authorized to conduct.

[Docket No. FAA-2001-10047, 68 FR 54561, Sept. 17, 2003, as amended by Docket FAA-2013-0485, Amdt. 91-345, 81 FR 90175, Dec. 13, 2016]

91.1067   Initial and recurrent flight attendant crewmember testing requirements

No program manager or owner may use a flight attendant crewmember, nor may any person serve as a flight attendant crewmember unless, since the beginning of the 12th month before that service, the program manager has determined by appropriate initial and recurrent testing that the person is knowledgeable and competent in the following areas as appropriate to assigned duties and responsibilities—

(a) Authority of the pilot in command;

(b) Passenger handling, including procedures to be followed in handling deranged persons or other persons whose conduct might jeopardize safety;

(c) Crewmember assignments, functions, and responsibilities during ditching and evacuation of persons who may need the assistance of another person to move expeditiously to an exit in an emergency;

(d) Briefing of passengers;

(e) Location and operation of portable fire extinguishers and other items of emergency equipment;

(f) Proper use of cabin equipment and controls;

(g) Location and operation of passenger oxygen equipment;

(h) Location and operation of all normal and emergency exits, including evacuation slides and escape ropes; and

(i) Seating of persons who may need assistance of another person to move rapidly to an exit in an emergency as prescribed by the program manager's operations manual.

91.1069 Flight crew: instrument proficiency check requirements

(a) No program manager or owner may use a pilot, nor may any person serve, as a pilot in command of an aircraft under IFR unless, since the beginning of the 6th month before that service, that pilot has passed an instrument proficiency check under this section administered by the Administrator or an authorized check pilot.

(b) No program manager or owner may use a pilot, nor may any person serve, as a second command pilot of an aircraft under IFR unless, since the beginning of the 12th month before that service, that pilot has passed an instrument proficiency check under this section administered by the Administrator or an authorized check pilot.

(c) No pilot may use any type of precision instrument approach procedure under IFR unless, since the beginning of the 6th month before that use, the pilot satisfactorily demonstrated that type of approach procedure. No pilot may use any type of nonprecision approach procedure under IFR unless, since the beginning of the 6th month before that use, the pilot has satisfactorily demonstrated either that type of approach procedure or any other two different types of nonprecision approach procedures. The instrument approach procedure or procedures must include at least one straight-in approach, one circling approach, and one missed approach. Each type of approach procedure demonstrated must be conducted to published minimums for that procedure.

(d) The instrument proficiency checks required by paragraphs (a) and (b) of this section consists of either an oral or written equipment test (or a combination) and a flight check under simulated or actual IFR conditions. The equipment test includes questions on emergency procedures, engine operation, fuel and lubrication systems, power settings, stall speeds, best engine-out speed, propeller and supercharger operations, and hydraulic, mechanical, and electrical systems, as appropriate. The flight check includes navigation by instruments, recovery from simulated emergencies, and standard instrument approaches involving navigational facilities which that pilot is to be authorized to use.

(e) Each pilot taking the instrument proficiency check must show that standard of competence required by 91.1065(d).

    (1) The instrument proficiency check must—

        (i) For a pilot in command of an aircraft requiring that the PIC hold an airline transport pilot certificate, include the procedures and maneuvers for an airline transport pilot certificate in the particular type of aircraft, if appropriate; and

        (ii) For a pilot in command of a rotorcraft or a second in command of any aircraft requiring that the SIC hold a commercial pilot certificate include the procedures and maneuvers for a commercial pilot certificate with an instrument rating and, if required, for the appropriate type rating.

    (2) The instrument proficiency check must be given by an authorized check pilot or by the Administrator.

(f) If the pilot is assigned to pilot only one type of aircraft, that pilot must take the instrument proficiency check required by paragraph (a) of this section in that type of aircraft.

(g) If the pilot in command is assigned to pilot more than one type of aircraft, that pilot must take the instrument proficiency check required by paragraph (a) of this section in each type of aircraft to which that pilot is assigned, in rotation, but not more than one flight check during each period described in paragraph (a) of this section.

(h) If the pilot in command is assigned to pilot both single-engine and multiengine aircraft, that pilot must initially take the instrument proficiency check required by paragraph (a) of this section in a multiengine aircraft, and each succeeding check alternately in single-engine and multiengine aircraft, but not more than one flight check during each period described in paragraph (a) of this section.

(i) All or portions of a required flight check may be given in an aircraft simulator or other appropriate training device, if approved by the Administrator.

91.1071 Crewmember: tests and checks, grace provisions, training to accepted standards

(a) If a crewmember who is required to take a test or a flight check under this subpart, completes the test or flight check in the month before or after the month in which it is required, that crewmember is considered to have completed the test or check in the month in which it is required.

(b) If a pilot being checked under this subpart fails any of the required maneuvers, the person giving the check may give additional training to the pilot during the course of the check. In addition to repeating the maneuvers failed, the person giving the check may require the pilot being checked to repeat any other maneuvers that are necessary to determine the pilot's proficiency. If the pilot being checked is unable to demonstrate satisfactory performance to the person conducting the check, the program manager may not use the pilot, nor may the pilot serve, as a flight crewmember in operations under this subpart until the pilot has satisfactorily completed the check. If a pilot who demonstrates unsatisfactory performance is employed as a pilot for a certificate holder operating under part 121, 125, or 135 of this chapter, he or she must notify that certificate holder of the unsatisfactory performance.

91.1073 Training program: general

(a) Each program manager must have a training program and must:

    (1) Establish, obtain the appropriate initial and final approval of, and provide a training program that meets this subpart and that ensures that each crewmember, including each flight attendant if the program manager uses a flight attendant crewmember, flight instructor, check pilot, and each person assigned duties for the carriage and handling of hazardous materials (as defined in 49 CFR 171.8) is adequately trained to perform these assigned duties.

    (2) Provide adequate ground and flight training facilities and properly qualified ground instructors for the training required by this subpart.

    (3) Provide and keep current for each aircraft type used and, if applicable, the particular variations within the aircraft type, appropriate training material, examinations, forms, instructions, and procedures for use in conducting the training and checks required by this subpart.

    (4) Provide enough flight instructors, check pilots, and simulator instructors to conduct required flight training and flight checks, and simulator training courses allowed under this subpart.

(b) Whenever a crewmember who is required to take recurrent training under this subpart completes the training in the month before, or the month after, the month in which that training is required, the crewmember is considered to have completed it in the month in which it was required.

(c) Each instructor, supervisor, or check pilot who is responsible for a particular ground training subject, segment of flight training, course of training, flight check, or competence check under this subpart must certify as to the proficiency and knowledge of the crewmember, flight instructor, or check pilot concerned upon completion of that training or check. That certification must be made a part of the crewmember's record. When the certification required by this paragraph is made by an entry in a computerized recordkeeping system, the certifying instructor, supervisor, or check pilot, must be identified with that entry. However, the signature of the certifying instructor, supervisor, or check pilot is not required for computerized entries.

FAR 91

(d) Training subjects that apply to more than one aircraft or crew-member position and that have been satisfactorily completed during previous training while employed by the program manager for another aircraft or another crewmember position, need not be repeated during subsequent training other than recurrent training.

(e) Aircraft simulators and other training devices may be used in the program manager's training program if approved by the Administrator.

(f) Each program manager is responsible for establishing safe and efficient crew management practices for all phases of flight in program operations including crew resource management training for all crewmembers used in program operations.

(g) If an aircraft simulator has been approved by the Administrator for use in the program manager's training program, the program manager must ensure that each pilot annually completes at least one flight training session in an approved simulator for at least one program aircraft. The training session may be the flight training portion of any of the pilot training or check requirements of this subpart, including the initial, transition, upgrade, requalification, differences, or recurrent training, or the accomplishment of a competency check or instrument proficiency check. If there is no approved simulator for that aircraft type in operation, then all flight training and checking must be accomplished in the aircraft.

91.1075   Training program: special rules

Other than the program manager, only the following are eligible under this subpart to conduct training, testing, and checking under contract or other arrangement to those persons subject to the requirements of this subpart.

(a) Another program manager operating under this subpart:

(b) A training center certificated under part 142 of this chapter to conduct training, testing, and checking required by this subpart if the training center—

(1) Holds applicable training specifications issued under part 142 of this chapter;

(2) Has facilities, training equipment, and courseware meeting the applicable requirements of part 142 of this chapter;

(3) Has approved curriculums, curriculum segments, and portions of curriculum segments applicable for use in training courses required by this subpart; and

(4) Has sufficient instructors and check pilots qualified under the applicable requirements of 91.1089 through 91.1095 to conduct training, testing, and checking to persons subject to the requirements of this subpart.

(c) A part 119 certificate holder operating under part 121 or part 135 of this chapter.

(d) As authorized by the Administrator, a training center that is not certificated under part 142 of this chapter.

91.1077   Training program and revision: initial and final approval

(a) To obtain initial and final approval of a training program, or a revision to an approved training program, each program manager must submit to the Administrator—

(1) An outline of the proposed or revised curriculum, that provides enough information for a preliminary evaluation of the proposed training program or revision; and

(2) Additional relevant information that may be requested by the Administrator.

(b) If the proposed training program or revision complies with this subpart, the Administrator grants initial approval in writing after which the program manager may conduct the training under that program. The Administrator then evaluates the effectiveness of the training program and advises the program manager of deficiencies, if any, that must be corrected.

(c) The Administrator grants final approval of the proposed training program or revision if the program manager shows that the training

conducted under the initial approval in paragraph (b) of this section ensures that each person who successfully completes the training is adequately trained to perform that person's assigned duties.

(d) Whenever the Administrator finds that revisions are necessary for the continued adequacy of a training program that has been granted final approval, the program manager must, after notification by the Administrator, make any changes in the program that are found necessary by the Administrator. Within 30 days after the program manager receives the notice, it may file a petition to reconsider the notice with the Administrator. The filing of a petition to reconsider stays the notice pending a decision by the Administrator. However, if the Administrator finds that there is an emergency that requires immediate action in the interest of safety, the Administrator may, upon a statement of the reasons, require a change effective without stay.

91.1079   Training program: curriculum

(a) Each program manager must prepare and keep current a written training program curriculum for each type of aircraft for each crewmember required for that type aircraft. The curriculum must include ground and flight training required by this subpart.

(b) Each training program curriculum must include the following:

(1) A list of principal ground training subjects, including emergency training subjects, that are provided.

(2) A list of all the training devices, mock-ups, systems trainers, procedures trainers, or other training aids that the program manager will use.

(3) Detailed descriptions or pictorial displays of the approved normal, abnormal, and emergency maneuvers, procedures and functions that will be performed during each flight training phase or flight check, indicating those maneuvers, procedures and functions that are to be performed during the inflight portions of flight training and flight checks.

91.1081   Crewmember training requirements

(a) Each program manager must include in its training program the following initial and transition ground training as appropriate to the particular assignment of the crewmember:

(1) Basic indoctrination ground training for newly hired crewmembers including instruction in at least the—

(i) Duties and responsibilities of crewmembers as applicable;

(ii) Appropriate provisions of this chapter;

(iii) Contents of the program manager's management specifications (not required for flight attendants); and

(iv) Appropriate portions of the program manager's operating manual.

(2) The initial and transition ground training in 91.1101 and 91.1105, as applicable.

(3) Emergency training in 91.1083.

(b) Each training program must provide the initial and transition flight training in 91.1103, as applicable.

(c) Each training program must provide recurrent ground and flight training as provided in 91.1107.

(d) Upgrade training in 91.1101 and 91.1103 for a particular type aircraft may be included in the training program for crewmembers who have qualified and served as second in command on that aircraft.

(e) In addition to initial, transition, upgrade and recurrent training, each training program must provide ground and flight training, instruction, and practice necessary to ensure that each crewmember—

(1) Remains adequately trained and currently proficient for each aircraft, crewmember position, and type of operation in which the crewmember serves; and

(2) Qualifies in new equipment, facilities, procedures, and techniques, including modifications to aircraft.

91.1083 Crewmember emergency training

(a) Each training program must provide emergency training under this section for each aircraft type, model, and configuration, each crewmember, and each kind of operation conducted, as appropriate for each crewmember and the program manager.

(b) Emergency training must provide the following:

(1) Instruction in emergency assignments and procedures, including coordination among crewmembers.

(2) Individual instruction in the location, function, and operation of emergency equipment including—

(i) Equipment used in ditching and evacuation;

(ii) First aid equipment and its proper use; and

(iii) Portable fire extinguishers, with emphasis on the type of extinguisher to be used on different classes of fires.

(3) Instruction in the handling of emergency situations including—

(i) Rapid decompression;

(ii) Fire in flight or on the surface and smoke control procedures with emphasis on electrical equipment and related circuit breakers found in cabin areas;

(iii) Ditching and evacuation;

(iv) Illness, injury, or other abnormal situations involving passengers or crewmembers; and

(v) Hijacking and other unusual situations.

(4) Review and discussion of previous aircraft accidents and incidents involving actual emergency situations.

(c) Each crewmember must perform at least the following emergency drills, using the proper emergency equipment and procedures, unless the Administrator finds that, for a particular drill, the crewmember can be adequately trained by demonstration:

(1) Ditching, if applicable.

(2) Emergency evacuation.

(3) Fire extinguishing and smoke control.

(4) Operation and use of emergency exits, including deployment and use of evacuation slides, if applicable.

(5) Use of crew and passenger oxygen.

(6) Removal of life rafts from the aircraft, inflation of the life rafts, use of lifelines, and boarding of passengers and crew, if applicable.

(7) Donning and inflation of life vests and the use of other individual flotation devices, if applicable.

(d) Crewmembers who serve in operations above 25,000 feet must receive instruction in the following:

(1) Respiration.

(2) Hypoxia.

(3) Duration of consciousness without supplemental oxygen at altitude.

(4) Gas expansion.

(5) Gas bubble formation.

(6) Physical phenomena and incidents of decompression.

91.1085 Hazardous materials recognition training

No program manager may use any person to perform, and no person may perform, any assigned duties and responsibilities for the handling or carriage of hazardous materials (as defined in 49 CFR 171.8), unless that person has received training in the recognition of hazardous materials.

91.1087 Approval of aircraft simulators and other training devices

(a) Training courses using aircraft simulators and other training devices may be included in the program manager's training program if approved by the Administrator.

(b) Each aircraft simulator and other training device that is used in a training course or in checks required under this subpart must meet the following requirements:

(1) It must be specifically approved for—

(i) The program manager; and

(ii) The particular maneuver, procedure, or crewmember function involved.

(2) It must maintain the performance, functional, and other characteristics that are required for approval.

(3) Additionally, for aircraft simulators, it must be—

(i) Approved for the type aircraft and, if applicable, the particular variation within type for which the training or check is being conducted; and

(ii) Modified to conform with any modification to the aircraft being simulated that changes the performance, functional, or other characteristics required for approval.

(c) A particular aircraft simulator or other training device may be used by more than one program manager.

(d) In granting initial and final approval of training programs or revisions to them, the Administrator considers the training devices, methods, and procedures listed in the program manager's curriculum under 91.1079.

91.1089 Qualifications: check pilots (aircraft) and check pilots (simulator)

(a) For the purposes of this section and 91.1093:

(1) A check pilot (aircraft) is a person who is qualified to conduct flight checks in an aircraft, in a flight simulator, or in a flight training device for a particular type aircraft.

(2) A check pilot (simulator) is a person who is qualified to conduct flight checks, but only in a flight simulator, in a flight training device, or both, for a particular type aircraft.

(3) Check pilots (aircraft) and check pilots (simulator) are those check pilots who perform the functions described in 91.1073(a)(4) and (c).

(b) No program manager may use a person, nor may any person serve as a check pilot (aircraft) in a training program established under this subpart unless, with respect to the aircraft type involved, that person—

(1) Holds the pilot certificates and ratings required to serve as a pilot in command in operations under this subpart;

(2) Has satisfactorily completed the training phases for the aircraft, including recurrent training, that are required to serve as a pilot in command in operations under this subpart;

(3) Has satisfactorily completed the proficiency or competency checks that are required to serve as a pilot in command in operations under this subpart;

(4) Has satisfactorily completed the applicable training requirements of 91.1093;

(5) Holds at least a Class III medical certificate unless serving as a required crewmember, in which case holds a Class I or Class II medical certificate as appropriate; and

(6) Has been approved by the Administrator for the check pilot duties involved.

(c) No program manager may use a person, nor may any person serve as a check pilot (simulator) in a training program established under this subpart unless, with respect to the aircraft type involved, that person meets the provisions of paragraph (b) of this section, or—

(1) Holds the applicable pilot certificates and ratings, except medical certificate, required to serve as a pilot in command in operations under this subpart;

(2) Has satisfactorily completed the appropriate training phases for the aircraft, including recurrent training, that are required to serve as a pilot in command in operations under this subpart;

(3) Has satisfactorily completed the appropriate proficiency or competency checks that are required to serve as a pilot in command in operations under this subpart;

(4) Has satisfactorily completed the applicable training requirements of 91.1093; and

(5) Has been approved by the Administrator for the check pilot (simulator) duties involved.

(d) Completion of the requirements in paragraphs (b)(2), (3), and (4) or (c)(2), (3), and (4) of this section, as applicable, must be entered in the individual's training record maintained by the program manager.

(e) A check pilot who does not hold an appropriate medical certificate may function as a check pilot (simulator), but may not serve as a flightcrew member in operations under this subpart.

(f) A check pilot (simulator) must accomplish the following—

(1) Fly at least two flight segments as a required crewmember for the type, class, or category aircraft involved within the 12-month period preceding the performance of any check pilot duty in a flight simulator; or

(2) Before performing any check pilot duty in a flight simulator, satisfactorily complete an approved line-observation program within the period prescribed by that program.

(g) The flight segments or line-observation program required in paragraph (f) of this section are considered to be completed in the month required if completed in the month before or the month after the month in which they are due.

91.1091   Qualifications: flight instructors (aircraft) and flight instructors (simulator)

(a) For the purposes of this section and 91.1095:

(1) A flight instructor (aircraft) is a person who is qualified to instruct in an aircraft, in a flight simulator, or in a flight training device for a particular type, class, or category aircraft.

(2) A flight instructor (simulator) is a person who is qualified to instruct in a flight simulator, in a flight training device, or in both, for a particular type, class, or category aircraft.

(3) Flight instructors (aircraft) and flight instructors (simulator) are those instructors who perform the functions described in 91.1073(a)(4) and (c).

(b) No program manager may use a person, nor may any person serve as a flight instructor (aircraft) in a training program established under this subpart unless, with respect to the type, class, or category aircraft involved, that person—

(1) Holds the pilot certificates and ratings required to serve as a pilot in command in operations under this subpart or part 121 or 135 of this chapter;

(2) Has satisfactorily completed the training phases for the aircraft, including recurrent training, that are required to serve as a pilot in command in operations under this subpart;

(3) Has satisfactorily completed the proficiency or competency checks that are required to serve as a pilot in command in operations under this subpart;

(4) Has satisfactorily completed the applicable training requirements of 91.1095; and

(5) Holds at least a Class III medical certificate.

(c) No program manager may use a person, nor may any person serve as a flight instructor (simulator) in a training program established under this subpart, unless, with respect to the type, class, or category aircraft involved, that person meets the provisions of paragraph (b) of this section, or—

(1) Holds the pilot certificates and ratings, except medical certificate, required to serve as a pilot in command in operations under this subpart or part 121 or 135 of this chapter;

(2) Has satisfactorily completed the appropriate training phases for the aircraft, including recurrent training, that are required to serve as a pilot in command in operations under this subpart;

(3) Has satisfactorily completed the appropriate proficiency or competency checks that are required to serve as a pilot in command in operations under this subpart; and

(4) Has satisfactorily completed the applicable training requirements of 91.1095.

(d) Completion of the requirements in paragraphs (b)(2), (3), and (4) or (c)(2), (3), and (4) of this section, as applicable, must be entered in the individual's training record maintained by the program manager.

(e) A pilot who does not hold a medical certificate may function as a flight instructor in an aircraft if functioning as a non-required crewmember, but may not serve as a flightcrew member in operations under this subpart.

(f) A flight instructor (simulator) must accomplish the following—

(1) Fly at least two flight segments as a required crewmember for the type, class, or category aircraft involved within the 12-month period preceding the performance of any flight instructor duty in a flight simulator; or

(2) Satisfactorily complete an approved line-observation program within the period prescribed by that program preceding the performance of any flight instructor duty in a flight simulator.

(g) The flight segments or line-observation program required in paragraph (f) of this section are considered completed in the month required if completed in the month before, or in the month after, the month in which they are due.

[Doc. No. FAA–2001–10047, 68 FR 54561, Sept. 17, 2003, as amended by Amdt. 91–322, 76 FR 31823, June 2, 2011]

91.1093   Initial and transition training and checking: check pilots (aircraft), check pilots (simulator)

(a) No program manager may use a person nor may any person serve as a check pilot unless—

(1) That person has satisfactorily completed initial or transition check pilot training; and

(2) Within the preceding 24 months, that person satisfactorily conducts a proficiency or competency check under the observation of an FAA inspector or an aircrew designated examiner employed by the program manager. The observation check may be accomplished in part or in full in an aircraft, in a flight simulator, or in a flight training device.

(b) The observation check required by paragraph (a)(2) of this section is considered to have been completed in the month required if completed in the month before or the month after the month in which it is due.

(c) The initial ground training for check pilots must include the following:

(1) Check pilot duties, functions, and responsibilities.

(2) The applicable provisions of the Code of Federal Regulations and the program manager's policies and procedures.

(3) The applicable methods, procedures, and techniques for conducting the required checks.

(4) Proper evaluation of student performance including the detection of—

    (i)   Improper and insufficient training; and

    (ii) Personal characteristics of an applicant that could adversely affect safety.

(5) The corrective action in the case of unsatisfactory checks.

(6) The approved methods, procedures, and limitations for performing the required normal, abnormal, and emergency procedures in the aircraft.

(d) The transition ground training for a check pilot must include the approved methods, procedures, and limitations for performing the required normal, abnormal, and emergency procedures applicable to the aircraft to which the check pilot is in transition.

(e) The initial and transition flight training for a check pilot (aircraft) must include the following—

(1) The safety measures for emergency situations that are likely to develop during a check;

(2) The potential results of improper, untimely, or nonexecution of safety measures during a check;

(3) Training and practice in conducting flight checks from the left and right pilot seats in the required normal, abnormal, and emergency procedures to ensure competence to conduct the pilot flight checks required by this subpart; and

(4) The safety measures to be taken from either pilot seat for emergency situations that are likely to develop during checking.

(f) The requirements of paragraph (e) of this section may be accomplished in full or in part in flight, in a flight simulator, or in a flight training device, as appropriate.

(g) The initial and transition flight training for a check pilot (simulator) must include the following:

(1) Training and practice in conducting flight checks in the required normal, abnormal, and emergency procedures to ensure competence to conduct the flight checks required by this subpart. This training and practice must be accomplished in a flight simulator or in a flight training device.

(2) Training in the operation of flight simulators, flight training devices, or both, to ensure competence to conduct the flight checks required by this subpart.

91.1095 Initial and transition training and checking: flight instructors (aircraft), flight instructors (simulator)

(a) No program manager may use a person nor may any person serve as a flight instructor unless—

(1) That person has satisfactorily completed initial or transition flight instructor training; and

(2) Within the preceding 24 months, that person satisfactorily conducts instruction under the observation of an FAA inspector, a program manager check pilot, or an aircrew designated examiner employed by the program manager. The observation check may be accomplished in part or in full in an aircraft, in a flight simulator, or in a flight training device.

(b) The observation check required by paragraph (a)(2) of this section is considered to have been completed in the month required if completed in the month before, or the month after, the month in which it is due.

(c) The initial ground training for flight instructors must include the following:

(1) Flight instructor duties, functions, and responsibilities.

(2) The applicable Code of Federal Regulations and the program manager's policies and procedures.

(3) The applicable methods, procedures, and techniques for conducting flight instruction.

(4) Proper evaluation of student performance including the detection of—

(i) Improper and insufficient training; and

(ii) Personal characteristics of an applicant that could adversely affect safety.

(5) The corrective action in the case of unsatisfactory training progress.

(6) The approved methods, procedures, and limitations for performing the required normal, abnormal, and emergency procedures in the aircraft.

(7) Except for holders of a flight instructor certificate—

(i) The fundamental principles of the teaching-learning process;

(ii) Teaching methods and procedures; and

(iii) The instructor-student relationship.

(d) The transition ground training for flight instructors must include the approved methods, procedures, and limitations for performing the required normal, abnormal, and emergency procedures applicable to the type, class, or category aircraft to which the flight instructor is in transition.

(e) The initial and transition flight training for flight instructors (aircraft) must include the following—

(1) The safety measures for emergency situations that are likely to develop during instruction;

(2) The potential results of improper or untimely safety measures during instruction;

(3) Training and practice from the left and right pilot seats in the required normal, abnormal, and emergency maneuvers to ensure competence to conduct the flight instruction required by this subpart; and

(4) The safety measures to be taken from either the left or right pilot seat for emergency situations that are likely to develop during instruction.

(f) The requirements of paragraph (e) of this section may be accomplished in full or in part in flight, in a flight simulator, or in a flight training device, as appropriate.

(g) The initial and transition flight training for a flight instructor (simulator) must include the following:

(1) Training and practice in the required normal, abnormal, and emergency procedures to ensure competence to conduct the flight instruction required by this subpart. These maneuvers and procedures must be accomplished in full or in part in a flight simulator or in a flight training device.

(2) Training in the operation of flight simulators, flight training devices, or both, to ensure competence to conduct the flight instruction required by this subpart.

91.1097 Pilot and flight attendant crewmember training programs

(a) Each program manager must establish and maintain an approved pilot training program, and each program manager who uses a flight attendant crewmember must establish and maintain an approved flight attendant training program, that is appropriate to the operations to which each pilot and flight attendant is to be assigned, and will ensure that they are adequately trained to meet the applicable knowledge and practical testing requirements of 91.1065 through 91.1071.

(b) Each program manager required to have a training program by paragraph (a) of this section must include in that program ground and flight training curriculums for—

(1) Initial training;

(2) Transition training;

(3) Upgrade training;

(4) Differences training;

(5) Recurrent training; and

(6) Requalification training.

(c) Each program manager must provide current and appropriate study materials for use by each required pilot and flight attendant.

(d) The program manager must furnish copies of the pilot and flight attendant crewmember training program, and all changes and additions, to the assigned representative of the Administrator. If the program manager uses training facilities of other persons, a copy of those training programs or appropriate portions used for those facilities must also be furnished. Curricula that follow FAA published curricula may be cited by reference in the copy of the training program furnished to the representative of the Administrator and need not be furnished with the program.

FAR 91

91.1099 Crewmember initial and recurrent training requirements

No program manager may use a person, nor may any person serve, as a crewmember in operations under this subpart unless that crewmember has completed the appropriate initial or recurrent training phase of the training program appropriate to the type of operation in which the crewmember is to serve since the beginning of the 12th month before that service.

91.1101 Pilots: initial, transition, and upgrade ground training

Initial, transition, and upgrade ground training for pilots must include instruction in at least the following, as applicable to their duties:

(a) General subjects—

(1) The program manager's flight locating procedures;

(2) Principles and methods for determining weight and balance, and runway limitations for takeoff and landing;

(3) Enough meteorology to ensure a practical knowledge of weather phenomena, including the principles of frontal systems, icing, fog, thunderstorms, windshear and, if appropriate, high altitude weather situations;

(4) Air traffic control systems, procedures, and phraseology;

(5) Navigation and the use of navigational aids, including instrument approach procedures;

(6) Normal and emergency communication procedures;

(7) Visual cues before and during descent below Decision Altitude or MDA; and

(8) Other instructions necessary to ensure the pilot's competence.

(b) For each aircraft type—

(1) A general description;

(2) Performance characteristics;

(3) Engines and propellers;

(4) Major components;

(5) Major aircraft systems (that is, flight controls, electrical, and hydraulic), other systems, as appropriate, principles of normal, abnormal, and emergency operations, appropriate procedures and limitations;

(6) Knowledge and procedures for—

(i) Recognizing and avoiding severe weather situations;

(ii) Escaping from severe weather situations, in case of inadvertent encounters, including low-altitude windshear (except that rotorcraft pilots are not required to be trained in escaping from low-altitude windshear);

(iii) Operating in or near thunderstorms (including best penetration altitudes), turbulent air (including clear air turbulence), inflight icing, hail, and other potentially hazardous meteorological conditions; and

(iv) Operating airplanes during ground icing conditions, (that is, any time conditions are such that frost, ice, or snow may reasonably be expected to adhere to the aircraft), if the program manager expects to authorize takeoffs in ground icing conditions, including:

(A) The use of holdover times when using deicing/anti-icing fluids;

(B) Airplane deicing/anti-icing procedures, including inspection and check procedures and responsibilities;

(C) Communications;

(D) Airplane surface contamination (that is, adherence of frost, ice, or snow) and critical area identification, and knowledge of how contamination adversely affects airplane performance and flight characteristics;

(E) Types and characteristics of deicing/anti-icing fluids, if used by the program manager;

(F) Cold weather preflight inspection procedures;

(G) Techniques for recognizing contamination on the airplane;

(7) Operating limitations;

(8) Fuel consumption and cruise control;

(9) Flight planning;

(10) Each normal and emergency procedure; and

(11) The approved Aircraft Flight Manual or equivalent.

91.1103 Pilots: initial, transition, upgrade, requalification, and differences flight training

(a) Initial, transition, upgrade, requalification, and differences training for pilots must include flight and practice in each of the maneuvers and procedures contained in each of the curriculums that are a part of the approved training program.

(b) The maneuvers and procedures required by paragraph (a) of this section must be performed in flight, except to the extent that certain maneuvers and procedures may be performed in an aircraft simulator, or an appropriate training device, as allowed by this subpart.

(c) If the program manager's approved training program includes a course of training using an aircraft simulator or other training device, each pilot must successfully complete—

(1) Training and practice in the simulator or training device in at least the maneuvers and procedures in this subpart that are capable of being performed in the aircraft simulator or training device; and

(2) A flight check in the aircraft or a check in the simulator or training device to the level of proficiency of a pilot in command or second in command, as applicable, in at least the maneuvers and procedures that are capable of being performed in an aircraft simulator or training device.

91.1105 Flight attendants: initial and transition ground training

Initial and transition ground training for flight attendants must include instruction in at least the following—

(a) General subjects—

(1) The authority of the pilot in command; and

(2) Passenger handling, including procedures to be followed in handling deranged persons or other persons whose conduct might jeopardize safety.

(b) For each aircraft type—

(1) A general description of the aircraft emphasizing physical characteristics that may have a bearing on ditching, evacuation, and inflight emergency procedures and on other related duties;

(2) The use of both the public address system and the means of communicating with other flight crewmembers, including emergency means in the case of attempted hijacking or other unusual situations; and

(3) Proper use of electrical galley equipment and the controls for cabin heat and ventilation.

91.1107 Recurrent training

(a) Each program manager must ensure that each crewmember receives recurrent training and is adequately trained and currently proficient for the type aircraft and crewmember position involved.

(b) Recurrent ground training for crewmembers must include at least the following:

(1) A quiz or other review to determine the crewmember's knowledge of the aircraft and crewmember position involved.

(2) Instruction as necessary in the subjects required for initial ground training by this subpart, as appropriate, including low-altitude windshear training and training on operating during ground icing conditions, as prescribed in 91.1097 and described in 91.1101, and emergency training.

(c) Recurrent flight training for pilots must include, at least, flight training in the maneuvers or procedures in this subpart, except that satisfactory completion of the check required by 91.1065 within the preceding 12 months may be substituted for recurrent flight training.

91.1109 Aircraft maintenance: inspection program

Each program manager must establish an aircraft inspection program for each make and model program aircraft and ensure each aircraft is inspected in accordance with that inspection program.

(a) The inspection program must be in writing and include at least the following information:

(1) Instructions and procedures for the conduct of inspections for the particular make and model aircraft, including necessary tests and checks. The instructions and procedures must set forth in detail the parts and areas of the airframe, engines, propellers, rotors, and appliances, including survival and emergency equipment required to be inspected.

(2) A schedule for performing the inspections that must be accomplished under the inspection program expressed in terms of the time in service, calendar time, number of system operations, or any combination thereof.

(3) The name and address of the person responsible for scheduling the inspections required by the inspection program. A copy of the inspection program must be made available to the person performing inspections on the aircraft and, upon request, to the Administrator.

(b) Each person desiring to establish or change an approved inspection program under this section must submit the inspection program for approval to the Flight Standards office that issued the program manager's management specifications. The inspection program must be derived from one of the following programs:

(1) An inspection program currently recommended by the manufacturer of the aircraft, aircraft engines, propellers, appliances, and survival and emergency equipment;

(2) An inspection program that is part of a continuous airworthiness maintenance program currently in use by a person holding an air carrier or operating certificate issued under part 119 of this chapter and operating that make and model aircraft under part 121 or 135 of this chapter;

(3) An aircraft inspection program approved under 135.419 of this chapter and currently in use under part 135 of this chapter by a person holding a certificate issued under part 119 of this chapter; or

(4) An airplane inspection program approved under 125.247 of this chapter and currently in use under part 125 of this chapter.

(5) An inspection program that is part of the program manager's continuous airworthiness maintenance program under 91.1411 through 91.1443.

(c) The Administrator may require revision of the inspection program approved under this section in accordance with the provisions of 91.415.

[Docket No. FAA-2001-10047, 68 FR 54561, Sept. 17, 2003, as amended by Docket FAA-2018-0119, Amdt. 91-350, 83 FR 9171, Mar. 5, 2018]

91.1111 Maintenance training

The program manager must ensure that all employees who are responsible for maintenance related to program aircraft undergo appropriate initial and annual recurrent training and are competent to perform those duties.

91.1113 Maintenance record keeping

Each fractional ownership program manager must keep (using the system specified in the manual required in 91.1025) the records specified in 91.417(a) for the periods specified in 91.417(b).

91.1115 Inoperable instruments and equipment

(a) No person may take off an aircraft with inoperable instruments or equipment installed unless the following conditions are met:

(1) An approved Minimum Equipment List exists for that aircraft.

(2) The program manager has been issued management specifications authorizing operations in accordance with an approved Minimum Equipment List. The flight crew must have direct access at all times prior to flight to all of the information contained in the approved Minimum Equipment List through printed or other means approved by the Administrator in the program manager's management specifications. An approved Minimum Equipment List, as authorized by the management specifications, constitutes an approved change to the type design without requiring recertification.

(3) The approved Minimum Equipment List must:

(i) Be prepared in accordance with the limitations specified in paragraph (b) of this section.

(ii) Provide for the operation of the aircraft with certain instruments and equipment in an inoperable condition.

(4) Records identifying the inoperable instruments and equipment and the information required by (a)(3)(ii) of this section must be available to the pilot.

(5) The aircraft is operated under all applicable conditions and limitations contained in the Minimum Equipment List and the management specifications authorizing use of the Minimum Equipment List.

(b) The following instruments and equipment may not be included in the Minimum Equipment List:

(1) Instruments and equipment that are either specifically or otherwise required by the airworthiness requirements under which the airplane is type certificated and that are essential for safe operations under all operating conditions.

(2) Instruments and equipment required by an airworthiness directive to be in operable condition unless the airworthiness directive provides otherwise.

(3) Instruments and equipment required for specific operations by this part.

(c) Notwithstanding paragraphs (b)(1) and (b)(3) of this section, an aircraft with inoperable instruments or equipment may be operated under a special flight permit under 21.197 and 21.199 of this chapter.

(d) A person authorized to use an approved Minimum Equipment List issued for a specific aircraft under part 121, 125, or 135 of this chapter must use that Minimum Equipment List to comply with this section.

91.1411 Continuous airworthiness maintenance program use by fractional ownership program manager

Fractional ownership program aircraft may be maintained under a continuous airworthiness maintenance program (CAMP) under 91.1413 through 91.1443. Any program manager who elects to maintain the program aircraft using a continuous airworthiness maintenance program must comply with 91.1413 through 91.1443.

91.1413 CAMP: responsibility for airworthiness

(a) For aircraft maintained in accordance with a Continuous Airworthiness Maintenance Program, each program manager is primarily responsible for the following:

(1) Maintaining the airworthiness of the program aircraft, including airframes, aircraft engines, propellers, rotors, appliances, and parts.

(2) Maintaining its aircraft in accordance with the requirements of this chapter.

(3) Repairing defects that occur between regularly scheduled maintenance required under part 43 of this chapter.

(b) Each program manager who maintains program aircraft under a CAMP must—

(1) Employ a Director of Maintenance or equivalent position. The Director of Maintenance must be a certificated mechanic with airframe and powerplant ratings who has responsibility for the maintenance program on all program aircraft maintained under a continuous airworthiness maintenance program. This person cannot also act as Chief Inspector.

(2) Employ a Chief Inspector or equivalent position. The Chief Inspector must be a certificated mechanic with airframe and powerplant ratings who has overall responsibility for inspection aspects of the CAMP. This person cannot also act as Director of Maintenance.

(3) Have the personnel to perform the maintenance of program aircraft, including airframes, aircraft engines, propellers, rotors, appliances, emergency equipment and parts, under its manual and this chapter; or make arrangements with another person for the performance of maintenance. However, the program manager must ensure that any maintenance, preventive maintenance, or alteration that is performed by another person is performed under the program manager's operating manual and this chapter.

91.1415   CAMP: mechanical reliability reports

(a) Each program manager who maintains program aircraft under a CAMP must report the occurrence or detection of each failure, malfunction, or defect in an aircraft concerning—

(1) Fires during flight and whether the related fire-warning system functioned properly;

(2) Fires during flight not protected by related fire-warning system;

(3) False fire-warning during flight;

(4) An exhaust system that causes damage during flight to the engine, adjacent structure, equipment, or components;

(5) An aircraft component that causes accumulation or circulation of smoke, vapor, or toxic or noxious fumes in the crew compartment or passenger cabin during flight;

(6) Engine shutdown during flight because of flameout;

(7) Engine shutdown during flight when external damage to the engine or aircraft structure occurs;

(8) Engine shutdown during flight because of foreign object ingestion or icing;

(9) Shutdown of more than one engine during flight;

(10) A propeller feathering system or ability of the system to control overspeed during flight;

(11) A fuel or fuel-dumping system that affects fuel flow or causes hazardous leakage during flight;

(12) An unwanted landing gear extension or retraction or opening or closing of landing gear doors during flight;

(13) Brake system components that result in loss of brake actuating force when the aircraft is in motion on the ground;

(14) Aircraft structure that requires major repair;

(15) Cracks, permanent deformation, or corrosion of aircraft structures, if more than the maximum acceptable to the manufacturer or the FAA; and

(16) Aircraft components or systems that result in taking emergency actions during flight (except action to shut down an engine).

(b) For the purpose of this section, during flight means the period from the moment the aircraft leaves the surface of the earth on takeoff until it touches down on landing.

(c) In addition to the reports required by paragraph (a) of this section, each program manager must report any other failure, malfunction, or defect in an aircraft that occurs or is detected at any time if, in the manager's opinion, the failure, malfunction, or defect has endangered or may endanger the safe operation of the aircraft.

(d) Each program manager must send each report required by this section, in writing, covering each 24-hour period beginning at 0900 hours local time of each day and ending at 0900 hours local time on the next day to the Flight Standards office that issued the program manager's management specifications. Each report of occurrences during a 24-hour period must be mailed or transmitted to that office within the next 72 hours. However, a report that is due on Saturday or Sunday may be mailed or transmitted on the following Monday and one that is due on a holiday may be mailed or transmitted on the next workday. For aircraft operated in areas where mail is not collected, reports may be mailed or transmitted within 72 hours after the aircraft returns to a point where the mail is collected.

(e) The program manager must transmit the reports required by this section on a form and in a manner prescribed by the Administrator, and must include as much of the following as is available:

(1) The type and identification number of the aircraft.

(2) The name of the program manager.

(3) The date.

(4) The nature of the failure, malfunction, or defect.

(5) Identification of the part and system involved, including available information pertaining to type designation of the major component and time since last overhaul, if known.

(6) Apparent cause of the failure, malfunction or defect (for example, wear, crack, design deficiency, or personnel error).

(7) Other pertinent information necessary for more complete identification, determination of seriousness, or corrective action.

(f) A program manager that is also the holder of a type certificate (including a supplemental type certificate), a Parts Manufacturer Approval, or a Technical Standard Order Authorization, or that is the licensee of a type certificate need not report a failure, malfunction, or defect under this section if the failure, malfunction, or defect has been reported by it under 21.3 of this chapter or under the accident reporting provisions of part 830 of the regulations of the National Transportation Safety Board.

(g) No person may withhold a report required by this section even when not all information required by this section is available.

(h) When the program manager receives additional information, including information from the manufacturer or other agency, concerning a report required by this section, the program manager must expeditiously submit it as a supplement to the first report and reference the date and place of submission of the first report.

[Docket No. FAA-2001-10047, 68 FR 54561, Sept. 17, 2003, as amended by Docket FAA-2018-0119, Amdt. 91-350, 83 FR 9171, Mar. 5, 2018]

91.1417   CAMP: mechanical interruption summary report

Each program manager who maintains program aircraft under a CAMP must mail or deliver, before the end of the 10th day of the following month, a summary report of the following occurrences in multiengine aircraft for the preceding month to the Flight Standards office that issued the management specifications:

(a) Each interruption to a flight, unscheduled change of aircraft en route, or unscheduled stop or diversion from a route, caused by known or suspected mechanical difficulties or malfunctions that are not required to be reported under 91.1415.

(b) The number of propeller featherings in flight, listed by type of propeller and engine and aircraft on which it was installed. Propeller featherings for training, demonstration, or flight check purposes need not be reported.

[Docket No. FAA-2001-10047, 68 FR 54561, Sept. 17, 2003, as amended by Docket FAA-2018-0119, Amdt. 91-350, 83 FR 9171, Mar. 5, 2018]

91.1423　CAMP: maintenance organization

(a) Each program manager who maintains program aircraft under a CAMP that has its personnel perform any of its maintenance (other than required inspections), preventive maintenance, or alterations, and each person with whom it arranges for the performance of that work, must have an organization adequate to perform the work.

(b) Each program manager who has personnel perform any inspections required by the program manager's manual under 91.1427(b) (2) or (3), (in this subpart referred to as required inspections), and each person with whom the program manager arranges for the performance of that work, must have an organization adequate to perform that work.

(c) Each person performing required inspections in addition to other maintenance, preventive maintenance, or alterations, must organize the performance of those functions so as to separate the required inspection functions from the other maintenance, preventive maintenance, or alteration functions. The separation must be below the level of administrative control at which overall responsibility for the required inspection functions and other maintenance, preventive maintenance, or alterations is exercised.

91.1425　CAMP: maintenance, preventive maintenance, and alteration programs

Each program manager who maintains program aircraft under a CAMP must have an inspection program and a program covering other maintenance, preventive maintenance, or alterations that ensures that—

(a) Maintenance, preventive maintenance, or alterations performed by its personnel, or by other persons, are performed under the program manager's manual;

(b) Competent personnel and adequate facilities and equipment are provided for the proper performance of maintenance, preventive maintenance, or alterations; and

(c) Each aircraft released to service is airworthy and has been properly maintained for operation under this part.

91.1427　CAMP: manual requirements

(a) Each program manager who maintains program aircraft under a CAMP must put in the operating manual the chart or description of the program manager's organization required by 91.1423 and a list of persons with whom it has arranged for the performance of any of its required inspections, and other maintenance, preventive maintenance, or alterations, including a general description of that work.

(b) Each program manager must put in the operating manual the programs required by 91.1425 that must be followed in performing maintenance, preventive maintenance, or alterations of that program manager's aircraft, including airframes, aircraft engines, propellers, rotors, appliances, emergency equipment, and parts, and must include at least the following:

(1) The method of performing routine and nonroutine maintenance (other than required inspections), preventive maintenance, or alterations.

(2) A designation of the items of maintenance and alteration that must be inspected (required inspections) including at least those that could result in a failure, malfunction, or defect endangering the safe operation of the aircraft, if not performed properly or if improper parts or materials are used.

(3) The method of performing required inspections and a designation by occupational title of personnel authorized to perform each required inspection.

(4) Procedures for the reinspection of work performed under previous required inspection findings (buy-back procedures).

(5) Procedures, standards, and limits necessary for required inspections and acceptance or rejection of the items required to be inspected and for periodic inspection and calibration of precision tools, measuring devices, and test equipment.

(6) Procedures to ensure that all required inspections are performed.

(7) Instructions to prevent any person who performs any item of work from performing any required inspection of that work.

(8) Instructions and procedures to prevent any decision of an inspector regarding any required inspection from being countermanded by persons other than supervisory personnel of the inspection unit, or a person at the level of administrative control that has overall responsibility for the management of both the required inspection functions and the other maintenance, preventive maintenance, or alterations functions.

(9) Procedures to ensure that maintenance (including required inspections), preventive maintenance, or alterations that are not completed because of work interruptions are properly completed before the aircraft is released to service.

(c) Each program manager must put in the manual a suitable system (which may include an electronic or coded system) that provides for the retention of the following information—

(1) A description (or reference to data acceptable to the Administrator) of the work performed;

(2) The name of the person performing the work if the work is performed by a person outside the organization of the program manager; and

(3) The name or other positive identification of the individual approving the work.

(d) For the purposes of this part, the program manager must prepare that part of its manual containing maintenance information and instructions, in whole or in part, in a format acceptable to the Administrator, that is retrievable in the English language.

91.1429　CAMP: required inspection personnel

(a) No person who maintains an aircraft under a CAMP may use any person to perform required inspections unless the person performing the inspection is appropriately certificated, properly trained, qualified, and authorized to do so.

(b) No person may allow any person to perform a required inspection unless, at the time the work was performed, the person performing that inspection is under the supervision and control of the chief inspector.

(c) No person may perform a required inspection if that person performed the item of work required to be inspected.

(d) Each program manager must maintain, or must ensure that each person with whom it arranges to perform required inspections maintains, a current listing of persons who have been trained, qualified, and authorized to conduct required inspections. The persons must be identified by name, occupational title, and the inspections that they are authorized to perform. The program manager (or person with whom it arranges to perform its required inspections) must give written information to each person so authorized, describing the extent of that person's responsibilities, authorities, and inspectional limitations. The list must be made available for inspection by the Administrator upon request.

91.1431　CAMP: continuing analysis and surveillance

(a) Each program manager who maintains program aircraft under a CAMP must establish and maintain a system for the continuing analysis and surveillance of the performance and effectiveness of its inspection program and the program covering other maintenance, preventive maintenance, and alterations and for the correction of any deficiency in those programs, regardless of whether those programs are carried out by employees of the program manager or by another person.

(b) Whenever the Administrator finds that the programs described in paragraph (a) of this section does not contain adequate procedures and standards to meet this part, the program manager must, after notification by the Administrator, make changes in those programs requested by the Administrator.

(c) A program manager may petition the Administrator to reconsider the notice to make a change in a program. The petition must be filed with the Executive Director, Flight Standards Service, within 30 days after the program manager receives the notice. Except in the case of an emergency requiring immediate action in the interest of safety, the filing of the petition stays the notice pending a decision by the Administrator.

[Docket No. FAA-2001-10047, 68 FR 54561, Sept. 17, 2003, as amended by Docket FAA-2018-0119, Amdt. 91-350, 83 FR 9171, Mar. 5, 2018]

91.1433 CAMP: maintenance and preventive maintenance training program

Each program manager who maintains program aircraft under a CAMP or a person performing maintenance or preventive maintenance functions for it must have a training program to ensure that each person (including inspection personnel) who determines the adequacy of work done is fully informed about procedures and techniques and new equipment in use and is competent to perform that person's duties.

91.1435 CAMP: certificate requirements

(a) Except for maintenance, preventive maintenance, alterations, and required inspections performed by repair stations located outside the United States certificated under the provisions of part 145 of this chapter, each person who is directly in charge of maintenance, preventive maintenance, or alterations for a CAMP, and each person performing required inspections for a CAMP must hold an appropriate airman certificate.

(b) For the purpose of this section, a person "directly in charge" is each person assigned to a position in which that person is responsible for the work of a shop or station that performs maintenance, preventive maintenance, alterations, or other functions affecting airworthiness. A person who is directly in charge need not physically observe and direct each worker constantly but must be available for consultation and decision on matters requiring instruction or decision from higher authority than that of the person performing the work.

91.1437 CAMP: authority to perform and approve maintenance

A program manager who maintains program aircraft under a CAMP may employ maintenance personnel, or make arrangements with other persons to perform maintenance and preventive maintenance as provided in its maintenance manual. Unless properly certificated, the program manager may not perform or approve maintenance for return to service.

91.1439 CAMP: maintenance recording requirements

(a) Each program manager who maintains program aircraft under a CAMP must keep (using the system specified in the manual required in 91.1427) the following records for the periods specified in paragraph (b) of this section:

(1) All the records necessary to show that all requirements for the issuance of an airworthiness release under 91.1443 have been met.

(2) Records containing the following information:

  (i) The total time in service of the airframe, engine, propeller, and rotor.

  (ii) The current status of life-limited parts of each airframe, engine, propeller, rotor, and appliance.

  (iii) The time since last overhaul of each item installed on the aircraft that are required to be overhauled on a specified time basis.

  (iv) The identification of the current inspection status of the aircraft, including the time since the last inspections required by the inspection program under which the aircraft and its appliances are maintained.

  (v) The current status of applicable airworthiness directives, including the date and methods of compliance, and, if the airworthiness directive involves recurring action, the time and date when the next action is required.

  (vi) A list of current major alterations and repairs to each airframe, engine, propeller, rotor, and appliance.

(b) Each program manager must retain the records required to be kept by this section for the following periods:

(1) Except for the records of the last complete overhaul of each airframe, engine, propeller, rotor, and appliance the records specified in paragraph (a)(1) of this section must be retained until the work is repeated or superseded by other work or for one year after the work is performed.

(2) The records of the last complete overhaul of each airframe, engine, propeller, rotor, and appliance must be retained until the work is superseded by work of equivalent scope and detail.

(3) The records specified in paragraph (a)(2) of this section must be retained as specified unless transferred with the aircraft at the time the aircraft is sold.

(c) The program manager must make all maintenance records required to be kept by this section available for inspection by the Administrator or any representative of the National Transportation Safety Board.

91.1441 CAMP: transfer of maintenance records

When a U.S.-registered fractional ownership program aircraft maintained under a CAMP is removed from the list of program aircraft in the management specifications, the program manager must transfer to the purchaser, at the time of the sale, the following records of that aircraft, in plain language form or in coded form that provides for the preservation and retrieval of information in a manner acceptable to the Administrator:

(a) The records specified in 91.1439(a)(2).

(b) The records specified in 91.1439(a)(1) that are not included in the records covered by paragraph (a) of this section, except that the purchaser may allow the program manager to keep physical custody of such records. However, custody of records by the program manager does not relieve the purchaser of its responsibility under 91.1439(c) to make the records available for inspection by the Administrator or any representative of the National Transportation Safety Board.

91.1443 CAMP: airworthiness release or aircraft maintenance log entry

(a) No program aircraft maintained under a CAMP may be operated after maintenance, preventive maintenance, or alterations are performed unless qualified, certificated personnel employed by the program manager prepare, or cause the person with whom the program manager arranges for the performance of the maintenance, preventive maintenance, or alterations, to prepare—

(1) An airworthiness release; or

(2) An appropriate entry in the aircraft maintenance log.

(b) The airworthiness release or log entry required by paragraph (a) of this section must—

(1) Be prepared in accordance with the procedure in the program manager's manual;

(2) Include a certification that—

  (i) The work was performed in accordance with the requirements of the program manager's manual;

  (ii) All items required to be inspected were inspected by an authorized person who determined that the work was satisfactorily completed;

  (iii) No known condition exists that would make the aircraft unairworthy;

(iv) So far as the work performed is concerned, the aircraft is in condition for safe operation; and

(3) Be signed by an authorized certificated mechanic.

(c) Notwithstanding paragraph (b)(3) of this section, after maintenance, preventive maintenance, or alterations performed by a repair station certificated under the provisions of part 145 of this chapter, the approval for return to service or log entry required by paragraph (a) of this section may be signed by a person authorized by that repair station.

(d) Instead of restating each of the conditions of the certification required by paragraph (b) of this section, the program manager may state in its manual that the signature of an authorized certificated mechanic or repairman constitutes that certification.

Subpart L — Continued Airworthiness and Safety Improvements

Source: Amdt. 91–297, 72 FR 63410, Nov. 8, 2007, unless otherwise noted.

91.1501 Purpose and definition

(a) This subpart requires operators to support the continued airworthiness of each airplane. These requirements may include, but are not limited to, revising the inspection program, incorporating design changes, and incorporating revisions to Instructions for Continued Airworthiness.

(b) [Reserved]

[Amdt. 91–297, 72 FR 63410, Nov. 8, 2007, as amended by Docket FAA-2018-0119, Amdt. 91–350, 83 FR 9171, Mar. 5, 2018]

91.1503 [Reserved]

91.1505 Repairs assessment for pressurized fuselages

(a) No person may operate an Airbus Model A300 (excluding the -600 series), British Aerospace Model BAC 1-11, Boeing Model 707, 720, 727, 737 or 747, McDonnell Douglas Model DC-8, DC-9/MD-80 or DC-10, Fokker Model F28, or Lockheed Model L-1011 airplane beyond applicable flight cycle implementation time specified below, or May 25, 2001, whichever occurs later, unless repair assessment guidelines applicable to the fuselage pressure boundary (fuselage skin, door skin, and bulkhead webs) are incorporated within its inspection program. The repair assessment guidelines must be approved by the responsible Aircraft Certification Service office for the type certificate for the affected airplane.

(1) For the Airbus Model A300 (excluding the –600 series), the flight cycle implementation time is:

(i) Model B2: 36,000 flights.

(ii) Model B4–100 (including Model B4–2C): 30,000 flights above the window line, and 36,000 flights below the window line.

(iii) Model B4–200: 25,500 flights above the window line, and 34,000 flights below the window line.

(2) For all models of the British Aerospace BAC 1–11, the flight cycle implementation time is 60,000 flights.

(3) For all models of the Boeing 707, the flight cycle implementation time is 15,000 flights.

(4) For all models of the Boeing 720, the flight cycle implementation time is 23,000 flights.

(5) For all models of the Boeing 727, the flight cycle implementation time is 45,000 flights.

(6) For all models of the Boeing 737, the flight cycle implementation time is 60,000 flights.

(7) For all models of the Boeing 747, the flight cycle implementation time is 15,000 flights.

(8) For all models of the McDonnell Douglas DC–8, the flight cycle implementation time is 30,000 flights.

(9) For all models of the McDonnell Douglas DC–9/MD–80, the flight cycle implementation time is 60,000 flights.

(10) For all models of the McDonnell Douglas DC–10, the flight cycle implementation time is 30,000 flights.

(11) For all models of the Lockheed L–1011, the flight cycle implementation time is 27,000 flights.

(12) For the Fokker F–28 Mark 1000, 2000, 3000, and 4000, the flight cycle implementation time is 60,000 flights.

(b) [Reserved]

[Doc. No. 29104, 65 FR 24125, Apr. 25, 2000; 65 FR 35703, June 5, 2000; 65 FR 50744, Aug. 21, 2000, as amended by Amdt. 91-266, 66 FR 23130, May 7, 2001; Amdt. 91-277, 67 FR 72834, Dec. 9, 2002; Amdt. 91-283, 69 FR 45941, July 30, 2004. Redesignated and amended by Amdt. 91-297, 72 FR 63410, Nov. 8, 2007; Docket FAA-2018-0119, Amdt. 91-350, 83 FR 9171, Mar. 5, 2018]

91.1507 Fuel tank system inspection program

(a) Except as provided in paragraph (g) of this section, this section applies to transport category, turbine-powered airplanes with a type certificate issued after January 1, 1958, that, as a result of original type certification or later increase in capacity, have—

(1) A maximum type-certificated passenger capacity of 30 or more, or

(2) A maximum payload capacity of 7,500 pounds or more.

(b) For each airplane on which an auxiliary fuel tank is installed under a field approval, before June 16, 2008, the operator must submit to the responsible Aircraft Certification Service Office proposed maintenance instructions for the tank that meet the requirements of Special Federal Aviation Regulation No. 88 (SFAR 88) of this chapter.

(c) After December 16, 2008, no operator may operate an airplane identified in paragraph (a) of this section unless the inspection program for that airplane has been revised to include applicable inspections, procedures, and limitations for fuel tank systems.

(d) The proposed fuel tank system inspection program revisions specified in paragraph (c) of this section must be based on fuel tank system Instructions for Continued Airworthiness (ICA) that have been developed in accordance with the applicable provisions of SFAR 88 of this chapter or §25.1529 and part 25, Appendix H, of this chapter, in effect on June 6, 2001 (including those developed for auxiliary fuel tanks, if any, installed under supplemental type certificates or other design approval) and that have been approved by the responsible Aircraft Certification Service Office.

(e) After December 16, 2008, before returning an airplane to service after any alterations for which fuel tank ICA are developed under SFAR 88, or under 25.1529 in effect on June 6, 2001, the operator must include in the inspection program for the airplane inspections and procedures for the fuel tank system based on those ICA.

(f) The fuel tank system inspection program changes identified in paragraphs (d) and (e) of this section and any later fuel tank system revisions must be submitted to the Flight Standards office responsible for review and approval.

(g) This section does not apply to the following airplane models:

(1) Bombardier CL–44

(2) Concorde

(3) deHavilland D.H. 106 Comet 4C

(4) VFW-Vereinigte Flugtechnische Werk VFW–614

(5) Illyushin Aviation IL 96T

(6) Bristol Aircraft Britannia 305

(7) Handley Page Herald Type 300

(8) Avions Marcel Dassault—Breguet Aviation Mercure 100C

(9) Airbus Caravelle

(10) Lockheed L–300

[Amdt. 91-297, 72 FR 63410, Nov. 8, 2007, as amended by Docket FAA-2018-0119, Amdt. 91-350, 83 FR 9172, Mar. 5, 2018]

Subpart M — Special Federal Aviation Regulations

91.1603   Special Federal Aviation Regulation No. 112— Prohibition Against Certain Flights in the Tripoli Flight Information Region (FIR) (HLLL).

(a) Applicability. This Special Federal Aviation Regulation (SFAR) applies to the following persons:

(1) All U.S. air carriers and U.S. commercial operators;

(2) All persons exercising the privileges of an airman certificate issued by the FAA, except when such persons are operating U.S.-registered aircraft for a foreign air carrier; and

(3) All operators of U.S.-registered civil aircraft, except when the operator of such aircraft is a foreign air carrier.

(b) Flight prohibition. Except as provided in paragraphs (c) and (d) of this section, no person described in paragraph (a) of this section may conduct flight operations in the following specified areas:

(1) The territory and airspace of Libya.

(2) Any portion of the Tripoli FIR (HLLL) that is outside the territory and airspace of Libya at altitudes below Flight Level (FL) 300.

(c) Permitted operations. This section does not prohibit persons described in paragraph (a) of this section from conducting the following flight operations in the Tripoli FIR (HLLL):

(1) Overflights of those portions of the Tripoli FIR (HLLL) that are outside the territory and airspace of Libya that occur at altitudes at or above Flight Level (FL) 300; or

(2) Flight operations in the Tripoli FIR (HLLL) that are conducted under a contract, grant, or cooperative agreement with a department, agency, or instrumentality of the U.S. Government (or under a subcontract between the prime contractor of the department, agency, or instrumentality and the person described in paragraph (a) of this section), with the approval of the FAA, or under an exemption issued by the FAA. The FAA will consider requests for approval or exemption in a timely manner, with the order of preference being: First, for those operations in support of U.S. Government-sponsored activities; second, for those operations in support of government-sponsored activities of a foreign country with the support of a U.S. Government department, agency, or instrumentality; and third, for all other operations.

(d) Emergency situations. In an emergency that requires immediate decision and action for the safety of the flight, the pilot in command of an aircraft may deviate from this section to the extent required by that emergency. Except for U.S. air carriers and commercial operators that are subject to the requirements of 14 CFR part 119, 121, 125, or 135, each person who deviates from this section must, within 10 days of the deviation, excluding Saturdays, Sundays, and Federal holidays, submit to the responsible Flight Standards Office a complete report of the operations of the aircraft involved in the deviation, including a description of the deviation and the reasons for it.

(e) Expiration. This Special Federal Aviation Regulation (SFAR) will remain in effect until March 20, 2023. The FAA may amend, rescind, or extend this SFAR, as necessary.

[Docket No FAA-2011-0246; Amdt. No.91-321E, 85 FR 45091, July 27, 2020]

91.1605   Special Federal Aviation Regulation No. 77 - Prohibition Against Certain Flights in the Baghdad Flight Information Region (FIR) (ORBB).

(a) Applicability. This section applies to the following persons:

(1) All U.S. air carriers and U.S. commercial operators;

(2) All persons exercising the privileges of an airman certificate issued by the FAA, except when such persons are operating U.S.-registered aircraft for a foreign air carrier; and

(3) All operators of civil aircraft registered in the United States, except when the operator of such aircraft is a foreign air carrier.

(b) Flight prohibition. Except as provided in paragraphs (c) and (d) of this section, no person described in paragraph (a) of this section may conduct flight operations in the Baghdad Flight Information Region (FIR) (ORBB) at altitudes below Flight Level (FL) 320.

(c) Permitted operations. This section does not prohibit persons described in paragraph (a) of this section from conducting flight operations in the Baghdad FIR (ORBB) at altitudes below FL320, provided that such flight operations occur under a contract, grant, or cooperative agreement with a department, agency, or instrumentality of the U.S. Government (or under a subcontract between the prime contractor of the department, agency, or instrumentality and the person described in paragraph (a) of this section) with the approval of the FAA, or under an exemption issued by the FAA. The FAA will consider requests for approval or exemption in a timely manner, with the order of preference being: first, for those operations in support of U.S. Government-sponsored activities; second, for those operations in support of government-sponsored activities of a foreign country with the support of a U.S. Government department, agency, or instrumentality; and third, for all other operations.

(d) Emergency situations. In an emergency that requires immediate decision and action for the safety of the flight, the pilot in command of an aircraft may deviate from this section to the extent required by that emergency. Except for U.S. air carriers and commercial operators that are subject to the requirements of part 119, 121, 125, or 135 of this chapter, each person who deviates from this section must, within 10 days of the deviation, excluding Saturdays, Sundays, and Federal holidays, submit to the responsible Flight Standards office a complete report of the operations of the aircraft involved in the deviation, including a description of the deviation and the reasons for it.

(e) Expiration. This SFAR will remain in effect until October 26, 2024. The FAA may amend, rescind, or extend this SFAR, as necessary.

[Docket No. FAA-2018-0927, Amdt. No. 91-353A, 85 FR 65693, Oct. 16, 2020, as amended by Amdt. No. 91-353B, 87 FR 57390, Sept. 20, 2022)]

91.1607   Special Federal Aviation Regulation No. 113 - Prohibition Against Certain Flights in Specified Areas of the Dnipro Flight Information Region (FIR) (UKDV).

(a) Applicability. This Special Federal Aviation Regulation (SFAR) applies to the following persons:

(1) All U.S. air carriers and U.S. commercial operators;

(2) All persons exercising the privileges of an airman certificate issued by the FAA, except when such persons are operating U.S.-registered aircraft for a foreign air carrier; and

(3) All operators of U.S.-registered civil aircraft, except when the operator of such aircraft is a foreign air carrier.

(b) Flight prohibition. Except as provided in paragraphs (c) and (d) of this section, no person described in paragraph (a) of this section may conduct flight operations in the Dnipro FIR (UKDV) from the surface to unlimited, east of a line drawn direct from ABDAR (471802N 351732E) along airway M853 to NIKAD (485946N 355519E), then along airway N604 to GOBUN (501806N 373824E). This prohibition applies to airways M853 and N604. This prohibition extends from the surface to unlimited and includes that portion of the Kyiv Upper Information Region (UIR)(UKBU) airspace within the lateral limits set forth in this paragraph (b) from the upper boundaries of the Dnipro FIR to unlimited.

(c) Permitted operations. This section does not prohibit persons described in paragraph (a) of this section from conducting flight operations in the specified areas described in paragraph (b) of this section, under the following circumstances:

(1) Operations are permitted to the extent necessary to take off from and land at the following three airports, subject to the approval of, and in accordance with the conditions established by, the appropriate authorities of Ukraine:

    (i) Kharkiv International Airport (UKHH);

    (ii) Dnipro International Airport (UKDD); and

    (iii) Zaporizhzhia International Airport (UKDE).

(2) Operations are permitted provided that they are conducted under a contract, grant, or cooperative agreement with a department, agency, or instrumentality of the U.S. Government (or under a subcontract between the prime contractor of the department, agency, or instrumentality of the U.S. Government and the person described in paragraph (a) of this section) with the approval of the FAA, or under an exemption issued by the FAA. The FAA will consider requests for approval or exemption in a timely manner, with the order of preference being: First, for those operations in support of U.S. Government-sponsored activities; second, for those operations in support of government-sponsored activities of a foreign country with the support of a U.S. Government department, agency, or instrumentality; and third, for all other operations.

(d) Emergency situations. In an emergency that requires immediate decision and action for the safety of the flight, the pilot in command of an aircraft may deviate from this section to the extent required by that emergency. Except for U.S. air carriers and commercial operators that are subject to the requirements of 14 CFR part 119, 121, 125, or 135, each person who deviates from this section must, within 10 days of the deviation, excluding Saturdays, Sundays, and Federal holidays, submit to the responsible Flight Standards office a complete report of the operations of the aircraft involved in the deviation, including a description of the deviation and the reasons for it.

(e) Expiration. This SFAR will remain in effect until October 27, 2023. The FAA may amend, rescind, or extend this SFAR as necessary.

[86 FR 55491, Oct. 6, 2021]

91.1609 Special Federal Aviation Regulation No. 114—Prohibition Against Certain Flights in the Damascus Flight Information Region (FIR) (OSTT).

(a) Applicability. This section applies to the following persons:

(1) All U.S. air carriers and U.S. commercial operators;

(2) All persons exercising the privileges of an airman certificate issued by the FAA, except when such persons are operating U.S.-registered aircraft for a foreign air carrier; and

(3) All operators of U.S.-registered civil aircraft, except when the operator of such aircraft is a foreign air carrier.

(b) Flight prohibition. Except as provided in paragraphs (c) and (d) of this section, no person described in paragraph (a) of this section may conduct flight operations in the Damascus Flight Information Region (FIR) (OSTT).

(c) Permitted operations. This section does not prohibit persons described in paragraph (a) of this section from conducting flight operations in the Damascus Flight Information Region (FIR) (OSTT), provided that such flight operations are conducted under a contract, grant, or cooperative agreement with a department, agency, or instrumentality of the U.S. government (or under a subcontract between the prime contractor of the department, agency, or instrumentality and the person described in paragraph (a) of this section) with the approval of the FAA, or under an exemption issued by the FAA. The FAA will consider requests for approval or exemption in a timely manner, with the order of preference being: First, for those operations in support of U.S. government-sponsored activities; second, for those operations in support of government-sponsored activities of a foreign country with the support of a U.S. government department, agency, or instrumentality; and third, for all other operations.

(d) Emergency situations. In an emergency that requires immediate decision and action for the safety of the flight, the pilot in command of an aircraft may deviate from this section to the extent required by that emergency. Except for U.S. air carriers and commercial operators that are subject to the requirements of 14 CFR part 119, 121, 125, or 135, each person who deviates from this section must, within 10 days of the deviation, excluding Saturdays, Sundays, and Federal holidays, submit to the responsible Flight Standards office a complete report of the operations of the aircraft involved in the deviation, including a description of the deviation and the reasons for it.

(e) Expiration. This SFAR will remain in effect until December 30, 2023. The FAA may amend, rescind, or extend this SFAR, as necessary.

[Docket FAA-2017-0768, Amdt. 91-348, 82 FR 40949, Aug. 29, 2017; Amdt. 91-348A, 82 FR 42592, Sept. 11, 2017, as amended by Amdt. No. 91-348B, 83 FR 63414, Dec. 10, 2018; Amdt. No. 91-348C; 85 FR 75845, Nov. 27, 2020]

91.1611 Special Federal Aviation Regulation No. 115—Prohibition Against Certain Flights in Specified Areas of the Sanaa Flight Information Region (FIR) (OYSC).

(a) Applicability. This Special Federal Aviation Regulation (SFAR) applies to the following persons:

(1) All U.S. air carriers and U.S. commercial operators;

(2) All persons exercising the privileges of an airman certificate issued by the FAA, except when such persons are operating U.S.-registered aircraft for a foreign air carrier; and

(3) All operators of U.S.-registered civil aircraft, except when the operator of such aircraft is a foreign air carrier.

(b) Flight prohibition. Except as provided in paragraphs (c) and (d) of this section, no person described in paragraph (a) of this section may conduct flight operations in the portion of the Sanaa Flight Information Region (FIR) (OYSC) that is west of a line drawn direct from KAPET (163322N 0530614E) to NODMA (152603N 0533359E), northwest of a line drawn direct from NODMA to ORBAT (140638N 0503924E) then from ORBAT to PAKER (115500N 0463500E), north of a line drawn direct from PAKER to PARIM (123142N 0432712E), and east of a line drawn direct from PARIM to RIBOK (154700N 0415230E). Use of jet route UN303 is not authorized.

(c) Permitted operations. This section does not prohibit persons described in paragraph (a) of this section from conducting flight operations in the Sanaa FIR (OYSC) under the following circumstances:

(1) Flight operations may be conducted in the Sanaa FIR (OYSC) in that airspace east of a line drawn direct from KAPET (163322N 0530614E) to NODMA (152603N 0533359E), southeast of a line drawn direct from NODMA to ORBAT (140638N 0503924E) then from ORBAT to PAKER (115500N 0463500E), south of a line drawn direct from PAKER to PARIM (123142N 0432712E), and west of a line drawn direct from PARIM to RIBOK (154700N 0415230E). Use of jet routes UT702 and M999 are authorized. All flight operations conducted under this subparagraph must be conducted subject to the approval of, and in accordance with the conditions established by, the appropriate authorities of Yemen.

(2) Flight operations may be conducted in the Sanaa FIR (OYSC) in that airspace west of a line drawn direct from KAPET (163322N 0530614E) to NODMA (152603N 0533359E), northwest of a line drawn direct from NODMA to ORBAT (140638N 0503924E) then from ORBAT to PAKER (115500N 0463500E), north of a line drawn direct from PAKER to PARIM (123142N 0432712E), and east of a line drawn direct from PARIM to RIBOK (154700N 0415230E) if such flight operations are conducted under a contract, grant, or cooperative agreement with a department, agency, or instrumentality

of the U.S. Government (or under a subcontract between the prime contractor of the U.S. Government department, agency, or instrumentality and the person subject to paragraph (a)), with the approval of the FAA, or under an exemption issued by the FAA. The FAA will consider requests for approval or exemption in a timely manner, with the order of preference being: First, for those operations in support of U.S. Government-sponsored activities; second, for those operations in support of government-sponsored activities of a foreign country with the support of a U.S. government department, agency, or instrumentality; and third, for all other operations.

(d) *Emergency situations.* In an emergency that requires immediate decision and action for the safety of the flight, the pilot in command of an aircraft may deviate from this section to the extent required by that emergency. Except for U.S. air carriers and commercial operators that are subject to the requirements of 14 CFR part 119, 121, 125, or 135, each person who deviates from this section must, within 10 days of the deviation, excluding Saturdays, Sundays, and Federal holidays, submit to the responsible Flight Standards office a complete report of the operations of the aircraft involved in the deviation, including a description of the deviation and the reasons for it.

(e) *Expiration.* This SFAR will remain in effect until January 7, 2025. The FAA may amend, rescind, or extend this SFAR, as necessary.

[Amdt. 91-340B, 84 FR 67665, Dec. 11, 2019, as amended by Amdt. 91-340C, 86 FR 69173, Dec. 7, 2021]

91.1613 Special Federal Aviation Regulation No. 107— Prohibition Against Certain Flights in the Territory and Airspace of Somalia

(a) *Applicability.* This Special Federal Aviation Regulation (SFAR) applies to the following persons:

(1) All U.S. air carriers and U.S. commercial operators;

(2) All persons exercising the privileges of an airman certificate issued by the FAA, except when such persons are operating U.S.-registered aircraft for a foreign air carrier; and

(3) All operators of U.S.-registered civil aircraft, except when the operator of such aircraft is a foreign air carrier.

(b) *Flight prohibition.* Except as provided in paragraphs (c) and (d) of this section, no person described in paragraph (a) of this section may conduct flight operations in the territory and airspace of Somalia at altitudes below Flight Level (FL) 260.

(c) *Permitted operations.* This section does not prohibit persons described in paragraph (a) of this section from conducting flight operations in the territory and airspace of Somalia under the following circumstances:

(1) Overflights of Somalia may be conducted at or above FL260 subject to the approval of, and in accordance with the conditions established by, the appropriate authorities of Somalia.

(2) Flight operations may be conducted in the territory and airspace of Somalia at altitudes below FL260 if such flight operations are conducted under a contract, grant, or cooperative agreement with a department, agency, or instrumentality of the U.S. Government (or under a subcontract between the prime contractor of the U.S. Government department, agency, or instrumentality and the person described in paragraph (a) of this section) with the approval of the FAA or under an exemption issued by the FAA. The FAA will consider requests for approval or exemption in a timely manner, with the order of preference being: First, for those operations in support of U.S. Government-sponsored activities; second, for those operations in support of government-sponsored activities of a foreign country with the support of a U.S. government department, agency, or instrumentality; and third, for all other operations.

(d) *Emergency situations.* In an emergency that requires immediate decision and action for the safety of the flight, the pilot in command of an aircraft may deviate from this section to the extent required by that emergency. Except for U.S. air carriers and commercial operators that are subject to the requirements of 14 CFR part 119, 121, 125, or 135, each person who deviates from this section must, within 10 days of the deviation, excluding Saturdays, Sundays, and Federal holidays, submit to the responsible Flight Standards office a complete report of the operations of the aircraft involved in the deviation, including a description of the deviation and the reasons for it.

(e) *Expiration.* This SFAR will remain in effect until January 7, 2023. The FAA may amend, rescind, or extend this SFAR as necessary.

[Docket FAA-2007-27602, Amdt.91-339, 81 FR 726, Jan. 7, 2016 as amended by Amdt. 91-339A, 82 FR 58550, Dec. 13, 2017; Docket FAA-2018-0119, Amdt. 91-350, 83 FR 9172, Mar. 5, 2018; Amdt 91-339B, 84 FR 67671, Dec. 11, 2019]

91.1615 Special Federal Aviation Regulation No. 79— Prohibition Against Certain Flights in the Pyongyang Flight Information Region (FIR) (ZKKP)

(a) *Applicability.* This Special Federal Aviation Regulation (SFAR) applies to the following persons:

(1) All U.S. air carriers and U.S. commercial operators;

(2) All persons exercising the privileges of an airman certificate issued by the FAA, except when such persons are operating U.S.-registered aircraft for a foreign air carrier; and

(3) All operators of U.S.-registered civil aircraft, except when the operator of such aircraft is a foreign air carrier.

(b) *Flight prohibition.* Except as provided in paragraphs (c) and (d) of this section, no person described in paragraph (a) of this section may conduct flight operations in the Pyongyang Flight Information Region (FIR) (ZKKP).

(c) *Permitted operations.* This section does not prohibit persons described in paragraph (a) of this section from conducting flight operations in the Pyongyang Flight Information Region (FIR) (ZKKP), provided that such flight operations are conducted under a contract, grant, or cooperative agreement with a department, agency, or instrumentality of the U.S. government (or under a subcontract between the prime contractor of the department, agency, or instrumentality and the person described in paragraph (a) of this section) with the approval of the FAA, or under an exemption issued by the FAA. The FAA will consider requests for approval or exemption in a timely manner, with the order of preference being: First, for those operations in support of U.S. government-sponsored activities; second, for those operations in support of government-sponsored activities of a foreign country with the support of a U.S. Government department agency, or instrumentality; and third, for all other operations.

(d) *Emergency situations.* In an emergency that requires immediate decision and action for the safety of the flight, the pilot in command of an aircraft may deviate from this section to the extent required by that emergency. Except for U.S. air carriers and commercial operators that are subject to the requirements of 14 CFR part 119, 121, 125, or 135, each person who deviates from this section must, within 10 days of the deviation, excluding Saturdays, Sundays, and Federal holidays, submit to the responsible Flight Standards Office a complete report of the operations of the aircraft involved in the deviation, including a description of the deviation and the reasons for it.

(e) *Expiration.* This SFAR will remain in effect until September 18 2023. The FAA may amend, rescind, or extend this SFAR, as necessary.

[Docket No. FAA-2018-0838, Amdt. No. 91-352, 83 FR 47064 Sept. 18, 2018, as amended by Amdt. No. 91-352A, 85 FR 55377 Sept. 8, 2020]

91.1617 Special Federal Aviation Regulation No. 117 - Prohibition Against Certain Flights in the Tehran Flight Information Region (FIR) (OIIX)

(a) Applicability. This Special Federal Aviation Regulation (SFAR) applies to the following persons:

(1) All U.S. air carriers and U.S. commercial operators;

(2) All persons exercising the privileges of an airman certificate issued by the FAA, except when such persons are operating U.S.-registered aircraft for a foreign air carrier; and

(3) All operators of U.S.-registered civil aircraft, except when the operator of such aircraft is a foreign air carrier.

(b) Flight prohibition. Except as provided in paragraphs (c) and (d) of this section, no person described in paragraph (a) of this section may conduct flight operations in the Tehran Flight Information Region (FIR) (OIIX).

(c) Permitted operations. This section does not prohibit persons described in paragraph (a) of this section from conducting flight operations in the Tehran FIR (OIIX), provided that such flight operations are conducted under a contract, grant, or cooperative agreement with a department, agency, or instrumentality of the U.S. Government (or under a subcontract between the prime contractor of the department, agency, or instrumentality and the person described in paragraph (a) of this section) with the approval of the FAA, or under an exemption issued by the FAA. The FAA will consider requests for approval or exemption in a timely manner, with the order of preference being: First, for those operations in support of U.S. Government-sponsored activities; second, for those operations in support of government-sponsored activities of a foreign country with the support of a U.S. Government department, agency, or instrumentality; and third, for all other operations.

(d) Emergency situations. In an emergency that requires immediate decision and action for the safety of the flight, the pilot in command of an aircraft may deviate from this section to the extent required by that emergency. Except for U.S. air carriers and commercial operators that are subject to the requirements of 14 CFR parts 119, 121, 125, or 135, each person who deviates from this section must, within 10 days of the deviation, excluding Saturdays, Sundays, and Federal holidays, submit to the responsible Flight Standards Office a complete report of the operations of the aircraft involved in the deviation, including a description of the deviation and the reasons for it.

(e) Expiration. This SFAR will remain in effect until October 31, 2024. The FAA may amend, rescind, or extend this SFAR, as necessary.

[Docket No. FAA-2020-0874, Amdt. No. 91-359, 85 FR 68440, Oct. 29, 2020, as amended by Amdt. No. 91-359A, 87 FR 57834, Sept. 20, 2022)]

Subpart N — Mitsubishi MU-2B Series Special Training, Experience, and Operating Requirements

Source: Docket FAA-2006-24981, Amdt. 91-344, 81 FR 61591, Sept. 7, 2016, unless otherwise noted.

91.1701 Applicability

(a) On and after November 7, 2016, all training conducted in an MU-2B must follow an approved MU-2B training program that meets the standards of this subpart.

(b) This subpart applies to all persons who operate a Mitsubishi MU-2B series airplane, including those who act as pilot in command, act as second-in-command, or other persons who manipulate the controls while under the supervision of a pilot in command.

(c) This subpart also applies to those persons who provide pilot training for a Mitsubishi MU-2B series airplane. The requirements in this subpart are in addition to the requirements of parts 61, 91, and 135 of this chapter.

91.1703 Compliance and eligibility

(a) Except as provided in paragraph (b) of this section, no person may manipulate the controls, act as PIC, act as second-in-command, or provide pilot training for a Mitsubishi MU-2B series airplane unless that person meets the requirements of this subpart.

(b) A person who does not meet the requirements of this subpart may manipulate the controls of a Mitsubishi MU-2B series airplane if a pilot in command who meets the requirements of this subpart is occupying a pilot station, no passengers or cargo are carried on board the airplane, and the flight is being conducted for one of the following reasons—

(1) The pilot in command is providing pilot training to the manipulator of the controls;

(2) The pilot in command is conducting a maintenance test flight with a second pilot or certificated mechanic; or

(3) The pilot in command is conducting simulated instrument flight and is using a safety pilot other than the pilot in command who manipulates the controls for the purposes of 91.109(b).

(c) A person is required to complete Initial/transition training if that person has fewer than—

(1) 50 hours of documented flight time manipulating the controls while serving as pilot in command of a Mitsubishi MU-2B series airplane in the preceding 24 months; or

(2) 500 hours of documented flight time manipulating the controls while serving as pilot in command of a Mitsubishi MU-2B series airplane.

(d) A person is eligible to receive Requalification training in lieu of Initial/transition training if that person has at least—

(1) 50 hours of documented flight time manipulating the controls while serving as pilot in command of a Mitsubishi MU-2B series airplane in the preceding 24 months; or

(2) 500 hours of documented flight time manipulating the controls while serving as pilot in command of a Mitsubishi MU-2B series airplane.

(e) A person is required to complete Recurrent training within the preceding 12 months. Successful completion of Initial/transition or Requalification training within the preceding 12 months satisfies the requirement of Recurrent training. A person must successfully complete Initial/transition training or Requalification training before being eligible to receive Recurrent training.

(f) Successful completion of Initial/transition training or Requalification training is a one-time requirement. A person may elect to retake Initial/transition training or Requalification training in lieu of Recurrent training.

(g) A person is required to complete Differences training in accordance with an FAA approved MU-2B training program if that person operates more than one MU-2B model as specified in 91.1707(c).

FAR 91

91.1705 Required pilot training

(a) Except as provided in 91.1703(b), no person may manipulate the controls, act as pilot in command, or act as second-in-command of a Mitsubishi MU-2B series airplane for the purpose of flight unless—

(1) The requirements for ground and flight training on Initial/transition, Requalification, Recurrent, and Differences training have been completed in accordance with an FAA approved MU-2B training program that meets the standards of this subpart; and

(2) That person's logbook has been endorsed in accordance with paragraph (f) of this section.

(b) Except as provided in 91.1703(b), no person may manipulate the controls, act as pilot in command, or act as second-in-command, of a Mitsubishi MU-2B series airplane for the purpose of flight unless—

(1) That person satisfactorily completes, if applicable, annual Recurrent pilot training on the Special Emphasis Items, and all items listed in the Training Course Final Phase Check in accordance with an FAA approved MU-2B training program that meets the standards of this subpart; and

(2) That person's logbook has been endorsed in accordance with paragraph (f) of this section.

(c) Satisfactory completion of the competency check required by 135.293 of this chapter within the preceding 12 calendar months may not be substituted for the Mitsubishi MU-2B series airplane annual recurrent flight training of this section.

(d) Satisfactory completion of a Federal Aviation Administration sponsored pilot proficiency program, as described in 61.56(e) of this chapter may not be substituted for the Mitsubishi MU-2B series airplane annual recurrent flight training of this section.

(e) If a person complies with the requirements of paragraph (a) or (b) of this section in the calendar month before or the calendar month after the month in which compliance with these paragraphs are required, that person is considered to have accomplished the training requirement in the month the training is due.

(f) The endorsement required under paragraph (a) and (b) of this section must be made by—

(1) A certificated flight instructor or a simulator instructor authorized by a Training Center certificated under part 142 of this chapter and meeting the qualifications of 91.1713; or

(2) For persons operating the Mitsubishi MU-2B series airplane for a 14 CFR part 119 certificate holder within the last 12 calendar months, the part 119 certificate holder's flight instructor if authorized by the FAA and if that flight instructor meets the requirements of 91.1713.

(g) All training conducted for a Mitsubishi MU-2B series airplane must be completed in accordance with an MU-2B series airplane checklist that has been accepted by the Federal Aviation Administration's MU-2B Flight Standardization Board or the applicable MU-2B series checklist (incorporated by reference, see 91.1721).

(h) MU-2B training programs must contain ground training and flight training sufficient to ensure pilot proficiency for the safe operation of MU-2B aircraft, including:

(1) A ground training curriculum sufficient to ensure pilot knowledge of MU-2B aircraft, aircraft systems, and procedures, necessary for safe operation; and

(2) Flight training curriculum including flight training maneuver profiles sufficient in number and detail to ensure pilot proficiency in all MU-2B operations for each MU-2B model in correlation with MU-2B limitations, procedures, aircraft performance, and MU-2B Cockpit Checklist procedures applicable to the MU-2B model being trained. A MU-2B training program must contain, at a minimum, the following flight training maneuver profiles applicable to the MU-2B model being trained:

   (i) Normal takeoff with 5- and 20- degrees flaps;

   (ii) Takeoff engine failure with 5- and 20- degrees flaps;

   (iii) Takeoff engine failure on runway or rejected takeoff;

   (iv) Takeoff engine failure after liftoff—unable to climb (may be completed in classroom or flight training device only);

   (v) Steep turns;

   (vi) Slow flight maneuvers;

   (vii) One engine inoperative maneuvering with loss of directional control;

   (viii) Approach to stall in clean configuration and with wings level;

   (ix) Approach to stall in takeoff configuration with 15- to 30- degrees bank;

   (x) Approach to stall in landing configuration with gear down and 40-degrees of flaps;

   (xi) Accelerated stall with no flaps;

   (xii) Emergency descent at low speed;

   (xiii) Emergency descent at high speed;

   (xiv) Unusual attitude recovery with the nose high;

   (xv) Unusual attitude recovery with the nose low;

   (xvi) Normal landing with 20- and 40-degrees flaps;

   (xvii) Go around and rejected landing;

   (xviii) No flap or 5-degrees flaps landing;

   (xix) One engine inoperative landing with 5- and 20- degrees flaps;

   (xx) Crosswind landing;

   (xxi) Instrument landing system (ILS) and missed approach;

   (xxii) Two engine missed approach;

   (xxiii) One engine inoperative ILS and missed approach;

   (xxiv) One engine inoperative missed approach;

   (xxv) Non-precision and missed approach;

   (xxvi) Non-precision continuous descent final approach and missed approach;

   (xxvii) One engine inoperative non-precision and missed approach;

   (xxviii) One engine inoperative non-precision CDFA and missed approach;

   (xxix) Circling approach at weather minimums;

   (xxx) One engine inoperative circling approach at weather minimums.

(3) Flight training must include a final phase check sufficient to document pilot proficiency in the flight training maneuver profiles at the completion of training; and

(4) Differences training for applicable MU-2B model variants sufficient to ensure pilot proficiency in each model operated. Current MU-2B differences requirements are specified in 91.1707(c). A person must complete Differences training if a person operates more than one MU-2B model as specified in 91.1707(c). Differences training between the factory type design K and M models of the MU-2B airplane, and the factory type design J and L models of the MU-2B airplane, may be accomplished with Level A training. All other factory type design differences training must be accomplished with Level B training unless otherwise specified in 91.1707(c) . A Level A or B differences training is not a recurring annual requirement. Once a person has completed Initial Level A or B Differences training between the applicable different models, no additional differences training between those models is required.

(5) Icing training sufficient to ensure pilot knowledge and safe operation of the MU-2B aircraft in icing conditions as established by the FAA;

(6) Ground and flight training programs must include training hours identified by 91.1707(a) for ground instruction, 91.1707(b) for flight instruction, and 91.1707(c) for differences training.

   (i) No training credit is given for second-in-command training and no credit is given for right seat time under this program. Only the sole manipulator of the controls of the MU-2B airplane, flight training device, or Level C or D simulator can receive training credit under this program;

   (ii) An MU-2B airplane must be operated in accordance with an FAA approved MU-2B training program that meets the standards of this subpart and the training hours in 91.1707.

(7) Endorsements given for compliance with paragraph (f) of this section must be appropriate to the content of that specific MU-2B training program's compliance with standards of this subpart.

91.1707   Training program hours

(a) Ground instruction hours are listed in the following table:

INITIAL/TRANSITION	REQUALIFICATION	RECURRENT
20 hours	12 hours	8 hours

(b) Flight instruction hours are listed in the following table:

INITIAL/TRANSITION	REQUALIFICATION	RECURRENT
12 hours with a minimum of 6 hours at level E	8 hours level C or level E	4 hours at level E, or 6 hours at level C

(c) Differences training hours are listed in the following table:

2 factory type design models concurrently	1.5 hours required at level B
More than 2 factory type design model concurrently	3 hours at level B
Each additional factory type design model added separately	1.5 hours at level B

(d) Definitions of levels of training as used in this subpart:

(1) LEVEL A Training—Training that is conducted through self-instruction by the pilot.

(2) LEVEL B Training—Training that is conducted in the classroom environment with the aid of a qualified instructor who meets the requirements of this subpart.

(3) LEVEL C Training—Training that is accomplished in an FAA-approved Level 5 or 6 flight training device. In addition to the basic FTD requirements, the FTD must be representative of the MU-2B cockpit controls and be specifically approved by the FAA for the MU-2B airplane.

(4) Level E Training—Training that must be accomplished in the MU-2B airplane, Level C simulator, or Level D simulator.

91.1709   Training program approval

To obtain approval for an MU-2B training program, training providers must submit a proposed training program to the Administrator.

(a) Only training programs approved by the Administrator may be used to satisfy the standards of this subpart.

(b) For part 91 training providers, training programs will be approved for 24 months, unless sooner superseded or rescinded.

(c) The Administrator may require revision of an approved MU-2B training program at any time.

(d) A training provider must present its approved training program and FAA approval documentation to any representative of the Administrator, upon request.

91.1711   Aeronautical experience

No person may act as a pilot in command of a Mitsubishi MU-2B series airplane for the purpose of flight unless that person holds an airplane category and multi-engine land class rating, and has logged a minimum of 100 flight hours of PIC time in multi-engine airplanes.

91.1713   Instruction, checking, and evaluation

(a) Flight Instructor (Airplane). No flight instructor may provide instruction or conduct a flight review in a Mitsubishi MU-2B series airplane unless that flight instructor

(1) Meets the pilot training and documentation requirements of 91.1705 before giving flight instruction in the Mitsubishi MU-2B series airplane;

(2) Meets the currency requirements of 91.1715(a) and 91.1715(c)

(3) Has a minimum total pilot time of 2,000 pilot-in-command hours and 800 pilot-in-command hours in multiengine airplanes; and

(4) Has:

(i) 300 pilot-in-command hours in the Mitsubishi MU-2B series airplane, 50 hours of which must have been within the preceding 12 months; or

(ii) 100 pilot-in-command hours in the Mitsubishi MU-2B series airplane, 25 hours of which must have been within the preceding 12 months, and 300 hours providing instruction in a FAA-approved Mitsubishi MU-2B simulator or FAA-approved Mitsubishi MU-2B flight training device, 25 hours of which must have been within the preceding 12 months.

(b) Flight Instructor (Simulator/Flight Training Device). No flight instructor may provide instruction for the Mitsubishi MU-2B series airplane unless that instructor meets the requirements of this paragraph—

(1) Each flight instructor who provides flight training for the Mitsubishi MU-2B series airplane must meet the pilot training and documentation requirements of 91.1705 before giving flight instruction for the Mitsubishi MU-2B series airplane;

(2) Each flight instructor who provides flight training for the Mitsubishi MU-2B series airplane must meet the currency requirements of 91.1715(c) before giving flight instruction for the Mitsubishi MU-2B series airplane;

(3) Each flight instructor who provides flight training for the Mitsubishi MU-2B series airplane must have:

(i) A minimum total pilot time of 2000 pilot-in-command hours and 800 pilot-in-command hours in multiengine airplanes; and

(ii) Within the preceding 12 months, either 50 hours of Mitsubishi MU-2B series airplane pilot-in-command experience or 50 hours providing simulator or flight training device instruction for the Mitsubishi MU-2B.

(c) Checking and evaluation. No person may provide checking or evaluation for the Mitsubishi MU-2B series airplane unless that person meets the requirements of this paragraph—

(1) For the purpose of checking, designated pilot examiners, training center evaluators, and check airmen must have completed the appropriate training in the Mitsubishi MU-2B series airplane in accordance with 91.1705;

(2) For checking conducted in the Mitsubishi MU-2B series airplane, each designated pilot examiner and check airman must have 100 hours pilot-in-command flight time in the Mitsubishi MU-2B series airplane and maintain currency in accordance with 91.1715.

91.1715   Currency requirements and flight review

(a) The takeoff and landing currency requirements of §61.57 of this chapter must be maintained in the Mitsubishi MU-2B series airplane. Takeoff and landings in other multiengine airplanes do not

FAR 91

meet the takeoff and landing currency requirements for the Mitsubishi MU-2B series plane. Takeoff and landings in either the short-body or long-body Mitsubishi MU-2B model airplane may be credited toward takeoff and landing currency for both Mitsubishi MU-2B model groups.

(b) Instrument experience obtained in other category and class of aircraft may be used to satisfy the instrument currency requirements of 61.57 of this chapter for the Mitsubishi MU-2B series airplane.

(c) Satisfactory completion of a flight review to satisfy the requirements of 61.56 of this chapter is valid for operation of a Mitsubishi MU-2B series airplane only if that flight review is conducted in a Mitsubishi MU-2B series airplane or an MU-2B Simulator approved for landings with an approved course conducted under part 142 of this chapter. The flight review for Mitsubishi MU-2B series airplanes must include the Special Emphasis Items, and all items listed in the Training Course Final Phase Check in accordance with an approved MU-2B Training Program.

(d) A person who successfully completes the Initial/transition, Requalification, or Recurrent training requirements under 91.1705 of this chapter also meet the requirements of 61.56 of this chapter and need not accomplish a separate flight review provided that at least 1 hour of the flight training was conducted in the Mitsubishi MU-2B series airplane or an MU-2B Simulator approved for landings with an approved course conducted under part 142 of this chapter.

[Docket FAA-2006-24981, Amdt. 91-344, 81 FR 61591, Sept. 7, 2016; Amdt. 91-344A, 82 FR 21472, May 9, 2017]

91.1717   Operating requirements

(a) Except as provided in paragraph (b) of this section, no person may operate a Mitsubishi MU-2B airplane in single pilot operations unless that airplane has a functional autopilot.

(b) A person may operate a Mitsubishi MU-2B airplane in single pilot operations without a functional autopilot when—

   (1) Operating under day visual flight rule requirements; or

   (2) Authorized under a FAA approved minimum equipment list for that airplane, operating under instrument flight rule requirements in daytime visual meteorological conditions.

(c) No person may operate a Mitsubishi MU-2B series airplane unless a copy of the appropriate Mitsubishi Heavy Industries MU-2B Airplane Flight Manual is carried on board the airplane and is accessible during each flight at the pilot station.

(d) No person may operate a Mitsubishi MU-2B series airplane unless an MU-2B series airplane checklist, appropriate for the model being operated and accepted by the Federal Aviation Administration MU-2B Flight Standardization Board, is accessible for each flight at the pilot station and is used by the flight crewmembers when operating the airplane.

(e) No person may operate a Mitsubishi MU-2B series airplane contrary to the standards of this subpart.

(f) If there are any differences between the training and operating requirements of this subpart and the MU-2B Airplane Flight Manual's procedures sections (Normal, Abnormal, and Emergency) and the MU-2B airplane series checklist incorporated by reference in 91.1721, the person operating the airplane must operate the airplane in accordance with the training specified in this subpart.

91.1719   Credit for prior training

Initial/transition, requalification, recurrent or Level B differences training conducted prior to November 7, 2016, compliant with SFAR No. 108, Section 3 of this part, is considered to be compliant with this subpart, if the student met the eligibility requirements for the applicable category of training and the student's instructor met the experience requirements of this subpart.

91.1721   Incorporation by reference

(a) The Mitsubishi Heavy Industries MU-2B Cockpit Checklists are incorporated by reference into this part. The Director of the Federal Register approved this incorporation by reference in accordance with 5 U.S.C. 552(a) and 1 CFR part 51. All approved material is available for inspection at U.S. Department of Transportation, Docket Management Facility, Room W 12-140, West Building Ground Floor, 1200 New Jersey Ave. SE., Washington, DC 20590-0001, or at the National Archives and Records Administration, call 202-741-6030, or go to: http://www.archives.gov/federal_register/code_of_federal_regulations/ibr_locations.html.

(b) Mitsubishi Heavy Industries America, Inc., 4951 Airport Parkway, Suite 530, Addison, TX 75001.

   (1) Mitsubishi Heavy Industries MU-2B Checklists:

      (i) Cockpit Checklist, Model MU-2B-60, Type Certificate A10SW, MHI Document No. YET06220C, accepted by FSB on February 12, 2007.

      (ii) Cockpit Checklist, Model MU-2B-40, Type Certificate A10SW, MHI Document No. YET06256A, accepted by FSB on February 12, 2007.

      (iii) Cockpit Checklist, Model MU-2B-36A, Type Certificate A10SW, MHI Document No. YET06257B, accepted by FSB on February 12, 2007.

      (iv) Cockpit Checklist, Model MU-2B-36, Type Certificate A2PC, MHI Document No. YET06252B, accepted by FSB on February 12, 2007.

      (v) Cockpit Checklist, Model MU-2B-35, Type Certificate A2PC, MHI Document No. YET06251B, accepted by FSB on February 12, 2007.

      (vi) Cockpit Checklist, Model MU-2B-30, Type Certificate A2PC, MHI Document No. YET06250A, accepted by FSB on March 2, 2007.

      (vii) Cockpit Checklist, Model MU-2B-26A, Type Certificate A10SW, MHI Document No. YET06255A, accepted by FSB on February 12, 2007.

      (viii) Cockpit Checklist, Model MU-2B-26, Type Certificate A2PC, MHI Document No. YET06249A, accepted by FSB on March 2, 2007.

      (ix) Cockpit Checklist, Model MU-2B-26, Type Certificate A10SW, MHI Document No. YET06254A, accepted by FSB on March 2, 2007.

      (x) Cockpit Checklist, Model MU-2B-25, Type Certificate A10SW, MHI Document No. YET06253A, accepted by FSB on March 2, 2007.

      (xi) Cockpit Checklist, Model MU-2B-25, Type Certificate A2PC, MHI Document No. YET06248A, accepted by FSB on March 2, 2007.

      (xii) Cockpit Checklist, Model MU-2B-20, Type Certificate A2PC, MHI Document No. YET06247A, accepted by FSB on February 12, 2007.

      (xiii)-(xiv) [Reserved]

      (xv) Cockpit Checklist, Model MU-2B-15, Type Certificate A2PC, MHI Document No. YET06246A, accepted by FSB on March 2, 2007.

      (xvi) Cockpit Checklist, Model MU-2B-10, Type Certificate A2PC, MHI Document No. YET06245A, accepted by FSB on March 2, 2007.

      (xvii) Cockpit Checklist, Model MU-2B, Type Certificate A2PC, MHI Document No. YET06244A, accepted by FSB on March 2, 2007.

   (2) [Reserved]

[Docket FAA-2006-24981, Amdt. 91-344, 81 FR 61591, Sept. 7, 2016; Amdt. 91-344A, 82 FR 21472, May 9, 2017]

Appendix A to Part 91 — Category II Operations: Manual, Instruments, Equipment, and Maintenance

1. Category II Manual

(a) Application for approval. An applicant for approval of a Category II manual or an amendment to an approved Category II manual must submit the proposed manual or amendment to the responsible Flight Standards office. If the application requests an evaluation program, it must include the following:

(1) The location of the aircraft and the place where the demonstrations are to be conducted; and

(2) The date the demonstrations are to commence (at least 10 days after filing the application).

(b) Contents. Each Category II manual must contain:

(1) The registration number, make, and model of the aircraft to which it applies;

(2) A maintenance program as specified in section 4 of this appendix; and

(3) The procedures and instructions related to recognition of decision height, use of runway visual range information, approach monitoring, the decision region (the region between the middle marker and the decision height), the maximum permissible deviations of the basic ILS indicator within the decision region, a missed approach, use of airborne low approach equipment, minimum altitude for the use of the autopilot, instrument and equipment failure warning systems, instrument failure, and other procedures, instructions, and limitations that may be found necessary by the Administrator.

2. Required Instruments and Equipment

The instruments and equipment listed in this section must be installed in each aircraft operated in a Category II operation. This section does not require duplication of instruments and equipment required by 91.205 or any other provisions of this chapter.

(a) Group I.

(1) Two localizer and glide slope receiving systems. Each system must provide a basic ILS display and each side of the instrument panel must have a basic ILS display. However, a single localizer antenna and a single glide slope antenna may be used.

(2) A communications system that does not affect the operation of at least one of the ILS systems.

(3) A marker beacon receiver that provides distinctive aural and visual indications of the outer and the middle markers.

(4) Two gyroscopic pitch and bank indicating systems.

(5) Two gyroscopic direction indicating systems.

(6) Two airspeed indicators.

(7) Two sensitive altimeters adjustable for barometric pressure, each having a placarded correction for altimeter scale error and for the wheel height of the aircraft. After June 26, 1979, two sensitive altimeters adjustable for barometric pressure, having markings at 20-foot intervals and each having a placarded correction for altimeter scale error and for the wheel height of the aircraft.

(8) Two vertical speed indicators.

(9) A flight control guidance system that consists of either an automatic approach coupler or a flight director system. A flight director system must display computed information as steering command in relation to an ILS localizer and, on the same instrument, either computed information as pitch command in relation to an ILS glide slope or basic ILS glide slope information. An automatic approach coupler must provide at least automatic steering in relation to an ILS localizer. The flight control guidance system may be operated from one of the receiving systems required by subparagraph (1) of this paragraph.

(10) For Category II operations with decision heights below 150 feet either a marker beacon receiver providing aural and visual indications of the inner marker or a radio altimeter.

(b) Group II.

(1) Warning systems for immediate detection by the pilot of system faults in items (1), (4), (5), and (9) of Group I and, if installed for use in Category III operations, the radio altimeter and autothrottle system.

(2) Dual controls.

(3) An externally vented static pressure system with an alternate static pressure source.

(4) A windshield wiper or equivalent means of providing adequate cockpit visibility for a safe visual transition by either pilot to touchdown and rollout.

(5) A heat source for each airspeed system pitot tube installed or an equivalent means of preventing malfunctioning due to icing of the pitot system.

3. Instruments and Equipment Approval

(a) General. The instruments and equipment required by section 2 of this appendix must be approved as provided in this section before being used in Category II operations. Before presenting an aircraft for approval of the instruments and equipment, it must be shown that since the beginning of the 12th calendar month before the date of submission—

(1) The ILS localizer and glide slope equipment were bench checked according to the manufacturer's instructions and found to meet those standards specified in RTCA Paper 23–63/DO–117 dated March 14, 1963, "Standard Adjustment Criteria for Airborne Localizer and Glide Slope Receivers," which may be obtained from the RTCA Secretariat, 1425 K St., NW., Washington, DC 20005.

(2) The altimeters and the static pressure systems were tested and inspected in accordance with appendix E to part 43 of this chapter; and

(3) All other instruments and items of equipment specified in section 2(a) of this appendix that are listed in the proposed maintenance program were bench checked and found to meet the manufacturer's specifications.

(b) Flight control guidance system. All components of the flight control guidance system must be approved as installed by the evaluation program specified in paragraph (e) of this section if they have not been approved for Category III operations under applicable type or supplemental type certification procedures. In addition, subsequent changes to make, model, or design of the components must be approved under this paragraph. Related systems or devices, such as the autothrottle and computed missed approach guidance system, must be approved in the same manner if they are to be used for Category II operations.

(c) Radio altimeter. A radio altimeter must meet the performance criteria of this paragraph for original approval and after each subsequent alteration.

(1) It must display to the flight crew clearly and positively the wheel height of the main landing gear above the terrain.

(2) It must display wheel height above the terrain to an accuracy of plus or minus 5 feet or 5 percent, whichever is greater, under the following conditions:

(i) Pitch angles of zero to plus or minus 5 degrees about the mean approach attitude.

(ii) Roll angles of zero to 20 degrees in either direction.

(iii) Forward velocities from minimum approach speed up to 200 knots.

(iv) Sink rates from zero to 15 feet per second at altitudes from 100 to 200 feet.

FAR 91

(3) Over level ground, it must track the actual altitude of the aircraft without significant lag or oscillation.

(4) With the aircraft at an altitude of 200 feet or less, any abrupt change in terrain representing no more than 10 percent of the aircraft's altitude must not cause the altimeter to unlock, and indicator response to such changes must not exceed 0.1 seconds and, in addition, if the system unlocks for greater changes, it must reacquire the signal in less than 1 second.

(5) Systems that contain a push-to-test feature must test the entire system (with or without an antenna) at a simulated altitude of less than 500 feet.

(6) The system must provide to the flight crew a positive failure warning display any time there is a loss of power or an absence of ground return signals within the designed range of operating altitudes.

(d) Other instruments and equipment. All other instruments and items of equipment required by 2 of this appendix must be capable of performing as necessary for Category II operations. Approval is also required after each subsequent alteration to these instruments and items of equipment.

(e) Evaluation program —

(1) Application. Approval by evaluation is requested as a part of the application for approval of the Category II manual.

(2) Demonstrations. Unless otherwise authorized by the Administrator, the evaluation program for each aircraft requires the demonstrations specified in this paragraph. At least 50 ILS approaches must be flown with at least five approaches on each of three different ILS facilities and no more than one half of the total approaches on any one ILS facility. All approaches shall be flown under simulated instrument conditions to a 100-foot decision height and 90 percent of the total approaches made must be successful. A successful approach is one in which—

(i) At the 100-foot decision height, the indicated airspeed and heading are satisfactory for a normal flare and landing (speed must be plus or minus 5 knots of programmed airspeed, but may not be less than computed threshold speed if autothrottles are used);

(ii) The aircraft at the 100-foot decision height, is positioned so that the cockpit is within, and tracking so as to remain within, the lateral confines of the runway extended;

(iii) Deviation from glide slope after leaving the outer marker does not exceed 50 percent of full-scale deflection as displayed on the ILS indicator;

(iv) No unusual roughness or excessive attitude changes occur after leaving the middle marker; and

(v) In the case of an aircraft equipped with an approach coupler, the aircraft is sufficiently in trim when the approach coupler is disconnected at the decision height to allow for the continuation of a normal approach and landing.

(3) Records. During the evaluation program the following information must be maintained by the applicant for the aircraft with respect to each approach and made available to the Administrator upon request:

(i) Each deficiency in airborne instruments and equipment that prevented the initiation of an approach.

(ii) The reasons for discontinuing an approach, including the altitude above the runway at which it was discontinued.

(iii) Speed control at the 100-foot decision height if auto throttles are used.

(iv) Trim condition of the aircraft upon disconnecting the auto coupler with respect to continuation to flare and landing.

(v) Position of the aircraft at the middle marker and at th decision height indicated both on a diagram of the bas ILS display and a diagram of the runway extended the middle marker. Estimated touchdown point must indicated on the runway diagram.

(vi) Compatibility of flight director with the auto coupler, applicable.

(vii) Quality of overall system performance.

(4) Evaluation. A final evaluation of the flight control guidanc system is made upon successful completion of the demonstra tions. If no hazardous tendencies have been displayed or ai otherwise known to exist, the system is approved as installec

4. Maintenance program

(a) Each maintenance program must contain the following:

(1) A list of each instrument and item of equipment specified in of this appendix that is installed in the aircraft and approve for Category II operations, including the make and model those specified in 2(a).

(2) A schedule that provides for the performance of inspection under subparagraph (5) of this paragraph within 3 calenda months after the date of the previous inspection. The inspec tion must be performed by a person authorized by part 4 of this chapter, except that each alternate inspection may t replaced by a functional flight check. This functional fligl check must be performed by a pilot holding a Category II pilc authorization for the type aircraft checked.

(3) A schedule that provides for the performance of bench check for each listed instrument and item of equipment that is spec fied in section 2(a) within 12 calendar months after the date c the previous bench check.

(4) A schedule that provides for the performance of a test and ir spection of each static pressure system in accordance with ap pendix E to part 43 of this chapter within 12 calendar month after the date of the previous test and inspection.

(5) The procedures for the performance of the periodic inspec tions and functional flight checks to determine the ability c each listed instrument and item of equipment specified in sec tion 2(a) of this appendix to perform as approved for Categor II operations including a procedure for recording functiona flight checks.

(6) A procedure for assuring that the pilot is informed of all de fects in listed instruments and items of equipment.

(7) A procedure for assuring that the condition of each listed in strument and item of equipment upon which maintenance i performed is at least equal to its Category II approval condi tion before it is returned to service for Category II operations

(8) A procedure for an entry in the maintenance records require by 43.9 of this chapter that shows the date, airport, and reason for each discontinued Category II operation because of a mal function of a listed instrument or item of equipment.

(b) Bench check. A bench check required by this section must compl with this paragraph.

(1) It must be performed by a certificated repair station holdin one of the following ratings as appropriate to the equipmen checked:

(i) An instrument rating.

(ii) A radio rating.

(2) It must consist of removal of an instrument or item of equip ment and performance of the following:

(i) A visual inspection for cleanliness, impending failure and the need for lubrication, repair, or replacement o parts;

(ii) Correction of items found by that visual inspection and

(iii) Calibration to at least the manufacturer's specifications unless otherwise specified in the approved Category II manual for the aircraft in which the instrument or item of equipment is installed.

(c) Extensions. After the completion of one maintenance cycle of 12 calendar months, a request to extend the period for checks, tests, and inspections is approved if it is shown that the performance of particular equipment justifies the requested extension.

[Doc. No. 18334, 54 FR 34325, Aug. 18, 1989, as amended by Amdt. 91-269, 66 FR 41116, Aug. 6, 2001; Docket FAA-2018-0119, Amdt. 91-350, 83 FR 9172, Mar. 5, 2018]

Appendix B to Part 91 — [Reserved]

Appendix C to Part 91 — [Reserved]

Appendix D to Part 91 — Airports/Locations: Special Operating Restrictions

Section 1. Locations at which the requirements of 91.215(b)(2) and 91.225 (d)(2) apply.

Locations at which the requirements of 91.215(b)(2) and 91.225(d)(2) apply. The requirements of 91.215(b)(2) and 91.225(d)(2) apply below 10,000 feet MSL within a 30-nautical-mile radius of each location in the following list.

Atlanta, GA (Hartsfield-Jackson Atlanta International Airport)
Baltimore, MD (Baltimore/Washington International Thurgood Marshall Airport)
Boston, MA (General Edward Lawrence Logan International Airport)
Camp Springs, MD (Joint Base Andrews)
Chantilly, VA (Washington Dulles International Airport)
Charlotte, NC (Charlotte/Douglas International Airport)
Chicago, IL Chicago-O'Hare International Airport)
Cleveland, OH (Cleveland-Hopkins International Airport)
Covington, KY (Cincinnati/Northern Kentucky International Airport)
Dallas, TX (Dallas/Fort Worth International Airport)
Denver, CO (Denver International Airport)
Detroit, MI (Detroit Metropolitan Wayne County Airport)
Honolulu, HI (Honolulu International Airport)
Houston, TX (George Bush Intercontinental/Houston Airport)
Houston, TX (William P. Hobby Airport)
Kansas City, MO (Kansas City International Airport)
Las Vegas, NV (McCarran International Airport)
Los Angeles, CA (Los Angeles International Airport)
Memphis, TN (Memphis International Airport)
Miami, FL (Miami International Airport)
Minneapolis, MN (Minneapolis-St. Paul International/Wold-Chamberlain Airport)
Newark, NJ (Newark Liberty International Airport)
New Orleans, LA (Louis Armstrong New Orleans International Airport)
New York, NY (John F. Kennedy International Airport)
New York, NY (LaGuardia Airport)
Orlando, FL (Orlando International Airport)
Philadelphia, PA (Philadelphia International Airport)
Phoenix, AZ (Phoenix Sky Harbor International Airport)
Pittsburgh, PA (Pittsburgh International Airport)
St. Louis, MO (Lambert-St. Louis International Airport)
Salt Lake City, UT (Salt Lake City International Airport)
San Diego, CA (Miramar Marine Corps Air Station)
San Diego, CA (San Diego International Airport)
San Francisco, CA (San Francisco International Airport)
Seattle, WA (Seattle-Tacoma International Airport)
Tampa, FL (Tampa International Airport)
Washington, DC (Ronald Reagan Washington National Airport)

Section 2. Airports at which the requirements of 91.215(b)(5)(ii) apply. [Reserved]

Section 3. Locations at which fixed-wing Special VFR operations are prohibited.

The Special VFR weather minimums of 91.157 do not apply to the following airports:
Atlanta, GA (Hartsfield-Jackson Atlanta International Airport)
Baltimore, MD (Baltimore/Washington International Thurgood Marshall Airport)
Boston, MA (General Edward Lawrence Logan International Airport)
Buffalo, NY (Greater Buffalo International Airport)
Camp Springs, MD (Joint Base Andrews)
Chicago, IL (Chicago-O'Hare International Airport)
Cleveland, OH (Cleveland-Hopkins International Airport)
Columbus, OH (Port Columbus International Airport)
Covington, KY (Cincinnati/Northern Kentucky International Airport)
Dallas, TX (Dallas/Fort Worth International Airport)
Dallas, TX (Dallas Love Field Airport)
Denver, CO (Denver International Airport)
Detroit, MI (Detroit Metropolitan Wayne County Airport)
Honolulu, HI (Honolulu International Airport)
Houston, TX (George Bush Intercontinental/Houston Airport)
Indianapolis, IN (Indianapolis International Airport)
Los Angeles, CA (Los Angeles International Airport)
Louisville, KY (Louisville International Airport-Standiford Field)
Memphis, TN (Memphis International Airport)
Miami, FL (Miami International Airport)
Minneapolis, MN (Minneapolis-St. Paul International/World-Chamberlain Airport)
Newark, NJ (Newark Liberty International Airport)
New York, NY (John F. Kennedy International Airport)
New York, NY (LaGuardia Airport)
New Orleans, LA (Louis Armstrong New Orleans International Airport Field)
Philadelphia, PA (Philadelphia International Airport)
Pittsburgh, PA (Pittsburgh International Airport)
Portland, OR (Portland International Airport)
San Francisco, CA (San Francisco International Airport)
Seattle, WA (Seattle-Tacoma International Airport)
St. Louis, MO (Lambert-St. Louis International Airport)
Tampa, FL (Tampa International Airport)
Washington, DC (Ronald Reagan Washington National Airport)

Section 4. Locations at which solo student, sport, and recreational pilot activity is not permitted.

Pursuant to 91.131(b)(2), solo student, sport, and recreational pilot operations are not permitted at any of the following airports.
Atlanta, GA (Hartsfield-Jackson Atlanta International Airport)
Boston, MA (General Edward Lawrence Logan International Airport)
Camp Springs, MD (Joint Base Andrews)
Chicago, IL (Chicago-O'Hare International Airport)
Dallas, TX (Dallas/Fort Worth International Airport)
Los Angeles, CA (Los Angeles International Airport)
Miami, FL (Miami International Airport)
Newark, NJ (Newark Liberty International Airport)
New York, NY (John F. Kennedy International Airport)
New York, NY (LaGuardia Airport)
San Francisco, CA (San Francisco International Airport)
Washington, DC (Ronald Reagan Washington National Airport)

[Amdt. 91-227, 56 FR 65661, Dec. 17, 1991]

Editorial Note: For Federal Register citations affecting Appendix D to Part 91, see the List of CFR Sections Affected, which appears in the Finding Aids section of the printed volume and at www.fdsys.gov.

Effective Date Note: By Amdt. 91-236, 59 FR 2918, Jan. 19, 1994, as corrected by Amdt. 91-237, 59 FR 6547, Feb. 11, 1994, appendix D to part 91 was amended in sections 1 and 3 in the Denver, CO entry by revising "Stapleton" to read "Denver" effective March 9, 1994. By Amdt. 91-238, 59 FR 10958, Mar. 9, 1994, the effective date was delayed to May 15, 1994. By Amdt. 91-241, 59 FR 24916, May 13, 1994, the effective date was suspended indefinitely.

FAR 91

Appendix E to Part 91 — Airplane Flight Recorder Specifications

PARAMETERS	RANGE	INSTALLED SYSTEM[1] MINIMUM ACCURACY (TO RECOVERED DATA)	SAMPLING INTERVAL (PER SECOND)	RESOLUTION[4] READ OUT
Relative Time (From Recorded on Prior to Takeoff)	8 hr minimum	+/-0.125% per hour	1	1 sec
Indicated Airspeed	Vso to VD (KIAS)	+/-5% or +/-10 kts., whichever is greater. Resolution 2 kts. below 175 KIAS.	1	1%[3]
Altitude	-1,000 ft. to max cert. alt. of A/C.	+/-100 to +/- 700 ft. (see Table 1, TSO C51-a).	1	25 to 150 ft.
Magnetic Heading	360 deg.	+/- 5 deg.	1	1 deg.
Vertical Acceleration	-3g to +6g	+/-0.2g in addition to +/-.3g maximum datum	4 (or 1 per second where peaks, ref. to 1g are recorded).	0.03g.
Longitudinal Acceleration	+/- 1.0 g	+/-1.5% max. range exuding datum error of +/- 5%	2	0.01g
Pitch Attitude	100% of usable	+/-2 deg.	1	0.8 deg.
Roll Attitude	+/- 60 deg. or 100% of usable range, whichever is greater.	+/-2 deg.	1	0.8 deg.
Stabilizer Trim Position, or Pitch Control Position	Full Range	+/-3% unless higher uniquely required.	1	1%[3]
Engine Power, Each Engine:	Full Range	+/- 3% unless higher uniquely required.	1	1%[3]
Fan or N[1] Speed or EPR or Cockpit indications Used for Aircraft Certification OR	Maximum Range	+/- 5%	1	1%[3]
Prop. speed and Torque (Sample Once/Sec as Close together as Practicable)			1 (prop Speed) / 1 (torque)	1%[3] / 1%[3]
Altitude Rate[2] (need depends on altitude resolution).	+/-8,000 fpm	+/-10%. Resolution 250 fpm below 12,000 ft. indicated.	1	250 fpm below 12,000
Angle of Attack[2] (need depends on altitude resolution).	-20 deg. to 40deg. or 100% of usable range	+/-2 deg.	1	0.8%[3]

[1] When data sources are aircraft instruments (except altimeters) of acceptable quality to fly the aircraft the recording system excluding these sensors (but including all other characacteristics of the recording system) shall contribute no more than half of the values in this column.
[2] If data from the altitude encoding altimeter (100 ft. resolution) is used, then either one of these parameters should also be recorded. If however, altitude is recorded at a minimum resolution of 25 feet, then these two parameters can be omitted.
[3] Percent of full range.
[4] This column applies to aircraft manufactured after October 11, 1991.
[5] For Pitch Control Position only, for all aircraft manufactured on or after April 6, 2012, the sampling interval (per second) is 8. Each input must be recorded at this rate. Alternately sampling inputs (interleaving) to meet this sampling interval is prohibited.

[Doc. No. 18334, 54 FR 34327, Aug. 18, 1989, as amended by Amdt. 91-300, 73 FR 12565, Mar. 7, 2008; 73 FR 15280, Mar. 21, 2008; Amdt. 91-313, 75 FR 17046, Apr. 5, 2010; Amdt. 91-329, 78 FR 39971, July 3, 2013]

Appendix F to Part 91 — Helicopter Flight Recorder Specifications

PARAMETERS	RANGE	INSTALLED SYSTEM[1] MINIMUM ACCURACY (TO RECOVERED DATA)	SAMPLING INTERVAL (PER SECOND)	RESOLUTION[3] READ OUT
Relative Time (From Recorded on Prior to Takeoff)	4 hr minimum	+/-0.125% per hour	1	1 sec.
Indicated Airspeed	VM in to VD (KIAS) (minimu airspeed signal attainable with installed pilot-static system)	+/-5% or +/-10 kts., which-ever is greater.	1	1kt.
Altitude	-1,000 ft. to 20,000 ft. pressure altitude.	+/-100 to +/- 700 ft. (see Table 1, TSO C51-a).	1	25 to 150 ft.
Magnetic Heading	360 deg.	+/- 5 deg.	1	1 deg.
Vertical Acceleration	-3g to +6g	+/-0.2g in addition to +/- 0.3g maximum datum	4 (or 1 per second where peaks, ref. to 1g are re-corded).	0.05g.
Longitudinal Acceleration	+/- 1.0 g	+/-1.5% max. range exud-ing datum error of +/- 5%	2	0.03g.
Pitch Attitude	100% of usable range	+/-2 deg.	1	0.8 deg.
Roll Attitude	+/- 60 deg. or 100% of usable range, whichever is greater.	+/-2 deg.	1	0.8 deg.
Altitude Rate	+/- 8,000 fpm	+/- 10% relolution 250 fpm below 12,000 ft. indicated.	1	250 fpm below 12,000.
Engine Power, Each Engine:				
Main Rotor Speed	Maximum Range	+/- 5%	1	1%[2]
Free or Power Turbine	Maximum Range	+/- 5%	1	1%[2]
Engine Torque	Maximum Range	+/- 5%	1	1%[2]
Flight Control Hydraulic Pressure				
Primary (Discrete)	High/Low		1	
Secondary - if applicable (Discrete).	High/Low		1	
Radio Transmitter Keying (Discrete)	On/Off		1	
Autopilot Engaged (Discrete).	Engaged or Disengaged		1	

[1] When data sources are aircraft instruments (except altimeters) of acceptable quality to fly the aircraft the recording system excluding these sensors (but including all other characteristics of the recording system) shall contribute no more than half of the values in this column.
[2] Percent of full range.
[3] This column applies to aircraft manufactured after October 11, 1991.
[4] For all aircraft manufactured on or after April 6, 2012, the sampling interval per second is 4.

[Doc. No. 18334, 54 FR 34328, Aug. 18, 1989; 54 FR 41211, Oct. 5, 1989; 54 FR 53036, Dec. 26, 1989; Amdt. 91–300, 73 FR 12565, Mar. 7, 2008; 73 FR 15280, Mar. 21, 2008]

FAR 91

Appendix G to Part 91 — Operations in Reduced Vertical Separation Minimum (RVSM) Airspace

Section 1. Definitions

Reduced Vertical Separation Minimum (RVSM) Airspace. Within RVSM airspace, air traffic control (ATC) separates aircraft by a minimum of 1,000 feet vertically between FL 290 and FL 410 inclusive. Air-traffic control notifies operators of RVSM airspace by providing route planning information.

RVSM Group Aircraft. Aircraft within a group of aircraft, approved as a group by the Administrator, in which each of the aircraft satisfy each of the following:

(a) The aircraft have been manufactured to the same design, and have been approved under the same type certificate, amended type certificate, or supplemental type certificate.

(b) The static system of each aircraft is installed in a manner and position that is the same as those of the other aircraft in the group. The same static source error correction is incorporated in each aircraft of the group.

(c) The avionics units installed in each aircraft to meet the minimum RVSM equipment requirements of this appendix are:

   (1) Manufactured to the same manufacturer specification and have the same part number; or

   (2) Of a different manufacturer or part number, if the applicant demonstrates that the equipment provides equivalent system performance.

RVSM Nongroup Aircraft. An aircraft that is approved for RVSM operations as an individual aircraft.

RVSM Flight envelope. An RVSM flight envelope includes the range of Mach number, weight divided by atmospheric pressure ratio, and altitudes over which an aircraft is approved to be operated in cruising flight within RVSM airspace. RVSM flight envelopes are defined as follows:

(a) The full RVSM flight envelope is bounded as follows:

   (1) The altitude flight envelope extends from FL 290 upward to the lowest altitude of the following:

      (i) FL 410 (the RVSM altitude limit);

      (ii) The maximum certificated altitude for the aircraft; or

      (iii) The altitude limited by cruise thrust, buffet, or other flight limitations.

   (2) The airspeed flight envelope extends:

      (i) From the airspeed of the slats/flaps-up maximum endurance (holding) airspeed, or the maneuvering airspeed, whichever is lower;

      (ii) To the maximum operating airspeed (Vmo/Mmo), or airspeed limited by cruise thrust buffet, or other flight limitations, whichever is lower.

   (3) All permissible gross weights within the flight envelopes defined in paragraphs (1) and (2) of this definition.

(b) The basic RVSM flight envelope is the same as the full RVSM flight envelope except that the airspeed flight envelope extends:

   (1) From the airspeed of the slats/flaps-up maximum endurance (holding) airspeed, or the maneuver airspeed, whichever is lower;

   (2) To the upper Mach/airspeed boundary defined for the full RVSM flight envelope, or a specified lower value not less than the long-range cruise Mach number plus .04 Mach, unless further limited by available cruise thrust, buffet, or other flight limitations.

Section 2 - Aircraft Approval

(a) Except as specified in Section 9 of this appendix, an operator may be authorized to conduct RVSM operations if the Administrator finds that its aircraft comply with this section.

(b) The applicant for authorization shall submit the appropriate data package for aircraft approval. The package must consist of at least the following:

(1) An identification of the RVSM aircraft group or the nongroup aircraft;

(2) A definition of the RVSM flight envelopes applicable to the subject aircraft;

(3) Documentation that establishes compliance with the applicable RVSM aircraft requirements of this section; and

(4) The conformity tests used to ensure that aircraft approved with the data package meet the RVSM aircraft requirements.

(c) Altitude-keeping equipment: All aircraft. To approve an aircraft group or a nongroup aircraft, the Administrator must find that the aircraft meets the following requirements:

(1) The aircraft must be equipped with two operational independent altitude measurement systems.

(2) The aircraft must be equipped with at least one automatic altitude control system that controls the aircraft altitude—

      (i) Within a tolerance band of ±65 feet about an acquired altitude when the aircraft is operated in straight and level flight under nonturbulent, nongust conditions; or

      (ii) Within a tolerance band of ±130 feet under nonturbulent, nongust conditions for aircraft for which application for type certification occurred on or before April 9, 1997 that are equipped with an automatic altitude control system with flight management/performance system inputs.

(3) The aircraft must be equipped with an altitude alert system that signals an alert when the altitude displayed to the flight crew deviates from the selected altitude by more than:

      (i) ±300 feet for aircraft for which application for type certification was made on or before April 9, 1997; or

      (ii) ±200 feet for aircraft for which application for type certification is made after April 9, 1997.

(d) Altimetry system error containment: Group aircraft for which application for type certification was made on or before April 9, 1997. To approve group aircraft for which application for type certification was made on or before April 9, 1997, the Administrator must find that the altimetry system error (ASE) is contained as follows:

(1) At the point in the basic RVSM flight envelope where mean ASE reaches its largest absolute value, the absolute value may not exceed 80 feet.

(2) At the point in the basic RVSM flight envelope where mean ASE plus three standard deviations reaches its largest absolute value, the absolute value may not exceed 200 feet.

(3) At the point in the full RVSM flight envelope where mean ASE reaches its largest absolute value, the absolute value may not exceed 120 feet.

(4) At the point in the full RVSM flight envelope where mean ASE plus three standard deviations reaches its largest absolute value, the absolute value may not exceed 245 feet.

(5) Necessary operating restrictions. If the applicant demonstrates that its aircraft otherwise comply with the ASE containment requirements, the Administrator may establish an operating restriction on that applicant's aircraft to restrict the aircraft from operating in areas of the basic RVSM flight envelope where the absolute value of mean ASE exceeds 80 feet, and/or the absolute value of mean ASE plus three standard deviations exceeds 200 feet; or from operating in areas of the full RVSM flight envelope where the absolute value of the mean ASE exceeds 120 feet and/or the absolute value of mean ASE plus three standard deviations exceeds 245 feet.

(e) Altimetry system error containment: Group aircraft for which application for type certification is made after April 9, 1997. To approve group aircraft for which application for type certification is made after April 9, 1997, the Administrator must find that the altimetry system error (ASE) is contained as follows:

(1) At the point in the full RVSM flight envelope where mean ASE reaches its largest absolute value, the absolute value may not exceed 80 feet.

(2) At the point in the full RVSM flight envelope where mean ASE plus three standard deviations reaches its largest absolute value, the absolute value may not exceed 200 feet.

(f) Altimetry system error containment: Nongroup aircraft. To approve a nongroup aircraft, the Administrator must find that the altimetry system error (ASE) is contained as follows:

(1) For each condition in the basic RVSM flight envelope, the largest combined absolute value for residual static source error plus the avionics error may not exceed 160 feet.

(2) For each condition in the full RVSM flight envelope, the largest combined absolute value for residual static source error plus the avionics error may not exceed 200 feet.

(g) Traffic Alert and Collision Avoidance System (TCAS) Compatibility With RVSM Operations: All aircraft. After March 31, 2002, unless otherwise authorized by the Administrator, if you operate an aircraft that is equipped with TCAS II in RVSM airspace, it must be a TCAS II that meets TSO C–119b (Version 7.0), or a later version.

(h) If the Administrator finds that the applicant's aircraft comply with this section, the Administrator notifies the applicant in writing.

Section 3. Operator Authorization

(a) Except as specified in Section 9 of this appendix, authority for an operator to conduct flight in airspace where RVSM is applied is issued in operations specifications, a Letter of Authorization, or management specifications issued under subpart K of this part, as appropriate. To issue an RVSM authorization under this section, the Administrator must find that the operator's aircraft have been approved in accordance with Section 2 of this appendix and the operator complies with this section.

(b) Except as specified in Section 9 of this appendix, an applicant seeking authorization to operate within RVSM airspace must apply in a form and manner prescribed by the Administrator. The application must include the following:

(1) [Reserved]

(2) For an applicant who operates under part 121 or 135 of this chapter or under subpart K of this part, initial and recurring pilot training requirements.

(3) Policies and procedures: An applicant who operates under part 121 or 135 of this chapter or under subpart K of this part must submit RVSM policies and procedures that will enable it to conduct RVSM operations safely.

(c) In a manner prescribed by the Administrator, an operator seeking authorization under this section must provide evidence that:

(1) It is capable to operate and maintain each aircraft or aircraft group for which it applies for approval to operate in RVSM airspace; and

(2) Each pilot has knowledge of RVSM requirements, policies, and procedures sufficient for the conduct of operations in RVSM airspace.

Section 4. RVSM Operations

(a) Each person requesting a clearance to operate within RVSM airspace shall correctly annotate the flight plan filed with air traffic control with the status of the operator and aircraft with regard to RVSM approval. Each operator shall verify RVSM applicability for the flight planned route through the appropriate flight planning information sources.

(b) No person may show, on the flight plan filed with air traffic control, an operator or aircraft as approved for RVSM operations, or operate on a route or in an area where RVSM approval is required, unless:

(1) The operator is authorized by the Administrator to perform such operations in accordance with Section 3 or Section 9 of this appendix, as applicable.

(2) The aircraft—

(i) Has been approved and complies with Section 2 this appendix; or

(ii) Complies with Section 9 of this appendix.

(3) Each pilot has knowledge of RVSM requirements, policies, and procedures sufficient for the conduct of operations in RVSM airspace.

Section 5. Deviation Authority Approval

The Administrator may authorize an aircraft operator to deviate from the requirements of 91.180 or 91.706 for a specific flight in RVSM airspace if:

(a) The operator submits a request in a time and manner acceptable to the Administrator; and

(b) At the time of filing the flight plan for that flight, ATC determines that the aircraft may be provided appropriate separation and that the flight will not interfere with, or impose a burden on, RVSM operations.

Section 6. Reporting Altitude-Keeping Errors

Each operator shall report to the Administrator each event in which the operator's aircraft has exhibited the following altitude-keeping performance:

(a) Total vertical error of 300 feet or more;

(b) Altimetry system error of 245 feet or more; or

(c) Assigned altitude deviation of 300 feet or more.

Section 7. Removal or Amendment of Authority

The Administrator may prohibit or restrict an operator from conducting operations in RVSM airspace, if the Administrator determines that the operator is not complying, or is unable to comply, with this appendix or subpart H of this part. Examples of reasons for amendment, revocation, or restriction include, but are not limited to, an operator's:

(a) Committing one or more altitude-keeping errors in RVSM airspace;

(b) Failing to make an effective and timely response to identify and correct an altitude-keeping error; or

(c) Failing to report an altitude-keeping error.

Section 8. Airspace Designation

RVSM may be applied in all ICAO Flight Information Regions (FIRs).

Section 9. Aircraft Equipped With Automatic Dependent Surveillance—Broadcast Out

An operator is authorized to conduct flight in airspace in which RVSM is applied provided:

(a) The aircraft is equipped with the following:

(1) Two operational independent altitude measurement systems.

(2) At least one automatic altitude control system that controls the aircraft altitude—

(i) Within a tolerance band of ±65 feet about an acquired altitude when the aircraft is operated in straight and level flight under nonturbulent, nongust conditions; or

(ii) Within a tolerance band of ±130 feet under nonturbulent, nongust conditions for aircraft for which application for type certification occurred on or before April 9, 1997, that are equipped with an automatic altitude control system with flight management/performance system inputs.

(3) An altitude alert system that signals an alert when the altitude displayed to the flightcrew deviates from the selected altitude by more than—

(i) ±300 feet for aircraft for which application for type certification was made on or before April 9, 1997; or

(ii) ±200 feet for aircraft for which application for type certification is made after April 9, 1997.

(4) A TCAS II that meets TSO C-119b (Version 7.0), or a later version, if equipped with TCAS II, unless otherwise authorized by the Administrator.

320

(5) Unless authorized by ATC or the foreign country where the aircraft is operated, an ADS-B Out system that meets the equipment performance requirements of 91.227 of this part. The aircraft must have its height-keeping performance monitored in a form and manner acceptable to the Administrator.

(b) The altimetry system error (ASE) of the aircraft does not exceed 200 feet when operating in RVSM airspace.

[Doc. No. 28870, 62 FR 17487, Apr. 9, 1997, as amended by Amdt. 91-261, 65 FR 5942, Feb. 7, 2000; Amdt. 91-271, 66 FR 63895, Dec. 10, 2001; Amdt. 91-274, 68 FR 54584, Sept. 17, 2003; Amdt. 91-276, 68 FR 70133, Dec. 17, 2003; Docket FAA-2015-1746, Amdt. 91-342, 81 FR 47017, July 20, 2016; Docket FAA-2016-9154, Amdt. 91-348, 82 FR 39664, Aug. 22, 2017; FAA-2017-0782, Amdt. No. 91-354, 83 FR 65492, Dec. 21, 2018]

PART 110 — GENERAL REQUIREMENTS

110.1   Applicability.
110.2   Definitions

Authority: 49 U.S.C. 106(g), 1153, 40101, 40102, 40103, 40113, 44105, 44106, 44111, 44701–44717, 44722, 44901, 44903, 44904, 44906, 44912, 44914, 44936, 44938, 46103, 46105.

Source: Doc. No. FAA–2009–0140, 76 FR 7486, Feb. 10, 2011, unless otherwise noted.

110.1   Applicability

This part governs all operations conducted under subchapter G of this chapter.

110.2   Definitions

For the purpose of this subchapter, the term—

All-cargo operation means any operation for compensation or hire that is other than a passenger-carrying operation or, if passengers are carried, they are only those specified in 121.583(a) or 135.85 of this chapter.

Commercial air tour means a flight conducted for compensation or hire in an airplane or helicopter where a purpose of the flight is sightseeing. The FAA may consider the following factors in determining whether a flight is a commercial air tour:

(1) Whether there was a holding out to the public of willingness to conduct a sightseeing flight for compensation or hire;

(2) Whether the person offering the flight provided a narrative that referred to areas or points of interest on the surface below the route of the flight;

(3) The area of operation;

(4) How often the person offering the flight conducts such flights;

(5) The route of flight;

(6) The inclusion of sightseeing flights as part of any travel arrangement package;

(7) Whether the flight in question would have been canceled based on poor visibility of the surface below the route of the flight; and

(8) Any other factors that the FAA considers appropriate.

Commuter operation means any scheduled operation conducted by any person operating one of the following types of aircraft with a frequency of operations of at least five round trips per week on at least one route between two or more points according to the published flight schedules:

(1) Airplanes, other than turbojet-powered airplanes, having a maximum passenger-seat configuration of 9 seats or less, excluding each crewmember seat, and a maximum payload capacity of 7,500 pounds or less; or

(2) Rotorcraft.

Direct air carrier means a person who provides or offers to provide air transportation and who has control over the operational functions performed in providing that transportation.

DOD commercial air carrier evaluator means a qualified Air Mobility Command, Survey and Analysis Office cockpit evaluator performing the duties specified in Public Law 99–661 when the evaluator is flying on an air carrier that is contracted or pursuing a contract with the U.S. Department of Defense (DOD).

Domestic operation means any scheduled operation conducted by any person operating any airplane described in paragraph (1) of this definition at locations described in paragraph (2) of this definition:

(1) Airplanes:

(i) Turbojet-powered airplanes;

(ii) Airplanes having a passenger-seat configuration of more than 9 passenger seats, excluding each crewmember seat; or

(iii) Airplanes having a payload capacity of more than 7,500 pounds.

(2) Locations:

(i) Between any points within the 48 contiguous States of the United States or the District of Columbia; or

(ii) Operations solely within the 48 contiguous States of the United States or the District of Columbia; or

(iii) Operations entirely within any State, territory, or possession of the United States; or

(iv) When specifically authorized by the Administrator, operations between any point within the 48 contiguous States of the United States or the District of Columbia and any specifically authorized point located outside the 48 contiguous States of the United States or the District of Columbia.

Empty weight means the weight of the airframe, engines, propellers, rotors, and fixed equipment. Empty weight excludes the weight of the crew and payload, but includes the weight of all fixed ballast, unusable fuel supply, undrainable oil, total quantity of engine coolant, and total quantity of hydraulic fluid.

Flag operation means any scheduled operation conducted by any person operating any airplane described in paragraph (1) of this definition at the locations described in paragraph (2) of this definition:

(1) Airplanes:

(i) Turbojet-powered airplanes;

(ii) Airplanes having a passenger-seat configuration of more than 9 passenger seats, excluding each crewmember seat; or

(iii) Airplanes having a payload capacity of more than 7,500 pounds.

(2) Locations:

(i) Between any point within the State of Alaska or the State of Hawaii or any territory or possession of the United States and any point outside the State of Alaska or the State of Hawaii or any territory or possession of the United States, respectively; or

(ii) Between any point within the 48 contiguous States of the United States or the District of Columbia and any point outside the 48 contiguous States of the United States and the District of Columbia.

(iii) Between any point outside the U.S. and another point outside the U.S.

Justifiable aircraft equipment means any equipment necessary for the operation of the aircraft. It does not include equipment or ballast specifically installed, permanently or otherwise, for the purpose of altering the empty weight of an aircraft to meet the maximum payload capacity.

Kind of operation means one of the various operations a certificate holder is authorized to conduct, as specified in its operations specifications, i.e., domestic, flag, supplemental, commuter, or on-demand operations.

Maximum payload capacity means:

(1) For an aircraft for which a maximum zero fuel weight is prescribed in FAA technical specifications, the maximum zero fuel weight, less empty weight, less all justifiable aircraft equipment, and less the operating load (consisting of minimum flightcrew, foods and beverages, and supplies and equipment related to foods and beverages, but not including disposable fuel or oil).

(2) For all other aircraft, the maximum certificated takeoff weight of an aircraft, less the empty weight, less all justifiable aircraft equipment, and less the operating load (consisting of minimum fuel load, oil, and flightcrew). The allowance for the weight of the crew, oil, and fuel is as follows:

(i) Crew—for each crewmember required by the Federal Aviation Regulations—

(A) For male flightcrew members—180 pounds.

(B) For female flightcrew members—140 pounds.

(C) For male flight attendants—180 pounds.

(D) For female flight attendants—130 pounds.

(E) For flight attendants not identified by gender—140 pounds.

(ii) Oil—350 pounds or the oil capacity as specified on the Type Certificate Data Sheet.

(iii) Fuel—the minimum weight of fuel required by the applicable Federal Aviation Regulations for a flight between domestic points 174 nautical miles apart under VFR weather conditions that does not involve extended overwater operations.

Maximum zero fuel weight means the maximum permissible weight of an aircraft with no disposable fuel or oil. The zero fuel weight figure may be found in either the aircraft type certificate data sheet, the approved Aircraft Flight Manual, or both.

Noncommon carriage means an aircraft operation for compensation or hire that does not involve a holding out to others.

On-demand operation means any operation for compensation or hire that is one of the following:

(1) Passenger-carrying operations conducted as a public charter under part 380 of this chapter or any operations in which the departure time, departure location, and arrival location are specifically negotiated with the customer or the customer's representative that are any of the following types of operations:

(i) Common carriage operations conducted with airplanes, including turbojet-powered airplanes, having a passenger-seat configuration of 30 seats or fewer, excluding each crewmember seat, and a payload capacity of 7,500 pounds or less, except that operations using a specific airplane that is also used in domestic or flag operations and that is so listed in the operations specifications as required by 119.49(a)(4) of this chapter for those operations are considered supplemental operations;

(ii) Noncommon or private carriage operations conducted with airplanes having a passenger-seat configuration of less than 20 seats, excluding each crewmember seat, and a payload capacity of less than 6,000 pounds; or

(iii) Any rotorcraft operation.

(2) Scheduled passenger-carrying operations conducted with one of the following types of aircraft with a frequency of operations of less than five round trips per week on at least one route between two or more points according to the published flight schedules:

(i) Airplanes, other than turbojet powered airplanes, having a maximum passenger-seat configuration of 9 seats or less, excluding each crewmember seat, and a maximum payload capacity of 7,500 pounds or less; or

(ii) Rotorcraft.

(3) All-cargo operations conducted with airplanes having a payload capacity of 7,500 pounds or less, or with rotorcraft.

Passenger-carrying operation means any aircraft operation carrying any person, unless the only persons on the aircraft are those identified in 121.583(a) or 135.85 of this chapter, as applicable. An aircraft used in a passenger-carrying operation may also carry cargo or mail in addition to passengers.

Principal base of operations means the primary operating location of a certificate holder as established by the certificate holder.

Provisional airport means an airport approved by the Administrator for use by a certificate holder for the purpose of providing service to a community when the regular airport used by the certificate holder is not available.

Regular airport means an airport used by a certificate holder in scheduled operations and listed in its operations specifications.

Scheduled operation means any common carriage passenger-carrying operation for compensation or hire conducted by an air carrier or commercial operator for which the certificate holder or its representative offers in advance the departure location, departure time, and arrival location. It does not include any passenger-carrying operation that is conducted as a public charter operation under part 380 of this chapter.

Supplemental operation means any common carriage operation for compensation or hire conducted with any airplane described in paragraph (1) of this definition that is a type of operation described in paragraph (2) of this definition:

(1) Airplanes:

(i) Airplanes having a passenger-seat configuration of more than 30 seats, excluding each crewmember seat;

(ii) Airplanes having a payload capacity of more than 7,500 pounds; or

(iii) Each propeller-powered airplane having a passenger-seat configuration of more than 9 seats and less than 31 seats, excluding each crewmember seat, that is also used in domestic or flag operations and that is so listed in the operations specifications as required by 119.49(a)(4) of this chapter for those operations; or

(iv) Each turbojet powered airplane having a passenger seat configuration of 1 or more and less than 31 seats, excluding each crewmember seat, that is also used in domestic or flag operations and that is so listed in the operations specifications as required by 119.49(a)(4) of this chapter for those operations.

(2) Types of operation:

(i) Operations for which the departure time, departure location, and arrival location are specifically negotiated with the customer or the customer's representative;

(ii) All-cargo operations; or

(iii) Passenger-carrying public charter operations conducted under part 380 of this chapter.

Wet lease means any leasing arrangement whereby a person agrees to provide an entire aircraft and at least one crewmember. A wet lease does not include a code-sharing arrangement.

When common carriage is not involved or operations not involving common carriage means any of the following:

(1) Noncommon carriage.

(2) Operations in which persons or cargo are transported without compensation or hire.

(3) Operations not involving the transportation of persons or cargo.

(4) Private carriage.

Years in service means the calendar time elapsed since an aircraft was issued its first U.S. or first foreign airworthiness certificate.

[Docket No. FAA-2009-0140, 76 FR 7486, Feb. 10, 2011, as amended by Docket FAA-2018-0119, Amdt. 110-2, 83 FR 9172, Mar. 5, 2018]

PART 119 — CERTIFICATION: AIR CARRIERS AND COMMERCIAL OPERATORS

Subpart A — General

Subpart B — Applicability of Operating Requirements to Different Kinds of Operations Under Parts 121, 125, and 135 of This Chapter

Subpart C — Certification, Operations Specifications, and Certain Other Requirements for Operations Conducted Under Part 121 or Part 135 of This Chapter

Authority: Pub. L. 111-216, sec. 215 (August 1, 2010); 49 U.S.C. 106(f), 106(g), 1153, 40101, 40102, 40103, 40113, 44105, 44106, 44111, 44701-44717, 44722, 44901, 44903, 44904, 44906, 44912, 44914, 44936, 44938, 46103, 46105.

Source: Docket No. 28154, 60 FR 65913, Dec. 20, 1995, unless otherwise noted.

Subpart A — General

119.1 Applicability

(a) This part applies to each person operating or intending to operate civil aircraft—

　(1) As an air carrier or commercial operator, or both, in air commerce; or

　(2) When common carriage is not involved, in operations of U.S.-registered civil airplanes with a seat configuration of 20 or more passengers, or a maximum payload capacity of 6,000 pounds or more.

(b) This part prescribes—

　(1) The types of air operator certificates issued by the Federal Aviation Administration, including air carrier certificates and operating certificates;

　(2) The certification requirements an operator must meet in order to obtain and hold a certificate authorizing operations under part 121, 125, or 135 of this chapter and operations specifications for each kind of operation to be conducted and each class and size of aircraft to be operated under part 121 or 135 of this chapter;

　(3) The requirements an operator must meet to conduct operations under part 121, 125, or 135 of this chapter and in operating each class and size of aircraft authorized in its operations specifications;

　(4) Requirements affecting wet leasing of aircraft and other arrangements for transportation by air;

　(5) Requirements for obtaining deviation authority to perform operations under a military contract and obtaining deviation authority to perform an emergency operation; and

　(6) Requirements for management personnel for operations conducted under part 121 or part 135 of this chapter.

(c) Persons subject to this part must comply with the other requirements of this chapter, except where those requirements are modified by or where additional requirements are imposed by part 119, 121, 125, or 135 of this chapter.

(d) This part does not govern operations conducted under part 91, subpart K (when common carriage is not involved) nor does it govern operations conducted under part 129, 133, 137, or 139 of this chapter.

(e) Except for operations when common carriage is not involved conducted with airplanes having a passenger-seat configuration of 20 seats or more, excluding any required crewmember seat, or a payload capacity of 6,000 pounds or more, this part does not apply to—

　(1) Student instruction;

　(2) Nonstop Commercial Air Tours conducted after September 11, 2007, in an airplane or helicopter having a standard airworthiness certificate and passenger-seat configuration of 30 seats or fewer and a maximum payload capacity of 7,500 pounds or less that begin and end at the same airport, and are conducted within a 25-statute mile radius of that airport, in compliance with the Letter of Authorization issued under 91.147 of this chapter. For nonstop Commercial Air Tours conducted in accordance with part 136, subpart B of this chapter, National Parks Air Tour Management, the requirements of part 119 of this chapter apply unless excepted in 136.37(g)(2). For Nonstop Commercial Air Tours conducted in the vicinity of the Grand Canyon National Park, Arizona, the requirements of SFAR 50–2, part 93, subpart U, and part 119 of this chapter, as applicable, apply.

　(3) Ferry or training flights;

　(4) Aerial work operations, including—

　　(i)　Crop dusting, seeding, spraying, and bird chasing;

　　(ii)　Banner towing;

　　(iii)　Aerial photography or survey;

FAR 119

(iv) Fire fighting;

(v) Helicopter operations in construction or repair work (but it does apply to transportation to and from the site of operations); and

(vi) Powerline or pipeline patrol;

(5) Sightseeing flights conducted in hot air balloons;

(6) Nonstop flights conducted within a 25-statute-mile radius of the airport of takeoff carrying persons or objects for the purpose of conducting intentional parachute operations.

(7) Helicopter flights conducted within a 25 statute mile radius of the airport of takeoff if—

(i) Not more than two passengers are carried in the helicopter in addition to the required flightcrew;

(ii) Each flight is made under day VFR conditions;

(iii) The helicopter used is certificated in the standard category and complies with the 100-hour inspection requirements of part 91 of this chapter;

(iv) The operator notifies the responsible Flight Standards office at least 72 hours before each flight and furnishes any essential information that the office requests;

(v) The number of flights does not exceed a total of six in any calendar year;

(vi) Each flight has been approved by the Administrator; and

(vii) Cargo is not carried in or on the helicopter;

(8) Operations conducted under part 133 of this chapter or 375 of this title;

(9) Emergency mail service conducted under 49 U.S.C. 41906;

(10) Operations conducted under the provisions of §91.321 of this chapter; or

(11) Small UAS operations conducted under part 107 of this chapter.

[Doc. No. 28154, 60 FR 65913, Dec. 20, 1995, as amended by Amdt. 119-4, 66 FR 23557, May 9, 2001; Amdt. 119-5, 67 FR 9554, Mar. 1, 2002; Amdt. 119-7, 68 FR 54584, Sept. 17, 2003; 72 FR 6911, Feb. 13, 2007; Docket FAA-2015-0150, Amdt. 119-18, 81 FR 42214, June 28, 2016; Docket FAA-2018-0119, Amdt. 119-19, 83 FR 9172, Mar. 5, 2018]

119.3 [Reserved]

119.5 Certifications, authorizations, and prohibitions

(a) A person authorized by the Administrator to conduct operations as a direct air carrier will be issued an Air Carrier Certificate.

(b) A person who is not authorized to conduct direct air carrier operations, but who is authorized by the Administrator to conduct operations as a U.S. commercial operator, will be issued an Operating Certificate.

(c) A person who is not authorized to conduct direct air carrier operations, but who is authorized by the Administrator to conduct operations when common carriage is not involved as an operator of U.S.-registered civil airplanes with a seat configuration of 20 or more passengers, or a maximum payload capacity of 6,000 pounds or more, will be issued an Operating Certificate.

(d) A person authorized to engage in common carriage under part 121 or part 135 of this chapter, or both, shall be issued only one certificate authorizing such common carriage, regardless of the kind of operation or the class or size of aircraft to be operated.

(e) A person authorized to engage in noncommon or private carriage under part 125 or part 135 of this chapter, or both, shall be issued only one certificate authorizing such carriage, regardless of the kind of operation or the class or size of aircraft to be operated.

(f) A person conducting operations under more than one paragraph of 119.21, 119.23, or 119.25 shall conduct those operations in compliance with—

(1) The requirements specified in each paragraph of those sections for the kind of operation conducted under that paragraph; and

(2) The appropriate authorizations, limitations, and procedures specified in the operations specifications for each kind of operation.

(g) No person may operate as a direct air carrier or as a commercial operator without, or in violation of, an appropriate certificate and appropriate operations specifications. No person may operate as a direct air carrier or as a commercial operator in violation of any deviation or exemption authority, if issued to that person or that person's representative.

(h) A person holding an Operating Certificate authorizing noncommon or private carriage operations shall not conduct any operations in common carriage. A person holding an Air Carrier Certificate or Operating Certificate authorizing common carriage operations shall not conduct any operations in noncommon carriage.

(i) No person may operate as a direct air carrier without holding appropriate economic authority from the Department of Transportation.

(j) A certificate holder under this part may not operate aircraft under part 121 or part 135 of this chapter in a geographical area unless its operations specifications specifically authorize the certificate holder to operate in that area.

(k) No person may advertise or otherwise offer to perform an operation subject to this part unless that person is authorized by the Federal Aviation Administration to conduct that operation.

(l) No person may operate an aircraft under this part, part 121 of this chapter, or part 135 of this chapter in violation of an air carrier operating certificate, operating certificate, or appropriate operations specifications issued under this part.

[Doc. No. 28154, 60 FR 65913, Dec. 20, 1995, as amended by Amdt. 119-3, 62 FR 13253, Mar. 19, 1997; 62 FR 15570, Apr. 1, 1997]

119.7 Operations specifications

(a) Each certificate holder's operations specifications must contain—

(1) The authorizations, limitations, and certain procedures under which each kind of operation, if applicable, is to be conducted; and

(2) Certain other procedures under which each class and size of aircraft is to be operated.

(b) Except for operations specifications paragraphs identifying authorized kinds of operations, operations specifications are not a part of a certificate.

119.9 Use of business names

(a) A certificate holder under this part may not operate an aircraft under part 121 or part 135 of this chapter using a business name other than a business name appearing in the certificate holder's operations specifications.

(b) No person may operate an aircraft under part 121 or part 135 of this chapter unless the name of the certificate holder who is operating the aircraft, or the air carrier or operating certificate number of the certificate holder who is operating the aircraft, is legibly displayed on the aircraft and is clearly visible and readable from the outside of the aircraft to a person standing on the ground at any time except during flight time. The means of displaying the name on the aircraft and its readability must be acceptable to the Administrator.

[Doc. No. 28154, 60 FR 65913, Dec. 20, 1995, as amended by Amdt. 119-3, 62 FR 13253, Mar. 19, 1997]

119.8 Safety Management Systems

(a) Certificate holders authorized to conduct operations under part 121 of this chapter must have a safety management system that meets the requirements of part 5 of this chapter and is acceptable to the Administrator by March 9, 2018.

(b) A person applying to the Administrator for an air carrier certificate or operating certificate to conduct operations under part 121 of this chapter after March 9, 2015, must demonstrate, as part of the application process under §119.35, that it has an SMS that meets the standards set forth in part 5 of this chapter and is acceptable to the Administrator.

[Doc. No. FAA-2009-0671, 80 FR 1328, Jan. 8, 2015]

Subpart B — Applicability of Operating Requirements to Different Kinds of Operations Under Parts 121, 125, and 135 of This Chapter

119.21 Commercial operators engaged in intrastate common carriage and direct air carriers

(a) Each person who conducts airplane operations as a commercial operator engaged in intrastate common carriage of persons or property for compensation or hire in air commerce, or as a direct air carrier, shall comply with the certification and operations specifications requirements in subpart C of this part, and shall conduct its:

(1) Domestic operations in accordance with the applicable requirements of part 121 of this chapter, and shall be issued operations specifications for those operations in accordance with those requirements. However, based on a showing of safety in air commerce, the Administrator may permit persons who conduct domestic operations between any point located within any of the following Alaskan islands and any point in the State of Alaska to comply with the requirements applicable to flag operations contained in subpart U of part 121 of this chapter:

   (i) The Aleutian Islands.

   (ii) The Pribilof Islands.

   (iii) The Shumagin Islands.

(2) Flag operations in accordance with the applicable requirements of part 121 of this chapter, and shall be issued operations specifications for those operations in accordance with those requirements.

(3) Supplemental operations in accordance with the applicable requirements of part 121 of this chapter, and shall be issued operations specifications for those operations in accordance with those requirements. However, based on a determination of safety in air commerce, the Administrator may authorize or require those operations to be conducted under paragraph (a)(1) or (a)(2) of this section.

(4) Commuter operations in accordance with the applicable requirements of part 135 of this chapter, and shall be issued operations specifications for those operations in accordance with those requirements.

(5) On-demand operations in accordance with the applicable requirements of part 135 of this chapter, and shall be issued operations specifications for those operations in accordance with those requirements.

(b) Persons who are subject to the requirements of paragraph (a)(4) of this section may conduct those operations in accordance with the requirements of paragraph (a)(1) or (a)(2) of this section, provided they obtain authorization from the Administrator.

(c) Persons who are subject to the requirements of paragraph (a)(5) of this section may conduct those operations in accordance with the requirements of paragraph (a)(3) of this section, provided they obtain authorization from the Administrator.

[Doc. No. 28154, 60 FR 65913, Dec. 20, 1995, as amended by Amdt. 119–2, 61 FR 30433, June 14, 1996; Amdt. 119–3, 62 FR 13254, Mar. 19, 1997]

119.23 Operators engaged in passenger-carrying operations, cargo operations, or both with airplanes when common carriage is not involved

(a) Each person who conducts operations when common carriage is not involved with airplanes having a passenger-seat configuration of 20 seats or more, excluding each crewmember seat, or a payload capacity of 6,000 pounds or more, shall, unless deviation authority is issued—

(1) Comply with the certification and operations specifications requirements of part 125 of this chapter;

(2) Conduct its operations with those airplanes in accordance with the requirements of part 125 of this chapter; and

(3) Be issued operations specifications in accordance with those requirements.

(b) Each person who conducts noncommon carriage (except as provided in 91.501(b) of this chapter) or private carriage operations for compensation or hire with airplanes having a passenger-seat configuration of less than 20 seats, excluding each crewmember seat, and a payload capacity of less than 6,000 pounds shall—

(1) Comply with the certification and operations specifications requirements in subpart C of this part;

(2) Conduct those operations in accordance with the requirements of part 135 of this chapter, except for those requirements applicable only to commuter operations; and

(3) Be issued operations specifications in accordance with those requirements.

[Doc. No. 28154, 60 FR 65913, Dec. 20, 1995, as amended by Amdt. 119–2, 61 FR 30434, June 14, 1996]

119.25 Rotorcraft operations: Direct air carriers and commercial operators

Each person who conducts rotorcraft operations for compensation or hire must comply with the certification and operations specifications requirements of Subpart C of this part, and shall conduct its:

(a) Commuter operations in accordance with the applicable requirements of part 135 of this chapter, and shall be issued operations specifications for those operations in accordance with those requirements.

(b) On-demand operations in accordance with the applicable requirements of part 135 of this chapter, and shall be issued operations specifications for those operations in accordance with those requirements.

Subpart C — Certification, Operations Specifications, and Certain Other Requirements for Operations Conducted Under Part 121 or Part 135 of This Chapter

119.31 Applicability

This subpart sets out certification requirements and prescribes the content of operations specifications and certain other requirements for operations conducted under part 121 or part 135 of this chapter.

119.33 General requirements

(a) A person may not operate as a direct air carrier unless that person—

(1) Is a citizen of the United States;

(2) Obtains an Air Carrier Certificate; and

(3) Obtains operations specifications that prescribe the authorizations, limitations, and procedures under which each kind of operation must be conducted.

(b) A person other than a direct air carrier may not conduct any commercial passenger or cargo aircraft operation for compensation or hire under part 121 or part 135 of this chapter unless that person—

(1) Is a citizen of the United States;

(2) Obtains an Operating Certificate; and

(3) Obtains operations specifications that prescribe the authorizations, limitations, and procedures under which each kind of operation must be conducted.

(c) Each applicant for a certificate under this part and each applicant for operations specifications authorizing a new kind of operation that is subject to 121.163 or 135.145 of this chapter shall conduct proving tests as authorized by the Administrator during the application process for authority to conduct operations under part 121 or part 135 of this chapter. All proving tests must be conducted in a manner acceptable to the Administrator. All prov-

FAR 119

ing tests must be conducted under the appropriate operating and maintenance requirements of part 121 or 135 of this chapter that would apply if the applicant were fully certificated. The Administrator will issue a letter of authorization to each person stating the various authorities under which the proving tests shall be conducted.

[Doc. No. 28154, 60 FR 65913, Dec. 20, 1995, as amended by Amdt. 119–2, 61 FR 30434, June 14, 1996]

119.35 Certificate application requirements for all operators

(a) A person applying to the Administrator for an Air Carrier Certificate or Operating Certificate under this part (applicant) must submit an application—

   (1) In a form and manner prescribed by the Administrator; and

   (2) Containing any information the Administrator requires the applicant to submit.

(b) Each applicant must submit the application to the Administrator at least 90 days before the date of intended operation.

[Doc. No. 28154, 62 FR 13254, Mar. 19, 1997; 62 FR 15570, Apr. 1, 1997]

119.36 Additional certificate application requirements for commercial operators

(a) Each applicant for the original issue of an operating certificate for the purpose of conducting intrastate common carriage operations under part 121 or part 135 of this chapter must submit an application in a form and manner prescribed by the Administrator to the responsible Flight Standards office.

(b) Each application submitted under paragraph (a) of this section must contain a signed statement showing the following:

   (1) For corporate applicants:

      (i) The name and address of each stockholder who owns 5 percent or more of the total voting stock of the corporation, and if that stockholder is not the sole beneficial owner of the stock, the name and address of each beneficial owner. An individual is considered to own the stock owned, directly or indirectly, by or for his or her spouse, children, grandchildren, or parents.

      (ii) The name and address of each director and each officer and each person employed or who will be employed in a management position described in 119.65 and 119.69, as applicable.

      (iii) The name and address of each person directly or indirectly controlling or controlled by the applicant and each person under direct or indirect control with the applicant.

   (2) For non-corporate applicants:

      (i) The name and address of each person having a financial interest therein and the nature and extent of that interest.

      (ii) The name and address of each person employed or who will be employed in a management position described in 119.65 and 119.69, as applicable.

(c) In addition, each applicant for the original issue of an operating certificate under paragraph (a) of this section must submit with the application a signed statement showing—

   (1) The nature and scope of its intended operation, including the name and address of each person, if any, with whom the applicant has a contract to provide services as a commercial operator and the scope, nature, date, and duration of each of those contracts; and

   (2) For applicants intending to conduct operations under part 121 of this chapter, the financial information listed in paragraph (e) of this section.

(d) Each applicant for, or holder of, a certificate issued under paragraph (a) of this section, shall notify the Administrator within 10 days after—

   (1) A change in any of the persons, or the names and addresses of any of the persons, submitted to the Administrator under paragraph (b)(1) or (b)(2) of this section; or

   (2) For applicants intending to conduct operations under part 121 of this chapter, a change in the financial information submitted to the Administrator under paragraph (e) of this section that occurs while the application for the issue is pending before the FAA and that would make the applicant's financial situation substantially less favorable than originally reported.

(e) Each applicant for the original issue of an operating certificate under paragraph (a) of this section who intends to conduct operations under part 121 of this chapter must submit the following financial information:

   (1) A balance sheet that shows assets, liabilities, and net worth, as of a date not more than 60 days before the date of application.

   (2) An itemization of liabilities more than 60 days past due on the balance sheet date, if any, showing each creditor's name and address, a description of the liability, and the amount and due date of the liability.

   (3) An itemization of claims in litigation, if any, against the applicant as of the date of application showing each claimant's name and address and a description and the amount of the claim.

   (4) A detailed projection of the proposed operation covering 6 complete months after the month in which the certificate is expected to be issued including—

      (i) Estimated amount and source of both operating and nonoperating revenue, including identification of its existing and anticipated income producing contracts and estimated revenue per mile or hour of operation by aircraft type;

      (ii) Estimated amount of operating and nonoperating expenses by expense objective classification; and

      (iii) Estimated net profit or loss for the period.

   (5) An estimate of the cash that will be needed for the proposed operations during the first 6 months after the month in which the certificate is expected to be issued, including—

      (i) Acquisition of property and equipment (explain);

      (ii) Retirement of debt (explain);

      (iii) Additional working capital (explain);

      (iv) Operating losses other than depreciation and amortization (explain); and

      (v) Other (explain).

   (6) An estimate of the cash that will be available during the first 6 months after the month in which the certificate is expected to be issued, from—

      (i) Sale of property or flight equipment (explain);

      (ii) New debt (explain);

      (iii) New equity (explain);

      (iv) Working capital reduction (explain);

      (v) Operations (profits) (explain);

      (vi) Depreciation and amortization (explain); and

      (vii) Other (explain).

   (7) A schedule of insurance coverage in effect on the balance sheet date showing insurance companies; policy numbers; types, amounts, and period of coverage; and special conditions, exclusions, and limitations.

   (8) Any other financial information that the Administrator requires to enable him or her to determine that the applicant has sufficient financial resources to conduct his or her operations with the degree of safety required in the public interest.

(f) Each financial statement containing financial information required by paragraph (e) of this section must be based on accounts prepared and maintained on an accrual basis in accordance with generally accepted accounting principles applied on a consistent basis, and must contain the name and address of the applicant's public accounting firm, if any. Information submitted must be signed by an officer, owner, or partner of the applicant or certificate holder.

[Doc. No. 28154, 62 FR 13254, Mar. 19, 1997; 62 FR 15570, Apr. 1, 1997, as amended by Docket FAA-2018-0119, Amdt. 119-19, 83 FR 9172, Mar. 5, 2018]

119.37 Contents of an Air Carrier Certificate or Operating Certificate

The Air Carrier Certificate or Operating Certificate includes—

(a) The certificate holder's name;

(b) The location of the certificate holder's principal base of operations;

(c) The certificate number;

(d) The certificate's effective date; and

(e) The name or the designator of the responsible Flight Standards office.

[Docket No. 28154, 60 FR 65913, Dec. 20, 1995, as amended by Docket FAA-2018-0119, Amdt. 119-19, 83 FR 9172, Mar. 5, 2018]

119.39 Issuing or denying a certificate

(a) An applicant may be issued an Air Carrier Certificate or Operating Certificate if, after investigation, the Administrator finds that the applicant—

(1) Meets the applicable requirements of this part;

(2) Holds the economic authority applicable to the kinds of operations to be conducted, issued by the Department of Transportation, if required; and

(3) Is properly and adequately equipped in accordance with the requirements of this chapter and is able to conduct a safe operation under appropriate provisions of part 121 or part 135 of this chapter and operations specifications issued under this part.

(b) An application for a certificate may be denied if the Administrator finds that—

(1) The applicant is not properly or adequately equipped or is not able to conduct safe operations under this subchapter;

(2) The applicant previously held an Air Carrier Certificate or Operating Certificate which was revoked;

(3) The applicant intends to or fills a key management position listed in 119.65(a) or 119.69(a), as applicable, with an individual who exercised control over or who held the same or a similar position with a certificate holder whose certificate was revoked, or is in the process of being revoked, and that individual materially contributed to the circumstances causing revocation or causing the revocation process;

(4) An individual who will have control over or have a substantial ownership interest in the applicant had the same or similar control or interest in a certificate holder whose certificate was revoked, or is in the process of being revoked, and that individual materially contributed to the circumstances causing revocation or causing the revocation process; or

(5) In the case of an applicant for an Operating Certificate for intrastate common carriage, that for financial reasons the applicant is not able to conduct a safe operation.

119.41 Amending a certificate

(a) The Administrator may amend any certificate issued under this part if—

(1) The Administrator determines, under 49 U.S.C. 44709 and part 13 of this chapter, that safety in air commerce and the public interest requires the amendment; or

(2) The certificate holder applies for the amendment and the responsible Flight Standards office determines that safety in air commerce and the public interest allows the amendment.

(b) When the Administrator proposes to issue an order amending, suspending, or revoking all or part of any certificate, the procedure in 13.19 of this chapter applies.

(c) When the certificate holder applies for an amendment of its certificate, the following procedure applies:

(1) The certificate holder must file an application to amend its certificate with the responsible Flight Standards office at least 15 days before the date proposed by the applicant for the amendment to become effective, unless the administrator approves filing within a shorter period; and

(2) The application must be submitted to the responsible Flight Standards office in the form and manner prescribed by the Administrator.

(d) When a certificate holder seeks reconsideration of a decision from the responsible Flight Standards office concerning amendments of a certificate, the following procedure applies:

(1) The petition for reconsideration must be made within 30 days after the certificate holder receives the notice of denial; and

(2) The certificate holder must petition for reconsideration to the Executive Director, Flight Standards Service.

[Docket No. 28154, 60 FR 65913, Dec. 20, 1995, as amended by Docket FAA-2018-0119, Amdt. 119-19, 83 FR 9172, Mar. 5, 2018]

119.43 Certificate holder's duty to maintain operations specifications

(a) Each certificate holder shall maintain a complete and separate set of its operations specifications at its principal base of operations.

(b) Each certificate holder shall insert pertinent excerpts of its operations specifications, or references thereto, in its manual and shall—

(1) Clearly identify each such excerpt as a part of its operations specifications; and

(2) State that compliance with each operations specifications requirement is mandatory.

(c) Each certificate holder shall keep each of its employees and other persons used in its operations informed of the provisions of its operations specifications that apply to that employee's or person's duties and responsibilities.

119.45 [Reserved]

119.47 Maintaining a principal base of operations, main operations base, and main maintenance base; change of address

(a) Each certificate holder must maintain a principal base of operations. Each certificate holder may also establish a main operations base and a main maintenance base which may be located at either the same location as the principal base of operations or at separate locations.

(b) At least 30 days before it proposes to establish or change the location of its principal base of operations, its main operations base, or its main maintenance base, a certificate holder must provide written notification to its responsible Flight Standards office.

[Docket No. 28154, 60 FR 65913, Dec. 20, 1995, as amended by Docket FAA-2018-0119, Amdt. 119-19, 83 FR 9172, Mar. 5, 2018]

FAR 119

119.49 Contents of operations specifications

(a) Each certificate holder conducting domestic, flag, or commuter operations must obtain operations specifications containing all of the following:

(1) The specific location of the certificate holder's principal base of operations and, if different, the address that shall serve as the primary point of contact for correspondence between the FAA and the certificate holder and the name and mailing address of the certificate holder's agent for service.

(2) Other business names under which the certificate holder may operate.

(3) Reference to the economic authority issued by the Department of Transportation, if required.

(4) Type of aircraft, registration markings, and serial numbers of each aircraft authorized for use, each regular and alternate airport to be used in scheduled operations, and, except for commuter operations, each provisional and refueling airport.

    (i) Subject to the approval of the Administrator with regard to form and content, the certificate holder may incorporate by reference the items listed in paragraph (a)(4) of this section into the certificate holder's operations specifications by maintaining a current listing of those items and by referring to the specific list in the applicable paragraph of the operations specifications.

    (ii) The certificate holder may not conduct any operation using any aircraft or airport not listed.

(5) Kinds of operations authorized.

(6) Authorization and limitations for routes and areas of operations.

(7) Airport limitations.

(8) Time limitations, or standards for determining time limitations, for overhauling, inspecting, and checking airframes, engines, propellers, rotors, appliances, and emergency equipment.

(9) Authorization for the method of controlling weight and balance of aircraft.

(10) Interline equipment interchange requirements, if relevant.

(11) Aircraft wet lease information required by 119.53(c).

(12) Any authorized deviation and exemption granted from any requirement of this chapter.

(13) An authorization permitting, or a prohibition against, accepting, handling, and transporting materials regulated as hazardous materials in transport under 49 CFR parts 171 through 180.

(14) Any other item the Administrator determines is necessary.

(b) Each certificate holder conducting supplemental operations must obtain operations specifications containing all of the following:

(1) The specific location of the certificate holder's principal base of operations, and, if different, the address that shall serve as the primary point of contact for correspondence between the FAA and the certificate holder and the name and mailing address of the certificate holder's agent for service.

(2) Other business names under which the certificate holder may operate.

(3) Reference to the economic authority issued by the Department of Transportation, if required.

(4) Type of aircraft, registration markings, and serial number of each aircraft authorized for use.

    (i) Subject to the approval of the Administrator with regard to form and content, the certificate holder may incorporate by reference the items listed in paragraph (b)(4) of this section into the certificate holder's operations specifications by maintaining a current listing of those items and by referring to the specific list in the applicable paragraph of the operations specifications.

    (ii) The certificate holder may not conduct any operation using any aircraft not listed.

(5) Kinds of operations authorized.

(6) Authorization and limitations for routes and areas of operations.

(7) Special airport authorizations and limitations.

(8) Time limitations, or standards for determining time limitations, for overhauling, inspecting, and checking airframes, engines, propellers, appliances, and emergency equipment.

(9) Authorization for the method of controlling weight and balance of aircraft.

(10) Aircraft wet lease information required by 119.53(c).

(11) Any authorization or requirement to conduct supplemental operations as provided by 119.21(a)(3).

(12) Any authorized deviation or exemption from any requirement of this chapter.

(13) An authorization permitting, or a prohibition against, accepting, handling, and transporting materials regulated as hazardous materials in transport under 49 CFR parts 171 through 180.

(14) Any other item the Administrator determines is necessary.

(c) Each certificate holder conducting on-demand operations must obtain operations specifications containing all of the following:

(1) The specific location of the certificate holder's principal base of operations, and if different, the address that shall serve as the primary point of contact for correspondence between the FAA and the name and mailing address of the certificate holder's agent for service.

(2) Other business names under which the certificate holder may operate.

(3) Reference to the economic authority issued by the Department of Transportation, if required.

(4) Kind and area of operations authorized.

(5) Category and class of aircraft that may be used in those operations.

(6) Type of aircraft, registration markings, and serial number of each aircraft that is subject to an airworthiness maintenance program required by 135.411(a)(2) of this chapter.

    (i) Subject to the approval of the Administrator with regard to form and content, the certificate holder may incorporate by reference the items listed in paragraph (c)(6) of this section into the certificate holder's operations specifications by maintaining a current listing of those items and by referring to the specific list in the applicable paragraph of the operations specifications.

    (ii) The certificate holder may not conduct any operation using any aircraft not listed.

(7) Registration markings of each aircraft that is to be inspected under an approved aircraft inspection program under 135.419 of this chapter.

(8) Time limitations or standards for determining time limitations, for overhauls, inspections, and checks for airframes, engines, propellers, rotors, appliances, and emergency equipment of aircraft that are subject to an airworthiness maintenance program required by 135.411(a)(2) of this chapter.

(9) Additional maintenance items required by the Administrator under 135.421 of this chapter.

(10) Aircraft wet lease information required by 119.53(c).

(11) Any authorized deviation or exemption from any requirement of this chapter.

(12) An authorization permitting, or a prohibition against, accepting, handling, and transporting materials regulated as hazardous materials in transport under 49 CFR parts 171 through 180.

(13) Any other item the Administrator determines is necessary.

[Docket No. 28154, 60 FR 65913, Dec. 20, 1995, as amended by Amdt. 119–10, 70 FR 58823, Oct. 7, 2005; Amdt. 119–13, 75 FR 26645, May 12, 2010]

119.51 Amending operations specifications

(a) The Administrator may amend any operations specifications issued under this part if—

(1) The Administrator determines that safety in air commerce and the public interest require the amendment; or

(2) The certificate holder applies for the amendment, and the Administrator determines that safety in air commerce and the public interest allows the amendment.

(b) Except as provided in paragraph (e) of this section, when the Administrator initiates an amendment to a certificate holder's operations specifications, the following procedure applies:

(1) The responsible Flight Standards office notifies the certificate holder in writing of the proposed amendment.

(2) The responsible Flight Standards office sets a reasonable period (but not less than 7 days) within which the certificate holder may submit written information, views, and arguments on the amendment.

(3) After considering all material presented, the responsible Flight Standards office notifies the certificate holder of—

(i) The adoption of the proposed amendment;

(ii) The partial adoption of the proposed amendment; or

(iii) The withdrawal of the proposed amendment.

4) If the responsible Flight Standards office issues an amendment to the operations specifications, it becomes effective not less than 30 days after the certificate holder receives notice of it unless—

(i) The responsible Flight Standards office finds under paragraph (e) of this section that there is an emergency requiring immediate action with respect to safety in air commerce; or

(ii) The certificate holder petitions for reconsideration of the amendment under paragraph (d) of this section.

(c) When the certificate holder applies for an amendment to its operations specifications, the following procedure applies:

(1) The certificate holder must file an application to amend its operations specifications—

(i) At least 90 days before the date proposed by the applicant for the amendment to become effective, unless a shorter time is approved, in cases of mergers; acquisitions of airline operational assets that require an additional showing of safety (e.g., proving tests); changes in the kind of operation as defined in 110.2; resumption of operations following a suspension of operations as a result of bankruptcy actions; or the initial introduction of aircraft not before proven for use in air carrier or commercial operator operations.

(ii) At least 15 days before the date proposed by the applicant for the amendment to become effective in all other cases.

(2) The application must be submitted to the responsible Flight Standards office in a form and manner prescribed by the Administrator.

(3) After considering all material presented, the responsible Flight Standards office notifies the certificate holder of—

(i) The adoption of the applied for amendment;

(ii) The partial adoption of the applied for amendment; or

(iii) The denial of the applied for amendment. The certificate holder may petition for reconsideration of a denial under paragraph (d) of this section.

(4) If the responsible Flight Standards office approves the amendment, following coordination with the certificate holder regarding its implementation, the amendment is effective on the date the Administrator approves it.

(d) When a certificate holder seeks reconsideration of a decision from the responsible Flight Standards office concerning the amendment of operations specifications, the following procedure applies:

(1) The certificate holder must petition for reconsideration of that decision within 30 days of the date that the certificate holder receives a notice of denial of the amendment to its operations specifications, or of the date it receives notice of an FAA-initiated amendment to its operations specifications, whichever circumstance applies.

(2) The certificate holder must address its petition to the Executive Director, Flight Standards Service.

(3) A petition for reconsideration, if filed within the 30-day period, suspends the effectiveness of any amendment issued by the responsible Flight Standards office unless the responsible Flight Standards office has found, under paragraph (e) of this section, that an emergency exists requiring immediate action with respect to safety in air transportation or air commerce.

(4) If a petition for reconsideration is not filed within 30 days, the procedures of paragraph (c) of this section apply.

(e) If the responsible Flight Standards office finds that an emergency exists requiring immediate action with respect to safety in air commerce or air transportation that makes the procedures set out in this section impracticable or contrary to the public interest:

(1) The responsible Flight Standards office amends the operations specifications and makes the amendment effective on the day the certificate holder receives notice of it.

(2) In the notice to the certificate holder, the responsible Flight Standards office articulates the reasons for its finding that an emergency exists requiring immediate action with respect to safety in air transportation or air commerce or that makes it impracticable or contrary to the public interest to stay the effectiveness of the amendment.

[Doc. No. 28154, 60 FR 65913, Dec. 20, 1995, as amended by Amdt. 119-14, 76 FR 7488, Feb. 10, 2011; Docket FAA-2018-0119, Amdt. 119-19, 83 FR 9172, Mar. 5, 2018]

119.53 Wet leasing of aircraft and other arrangements for transportation by air

(a) Unless otherwise authorized by the Administrator, prior to conducting operations involving a wet lease, each certificate holder under this part authorized to conduct common carriage operations under this subchapter shall provide the Administrator with a copy of the wet lease to be executed which would lease the aircraft to any other person engaged in common carriage operations under this subchapter, including foreign air carriers, or to any other foreign person engaged in common carriage wholly outside the United States.

(b) No certificate holder under this part may wet lease from a foreign air carrier or any other foreign person or any person not authorized to engage in common carriage.

(c) Upon receiving a copy of a wet lease, the Administrator determines which party to the agreement has operational control of the aircraft and issues amendments to the operations specifications of each party to the agreement, as needed. The lessor must provide the following information to be incorporated into the operations specifications of both parties, as needed.

(1) The names of the parties to the agreement and the duration thereof.

(2) The nationality and registration markings of each aircraft involved in the agreement.

(3) The kind of operation (e.g., domestic, flag, supplemental, commuter, or on-demand).

(4) The airports or areas of operation.

(5) A statement specifying the party deemed to have operational control and the times, airports, or areas under which such operational control is exercised.

(d) In making the determination of paragraph (c) of this section, the Administrator will consider the following:

(1) Crewmembers and training.

(2) Airworthiness and performance of maintenance.

(3) Dispatch.

(4) Servicing the aircraft.

(5) Scheduling.

(6) Any other factor the Administrator considers relevant.

(e) Other arrangements for transportation by air: Except as provided in paragraph (f) of this section, a certificate holder under this part operating under part 121 or 135 of this chapter may not conduct any operation for another certificate holder under this part or a foreign air carrier under part 129 of this chapter or a foreign person engaged in common carriage wholly outside the United States unless it holds applicable Department of Transportation economic authority, if required, and is authorized under its operations specifications to conduct the same kinds of operations (as defined in 110.2). The certificate holder conducting the substitute operation must conduct that operation in accordance with the same operations authority held by the certificate holder arranging for the substitute operation. These substitute operations must be conducted between airports for which the substitute certificate holder holds authority for scheduled operations or within areas of operations for which the substitute certificate holder has authority for supplemental or on-demand operations.

(f) A certificate holder under this part may, if authorized by the Department of Transportation under 380.3 of this title and the Administrator in the case of interstate commuter, interstate domestic, and flag operations, or the Administrator in the case of scheduled intrastate common carriage operations, conduct one or more flights for passengers who are stranded because of the cancellation of their scheduled flights. These flights must be conducted under the rules of part 121 or part 135 of this chapter applicable to supplemental or on-demand operations.

[Doc. No. 28154, 60 FR 65913, Dec. 20, 1995, as amended by Amdt. 119–14, 76 FR 7488, Feb. 10, 2011]

119.55   Obtaining deviation authority to perform operations under a U.S. military contract

(a) The Administrator may authorize a certificate holder that is autho(a) The Administrator may authorize a certificate holder that is authorized to conduct supplemental or on-demand operations to deviate from the applicable requirements of this part, part 117, part 121, or part 135 of this chapter in order to perform operations under a U.S. military contract.

(b) A certificate holder that has a contract with the U.S. Department of Defense's Air Mobility Command (AMC) must submit a request for deviation authority to AMC. AMC will review the requests, then forward the carriers' consolidated requests, along with AMC's recommendations, to the FAA for review and action.

(c) The Administrator may authorize a deviation to perform operations under a U.S. military contract under the following conditions—

(1) The Department of Defense certifies to the Administrator that the operation is essential to the national defense;

(2) The Department of Defense further certifies that the certificate holder cannot perform the operation without deviation authority;

(3) The certificate holder will perform the operation under a contract or subcontract for the benefit of a U.S. armed service; and

(4) The Administrator finds that the deviation is based on grounds other than economic advantage either to the certificate holder or to the United States.

(d) In the case where the Administrator authorizes a deviation under this section, the Administrator will issue an appropriate amendment to the certificate holder's operations specifications.

(e) The Administrator may, at any time, terminate any grant of deviation authority issued under this section.

[Doc. No. 28154, 60 FR 65913, Dec. 20, 1995, as amended by Amdt. 119–16, 77 FR 402, Jan. 4, 2012]

119.57   Obtaining deviation authority to perform an emergency operation

(a) In emergency conditions, the Administrator may authorize deviations if—

(1) Those conditions necessitate the transportation of persons or supplies for the protection of life or property; and

(2) The Administrator finds that a deviation is necessary for the expeditious conduct of the operations.

(b) When the Administrator authorizes deviations for operations under emergency conditions—

(1) The Administrator will issue an appropriate amendment to the certificate holder's operations specifications; or

(2) If the nature of the emergency does not permit timely amendment of the operations specifications—

(i) The Administrator may authorize the deviation orally; and

(ii) The certificate holder shall provide documentation describing the nature of the emergency to the responsible Flight Standards office within 24 hours after completing the operation.

[Docket No. 28154, 60 FR 65913, Dec. 20, 1995, as amended by Docket FAA-2018-0119, Amdt. 119-19, 83 FR 9172, Mar. 5, 2018]

119.59   Conducting tests and inspections

(a) At any time or place, the Administrator may conduct an inspection or test to determine whether a certificate holder under this part is complying with title 49 of the United States Code, applicable regulations, the certificate, or the certificate holder's operations specifications.

(b) The certificate holder must—

(1) Make available to the Administrator at the certificate holder's principal base of operations—

(i) The certificate holder's Air Carrier Certificate or the certificate holder's Operating Certificate and the certificate holder's operations specifications; and

(ii) A current listing that will include the location and persons responsible for each record, document, and report required to be kept by the certificate holder under title 49 of the United States Code applicable to the operation of the certificate holder.

(2) Allow the Administrator to make any test or inspection to determine compliance respecting any matter stated in paragraph (a) of this section.

(c) Each employee of, or person used by, the certificate holder who is responsible for maintaining the certificate holder's records must make those records available to the Administrator.

(d) The Administrator may determine a certificate holder's continued eligibility to hold its certificate and/or operations specifications on any grounds listed in paragraph (a) of this section, or any other appropriate grounds.

(e) Failure by any certificate holder to make available to the Administrator upon request, the certificate, operations specifications, or any required record, document, or report is grounds for suspension of all or any part of the certificate holder's certificate and operations specifications.

(f) In the case of operators conducting intrastate common carriage operations, these inspections and tests include inspections and tests of financial books and records.

119.61   Duration and surrender of certificate and operations specifications

(a) An Air Carrier Certificate or Operating Certificate issued under this part is effective until—

(1) The certificate holder surrenders it to the Administrator; or

(2) The Administrator suspends, revokes, or otherwise terminates the certificate.

(b) Operations specifications issued under this part, part 121, or part 135 of this chapter are effective unless—

(1) The Administrator suspends, revokes, or otherwise terminates the certificate;

(2) The operations specifications are amended as provided in 119.51;

(3) The certificate holder does not conduct a kind of operation for more than the time specified in 119.63 and fails to follow the procedures of 119.63 upon resuming that kind of operation; or

(4) The Administrator suspends or revokes the operations specifications for a kind of operation.

(c) Within 30 days after a certificate holder terminates operations under part 135 of this chapter, the operating certificate and operations specifications must be surrendered by the certificate holder to the responsible Flight Standards office.

Docket No. 28154, 60 FR 65913, Dec. 20, 1995, as amended by Docket FAA-2018-0119, Amdt. 119-19, 83 FR 9172, Mar. 5, 2018]

119.63   Recency of operation

(a) Except as provided in paragraph (b) of this section, no certificate holder may conduct a kind of operation for which it holds authority in its operations specifications unless the certificate holder has conducted that kind of operation within the preceding number of consecutive calendar days specified in this paragraph:

(1) For domestic, flag, or commuter operations—30 days.

(2) For supplemental or on-demand operations—90 days, except that if the certificate holder has authority to conduct domestic, flag, or commuter operations, and has conducted domestic, flag or commuter operations within the previous 30 days, this paragraph does not apply.

(b) If a certificate holder does not conduct a kind of operation for which it is authorized in its operations specifications within the number of calendar days specified in paragraph (a) of this section, it shall not conduct such kind of operation unless—

(1) It advises the Administrator at least 5 consecutive calendar days before resumption of that kind of operation; and

(2) It makes itself available and accessible during the 5 consecutive calendar day period in the event that the FAA decides to conduct a full inspection reexamination to determine whether the certificate holder remains properly and adequately equipped and able to conduct a safe operation.

Doc. No. 28154, 60 FR 65913, Dec. 20, 1995, as amended by Amdt. 119–2, 61 FR 30434, June 14, 1996]

119.65   Management personnel required for operations conducted under part 121 of this chapter

(a) Each certificate holder must have sufficient qualified management and technical personnel to ensure the highest degree of safety in its operations. The certificate holder must have qualified personnel serving full-time in the following or equivalent positions:

(1) Director of Safety.

(2) Director of Operations.

(3) Chief Pilot.

(4) Director of Maintenance.

(5) Chief Inspector.

(b) The Administrator may approve positions or numbers of positions other than those listed in paragraph (a) of this section for a particular operation if the certificate holder shows that it can perform the operation with the highest degree of safety under the direction of fewer or different categories of management personnel due to—

(1) The kind of operation involved;

(2) The number and type of airplanes used; and

(3) The area of operations.

(c) The title of the positions required under paragraph (a) of this section or the title and number of equivalent positions approved under paragraph (b) of this section shall be set forth in the certificate holder's operations specifications.

(d) The individuals who serve in the positions required or approved under paragraph (a) or (b) of this section and anyone in a position to exercise control over operations conducted under the operating certificate must—

(1) Be qualified through training, experience, and expertise;

(2) To the extent of their responsibilities, have a full understanding of the following materials with respect to the certificate holder's operation—

   (i) Aviation safety standards and safe operating practices;

   (ii) 14 CFR Chapter I (Federal Aviation Regulations);

   (iii) The certificate holder's operations specifications;

   (iv) All appropriate maintenance and airworthiness requirements of this chapter (e.g., parts 1, 21, 23, 25, 43, 45, 47, 65, 91, and 121 of this chapter); and

   (v) The manual required by 121.133 of this chapter; and

(3) Discharge their duties to meet applicable legal requirements and to maintain safe operations.

(e) Each certificate holder must:

(1) State in the general policy provisions of the manual required by 121.133 of this chapter, the duties, responsibilities, and authority of personnel required under paragraph (a) of this section;

(2) List in the manual the names and business addresses of the individuals assigned to those positions; and

(3) Notify the responsible Flight Standards office within 10 days of any change in personnel or any vacancy in any position listed.

[Docket No. 28154, 60 FR 65913, Dec. 20, 1995, as amended by Docket FAA-2018-0119, Amdt. 119-19, 83 FR 9172, Mar. 5, 2018]

119.67   Management personnel: Qualifications for operations conducted under part 121 of this chapter

(a) To serve as Director of Operations under 119.65(a) a person must—

(1) Hold an airline transport pilot certificate;

(2) Have at least 3 years supervisory or managerial experience within the last 6 years in a position that exercised operational control over any operations conducted with large airplanes under part 121 or part 135 of this chapter, or if the certificate holder uses only small airplanes in its operations, the experience may be obtained in large or small airplanes; and

(3) In the case of a person becoming a Director of Operations—

   (i) For the first time ever, have at least 3 years experience, within the past 6 years, as pilot in command of a large airplane operated under part 121 or part 135 of this chapter, if the certificate holder operates large airplanes. If the certificate holder uses only small airplanes in its operation, the experience may be obtained in either large or small airplanes.

   (ii) In the case of a person with previous experience as a Director of Operations, have at least 3 years experience as pilot in command of a large airplane operated under part 121 or part 135 of this chapter, if the certificate holder operates large airplanes. If the certificate holder uses only small airplanes in its operation, the experience may be obtained in either large or small airplanes.

(b) To serve as Chief Pilot under 119.65(a) a person must hold an airline transport pilot certificate with appropriate ratings for at least one of the airplanes used in the certificate holder's operation and:

(1) In the case of a person becoming a Chief Pilot for the first time ever, have at least 3 years experience, within the past 6 years, as pilot in command of a large airplane operated under part 121 or part 135 of this chapter, if the certificate holder operates large airplanes. If the certificate holder uses only small airplanes in its operation, the experience may be obtained in either large or small airplanes.

(2) In the case of a person with previous experience as a Chief Pilot, have at least 3 years experience, as pilot in command of a large airplane operated under part 121 or part 135 of this chapter, if the certificate holder operates large airplanes. If the certificate holder uses only small airplanes in its operation, the experience may be obtained in either large or small airplanes.

FAR 119

(c) To serve as Director of Maintenance under 119.65(a) a person must—

   (1) Hold a mechanic certificate with airframe and powerplant ratings;

   (2) Have 1 year of experience in a position responsible for returning airplanes to service;

   (3) Have at least 1 year of experience in a supervisory capacity under either paragraph (c)(4)(i) or (c)(4)(ii) of this section maintaining the same category and class of airplane as the certificate holder uses; and

   (4) Have 3 years experience within the past 6 years in one or a combination of the following—

      (i) Maintaining large airplanes with 10 or more passenger seats, including at the time of appointment as Director of Maintenance, experience in maintaining the same category and class of airplane as the certificate holder uses; or

      (ii) Repairing airplanes in a certificated airframe repair station that is rated to maintain airplanes in the same category and class of airplane as the certificate holder uses.

(d) To serve as Chief Inspector under 119.65(a) a person must—

   (1) Hold a mechanic certificate with both airframe and powerplant ratings, and have held these ratings for at least 3 years;

   (2) Have at least 3 years of maintenance experience on different types of large airplanes with 10 or more passenger seats with an air carrier or certificated repair station, 1 year of which must have been as maintenance inspector; and

   (3) Have at least 1 year of experience in a supervisory capacity maintaining the same category and class of aircraft as the certificate holder uses.

(e) A certificate holder may request a deviation to employ a person who does not meet the appropriate airman experience, managerial experience, or supervisory experience requirements of this section if the Manager of the Air Transportation Division, AFS–200, or the Manager of the Aircraft Maintenance Division, AFS–300, as appropriate, finds that the person has comparable experience, and can effectively perform the functions associated with the position in accordance with the requirements of this chapter and the procedures outlined in the certificate holder's manual. Grants of deviation under this paragraph may be granted after consideration of the size and scope of the operation and the qualifications of the intended personnel. The Administrator may, at any time, terminate any grant of deviation authority issued under this paragraph.

[Doc. No. 28154, 60 FR 65913, Dec. 20, 1995, as amended by Amdt. 119–2, 61 FR 30434, June 14, 1996; Amdt. 119–3, 62 FR 13255, Mar. 19, 1997]

119.69 Management personnel required for operations conducted under part 135 of this chapter

(a) Each certificate holder must have sufficient qualified management and technical personnel to ensure the safety of its operations. Except for a certificate holder using only one pilot in its operations, the certificate holder must have qualified personnel serving in the following or equivalent positions:

   (1) Director of Operations.

   (2) Chief Pilot.

   (3) Director of Maintenance.

(b) The Administrator may approve positions or numbers of positions other than those listed in paragraph (a) of this section for a particular operation if the certificate holder shows that it can perform the operation with the highest degree of safety under the direction of fewer or different categories of management personnel due to—

   (1) The kind of operation involved;

   (2) The number and type of aircraft used; and

   (3) The area of operations.

(c) The title of the positions required under paragraph (a) of this section or the title and number of equivalent positions approved under paragraph (b) of this section shall be set forth in the certificate holder's operations specifications.

(d) The individuals who serve in the positions required or approved under paragraph (a) or (b) of this section and anyone in a position to exercise control over operations conducted under the operating certificate must—

   (1) Be qualified through training, experience, and expertise;

   (2) To the extent of their responsibilities, have a full understanding of the following material with respect to the certificate holder's operation—

      (i) Aviation safety standards and safe operating practices;

      (ii) 14 CFR Chapter I (Federal Aviation Regulations);

      (iii) The certificate holder's operations specifications;

      (iv) All appropriate maintenance and airworthiness requirements of this chapter (e.g., parts 1, 21, 23, 25, 43, 45, 47, 65, 91, and 135 of this chapter); and

      (v) The manual required by 135.21 of this chapter; and

   (3) Discharge their duties to meet applicable legal requirements and to maintain safe operations.

(e) Each certificate holder must—

   (1) State in the general policy provisions of the manual required by 135.21 of this chapter, the duties, responsibilities, and authority of personnel required or approved under paragraph (a) or (b), respectively, of this section;

   (2) List in the manual the names and business addresses of the individuals assigned to those positions; and

   (3) Notify the responsible Flight Standards office within 10 days of any change in personnel or any vacancy in any position listed.

[Docket No. 28154, 60 FR 65913, Dec. 20, 1995, as amended by Docket FAA-2018-0119, Amdt. 119-19, 83 FR 9172, Mar. 5, 2018]

119.71 Management personnel: Qualifications for operations conducted under part 135 of this chapter

(a) To serve as Director of Operations under 119.69(a) for a certificate holder conducting any operations for which the pilot in command is required to hold an airline transport pilot certificate, a person must hold an airline transport pilot certificate and either:

   (1) Have at least 3 years supervisory or managerial experience within the last 6 years in a position that exercised operational control over any operations conducted under part 121 or part 135 of this chapter; or

   (2) In the case of a person becoming Director of Operations—

      (i) For the first time ever, have at least 3 years experience within the past 6 years, as pilot in command of an aircraft operated under part 121 or part 135 of this chapter.

      (ii) In the case of a person with previous experience as a Director of Operations, have at least 3 years experience as pilot in command of an aircraft operated under part 121 or part 135 of this chapter.

(b) To serve as Director of Operations under 119.69(a) for a certificate holder that only conducts operations for which the pilot in command is required to hold a commercial pilot certificate, a person must hold at least a commercial pilot certificate. If an instrument rating is required for any pilot in command for that certificate holder, the Director of Operations must also hold an instrument rating. In addition, the Director of Operations must either—

   (1) Have at least 3 years supervisory or managerial experience within the last 6 years in a position that exercised operational control over any operations conducted under part 121 or part

135 of this chapter; or

(2) In the case of a person becoming Director of Operations—

    (i) For the first time ever, have at least 3 years experience, within the past 6 years, as pilot in command of an aircraft operated under part 121 or part 135 of this chapter.

    (ii) In the case of a person with previous experience as a Director of Operations, have at least 3 years experience as pilot in command of an aircraft operated under part 121 or part 135 of this chapter.

(c) To serve as Chief Pilot under 119.69(a) for a certificate holder conducting any operation for which the pilot in command is required to hold an airline transport pilot certificate a person must hold an airline transport pilot certificate with appropriate ratings and be qualified to serve as pilot in command in at least one aircraft used in the certificate holder's operation and:

(1) In the case of a person becoming a Chief Pilot for the first time ever, have at least 3 years experience, within the past 6 years, as pilot in command of an aircraft operated under part 121 or part 135 of this chapter.

(2) In the case of a person with previous experience as a Chief Pilot, have at least 3 years experience as pilot in command of an aircraft operated under part 121 or part 135 of this chapter.

(d) To serve as Chief Pilot under 119.69(a) for a certificate holder that only conducts operations for which the pilot in command is required to hold a commercial pilot certificate, a person must hold at least a commercial pilot certificate. If an instrument rating is required for any pilot in command for that certificate holder, the Chief Pilot must also hold an instrument rating. The Chief Pilot must be qualified to serve as pilot in command in at least one aircraft used in the certificate holder's operation. In addition, the Chief Pilot must:

(1) In the case of a person becoming a Chief Pilot for the first time ever, have at least 3 years experience, within the past 6 years, as pilot in command of an aircraft operated under part 121 or part 135 of this chapter.

(2) In the case of a person with previous experience as a Chief Pilot, have at least 3 years experience as pilot in command of an aircraft operated under part 121 or part 135 of this chapter.

(e) To serve as Director of Maintenance under 119.69(a) a person must hold a mechanic certificate with airframe and powerplant ratings and either:

(1) Have 3 years of experience within the past 6 years maintaining aircraft as a certificated mechanic, including, at the time of appointment as Director of Maintenance, experience in maintaining the same category and class of aircraft as the certificate holder uses; or

(2) Have 3 years of experience within the past 6 years repairing aircraft in a certificated airframe repair station, including 1 year in the capacity of approving aircraft for return to service.

(f) A certificate holder may request a deviation to employ a person who does not meet the appropriate airmen experience requirements, managerial experience requirements, or supervisory experience requirements of this section if the Manager of the Air Transportation Division, AFS–200, or the Manager of the Aircraft Maintenance Division, AFS–300, as appropriate, find that the person has comparable experience, and can effectively perform the functions associated with the position in accordance with the requirements of this chapter and the procedures outlined in the certificate holder's manual. The Administrator may, at any time, terminate any grant of deviation authority issued under this paragraph.

[Doc. No. 28154, 60 FR 65913, Dec. 20, 1995, as amended by Amdt. 119–3, 62 FR 13255, Mar. 19, 1997; Amdt. 119–12, 72 FR 54816, Sept. 27, 2007]

119.73 Employment of former FAA employees

(a) Except as specified in paragraph (c) of this section, no certificate holder conducting operations under part 121 or 135 of this chapter may knowingly employ or make a contractual arrangement which permits an individual to act as an agent or representative of the certificate holder in any matter before the Federal Aviation Administration if the individual, in the preceding 2 years—

(1) Served as, or was directly responsible for the oversight of, a Flight Standards Service aviation safety inspector; and

(2) Had direct responsibility to inspect, or oversee the inspection of, the operations of the certificate holder.

(b) For the purpose of this section, an individual shall be considered to be acting as an agent or representative of a certificate holder in a matter before the agency if the individual makes any written or oral communication on behalf of the certificate holder to the agency (or any of its officers or employees) in connection with a particular matter, whether or not involving a specific party and without regard to whether the individual has participated in, or had responsibility for, the particular matter while serving as a Flight Standards Service aviation safety inspector.

(c) The provisions of this section do not prohibit a certificate holder from knowingly employing or making a contractual arrangement which permits an individual to act as an agent or representative of the certificate holder in any matter before the Federal Aviation Administration if the individual was employed by the certificate holder before October 21, 2011.

[Doc. No. FAA–2008–1154, 76 FR 52235, Aug. 22, 2011]

FAR 119

PART 121 — OPERATING REQUIREMENTS: DOMESTIC, FLAG, AND SUPPLEMENTAL OPERATIONS

Authority: 49 U.S.C. 106(f), 106(g), 40103, 40113, 40119, 41706, 42301 preceding note added by Pub. L. 112-95, sec. 412, 126 Stat. 89, 44101, 44701-44702, 44705, 44709-44711, 44713, 44716-44717, 44722, 44729, 44732; 46105; Pub. L. 111-216, 124 Stat. 2348 (49 U.S.C. 44701 note); Pub. L. 112-95 126 Stat 62 (49 U.S.C. 44732 note).

Subpart J — Special Airworthiness Requirements

Source: Docket No. 6258, 29 FR 19202, Dec. 31, 1964, unless otherwise noted.

121.211   Applicability

(a) This subpart prescribes special airworthiness requirements applicable to certificate holders as stated in paragraphs (b) through (e) of this section.

(b) Except as provided in paragraph (d) of this section, each airplane type certificated under Aero Bulletin 7A or part 04 of the Civil Air Regulations in effect before November 1, 1946 must meet the special airworthiness requirements in 121.215 through 121.283.

(c) Each certificate holder must comply with the requirements of 121.285 through 121.291.

(d) If the Administrator determines that, for a particular model of airplane used in cargo service, literal compliance with any requirement under paragraph (b) of this section would be extremely difficult and that compliance would not contribute materially to the objective sought, he may require compliance only with those requirements that are necessary to accomplish the basic objectives of this part.

(e) No person may operate under this part a nontransport category airplane type certificated after December 31, 1964, unless the airplane meets the special airworthiness requirements in 121.293.

[Doc. No. 28154, 60 FR 65928, Dec. 20, 1995]

121.213   [Reserved]

121.215   Cabin interiors

(a) Except as provided in 121.312, each compartment used by the crew or passengers must meet the requirements of this section.

(b) Materials must be at least flash resistant.

(c) The wall and ceiling linings and the covering of upholstering, floors, and furnishings must be flame resistant.

(d) Each compartment where smoking is to be allowed must be equipped with self-contained ash trays that are completely removable and other compartments must be placarded against smoking.

(e) Each receptacle for used towels, papers, and wastes must be of fire-resistant material and must have a cover or other means of containing possible fires started in the receptacles.

[Doc. No. 6258, 29 FR 19202, Dec. 31, 1964, as amended by Amdt. 121–84, 37 FR 3974, Feb. 24, 1972]

121.217 Internal doors

In any case where internal doors are equipped with louvres or other ventilating means, there must be a means convenient to the crew for closing the flow of air through the door when necessary.

121.219 Ventilation

Each passenger or crew compartment must be suitably ventilated. Carbon monoxide concentration may not be more than one part in 20,000 parts of air, and fuel fumes may not be present. In any case where partitions between compartments have louvres or other means allowing air to flow between compartments, there must be a means convenient to the crew for closing the flow of air through the partitions, when necessary.

121.221 Fire precautions

(a) Each compartment must be designed so that, when used for storing cargo or baggage, it meets the following requirements:

(1) No compartment may include controls, wiring, lines, equipment, or accessories that would upon damage or failure, affect the safe operation of the airplane unless the item is adequately shielded, isolated, or otherwise protected so that it cannot be damaged by movement of cargo in the compartment and so that damage to or failure of the item would not create a fire hazard in the compartment.

(2) Cargo or baggage may not interfere with the functioning of the fire-protective features of the compartment.

(3) Materials used in the construction of the compartments, including tie-down equipment, must be at least flame resistant.

(4) Each compartment must include provisions for safeguarding against fires according to the classifications set forth in paragraphs (b) through (f) of this section.

(b) Class A. Cargo and baggage compartments are classified in the "A" category if—

(1) A fire therein would be readily discernible to a member of the crew while at his station; and

(2) All parts of the compartment are easily accessible in flight.

There must be a hand fire extinguisher available for each Class A compartment.

(c) Class B. Cargo and baggage compartments are classified in the "B" category if enough access is provided while in flight to enable a member of the crew to effectively reach all of the compartment and its contents with a hand fire extinguisher and the compartment is so designed that, when the access provisions are being used, no hazardous amount of smoke, flames, or extinguishing agent enters any compartment occupied by the crew or passengers. Each Class B compartment must comply with the following:

(1) It must have a separate approved smoke or fire detector system to give warning at the pilot or flight engineer station.

(2) There must be a hand fire extinguisher available for the compartment.

(3) It must be lined with fire-resistant material, except that additional service lining of flame-resistant material may be used.

(d) Class C. Cargo and baggage compartments are classified in the "C" category if they do not conform with the requirements for the "A", "B", "D", or "E" categories. Each Class C compartment must comply with the following:

(1) It must have a separate approved smoke or fire detector system to give warning at the pilot or flight engineer station.

(2) It must have an approved built-in fire-extinguishing system controlled from the pilot or flight engineer station.

(3) It must be designed to exclude hazardous quantities of smoke, flames, or extinguishing agents from entering into any compartment occupied by the crew or passengers.

(4) It must have ventilation and draft controlled so that the extinguishing agent provided can control any fire that may start in the compartment.

(5) It must be lined with fire-resistant material, except that additional service lining of flame-resistant material may be used.

(e) Class D. Cargo and baggage compartments are classified in the "D" category if they are so designed and constructed that a fire occurring therein will be completely confined without endangering the safety of the airplane or the occupants. Each Class D compartment must comply with the following:

(1) It must have a means to exclude hazardous quantities of smoke, flames, or noxious gases from entering any compartment occupied by the crew or passengers.

(2) Ventilation and drafts must be controlled within each compartment so that any fire likely to occur in the compartment will not progress beyond safe limits.

(3) It must be completely lined with fire-resistant material.

(4) Consideration must be given to the effect of heat within the compartment on adjacent critical parts of the airplane.

(f) Class E. On airplanes used for the carriage of cargo only, the cabin area may be classified as a Class "E" compartment. Each Class E compartment must comply with the following:

(1) It must be completely lined with fire-resistant material.

(2) It must have a separate system of an approved type smoke or fire detector to give warning at the pilot or flight engineer station.

(3) It must have a means to shut off the ventilating air flow to or within the compartment and the controls for that means must be accessible to the flight crew in the crew compartment.

(4) It must have a means to exclude hazardous quantities of smoke, flames, or noxious gases from entering the flight crew compartment.

(5) Required crew emergency exits must be accessible under all cargo loading conditions.

121.223 Proof of compliance with 121.221

Compliance with those provisions of 121.221 that refer to compartment accessibility, the entry of hazardous quantities of smoke or extinguishing agent into compartments occupied by the crew or passengers, and the dissipation of the extinguishing agent in Class "C" compartments must be shown by tests in flight. During these tests it must be shown that no inadvertent operation of smoke or fire detectors in other compartments within the airplane would occur as a result of fire contained in any one compartment, either during the time it is being extinguished, or thereafter, unless the extinguishing system floods those compartments simultaneously.

121.225 Propeller deicing fluid

If combustible fluid is used for propeller deicing, the certificate holder must comply with 121.255.

121.227 Pressure cross-feed arrangements

(a) Pressure cross-feed lines may not pass through parts of the airplane used for carrying persons or cargo unless—

(1) There is a means to allow crewmembers to shut off the supply of fuel to these lines; or

(2) The lines are enclosed in a fuel and fume-proof enclosure that is ventilated and drained to the exterior of the airplane.

However, such an enclosure need not be used if those lines incorporate no fittings on or within the personnel or cargo areas and are suitably routed or protected to prevent accidental damage.

(b) Lines that can be isolated from the rest of the fuel system by valves at each end must incorporate provisions for relieving excessive pressures that may result from exposure of the isolated line to high temperatures.

121.229 Location of fuel tanks

(a) Fuel tanks must be located in accordance with 121.255.

(b) No part of the engine nacelle skin that lies immediately behind a major air outlet from the engine compartment may be used as the wall of an integral tank.

c) Fuel tanks must be isolated from personnel compartments by means of fume- and fuel-proof enclosures.

121.231 Fuel system lines and fittings

a) Fuel lines must be installed and supported so as to prevent excessive vibration and so as to be adequate to withstand loads due to fuel pressure and accelerated flight conditions.

b) Lines connected to components of the airplanes between which there may be relative motion must incorporate provisions for flexibility.

c) Flexible connections in lines that may be under pressure and subject to axial loading must use flexible hose assemblies rather than hose clamp connections.

d) Flexible hose must be of an acceptable type or proven suitable for the particular application.

121.233 Fuel lines and fittings in designated fire zones

Fuel lines and fittings in each designated fire zone must comply with 121.259.

121.235 Fuel valves

Each fuel valve must—

a) Comply with 121.257;

b) Have positive stops or suitable index provisions in the "on" and "off" positions; and

c) Be supported so that loads resulting from its operation or from accelerated flight conditions are not transmitted to the lines connected to the valve.

121.237 Oil lines and fittings in designated fire zones

Oil line and fittings in each designated fire zone must comply with 121.259.

121.239 Oil valves

a) Each oil valve must—

(1) Comply with 121.257;

(2) Have positive stops or suitable index provisions in the "on" and "off" positions; and

(3) Be supported so that loads resulting from its operation or from accelerated flight conditions are not transmitted to the lines attached to the valve.

b) The closing of an oil shutoff means must not prevent feathering the propeller, unless equivalent safety provisions are incorporated.

121.241 Oil system drains

Accessible drains incorporating either a manual or automatic means for positive locking in the closed position, must be provided to allow safe drainage of the entire oil system.

121.243 Engine breather lines

(a) Engine breather lines must be so arranged that condensed water vapor that may freeze and obstruct the line cannot accumulate at any point.

(b) Engine breathers must discharge in a location that does not constitute a fire hazard in case foaming occurs and so that oil emitted from the line does not impinge upon the pilots' windshield.

(c) Engine breathers may not discharge into the engine air induction system.

121.245 Fire walls

Each engine, auxiliary power unit, fuel-burning heater, or other item of combustion equipment that is intended for operation in flight must be isolated from the rest of the airplane by means of firewalls or shrouds, or by other equivalent means.

121.247 Fire-wall construction

Each fire wall and shroud must—

(a) Be so made that no hazardous quantity of air, fluids, or flame can pass from the engine compartment to other parts of the airplane;

(b) Have all openings in the fire wall or shroud sealed with close-fitting fire-proof grommets, bushings, or firewall fittings;

(c) Be made of fireproof material; and

(d) Be protected against corrosion.

121.249 Cowling

(a) Cowling must be made and supported so as to resist the vibration inertia, and air loads to which it may be normally subjected.

(b) Provisions must be made to allow rapid and complete drainage of the cowling in normal ground and flight attitudes. Drains must not discharge in locations constituting a fire hazard. Parts of the cowling that are subjected to high temperatures because they are near exhaust system parts or because of exhaust gas impingement must be made of fireproof material. Unless otherwise specified in these regulations all other parts of the cowling must be made of material that is at least fire resistant.

121.251 Engine accessory section diaphragm

Unless equivalent protection can be shown by other means, a diaphragm that complies with 121.247 must be provided on air-cooled engines to isolate the engine power section and all parts of the exhaust system from the engine accessory compartment.

121.253 Powerplant fire protection

(a) Designated fire zones must be protected from fire by compliance with 121.255 through 121.261.

(b) Designated fire zones are—

(1) Engine accessory sections;

(2) Installations where no isolation is provided between the engine and accessory compartment; and

(3) Areas that contain auxiliary power units, fuel-burning heaters, and other combustion equipment.

121.255 Flammable fluids

(a) No tanks or reservoirs that are a part of a system containing flammable fluids or gases may be located in designated fire zones, except where the fluid contained, the design of the system, the materials used in the tank, the shutoff means, and the connections, lines, and controls provide equivalent safety.

(b) At least one-half inch of clear airspace must be provided between any tank or reservoir and a firewall or shroud isolating a designated fire zone.

121.257 Shutoff means

(a) Each engine must have a means for shutting off or otherwise preventing hazardous amounts of fuel, oil, deicer, and other flammable fluids from flowing into, within, or through any designated fire zone. However, means need not be provided to shut off flow in lines that are an integral part of an engine.

(b) The shutoff means must allow an emergency operating sequence that is compatible with the emergency operation of other equipment, such as feathering the propeller, to facilitate rapid and effective control of fires.

(c) Shutoff means must be located outside of designated fire zones, unless equivalent safety is provided, and it must be shown that no hazardous amount of flammable fluid will drain into any designated fire zone after a shut off.

(d) Adequate provisions must be made to guard against inadvertent operation of the shutoff means and to make it possible for the crew to reopen the shutoff means after it has been closed.

121.259 Lines and fittings

(a) Each line, and its fittings, that is located in a designated fire zone, if it carries flammable fluids or gases under pressure, or is attached directly to the engine, or is subject to relative motion between components (except lines and fittings forming an integral part of the engine), must be flexible and fire-resistant with fire-resistant, factory-fixed, detachable, or other approved fire-resistant ends.

(b) Lines and fittings that are not subject to pressure or to relative motion between components must be of fire-resistant materials.

121.261   Vent and drain lines

All vent and drain lines and their fittings, that are located in a designated fire zone must, if they carry flammable fluids or gases, comply with 121.259, if the Administrator finds that the rupture or breakage of any vent or drain line may result in a fire hazard.

121.263   Fire-extinguishing systems

(a) Unless the certificate holder shows that equivalent protection against destruction of the airplane in case of fire is provided by the use of fireproof materials in the nacelle and other components that would be subjected to flame, fire-extinguishing systems must be provided to serve all designated fire zones.

(b) Materials in the fire-extinguishing system must not react chemically with the extinguishing agent so as to be a hazard.

121.265   Fire-extinguishing agents

Only methyl bromide, carbon dioxide, or another agent that has been shown to provide equivalent extinguishing action may be used as a fire-extinguishing agent. If methyl bromide or any other toxic extinguishing agent is used, provisions must be made to prevent harmful concentrations of fluid or fluid vapors from entering any personnel compartment either because of leakage during normal operation of the airplane or because of discharging the fire extinguisher on the ground or in flight when there is a defect in the extinguishing system. If a methyl bromide system is used, the containers must be charged with dry agent and sealed by the fire-extinguisher manufacturer or some other person using satisfactory recharging equipment. If carbon dioxide is used, it must not be possible to discharge enough gas into the personnel compartments to create a danger of suffocating the occupants.

121.267   Extinguishing agent container pressure relief

Extinguishing agent containers must be provided with a pressure relief to prevent bursting of the container because of excessive internal pressures. The discharge line from the relief connection must terminate outside the airplane in a place convenient for inspection on the ground. An indicator must be provided at the discharge end of the line to provide a visual indication when the container has discharged.

121.269   Extinguishing agent container compartment temperature

Precautions must be taken to insure that the extinguishing agent containers are installed in places where reasonable temperatures can be maintained for effective use of the extinguishing system.

121.271   Fire-extinguishing system materials

(a) Except as provided in paragraph (b) of this section, each component of a fire-extinguishing system that is in a designated fire zone must be made of fireproof materials.

(b) Connections that are subject to relative motion between components of the airplane must be made of flexible materials that are at least fire-resistant and be located so as to minimize the probability of failure.

121.273   Fire-detector systems

Enough quick-acting fire detectors must be provided in each designated fire zone to assure the detection of any fire that may occur in that zone.

121.275   Fire detectors

Fire detectors must be made and installed in a manner that assures their ability to resist, without failure, all vibration, inertia, and other loads to which they may be normally subjected. Fire detectors must be unaffected by exposure to fumes, oil, water, or other fluids that may be present.

121.277   Protection of other airplane components agains fire

(a) Except as provided in paragraph (b) of this section, all airplan surfaces aft of the nacelles in the area of one nacelle diameter c both sides of the nacelle centerline must be made of material th is at least fire resistant.

(b) Paragraph (a) of this section does not apply to tail surfaces ly ing behind nacelles unless the dimensional configuration of th airplane is such that the tail surfaces could be affected readily b heat, flames, or sparks emanating from a designated fire zone c from the engine compartment of any nacelle.

121.279   Control of engine rotation

(a) Except as provided in paragraph (b) of this section, each airplan must have a means of individually stopping and restarting the r tation of any engine in flight.

(b) In the case of turbine engine installations, a means of stopping th rotation need be provided only if the Administrator finds that rota tion could jeopardize the safety of the airplane.

121.281   Fuel system independence

(a) Each airplane fuel system must be arranged so that the failure c any one component does not result in the irrecoverable loss c power of more than one engine.

(b) A separate fuel tank need not be provided for each engine if th certificate holder shows that the fuel system incorporates feature that provide equivalent safety.

121.283   Induction system ice prevention

A means for preventing the malfunctioning of each engine due to ic accumulation in the engine air induction system must be provided fc each airplane.

121.285   Carriage of cargo in passenger compartments

(a) Except as provided in paragraph (b), (c), or (d) or this section, n certificate holder may carry cargo in the passenger compartmen of an airplane.

(b) Cargo may be carried anywhere in the passenger compartment i it is carried in an approved cargo bin that meets the followin, requirements:

(1) The bin must withstand the load factors and emergency land ing conditions applicable to the passenger seats of the airplan in which the bin is installed, multiplied by a factor of 1.15, us ing the combined weight of the bin and the maximum weigh of cargo that may be carried in the bin.

(2) The maximum weight of cargo that the bin is approved t carry and any instructions necessary to insure proper weigh distribution within the bin must be conspicuously marked o the bin.

(3) The bin may not impose any load on the floor or other structur of the airplane that exceeds the load limitations of that structur

(4) The bin must be attached to the seat tracks or to the floor struc ture of the airplane, and its attachment must withstand the loa factors and emergency landing conditions applicable to th passenger seats of the airplane in which the bin is installed multiplied by either the factor 1.15 or the seat attachment fac tor specified for the airplane, whichever is greater, using th combined weight of the bin and the maximum weight of carg that may be carried in the bin.

(5) The bin may not be installed in a position that restricts access to or use of any required emergency exit, or of the aisle in th passenger compartment.

(6) The bin must be fully enclosed and made of material that is a least flame resistant.

(7) Suitable safeguards must be provided within the bin to preven the cargo from shifting under emergency landing conditions.

(8) The bin may not be installed in a position that obscures any passenger's view of the "seat belt" sign "no smoking" sign

or any required exit sign, unless an auxiliary sign or other approved means for proper notification of the passenger is provided.

c) Cargo may be carried aft of a bulkhead or divider in any passenger compartment provided the cargo is restrained to the load factors in 25.561(b)(3) and is loaded as follows:

(1) It is properly secured by a safety belt or other tiedown having enough strength to eliminate the possibility of shifting under all normally anticipated flight and ground conditions.

(2) It is packaged or covered in a manner to avoid possible injury to passengers and passenger compartment occupants.

(3) It does not impose any load on seats or the floor structure that exceeds the load limitation for those components.

(4) Its location does not restrict access to or use of any required emergency or regular exit, or of the aisle in the passenger compartment.

(5) Its location does not obscure any passenger's view of the "seat belt" sign, "no smoking" sign, or required exit sign, unless an auxiliary sign or other approved means for proper notification of the passenger is provided.

(d) Cargo, including carry-on baggage, may be carried anywhere in the passenger compartment of a nontransport category airplane type certificated after December 31, 1964, if it is carried in an approved cargo rack, bin, or compartment installed in or on the airplane, if it is secured by an approved means, or if it is carried in accordance with each of the following:

(1) For cargo, it is properly secured by a safety belt or other tiedown having enough strength to eliminate the possibility of shifting under all normally anticipated flight and ground conditions, or for carry-on baggage, it is restrained so as to prevent its movement during air turbulence.

(2) It is packaged or covered to avoid possible injury to occupants.

(3) It does not impose any load on seats or in the floor structure that exceeds the load limitation for those components.

(4) It is not located in a position that obstructs the access to, or use of, any required emergency or regular exit, or the use of the aisle between the crew and the passenger compartment, or is located in a position that obscures any passenger's view of the "seat belt" sign, "no smoking" sign or placard, or any required exit sign, unless an auxiliary sign or other approved means for proper notification of the passengers is provided.

(5) It is not carried directly above seated occupants.

(6) It is stowed in compliance with this section for takeoff and landing.

(7) For cargo-only operations, paragraph (d)(4) of this section does not apply if the cargo is loaded so that at least one emergency or regular exit is available to provide all occupants of the airplane a means of unobstructed exit from the airplane if an emergency occurs.

[Doc. No. 6258, 29 FR 19202, Dec. 31, 1964, as amended by Amdt. 121–179, 47 FR 33390, Aug. 2, 1982; Amdt. 121–251, 60 FR 65928, Dec. 20, 1995]

121.287 Carriage of cargo in cargo compartments

When cargo is carried in cargo compartments that are designed to require the physical entry of a crewmember to extinguish any fire that may occur during flight, the cargo must be loaded so as to allow a crewmember to effectively reach all parts of the compartment with the contents of a hand fire extinguisher.

121.289 Landing gear: Aural warning device

(a) Except for airplanes that comply with the requirements of 25.729 of this chapter on or after January 6, 1992, each airplane must have a landing gear aural warning device that functions continuously under the following conditions:

(1) For airplanes with an established approach wing-flap position, whenever the wing flaps are extended beyond the maximum certificated approach climb configuration position in the Airplane Flight Manual and the landing gear is not fully extended and locked.

(2) For airplanes without an established approach climb wing-flap position, whenever the wing flaps are extended beyond the position at which landing gear extension is normally performed and the landing gear is not fully extended and locked.

(b) The warning system required by paragraph (a) of this section—

(1) May not have a manual shutoff;

(2) Must be in addition to the throttle-actuated device installed under the type certification airworthiness requirements; and

(3) May utilize any part of the throttle-actuated system including the aural warning device.

(c) The flap position sensing unit may be installed at any suitable place in the airplane.

[Doc. No. 6258, 29 FR 19202, Dec. 31, 1964, as amended by Amdt. 121–3, 30 FR 3638, Mar. 19, 1965; Amdt. 121–130, 41 FR 47229, Oct. 28, 1976; Amdt. 121–227, 56 FR 63762, Dec. 5, 1991; Amdt. 121–251, 60 FR 65929, Dec. 20, 1995]

121.291 Demonstration of emergency evacuation procedures

(a) Except as provided in paragraph (a)(1) of this section, each certificate holder must conduct an actual demonstration of emergency evacuation procedures in accordance with paragraph (a) of appendix D to this part to show that each type and model of airplane with a seating capacity of more than 44 passengers to be used in its passenger-carrying operations allows the evacuation of the full capacity, including crewmembers, in 90 seconds or less.

(1) An actual demonstration need not be conducted if that airplane type and model has been shown to be in compliance with this paragraph in effect on or after October 24, 1967, or, if during type certification, with 25.803 of this chapter in effect on or after December 1, 1978.

(2) Any actual demonstration conducted after September 27, 1993, must be in accordance with paragraph (a) of appendix D to this part in effect on or after that date or with 25.803 in effect on or after that date.

(b) Each certificate holder conducting operations with airplanes with a seating capacity of more than 44 passengers must conduct a partial demonstration of emergency evacuation procedures in accordance with paragraph (c) of this section upon:

(1) Initial introduction of a type and model of airplane into passenger-carrying operation;

(2) Changing the number, location, or emergency evacuation duties or procedures of flight attendants who are required by 121.391; or

(3) Changing the number, location, type of emergency exits, or type of opening mechanism on emergency exits available for evacuation.

(c) In conducting the partial demonstration required by paragraph (b) of this section, each certificate holder must:

(1) Demonstrate the effectiveness of its crewmember emergency training and evacuation procedures by conducting a demonstration, not requiring passengers and observed by the Administrator, in which the flight attendants for that type and model of airplane, using that operator's line operating procedures, open 50 percent of the required floor-level emergency exits and 50 percent of the required non-floor-level emergency exits whose opening by a flight attendant is defined as an emergency evacuation duty under 121.397, and deploy 50 percent of the exit slides. The exits and slides will be selected by the administrator and must be ready for use within 15 seconds;

(2) Apply for and obtain approval from the responsible Flight Standards office before conducting the demonstration;

FAR 121

(3) Use flight attendants in this demonstration who have been selected at random by the Administrator, have completed the certificate holder's FAA-approved training program for the type and model of airplane, and have passed a written or practical examination on the emergency equipment and procedures; and

(4) Apply for and obtain approval from the responsible Flight Standards office before commencing operations with this type and model airplane.

[Doc. No. 21269, 46 FR 61453, Dec. 17, 1981, as amended by Amdt. 121-233, 58 FR 45230, Aug. 26, 1993; Amdt. 121-251, 60 FR 65929, Dec. 20, 1995; Amdt. 121-307, 69 FR 67499, Nov. 17, 2004; Docket FAA-2018-0119, Amdt. 121-380, 83 FR 9172, Mar. 5, 2018]

(d) Each certificate holder operating or proposing to operate one or more landplanes in extended overwater operations, or otherwise required to have certain equipment under 121.339, must show, by simulated ditching conducted in accordance with paragraph (b) of appendix D to this part, that it has the ability to efficiently carry out its ditching procedures. For certificate holders subject to 121.2(a)(1), this paragraph applies only when a new type or model airplane is introduced into the certificate holder's operations after January 19, 1996.

(e) For a type and model airplane for which the simulated ditching specified in paragraph (d) has been conducted by a part 121 certificate holder, the requirements of paragraphs (b)(2), (b)(4), and (b)(5) of appendix D to this part are complied with if each life raft is removed from stowage, one life raft is launched and inflated (or one slide life raft is inflated) and crewmembers assigned to the inflated life raft display and describe the use of each item of required emergency equipment. The life raft or slide life raft to be inflated will be selected by the Administrator.

[Doc. No. 21269, 46 FR 61453, Dec. 17, 1981, as amended by Amdt. 121–233, 58 FR 45230, Aug. 26, 1993; Amdt. 121–251, 60 FR 65929, Dec. 20, 1995; Amdt. 121–307, 69 FR 67499, Nov. 17, 2004]

121.293 Special airworthiness requirements for nontransport category airplanes type certificated after December 31, 1964

No certificate holder may operate a nontransport category airplane manufactured after December 20, 1999 unless the airplane contains a takeoff warning system that meets the requirements of 14 CFR 25.703. However, the takeoff warning system does not have to cover any device for which it has been demonstrated that takeoff with that device in the most adverse position would not create a hazardous condition.

[Doc. No. 28154, 60 FR 65929, Dec. 20, 1995]

121.295 Location for a suspect device

After November 28, 2009, all airplanes with a maximum certificated passenger seating capacity of more than 60 persons must have a location where a suspected explosive or incendiary device found in flight can be placed to minimize the risk to the airplane.

[Doc. No. FAA–2006–26722, 73 FR 63880, Oct. 28, 2008]

121.321 Operations in icing.

After October 21, 2013, no person may operate an airplane with a certificated maximum takeoff weight less than 60,000 pounds in conditions conducive to airframe icing unless it complies with this section. As used in this section, the phrase "conditions conducive to airframe icing" means visible moisture at or below a static air temperature of 5 °C or a total air temperature of 10 °C, unless the approved Airplane Flight Manual provides another definition.

(a) When operating in conditions conducive to airframe icing, compliance must be shown with paragraph (a)(1), or (2), or (3) of this section.

(1) The airplane must be equipped with a certificated primary airframe ice detection system.

    (i) The airframe ice protection system must be activated automatically, or manually by the flightcrew, when the primary ice detection system indicates activation is necessary.

    (ii) When the airframe ice protection system is activated, any other procedures in the Airplane Flight Manual for operating in icing conditions must be initiated.

(2) Visual cues of the first sign of ice formation anywhere on the airplane and a certificated advisory airframe ice detection system must be provided.

    (i) The airframe ice protection system must be activated when any of the visual cues are observed or when the advisory airframe ice detection system indicates activation is necessary, whichever occurs first.

    (ii) When the airframe ice protection system is activated, any other procedures in the Airplane Flight Manual for operating in icing conditions must be initiated.

(3) If the airplane is not equipped to comply with the provision of paragraph (a)(1) or (2) of this section, then the following apply:

    (i) When operating in conditions conducive to airframe icing, the airframe ice protection system must be activated prior to, and operated during, the following phases of flight:

        (A) Takeoff climb after second segment,

        (B) En route climb,

        (C) Go-around climb,

        (D) Holding,

        (E) Maneuvering for approach and landing, and

        (F) Any other operation at approach or holding airspeeds.

    (ii) During any other phase of flight, the airframe ice protection system must be activated and operated at the first sign of ice formation anywhere on the airplane unless the Airplane Flight Manual specifies that the airframe ice protection system should not be used or provides other operational instructions.

    (iii) Any additional procedures for operation in conditions conducive to icing specified in the Airplane Flight Manual or in the manual required by 121.133 must be initiated.

(b) If the procedures specified in paragraph (a)(3)(i) of this section are specifically prohibited in the Airplane Flight Manual, compliance must be shown with the requirements of paragraph (a)(1) or (2) of this section.

(c) Procedures necessary for safe operation of the airframe ice protection system must be established and documented in:

(1) The Airplane Flight Manual for airplanes that comply with paragraph (a)(1) or (2) of this section, or

(2) The Airplane Flight Manual or in the manual required by 121.133 for airplanes that comply with paragraph (a)(3) of this section.

(d) Procedures for operation of the airframe ice protection system must include initial activation, operation after initial activation and deactivation. Procedures for operation after initial activation of the ice protection system must address—

(1) Continuous operation,

(2) Automatic cycling,

(3) Manual cycling if the airplane is equipped with an ice detection system that alerts the flightcrew each time the ice protection system must be cycled, or

(4) Manual cycling based on a time interval if the airplane type is not equipped with features necessary to implement (d)(1)-(3) of this section.

(e) System installations used to comply with paragraph (a)(1) or (a)(2) of this section must be approved through an amended or supplemental type certificate in accordance with part 21 of this chapter.

[Doc. No. FAA-2009-0675, 78 FR 15876, Mar. 13, 2013]

Subpart L — Maintenance, Preventive Maintenance, and Alterations

Source: Docket No. 6258, 29 FR 19210, Dec. 31, 1964, unless otherwise noted.

121.361 Applicability

(a) Except as provided by paragraph (b) of this section, this subpart prescribes requirements for maintenance, preventive maintenance, and alterations for all certificate holders.

(b) The Administrator may amend a certificate holder's operations specifications to permit deviation from those provisions of this subpart that would prevent the return to service and use of airframe components, powerplants, appliances, and spare parts thereof because those items have been maintained, altered, or inspected by persons employed outside the United States who do not hold U.S. airman certificates. Each certificate holder who uses parts under this deviation must provide for surveillance of facilities and practices to assure that all work performed on these parts is accomplished in accordance with the certificate holder's manual.

[Doc. No. 8754, 33 FR 14406, Sept. 25, 1968]

121.363 Responsibility for airworthiness

(a) Each certificate holder is primarily responsible for—

(1) The airworthiness of its aircraft, including airframes, aircraft engines, propellers, appliances, and parts thereof; and

(2) The performance of the maintenance, preventive maintenance, and alteration of its aircraft, including airframes, aircraft engines, propellers, appliances, emergency equipment, and parts thereof, in accordance with its manual and the regulations of this chapter.

(b) A certificate holder may make arrangements with another person for the performance of any maintenance, preventive maintenance, or alterations. However, this does not relieve the certificate holder of the responsibility specified in paragraph (a) of this section.

[Doc. No. 6258, 29 FR 19210, Dec. 31, 1964, as amended by Amdt. 121–106, 38 FR 22378, Aug. 20, 1973]

121.365 Maintenance, preventive maintenance, and alteration organization

(a) Each certificate holder that performs any of its maintenance (other than required inspections), preventive maintenance, or alterations, and each person with whom it arranges for the performance of that work must have an organization adequate to perform the work.

(b) Each certificate holder that performs any inspections required by its manual in accordance with 121.369(b)(2) or (3) (in this subpart referred to as required inspections) and each person with whom it arranges for the performance of that work must have an organization adequate to perform that work.

(c) Each person performing required inspections in addition to other maintenance, preventive maintenance, or alterations, shall organize the performance of those functions so as to separate the required inspection functions from the other maintenance, preventive maintenance, and alteration functions. The separation shall be below the level of administrative control at which overall responsibility for the required inspection functions and other maintenance, preventive maintenance, and alteration functions are exercised.

[Doc. No. 6258, 29 FR 19210, Dec. 31, 1964, as amended by Amdt. 121–3, 30 FR 3639, Mar. 19, 1965]

121.367 Maintenance, preventive maintenance, and alterations programs

Each certificate holder shall have an inspection program and a program covering other maintenance, preventive maintenance, and alterations that ensures that—

(a) Maintenance, preventive maintenance, and alterations performed by it, or by other persons, are performed in accordance with the certificate holder's manual;

(b) Competent personnel and adequate facilities and equipment are provided for the proper performance of maintenance, preventive maintenance, and alterations; and

(c) Each aircraft released to service is airworthy and has been properly maintained for operation under this part.

Doc. No. 6258, 29 FR 19210, Dec. 31, 1964, as amended by Amdt. 121–100, 37 FR 28053, Dec. 20, 1972]

121.368 Contract maintenance

(a) A certificate holder may arrange with another person for the performance of maintenance, preventive maintenance, and alterations as authorized in §121.379(a) only if the certificate holder has met all the requirements in this section. For purposes of this section—

(1) A maintenance provider is any person who performs maintenance, preventive maintenance, or an alteration for a certificate holder other than a person who is trained by and employed directly by that certificate holder.

(2) Covered work means any of the following:

(i) Essential maintenance that could result in a failure, malfunction, or defect endangering the safe operation of an aircraft if not performed properly or if improper parts or materials are used;

(ii) Regularly scheduled maintenance; or

(iii) A required inspection item on an aircraft.

(3) Directly in charge means having responsibility for covered work performed by a maintenance provider. A representative of the certificate holder directly in charge of covered work does not need to physically observe and direct each maintenance provider constantly, but must be available for consultation on matters requiring instruction or decision.

(b) Each certificate holder must be directly in charge of all covered work done for it by a maintenance provider.

(c) Each maintenance provider must perform all covered work in accordance with the certificate holder's maintenance manual.

(d) No maintenance provider may perform covered work unless that work is carried out under the supervision and control of the certificate holder.

(e) Each certificate holder who contracts for maintenance, preventive maintenance, or alterations must develop and implement policies, procedures, methods, and instructions for the accomplishment of all contracted maintenance, preventive maintenance, and alterations. These policies, procedures, methods, and instructions must provide for the maintenance, preventive maintenance, and alterations to be performed in accordance with the certificate holder's maintenance program and maintenance manual.

(f) Each certificate holder who contracts for maintenance, preventive maintenance, or alterations must ensure that its system for the continuing analysis and surveillance of the maintenance, preventive maintenance, and alterations carried out by the maintenance provider, as required by §121.373(a), contains procedures for oversight of all contracted covered work.

(g) The policies, procedures, methods, and instructions required by paragraphs (e) and (f) of this section must be acceptable to the FAA and included in the certificate holder's maintenance manual as required by 121.369(b)(10).

(h) Each certificate holder who contracts for maintenance, preventive maintenance, or alterations must provide to its responsible Flight Standards office, in a format acceptable to the FAA, a list that includes the name and physical (street) address, or addresses, where the work is carried out for each maintenance provider that performs work for the certificate holder, and a description of the type of maintenance, preventive maintenance, or alteration that is to be performed at each location. The list must be updated with any changes, including additions or deletions, and the updated list provided to the FAA in a format acceptable to the FAA by the last day of each calendar month.

[Docket FAA-2011-1136, Amdt. 121-371, 80 FR 11546, Mar. 4, 2015, as amended by Docket FAA-2018-0119, Amdt. 121-380, 83 FR 9173, Mar. 5, 2018]

121.369　Manual requirements

(a) The certificate holder shall put in its manual a chart or description of the certificate holder's organization required by 121.365 and a list of persons with whom it has arranged for the performance of any of its required inspections, other maintenance, preventive maintenance, or alterations, including a general description of that work.

(b) The certificate holder's manual must contain the programs required by 121.367 that must be followed in performing maintenance, preventive maintenance, and alterations of that certificate holder's airplanes, including airframes, aircraft engines, propellers, appliances, emergency equipment, and parts thereof, and must include at least the following:

(1) The method of performing routine and nonroutine maintenance (other than required inspections), preventive maintenance, and alterations.

(2) A designation of the items of maintenance and alteration that must be inspected (required inspections), including at least those that could result in a failure, malfunction, or defect endangering the safe operation of the aircraft, if not performed properly or if improper parts or materials are used.

(3) The method of performing required inspections and a designation by occupational title of personnel authorized to perform each required inspection.

(4) Procedures for the reinspection of work performed pursuant to previous required inspection findings (buy-back procedures).

(5) Procedures, standards, and limits necessary for required inspections and acceptance or rejection of the items required to be inspected and for periodic inspection and calibration of precision tools, measuring devices, and test equipment.

(6) Procedures to ensure that all required inspections are performed.

(7) Instructions to prevent any person who performs any item of work from performing any required inspection of that work.

(8) Instructions and procedures to prevent any decision of an inspector, regarding any required inspection from being countermanded by persons other than supervisory personnel of the inspection unit, or a person at that level of administrative control that has overall responsibility for the management of both the required inspection functions and the other maintenance, preventive maintenance, and alterations functions.

(9) Procedures to ensure that required inspections, other maintenance, preventive maintenance, and alterations that are not completed as a result of shift changes or similar work interruptions are properly completed before the aircraft is released to service.

(10) Policies, procedures, methods, and instructions for the accomplishment of all maintenance, preventive maintenance, and alterations carried out by a maintenance provider. These policies, procedures, methods, and instructions must be acceptable to the FAA and provide for the maintenance, preventive maintenance, and alterations to be performed in accordance with the certificate holder's maintenance program and maintenance manual.

(c) The certificate holder must set forth in its manual a suitable system (which may include a coded system) that provides for preservation and retrieval of information in a manner acceptable to the Administrator and that provides—

(1) A description (or reference to data acceptable to the Administrator) of the work performed;

(2) The name of the person performing the work if the work is performed by a person outside the organization of the certificate holder; and

(3) The name or other positive identification of the individual approving the work.

[Doc. No. 6258, 29 FR 19210, Dec. 31, 1964, as amended by Amdt. 121–94, 37 FR 15983, Aug. 9, 1972; Amdt. 121–106, 38 FR 22378, Aug. 20, 1973]

121.370　[Reserved]

121.370a　[Reserved]

121.371　Required inspection personnel

(a) No person may use any person to perform required inspections unless the person performing the inspection is appropriately certificated, properly trained, qualified, and authorized to do so.

(b) No person may allow any person to perform a required inspection unless, at that time, the person performing that inspection is under the supervision and control of an inspection unit.

(c) No person may perform a required inspection if he performed the item of work required to be inspected.

(d) Each certificate holder shall maintain, or shall determine that each person with whom it arranges to perform its required inspections maintains, a current listing of persons who have been trained, qualified, and authorized to conduct required inspections. The persons must be identified by name, occupational title, and the inspections that they are authorized to perform. The certificate holder (or person with whom it arranges to perform its required inspections) shall give written information to each person so authorized describing the extent of his responsibilities, authorities, and inspectional limitations. The list shall be made available for inspection by the Administrator upon request.

121.373　Continuing analysis and surveillance

(a) Each certificate holder shall establish and maintain a system for the continuing analysis and surveillance of the performance and effectiveness of its inspection program and the program covering other maintenance, preventive maintenance, and alterations and for the correction of any deficiency in those programs, regardless of whether those programs are carried out by the certificate holder or by another person.

(b) Whenever the Administrator finds that either or both of the programs described in paragraph (a) of this section does not contain adequate procedures and standards to meet the requirements of this part, the certificate holder shall, after notification by the Administrator, make any changes in those programs that are necessary to meet those requirements.

(c) A certificate holder may petition the Administrator to reconsider the notice to make a change in a program. The petition must be filed with the responsible Flight Standards office charged with the overall inspection of the certificate holder's operations within 30 days after the certificate holder receives the notice. Except in the case of an emergency requiring immediate action in the interest of safety, the filing of the petition stays the notice pending a decision by the Administrator.

[Doc. No. 6258, 29 FR 19210, Dec. 31, 1964, as amended by Amdt. 121-207, 54 FR 39293, Sept. 25, 1989; Amdt. 121-253, 61 FR 2611, Jan. 26, 1996; Docket FAA-2018-0119, Amdt. 121-380, 83 FR 9173, Mar. 5, 2018]

121.374　Continuous airworthiness maintenance program (CAMP) for two-engine ETOPS

In order to conduct an ETOPS flight using a two-engine airplane, each certificate holder must develop and comply with the ETOPS continuous airworthiness maintenance program, as authorized in the certificate holder's operations specifications, for each airplane-engine combination used in ETOPS. The certificate holder must develop this ETOPS CAMP by supplementing the manufacturer's maintenance program or the CAMP currently approved for the certificate holder. This ETOPS CAMP must include the following elements:

(a) ETOPS maintenance document. The certificate holder must have an ETOPS maintenance document for use by each person involved in ETOPS.

(1) The document must—

(i) List each ETOPS significant system,

(ii) Refer to or include all of the ETOPS maintenance elements in this section,

 (iii) Refer to or include all supportive programs and procedures,

 (iv) Refer to or include all duties and responsibilities, and

 (v) Clearly state where referenced material is located in the certificate holder's document system.

(b) ETOPS pre-departure service check. Except as provided in Appendix P of this part, the certificate holder must develop a pre-departure check tailored to their specific operation.

(1) The certificate holder must complete a pre-departure service check immediately before each ETOPS flight.

(2) At a minimum, this check must—

 (i) Verify the condition of all ETOPS Significant Systems;

 (ii) Verify the overall status of the airplane by reviewing applicable maintenance records; and

 (iii) Include an interior and exterior inspection to include a determination of engine and APU oil levels and consumption rates.

(3) An appropriately trained maintenance person, who is ETOPS qualified, must accomplish and certify by signature ETOPS specific tasks. Before an ETOPS flight may commence, an ETOPS pre-departure service check (PDSC) Signatory Person, who has been authorized by the certificate holder, must certify by signature, that the ETOPS PDSC has been completed.

(4) For the purposes of this paragraph (b) only, the following definitions apply:

 (i) ETOPS qualified person: A person is ETOPS qualified when that person satisfactorily completes the operator's ETOPS training program and is authorized by the certificate holder.

 (ii) ETOPS PDSC Signatory Person: A person is an ETOPS PDSC Signatory Person when that person is ETOPS qualified and that person:

  (A) When certifying the completion of the ETOPS PDSC in the United States:

   (1) Works for an operator authorized to engage in part 121 operation or works for a part 145 repair station; and

   (2) Holds a U.S. Mechanic's Certificate with airframe and powerplant ratings.

  (B) When certifying the completion of the ETOPS PDSC outside of the U.S. holds a certificate in accordance with 43.17(c)(1) of this chapter; or

  (C) When certifying the completion of the ETOPS PDSC outside the U.S. holds the certificates needed or has the requisite experience or training to return aircraft to service on behalf of an ETOPS maintenance entity.

 (iii) ETOPS maintenance entity: An entity authorized to perform ETOPS maintenance and complete ETOPS PDSC and that entity is:

  (A) Certificated to engage in part 121 operations;

  (B) Repair station certificated under part 145 of this chapter; or

  (C) Entity authorized pursuant to 43.17(c)(2) of this chapter.

(c) Limitations on dual maintenance.

(1) Except as specified in paragraph (c)(2), the certificate holder may not perform scheduled or unscheduled dual maintenance during the same maintenance visit on the same or a substantially similar ETOPS Significant System listed in the ETOPS maintenance document, if the improper maintenance could result in the failure of an ETOPS Significant System.

(2) In the event dual maintenance as defined in paragraph (c)(1) of this section cannot be avoided, the certificate holder may perform maintenance provided:

 (i) The maintenance action on each affected ETOPS Significant System is performed by a different technician, or

 (ii) The maintenance action on each affected ETOPS Significant System is performed by the same technician under the direct supervision of a second qualified individual; and

 (iii) For either paragraph (c)(2)(i) or (ii) of this section, a qualified individual conducts a ground verification test and any in-flight verification test required under the program developed pursuant to paragraph (d) of this section.

(d) Verification program. The certificate holder must develop and maintain a program for the resolution of discrepancies that will ensure the effectiveness of maintenance actions taken on ETOPS Significant Systems. The verification program must identify potential problems and verify satisfactory corrective action. The verification program must include ground verification and in-flight verification policy and procedures. The certificate holder must establish procedures to indicate clearly who is going to initiate the verification action and what action is necessary. The verification action may be performed on an ETOPS revenue flight provided the verification action is documented as satisfactorily completed upon reaching the ETOPS Entry Point.

(e) Task identification. The certificate holder must identify all ETOPS-specific tasks. An appropriately trained mechanic who is ETOPS qualified must accomplish and certify by signature that the ETOPS-specific task has been completed.

(f) Centralized maintenance control procedures. The certificate holder must develop and maintain procedures for centralized maintenance control for ETOPS.

(g) Parts control program. The certificate holder must develop an ETOPS parts control program to ensure the proper identification of parts used to maintain the configuration of airplanes used in ETOPS.

(h) Reliability program. The certificate holder must have an ETOPS reliability program. This program must be the certificate holder's existing reliability program or its Continuing Analysis and Surveillance System (CASS) supplemented for ETOPS. This program must be event-oriented and include procedures to report the events listed below, as follows:

(1) The certificate holder must report the following events within 96 hours of the occurrence to its certificate holding district office (CHDO):

 (i) IFSDs, except planned IFSDs performed for flight training.

 (ii) Diversions and turnbacks for failures, malfunctions, or defects associated with any airplane or engine system.

 (iii) Uncommanded power or thrust changes or surges.

 (iv) Inability to control the engine or obtain desired power or thrust.

 (v) Inadvertent fuel loss or unavailability, or uncorrectable fuel imbalance in flight.

 (vi) Failures, malfunctions or defects associated with ETOPS Significant Systems.

 (vii) Any event that would jeopardize the safe flight and landing of the airplane on an ETOPS flight.

(2) The certificate holder must investigate the cause of each event listed in paragraph (h)(1) of this section and submit findings and a description of corrective action to its responsible Flight Standards office. The report must include the information specified in 121.703(e). The corrective action must be acceptable to its responsible Flight Standards office.

(i) Propulsion system monitoring.

(1) If the IFSD rate (computed on a 12-month rolling average) for an engine installed as part of an airplane-engine combination

exceeds the following values, the certificate holder must do a comprehensive review of its operations to identify any common cause effects and systemic errors. The IFSD rate must be computed using all engines of that type in the certificate holder's entire fleet of airplanes approved for ETOPS.

(i)   A rate of 0.05 per 1,000 engine hours for ETOPS up to and including 120 minutes.

(ii)   A rate of 0.03 per 1,000 engine hours for ETOPS beyond 120-minutes up to and including 207 minutes in the North Pacific Area of Operation and up to and including 180 minutes elsewhere.

(iii) A rate of 0.02 per 1,000 engine hours for ETOPS beyond 207 minutes in the North Pacific Area of Operation and beyond 180 minutes elsewhere.

(2) Within 30 days of exceeding the rates above, the certificate holder must submit a report of investigation and any necessary corrective action taken to its responsible Flight Standards office.

(j) Engine condition monitoring.

(1) The certificate holder must have an engine condition monitoring program to detect deterioration at an early stage and to allow for corrective action before safe operation is affected.

(2) This program must describe the parameters to be monitored, the method of data collection, the method of analyzing data, and the process for taking corrective action.

(3) The program must ensure that engine-limit margins are maintained so that a prolonged engine-inoperative diversion may be conducted at approved power levels and in all expected environmental conditions without exceeding approved engine limits. This includes approved limits for items such as rotor speeds and exhaust gas temperatures.

(k) Oil-consumption monitoring. The certificate holder must have an engine oil consumption monitoring program to ensure that there is enough oil to complete each ETOPS flight. APU oil consumption must be included if an APU is required for ETOPS. The operator's oil consumption limit may not exceed the manufacturer's recommendation. Monitoring must be continuous and include oil added at each ETOPS departure point. The program must compare the amount of oil added at each ETOPS departure point with the running average consumption to identify sudden increases.

(l) APU in-flight start program. If the airplane type certificate requires an APU but does not require the APU to run during the ETOPS portion of the flight, the certificate holder must develop and maintain a program acceptable to the FAA for cold soak in-flight start-and-run reliability.

(m) Maintenance training. For each airplane-engine combination, the certificate holder must develop a maintenance training program that provides training adequate to support ETOPS. It must include ETOPS specific training for all persons involved in ETOPS maintenance that focuses on the special nature of ETOPS. This training must be in addition to the operator's maintenance training program used to qualify individuals to perform work on specific airplanes and engines.

(n) Configuration, maintenance, and procedures (CMP) document. If an airplane-engine combination has a CMP document, the certificate holder must use a system that ensures compliance with the applicable FAA-approved document.

(o) Procedural changes. Each substantial change to the maintenance or training procedures that were used to qualify the certificate holder for ETOPS, must be submitted to the responsible Flight Standards office for review. The certificate holder cannot implement a change until its responsible Flight Standards office notifies the certificate holder that the review is complete.

[Doc. No. FAA-2002-6717, 72 FR 1880, Jan. 16, 2007, as amended by Amdt. 121-329, 72 FR 7348, Feb. 15, 2007; Amdt. 121-329, 72 FR 26541, May 10, 2007; Amdt. 121-339, 73 FR 33881, June 16, 2008; Docket FAA-2018-0119, Amdt. 121-380, 83 FR 9173, Mar. 5, 2018]

121.375   Maintenance and preventive maintenance training program

Each certificate holder or person performing maintenance or preventive maintenance functions for it shall have a training program to ensure that each person (including inspection personnel) who determines the adequacy of work done is fully informed about procedures and techniques and new equipment in use and is competent to perform his duties.

121.377   Maintenance and preventive maintenance personnel duty time limitations

Within the United States, each certificate holder (or person performing maintenance or preventive maintenance functions for it) shall relieve each person performing maintenance or preventive maintenance from duty for a period of at least 24 consecutive hours during any seven consecutive days, or the equivalent thereof within any one calendar month.

121.378   Certificate requirements

(a) Except for maintenance, preventive maintenance, alterations, and required inspections performed by a certificated repair station that is located outside the United States, each person who is directly in charge of maintenance, preventive maintenance, or alterations, and each person performing required inspections must hold an appropriate airman certificate.

(b) For the purposes of this section, a person directly in charge is each person assigned to a position in which he is responsible for the work of a shop or station that performs maintenance, preventive maintenance, alterations, or other functions affecting aircraft airworthiness. A person who is directly in charge need not physically observe and direct each worker constantly but must be available for consultation and decision on matters requiring instruction or decision from higher authority than that of the persons performing the work.

[Doc. No. 6258, 29 FR 19210, Dec. 31, 1964, as amended by Amdt. 121–21, 31 FR 10618, Aug. 9, 1966; Amdt. 121–286, 66 FR 41116, Aug. 6, 2001]

121.379   Authority to perform and approve maintenance, preventive maintenance, and alterations

(a) A certificate holder may perform, or it may make arrangements with other persons to perform, maintenance, preventive maintenance, and alterations as provided in its continuous airworthiness maintenance program and its maintenance manual. In addition, a certificate holder may perform these functions for another certificate holder as provided in the continuous airworthiness maintenance program and maintenance manual of the other certificate holder.

(b) A certificate holder may approve any aircraft, airframe, aircraft engine, propeller, or appliance for return to service after maintenance, preventive maintenance, or alterations that are performed under paragraph (a) of this section. However, in the case of a major repair or major alteration, the work must have been done in accordance with technical data approved by the Administrator.

[Doc. No. 10289, 35 FR 16793, Oct. 30, 1970]

121.380   Maintenance recording requirements

(a) Each certificate holder shall keep (using the system specified in the manual required in 121.369) the following records for the periods specified in paragraph (c) of this section:

(1) All the records necessary to show that all requirements for the issuance of an airworthiness release under 121.709 have been met.

(2) Records containing the following information:

(i)   The total time in service of the airframe.

(ii)   Except as provided in paragraph (b) of this section, the total time in service of each engine and propeller.

(iii) The current status of life-limited parts of each airframe, engine, propeller, and appliance.

(iv) The time since last overhaul of all items installed on the aircraft which are required to be overhauled on a specified time basis.

(v) The identification of the current inspection status of the aircraft, including the times since the last inspections required by the inspection program under which the aircraft and its appliances are maintained.

(vi) The current status of applicable airworthiness directives, including the date and methods of compliance, and, if the airworthiness directive involves recurring action, the time and date when the next action is required.

(vii) A list of current major alterations to each airframe, engine, propeller, and appliance.

(b) A certificate holder need not record the total time in service of an engine or propeller on a transport category cargo airplane, a transport category airplane that has a passenger seat configuration of more than 30 seats, or a nontransport category airplane type certificated before January 1, 1958, until the following, whichever occurs first:

(1) March 20, 1997; or

(2) The date of the first overhaul of the engine or propeller, as applicable, after January 19, 1996.

(c) Each certificate holder shall retain the records required to be kept by this section for the following periods:

(1) Except for the records of the last complete overhaul of each airframe, engine, propeller, and appliance, the records specified in paragraph (a)(1) of this section shall be retained until the work is repeated or superseded by other work or for one year after the work is performed.

(2) The records of the last complete overhaul of each airframe, engine, propeller, and appliance shall be retained until the work is superseded by work of equivalent scope and detail.

(3) The records specified in paragraph (a)(2) of this section shall be retained and transferred with the aircraft at the time the aircraft is sold.

(d) The certificate holder shall make all maintenance records required to be kept by this section available for inspection by the Administrator or any authorized representative of the National Transportation Safety Board (NTSB).

[Doc. No. 10658, 37 FR 15983, Aug. 9, 1972, as amended by Amdt. 121–251, 60 FR 65933, Dec. 20, 1995; Amdt. 121–321, 71 FR 536, Jan. 4, 2006]

121.380a Transfer of maintenance records

Each certificate holder who sells a U.S. registered aircraft shall transfer to the purchaser, at the time of sale, the following records of that aircraft, in plain language form or in coded form at the election of the purchaser, if the coded form provides for the preservation and retrieval of information in a manner acceptable to the Administrator:

(a) The record specified in 121.380(a)(2).

(b) The records specified in 121.380(a)(1) which are not included in the records covered by paragraph (a) of this section, except that the purchaser may permit the seller to keep physical custody of such records. However, custody of records in the seller does not relieve the purchaser of his responsibility under 121.380(c) to make the records available for inspection by the Administrator or any authorized representative of the National Transportation Safety Board (NTSB).

[Doc. No. 10658, 37 FR 15984, Aug. 9, 1972]

Subpart AA — Continued Airworthiness and Safety Improvements

Source: Amdt. 121–336, 72 FR 63411, Nov. 8, 2007, unless otherwise noted.

121.1101 Purpose and definition

(a) This subpart requires persons holding an air carrier or operating certificate under part 119 of this chapter to support the continued airworthiness of each airplane. These requirements may include, but are not limited to, revising the maintenance program, incorporating design changes, and incorporating revisions to Instructions for Continued Airworthiness.

(b) [Reserved]

[Amdt. 121–336, 72 FR 63411, Nov. 8, 2007, as amended by Docket FAA-2018-0119, Amdt. 121–380, 83 FR 9173, Mar. 5, 2018]

121.1103 [Reserved]

121.1105 Aging airplane inspections and records reviews

(a) Applicability. This section applies to all airplanes operated by a certificate holder under this part, except for those airplanes operated between any point within the State of Alaska and any other point within the State of Alaska.

(b) Operation after inspection and records review. After the dates specified in this paragraph, a certificate holder may not operate an airplane under this part unless the Administrator has notified the certificate holder that the Administrator has completed the aging airplane inspection and records review required by this section. During the inspection and records review, the certificate holder must demonstrate to the Administrator that the maintenance of age-sensitive parts and components of the airplane has been adequate and timely enough to ensure the highest degree of safety.

(1) Airplanes exceeding 24 years in service on December 8, 2003; initial and repetitive inspections and records reviews. For an airplane that has exceeded 24 years in service on December 8, 2003, no later than December 5, 2007, and thereafter at intervals not to exceed 7 years.

(2) Airplanes exceeding 14 years in service but not 24 years in service on December 8, 2003; initial and repetitive inspections and records reviews. For an airplane that has exceeded 14 years in service but not 24 years in service on December 8, 2003, no later than December 4, 2008, and thereafter at intervals not to exceed 7 years.

(3) Airplanes not exceeding 14 years in service on December 8, 2003; initial and repetitive inspections and records reviews. For an airplane that has not exceeded 14 years in service on December 8, 2003, no later than 5 years after the start of the airplane's 15th year in service and thereafter at intervals not to exceed 7 years.

(c) Unforeseen schedule conflict. In the event of an unforeseen scheduling conflict for a specific airplane, the Administrator may approve an extension of up to 90 days beyond an interval specified in paragraph (b) of this section.

(d) Airplane and records availability. The certificate holder must make available to the Administrator each airplane for which an inspection and records review is required under this section, in a condition for inspection specified by the Administrator, together with records containing the following information:

(1) Total years in service of the airplane;

(2) Total time in service of the airframe;

(3) Total flight cycles of the airframe;

(4) Date of the last inspection and records review required by this section;

(5) Current status of life-limited parts of the airframe;

(6) Time since the last overhaul of all structural components required to be overhauled on a specific time basis;

(7) Current inspection status of the airplane, including the time since the last inspection required by the inspection program under which the airplane is maintained;

(8) Current status of applicable airworthiness directives, including the date and methods of compliance, and if the airworthiness directive involves recurring action, the time and date when the next action is required;

(9) A list of major structural alterations; and

FAR 121

(10) A report of major structural repairs and the current inspection status for those repairs.

(e) *Notification to Administrator.* Each certificate holder must notify the Administrator at least 60 days before the date on which the airplane and airplane records will be made available for the inspection and records review.

[Doc. No. FAA–1999–5401, 67 FR 72761, Dec. 6, 2002, as amended by Amdt. 121–284, 70 FR 5532, Feb. 2, 2005; Amdt. 121–310, 70 FR 23936, May 6, 2005. Redesignated by Amdt. 121–336, 72 FR 63412, Nov. 8, 2007]

121.1107 Repairs assessment for pressurized fuselages

(a) No certificate holder may operate an Airbus Model A300 (excluding the -600 series), British Aerospace Model BAC 1-11, Boeing Model 707, 720, 727, 737, or 747, McDonnell Douglas Model DC-8, DC-9/MD-80 or DC-10, Fokker Model F28, or Lockheed Model L-1011 airplane beyond the applicable flight cycle implementation time specified below, or May 25, 2001, whichever occurs later, unless operations specifications have been issued to reference repair assessment guidelines applicable to the fuselage pressure boundary (fuselage skin, door skin, and bulkhead webs), and those guidelines are incorporated in its maintenance program. The repair assessment guidelines must be approved by the responsible Aircraft Certification office for the type certificate for the affected airplane.

(1) For the Airbus Model A300 (excluding the –600 series), the flight cycle implementation time is:

(i) Model B2: 36,000 flights.

(ii) Model B4–100 (including Model B4–2C): 30,000 flights above the window line, and 36,000 flights below the window line.

(iii) Model B4–200: 25,500 flights above the window line, and 34,000 flights below the window line.

(2) For all models of the British Aerospace BAC 1–11, the flight cycle implementation time is 60,000 flights.

(3) For all models of the Boeing 707, the flight cycle implementation time is 15,000 flights.

(4) For all models of the Boeing 720, the flight cycle implementation time is 23,000 flights.

(5) For all models of the Boeing 727, the flight cycle implementation time is 45,000 flights.

(6) For all models of the Boeing 737, the flight cycle implementation time is 60,000 flights.

(7) For all models of the Boeing 747, the flight cycle implementation time is 15,000 flights.

(8) For all models of the McDonnell Douglas DC–8, the flight cycle implementation time is 30,000 flights.

(9) For all models of the McDonnell Douglas DC–9/MD–80, the flight cycle implementation time is 60,000 flights.

(10) For all models of the McDonnell Douglas DC–10, the flight cycle implementation time is 30,000 flights.

(11) For all models of the Lockheed L–1011, the flight cycle implementation time is 27,000 flights.

(12) For the Fokker F–28 Mark 1000, 2000, 3000, and 4000, the flight cycle implementation time is 60,000 flights.

(b) [Reserved]

[Doc. No. 29104, 65 FR 24125, Apr. 25, 2000; 65 FR 50744, Aug. 21, 2000, as amended by Amdt. 121-282, 66 FR 23130, May 7, 2001; Amdt. 121-305, 69 FR 45942, July 30, 2004. Redesignated and amended by Amdt. 121-336, 72 FR 63412, Nov. 8, 2007; Docket FAA-2018-0119, Amdt. 121-380, 83 FR 9173, Mar. 5, 2018]

121.1109 Supplemental inspections

(a) *Applicability.* Except as specified in paragraph (b) of this section, this section applies to transport category, turbine powered airplanes with a type certificate issued after January 1, 1958, that

as a result of original type certification or later increase in capacity have—

(1) A maximum type certificated passenger seating capacity of 30 or more; or

(2) A maximum payload capacity of 7,500 pounds or more.

(b) *Exception.* This section does not apply to an airplane operated by a certificate holder under this part between any point within the State of Alaska and any other point within the State of Alaska.

(c) *General requirements.* After December 20, 2010, a certificate holder may not operate an airplane under this part unless the following requirements have been met:

(1) *Baseline Structure.* The certificate holder's maintenance program for the airplane includes FAA-approved damage-tolerance-based inspections and procedures for airplane structure susceptible to fatigue cracking that could contribute to a catastrophic failure. For the purpose of this section, this structure is termed "fatigue critical structure."

(2) *Adverse effects of repairs, alterations, and modifications.* The maintenance program for the airplane includes a means for addressing the adverse effects repairs, alterations, and modifications may have on fatigue critical structure and on inspections required by paragraph (c)(1) of this section. The means for addressing these adverse effects must be approved by the responsible Aircraft Certification Service office.

(3) *Changes to maintenance program.* The changes made to the maintenance program required by paragraphs (c)(1) and (c) (2) of this section, and any later revisions to these changes, must be submitted to the Principal Maintenance Inspector for review and approval.

[Doc. No. FAA-1999-5401, 70 FR 5532, Feb. 2, 2005. Redesignated by Amdt. 121-336, 72 FR 63412, Nov. 8, 2007; Amdt. 121-337, 72 FR 70508, Dec. 12, 2007; Docket FAA-2018-0119, Amdt. 121-380, 83 FR 9173, Mar. 5, 2018]

121.1111 Electrical wiring interconnection systems (EWIS) maintenance program

(a) Except as provided in paragraph (f) of this section, this section applies to transport category, turbine-powered airplanes with a type certificate issued after January 1, 1958, that, as a result of original type certification or later increase in capacity, have—

(1) A maximum type-certificated passenger capacity of 30 or more, or

(2) A maximum payload capacity of 7500 pounds or more.

(b) After March 10, 2011, no certificate holder may operate an airplane identified in paragraph (a) of this section unless the maintenance program for that airplane includes inspections and procedures for electrical wiring interconnection systems (EWIS).

(c) The proposed EWIS maintenance program changes must be based on EWIS Instructions for Continued Airworthiness (ICA) that have been developed in accordance with the provisions of Appendix H of part 25 of this chapter applicable to each affected airplane (including those ICA developed for supplemental type certificates installed on each airplane) and that have been approved by the responsible Aircraft Certification Service office.

(1) For airplanes subject to 26.11 of this chapter, the EWIS ICA must comply with paragraphs H25.5(a)(1) and (b).

(2) For airplanes subject to 25.1729 of this chapter, the EWIS ICA must comply with paragraph H25.4 and all of paragraph H25.5.

(d) After March 10, 2011, before returning an airplane to service after any alterations for which EWIS ICA are developed, the certificate holder must include in the airplane's maintenance program inspections and procedures for EWIS based on those ICA.

(e) The EWIS maintenance program changes identified in paragraphs (c) and (d) of this section and any later EWIS revisions must be submitted to the Principal Inspector for review and approval.

(f) This section does not apply to the following airplane models:

(1) Lockheed L–188

(2) Bombardier CL–44

(3) Mitsubishi YS–11

(4) British Aerospace BAC 1–11

(5) Concorde

(6) deHavilland D.H. 106 Comet 4C

(7) VFW-Vereinigte Flugtechnische Werk VFW–614

(8) Illyushin Aviation IL 96T

(9) Bristol Aircraft Britannia 305

(10) Handley Page Herald Type 300

(11) Avions Marcel Dassault—Breguet Aviation Mercure 100C

(12) Airbus Caravelle

(13) Lockheed L–300

[Amdt. 121-336, 72 FR 63411, Nov. 8, 2007, as amended by Docket FAA-2018-0119, Amdt. 121-380, 83 FR 9173, Mar. 5, 2018]

121.1113 Fuel tank system maintenance program

(a) Except as provided in paragraph (g) of this section, this section applies to transport category, turbine-powered airplanes with a type certificate issued after January 1, 1958, that, as a result of original type certification or later increase in capacity, have—

(1) A maximum type-certificated passenger capacity of 30 or more, or

(2) A maximum payload capacity of 7500 pounds or more.

(b) For each airplane on which an auxiliary fuel tank is installed under a field approval, before June 16, 2008, the certificate holder must submit to the responsible Aircraft Certification Service office proposed maintenance instructions for the tank that meet the requirements of Special Federal Aviation Regulation No. 88 (SFAR 88) of this chapter.

(c) After December 16, 2008, no certificate holder may operate an airplane identified in paragraph (a) of this section unless the maintenance program for that airplane has been revised to include applicable inspections, procedures, and limitations for fuel tanks systems.

(d) The proposed fuel tank system maintenance program revisions must be based on fuel tank system Instructions for Continued Airworthiness (ICA) that have been developed in accordance with the applicable provisions of SFAR 88 of this chapter or §25.1529 and part 25, Appendix H, of this chapter, in effect on June 6, 2001 (including those developed for auxiliary fuel tanks, if any, installed under supplemental type certificates or other design approval) and that have been approved by the responsible Aircraft Certification Service office.

(e) After December 16, 2008, before returning an aircraft to service after any alteration for which fuel tank ICA are developed under SFAR 88 or under 25.1529 in effect on June 6, 2001, the certificate holder must include in the maintenance program for the airplane inspections and procedures for the fuel tank system based on those ICA.

(f) The fuel tank system maintenance program changes identified in paragraphs (d) and (e) of this section and any later fuel tank system revisions must be submitted to the Principal Inspector for review and approval.

(g) This section does not apply to the following airplane models:

(1) Bombardier CL–44

(2) Concorde

(3) deHavilland D.H. 106 Comet 4C

(4) VFW–Vereinigte Flugtechnische Werk VFW–614

(5) Illyushin Aviation IL 96T

(6) Bristol Aircraft Britannia 305

(7) Handley Page Herald Type 300

(8) Avions Marcel Dassault—Breguet Aviation Mercure 100C

(9) Airbus Caravelle

(10) Lockheed L–300

[Amdt. 121-336, 72 FR 63411, Nov. 8, 2007, as amended by Docket FAA-2018-0119, Amdt. 121-380, 83 FR 9173, Mar. 5, 2018]

121.1115 Limit of validity

(a) *Applicability.* This section applies to certificate holders operating any transport category, turbine-powered airplane with a maximum takeoff gross weight greater than 75,000 pounds and a type certificate issued after January 1, 1958, regardless of whether the maximum takeoff gross weight is a result of an original type certificate or a later design change. This section also applies to certificate holders operating any transport category, turbine-powered airplane with a type certificate issued after January 1, 1958, regardless of the maximum takeoff gross weight, for which a limit of validity of the engineering data that supports the structural maintenance program (hereafter referred to as LOV) is required in accordance with 25.571 or 26.21 of this chapter after January 14, 2011.

(b) *Limit of validity.* No certificate holder may operate an airplane identified in paragraph (a) of this section after the applicable date identified in Table 1 of this section unless an Airworthiness Limitations section approved under Appendix H to part 25 or 26.21 of this chapter is incorporated into its maintenance program. The ALS must—

(1) Include an LOV approved under 25.571 or 26.21 of this chapter, as applicable, except as provided in paragraph (f) of this section; and

(2) Be clearly distinguishable within its maintenance program.

(c) *Operation of airplanes excluded from 26.21.* No certificate holder may operate an airplane identified in 26.21(g) of this chapter after July 14, 2013, unless an Airworthiness Limitations section approved under Appendix H to part 25 or 26.21 of this chapter is incorporated into its maintenance program. The ALS must—

(1) Include an LOV approved under 25.571 or 26.21 of this chapter, as applicable, except as provided in paragraph (f) of this section; and

(2) Be clearly distinguishable within its maintenance program.

(d) *Extended limit of validity.* No certificate holder may operate an airplane beyond the LOV, or extended LOV, specified in paragraph (b)(1), (c), (d), or (f) of this section, as applicable, unless the following conditions are met:

(1) An ALS must be incorporated into its maintenance program that—

(i) Includes an extended LOV and any widespread fatigue damage airworthiness limitation items approved under 26.23 of this chapter; and

(ii) Is approved under 26.23 of this chapter.

(2) The extended LOV and the airworthiness limitation items pertaining to widespread fatigue damage must be clearly distinguishable within its maintenance program.

(e) *Principal Maintenance Inspector approval.* Certificate holders must submit the maintenance program revisions required by paragraphs (b), (c), and (d) of this section to the Principal Maintenance Inspector for review and approval.

FAR 121

(f) *Exception.* For any airplane for which an LOV has not been approved as of the applicable compliance date specified in paragraph (c) or Table 1 of this section, instead of including an approved LOV in the ALS, an operator must include the applicable default LOV specified in Table 1 or Table 2 of this section, as applicable, in the ALS.

[Doc. No. FAA–2006–24281, 75 FR 69785, Nov. 15, 2010, as amended at Doc. No. FAA–2006–24281, 77 FR 30878, May 24, 2012]

TABLE 1 TO 121.1115 — AIRPLANES SUBJECT TO 26.21		
AIRPLANE MODEL	COMPLIANCE DATE— MONTHS AFTER JANUARY 14, 2011	DEFAULT LOV [FLIGHT CYCLES (FC) OR FLIGHT HOURS (FH)]
Airbus— Existing[1] Models Only:		
A300 B2-1A, B2-1C, B2K-3C, B2-203	30	48,000 FC
A300 B4-2C, B4-103	30	40,000 FC
A300 B4-203	30	34,000 FC
A300-600 Series	60	30,000 FC/67,500 FH
A310-200 Series	60	40,000 FC/60,000 FH
A310-300 Series	60	35,000 FC/60,000 FH
A318 Series	60	48,000 FC/60,000 FH
A319 Series	60	48,000 FC/60,000 FH
A320-100 Series	60	48,000 FC 48,000 FH
A320-200 Series	60	48,000 FC/60,000 FH
A321 Series	60	48,000 FC/60,000 FH
A330-200, -300 Series (except WV050 family) (non enhanced)	60	40,000 FC/60,000 FH
A330-200, -300 Series WV050 family (enhanced)	60	33,000 FC/100,000 FH
A330-200 Freighter Series	60	See NOTE
A340-200, -300 Series (except WV 027 and WV 050 family) (non enhanced)	60	20,000 FC/80,000 FH
A340-200, -300 Series WV 027 (non enhanced)	60	30,000 FC/60,000 FH
A340-300 Series WV 050 family (enhanced)	60	20,000 FC/100,000 FH
A340-500, -600 Series	60	16,600 FC/100,000 FH
A380-800 Series	72	See NOTE
Boeing—Existing[1] Models Only:		
717	60	60,000 FC/60,000 FH
727 (all series)	30	60,000 FC
737 (Classics): 737-100, -200, -200C, -300, -400, -500	30	75,000 FC
737 (NG): 737-600, -700, -700C, -800, -900, -900ER	60	75,000 FC
747 (Classics): 747-100, -100B, -100B SUD, -200B, -200C, -200F, -300, 747SP, 747SR	30	20,000 FC
747-400: 747-400, -400D, -440F	60	20,000 FC
757	60	50,000 FC
767	60	50,000 FC
777-200, -300	60	40,000 FC
777-200LR, 777-300ER	60	40,000 FC
777F	72	11,000 FC
Bombardier—Existing[1] Models Only:		
CL-600: 2D15 (Regional Jet eries 705), 2D24 (Regional Jet Series 900)	72	60,000 FC
Embraer—Existing[1] Models Only:		
ERJ 170	72	See NOTE
ERJ 190	72	See NOTE
Fokker—Existing[1] Models Only:		
F.28 Mark 0070, Mark 0100	30	90,000 FC
Lockhead—Existing[1] Models Only:		
L-1011	30	36,000 FC
188	30	26,000 FC
382 (all series)	30	20,000 FC/50,000 FH
McDonnell Douglas—Existing[1] Models Only:		
DC-8, -8F	30	50,000 FC/50,000 FH
DC-9 (except for MD-80 models)	30	100,000 FC/100,000 FH
MD-80 (DC-9-81, -82, -83, -87, MD-88)	30	50,000 FC/50,000 FH
MD-90	60	60,000 FC/90,000 FH
DC-10-10, -15	30	42,000 FC/60,000 FH

TABLE 1 TO 121.1115 *CONTINUED*		
AIRPLANE MODEL	COMPLIANCE DATE— MONTHS AFTER JANUARY 14, 2011	DEFAULT LOV [FLIGHT CYCLES (FC) OR FLIGHT HOURS (FH)]
McDonnell Douglas—Existing[1] Models Only: *Continued*		
DC-10-30, -40, -10F, -30F, -40F	30	30,000 FC/60,000 FH
MD-10-10F	60	42,000 FC/60,000 FH
MD-10-30F	60	30,000 FC/60,000 FH
MD-11, MD-11F	60	20,000 FC/60,000 FH
Maximum Takeoff Gross Weight Changes:		
All airplanes whose maximum takeoff gross weight has been decreased to 75,000 pounds or below after January 14, 2011, or increased to greater than 75,000 pounds at any time by an amended type certificate or supplemental type certificate.	30, or within 12 months after the LOV is approved, or before operating the airplane, whichever occurs latest	Not applicable
All Other Airplane Models (TCs and amended TCs) not listed in Table 2	72, or within 12 months after the LOV is approved, or before operating the airplane, whichever occurs latest	Not applicable
[1]Type certificated as of January 14, 2011		
Note: Airplane operation limitation is stated in the Airworthiness Limitation section		

TABLE 2 TO 121.1115 — AIRPLANES SUBJECT TO 26.21	
AIRPLANE MODEL	DEFAULT LOV [FLIGHT CYCLES (FC) OR FLIGHT HOURS (FH)]
Airbus:	
Caravelle	15,000 FC/24,000 FH
Avions Marcel Dassault:	
Breguet Aviation Mercure 100C	20,000 FC/16,000 FH
Boeing:	
Boeing 707 (-100 Series and -200 Series)	20,000 FC
Boeing 707 (-300 Series and -400 Series)	20,000 FC
Boeing 720	30,000 FC
Bombardier:	
CL-44D4 and CL-44J	20,000 FC
BD-700	15,000 FH
Bristol Aeroplane Company:	
Britannia 305	10,000 FC
British Aerospace Airbus, Ltd:	
BAC 1-11 (all models)	85,000 FC
British Aerospace (Commercial Aircraft) Ltd.:	
Armstrong Whitworth Argosy A.W. 650 Series 101	20,000 FC

TABLE 2 TO 121.1115 *CONTINUED*	
AIRPLANE MODEL	DEFAULT LOV [FLIGHT CYCLES (FC) OR FLIGHT HOURS (FH)]
BAE Systems (Operations) Ltd.:	
BAe 146-100A (all models)	50,000 FC
BAe 146-200-07	50,000 FC
BAe 146-200-07 Dev	50,000 FC
BAe 146-200-11	50,000 FC
BAe 146-200-07A	47,000 FC
BAe 146-200-11 Dev	43,000 FC
BAe 146-300 (all models)	40,000 FC
Avro 146-RJ70A (all models)	40,000 FC
Avro 146-RJ85A and 146-RJ100A (all models)	50,000 FC
D & R Nevada, LLC:	
Convair Model 22	1,000 FC/1,000 FH
Convair Model 23M	1,000 FC/1,000 FH
deHavilland Aircraft Company, Ltd.:	
D.H. 106 Comet 4C	8,000 FH
Gulfstream	
GV	40,000 FH
GV-SP	40,000 FH
Ilyushin Aviation Complex:	
IL-96T	10,000 FC/30,000 FH
Lockheed:	
300-50A01 (USAF C 141A)	20,000 FC

121.1117   Flammability reduction means

(a) Applicability. Except as provided in paragraph (o) of this section, this section applies to transport category, turbine-powered airplanes with a type certificate issued after January 1, 1958, that, as a result of original type certification or later increase in capacity have:

   (1) A maximum type-certificated passenger capacity of 30 or more, or

   (2) A maximum payload capacity of 7,500 pounds or more.

(b) New Production Airplanes. Except in accordance with 121.628, no certificate holder may operate an airplane identified in Table 1 of this section (including all-cargo airplanes) for which the State of Manufacture issued the original certificate of airworthiness or export airworthiness approval after December 27, 2010 unless an Ignition Mitigation Means (IMM) or Flammability Reduction Means (FRM) meeting the requirements of 26.33 of this chapter is operational.

TABLE 1	
MODEL—BOEING	MODEL—AIRBUS
747 Series	A318, A319, A320, A321 Series
737 Series	A330, A340 Series
777 Series	
767 Series	

(c) Auxiliary Fuel Tanks . After the applicable date stated in paragraph (e) of this section, no certificate holder may operate any airplane subject to 26.33 of this chapter that has an Auxiliary Fuel Tank installed pursuant to a field approval, unless the following requirements are met:

   (1) The certificate holder complies with 14 CFR 26.35 by the applicable date stated in that section.

   (2) The certificate holder installs Flammability Impact Mitigation Means (FIMM), if applicable, that is approved by the responsible Aircraft Certification Service office.

   (3) Except in accordance with 121.628, the FIMM, if applicable, is operational.

(d) Retrofit. Except as provided in paragraphs (j), (k), and (l) of this section, after the dates specified in paragraph (e) of this section, no certificate holder may operate an airplane to which this section applies unless the requirements of paragraphs (d)(1) and (d)(2) of this section are met.

   (1) IMM, FRM or FIMM, if required by §§26.33, 26.35, or 26.37 of this chapter, that are approved by the responsible Aircraft Certification Service office, are installed within the compliance times specified in paragraph (e) of this section.

   (2) Except in accordance with 121.628, the IMM, FRM or FIMM, as applicable, are operational.

(e) Compliance Times. Except as provided in paragraphs (k) and (l) of this section, the installations required by paragraph (d) of this section must be accomplished no later than the applicable dates specified in paragraph (e)(1), (e)(2), or (e)(3) of this section.

   (1) Fifty percent of each certificate holder's fleet identified in paragraph (d)(1) of this section must be modified no later than December 26, 2014.

   (2) One hundred percent of each certificate holder's fleet identified in paragraph (d)(1) of this section must be modified no later than December 26, 2017.

   (3) For those certificate holders that have only one airplane of a model identified in Table 1 of this section, the airplane must be modified no later than December 26, 2017.

(f) Compliance After Installation. Except in accordance with 121.628, no certificate holder may—

   (1) Operate an airplane on which IMM or FRM has been installed before the dates specified in paragraph (e) of this section unless the IMM or FRM is operational, or

   (2) Deactivate or remove an IMM or FRM once installed unless it is replaced by a means that complies with paragraph (d) of this section.

(g) Maintenance Program Revisions. No certificate holder may operate an airplane for which airworthiness limitations have been approved by the responsible Aircraft Certification Service office in accordance with 26.33, 26.35, or 26.37 of this chapter after the airplane is modified in accordance with paragraph (d) of this section unless the maintenance program for that airplane is revised to include those applicable airworthiness limitations.

(h) After the maintenance program is revised as required by paragraph (g) of this section, before returning an airplane to service after any alteration for which airworthiness limitations are required by 25.981, 26.33, or 26.37 of this chapter, the certificate holder must revise the maintenance program for the airplane to include those airworthiness limitations.

(i) The maintenance program changes identified in paragraphs (g) and (h) of this section must be submitted to the operator's Principal Maintenance Inspector responsible for review and approval prior to incorporation.

(j) The requirements of paragraph (d) of this section do not apply to airplanes operated in all-cargo service, but those airplanes are subject to paragraph (f) of this section.

(k) The compliance dates specified in paragraph (e) of this section may be extended by one year, provided that—

   (1) No later than March 26, 2009, the certificate holder notifies its assigned Flight Standards Office or Principal Inspector that it intends to comply with this paragraph;

   (2) No later than June 24, 2009, the certificate holder applies for an amendment to its operations specification in accordance with 119.51 of this chapter and revises the manual required by 121.133 to include a requirement for the airplane models specified in Table 2 of this section to use ground air conditioning systems for actual gate times of more than 30 minutes, when available at the gate and operational, whenever the ambient temperature exceeds 60 degrees Fahrenheit; and

   (3) Thereafter, the certificate holder uses ground air conditioning systems as described in paragraph (k)(2) of this section on each airplane subject to the extension.

TABLE 2	
Model—Boeing	Model—Airbus
747 Series	A318, A319, A320, A321 Series
737 Series	A300, A310 Series
777 Series	A330, A340 Series
767 Series	
757 Series	

(l) For any certificate holder for which the operating certificate is issued after December 26, 2008, the compliance date specified in paragraph (e) of this section may be extended by one year, provided that the certificate holder meets the requirements of paragraph (k)(2) of this section when its initial operations specifications are issued and, thereafter, uses ground air conditioning systems as described in paragraph (k)(2) of this section on each airplane subject to the extension.

(m) After the date by which any person is required by this section to modify 100 percent of the affected fleet, no certificate holder may operate in passenger service any airplane model specified in Table 2 of this section unless the airplane has been modified to comply with 26.33(c) of this chapter.

(n) No certificate holder may operate any airplane on which an auxiliary fuel tank is installed after December 26, 2017 unless the FAA has certified the tank as compliant with 25.981 of this chapter, in effect on December 26, 2008.

(o) Exclusions . The requirements of this section do not apply to the following airplane models:

  (1) Convair CV–240, 340, 440, including turbine powered conversions.

  (2) Lockheed L–188 Electra.

  (3) Vickers VC-10.

  (4) Douglas DC–3, including turbine powered conversions.

  (5) Bombardier CL–44.

  (6) Mitsubishi YS–11.

  (7) BAC 1–11.

  (8) Concorde.

  (9) deHavilland D.H. 106 Comet 4C.

  (10) VFW—Vereinigte Flugtechnische VFW–614.

  (11) Illyushin Aviation IL 96T.

  (12) Bristol Aircraft Britannia 305.

  (13) Handley Page Herald Type 300.

  (14) Avions Marcel Dassault—Breguet Aviation Mercure 100C.

  (15) Airbus Caravelle.

  (16) Fokker F–27/Fairchild Hiller FH–227.

  (17) Lockheed L–300.

[Doc. No. FAA-2005-22997, 73 FR 42501, July 21, 2008, as amended by Amdt. 121-345, 74 FR 31619, July 2, 2009; Docket FAA-2018-0119, Amdt. 121-380, 83 FR 9173, Mar. 5, 2018]

121.1119   Fuel tank vent explosion protection.

(a) Applicability. This section applies to transport category, turbine-powered airplanes with a type certificate issued after January 1, 1958, that have:

  (1) A maximum type-certificated passenger capacity of 30 or more; or

  (2) A maximum payload capacity of 7,500 pounds or more.

(b) New production airplanes. No certificate holder may operate an airplane for which the State of Manufacture issued the original certificate of airworthiness or export airworthiness approval after August 23, 2018 unless means, approved by the Administrator, to prevent fuel tank explosions caused by propagation of flames from outside the fuel tank vents into the fuel tank vapor spaces are installed and operational.

[Docket FAA-2014-0500, Amdt. 121-375, 81 FR 41208, June 24, 2016]

PART 125 — CERTIFICATION AND OPERATIONS: AIRPLANES HAVING A SEATING CAPACITY OF 20 OR MORE PASSENGERS OR A MAXIMUM PAYLOAD CAPACITY OF 6,000 POUNDS OR MORE; AND RULES GOVERNING PERSONS ON BOARD SUCH AIRCRAFT

FAR 125

Authority: 49 U.S.C. 106(f), 106(g), 40113, 44701-44702, 44705, 44710-44711, 44713, 44716-44717, 44722.

Source: Docket No. 19779, 45 FR 67235, Oct. 9, 1980, unless otherwise noted.

Special Federal Aviation Regulation No. 89

Editorial Note: For the text of SFAR No. 89, see part 121 of this chapter.

Special Federal Aviation Regulation No. 97

Editorial Note: For the text of SFAR No. 97, see part 91 of this chapter.

Subpart A — General

125.1 Applicability

(a) Except as provided in paragraphs (b), (c) and (d) of this section, this part prescribes rules governing the operations of U.S.-registered civil airplanes which have a seating configuration of 20 or more passengers or a maximum payload capacity of 6,000 pounds or more when common carriage is not involved.

(b) The rules of this part do not apply to the operations of airplanes specified in paragraph (a) of this section, when—

(1) They are required to be operated under part 121, 129, 135, or 137 of this chapter;

(2) They have been issued restricted, limited, or provisional airworthiness certificates, special flight permits, or experimental certificates;

(3) They are being operated by a part 125 certificate holder without carrying passengers or cargo under part 91 for training, ferrying, positioning, or maintenance purposes;

(4) They are being operated under part 91 by an operator certificated to operate those airplanes under the rules of parts 121, 135, or 137 of this chapter, they are being operated under the applicable rules of part 121 or part 135 of this chapter by an applicant for a certificate under part 119 of this chapter or they are being operated by a foreign air carrier or a foreign person engaged in common carriage solely outside the United States under part 91 of this chapter;

(5) They are being operated under a deviation authority issued under 125.3;

(6) They are being operated under part 91, subpart K by a fractional owner as defined in 91.1001 of this chapter; or

(7) They are being operated by a fractional ownership program manager as defined in 91.1001 of this chapter, for training, ferrying, positioning, maintenance, or demonstration purposes under part 91 of this chapter and without carrying passengers or cargo for compensation or hire except as permitted for demonstration flights under 91.501(b)(3) of this chapter.

(c) The rules of this part, except 125.247, do not apply to the operation of airplanes specified in paragraph (a) when they are operated outside the United States by a person who is not a citizen of the United States.

(d) The provisions of this part apply to each person on board an aircraft being operated under this part, unless otherwise specified.

(e) This part also establishes requirements for operators to take actions to support the continued airworthiness of each airplane.

[Doc. No. 19779, 45 FR 67235, Oct. 9, 1980, as amended by Amdt. 125–4, 47 FR 44719, Oct. 12, 1982; Amdt. 125–5, 49 FR 34816, Sept. 4, 1984; Amdt. 125–6, 51 FR 873, Jan. 8, 1986; Amdt. 125–9, 52 FR 20028, May 28, 1987; Amdt. 121–251, 60 FR 65937, Dec. 20, 1995; Amdt. 125–31, 64 FR 1080, Jan. 7, 1999; Amdt. 125–44, 68 FR 54585, Sept. 17, 2003; Amdt. 125–53, 72 FR 63412, Nov. 8, 2007]

125.3 Deviation authority

(a) The Administrator may, upon consideration of the circumstances of a particular operation, issue deviation authority providing relief from specified sections of part 125. This deviation authority will be issued as a Letter of Deviation Authority.

(b) A Letter of Deviation Authority may be terminated or amended at any time by the Administrator.

(c) A request for deviation authority must be submitted to the responsible Flight Standards office, not less than 60 days prior to the date of intended operations. A request for deviation authority must contain a complete statement of the circumstances and justification for the deviation requested.

(d) After February 2, 2012, no deviation authority from the flight data recorder requirements of this part will be granted. Any previously issued deviation from the flight data recorder requirements of this part is no longer valid.

[Doc. No. 19779, 45 FR 67235, Oct. 9, 1980, as amended by Amdt. 125-13, 54 FR 39294, Sept. 25, 1989; Amdt. 125-56, 73 FR 73179, Dec. 2, 2008; Docket FAA-2018-0119, Amdt. 125-68, 83 FR 9173, Mar. 5, 2018]

125.5 Operating certificate and operations specifications required

(a) After February 3, 1981, no person may engage in operations governed by this part unless that person holds a certificate and operations specification or appropriate deviation authority.

(b) Applicants who file an application before June 1, 1981 shall continue to operate under the rules applicable to their operations on February 2, 1981 until the application for an operating certificate required by this part has been denied or the operating certificate and operations specifications required by this part have been issued.

(c) The rules of this part which apply to a certificate holder also apply to any person who engages in any operation governed by this part without an appropriate certificate and operations specifications required by this part or a Letter of Deviation Authority issued under 125.3.

[Doc. No. 19779, 45 FR 67235, Oct. 9, 1980, as amended by Amdt. 125–1A, 46 FR 10903, Feb. 5, 1981]

125.7 Display of certificate

(a) The certificate holder must display a true copy of the certificate in each of its aircraft.

(b) Each operator holding a Letter of Deviation Authority issued under this part must carry a true copy in each of its airplanes.

125.9 Definitions

(a) For the purposes of this part, maximum payload capacity means:

(1) For an airplane for which a maximum zero fuel weight is prescribed in FAA technical specifications, the maximum zero fuel weight, less empty weight, less all justifiable airplane equipment, and less the operating load (consisting of minimum flightcrew, foods and beverages and supplies and equipment related to foods and beverages, but not including disposable fuel or oil):

(2) For all other airplanes, the maximum certificated takeoff weight of an airplane, less the empty weight, less all justifiable airplane equipment, and less the operating load (consisting of minimum fuel load, oil, and flightcrew). The allowance for the weight of the crew, oil, and fuel is as follows:

(i) Crew—200 pounds for each crewmember required under this chapter

(ii) Oil—350 pounds.

(iii) Fuel—the minimum weight of fuel required under this chapter for a flight between domestic points 174 nautical miles apart under VFR weather conditions that does not involve extended overwater operations.

(b) For the purposes of this part, empty weight means the weight of the airframe, engines, propellers, and fixed equipment. Empty weight excludes the weight of the crew and payload, but includes the weight of all fixed ballast, unusable fuel supply, undrainable oil, total quantity of engine coolant, and total quantity of hydraulic fluid.

(c) For the purposes of this part, maximum zero fuel weight means the maximum permissible weight of an airplane with no disposable fuel or oil. The zero fuel weight figure may be found in either the airplane type certificate data sheet or the approved Airplane Flight Manual, or both.

(d) For the purposes of this section, justifiable airplane equipment means any equipment necessary for the operation of the airplane. It does not include equipment or ballast specifically installed, permanently or otherwise, for the purpose of altering the empty weight of an airplane to meet the maximum payload capacity.

125.11 Certificate eligibility and prohibited operations

(a) No person is eligible for a certificate or operations specifications under this part if the person holds the appropriate operating certificate and/or operations specifications necessary to conduct operations under part 121, 129 or 135 of this chapter.

(b) No certificate holder may conduct any operation which results directly or indirectly from any person's holding out to the public to furnish transportation.

(c) No person holding operations specifications under this part may operate or list on its operations specifications any aircraft listed on any operations specifications or other required aircraft listing under part 121, 129, or 135 of this chapter.

[Doc. No. 19779, 45 FR 67235, Oct. 9, 1980 as amended by Amdt. 125–9, 52 FR 20028, May 28, 1987]

Subpart B — Certification Rules and Miscellaneous Requirements

125.21 Application for operating certificate

(a) Each applicant for the issuance of an operating certificate must submit an application in a form and manner prescribed by the Administrator to the responsible Flight Standards office in whose area the applicant proposes to establish or has established its principal operations base. The application must be submitted at least 60 days before the date of intended operations.

(b) Each application submitted under paragraph (a) of this section must contain a signed statement showing the following:

(1) The name and address of each director and each officer or person employed or who will be employed in a management position described in 125.25.

(2) A list of flight crewmembers with the type of airman certificate held, including ratings and certificate numbers.

[Docket No. 19779, 45 FR 67235, Oct. 9, 1980, as amended by Docket FAA-2018-0119, Amdt. 125-68, 83 FR 9173, Mar. 5, 2018]

125.23 Rules applicable to operations subject to this part

Each person operating an airplane in operations under this part shall—

(a) While operating inside the United States, comply with the applicable rules in part 91 of this chapter; and

(b) While operating outside the United States, comply with Annex 2, Rules of the Air, to the Convention on International Civil Aviation or the regulations of any foreign country, whichever applies, and with any rules of parts 61 and 91 of this chapter and this part that are more restrictive than that Annex or those regulations and that can be complied with without violating that Annex or those regulations. Annex 2 is incorporated by reference in 91.703(b) of this chapter.

[Doc. No. 19779, 45 FR 67235, Oct. 9, 1980, as amended by Amdt. 125–12, 54 FR 34331, Aug. 18, 1989]

FAR 125

125.25 Management personnel required

(a) Each applicant for a certificate under this part must show that it has enough management personnel, including at least a director of operations, to assure that its operations are conducted in accordance with the requirements of this part.

(b) Each applicant shall—

(1) Set forth the duties, responsibilities, and authority of each of its management personnel in the general policy section of its manual;

(2) List in the manual the names and addresses of each of its management personnel;

(3) Designate a person as responsible for the scheduling of inspections required by the manual and for the updating of the approved weight and balance system on all airplanes.

(c) Each certificate holder shall notify the responsible Flight Standards office charged with the overall inspection of the certificate holder of any change made in the assignment of persons to the listed positions within 10 days, excluding Saturdays, Sundays, and Federal holidays, of such change.

[Docket No. 19779, 45 FR 67235, Oct. 9, 1980, as amended by Docket FAA-2018-0119, Amdt. 125-68, 83 FR 9173, Mar. 5, 2018]

125.26 Employment of former FAA employees

(a) Except as specified in paragraph (c) of this section, no certificate holder may knowingly employ or make a contractual arrangement which permits an individual to act as an agent or representative of the certificate holder in any matter before the Federal Aviation Administration if the individual, in the preceding 2 years—

(1) Served as, or was directly responsible for the oversight of, a Flight Standards Service aviation safety inspector; and

(2) Had direct responsibility to inspect, or oversee the inspection of, the operations of the certificate holder.

(b) For the purpose of this section, an individual shall be considered to be acting as an agent or representative of a certificate holder in a matter before the agency if the individual makes any written or oral communication on behalf of the certificate holder to the agency (or any of its officers or employees) in connection with a particular matter, whether or not involving a specific party and without regard to whether the individual has participated in, or had responsibility for, the particular matter while serving as a Flight Standards Service aviation safety inspector.

(c) The provisions of this section do not prohibit a certificate holder from knowingly employing or making a contractual arrangement which permits an individual to act as an agent or representative of the certificate holder in any matter before the Federal Aviation Administration if the individual was employed by the certificate holder before October 21, 2011.

[Doc. No. FAA–2008–1154, 76 FR 52235, Aug. 22, 2011]

125.27 Issue of certificate

(a) An applicant for a certificate under this subpart is entitled to a certificate if the Administrator finds that the applicant is properly and adequately equipped and able to conduct a safe operation in accordance with the requirements of this part and the operations specifications provided for in this part.

(b) The Administrator may deny an application for a certificate under this subpart if the Administrator finds—

(1) That an operating certificate required under this part or part 121, 123, or 135 of this chapter previously issued to the applicant was revoked; or

(2) That a person who was employed in a management position under 125.25 of this part with (or has exercised control with respect to) any certificate holder under part 121, 123, 125, or 135 of this chapter whose operating certificate has been revoked, will be employed in any of those positions or a similar position with the applicant and that the person's employment or control contributed materially to the reasons for revoking that certificate.

125.29 Duration of certificate

(a) A certificate issued under this part is effective until surrendered, suspended, or revoked.

(b) The Administrator may suspend or revoke a certificate under section 609 of the Federal Aviation Act of 1958 and the applicable procedures of part 13 of this chapter for any cause that, at the time of suspension or revocation, would have been grounds for denying an application for a certificate.

(c) If the Administrator suspends or revokes a certificate or it is otherwise terminated, the holder of that certificate shall return it to the Administrator.

125.31 Contents of certificate and operations specifications

(a) Each certificate issued under this part contains the following:

(1) The holder's name.

(2) A description of the operations authorized.

(3) The date it is issued.

(b) The operations specifications issued under this part contain the following:

(1) The kinds of operations authorized.

(2) The types and registration numbers of airplanes authorized for use.

(3) Approval of the provisions of the operator's manual relating to airplane inspections, together with necessary conditions and limitations.

(4) Registration numbers of airplanes that are to be inspected under an approved airplane inspection program under 125.247.

(5) Procedures for control of weight and balance of airplanes.

(6) Any other item that the Administrator determines is necessary to cover a particular situation.

125.33 Operations specifications not a part of certificate

Operations specifications are not a part of an operating certificate.

125.35 Amendment of operations specifications

(a) The responsible Flight Standards office charged with the overall inspection of the certificate holder may amend any operations specifications issued under this part if—

(1) It determines that safety in air commerce requires that amendment; or

(2) Upon application by the holder, the responsible Flight Standards office determines that safety in air commerce allows that amendment.

(b) The certificate holder must file an application to amend operations specifications at least 15 days before the date proposed by the applicant for the amendment to become effective, unless a shorter filing period is approved. The application must be on a form and in a manner prescribed by the Administrator and be submitted to the responsible Flight Standards office charged with the overall inspection of the certificate holder.

(c) Within 30 days after a notice of refusal to approve a holder's application for amendment is received, the holder may petition the Executive Director, Flight Standards Service, to reconsider the refusal to amend.

(d) When the responsible Flight Standards office charged with the overall inspection of the certificate holder amends operations specifications, the responsible Flight Standards office gives notice in writing to the holder of a proposed amendment to the operations specifications, fixing a period of not less than 7 days within which the holder may submit written information, views, and arguments concerning the proposed amendment. After consideration of all relevant matter presented, the responsible Flight Standards office notifies the holder of any amendment adopted, or a rescission of the notice. That amendment becomes effective not less than 30 days after the holder receives notice of the adoption of the amendment, unless the holder petitions the Executive Director, Flight

Standards Service, for reconsideration of the amendment. In that case, the effective date of the amendment is stayed pending a decision by the Executive Director. If the Executive Director finds there is an emergency requiring immediate action as to safety in air commerce that makes the provisions of this paragraph impracticable or contrary to the public interest, the Executive Director notifies the certificate holder that the amendment is effective on the date of receipt, without previous notice.

[Doc. No. 19779, 45 FR 67235, Oct. 9, 1980, as amended by Amdt. 125-13, 54 FR 39294, Sept. 25, 1989; Docket FAA-2018-0119, Amdt. 125-68, 83 FR 9173, 9174, Mar. 5, 2018]

125.37 Duty period limitations

(a) Each flight crewmember and flight attendant must be relieved from all duty for at least 8 consecutive hours during any 24-hour period.

(b) The Administrator may specify rest, flight time, and duty time limitations in the operations specifications that are other than those specified in paragraph (a) of this section.

[Doc. No. 19779, 45 FR 67235, Oct. 9, 1980, as amended by Amdt. 125-21, 59 FR 42993, Aug. 19, 1994]

125.39 Carriage of narcotic drugs, marihuana, and depressant or stimulant drugs or substances

If the holder of a certificate issued under this part permits any airplane owned or leased by that holder to be engaged in any operation that the certificate holder knows to be in violation of 91.19(a) of this chapter, that operation is a basis for suspending or revoking the certificate.

[Doc. No. 19779, 45 FR 67235, Oct. 9, 1980, as amended by Amdt. 125-12, 54 FR 34331, Aug. 18, 1989]

125.41 Availability of certificate and operations specifications

Each certificate holder shall make its operating certificate and operations specifications available for inspection by the Administrator at its principal operations base.

125.43 Use of operations specifications

(a) Each certificate holder shall keep each of its employees informed of the provisions of its operations specifications that apply to the employee's duties and responsibilities.

(b) Each certificate holder shall maintain a complete and separate set of its operations specifications. In addition, each certificate holder shall insert pertinent excerpts of its operations specifications, or reference thereto, in its manual in such a manner that they retain their identity as operations specifications.

125.45 Inspection authority

Each certificate holder shall allow the Administrator, at any time or place, to make any inspections or tests to determine its compliance with the Federal Aviation Act of 1958, the Federal Aviation Regulations, its operating certificate and operations specifications, its letter of deviation authority, or its eligibility to continue to hold its certificate or its letter of deviation authority.

125.47 Change of address

Each certificate holder shall notify the responsible Flight Standards office charged with the overall inspection of its operations, in writing, at least 30 days in advance, of any change in the address of its principal business office, its principal operations base, or its principal maintenance base.

[Docket No. 19779, 45 FR 67235, Oct. 9, 1980, as amended by Docket FAA-2018-0119, Amdt. 125-68, 83 FR 9173, Mar. 5, 2018]

125.49 Airport requirements

(a) No certificate holder may use any airport unless it is adequate for the proposed operation, considering such items as size, surface, obstructions, and lighting.

(b) No pilot of an airplane carrying passengers at night may take off from, or land on, an airport unless—

(1) That pilot has determined the wind direction from an illuminated wind direction indicator or local ground communications, or, in the case of takeoff, that pilot's personal observations; and

(2) The limits of the area to be used for landing or takeoff are clearly shown by boundary or runway marker lights.

(c) For the purposes of paragraph (b) of this section, if the area to be used for takeoff or landing is marked by flare pots or lanterns, their use must be approved by the Administrator.

125.51 En route navigation facilities

(a) Except as provided in paragraph (b) of this section, no certificate holder may conduct any operation over a route (including to any destination, refueling or alternate airports) unless suitable navigation aids are available over the route to navigate the airplane along the route within the degree of accuracy required for ATC. Navigation aids required for routes outside of controlled airspace are listed in the certificate holder's operations specifications except for those aids required for routes to alternate airports.

(b) Navigation aids are not required for any of the following operations—

(1) Day VFR operations that the certificate holder shows can be conducted safely by pilotage because of the characteristics of the terrain;

(2) Night VFR operations on routes that the certificate holder shows have reliably lighted landmarks adequate for safe operations; and

(3) Other operations approved by the responsible Flight Standards office.

[Doc. No. FAA-2002-14002, 72 FR 31682, June 7, 2007, as amended by Docket FAA-2018-0119, Amdt. 125-68, 83 FR 9174, Mar. 5, 2018]

125.53 Flight locating requirements

(a) Each certificate holder must have procedures established for locating each flight for which an FAA flight plan is not filed that—

(1) Provide the certificate holder with at least the information required to be included in a VFR flight plan;

(2) Provide for timely notification of an FAA facility or search and rescue facility, if an airplane is overdue or missing; and

(3) Provide the certificate holder with the location, date, and estimated time for reestablishing radio or telephone communications, if the flight will operate in an area where communications cannot be maintained.

(b) Flight locating information shall be retained at the certificate holder's principal operations base, or at other places designated by the certificate holder in the flight locating procedures, until the completion of the flight.

(c) Each certificate holder shall furnish the representative of the Administrator assigned to it with a copy of its flight locating procedures and any changes or additions, unless those procedures are included in a manual required under this part.

Subpart C — Manual Requirements

125.71 Preparation

(a) Each certificate holder shall prepare and keep current a manual setting forth the certificate holder's procedures and policies acceptable to the Administrator. This manual must be used by the certificate holder's flight, ground, and maintenance personnel in conducting its operations. However, the Administrator may authorize a deviation from this paragraph if the Administrator finds that, because of the limited size of the operation, all or part of the manual is not necessary for guidance of flight, ground, or maintenance personnel.

(b) Each certificate holder shall maintain at least one copy of the manual at its principal operations base.

(c) The manual must not be contrary to any applicable Federal regulations, foreign regulation applicable to the certificate holder's operations in foreign countries, or the certificate holder's operating certificate or operations specifications.

(d) A copy of the manual, or appropriate portions of the manual (and changes and additions) shall be made available to maintenance and ground operations personnel by the certificate holder and furnished to—

(1) Its flight crewmembers; and

(2) The responsible Flight Standards office charged with the overall inspection of its operations.

(e) Each employee of the certificate holder to whom a manual or appropriate portions of it are furnished under paragraph (d)(1) of this section shall keep it up to date with the changes and additions furnished to them.

(f) For the purpose of complying with paragraph (d) of this section, a certificate holder may furnish the persons listed therein with the maintenance part of its manual in printed form or other form, acceptable to the Administrator, that is retrievable in the English language. If the certificate holder furnishes the maintenance part of the manual in other than printed form, it must ensure there is a compatible reading device available to those persons that provides a legible image of the maintenance information and instructions or a system that is able to retrieve the maintenance information and instructions in the English language.

(g) If a certificate holder conducts airplane inspections or maintenance at specified stations where it keeps the approved inspection program manual, it is not required to carry the manual aboard the airplane en route to those stations.

[Doc. No. 19779, 45 FR 67235, Oct. 9, 1980, as amended by Amdt. 125-28, 62 FR 13257, Mar. 19, 1997; Docket FAA-2018-0119, Amdt. 125-68, 83 FR 9173, Mar. 5, 2018]

125.73   Contents

Each manual shall have the date of the last revision and revision number on each revised page. The manual must include—

(a) The name of each management person who is authorized to act for the certificate holder, the person's assigned area of responsibility, and the person's duties, responsibilities, and authority;

(b) Procedures for ensuring compliance with airplane weight and balance limitations;

(c) Copies of the certificate holder's operations specifications or appropriate extracted information, including area of operations authorized, category and class of airplane authorized, crew complements, and types of operations authorized;

(d) Procedures for complying with accident notification requirements;

(e) Procedures for ensuring that the pilot in command knows that required airworthiness inspections have been made and that the airplane has been approved for return to service in compliance with applicable maintenance requirements;

(f) Procedures for reporting and recording mechanical irregularities that come to the attention of the pilot in command before, during, and after completion of a flight;

(g) Procedures to be followed by the pilot in command for determining that mechanical irregularities or defects reported for previous flights have been corrected or that correction has been deferred;

(h) Procedures to be followed by the pilot in command to obtain maintenance, preventive maintenance, and servicing of the airplane at a place where previous arrangements have not been made by the operator, when the pilot is authorized to so act for the operator;

(i) Procedures for the release for, or continuation of, flight if any item of equipment required for the particular type of operation becomes inoperative or unserviceable en route;

(j) Procedures for refueling airplanes, eliminating fuel contamination, protecting from fire (including electrostatic protection), and supervising and protecting passengers during refueling;

(k) Procedures to be followed by the pilot in command in the briefing under 125.327;

(l) Flight locating procedures, when applicable;

(m) Procedures for ensuring compliance with emergency procedures, including a list of the functions assigned each category of required crewmembers in connection with an emergency and emergency evacuation;

(n) The approved airplane inspection program;

(o) Procedures and instructions to enable personnel to recognize hazardous materials, as defined in title 49 CFR, and if these materials are to be carried, stored, or handled, procedures and instructions for—

(1) Accepting shipment of hazardous material required by title 49 CFR, to assure proper packaging, marking, labeling, shipping documents, compatibility of articles, and instructions on their loading, storage, and handling;

(2) Notification and reporting hazardous material incidents as required by title 49 CFR; and

(3) Notification of the pilot in command when there are hazardous materials aboard, as required by title 49 CFR;

(p) Procedures for the evacuation of persons who may need the assistance of another person to move expeditiously to an exit if an emergency occurs;

(q) The identity of each person who will administer tests required by this part, including the designation of the tests authorized to be given by the person; and

(r) Other procedures and policy instructions regarding the certificate holder's operations that are issued by the certificate holder.

125.75   Airplane Flight Manual

(a) Each certificate holder shall keep a current approved Airplane Flight Manual or approved equivalent for each type airplane that it operates.

(b) Each certificate holder shall carry the approved Airplane Flight Manual or the approved equivalent aboard each airplane it operates. A certificate holder may elect to carry a combination of the manuals required by this section and 125.71. If it so elects, the certificate holder may revise the operating procedures sections and modify the presentation of performance from the applicable Airplane Flight Manual if the revised operating procedures and modified performance data presentation are approved by the Administrator.

Subpart D—Airplane Requirements

125.91   Airplane requirements: General

(a) No certificate holder may operate an airplane governed by this part unless it—

(1) Carries an appropriate current airworthiness certificate issued under this chapter; and

(2) Is in an airworthy condition and meets the applicable airworthiness requirements of this chapter, including those relating to identification and equipment.

(b) No person may operate an airplane unless the current empty weight and center of gravity are calculated from the values established by actual weighing of the airplane within the preceding 36 calendar months.

(c) Paragraph (b) of this section does not apply to airplanes issued an original airworthiness certificate within the preceding 36 calendar months.

125.93   Airplane limitations

No certificate holder may operate a land airplane (other than a DC–3, C–46, CV–240, CV–340, CV–440, CV–580, CV–600, CV–640, or Martin 404) in an extended overwater operation unless it is certificated or approved as adequate for ditching under the ditching provisions of part 25 of this chapter.

Subpart E — Special Airworthiness Requirements

125.111   General

(a) Except as provided in paragraph (b) of this section, no certificate holder may use an airplane powered by airplane engines rated at more than 600 horsepower each for maximum continuous operation unless that airplane meets the requirements of 125.113 through 125.181.

(b) If the Administrator determines that, for a particular model of airplane used in cargo service, literal compliance with any requirement under paragraph (a) of this section would be extremely difficult and that compliance would not contribute materially to the objective sought, the Administrator may require compliance with only those requirements that are necessary to accomplish the basic objectives of this part.

(c) This section does not apply to any airplane certificated under—

(1) Part 4b of the Civil Air Regulations in effect after October 31, 1946;

(2) Part 25 of this chapter; or

(3) Special Civil Air Regulation 422, 422A, or 422B.

125.113   Cabin interiors

(a) Upon the first major overhaul of an airplane cabin or refurbishing of the cabin interior, all materials in each compartment used by the crew or passengers that do not meet the following requirements must be replaced with materials that meet these requirements:

(1) For an airplane for which the application for the type certificate was filed prior to May 1, 1972, 25.853 in effect on April 30, 1972.

(2) For an airplane for which the application for the type certificate was filed on or after May 1, 1972, the materials requirement under which the airplane was type certificated.

(b) Except as provided in paragraph (a) of this section, each compartment used by the crew or passengers must meet the following requirements:

(1) Materials must be at least flash resistant.

(2) The wall and ceiling linings and the covering of upholstering, floors, and furnishings must be flame resistant.

(3) Each compartment where smoking is to be allowed must be equipped with self-contained ash trays that are completely removable and other compartments must be placarded against smoking.

(4) Each receptacle for used towels, papers, and wastes must be of fire-resistant material and must have a cover or other means of containing possible fires started in the receptacles.

(c) Thermal/acoustic insulation materials. For transport category airplanes type certificated after January 1, 1958:

(1) For airplanes manufactured before September 2, 2005, when thermal/acoustic insulation is installed in the fuselage as replacements after September 2, 2005, the insulation must meet the flame propagation requirements of 25.856 of this chapter, effective September 2, 2003, if it is:

(i)   of a blanket construction or

(ii)   Installed around air ducting.

(2) For airplanes manufactured after September 2, 2005, thermal/acoustic insulation materials installed in the fuselage must meet the flame propagation requirements of 25.856 of this chapter, effective September 2, 2003.

[Doc. No. 19799, 45 FR 67235, Oct. 9, 1980, as amended by Amdt. 125–43, 68 FR 45084, July 31, 2003; Amdt. 125–50, 70 FR 77752, Dec. 30, 2005]

125.115   Internal doors

In any case where internal doors are equipped with louvres or other ventilating means, there must be a means convenient to the crew for closing the flow of air through the door when necessary.

125.117   Ventilation

Each passenger or crew compartment must be suitably ventilated. Carbon monoxide concentration may not be more than one part in 20,000 parts of air, and fuel fumes may not be present. In any case where partitions between compartments have louvres or other means allowing air to flow between compartments, there must be a means convenient to the crew for closing the flow of air through the partitions when necessary.

125.119   Fire precautions

(a) Each compartment must be designed so that, when used for storing cargo or baggage, it meets the following requirements:

(1) No compartment may include controls, wiring, lines, equipment, or accessories that would upon damage or failure, affect the safe operation of the airplane unless the item is adequately shielded, isolated, or otherwise protected so that it cannot be damaged by movement of cargo in the compartment and so that damage to or failure of the item would not create a fire hazard in the compartment.

(2) Cargo or baggage may not interfere with the functioning of the fire-protective features of the compartment.

(3) Materials used in the construction of the compartments, including tie-down equipment, must be at least flame resistant.

(4) Each compartment must include provisions for safeguarding against fires according to the classifications set forth in paragraphs (b) through (f) of this section.

(b) Class A. Cargo and baggage compartments are classified in the "A" category if a fire therein would be readily discernible to a member of the crew while at that crewmember's station, and all parts of the compartment are easily accessible in flight. There must be a hand fire extinguisher available for each Class A compartment.

(c) Class B. Cargo and baggage compartments are classified in the "B" category if enough access is provided while in flight to enable a member of the crew to effectively reach all of the compartment and its contents with a hand fire extinguisher and the compartment is so designed that, when the access provisions are being used, no hazardous amount of smoke, flames, or extinguishing agent enters any compartment occupied by the crew or passengers. Each Class B compartment must comply with the following:

(1) It must have a separate approved smoke or fire detector system to give warning at the pilot or flight engineer station.

(2) There must be a hand-held fire extinguisher available for the compartment.

(3) It must be lined with fire-resistant material, except that additional service lining of flame-resistant material may be used.

(d) Class C. Cargo and baggage compartments are classified in the "C" category if they do not conform with the requirements for the "A", "B", "D", or "E" categories. Each Class C compartment must comply with the following:

(1) It must have a separate approved smoke or fire detector system to give warning at the pilot or flight engineer station.

(2) It must have an approved built-in fire-extinguishing system controlled from the pilot or flight engineer station.

(3) It must be designed to exclude hazardous quantities of smoke, flames, or extinguishing agents from entering into any compartment occupied by the crew or passengers.

(4) It must have ventilation and draft control so that the extinguishing agent provided can control any fire that may start in the compartment.

(5) It must be lined with fire-resistant material, except that additional service lining of flame-resistant material may be used.

(e) Class D. Cargo and baggage compartments are classified in the "D" category if they are so designed and constructed that a fire occurring therein will be completely confined without endangering the safety of the airplane or the occupants. Each Class D compartment must comply with the following:

(1) It must have a means to exclude hazardous quantities of smoke, flames, or noxious gases from entering any compartment occupied by the crew or passengers.

(2) Ventilation and drafts must be controlled within each compartment so that any fire likely to occur in the compartment will not progress beyond safe limits.

360 Part 125—Certification and Operations of Large AirplanesPart 125—Certification and Operations of Large Airplanes

(3) It must be completely lined with fire-resistant material.

(4) Consideration must be given to the effect of heat within the compartment on adjacent critical parts of the airplane.

(f) Class E. On airplanes used for the carriage of cargo only, the cabin area may be classified as a Class "E" compartment. Each Class E compartment must comply with the following:

(1) It must be completely lined with fire-resistant material.

(2) It must have a separate system of an approved type smoke or fire detector to give warning at the pilot or flight engineer station.

(3) It must have a means to shut off the ventilating air flow to or within the compartment and the controls for that means must be accessible to the flightcrew in the crew compartment.

(4) It must have a means to exclude hazardous quantities of smoke, flames, or noxious gases from entering the flightcrew compartment.

(5) Required crew emergency exits must be accessible under all cargo loading conditions.

125.121   Proof of compliance with 125.119

Compliance with those provisions of 125.119 that refer to compartment accessibility, the entry of hazardous quantities of smoke or extinguishing agent into compartment occupied by the crew or passengers, and the dissipation of the extinguishing agent in Class "C" compartments must be shown by tests in flight. During these tests it must be shown that no inadvertent operation of smoke or fire detectors in other compartments within the airplane would occur as a result of fire contained in any one compartment, either during the time it is being extinguished, or thereafter, unless the extinguishing system floods those compartments simultaneously.

125.123   Propeller deicing fluid

If combustible fluid is used for propeller deicing, the certificate holder must comply with 125.153.

125.125   Pressure cross-feed arrangements

(a) Pressure cross-feed lines may not pass through parts of the airplane used for carrying persons or cargo unless there is a means to allow crewmembers to shut off the supply of fuel to these lines or the lines are enclosed in a fuel and fume-proof enclosure that is ventilated and drained to the exterior of the airplane. However, such an enclosure need not be used if those lines incorporate no fittings on or within the personnel or cargo areas and are suitably routed or protected to prevent accidental damage.

(b) Lines that can be isolated from the rest of the fuel system by valves at each end must incorporate provisions for relieving excessive pressures that may result from exposure of the isolated line to high temperatures.

125.127   Location of fuel tanks

(a) Fuel tanks must be located in accordance with 125.153.

(b) No part of the engine nacelle skin that lies immediately behind a major air outlet from the engine compartment may be used as the wall of an integral tank.

(c) Fuel tanks must be isolated from personnel compartments by means of fume- and fuel-proof enclosures.

125.129   Fuel system lines and fittings

(a) Fuel lines must be installed and supported so as to prevent excessive vibration and so as to be adequate to withstand loads due to fuel pressure and accelerated flight conditions.

(b) Lines connected to components of the airplane between which there may be relative motion must incorporate provisions for flexibility.

(c) Flexible connections in lines that may be under pressure and subject to axial loading must use flexible hose assemblies rather than hose clamp connections.

(d) Flexible hoses must be of an acceptable type or proven suitable for the particular application.

125.131   Fuel lines and fittings in designated fire zones

Fuel lines and fittings in each designated fire zone must comply with 125.157.

125.133   Fuel valves

Each fuel valve must—

(a) Comply with 125.155;

(b) Have positive stops or suitable index provisions in the "on" and "off" positions; and

(c) Be supported so that loads resulting from its operation or from accelerated flight conditions are not transmitted to the lines connected to the valve.

125.135   Oil lines and fittings in designated fire zones

Oil lines and fittings in each designated fire zone must comply with 125.157.

125.137   Oil valves

(a) Each oil valve must—

(1) Comply with 125.155;

(2) Have positive stops or suitable index provisions in the "on" and "off" positions; and

(3) Be supported so that loads resulting from its operation or from accelerated flight conditions are not transmitted to the lines attached to the valve.

(b) The closing of an oil shutoff means must not prevent feathering the propeller, unless equivalent safety provisions are incorporated.

125.139   Oil system drains

Accessible drains incorporating either a manual or automatic means for positive locking in the closed position must be provided to allow safe drainage of the entire oil system.

125.141   Engine breather lines

(a) Engine breather lines must be so arranged that condensed water vapor that may freeze and obstruct the line cannot accumulate at any point.

(b) Engine breathers must discharge in a location that does not constitute a fire hazard in case foaming occurs and so that oil emitted from the line does not impinge upon the pilots' windshield.

(c) Engine breathers may not discharge into the engine air induction system.

125.143   Firewalls

Each engine, auxiliary power unit, fuel-burning heater, or other item of combusting equipment that is intended for operation in flight must be isolated from the rest of the airplane by means of firewalls or shrouds, or by other equivalent means.

125.145   Firewall construction

Each firewall and shroud must—

(a) Be so made that no hazardous quantity of air, fluids, or flame can pass from the engine compartment to other parts of the airplane;

(b) Have all openings in the firewall or shroud sealed with close-fitting fireproof grommets, bushings, or firewall fittings;

(c) Be made of fireproof material; and

(d) Be protected against corrosion.

125.147   Cowling

(a) Cowling must be made and supported so as to resist the vibration, inertia, and air loads to which it may be normally subjected.

(b) Provisions must be made to allow rapid and complete drainage of the cowling in normal ground and flight attitudes. Drains must not discharge in locations constituting a fire hazard. Parts of the cowling that are subjected to high temperatures because they are near exhaust system parts or because of exhaust gas impingement must be made of fireproof material. Unless otherwise specified in these regulations, all other parts of the cowling must be made of material that is at least fire resistant.

25.149 Engine accessory section diaphragm

Unless equivalent protection can be shown by other means, a diaphragm that complies with 125.145 must be provided on air-cooled engines to isolate the engine power section and all parts of the exhaust system from the engine accessory compartment.

25.151 Powerplant fire protection

a) Designated fire zones must be protected from fire by compliance with 125.153 through 125.159.

b) Designated fire zones are—

(1) Engine accessory sections;

(2) Installations where no isolation is provided between the engine and accessory compartment; and

(3) Areas that contain auxiliary power units, fuel-burning heaters, and other combustion equipment.

25.153 Flammable fluids

a) No tanks or reservoirs that are a part of a system containing flammable fluids or gases may be located in designated fire zones, except where the fluid contained, the design of the system, the materials used in the tank, the shutoff means, and the connections, lines, and controls provide equivalent safety.

b) At least one-half inch of clear airspace must be provided between any tank or reservoir and a firewall or shroud isolating a designated fire zone.

25.155 Shutoff means

a) Each engine must have a means for shutting off or otherwise preventing hazardous amounts of fuel, oil, deicer, and other flammable fluids from flowing into, within, or through any designated fire zone. However, means need not be provided to shut off flow in lines that are an integral part of an engine.

b) The shutoff means must allow an emergency operating sequence that is compatible with the emergency operation of other equipment, such as feathering the propeller, to facilitate rapid and effective control of fires.

c) Shutoff means must be located outside of designated fire zones, unless equivalent safety is provided, and it must be shown that no hazardous amount of flammable fluid will drain into any designated fire zone after a shutoff.

d) Adequate provisions must be made to guard against inadvertent operation of the shutoff means and to make it possible for the crew to reopen the shutoff means after it has been closed.

125.157 Lines and fittings

(a) Each line, and its fittings, that is located in a designated fire zone, if it carries flammable fluids or gases under pressure, or is attached directly to the engine, or is subject to relative motion between components (except lines and fittings forming an integral part of the engine), must be flexible and fire-resistant with fire-resistant, factory-fixed, detachable, or other approved fire-resistant ends.

(b) Lines and fittings that are not subject to pressure or to relative motion between components must be of fire-resistant materials.

125.159 Vent and drain lines

All vent and drain lines, and their fittings, that are located in a designated fire zone must, if they carry flammable fluids or gases, comply with 125.157, if the Administrator finds that the rupture or breakage of any vent or drain line may result in a fire hazard.

125.161 Fire-extinguishing systems

(a) Unless the certificate holder shows that equivalent protection against destruction of the airplane in case of fire is provided by the use of fireproof materials in the nacelle and other components that would be subjected to flame, fire-extinguishing systems must be provided to serve all designated fire zones.

(b) Materials in the fire-extinguishing system must not react chemically with the extinguishing agent so as to be a hazard.

125.163 Fire-extinguishing agents

Only methyl bromide, carbon dioxide, or another agent that has been shown to provide equivalent extinguishing action may be used as a fire-extinguishing agent. If methyl bromide or any other toxic extinguishing agent is used, provisions must be made to prevent harmful concentrations of fluid or fluid vapors from entering any personnel compartment either because of leakage during normal operation of the airplane or because of discharging the fire extinguisher on the ground or in flight when there is a defect in the extinguishing system. If a methyl bromide system is used, the containers must be charged with dry agent and sealed by the fire-extinguisher manufacturer or some other person using satisfactory recharging equipment. If carbon dioxide is used, it must not be possible to discharge enough gas into the personnel compartments to create a danger of suffocating the occupants.

125.165 Extinguishing agent container pressure relief

Extinguishing agent containers must be provided with a pressure relief to prevent bursting of the container because of excessive internal pressures. The discharge line from the relief connection must terminate outside the airplane in a place convenient for inspection on the ground. An indicator must be provided at the discharge end of the line to provide a visual indication when the container has discharged.

125.167 Extinguishing agent container compartment temperature

Precautions must be taken to ensure that the extinguishing agent containers are installed in places where reasonable temperatures can be maintained for effective use of the extinguishing system.

125.169 Fire-extinguishing system materials

(a) Except as provided in paragraph (b) of this section, each component of a fire-extinguishing system that is in a designated fire zone must be made of fireproof materials.

(b) Connections that are subject to relative motion between components of the airplane must be made of flexible materials that are at least fire-resistant and be located so as to minimize the probability of failure.

125.171 Fire-detector systems

Enough quick-acting fire detectors must be provided in each designated fire zone to assure the detection of any fire that may occur in that zone.

125.173 Fire detectors

Fire detectors must be made and installed in a manner that assures their ability to resist, without failure, all vibration, inertia, and other loads to which they may be normally subjected. Fire detectors must be unaffected by exposure to fumes, oil, water, or other fluids that may be present.

125.175 Protection of other airplane components against fire

(a) Except as provided in paragraph (b) of this section, all airplane surfaces aft of the nacelles in the area of one nacelle diameter on both sides of the nacelle centerline must be made of material that is at least fire resistant.

(b) Paragraph (a) of this section does not apply to tail surfaces lying behind nacelles unless the dimensional configuration of the airplane is such that the tail surfaces could be affected readily by heat, flames, or sparks emanating from a designated fire zone or from the engine from a designated fire zone or from the engine compartment of any nacelle.

125.177 Control of engine rotation

(a) Except as provided in paragraph (b) of this section, each airplane must have a means of individually stopping and restarting the rotation of any engine in flight.

(b) In the case of turbine engine installations, a means of stopping rotation need be provided only if the Administrator finds that rotation could jeopardize the safety of the airplane.

FAR 125

125.179   Fuel system independence

(a) Each airplane fuel system must be arranged so that the failure of any one component does not result in the irrecoverable loss of power of more than one engine.

(b) A separate fuel tank need not be provided for each engine if the certificate holder shows that the fuel system incorporates features that provide equivalent safety.

125.181   Induction system ice prevention.

A means for preventing the malfunctioning of each engine due to ice accumulation in the engine air induction system must be provided for each airplane.

125.183   Carriage of cargo in passenger compartments

(a) Except as provided in paragraph (b) or (c) of this section, no certificate holder may carry cargo in the passenger compartment of an airplane.

(b) Cargo may be carried aft of the foremost seated passengers if it is carried in an approved cargo bin that meets the following requirements:

(1) The bin must withstand the load factors and emergency landing conditions applicable to the passenger seats of the airplane in which the bin is installed, multiplied by a factor of 1.15, using the combined weight of the bin and the maximum weight of cargo that may be carried in the bin.

(2) The maximum weight of cargo that the bin is approved to carry and any instructions necessary to ensure proper weight distribution within the bin must be conspicuously marked on the bin.

(3) The bin may not impose any load on the floor or other structure of the airplane that exceeds the load limitations of that structure.

(4) The bin must be attached to the seat tracks or to the floor structure of the airplane, and its attachment must withstand the load factors and emergency landing conditions applicable to the passenger seats of the airplane in which the bin is installed, multiplied by either the factor 1.15 or the seat attachment factor specified for the airplane, whichever is greater, using the combined weight of the bin and the maximum weight of cargo that may be carried in the bin.

(5) The bin may not be installed in a position that restricts access to or use of any required emergency exit, or of the aisle in the passenger compartment.

(6) The bin must be fully enclosed and made of material that is at least flame-resistant.

(7) Suitable safeguards must be provided within the bin to prevent the cargo from shifting under emergency landing conditions.

(8) The bin may not be installed in a position that obscures any passenger's view of the "seat belt" sign, "no smoking" sign, or any required exit sign, unless an auxiliary sign or other approved means for proper notification of the passenger is provided.

(c) All cargo may be carried forward of the foremost seated passengers and carry-on baggage may be carried alongside the foremost seated passengers if the cargo (including carry-on baggage) is carried either in approved bins as specified in paragraph (b) of this section or in accordance with the following:

(1) It is properly secured by a safety belt or other tie down having enough strength to eliminate the possibility of shifting under all normally anticipated flight and ground conditions.

(2) It is packaged or covered in a manner to avoid possible injury to passengers.

(3) It does not impose any load on seats or the floor structure that exceeds the load limitation for those components.

(4) Its location does not restrict access to or use of any required emergency or regular exit, or of the aisle in the passenger compartment.

(5) Its location does not obscure any passenger's view of the "seat belt" sign, "no smoking" sign, or required exit sign, unless a auxiliary sign or other approved means for proper notification of the passenger is provided.

125.185   Carriage of cargo in cargo compartments

When cargo is carried in cargo compartments that are designed to require the physical entry of a crewmember to extinguish any fire that may occur during flight, the cargo must be loaded so as to allow a crewmember to effectively reach all parts of the compartment with the contents of a hand-held fire extinguisher.

125.187   Landing gear: aural warning device

(a) Except for airplanes that comply with the requirements of 25.72 of this chapter on or after January 6, 1992, each airplane must have a landing gear aural warning device that functions continuously under the following conditions:

(1) For airplanes with an established approach wing-flap position, whenever the wing flaps are extended beyond the maximum certificated approach climb configuration position in the Airplane Flight Manual and the landing gear is not fully extended and locked.

(2) For airplanes without an established approach climb wing-flap position, whenever the wing flaps are extended beyond the position at which landing gear extension is normally performed and the landing gear is not fully extended and locked.

(b) The warning system required by paragraph (a) of this section—

(1) May not have a manual shutoff;

(2) Must be in addition to the throttle-actuated device installed under the type certification airworthiness requirements; and

(3) May utilize any part of the throttle-actuated system including the aural warning device.

(c) The flap position sensing unit may be installed at any suitable place in the airplane.

[Doc. No. 19779, 45 FR 67235, Oct. 9, 1980, as amended by Amdt 125–16, 56 FR 63762, Dec. 5, 1991]

125.189   Demonstration of emergency evacuation procedures

(a) Each certificate holder must show, by actual demonstration conducted in accordance with paragraph (a) of appendix B of this part, that the emergency evacuation procedures for each type and model of airplane with a seating of more than 44 passengers, that is used in its passenger-carrying operations, allow the evacuation of the full seating capacity, including crewmembers, in 90 seconds or less, in each of the following circumstances:

(1) A demonstration must be conducted by the certificate holder upon the initial introduction of a type and model of airplane into passenger-carrying operations. However, the demonstration need not be repeated for any airplane type or model that has the same number and type of exits, the same cabin configuration, and the same emergency equipment as any other airplane used by the certificate holder in successfully demonstrating emergency evacuation in compliance with this paragraph.

(2) A demonstration must be conducted—

(i) Upon increasing by more than 5 percent the passenger seating capacity for which successful demonstration has been conducted; or

(ii) Upon a major change in the passenger cabin interior configuration that will affect the emergency evacuation of passengers.

(b) If a certificate holder has conducted a successful demonstration required by 121.291(a) in the same type airplane as a part 121 or part 123 certificate holder, it need not conduct a demonstration under this paragraph in that type airplane to achieve certification under part 125.

c) Each certificate holder operating or proposing to operate one or more landplanes in extended overwater operations, or otherwise required to have certain equipment under 125.209, must show, by a simulated ditching conducted in accordance with paragraph (b) of appendix B of this part, that it has the ability to efficiently carry out its ditching procedures.

d) If a certificate holder has conducted a successful demonstration required by 121.291(b) in the same type airplane as a part 121 or part 123 certificate holder, it need not conduct a demonstration under this paragraph in that type airplane to achieve certification under part 125.

Subpart F — Instrument and Equipment Requirements

125.201 Inoperable instruments and equipment

(a) No person may take off an airplane with inoperable instruments or equipment installed unless the following conditions are met:

(1) An approved Minimum Equipment List exists for that airplane.

(2) The responsible Flight Standards office having certification responsibility has issued the certificate holder operations specifications authorizing operations in accordance with an approved Minimum Equipment List. The flight crew shall have direct access at all times prior to flight to all of the information contained in the approved Minimum Equipment List through printed or other means approved by the Administrator in the certificate holders operations specifications. An approved Minimum Equipment List, as authorized by the operations specifications, constitutes an approved change to the type design without requiring recertification.

(3) The approved Minimum Equipment List must:

(i) Be prepared in accordance with the limitations specified in paragraph (b) of this section.

(ii) Provide for the operation of the airplane with certain instruments and equipment in an inoperable condition.

(4) Records identifying the inoperable instruments and equipment and the information required by paragraph (a)(3)(ii) of this section must be available to the pilot.

(5) The airplane is operated under all applicable conditions and limitations contained in the Minimum Equipment List and the operations specifications authorizing use of the Minimum Equipment List.

(b) The following instruments and equipment may not be included in the Minimum Equipment List:

(1) Instruments and equipment that are either specifically or otherwise required by the airworthiness requirements under which the airplane is type certificated and which are essential for safe operations under all operating conditions.

(2) Instruments and equipment required by an airworthiness directive to be in operable condition unless the airworthiness directive provides otherwise.

(3) Instruments and equipment required for specific operations by this part.

(c) Notwithstanding paragraphs (b)(1) and (b)(3) of this section, an airplane with inoperable instruments or equipment may be operated under a special flight permit under 21.197 and 21.199 of this chapter.

[Doc. No. 25780, 56 FR 12310, Mar. 22, 1991, as amended by Docket FAA-2018-0119, Amdt. 125-68, 83 FR 9174, Mar. 5, 2018]

125.203 Communication and navigation equipment

(a) Communication equipment—general. No person may operate an airplane unless it has two-way radio communication equipment able, at least in flight, to transmit to, and receive from, appropriate facilities 22 nautical miles away.

(b) Navigation equipment for operations over the top. No person may operate an airplane over the top unless it has navigation equipment suitable for the route to be flown.

(c) Communication and navigation equipment for IFR or extended over-water operations—General. Except as provided in paragraph (f) of this section, no person may operate an airplane carrying passengers under IFR or in extended over-water operations unless—

(1) The en route navigation aids necessary for navigating the airplane along the route (e.g., ATS routes, arrival and departure routes, and instrument approach procedures, including missed approach procedures if a missed approach routing is specified in the procedure) are available and suitable for use by the aircraft navigation systems required by this section;

(2) The airplane used in those operations is equipped with at least the following equipment—

(i) Except as provided in paragraph (d) of this section, two approved independent navigation systems suitable for navigating the airplane along the route within the degree of accuracy required for ATC;

(ii) One marker beacon receiver providing visual and aural signals;

(iii) One ILS receiver;

(iv) Two transmitters;

(v) Two microphones;

(vi) Two headsets or one headset and one speaker; and

(vii) Two independent communication systems, one of which must have two-way voice communication capability, capable of transmitting to, and receiving from, at least one appropriate facility from any place on the route to be flown; and

(3) Any RNAV system used to meet the navigation equipment requirements of this section is authorized in the certificate holder's operations specifications.

(d) Use of a single independent navigation system for operations under IFR—not for extended overwater operations. Notwithstanding the requirements of paragraph (c)(2)(i) of this section, the airplane may be equipped with a single independent navigation system suitable for navigating the airplane along the route to be flown within the degree of accuracy required for ATC if—

(1) It can be shown that the airplane is equipped with at least one other independent navigation system suitable, in the event of loss of the navigation capability of the single independent navigation system permitted by this paragraph at any point along the route, for proceeding safely to a suitable airport and completing an instrument approach; and

(2) The airplane has sufficient fuel so that the flight may proceed safely to a suitable airport by use of the remaining navigation system, and complete an instrument approach and land.

(e) Use of VOR navigation equipment. If VOR navigation equipment is required by paragraph (c) or (d) of this section, no person may operate an airplane unless it is equipped with at least one approved DME or a suitable RNAV system.

(f) Extended over-water operations. Notwithstanding the requirements of paragraph (c) of this section, installation and use of a single long-range navigation system and a single long-range communication system for extended over-water operations in certain geographic areas may be authorized by the Administrator and approved in the certificate holder's operations specifications. The following are among the operational factors the Administrator may consider in granting an authorization:

(1) The ability of the flight crew to navigate the airplane along the route to be flown within the degree of accuracy required for ATC;

(2) The length of the route being flown; and

(3) The duration of the very high frequency communications gap.

[Doc. No. FAA-2002-14002, 72 FR 31682, June 7, 2007]

125.204 Portable electronic devices

(a) Except as provided in paragraph (b) of this section, no person may operate, nor may any operator or pilot in command of an aircraft

FAR 125

364

allow the operation of, any portable electronic device on any U.S.-registered civil aircraft operating under this part.

(b) Paragraph (a) of this section does not apply to—

(1) Portable voice recorders;

(2) Hearing aids;

(3) Heart pacemakers;

(4) Electric shavers;

(5) Portable oxygen concentrators that comply with the requirements in 125.219; or

(6) Any other portable electronic device that the Part 125 certificate holder has determined will not cause interference with the navigation or communication system of the aircraft on which it is to be used.

(c) The determination required by paragraph (b)(6) of this section shall be made by that Part 125 certificate holder operating the particular device to be used.

[Doc. No. FAA-1998-4954, 64 FR 1080, Jan. 7, 1999, as amended by Docket FAA-2014-0554, Amdt. 125-65, 81 FR 33118, May 24, 2016]

125.205 Equipment requirements: airplanes under IFR

No person may operate an airplane under IFR unless it has—

(a) A vertical speed indicator;

(b) A free-air temperature indicator;

(c) A heated pitot tube for each airspeed indicator;

(d) A power failure warning device or vacuum indicator to show the power available for gyroscopic instruments from each power source;

(e) An alternate source of static pressure for the altimeter and the airspeed and vertical speed indicators;

(f) At least two generators each of which is on a separate engine, or which any combination of one-half of the total number are rated sufficiently to supply the electrical loads of all required instruments and equipment necessary for safe emergency operation of the airplane; and

(g) Two independent sources of energy (with means of selecting either), of which at least one is an engine-driven pump or generator, each of which is able to drive all gyroscopic instruments and installed so that failure of one instrument or source does not interfere with the energy supply to the remaining instruments or the other energy source. For the purposes of this paragraph, each engine-driven source of energy must be on a different engine.

(h) For the purposes of paragraph (f) of this section, a continuous inflight electrical load includes one that draws current continuously during flight, such as radio equipment, electrically driven instruments, and lights, but does not include occasional intermittent loads.

(i) An airspeed indicating system with heated pitot tube or equivalent means for preventing malfunctioning due to icing.

(j) A sensitive altimeter.

(k) Instrument lights providing enough light to make each required instrument, switch, or similar instrument easily readable and installed so that the direct rays are shielded from the flight crewmembers' eyes and that no objectionable reflections are visible to them. There must be a means of controlling the intensity of illumination unless it is shown that nondimming instrument lights are satisfactory.

125.206 Pitot heat indication systems

(a) Except as provided in paragraph (b) of this section, after April 12, 1981, no person may operate a transport category airplane equipped with a flight instrument pitot heating system unless the airplane is equipped with an operable pitot heat indication system that complies with 25.1326 of this chapter in effect on April 12, 1978.

(b) A certificate holder may obtain an extension of the April 12, 1981, compliance date specified in paragraph (a) of this section, but not beyond April 12, 1983, from the Executive Director, Flight Standards Service if the certificate holder—

(1) Shows that due to circumstances beyond its control it cannot comply by the specified compliance date; and

(2) Submits by the specified compliance date a schedule for compliance acceptable to the Executive Director, indicating that compliance will be achieved at the earliest practicable date.

[Doc. No. 18904, 46 FR 43806, Aug. 31, 1981, as amended by Amdt 125-13, 54 FR 39294, Sept. 25, 1989; Docket FAA-2018-0119, Amdt 125-68, 83 FR 9174, Mar. 5, 2018]

125.207 Emergency equipment requirements

(a) No person may operate an airplane having a seating capacity of 20 or more passengers unless it is equipped with the following emergency equipment:

(1) One approved first aid kit for treatment of injuries likely to occur in flight or in a minor accident, which meets the following specifications and requirements:

(i) Each first aid kit must be dust and moisture proof and contain only materials that either meet Federal Specifications GGK–391a, as revised, or as approved by the Administrator.

(ii) Required first aid kits must be readily accessible to the cabin flight attendants.

(iii) Except as provided in paragraph (a)(1)(iv) of this section, at time of takeoff, each first aid kit must contain at least the following or other contents approved by the Administrator:

CONTENTS	QUANTITY
Adhesive bandage compressors, 1 in	16
Antiseptic swabs	20
Ammonia inhalants	10
Bandage compressors, 4 in	8
Triangular bandage compressors, 40 in	5
Arm splint, noninflatable	1
Leg splint, noninflatable	1
Roller bandage, 4 in	4
Adhesive tape, 1-in standard roll	2
Bandage scissors	1
Protective latex gloves or equivalent nonpermeable gloves	1 Pair

(iv) Protective latex gloves or equivalent nonpermeable gloves may be placed in the first aid kit or in a location that is readily accessible to crewmembers.

(2) A crash axe carried so as to be accessible to the crew but inaccessible to passengers during normal operations.

(3) Signs that are visible to all occupants to notify them when smoking is prohibited and when safety belts should be fastened. The signs must be so constructed that they can be turned on and off by a crewmember. They must be turned on for each takeoff and each landing and when otherwise considered to be necessary by the pilot in command.

(4) The additional emergency equipment specified in appendix A of this part.

(b) Megaphones. Each passenger-carrying airplane must have a portable battery-powered megaphone or megaphones readily accessible to the crewmembers assigned to direct emergency evacuation, installed as follows:

(1) One megaphone on each airplane with a seating capacity of more than 60 and less than 100 passengers, at the most rearward location in the passenger cabin where it would be readily accessible to a normal flight attendant seat. However, the Administrator may grant a deviation from the requirements of this paragraph if the Administrator finds that a different location would be more useful for evacuation of persons during an emergency.

(2) Two megaphones in the passenger cabin on each airplane with a seating capacity of more than 99 and less than 200 passengers, one installed at the forward end and the other at the most rearward location where it would be readily accessible to a normal flight attendant seat.

(3) Three megaphones in the passenger cabin on each airplane with a seating capacity of more than 199 passengers, one installed at the forward end, one installed at the most rearward location where it would be readily accessible to a normal flight attendant seat, and one installed in a readily accessible location in the mid-section of the airplane.

[Doc. No. 19779, 45 FR 67235, Oct. 9, 1980, as amended by Amdt. 125–19, 59 FR 1781, Jan. 12, 1994; Amdt. 125–22, 59 FR 52643, Oct. 18, 1994; 59 FR 55208, Nov. 4, 1994]

125.209   Emergency equipment: extended overwater operations

(a) No person may operate an airplane in extended overwater operations unless it carries, installed in conspicuously marked locations easily accessible to the occupants if a ditching occurs, the following equipment:

(1) An approved life preserver equipped with an approved survivor locator light, or an approved flotation means, for each occupant of the aircraft. The life preserver or other flotation means must be easily accessible to each seated occupant. If a flotation means other than a life preserver is used, it must be readily removable from the airplane.

(2) Enough approved life rafts (with proper buoyancy) to carry all occupants of the airplane, and at least the following equipment for each raft clearly marked for easy identification—

   (i)   One canopy (for sail, sunshade, or rain catcher);

   (ii)   One radar reflector (or similar device);

   (iii)   One life raft repair kit;

   (iv)   One bailing bucket;

   (v)   One signaling mirror;

   (vi)   One police whistle;

   (vii)   One raft knife;

   (viii) One CO_2 bottle for emergency inflation;

   (ix)   One inflation pump;

   (x)   Two oars;

   (xi)   One 75-foot retaining line;

   (xii)   One magnetic compass;

   (xiii) One dye marker;

   (xiv)   One flashlight having at least two size "D" cells or equivalent;

   (xv)   At least one approved pyrotechnic signaling device;

   (xvi)   A 2-day supply of emergency food rations supplying at least 1,000 calories a day for each person;

   (xvii) One sea water desalting kit for each two persons that raft is rated to carry, or two pints of water for each person the raft is rated to carry;

   (xviii) One fishing kit; and

   (xix)   One book on survival appropriate for the area in which the airplane is operated.

(b) No person may operate an airplane in extended overwater operations unless there is attached to one of the life rafts required by paragraph (a) of this section, an approved survival type emergency locator transmitter. Batteries used in this transmitter must be replaced (or recharged, if the batteries are rechargeable) when the transmitter has been in use for more than one cumulative hour, or, when 50 percent of their useful life (or for rechargeable batteries, 50 percent of their useful life of charge) has expired, as established by the transmitter manufacturer under its approval. The new expiration date for replacing (or recharging) the battery must be legibly marked on the outside of the transmitter. The battery useful life (or useful life of charge) requirements of this paragraph do not apply to batteries (such as water-activated batteries) that are essentially unaffected during probable storage intervals.

[Doc. No. 19779, 45 FR 67235, Oct. 9, 1980, as amended by Amdt. 125–20, 59 FR 32058, June 21, 1994]

125.211   Seat and safety belts

(a) No person may operate an airplane unless there are available during the takeoff, en route flight, and landing—

(1) An approved seat or berth for each person on board the airplane who is at least 2 years old; and

(2) An approved safety belt for separate use by each person on board the airplane who is at least 2 years old, except that two persons occupying a berth may share one approved safety belt and two persons occupying a multiple lounge or divan seat may share one approved safety belt during en route flight only.

(b) Except as provided in paragraphs (b)(1) and (b)(2) of this section, each person on board an airplane operated under this part shall occupy an approved seat or berth with a separate safety belt properly secured about him or her during movement on the surface, takeoff, and landing. A safety belt provided for the occupant of a seat may not be used for more than one person who has reached his or her second birthday. Notwithstanding the preceding requirements, a child may:

(1) Be held by an adult who is occupying an approved seat or berth, provided the child has not reached his or her second birthday and the child does not occupy or use any restraining device; or

(2) Notwithstanding any other requirement of this chapter, occupy an approved child restraint system furnished by the certificate holder or one of the persons described in paragraph (b)(2)(i) of this section, provided:

   (i) The child is accompanied by a parent, guardian, or attendant designated by the child's parent or guardian to attend to the safety of the child during the flight;

   (ii) Except as provided in paragraph (b)(2)(ii)(D) of this section, the approved child restraint system bears one or more labels as follows:

   (A) Seats manufactured to U.S. standards between January 1, 1981, and February 25, 1985, must bear the label: "This child restraint system conforms to all applicable Federal motor vehicle safety standards";

   (B) Seats manufactured to U.S. standards on or after February 26, 1985, must bear two labels:

      (1) "This child restraint system conforms to all applicable Federal motor vehicle safety standards"; and

      (2) "THIS RESTRAINT IS CERTIFIED FOR USE IN MOTOR VEHICLES AND AIRCRAFT" in red lettering;

   (C) Seats that do not qualify under paragraphs (b)(2)(ii)(A) and (b)(2)(ii)(B) of this section must bear a label or markings showing:

      (1) That the seat was approved by a foreign government;

      (2) That the seat was manufactured under the standards of the United Nations;

      (3) That the seat or child restraint device furnished by the certificate holder was approved by the FAA through Type Certificate or Supplemental Type Certificate; or

      (4) That the seat or child restraint device furnished by the certificate holder, or one of the persons described in paragraph (b)(2)(i) of this section, was approved by the FAA in accordance with 21.8(d) of this chapter or Technical Standard Order C-100b, or a later version. The child restraint device manufactured by AmSafe, Inc. (CARES, Part No. 4082) and approved by the FAA in accordance with 21.305(d) (2010 ed.) of this chapter may continue to bear a label or markings showing FAA approval in accordance with 21.305(d) (2010 ed.) of this chapter.

FAR 125

(D) Except as provided in 125.211(b)(2)(ii)(C)(3) and 125.211(b)(2)(ii)(C)(4), booster-type child restraint systems (as defined in Federal Motor Vehicle Safety Standard No. 213 (49 CFR 571.213)), vest- and harness-type child restraint systems, and lap held child restraints are not approved for use in aircraft; and

(iii) The certificate holder complies with the following requirements:

(A) The restraint system must be properly secured to an approved forward-facing seat or berth;

(B) The child must be properly secured in the restraint system and must not exceed the specified weight limit for the restraint system; and

(C) The restraint system must bear the appropriate label(s).

(c) Except as provided in paragraph (c)(3) of this section, the following prohibitions apply to certificate holders:

(1) Except as provided in 125.211(b)(2)(ii)(C)(3) and 125.211(b)(2)(ii)(C(4), no certificate holder may permit a child, in an aircraft, to occupy a booster-type child restraint system, a vest-type child restraint system, a harness-type child restraint system, or a lap held child restraint system during take off, landing, and movement on the surface.

(2) Except as required in paragraph (c)(1) of this section, no certificate holder may prohibit a child, if requested by the child's parent, guardian, or designated attendant, from occupying a child restraint system furnished by the child's parent, guardian, or designated attendant provided:

(i) The child holds a ticket for an approved seat or berth or such seat or berth is otherwise made available by the certificate holder for the child's use;

(ii) The requirements of paragraph (b)(2)(i) of this section are met;

(iii) The requirements of paragraph (b)(2)(iii) of this section are met; and

(iv) The child restraint system has one or more of the labels described in paragraphs (b)(2)(ii)(A) through (b)(2)(ii)(C) of this section.

(3) This section does not prohibit the certificate holder from providing child restraint systems authorized by this section or, consistent with safe operating practices, determining the most appropriate passenger seat location for the child restraint system.

(d) Each sideward facing seat must comply with the applicable requirements of 25.785(c) of this chapter.

(e) No certificate holder may take off or land an airplane unless each passenger seat back is in the upright position. Each passenger shall comply with instructions given by a crewmember in compliance with this paragraph. This paragraph does not apply to seats on which cargo or persons who are unable to sit erect for a medical reason are carried in accordance with procedures in the certificate holder's manual if the seat back does not obstruct any passenger's access to the aisle or to any emergency exit.

(f) Each occupant of a seat equipped with a shoulder harness must fasten the shoulder harness during takeoff and landing, except that, in the case of crewmembers, the shoulder harness need not be fastened if the crewmember cannot perform his required duties with the shoulder harness fastened.

[Doc. No. 19799, 45 FR 67235, Oct. 9, 1980, as amended by Amdt. 125-17, 57 FR 42674, Sept. 15, 1992; Amdt. 125-26, 61 FR 28422, June 4, 1996; Amdt. 125-48, 70 FR 50907, Aug. 26, 2005; Amdt. 125-51, 71 FR 40009, July 14, 2006; 71 FR 59373, Oct. 10, 2006; Amdt. 125-64, 79 FR 28812, May 20, 2014]

125.213   Miscellaneous equipment

No person may conduct any operation unless the following equipment is installed in the airplane:

(a) If protective fuses are installed on an airplane, the number of spare fuses approved for the airplane and appropriately described in the certificate holder's manual.

(b) A windshield wiper or equivalent for each pilot station.

(c) A power supply and distribution system that meets the requirements of 25.1309, 25.1331, 25.1351 (a) and (b) (1) through (4), 25.1353, 25.1355, and 25.1431(b) or that is able to produce and distribute the load for the required instruments and equipment, with use of an external power supply if any one power source or component of the power distribution system fails. The use of common elements in the system may be approved if the Administrator finds that they are designed to be reasonably protected against malfunctioning. Engine-driven sources of energy, when used, must be on separate engines.

(d) A means for indicating the adequacy of the power being supplied to required flight instruments.

(e) Two independent static pressure systems, vented to the outside atmospheric pressure so that they will be least affected by air flow variation or moisture or other foreign matter, and installed so as to be airtight except for the vent. When a means is provided for transferring an instrument from its primary operating system to an alternative system, the means must include a positive positioning control and must be marked to indicate clearly which system is being used.

(f) A placard on each door that is the means of access to a required passenger emergency exit to indicate that it must be open during takeoff and landing.

(g) A means for the crew, in an emergency, to unlock each door that leads to a compartment that is normally accessible to passengers and that can be locked by passengers.

125.215   Operating information required

(a) The operator of an airplane must provide the following materials, in current and appropriate form, accessible to the pilot at the pilot station, and the pilot shall use them:

(1) A cockpit checklist.

(2) An emergency cockpit checklist containing the procedures required by paragraph (c) of this section, as appropriate.

(3) Pertinent aeronautical charts.

(4) For IFR operations, each pertinent navigational en route, terminal area, and approach and letdown chart;

(5) One-engine-inoperative climb performance data and, if the airplane is approved for use in IFR or over-the-top operations, that data must be sufficient to enable the pilot to determine that the airplane is capable of carrying passengers over-the-top or in IFR conditions at a weight that will allow it to climb, with the critical engine inoperative, at least 50 feet a minute when operating at the MEA's of the route to be flown or 5,000 feet MSL, whichever is higher.

(b) Each cockpit checklist required by paragraph (a)(1) of this section must contain the following procedures:

(1) Before starting engines;

(2) Before take-off;

(3) Cruise;

(4) Before landing;

(5) After landing;

(6) Stopping engines.

(c) Each emergency cockpit checklist required by paragraph (a)(2) of this section must contain the following procedures, as appropriate:

(1) Emergency operation of fuel, hydraulic, electrical, and mechanical systems.

(2) Emergency operation of instruments and controls.

(3) Engine inoperative procedures.

(4) Any other emergency procedures necessary for safety.

125.217 Passenger information

(a) Except as provided in paragraph (b) of this section, no person may operate an airplane carrying passengers unless it is equipped with signs that meet the requirements of 25.791 of this chapter and that are visible to passengers and flight attendants to notify them when smoking is prohibited and when safety belts must be fastened. The signs must be so constructed that the crew can turn them on and off. They must be turned on during airplane movement on the surface, for each takeoff, for each landing, and when otherwise considered to be necessary by the pilot in command.

(b) No passenger or crewmember may smoke while any "No Smoking" sign is lighted nor may any passenger or crewmember smoke in any lavatory.

(c) Each passenger required by 125.211(b) to occupy a seat or berth shall fasten his or her safety belt about him or her and keep it fastened while any "Fasten Seat Belt" sign is lighted.

(d) Each passenger shall comply with instructions given him or her by crewmembers regarding compliance with paragraphs (b) and (c) of this section.

[Doc. No. 26142, 57 FR 42675, Sept. 15, 1992]

125.219 Oxygen and portable oxygen concentrators for medical use by passengers

(a) Except as provided in paragraphs (d) and (f) of this section, no certificate holder may allow the carriage or operation of equipment for the storage, generation or dispensing of medical oxygen unless the conditions in paragraphs (a) through (c) of this section are satisfied. Beginning August 22, 2016, a certificate holder may allow a passenger to carry and operate a portable oxygen concentrator when the conditions in paragraphs (b) and (f) of this section are satisfied.

(1) The equipment must be—

(i) Of an approved type or in conformity with the manufacturing, packaging, marking, labeling, and maintenance requirements of title 49 CFR parts 171, 172, and 173, except 173.24(a)(1);

(ii) When owned by the certificate holder, maintained under the certificate holder's approved maintenance program;

(iii) Free of flammable contaminants on all exterior surfaces;

(iv) Constructed so that all valves, fittings, and gauges are protected from damage during that carriage or operation; and

(v) Appropriately secured.

(2) When the oxygen is stored in the form of a liquid, the equipment must have been under the certificate holder's approved maintenance program since its purchase new or since the storage container was last purged.

(3) When the oxygen is stored in the form of a compressed gas as defined in title 49 CFR 173.115(b)—

(i) When owned by the certificate holder, it must be maintained under its approved maintenance program; and

(ii) The pressure in any oxygen cylinder must not exceed the rated cylinder pressure.

(4) The pilot in command must be advised when the equipment is on board and when it is intended to be used.

(5) The equipment must be stowed, and each person using the equipment must be seated so as not to restrict access to or use of any required emergency or regular exit or of the aisle in the passenger compartment.

(b) No person may smoke or create an open flame and no certificate holder may allow any person to smoke or create an open flame within 10 feet of oxygen storage and dispensing equipment carried under paragraph (a) of this section or a portable oxygen concentrator carried and operated under paragraph (f) of this section.

(c) No certificate holder may allow any person other than a person trained in the use of medical oxygen equipment to connect or disconnect oxygen bottles or any other ancillary component while any passenger is aboard the airplane.

(d) Paragraph (a)(1)(i) of this section does not apply when that equipment is furnished by a professional or medical emergency service for use on board an airplane in a medical emergency when no other practical means of transportation (including any other properly equipped certificate holder) is reasonably available and the person carried under the medical emergency is accompanied by a person trained in the use of medical oxygen.

(e) Each certificate holder who, under the authority of paragraph (d) of this section, deviates from paragraph (a)(1)(i) of this section under a medical emergency shall, within 10 days, excluding Saturdays, Sundays, and Federal holidays, after the deviation, send to the responsible Flight Standards office charged with the overall inspection of the certificate holder a complete report of the operation involved, including a description of the deviation and the reasons for it.

(f) Portable oxygen concentrators—

(1) Acceptance criteria. A passenger may carry or operate a portable oxygen concentrator for personal use on board an aircraft and a certificate holder may allow a passenger to carry or operate a portable oxygen concentrator on board an aircraft operated under this part during all phases of flight if the portable oxygen concentrator satisfies all of the requirements in this paragraph (f):

(i) Is legally marketed in the United States in accordance with Food and Drug Administration requirements in title 21 of the CFR;

(ii) Does not radiate radio frequency emissions that interfere with aircraft systems;

(iii) Generates a maximum oxygen pressure of less than 200 kPa gauge (29.0 psig/43.8 psia) at 20 °C (68 °F);

(iv) Does not contain any hazardous materials subject to the Hazardous Materials Regulations (49 CFR parts 171 through 180) except as provided in 49 CFR 175.10 for batteries used to power portable electronic devices and that do not require aircraft operator approval; and

(v) Bears a label on the exterior of the device applied in a manner that ensures the label will remain affixed for the life of the device and containing the following certification statement in red lettering: "The manufacturer of this POC has determined this device conforms to all applicable FAA acceptance criteria for POC carriage and use on board aircraft." The label requirements in this paragraph (f)(1)(v) do not apply to the following portable oxygen concentrators approved by the FAA for use on board aircraft prior to May 24, 2016:

(A) AirSep Focus;

(B) AirSep FreeStyle;

(C) AirSep FreeStyle 5;

(D) AirSep LifeStyle;

(E) Delphi RS-00400;

(F) DeVilbiss Healthcare iGo;

(G) Inogen One;

(H) Inogen One G2;

(I) Inogen One G3;

(J) Inova Labs LifeChoice;

(K) Inova Labs LifeChoice Activox;

(L) International Biophysics LifeChoice;

(M) Invacare Solo2;

(N) Invacare XPO2;

(O) Oxlife Independence Oxygen Concentrator;

(P) Oxus RS-00400;

(Q) Precision Medical EasyPulse;

(R) Respironics EverGo;

(S) Respironics SimplyGo;

(T) SeQual Eclipse;

(U) SeQual eQuinox Oxygen System (model 4000);

(V) SeQual Oxywell Oxygen System (model 4000);

(W) SeQual SAROS; and

(X) VBox Trooper Oxygen Concentrator.

(2) *Operating requirements.* Portable oxygen concentrators that satisfy the acceptance criteria identified in paragraph (f)(1) of this section may be carried or used by a passenger on an aircraft provided the aircraft operator ensures that all of the conditions in this paragraph (f)(2) are satisfied:

    (i) *Exit seats.* No person operating a portable oxygen concentrator is permitted to occupy an exit seat.

    (ii) *Stowage of device.* During movement on the surface, takeoff and landing, the device must be stowed under the seat in front of the user, or in another approved stowage location so that it does not block the aisle way or the entryway to the row. If the device is to be operated by the user, it must be operated only at a seat location that does not restrict any passenger's access to, or use of, any required emergency or regular exit, or the aisle(s) in the passenger compartment.

[Docket No. 19779, 45 FR 67235, Oct. 9, 1980, as amended by Docket FAA-2014-0554, Amdt. 125-65, 81 FR 33119, May 24, 2016; Docket FAA-2018-0119, Amdt. 125-68, 83 FR 9173, Mar. 5, 2018]

125.221   Icing conditions: operating limitations

(a) No pilot may take off an airplane that has frost, ice, or snow adhering to any propeller, windshield, stabilizing or control surface; to a powerplant installation; or to an airspeed, altimeter, rate of climb, flight attitude instrument system, or wing, except that takeoffs may be made with frost under the wing in the area of the fuel tanks if authorized by the FAA.

(b) No certificate holder may authorize an airplane to take off and no pilot may take off an airplane any time conditions are such that frost, ice, or snow may reasonably be expected to adhere to the airplane unless the pilot has completed the testing required under 125.287(a)(9) and unless one of the following requirements is met:

(1) A pretakeoff contamination check, that has been established by the certificate holder and approved by the Administrator for the specific airplane type, has been completed within 5 minutes prior to beginning takeoff. A pretakeoff contamination check is a check to make sure the wings and control surfaces are free of frost, ice, or snow.

(2) The certificate holder has an approved alternative procedure and under that procedure the airplane is determined to be free of frost, ice, or snow.

(3) The certificate holder has an approved deicing/anti-icing program that complies with 121.629(c) of this chapter and the takeoff complies with that program.

(c) No pilot may fly under IFR into known or forecast light or moderate icing conditions, or under VFR into known light or moderate icing conditions, unless—

(1) The aircraft has functioning deicing or anti-icing equipment protecting each propeller, windshield, wing, stabilizing or control surface, and each airspeed, altimeter, rate of climb, or flight attitude instrument system;

(2) The airplane has ice protection provisions that meet appendix G of this part; or

(3) The airplane meets transport category airplane type certification provisions, including the requirements for certification for flight in icing conditions.

(d) Except for an airplane that has ice protection provisions that meet appendix C of this part or those for transport category airplane type certification, no pilot may fly an airplane into known or forecast severe icing conditions.

(e) If current weather reports and briefing information relied upon by the pilot in command indicate that the forecast icing condition that would otherwise prohibit the flight will not be encountered during the flight because of changed weather conditions since the forecast, the restrictions in paragraphs (b) and (c) of this section based on forecast conditions do not apply.

[45 FR 67235, Oct. 9, 1980, as amended by Amdt. 125–18, 58 FR 69629, Dec. 30, 1993; Amdt. 125-58, 74 FR 62696, Dec. 1 2009]

125.223   Airborne weather radar equipment requirements

(a) No person may operate an airplane governed by this part in passenger-carrying operations unless approved airborne weather radar equipment is installed in the airplane.

(b) No person may begin a flight under IFR or night VFR conditions when current weather reports indicate that thunderstorms, or other potentially hazardous weather conditions that can be detected with airborne weather radar equipment, may reasonably be expected along the route to be flown, unless the airborne weather radar equipment required by paragraph (a) of this section is in satisfactory operating condition.

(c) If the airborne weather radar equipment becomes inoperative en route, the airplane must be operated under the instructions and procedures specified for that event in the manual required by 125.71.

(d) This section does not apply to airplanes used solely within the State of Hawaii, within the State of Alaska, within that part of Canada west of longitude 130 degrees W, between latitude 70 degrees N, and latitude 53 degrees N, or during any training, test, or ferry flight.

(e) Without regard to any other provision of this part, an alternate electrical power supply is not required for airborne weather radar equipment.

125.224   Collision avoidance system

Effective January 1, 2005, any airplane you operate under this part 125 must be equipped and operated according to the following table:

COLLISION AVOIDANCE SYSTEMS	
IF YOU OPERATE ANY	THEN YOU MUST OPERATE THAT AIRPLANE WITH:
(a) Turbine-powered airplane of more than 33,000 pounds maximum certificated takeoff weight	(1) An appropriate class of Mode S transponder that meets Technical Standard Order (TSO) C–112, or a later version, and one of the following approved units:
	(i) TCAS II that meets TSO C–119b (version 7.0), or a later version.
	(ii) TCAS II that meets TSO C–119a (version 6.04A Enhanced) that was installed in that airplane before May 1, 2003. If that TCAS II version 6.04A Enhanced no longer can be repaired to TSO C–119a standards, it must be replaced with a TCAS II that meets TSO C–119b (version 7.0), or a later version.
	(iii) A collision avoidance system equivalent to TSO C–119b (version 7.0), or a later version, capable of coordinating with units that meet TSO C–119a (version 6.04A Enhanced), or a later version.
(b) Piston-powered airplane of more than 33,000 pounds maximum certificated takeoff weight	(1) TCAS I that meets TSO C–118, or a later version, or (2) A collision avoidance system equivalent to TSO C–118, or a later version, or (1)(3) A collision avoidance system and Mode S transponder that meet paragraph (a)(1) of this section.

[Doc. No. FAA–2001–10910, 68 FR 15903, Apr. 1, 2003]

125.225 Flight data recorders

(a) Except as provided in paragraph (d) of this section, after October 11, 1991, no person may operate a large airplane type certificated before October 1, 1969, for operations above 25,000 feet altitude, nor a multiengine, turbine powered airplane type certificated before October 1, 1969, unless it is equipped with one or more approved flight recorders that utilize a digital method of recording and storing data and a method of readily retrieving that data from the storage medium. The following information must be able to be determined within the ranges, accuracies, resolution, and recording intervals specified in appendix D of this part:

(1) Time;

(2) Altitude;

(3) Airspeed;

(4) Vertical acceleration;

(5) Heading;

(6) Time of each radio transmission to or from air traffic control;

(7) Pitch attitude;

(8) Roll attitude;

(9) Longitudinal acceleration;

(10) Control column or pitch control surface position; and

(11) Thrust of each engine.

(b) Except as provided in paragraph (d) of this section, after October 11, 1991, no person may operate a large airplane type certificated after September 30, 1969, for operations above 25,000 feet altitude, nor a multiengine, turbine powered airplane type certificated after September 30, 1969, unless it is equipped with one or more approved flight recorders that utilize a digital method of recording and storing data and a method of readily retrieving that data from the storage medium. The following information must be able to be determined within the ranges, accuracies, resolutions, and recording intervals specified in appendix D of this part:

(1) Time;

(2) Altitude;

(3) Airspeed;

(4) Vertical acceleration;

(5) Heading;

(6) Time of each radio transmission either to or from air traffic control;

(7) Pitch attitude;

(8) Roll attitude;

(9) Longitudinal acceleration;

(10) Pitch trim position;

(11) Control column or pitch control surface position;

(12) Control wheel or lateral control surface position;

(13) Rudder pedal or yaw control surface position;

(14) Thrust of each engine;

(15) Position of each trust reverser;

(16) Trailing edge flap or cockpit flap control position; and

(17) Leading edge flap or cockpit flap control position.

(c) After October 11, 1991, no person may operate a large airplane equipped with a digital data bus and ARINC 717 digital flight data acquisition unit (DFDAU) or equivalent unless it is equipped with one or more approved flight recorders that utilize a digital method of recording and storing data and a method of readily retrieving that data from the storage medium. Any parameters specified in appendix D of this part that are available on the digital data bus must be recorded within the ranges, accuracies, resolutions, and sampling intervals specified.

(d) No person may operate under this part an airplane that is manufactured after October 11, 1991, unless it is equipped with one or more approved flight recorders that utilize a digital method of recording and storing data and a method of readily retrieving that data from the storage medium. The parameters specified in appendix D of this part must be recorded within the ranges, accuracies, resolutions and sampling intervals specified. For the purpose of this section, "manufactured" means the point in time at which the airplane inspection acceptance records reflect that the airplane is complete and meets the FAA-approved type design data.

(e) Whenever a flight recorder required by this section is installed, it must be operated continuously from the instant the airplane begins the takeoff roll until it has completed the landing roll at an airport.

(f) Except as provided in paragraph (g) of this section, and except for recorded data erased as authorized in this paragraph, each certificate holder shall keep the recorded data prescribed in paragraph (a), (b), (c), or (d) of this section, as applicable, until the airplane has been operated for at least 25 hours of the operating time specified in 125.227(a) of this chapter. A total of 1 hour of recorded data may be erased for the purpose of testing the flight recorder or the flight recorder system. Any erasure made in accordance with this paragraph must be of the oldest recorded data accumulated at the time of testing. Except as provided in paragraph (g) of this section, no record need be kept more than 60 days.

(g) In the event of an accident or occurrence that requires immediate notification of the National Transportation Safety Board under 49 CFR part 830 and that results in termination of the flight, the certificate holder shall remove the recording media from the airplane and keep the recorded data required by paragraph (a), (b), (c), or (d) of this section, as applicable, for at least 60 days or for a longer period upon the request of the Board or the Administrator.

(h) Each flight recorder required by this section must be installed in accordance with the requirements of 25.1459 of this chapter in effect on August 31, 1977. The correlation required by 25.1459(c) of this chapter need be established only on one airplane of any group of airplanes.

(1) That are of the same type;

(2) On which the flight recorder models and their installations are the same; and

(3) On which there are no differences in the type design with respect to the installation of the first pilot's instruments associated with the flight recorder. The most recent instrument calibration, including the recording medium from which this calibration is derived, and the recorder correlation must be retained by the certificate holder.

(i) Each flight recorder required by this section that records the data specified in paragraphs (a), (b), (c), or (d) of this section must have an approved device to assist in locating that recorder under water.

(j) After August 20, 2001, this section applies only to the airplane models listed in 125.226(l)(2). All other airplanes must comply with the requirements of 125.226.

[Doc. No. 25530, 53 FR 26148, July 11, 1988; 53 FR 30906, Aug. 16, 1988; Amdt. 125–54, 73 FR 12568, Mar. 7, 2008]

125.226 Digital flight data recorders

(a) Except as provided in paragraph (l) of this section, no person may operate under this part a turbine-engine-powered transport category airplane unless it is equipped with one or more approved flight recorders that use a digital method of recording and storing data and a method of readily retrieving that data from the storage medium. The operational parameters required to be recorded by digital flight data recorders required by this section are as follows: the phrase "when an information source is installed" following a parameter indicates that recording of that parameter is not intended to require a change in installed equipment:

(1) Time;

(2) Pressure altitude;

(3) Indicated airspeed;

(4) Heading—primary flight crew reference (if selectable, record discrete, true or magnetic);

FAR 125

(5) Normal acceleration (Vertical);

(6) Pitch attitude;

(7) Roll attitude;

(8) Manual radio transmitter keying, or CVR/DFDR synchronization reference;

(9) Thrust/power of each engine—primary flight crew reference;

(10) Autopilot engagement status;

(11) Longitudinal acceleration;

(12) Pitch control input;

(13) Lateral control input;

(14) Rudder pedal input;

(15) Primary pitch control surface position;

(16) Primary lateral control surface position;

(17) Primary yaw control surface position;

(18) Lateral acceleration;

(19) Pitch trim surface position or parameters of paragraph (a)(82) of this section if currently recorded;

(20) Trailing edge flap or cockpit flap control selection (except when parameters of paragraph (a)(85) of this section apply);

(21) Leading edge flap or cockpit flap control selection (except when parameters of paragraph (a)(86) of this section apply);

(22) Each Thrust reverser position (or equivalent for propeller airplane);

(23) Ground spoiler position or speed brake selection (except when parameters of paragraph (a)(87) of this section apply);

(24) Outside or total air temperature;

(25) Automatic Flight Control System (AFCS) modes and engagement status, including autothrottle;

(26) Radio altitude (when an information source is installed);

(27) Localizer deviation, MLS Azimuth;

(28) Glideslope deviation, MLS Elevation;

(29) Marker beacon passage;

(30) Master warning;

(31) Air/ground sensor (primary airplane system reference nose or main gear);

(32) Angle of attack (when information source is installed);

(33) Hydraulic pressure low (each system);

(34) Ground speed (when an information source is installed);

(35) Ground proximity warning system;

(36) Landing gear position or landing gear cockpit control selection;

(37) Drift angle (when an information source is installed);

(38) Wind speed and direction (when an information source is installed);

(39) Latitude and longitude (when an information source is installed);

(40) Stick shaker/pusher (when an information source is installed);

(41) Windshear (when an information source is installed);

(42) Throttle/power lever position;

(43) Additional engine parameters (as designed in appendix E of this part);

(44) Traffic alert and collision avoidance system;

(45) DME 1 and 2 distances;

(46) Nav 1 and 2 selected frequency;

(47) Selected barometric setting (when an information source is installed);

(48) Selected altitude (when an information source is installed);

(49) Selected speed (when an information source is installed);

(50) Selected mach (when an information source is installed);

(51) Selected vertical speed (when an information source is installed);

(52) Selected heading (when an information source is installed);

(53) Selected flight path (when an information source is installed);

(54) Selected decision height (when an information source is installed);

(55) EFIS display format;

(56) Multi-function/engine/alerts display format;

(57) Thrust command (when an information source is installed);

(58) Thrust target (when an information source is installed);

(59) Fuel quantity in CG trim tank (when an information source is installed);

(60) Primary Navigation System Reference;

(61) Icing (when an information source is installed);

(62) Engine warning each engine vibration (when an information source is installed);

(63) Engine warning each engine over temp. (when an information source is installed);

(64) Engine warning each engine oil pressure low (when an information source is installed);

(65) Engine warning each engine over speed (when an information source is installed);

(66) Yaw trim surface position;

(67) Roll trim surface position;

(68) Brake pressure (selected system);

(69) Brake pedal application (left and right);

(70) Yaw of sideslip angle (when an information source is installed);

(71) Engine bleed valve position (when an information source is installed);

(72) De-icing or anti-icing system selection (when an information source is installed);

(73) Computed center of gravity (when an information source is installed);

(74) AC electrical bus status;

(75) DC electrical bus status;

(76) APU bleed valve position (when an information source is installed);

(77) Hydraulic pressure (each system);

(78) Loss of cabin pressure;

(79) Computer failure;

(80) Heads-up display (when an information source is installed);

(81) Para-visual display (when an information source is installed);

(82) Cockpit trim control input position-pitch;

(83) Cockpit trim control input position—roll;

(84) Cockpit trim control input position—yaw;

(85) Trailing edge flap and cockpit flap control position;

(86) Leading edge flap and cockpit flap control position;

(87) Ground spoiler position and speed brake selection; and

(88) All cockpit flight control input forces (control wheel, control column, rudder pedal).

(b) For all turbine-engine powered transport category airplanes manufactured on or before October 11, 1991, by August 20, 2001—

(1) For airplanes not equipped as of July 16, 1996, with a flight data acquisition unit (FDAU), the parameters listed in para-

graphs (a)(1) through (a)(18) of this section must be recorded within the ranges and accuracies specified in Appendix D of this part, and—

    (i) For airplanes with more than two engines, the parameter described in paragraph (a)(18) is not required unless sufficient capacity is available on the existing recorder to record that parameter.

    (ii) Parameters listed in paragraphs (a)(12) through (a)(17) each may be recorded from a single source.

(2) For airplanes that were equipped as of July 16, 1996, with a flight data acquisition unit (FDAU), the parameters listed in paragraphs (a)(1) through (a)(22) of this section must be recorded within the ranges, accuracies, and recording intervals specified in Appendix E of this part. Parameters listed in paragraphs (a)(12) through (a)(17) each may be recorded from a single source.

(3) The approved flight recorder required by this section must be installed at the earliest time practicable, but no later than the next heavy maintenance check after August 18, 1999 and no later than August 20, 2001. A heavy maintenance check is considered to be any time an airplane is scheduled to be out of service for 4 or more days and is scheduled to include access to major structural components.

(c) For all turbine-engine-powered transport category airplanes manufactured on or before October 11, 1991—

(1) That were equipped as of July 16, 1996, with one or more digital data bus(es) and an ARINC 717 digital flight data acquisition unit (DFDAU) or equivalent, the parameters specified in paragraphs (a)(1) through (a)(22) of this section must be recorded within the ranges, accuracies, resolutions, and sampling intervals specified in Appendix E of this part by August 20, 2001. Parameters listed in paragraphs (a)(12) through (a)(14) each may be recorded from a single source.

(2) Commensurate with the capacity of the recording system (DFDAU or equivalent and the DFDR), all additional parameters for which information sources are installed and which are connected to the recording system must be recorded within the ranges, accuracies, resolutions, and sampling intervals specified in Appendix E of this part by August 20, 2001.

(3) That were subject to 125.225(e) of this part, all conditions of 125.225(c) must continue to be met until compliance with paragraph (c)(1) of this section is accomplished.

(d) For all turbine-engine-powered transport category airplanes that were manufactured after October 11, 1991—

(1) The parameters listed in paragraphs (a)(1) through (a)(34) of this section must be recorded within the ranges, accuracies, resolutions, and recording intervals specified in Appendix E of this part by August 20, 2001. Paramaters listed in paragraphs (a)(12) through (a)(14) each may be recorded from a single source.

(2) Commensurate with the capacity of the recording system, all additional parameters for which information sources are installed and which are connected to the recording system, must be recorded within the ranges, accuracies, resolutions, and sampling intervals specified in Appendix E of this part by August 20, 2001.

(e) For all turbine-engine-powered transport category airplanes that are manufactured after August 18, 2000—

(1) The parameters listed in paragraph (a) (1) through (57) of this section must be recorded within the ranges, accuracies, resolutions, and recording intervals specified in Appendix E of this part.

(2) Commensurate with the capacity of the recording system, all additional parameters for which information sources are installed and which are connected to the recording system, must be recorded within the ranges, accuracies, resolutions, and sampling intervals specified in Appendix E of this part.

(f) For all turbine-engine-powered transport category airplanes that are manufactured after August 19, 2002—

(1) The parameters listed in paragraphs (a)(1) through (a)(88) of this section must be recorded within the ranges, accuracies, resolutions, and recording intervals specified in Appendix E of this part.

(g) Whenever a flight data recorder required by this section is installed, it must be operated continuously from the instant the airplane begins its takeoff roll until it has completed its landing roll.

(h) Except as provided in paragraph (i) of this section, and except for recorded data erased as authorized in this paragraph, each certificate holder shall keep the recorded data prescribed by this section, as appropriate, until the airplane has been operated for at least 25 hours of the operating time specified in 121.359(a) of this part. A total of 1 hour of recorded data may be erased for the purpose of testing the flight recorder or the flight recorder system. Any erasure made in accordance with this paragraph must be of the oldest recorded data accumulated at the time of testing. Except as provided in paragraph (i) of this section, no record need to be kept more than 60 days.

(i) In the event of an accident or occurrence that requires immediate notification of the National Transportation Safety Board under 49 CFR 830 of its regulations and that results in termination of the flight, the certificate holder shall remove the recorder from the airplane and keep the recorder data prescribed by this section, as appropriate, for at least 60 days or for a longer period upon the request of the Board or the Administrator.

(j) Each flight data recorder system required by this section must be installed in accordance with the requirements of 25.1459 (a) (except paragraphs (a)(3)(ii) and (7)), (b), (d) and (e) of this chapter. A correlation must be established between the values recorded by the flight data recorder and the corresponding values being measured. The correlation must contain a sufficient number of correlation points to accurately establish the conversion from the recorded values to engineering units or discrete state over the full operating range of the parameter. Except for airplanes having separate altitude and airspeed sensors that are an integral part of the flight data recorder system, a single correlation may be established for any group of airplanes—

(1) That are of the same type;

(2) On which the flight recorder system and its installation are the same; and

(3) On which there is no difference in the type design with respect to the installation of those sensors associated with the flight data recorder system. Documentation sufficient to convert recorded data into the engineering units and discrete values specified in the applicable appendix must be maintained by the certificate holder.

(k) Each flight data recorder required by this section must have an approved device to assist in locating that recorder under water.

(l) The following airplanes that were manufactured before August 18, 1997 need not comply with this section, but must continue to comply with applicable paragraphs of 125.225 of this chapter, as appropriate:

(1) Airplanes that meet the Stage 2 noise levels of part 36 of this chapter and are subject to 91.801(c) of this chapter, until January 1, 2000. On and after January 1, 2000, any Stage 2 airplane otherwise allowed to be operated under Part 91 of this chapter must comply with the applicable flight data recorder requirements of this section for that airplane.

(2) British Aerospace 1–11, General Dynamics Convair 580, General Dynamics Convair 600, General Dynamics Convair 640, deHavilland Aircraft Company Ltd. DHC–7, Fairchild Industries FH 227, Fokker F–27 (except Mark 50), F–28 Mark 1000 and Mark 4000, Gulfstream Aerospace G–159, Jetstream 4100 Series, Lockheed Aircraft Corporation Electra 10–A, Lockheed Aircraft Corporation Electra 10–B, Lockheed Aircraft Corporation Electra 10–E, Lockheed Aircraft Corporation Electra L–188, Lockheed Martin Model 382 (L–100) Hercules, Maryland Air Industries, Inc. F27, Mitsubishi Heavy Industries, Ltd. YS–11, Short Bros. Limited SD3–30, Short Bros. Limited SD3–60.

(m) All aircraft subject to the requirements of this section that are manufactured on or after April 7, 2010, must have a flight data recorder installed that also—

   (1) Meets the requirements in 25.1459(a)(3), (a)(7), and (a)(8) of this chapter; and

   (2) Retains the 25 hours of recorded information required in paragraph (f) of this section using a recorder that meets the standards of TSO–C124a, or later revision.

(n) In addition to all other applicable requirements of this section, all Boeing 737 model airplanes manufactured after August 18, 2000 must record the parameters listed in paragraphs (a)(88) through (a)(91) of this section within the ranges, accuracies, resolutions and recording intervals specified in Appendix E to this part. Compliance with this paragraph is required no later than February 2, 2001.

[Doc. No. 28109, 62 FR 38387, July 17, 1997; 62 FR 48135, Sept. 12, 1997, as amended by Amdt. 125–42, 68 FR 42937, July 18, 2003; 68 FR 50069, Aug. 20, 2003; Amdt. 125–54, 73 FR 12568, Mar. 7, 2008; Amdt. 125-54, 74 FR 32801, 32804 July 9, 2009]

125.227   Cockpit voice recorders

(a) No certificate holder may operate a large turbine engine powered airplane or a large pressurized airplane with four reciprocating engines unless an approved cockpit voice recorder is installed in that airplane and is operated continuously from the start of the use of the checklist (before starting engines for the purpose of flight) to completion of the final checklist at the termination of the flight.

(b) Each certificate holder shall establish a schedule for completion, before the prescribed dates, of the cockpit voice recorder installations required by paragraph (a) of this section. In addition, the certificate holder shall identify any airplane specified in paragraph (a) of this section he intends to discontinue using before the prescribed dates.

(c) The cockpit voice recorder required by this section must also meet the following standards:

   (1) The requirements of part 25 of this chapter in effect after October 11, 1991.

   (2) After September 1, 1980, each recorder container must—

      (i) Be either bright orange or bright yellow;

      (ii) Have reflective tape affixed to the external surface to facilitate its location under water; and

      (iii) Have an approved underwater locating device on or adjacent to the container which is secured in such a manner that it is not likely to be separated during crash impact, unless the cockpit voice recorder and the flight recorder, required by 125.225 of this chapter, are installed adjacent to each other in such a manner that they are not likely to be separated during crash impact.

(d) In complying with this section, an approved cockpit voice recorder having an erasure feature may be used so that, at any time during the operation of the recorder, information recorded more than 30 minutes earlier may be erased or otherwise obliterated.

(e) For those aircraft equipped to record the uninterrupted audio signals received by a boom or a mask microphone the flight crewmembers are required to use the boom microphone below 18,000 feet mean sea level. No person may operate a large turbine engine powered airplane or a large pressurized airplane with four reciprocating engines manufactured after October 11, 1991, or on which a cockpit voice recorder has been installed after October 11, 1991, unless it is equipped to record the uninterrupted audio signal received by a boom or mask microphone in accordance with 25.1457(c)(5) of this chapter.

(f) In the event of an accident or occurrence requiring immediate notification of the National Transportation Safety Board under 49 CFR part 830 of its regulations, which results in the termination of the flight, the certificate holder shall keep the recorded information for at least 60 days or, if requested by the Administrator or the Board, for a longer period. Information obtained from the record is used to assist in determining the cause of accidents or occur-

rences in connection with investigations under 49 CFR part 830. The Administrator does not use the record in any civil penalty or certificate action.

(g) By April 7, 2012, all turbine engine-powered airplanes subject to this section that are manufactured before April 7, 2010, must have a cockpit voice recorder installed that also—

   (1) Meets the requirements of 25.1457(a)(3), (a)(4), (a)(5), and (d)(6) of this chapter;

   (2) Retains at least the last 2 hours of recorded information using a recorder that meets the standards of TSO–C123a, or later revision; and

   (3) Is operated continuously from the start of the use of the checklist (before starting the engines for the purpose of flight), to the completion of the final checklist at the termination of the flight.

(h) All turbine engine-powered airplanes subject to this section that are manufactured on or after April 7, 2010, must have a cockpit voice recorder installed that also—

   (1) Is installed in accordance wtih the requirements of 25.1457 (except for paragraph (a)(6)) of this chapter;

   (2) Retains at least the last 2 hours of recorded information using a recorder that meets the standards of TSO–C123a, or later revision; and

   (3) Is operated continuously from the start of the use of the checklist (before starting the engines for the purpose of flight), to the completion of the final checklist at the termination of the flight.

   (4) For all airplanes manufactured on or afer December 6, 2010, also meets the requirements of 25.1457 (a)(6) of this chapter.

(i) All airplanes required by this part to have a cockpit voice recorder and a flight data recorder, that install datalink communication equipment on or after December 6, 2010, must record all datalink messages as required by the certification rule applicable to the airplane.

Doc. No. 25530, 53 FR 26149, July 11, 1988, as amended by Amdt. 125–54, 73 FR 12568, Mar. 7, 2008; Amdt. 125-54, 74 FR 32801, July 9, 2009; Amdt. 125-60, 75 FR 17046, Apr. 5, 2010]

125.228   Flight data recorders: filtered data

(a) A flight data signal is filtered when an original sensor signal has been changed in any way, other than changes necessary to:

   (1) Accomplish analog to digital conversion of the signal;

   (2) Format a digital signal to be DFDR compatible; or

   (3) Eliminate a high frequency component of a signal that is outside the operational bandwidth of the sensor.

(b) An original sensor signal for any flight recorder parameter required to be recorded under 125.226 may be filtered only if the recorded signal value continues to meet the requirements of Appendix D or E of this part, as applicable.

(c) For a parameter described in 125.226(a) (12) through (17), (42), or Appendix D of this part, if the recorded signal value is filtered and does not meet the requirements of Appendix D or E of this part, as applicable, the certificate holder must:

   (1) Remove the filtering and ensure that the recorded signal value meets the requirements of Appendix D or E of this part, as applicable; or

   (2) Demonstrate by test and analysis that the original sensor signal value can be reconstructed from the recorded data. This demonstration requires that:

      (i) The FAA determine that the procedure and the test results submitted by the certificate holder as its compliance with paragraph (c)(2) of this section are repeatable; and

      (ii) The certificate holder maintains documentation of the procedure required to reconstruct the original sensor signal value. This documentation is also subject to the requirements of 125.226(i).

(d) Compliance. Compliance is required as follows:

(1) No later than October 20, 2011, each operator must determine, for each airplane it operates, whether the airplane's DFDR system is filtering any of the parameters listed in paragraph (c) of this section. The operator must create a record of the determination for each airplane it operates, and maintain it as part of the correlation documentation required by 125.226 (j)(3) of this part.

(2) For airplanes that are not filtering any listed parameter, no further action is required unless the airplanes' DFDR system is modified in a manner that would cause it to meet the definition of filtering on any listed parameter.

(3) For airplanes found to be filtering a parameter listed in paragraph (c) of this section, the operator must either:

   (i) No later than April 21, 2014, remove the filtering; or

   (II) No later that April 22, 2013, submit the necessary procedure and test results required by paragraph (c)(2) of this section.

(4) After April 21, 2014, no aircraft flight data recording system may filter any parameter listed in paragraph (c) of this section that does not meet the requirements of Appendix D or E of this part, unless the certificate holder possesses test and analysis procedures and the test results that have been approved by the FAA. All records of tests, analysis and procedures used to comply with this section must be maintained as part of the correlation documentation required by 125.226(j)(3) of this part.

[Doc. No. FAA–2006–26135, 75 FR 7356, Feb. 19, 2010]

Subpart G — Maintenance

125.241   Applicability

This subpart prescribes rules, in addition to those prescribed in other parts of this chapter, for the maintenance of airplanes, airframes, aircraft engines, propellers, appliances, each item of survival and emergency equipment, and their component parts operated under this part.

125.243   Certificate holder's responsibilities

(a) With regard to airplanes, including airframes, aircraft engines, propellers, appliances, and survival and emergency equipment, operated by a certificate holder, that certificate holder is primarily responsible for—

(1) Airworthiness;

(2) The performance of maintenance, preventive maintenance, and alteration in accordance with applicable regulations and the certificate holder's manual;

(3) The scheduling and performance of inspections required by this part; and

(4) Ensuring that maintenance personnel make entries in the airplane maintenance log and maintenance records which meet the requirements of part 43 of this chapter and the certificate holder's manual, and which indicate that the airplane has been approved for return to service after maintenance, preventive maintenance, or alteration has been performed.

125.245   Organization required to perform maintenance, preventive maintenance, and alteration

The certificate holder must ensure that each person with whom it arranges for the performance of maintenance, preventive maintenance, alteration, or required inspection items identified in the certificate holder's manual in accordance with 125.249(a)(3)(ii) must have an organization adequate to perform that work.

125.247   Inspection programs and maintenance

(a) No person may operate an airplane subject to this part unless

(1) The replacement times for life-limited parts specified in the aircraft type certificate data sheets, or other documents approved by the Administrator, are complied with;

(2) Defects disclosed between inspections, or as a result of inspection, have been corrected in accordance with part 43 of this chapter; and

(3) The airplane, including airframe, aircraft engines, propellers, appliances, and survival and emergency equipment, and their component parts, is inspected in accordance with an inspection program approved by the Administrator.

(b) The inspection program specified in paragraph (a)(3) of this section must include at least the following:

(1) Instructions, procedures, and standards for the conduct of inspections for the particular make and model of airplane, including necessary tests and checks. The instructions and procedures must set forth in detail the parts and areas of the airframe, aircraft engines, propellers, appliances, and survival and emergency equipment required to be inspected.

(2) A schedule for the performance of inspections that must be performed under the program, expressed in terms of the time in service, calendar time, number of system operations, or any combination of these.

(c) No person may be used to perform the inspections required by this part unless that person is authorized to perform maintenance under part 43 of this chapter.

(d) No person may operate an airplane subject to this part unless—

(1) The installed engines have been maintained in accordance with the overhaul periods recommended by the manufacturer or a program approved by the Administrator; and

(2) The engine overhaul periods are specified in the inspection programs required by 125.247(a)(3).

(e) Inspection programs which may be approved for use under this part include, but are not limited to—

(1) A continuous inspection program which is a part of a current continuous airworthiness program approved for use by a certificate holder under part 121 or part 135 of this chapter;

(2) Inspection programs currently recommended by the manufacturer of the airplane, aircraft engines, propellers, appliances, or survival and emergency equipment; or

(3) An inspection program developed by a certificate holder under this part.

[Doc. No. 19779, 45 FR 67235, Oct. 9, 1980, as amended by Amdt. 125–2, 46 FR 24409, Apr. 30, 1981]

125.248   [Reserved]

125.249   Maintenance manual requirements

(a) Each certificate holder's manual required by 125.71 of this part shall contain, in addition to the items required by 125.73 of this part, at least the following:

(1) A description of the certificate holders maintenance organization, when the certificate holder has such an organization.

(2) A list of those persons with whom the certificate holder has arranged for performance of inspections under this part. The list shall include the persons' names and addresses.

(3) The inspection programs required by 125.247 of this part to be followed in the performance of inspections under this part including—

   (i) The method of performing routine and nonroutine inspections (other than required inspections);

   (ii) The designation of the items that must be inspected (required inspections), including at least those which if improperly accomplished could result in a failure, malfunction, or defect endangering the safe operation of the airplane;

   (iii) The method of performing required inspections;

   (iv) Procedures for the inspection of work performed under previously required inspection findings ("buy-back procedures");

   (v) Procedures, standards, and limits necessary for required inspections and acceptance or rejection of the items required to be inspected;

FAR 125

(vi) Instructions to prevent any person who performs any item of work from performing any required inspection of that work; and

(vii) Procedures to ensure that work interruptions do not adversely affect required inspections and to ensure required inspections are properly completed before the airplane is released to service.

(b) In addition, each certificate holder's manual shall contain a suitable system which may include a coded system that provides for the retention of the following:

(1) A description (or reference to data acceptable to the Administrator) of the work performed.

(2) The name of the person performing the work and the person's certificate type and number.

(3) The name of the person approving the work and the person's certificate type and number.

125.251   Required inspection personnel

(a) No person may use any person to perform required inspections unless the person performing the inspection is appropriately certificated, properly trained, qualified, and authorized to do so.

(b) No person may perform a required inspection if that person performed the item of work required to be inspected.

Subpart H — Airman and Crewmember Requirements

125.261   Airman: Limitations on use of services

(a) No certificate holder may use any person as an airman nor may any person serve as an airman unless that person—

(1) Holds an appropriate current airman certificate issued by the FAA;

(2) Has any required appropriate current airman and medical certificates in that person's possession while engaged in operations under this part; and

(3) Is otherwise qualified for the operation for which that person is to be used.

(b) Each airman covered by paragraph (a) of this section shall present the certificates for inspection upon the request of the Administrator.

125.263   Composition of flight crew

(a) No certificate holder may operate an airplane with less than the minimum flightcrew specified in the type certificate and the Airplane Flight Manual approved for that type airplane and required by this part for the kind of operation being conducted.

(b) In any case in which this part requires the performance of two or more functions for which an airman certificate is necessary, that requirement is not satisfied by the performance of multiple functions at the same time by one airman.

(c) On each flight requiring a flight engineer, at least one flight crewmember, other than the flight engineer, must be qualified to provide emergency performance of the flight engineer's functions for the safe completion of the flight if the flight engineer becomes ill or is otherwise incapacitated. A pilot need not hold a flight engineer's certificate to perform the flight engineer's functions in such a situation.

125.265   Flight engineer requirements

(a) No person may operate an airplane for which a flight engineer is required by the type certification requirements without a flight crewmember holding a current flight engineer certificate.

(b) No person may serve as a required flight engineer on an airplane unless, within the preceding 6 calendar months, that person has had at least 50 hours of flight time as a flight engineer on that type airplane, or the Administrator has checked that person on that type airplane and determined that person is familiar and competent with all essential current information and operating procedures.

125.267   Flight navigator and long-range navigation equipment

(a) No certificate holder may operate an airplane outside the 48 conterminous States and the District of Columbia when its position cannot be reliably fixed for a period of more than 1 hour, without—

(1) A flight crewmember who holds a current flight navigator certificate; or

(2) Two independent, properly functioning, and approved long-range means of navigation which enable a reliable determination to be made of the position of the airplane by each pilot seated at that person's duty station.

(b) Operations where a flight navigator or long-range navigation equipment, or both, are required are specified in the operations specifications of the operator.

125.269   Flight attendants

(a) Each certificate holder shall provide at least the following flight attendants on each passenger-carrying airplane used:

(1) For airplanes having more than 19 but less than 51 passengers—one flight attendant.

(2) For airplanes having more than 50 but less than 101 passengers—two flight attendants.

(3) For airplanes having more than 100 passengers—two flight attendants plus one additional flight attendant for each unit (or part of a unit) of 50 passengers above 100 passengers.

(b) The number of flight attendants approved under paragraphs (a) and (b) of this section are set forth in the certificate holder's operations specifications.

(c) During takeoff and landing, flight attendants required by this section shall be located as near as practicable to required floor level exits and shall be uniformly distributed throughout the airplane to provide the most effective egress of passengers in event of an emergency evacuation.

125.271   Emergency and emergency evacuation duties

(a) Each certificate holder shall, for each type and model of airplane, assign to each category of required crewmember, as appropriate, the necessary functions to be performed in an emergency or a situation requiring emergency evacuation. The certificate holder shall show those functions are realistic, can be practically accomplished, and will meet any reasonably anticipated emergency, including the possible incapacitation of individual crewmembers or their inability to reach the passenger cabin because of shifting cargo in combination cargo-passenger airplanes.

(b) The certificate holder shall describe in its manual the functions of each category of required crewmembers under paragraph (a) of this section.

Subpart I — Flight Crewmember Requirements

125.281   Pilot-in-command qualifications

No certificate holder may use any person, nor may any person serve, as pilot in command of an airplane unless that person—

(a) Holds at least a commercial pilot certificate, an appropriate category, class, and type rating, and an instrument rating; and

(b) Has had at least 1,200 hours of flight time as a pilot, including 500 hours of cross-country flight time, 100 hours of night flight time, including at least 10 night takeoffs and landings, and 75 hours of actual or simulated instrument flight time, at least 50 hours of which were actual flight.

125.283   Second-in-command qualifications

No certificate holder may use any person, nor may any person serve, as second in command of an airplane unless that person—

(a) Holds at least a commercial pilot certificate with appropriate category and class ratings, and an instrument rating; and

(b) For flight under IFR, meets the recent instrument experience requirements prescribed for a pilot in command in part 61 of this chapter.

125.285 Pilot qualifications: recent experience

(a) No certificate holder may use any person, nor may any person serve, as a required pilot flight crewmember unless within the preceding 90 calendar days that person has made at least three takeoffs and landings in the type airplane in which that person is to serve. The takeoffs and landings required by this paragraph may be performed in a flight simulator if the flight simulator is qualified and approved by the Administrator for such purpose. However, any person who fails to qualify for a 90-consecutive-day period following the date of that person's last qualification under this paragraph must reestablish recency of experience as provided in paragraph (b) of this section.

(b) A required pilot flight crewmember who has not met the requirements of paragraph (a) of this section may reestablish recency of experience by making at least three takeoffs and landings under the supervision of an authorized check airman, in accordance with the following:

(1) At least one takeoff must be made with a simulated failure of the most critical powerplant.

(2) At least one landing must be made from an ILS approach to the lowest ILS minimums authorized for the certificate holder.

(3) At least one landing must be made to a complete stop.

(c) A required pilot flight crewmember who performs the maneuvers required by paragraph (b) of this section in a qualified and approved flight simulator, as prescribed in paragraph (a) of this section, must—

(1) Have previously logged 100 hours of flight time in the same type airplane in which the pilot is to serve; and

(2) Be observed on the first two landings made in operations under this part by an authorized check airman who acts as pilot in command and occupies a pilot seat. The landings must be made in weather minimums that are not less than those contained in the certificate holder's operations specifications for Category I operations and must be made within 45 days following completion of simulator testing.

(d) An authorized check airman who observes the takeoffs and landings prescribed in paragraphs (b) and (c)(3) of this section shall certify that the person being observed is proficient and qualified to perform flight duty in operations under this part, and may require any additional maneuvers that are determined necessary to make this certifying statement.

[Doc. No. 19779, 45 FR 67235, Oct. 9, 1980, as amended by Amdt. 125–27, 61 FR 34561, July 2, 1996]

125.287 Initial and recurrent pilot testing requirements

(a) No certificate holder may use any person, nor may any person serve as a pilot, unless, since the beginning of the 12th calendar month before that service, that person has passed a written or oral test, given by the Administrator or an authorized check airman on that person's knowledge in the following areas—

(1) The appropriate provisions of parts 61, 91, and 125 of this chapter and the operations specifications and the manual of the certificate holder;

(2) For each type of airplane to be flown by the pilot, the airplane powerplant, major components and systems, major appliances, performance and operating limitations, standard and emergency operating procedures, and the contents of the approved Airplane Flight Manual or approved equivalent, as applicable;

(3) For each type of airplane to be flown by the pilot, the method of determining compliance with weight and balance limitations for takeoff, landing, and en route operations;

(4) Navigation and use of air navigation aids appropriate to the operation of pilot authorization, including, when applicable, instrument approach facilities and procedures;

(5) Air traffic control procedures, including IFR procedures when applicable;

(6) Meteorology in general, including the principles of frontal systems, icing, fog, thunderstorms, and windshear, and, if ap-

propriate for the operation of the certificate holder, high altitude weather;

(7) Procedures for avoiding operations in thunderstorms and hail, and for operating in turbulent air or in icing conditions;

(8) New equipment, procedures, or techniques, as appropriate;

(9) Knowledge and procedures for operating during ground icing conditions, (i.e., any time conditions are such that frost, ice, or snow may reasonably be expected to adhere to the airplane), if the certificate holder expects to authorize takeoffs in ground icing conditions, including:

(i) The use of holdover times when using deicing/anti-icing fluids.

(ii) Airplane deicing/anti-icing procedures, including inspection and check procedures and responsibilities.

(iii) Communications.

(iv) Airplane surface contamination (i.e., adherence of frost, ice, or snow) and critical area identification, and knowledge of how contamination adversely affects airplane performance and flight characteristics.

(v) Types and characteristics of deicing/anti-icing fluids, if used by the certificate holder.

(vi) Cold weather preflight inspection procedures.

(vii) Techniques for recognizing contamination on the airplane.

(b) No certificate holder may use any person, nor may any person serve, as a pilot in any airplane unless, since the beginning of the 12th calendar month before that service, that person has passed a competency check given by the Administrator or an authorized check airman in that type of airplane to determine that person's competence in practical skills and techniques in that airplane or type of airplane. The extent of the competency check shall be determined by the Administrator or authorized check airman conducting the competency check. The competency check may include any of the maneuvers and procedures currently required for the original issuance of the particular pilot certificate required for the operations authorized and appropriate to the category, class, and type of airplane involved. For the purposes of this paragraph, type, as to an airplane, means any one of a group of airplanes determined by the Administrator to have a similar means of propulsion, the same manufacturer, and no significantly different handling or flight characteristics.

(c) The instrument proficiency check required by 125.291 may be substituted for the competency check required by this section for the type of airplane used in the check.

(d) For the purposes of this part, competent performance of a procedure or maneuver by a person to be used as a pilot requires that the pilot be the obvious master of the airplane with the successful outcome of the maneuver never in doubt.

(e) The Administrator or authorized check airman certifies the competency of each pilot who passes the knowledge or flight check in the certificate holder's pilot records.

(f) Portions of a required competency check may be given in an airplane simulator or other appropriate training device, if approved by the Administrator.

(g) If the certificate holder is authorized to conduct EFVS operations, the competency check in paragraph (b) of this section must include tasks appropriate to the EFVS operations the certificate holder is authorized to conduct.

[45 FR 67235, Oct. 9, 1980, as amended by Amdt. 125-18, 58 FR 69629, Dec. 30, 1993; Docket FAA-2013-0485, Amdt. 125-66, 81 FR 90176, Dec. 13, 2016]

125.289 Initial and recurrent flight attendant crewmember testing requirements

No certificate holder may use any person, nor may any person serve, as a flight attendant crewmember, unless, since the beginning of the 12th calendar month before that service, the certificate holder has de-

FAR 125

termined by appropriate initial and recurrent testing that the person is knowledgeable and competent in the following areas as appropriate to assigned duties and responsibilities:

(a) Authority of the pilot in command;

(b) Passenger handling, including procedures to be followed in handling deranged persons or other persons whose conduct might jeopardize safety;

(c) Crewmember assignments, functions, and responsibilities during ditching and evacuation of persons who may need the assistance of another person to move expeditiously to an exit in an emergency;

(d) Briefing of passengers;

(e) Location and operation of portable fire extinguishers and other items of emergency equipment;

(f) Proper use of cabin equipment and controls;

(g) Location and operation of passenger oxygen equipment;

(h) Location and operation of all normal and emergency exits, including evacuation chutes and escape ropes; and

(i) Seating of persons who may need assistance of another person to move rapidly to an exit in an emergency as prescribed by the certificate holder's operations manual.

125.291   Pilot in command: Instrument proficiency check requirements

(a) No certificate holder may use any person, nor may any person serve, as a pilot in command of an airplane under IFR unless, since the beginning of the sixth calendar month before that service, that person has passed an instrument proficiency check and the Administrator or an authorized check airman has so certified in a letter of competency.

(b) No pilot may use any type of precision instrument approach procedure under IFR unless, since the beginning of the sixth calendar month before that use, the pilot has satisfactorily demonstrated that type of approach procedure and has been issued a letter of competency under paragraph (g) of this section. No pilot may use any type of nonprecision approach procedure under IFR unless, since the beginning of the sixth calendar month before that use, the pilot has satisfactorily demonstrated either that type of approach procedure or any other two different types of nonprecision approach procedures and has been issued a letter of competency under paragraph (g) of this section. The instrument approach procedure or procedures must include at least one straight-in approach, one circling approach, and one missed approach. Each type of approach procedure demonstrated must be conducted to published minimums for that procedure.

(c) The instrument proficiency check required by paragraph (a) of this section consists of an oral or written equipment test and a flight check under simulated or actual IFR conditions. The equipment test includes questions on emergency procedures, engine operation, fuel and lubrication systems, power settings, stall speeds, best engine-out speed, propeller and supercharge operations, and hydraulic, mechanical, and electrical systems, as appropriate. The flight check includes navigation by instruments, recovery from simulated emergencies, and standard instrument approaches involving navigational facilities which that pilot is to be authorized to use.

(1) For a pilot in command of an airplane, the instrument proficiency check must include the procedures and maneuvers for a commercial pilot certificate with an instrument rating and, if required, for the appropriate type rating.

(2) The instrument proficiency check must be given by an authorized check airman or by the Administrator.

(d) If the pilot in command is assigned to pilot only one type of airplane, that pilot must take the instrument proficiency check required by paragraph (a) of this section in that type of airplane.

(e) If the pilot in command is assigned to pilot more than one type of airplane, that pilot must take the instrument proficiency check

required by paragraph (a) of this section in each type of airplane to which that pilot is assigned, in rotation, but not more than one flight check during each period described in paragraph (a) of this section.

(f) Portions of a required flight check may be given in an airplane simulator or other appropriate training device, if approved by the Administrator.

(g) The Administrator or authorized check airman issues a letter of competency to each pilot who passes the instrument proficiency check. The letter of competency contains a list of the types of instrument approach procedures and facilities authorized.

125.293   Crewmember: tests and checks, grace provisions, accepted standards

(a) If a crewmember who is required to take a test or a flight check under this part completes the test or flight check in the calendar month before or after the calendar month in which it is required, that crewmember is considered to have completed the test or check in the calendar month in which it is required.

(b) If a pilot being checked under this subpart fails any of the required maneuvers, the person giving the check may give additional training to the pilot during the course of the check. In addition to repeating the maneuvers failed, the person giving the check may require the pilot being checked to repeat any other maneuvers that are necessary to determine the pilot's proficiency. If the pilot being checked is unable to demonstrate satisfactory performance to the person conducting the check, the certificate holder may not use the pilot, nor may the pilot serve, in the capacity for which the pilot is being checked in operations under this part until the pilot has satisfactorily completed the check.

125.295   Check airman authorization: application and issue

Each certificate holder desiring FAA approval of a check airman shall submit a request in writing to the responsible Flight Standards office charged with the overall inspection of the certificate holder. The Administrator may issue a letter of authority to each check airman if that airman passes the appropriate oral and flight test. The letter of authority lists the tests and checks in this part that the check airman is qualified to give, and the category, class and type airplane, where appropriate, for which the check airman is qualified.

[Docket No. 19779, 45 FR 67235, Oct. 9, 1980, as amended by Docket FAA-2018-0119, Amdt. 125-68, 83 FR 9173, Mar. 5, 2018]

125.296   Training, testing, and checking conducted by training centers: special rules

A crewmember who has successfully completed training, testing, or checking in accordance with an approved training program that meets the requirements of this part and that is conducted in accordance with an approved course conducted by a training center certificated under part 142 of this chapter, is considered to meet applicable requirements of this part.

[Doc. No. 26933, 61 FR 34561, July 2, 1996]

125.297   Approval of flight simulators and flight training devices

(a) Flight simulators and flight training devices approved by the Administrator may be used in training, testing, and checking required by this subpart.

(b) Each flight simulator and flight training device that is used in training, testing, and checking required under this subpart must be used in accordance with an approved training course conducted by a training center certificated under part 142 of this chapter, or meet the following requirements:

(1) It must be specifically approved for—

(i) The certificate holder;

(ii) The type airplane and, if applicable, the particular variation within type for which the check is being conducted; and

(iii) The particular maneuver, procedure, or crewmember function involved.

(2) It must maintain the performance, functional, and other characteristics that are required for approval.

(3) It must be modified to conform with any modification to the airplane being simulated that changes the performance, functional, or other characteristics required for approval.

[Doc. No. 19779, 45 FR 67235, Oct. 9, 1980, as amended by Amdt. 125–27, 61 FR 34561, July 2, 1996]

Subpart J — Flight Operations

125.311   Flight crewmembers at controls

(a) Except as provided in paragraph (b) of this section, each required flight crewmember on flight deck duty must remain at the assigned duty station with seat belt fastened while the airplane is taking off or landing and while it is en route.

(b) A required flight crewmember may leave the assigned duty station—

(1) If the crewmember's absence is necessary for the performance of duties in connection with the operation of the airplane;

(2) If the crewmember's absence is in connection with physiological needs; or

(3) If the crewmember is taking a rest period and relief is provided—

(i) In the case of the assigned pilot in command, by a pilot qualified to act as pilot in command.

(ii) In the case of the assigned second in command, by a pilot qualified to act as second in command of that airplane during en route operations. However, the relief pilot need not meet the recent experience requirements of 125.285.

125.313   Manipulation of controls when carrying passengers

No pilot in command may allow any person to manipulate the controls of an airplane while carrying passengers during flight, nor may any person manipulate the controls while carrying passengers during flight, unless that person is a qualified pilot of the certificate holder operating that airplane.

125.315   Admission to flight deck

(a) No person may admit any person to the flight deck of an airplane unless the person being admitted is—

(1) A crewmember;

(2) An FAA inspector or an authorized representative of the National Transportation Safety Board who is performing official duties; or

(3) Any person who has the permission of the pilot in command.

(b) No person may admit any person to the flight deck unless there is a seat available for the use of that person in the passenger compartment, except—

(1) An FAA inspector or an authorized representative of the Administrator or National Transportation Safety Board who is checking or observing flight operations; or

(2) A certificated airman employed by the certificate holder whose duties require an airman certificate.

125.317   Inspector's credentials: admission to pilots' compartment: forward observer's seat

(a) Whenever, in performing the duties of conducting an inspection, an FAA inspector presents an Aviation Safety Inspector credential, FAA Form 110A, to the pilot in command of an airplane operated by the certificate holder, the inspector must be given free and uninterrupted access to the pilot compartment of that airplane. However, this paragraph does not limit the emergency authority of the pilot in command to exclude any person from the pilot compartment in the interest of safety.

(b) A forward observer's seat on the flight deck, or forward passenger seat with headset or speaker, must be provided for use by the Administrator while conducting en route inspections. The suitability of the location of the seat and the headset or speaker for use in conducting en route inspections is determined by the Administrator.

125.319   Emergencies

(a) In an emergency situation that requires immediate decision and action, the pilot in command may take any action considered necessary under the circumstances. In such a case, the pilot in command may deviate from prescribed operations, procedures and methods, weather minimums, and this chapter, to the extent required in the interests of safety.

(b) In an emergency situation arising during flight that requires immediate decision and action by appropriate management personnel in the case of operations conducted with a flight following service and which is known to them, those personnel shall advise the pilot in command of the emergency, shall ascertain the decision of the pilot in command, and shall have the decision recorded. If they cannot communicate with the pilot, they shall declare an emergency and take any action that they consider necessary under the circumstances.

(c) Whenever emergency authority is exercised, the pilot in command or the appropriate management personnel shall keep the appropriate ground radio station fully informed of the progress of the flight. The person declaring the emergency shall send a written report of any deviation, through the operator's director of operations, to the Administrator within 10 days, exclusive of Saturdays, Sundays, and Federal holidays, after the flight is completed or, in the case of operations outside the United States, upon return to the home base.

125.321   Reporting potentially hazardous meteorological conditions and irregularities of ground and navigation facilities

Whenever the pilot in command encounters a meteorological condition or an irregularity in a ground facility or navigation aid in flight, the knowledge of which the pilot in command considers essential to the safety of other flights, the pilot in command shall notify an appropriate ground station as soon as practicable.

[Doc. No. 19779, 45 FR 67235, Oct. 9, 1980, as amended by Amdt. 125–52, 72 FR 31683, June 7, 2007]

125.323   Reporting mechanical irregularities

The pilot in command shall ensure that all mechanical irregularities occurring during flight are entered in the maintenance log of the airplane at the next place of landing. Before each flight, the pilot in command shall ascertain the status of each irregularity entered in the log at the end of the preceding flight.

125.325   Instrument approach procedures and IFR landing minimums.

Except as specified in 91.176 of this chapter, no person may make an instrument approach at an airport except in accordance with IFR weather minimums and unless the type of instrument approach procedure to be used is listed in the certificate holder's operations specifications.

[Docket FAA-2013-0485, Amdt. 125-66, 81 FR 90176, Dec. 13, 2016]

125.327   Briefing of passengers before flight

(a) Before each takeoff, each pilot in command of an airplane carrying passengers shall ensure that all passengers have been orally briefed on—

(1) Smoking. Each passenger shall be briefed on when, where, and under what conditions smoking is prohibited. This briefing shall include a statement that the Federal Aviation Regulations require passenger compliance with the lighted passenger information signs, posted placards, areas designated for safety purposes as no smoking areas, and crewmember instructions with regard to these items.

(2) The use of safety belts, including instructions on how to fasten and unfasten the safety belts. Each passenger shall be briefed on when, where, and under what conditions the safety belt must be fastened about him or her. This briefing shall include a statement that the Federal Aviation Regulations require passenger compliance with lighted passenger information signs and crewmember instructions concerning the use of safety belts.

(3) The placement of seat backs in an upright position before takeoff and landing;

(4) Location and means for opening the passenger entry door and emergency exits;

(5) Location of survival equipment;

(6) If the flight involves extended overwater operation, ditching procedures and the use of required flotation equipment;

(7) If the flight involves operations above 12,000 feet MSL, the normal and emergency use of oxygen; and

(8) Location and operation of fire extinguishers.

(b) Before each takeoff, the pilot in command shall ensure that each person who may need the assistance of another person to move expeditiously to an exit if an emergency occurs and that person's attendant, if any, has received a briefing as to the procedures to be followed if an evacuation occurs. This paragraph does not apply to a person who has been given a briefing before a previous leg of a flight in the same airplane.

(c) The oral briefing required by paragraph (a) of this section shall be given by the pilot in command or a member of the crew. It shall be supplemented by printed cards for the use of each passenger containing—

(1) A diagram and method of operating the emergency exits; and

(2) Other instructions necessary for the use of emergency equipment on board the airplane.

Each card used under this paragraph must be carried in the airplane in locations convenient for the use of each passenger and must contain information that is appropriate to the airplane on which it is to be used.

(d) The certificate holder shall describe in its manual the procedure to be followed in the briefing required by paragraph (a) of this section.

(e) If the airplane does not proceed directly over water after takeoff, no part of the briefing required by paragraph (a)(6) of this section has to be given before takeoff but the briefing required by paragraph (a)(6) must be given before reaching the overwater part of the flight.

[Doc. No. 19779, 45 FR 67235, Oct. 9, 1980, as amended by Amdt. 125–17, 57 FR 42675, Sept. 15, 1992]

125.328   Prohibition on crew interference

No person may assault, threaten, intimidate, or interfere with a crewmember in the performance of the crewmember's duties aboard an aircraft being operated under this part.

[Doc. No. FAA–1998–4954, 64 FR 1080, Jan. 7, 1999]

125.329   Minimum altitudes for use of autopilot

(a) Definitions. For purpose of this section—

(1) Altitudes for takeoff/initial climb and go-around/missed approach are defined as above the airport elevation.

(2) Altitudes for en route operations are defined as above terrain elevation.

(3) Altitudes for approach are defined as above the touchdown zone elevation (TDZE), unless the altitude is specifically in reference to DA (H) or MDA, in which case the altitude is defined by reference to the DA(H) or MDA itself.

(b) Takeoff and initial climb. No person may use an autopilot for takeoff or initial climb below the higher of 500 feet or an altitude that is no lower than twice the altitude loss specified in the Airplane Flight Manual (AFM), except as follows—

(1) At a minimum engagement altitude specified in the AFM; or

(2) At an altitude specified by the Administrator, whichever is greater.

(c En route. No person may use an autopilot en route, including climb and descent, below the following—

(1) 500 feet;

(2) At an altitude that is no lower than twice the altitude loss specified in the AFM for an autopilot malfunction in cruise conditions; or

(3) At an altitude specified by the Administrator, whichever is greater.

(d) Approach. No person may use an autopilot at an altitude lower than 50 feet below the DA(H) or MDA for the instrument procedure being flown, except as follows—

(1) For autopilots with an AFM specified altitude loss for approach operations—

(i)   An altitude no lower than twice the specified altitude loss if higher than 50 feet below the MDA or DA(H);

(ii) An altitude no lower than 50 feet higher than the altitude loss specified in the AFM, when the following conditions are met—

(A) Reported weather conditions are less than the basic VFR weather conditions in 91.155 of this chapter;

(B) Suitable visual references specified in 91.175 of this chapter have been established on the instrument approach procedure; and

(C) The autopilot is coupled and receiving both lateral and vertical path references;

(iii) An altitude no lower than the higher of the altitude loss specified in the AFM or 50 feet above the TDZE, when the following conditions are met—

(A) Reported weather conditions are equal to or better than the basic VFR weather conditions in 91.155 of this chapter; and

(B) The autopilot is coupled and receiving both lateral and vertical path references; or

(iv) A greater altitude specified by the Administrator.

(2) For autopilots with AFM specified approach altitude limitations, the greater of—

(i)   The minimum use altitude specified for the coupled approach mode selected;

(ii) 50 feet; or

(iii) An altitude specified by Administrator.

(3) For autopilots with an AFM specified negligible or zero altitude loss for an autopilot approach mode malfunction, the greater of—

(i) 50 feet; or

(ii) An altitude specified by Administrator.

(4) If executing an autopilot coupled go-around or missed approach using a certificated and functioning autopilot in accordance with paragraph (e) in this section.

(e) Go-Around/Missed Approach. No person may engage an autopilot during a go-around or missed approach below the minimum engagement altitude specified for takeoff and initial climb in paragraph (b) in this section. An autopilot minimum use altitude does not apply to a go-around/missed approach initiated with an engaged autopilot. Performing a go-around or missed approach with an engaged autopilot must not adversely affect safe obstacle clearance.

(f) Landing. Notwithstanding paragraph (d) of this section, autopilot minimum use altitudes do not apply to autopilot operations when an approved automatic landing system mode is being used for landing. Automatic landing systems must be authorized in an operations specification issued to the operator.

[Doc. No. FAA-2012-1059, 79 FR 6087, Feb. 3, 2014]

125.331　Carriage of persons without compliance with the passenger-carrying provisions of this part

The following persons may be carried aboard an airplane without complying with the passenger-carrying requirements of this part:

(a) A crewmember.

(b) A person necessary for the safe handling of animals on the airplane.

(c) A person necessary for the safe handling of hazardous materials (as defined in subchapter C of title 49 CFR).

(d) A person performing duty as a security or honor guard accompanying a shipment made by or under the authority of the U.S. Government.

(e) A military courier or a military route supervisor carried by a military cargo contract operator if that carriage is specifically authorized by the appropriate military service.

(f) An authorized representative of the Administrator conducting an en route inspection.

(g) A person authorized by the Administrator.

125.333　Stowage of food, beverage, and passenger service equipment during airplane movement on the surface, takeoff, and landing

(a) No certificate holder may move an airplane on the surface, take off, or land when any food, beverage, or tableware furnished by the certificate holder is located at any passenger seat.

(b) No certificate holder may move an airplane on the surface, take off, or land unless each food and beverage tray and seat back tray table is secured in its stowed position.

(c) No certificate holder may permit an airplane to move on the surface, take off, or land unless each passenger serving cart is secured in its stowed position.

(d) Each passenger shall comply with instructions given by a crewmember with regard to compliance with this section.

[Doc. No. 26142, 57 FR 42675, Sept. 15, 1992]

Subpart K — Flight Release Rules

125.351　Flight release authority

(a) No person may start a flight without authority from the person authorized by the certificate holder to exercise operational control over the flight.

(b) No person may start a flight unless the pilot in command or the person authorized by the cetificate holder to exercise operational control over the flight has executed a flight release setting forth the conditions under which the flight will be conducted. The pilot in command may sign the flight release only when both the pilot in command and the person authorized to exercise operational control believe the flight can be made safely, unless the pilot in command is authorized by the certificate holder to exercise operational control and execute the flight release without the approval of any other person.

(c) No person may continue a flight from an intermediate airport without a new flight release if the airplane has been on the ground more than 6 hours.

125.353　Facilities and services

During a flight, the pilot in command shall obtain any additional available information of meteorological conditions and irregularities of facilities and services that may affect the safety of the flight.

125.355　Airplane equipment

No person may release an airplane unless it is airworthy and is equipped as prescribed.

125.357　Communication and navigation facilities

No person may release an airplane over any route or route segment unless communication and navigation facilities equal to those required by 125.51 are in satisfactory operating condition.

125.359　Flight release under VFR

No person may release an airplane for VFR operation unless the ceiling and visibility en route, as indicated by available weather reports or forecasts, or any combination thereof, are and will remain at or above applicable VFR minimums until the airplane arrives at the airport or airports specified in the flight release.

125.361　Flight release under IFR or over-the-top

Except as provided in 125.363, no person may release an airplane for operations under IFR or over-the-top unless appropriate weather reports or forecasts, or any combination thereof, indicate that the weather conditions will be at or above the authorized minimums at the estimated time of arrival at the airport or airports to which released.

125.363　Flight release over water

(a) No person may release an airplane for a flight that involves extended overwater operation unless appropriate weather reports or forecasts, or any combination thereof, indicate that the weather conditions will be at or above the authorized minimums at the estimated time of arrival at any airport to which released or to any required alternate airport.

(b) Each certificate holder shall conduct extended overwater operations under IFR unless it shows that operating under IFR is not necessary for safety.

(c) Each certificate holder shall conduct other overwater operations under IFR if the Administrator determines that operation under IFR is necessary for safety.

(d) Each authorization to conduct extended overwater operations under VFR and each requirement to conduct other overwater operations under IFR will be specified in the operations specifications.

125.365　Alternate airport for departure

(a) If the weather conditions at the airport of takeoff are below the landing minimums in the certificate holder's operations specifications for that airport, no person may release an airplane from that airport unless the flight release specifies an alternate airport located within the following distances from the airport of takeoff:

(1) Airplanes having two engines. Not more than 1 hour from the departure airport at normal cruising speed in still air with one engine inoperative.

(2) Airplanes having three or more engines. Not more than 2 hours from the departure airport at normal cruising speed in still air with one engine inoperative.

(b) For the purposes of paragraph (a) of this section, the alternate airport weather conditions must meet the requirements of the certificate holder's operations specifications.

(c) No person may release an airplane from an airport unless that person lists each required alternate airport in the flight release.

125.367　Alternate airport for destination: IFR or over-the-top

(a) Except as provided in paragraph (b) of this section, each person releasing an airplane for operation under IFR or over-the-top shall list at least one alternate airport for each destination airport in the flight release.

(b) An alternate airport need not be designated for IFR or over-the-top operations where the airplane carries enough fuel to meet the requirements of 125.375 and 125.377 for flights outside the 48 conterminous States and the District of Columbia over routes without an available alternate airport for a particular airport of destination.

(c) For the purposes of paragraph (a) of this section, the weather requirements at the alternate airport must meet the requirements of the operator's operations specifications.

(d) No person may release a flight unless that person lists each required alternate airport in the flight release.

125.369　Alternate airport weather minimums

No person may list an airport as an alternate airport in the flight release unless the appropriate weather reports or forecasts, or any combina-

FAR
125

tion thereof, indicate that the weather conditions will be at or above the alternate weather minimums specified in the certificate holder's operations specifications for that airport when the flight arrives.

125.371 Continuing flight in unsafe conditions

(a) No pilot in command may allow a flight to continue toward any airport to which it has been released if, in the opinion of the pilot in command, the flight cannot be completed safely, unless, in the opinion of the pilot in command, there is no safer procedure. In that event, continuation toward that airport is an emergency situation.

125.373 Original flight release or amendment of flight release

(a) A certificate holder may specify any airport authorized for the type of airplane as a destination for the purpose of original release.

(b) No person may allow a flight to continue to an airport to which it has been released unless the weather conditions at an alternate airport that was specified in the flight release are forecast to be at or above the alternate minimums specified in the operations specifications for that airport at the time the airplane would arrive at the alternate airport. However, the flight release may be amended en route to include any alternate airport that is within the fuel range of the airplane as specified in 125.375 or 125.377.

(c) No person may change an original destination or alternate airport that is specified in the original flight release to another airport while the airplane is en route unless the other airport is authorized for that type of airplane.

(d) Each person who amends a flight release en route shall record that amendment.

125.375 Fuel supply: nonturbine and turbopropeller-powered airplanes

(a) Except as provided in paragraph (b) of this section, no person may release for flight or take off a nonturbine or turbopropeller-powered airplane unless, considering the wind and other weather conditions expected, it has enough fuel—

(1) To fly to and land at the airport to which it is released;

(2) Thereafter, to fly to and land at the most distant alternate airport specified in the flight release; and

(3) Thereafter, to fly for 45 minutes at normal cruising fuel consumption.

(b) If the airplane is released for any flight other than from one point in the conterminous United States to another point in the conterminous United States, it must carry enough fuel to meet the requirements of paragraphs (a)(1) and (2) of this section and thereafter fly for 30 minutes plus 15 percent of the total time required to fly at normal cruising fuel consumption to the airports specified in paragraphs (a)(1) and (2) of this section, or fly for 90 minutes at normal cruising fuel consumption, whichever is less.

(c) No person may release a nonturbine or turbopropeller-powered airplane to an airport for which an alternate is not specified under 125.367(b) unless it has enough fuel, considering wind and other weather conditions expected, to fly to that airport and thereafter to fly for 3 hours at normal cruising fuel consumption.

125.377 Fuel supply: turbine-engine-powered airplanes other than turbopropeller

(a) Except as provided in paragraph (b) of this section, no person may release for flight or takeoff a turbine-powered airplane (other than a turbopropeller-powered airplane) unless, considering the wind and other weather conditions expected, it has enough fuel—

(1) To fly to and land at the airport to which it is released;

(2) Thereafter, to fly to and land at the most distant alternate airport specified in the flight release; and

(3) Thereafter, to fly for 45 minutes at normal cruising fuel consumption.

(b) For any operation outside the 48 conterminous United States and

the District of Columbia, unless authorized by the Administrator in the operations specifications, no person may release for flight or take off a turbine-engine powered airplane (other than a turbopropeller-powered airplane) unless, considering wind and other weather conditions expected, it has enough fuel—

(1) To fly and land at the airport to which it is released;

(2) After that, to fly for a period of 10 percent of the total time required to fly from the airport of departure and land at the airport to which it was released;

(3) After that, to fly to and land at the most distant alternate airport specified in the flight release, if an alternate is required; and

(4) After that, to fly for 30 minutes at holding speed at 1,500 feet above the alternate airport (or the destination airport if no alternate is required) under standard temperature conditions.

(c) No person may release a turbine-engine-powered airplane (other than a turbopropeller airplane) to an airport for which an alternate is not specified under 125.367(b) unless it has enough fuel, considering wind and other weather conditions expected, to fly to that airport and thereafter to fly for at least 2 hours at normal cruising fuel consumption.

(d) The Administrator may amend the operations specifications of a certificate holder to require more fuel than any of the minimums stated in paragraph (a) or (b) of this section if the Administrator finds that additional fuel is necessary on a particular route in the interest of safety.

125.379 Landing weather minimums: IFR

(a) If the pilot in command of an airplane has not served 100 hours as pilot in command in the type of airplane being operated, the MDA or DA/DH and visibility landing minimums in the certificate holder's operations specification are increased by 100 feet and one-half mile (or the RVR equivalent). The MDA or DA/DH and visibility minimums need not be increased above those applicable to the airport when used as an alternate airport, but in no event may the landing minimums be less than a 300-foot ceiling and 1 mile of visibility.

(b) The 100 hours of pilot-in-command experience required by paragraph (a) may be reduced (not to exceed 50 percent) by substituting one landing in operations under this part in the type of airplane for 1 required hour of pilot-in-command experience if the pilot has at least 100 hours as pilot in command of another type airplane in operations under this part.

(c) Category II minimums, when authorized in the certificate holder's operations specifications, do not apply until the pilot in command subject to paragraph (a) of this section meets the requirements of that paragraph in the type of airplane the pilot is operating.

[Doc. No. 19779, 45 FR 67235, Oct. 9, 1980, as amended by Amdt 125–52, 72 FR 31683, June 7, 2007]

125.381 Takeoff and landing weather minimums: IFR

(a) Regardless of any clearance from ATC, if the reported weather conditions are less than that specified in the certificate holder's operations specifications, no pilot may—

(1) Take off an airplane under IFR; or

(2) Except as provided in paragraphs (c) and (d) of this section land an airplane under IFR.

(b) Except as provided in paragraphs (c) and (d) of this section, no pilot may execute an instrument approach procedure if the latest reported visibility is less than the landing minimums specified in the certificate holder's operations specifications.

(c) A pilot who initiates an instrument approach procedure based on a weather report that indicates that the specified visibility minimums exist and subsequently receives another weather report that indicates that conditions are below the minimum requirements may continue the approach only if either the requirements of 91.176 of this chapter, or the following conditions are met—

(1) The later weather report is received when the airplane is in one of the following approach phases:

(i) The airplane is on a ILS approach and has passed the final approach fix;

(ii) The airplane is on an ASR or PAR final approach and has been turned over to the final approach controller; or

(iii) The airplane is on a nonprecision final approach and the airplane—

(A) Has passed the appropriate facility or final approach fix; or

(B) Where a final approach fix is not specified, has completed the procedure turn and is established inbound toward the airport on the final approach course within the distance prescribed in the procedure; and

(2) The pilot in command finds, on reaching the authorized MDA, or DA/DH, that the actual weather conditions are at or above the minimums prescribed for the procedure being used.

(d) A pilot may execute an instrument approach procedure, or continue the approach, at an airport when the visibility is reported to be less than the visibility minimums prescribed for that procedure if the pilot uses an operable EFVS in accordance with 91.176 of this chapter and the certificate holder's operations specifications for EFVS operations, or for a holder of a part 125 letter of deviation authority, a letter of authorization for the use of EFVS.

[Doc. No. 19779, 45 FR 67235, Oct. 9, 1980, as amended by Amdt. 125-2, 46 FR 24409, Apr. 30, 1981; Amdt. 125-45, 69 FR 1641, Jan. 9, 2004; Amdt. 125-52, 72 FR 31683, June 7, 2007; Docket FAA-2013-0485, Amdt. 125-66, 81 FR 90177, Dec. 13, 2016]

125.383 Load manifest

(a) Each certificate holder is responsible for the preparation and accuracy of a load manifest in duplicate containing information concerning the loading of the airplane. The manifest must be prepared before each takeoff and must include—

(1) The number of passengers;

(2) The total weight of the loaded airplane;

(3) The maximum allowable takeoff and landing weights for that flight;

(4) The center of gravity limits;

(5) The center of gravity of the loaded airplane, except that the actual center of gravity need not be computed if the airplane is loaded according to a loading schedule or other approved method that ensures that the center of gravity of the loaded airplane is within approved limits. In those cases, an entry shall be made on the manifest indicating that the center of gravity is within limits according to a loading schedule or other approved method:

(6) The registration number of the airplane;

(7) The origin and destination ; and

(8) Names of passengers.

(b) The pilot in command of an airplane for which a load manifest must be prepared shall carry a copy of the completed load manifest in the airplane to its destination. The certificate holder shall keep copies of completed load manifests for at least 30 days at its principal operations base, or at another location used by it and approved by the Administrator.

Subpart L — Records and Reports

125.401 Crewmember record

(a) Each certificate holder shall—

(1) Maintain current records of each crewmember that show whether or not that crewmember complies with this chapter (e.g., proficiency checks, airplane qualifications, any required physical examinations, and flight time records); and

(2) Record each action taken concerning the release from employment or physical or professional disqualification of any flight crewmember and keep the record for at least 6 months thereafter.

(b) Each certificate holder shall maintain the records required by paragraph (a) of this section at its principal operations base, or at another location used by it and approved by the Administrator.

(c) Computer record systems approved by the Administrator may be used in complying with the requirements of paragraph (a) of this section.

125.403 Flight release form

(a) The flight release may be in any form but must contain at least the following information concerning each flight:

(1) Company or organization name.

(2) Make, model, and registration number of the airplane being used.

(3) Date of flight.

(4) Name and duty assignment of each crewmember.

(5) Departure airport, destination airports, alternate airports, and route.

(6) Minimum fuel supply (in gallons or pounds).

(7) A statement of the type of operation (e.g., IFR, VFR).

(b) The airplane flight release must contain, or have attached to it, weather reports, available weather forecasts, or a combination thereof.

125.405 Disposition of load manifest, flight release, and flight plans

(a) The pilot in command of an airplane shall carry in the airplane to its destination the original or a signed copy of the—

(1) Load manifest required by 125.383;

(2) Flight release;

(3) Airworthiness release; and

(4) Flight plan, including route.

(b) If a flight originates at the principal operations base of the certificate holder, it shall retain at that base a signed copy of each document listed in paragraph (a) of this section.

(c) Except as provided in paragraph (d) of this section, if a flight originates at a place other than the principal operations base of the certificate holder, the pilot in command (or another person not aboard the airplane who is authorized by the operator) shall, before or immediately after departure of the flight, mail signed copies of the documents listed in paragraph (a) of this section to the principal operations base.

(d) If a flight originates at a place other than the principal operations base of the certificate holder and there is at that place a person to manage the flight departure for the operator who does not depart on the airplane, signed copies of the documents listed in paragraph (a) of this section may be retained at that place for not more than 30 days before being sent to the principal operations base of the certificate holder. However, the documents for a particular flight need not be further retained at that place or be sent to the principal operations base, if the originals or other copies of them have been previously returned to the principal operations base.

(e) The certificate holder shall:

(1) Identify in its operations manual the person having custody of the copies of documents retained in accordance with paragraph (d) of this section; and

(2) Retain at its principal operations base either the original or a copy of the records required by this section for at least 30 days.

125.407 Maintenance log: airplanes

(a) Each person who takes corrective action or defers action concerning a reported or observed failure or malfunction of an airframe, aircraft engine, propeller, or appliance shall record the action taken in the airplane maintenance log in accordance with part 43 of this chapter.

(b) Each certificate holder shall establish a procedure for keeping copies of the airplane maintenance log required by this section in the airplane for access by appropriate personnel and shall include that procedure in the manual required by 125.249.

125.409 Service difficulty reports

(a) Each certificate holder shall report the occurrence or detection of each failure, malfunction, or defect, in a form and manner prescribed by the Administrator.

(b) Each certificate holder shall submit each report required by this section, covering each 24-hour period beginning at 0900 local time of each day and ending at 0900 local time on the next day, to the FAA office in Oklahoma City, Oklahoma. Each report of occurrences during a 24-hour period shall be submitted to the collection point within the next 96 hours. However, a report due on a Saturday or Sunday may be submitted on the following Monday, and a report due on a holiday may be submitted on the next work day.

[Doc. No. 19779, 45 FR 67235, Oct. 9, 1980, as amended by Amdt. 125–49, 70 FR 76979, Dec. 29, 2005]

125.411 Airworthiness release or maintenance record entry

(a) No certificate holder may operate an airplane after maintenance, preventive maintenance, or alteration is performed on the airplane unless the person performing that maintenance, preventive maintenance, or alteration prepares or causes to be prepared—

(1) An airworthiness release; or

(2) An entry in the aircraft maintenance records in accordance with the certificate holder's manual.

(b) The airworthiness release or maintenance record entry required by paragraph (a) of this section must—

(1) Be prepared in accordance with the procedures set forth in the certificate holder's manual;

(2) Include a certification that—

    (i) The work was performed in accordance with the requirements of the certificate holder's manual;

    (ii) All items required to be inspected were inspected by an authorized person who determined that the work was satisfactorily completed;

    (iii) No known condition exists that would make the airplane unairworthy; and

    (iv) So far as the work performed is concerned, the airplane is in condition for safe operation; and

(3) Be signed by a person authorized in part 43 of this chapter to perform maintenance, preventive maintenance, and alteration.

(c) When an airworthiness release form is prepared, the certificate holder must give a copy to the pilot in command and keep a record of it for at least 60 days.

(d) Instead of restating each of the conditions of the certification required by paragraph (b) of this section, the certificate holder may state in its manual that the signature of a person authorized in part 43 of this chapter constitutes that certification.

Subpart M — Continued Airworthiness and Safety Improvements

Source: Amdt. 125–53, 72 FR 63412, Nov. 8, 2007, unless otherwise noted.

125.501 Purpose and definition

(a) This subpart requires operators to support the continued airworthiness of each airplane. These requirements may include, but are not limited to, revising the inspection program, incorporating design changes, and incorporating revisions to Instructions for Continued Airworthiness.

(b) [Reserved]

[Amdt. 125–53, 72 FR 63412, Nov. 8, 2007, as amended by Docket FAA-2018-0119, Amdt. 125-68, 83 FR 9174, Mar. 5, 2018]

125.503 [Reserved]

125.505 Repairs assessment for pressurized fuselages

(a) No person may operate an Airbus Model A300 (excluding the -600 series), British Aerospace Model BAC 1-11, Boeing Model 707, 720, 727, 737 or 747, McDonnell Douglas Model DC-8, DC-9/MD-80 or DC-10, Fokker Model F28, or Lockheed Model L-1011 beyond the applicable flight cycle implementation time specified below, or May 25, 2001, whichever occurs later, unless operations specifications have been issued to reference repair assessment guidelines applicable to the fuselage pressure boundary (fuselage skin, door skin, and bulkhead webs), and those guidelines are incorporated in its maintenance program. The repair assessment guidelines must be approved by the responsible Aircraft Certification Service office for the type certificate for the affected airplane.

(1) For the Airbus Model A300 (excluding the –600 series), the flight cycle implementation time is:

    (i) Model B2: 36,000 flights.

    (ii) Model B4–100 (including Model B4–2C): 30,000 flights above the window line, and 36,000 flights below the window line.

    (iii) Model B4–200: 25,500 flights above the window line, and 34,000 flights below the window line.

(2) For all models of the British Aerospace BAC 1–11, the flight cycle implementation time is 60,000 flights.

(3) For all models of the Boeing 707, the flight cycle implementation time is 15,000 flights.

(4) For all models of the Boeing 720, the flight cycle implementation time is 23,000 flights.

(5) For all models of the Boeing 727, the flight cycle implementation time is 45,000 flights.

(6) For all models of the Boeing 737, the flight cycle implementation time is 60,000 flights.

(7) For all models of the Boeing 747, the flight cycle implementation time is 15,000 flights.

(8) For all models of the McDonnell Douglas DC–8, the flight cycle implementation time is 30,000 flights.

(9) For all models of the McDonnell Douglas DC–9/MD–80, the flight cycle implementation time is 60,000 flights.

(10) For all models of the McDonnell Douglas DC–10, the flight cycle implementation time is 30,000 flights.

(11) For all models of the Lockheed L–1011, the flight cycle implementation time is 27,000 flights.

(12) For the Fokker F–28 Mark, 1000, 2000, 3000, and 4000, the flight cycle implementation time is 60,000 flights.

(b) [Reserved]

[Doc. No. 29104, 65 FR 24126, Apr. 25, 2000; 65 FR 50744, Aug. 21, 2000, as amended by Amdt. 125-36, 66 FR 23131, May 7, 2001; Amdt. 125-40, 67 FR 72834, Dec. 9, 2002; Amdt. 125-46, 69 FR 45942, July 30, 2004. Redesignated by Amdt. 125-53, 72 FR 63412, Nov. 8, 2007; Docket FAA-2018-0119, Amdt. 125-68, 83 FR 9174, Mar. 5, 2018]

125.507 Fuel tank system inspection program

(a) Except as provided in paragraph (g) of this section, this section applies to transport category, turbine-powered airplanes with a type certificate issued after January 1, 1958, that, as a result of original type certification or later increase in capacity, have—

(1) A maximum type-certificated passenger capacity of 30 or more, or

(2) A maximum payload capacity of 7500 pounds or more.

(b) For each airplane on which an auxiliary fuel tank is installed under a field approval, before June 16, 2008, the certificate holder must submit to the responsible Aircraft Certification Service office proposed maintenance instructions for the tank that meet the requirements of Special Federal Aviation Regulation No. 88 (SFAR 88) of this chapter.

(c) After December 16, 2008, no certificate holder may operate an airplane identified in paragraph (a) of this section unless the inspection program for that airplane has been revised to include applicable inspections, procedures, and limitations for fuel tank systems.

(d) The proposed fuel tank system inspection program revisions must be based on fuel tank system Instructions for Continued Airworthiness (ICA) that have been developed in accordance with the applicable provisions of SFAR 88 of this chapter or 25.1529 and part 25, Appendix H, of this chapter, in effect on June 6, 2001 (including those developed for auxiliary fuel tanks, if any, installed under supplemental type certificates or other design approval) and that have been approved by the responsible Aircraft Certification Service office.

(e) After December 16, 2008, before returning an aircraft to service after any alteration for which fuel tank ICA are developed under SFAR 88, or under 25.1529 in effect on June 6, 2001, the certificate holder must include in the inspection program for the airplane inspections and procedures for the fuel tank system based on those ICA.

(f) The fuel tank system inspection program changes identified in paragraphs (d) and (e) of this section and any later fuel tank system revisions must be submitted to the Principal Inspector for review and approval.

(g) This section does not apply to the following airplane models:

  (1) Bombardier CL–44

  (2) Concorde

  (3) deHavilland D.H. 106 Comet 4C

  (4) VFW–Vereinigte Flugtechnische Werk VFW–614

  (5) Illyushin Aviation IL 96T

  (6) Bristol Aircraft Britannia 305

  (7) Handley Page Herald Type 300

  (8) Avions Marcel Dassault—Breguet Aviation Mercure 100C

  (9) Airbus Caravelle

  (10) Lockheed L–300

[Amdt. 125–53, 72 FR 63412, Nov. 8, 2007, as amended by Docket FAA-2018-0119, Amdt. 125-68, 83 FR 9174, Mar. 5, 2018]

125.509 Flammability reduction means

(a) Applicability. Except as provided in paragraph (m) of this section, this section applies to transport category, turbine-powered airplanes with a type certificate issued after January 1, 1958, that, as a result of original type certification or later increase in capacity have:

  (1) A maximum type-certificated passenger capacity of 30 or more, or

  (2) A maximum payload capacity of 7,500 pounds or more.

(b) New Production Airplanes. Except in accordance with 125.201, no person may operate an airplane identified in Table 1 of this section (including all-cargo airplanes) for which the State of Manufacture issued the original certificate of airworthiness or export airworthiness approval after December 27, 2010 unless an Ignition Mitigation Means (IMM) or Flammability Reduction Means (FRM) meeting the requirements of 26.33 of this chapter is operational.

TABLE 1	
Model—Boeing	Model—Airbus
747 Series	A318, A319, A320, A321 Series
737 Series	A330, A340 Series
777 Series	
767 Series	

(c) Auxiliary Fuel Tanks. After the applicable date stated in paragraph (e) of this section, no person may operate any airplane subject to 26.33 of this chapter that has an Auxiliary Fuel Tank installed pursuant to a field approval, unless the following requirements are met:

  (1) The person complies with 14 CFR 26.35 by the applicable date stated in that section.

  (2) The person installs Flammability Impact Mitigation Means (FIMM), if applicable, that is approved by the responsible Aircraft Certification Service office.(3)   Except   in accordance with 125.201, the FIMM, if applicable, are operational.

(d) Retrofit. Except as provided in paragraph (j) of this section, after the dates specified in paragraph (e) of this section, no person may operate an airplane to which this section applies unless the requirements of paragraphs (d)(1) and (d)(2) of this section are met.

  (1) Ignition Mitigation Means (IMM), Flammability Reduction Means (FRM), or FIMM, if required by 26.33, 26.35, or 26.37 of this chapter, that are approved by the responsible Aircraft Certification Service office, are installed within the compliance times specified in paragraph (e) of this section.

  (2) Except in accordance with 125.201 of this part, the IMM, FRM or FIMM, as applicable, are operational.

(e) Compliance Times. The installations required by paragraph (d) of this section must be accomplished no later than the applicable dates specified in paragraph (e)(1), (e)(2) or (e)(3) of this section.

  (1) Fifty percent of each person's fleet of airplanes subject to paragraph (d)(1) of this section must be modified no later than December 26, 2014.

  (2) One hundred percent of each person's fleet of airplanes subject to paragraph (d)(1) of this section must be modified no later than December 26, 2017.

  (3) For those persons that have only one airplane of a model identified in Table 1 of this section, the airplane must be modified no later than December 26, 2017.

(f) Compliance after Installation. Except in accordance with 125.201, no person may—

  (1) Operate an airplane on which IMM or FRM has been installed before the dates specified in paragraph (e) of this section unless the IMM or FRM is operational, or

  (2) Deactivate or remove an IMM or FRM once installed unless it is replaced by a means that complies with paragraph (d) of this section.

(g) Inspection Program Revisions. No person may operate an airplane for which airworthiness limitations have been approved by the responsible Aircraft Certification Service office in accordance with 26.33, 26.35, or 26.37 of this chapter after the airplane is modified in accordance with paragraph (d) of this section unless the inspection program for that airplane is revised to include those applicable airworthiness limitations.

(h) After the inspection program is revised as required by paragraph (g) of this section, before returning an airplane to service after any alteration for which airworthiness limitations are required by 25.981, 26.33, 26.35, or 26.37 of this chapter, the person must revise the inspection program for the airplane to include those airworthiness limitations.

(i) The inspection program changes identified in paragraphs (g) and (h) of this section must be submitted to the operator's assigned Flight Standards office responsible for review and approval prior to incorporation.

(j) The requirements of paragraph (d) of this section do not apply to airplanes operated in all-cargo service, but those airplanes are subject to paragraph (f) of this section.

(k) After the date by which any person is required by this section to modify 100 percent of the affected fleet, no person may operate in passenger service any airplane model specified in Table 2 of this section unless the airplane has been modified to comply with 26.33(c) of this chapter.

FAR 125

TABLE 2	
Model—Boeing	Model—Airbus
747 Series	A318, A319, A320, A321 Series
737 Series	Z300, A310 Series
777 Series	A330, A340 Series
767 Series	
757	

(l) No person may operate any airplane on which an auxiliary fuel tank is installed after December 26, 2017 unless the FAA has certified the tank as compliant with 25.981 of this chapter, in effect on December 26, 2008.

(m) Exclusions. The requirements of this section do not apply to the following airplane models:

(1) Convair CV–240, 340, 440, including turbine powered conversions.

(2) Lockheed L–188 Electra.

(3) Vickers VC-10.

(4) Douglas DC–3, including turbine powered conversions.

(5) Bombardier CL–44.

(6) Mitsubishi YS–11.

(7) BAC 1–11.

(8) Concorde.

(9) deHavilland D.H. 106 Comet 4C.

(10) VFW—Vereinigte Flugtechnische VFW–614.

(11) Illyushin Aviation IL 96T.

(12) Bristol Aircraft Britannia 305.

(13) Handley Page Herald Type 300.

(14) Avions Marcel Dassault—Breguet Aviation Mercure 100C.

(15) Airbus Caravelle.

(16) Fokker F–27/Fairchild Hiller FH–227.

(17) Lockheed L–300.

[Doc. No. FAA-2005-22997, 73 FR 42502, July 21, 2008, as amended by Amdt. 125-57, 74 FR 31619, July 2, 2009; Docket FAA-2018-0119, Amdt. 125-68, 83 FR 9174, Mar. 5, 2018]

Appendix A to Part 125 — Additional Emergency Equipment

(a) Means for emergency evacuation. Each passenger-carrying landplane emergency exit (other than over-the-wing) that is more that 6 feet from the ground with the airplane on the ground and the landing gear extended must have an approved means to assist the occupants in descending to the ground. The assisting means for a floor level emergency exit must meet the requirements of 25.809(f)(1) of this chapter in effect on April 30, 1972, except that, for any airplane for which the application for the type certificate was filed after that date, it must meet the requirements under which the airplane was type certificated. An assisting means that deploys automatically must be armed during taxiing, takeoffs, and landings. However, if the Administrator finds that the design of the exit makes compliance impractical, the Administrator may grant a deviation from the requirement of automatic deployment if the assisting means automatically erects upon deployment and, with respect to required emergency exits, if an emergency evacuation demonstration is conducted in accordance with 125.189. This paragraph does not apply to the rear window emergency exit of DC-3 airplanes operated with less than 36 occupants, including crewmembers, and less than five exits authorized for passenger use.

(b) Interior emergency exit marking. The following must be complied with for each passenger-carrying airplane:

(1) Each passenger emergency exit, its means of access, and means of opening must be conspicuously marked. The identity and location of each passenger emergency exit must be recognizable from a distance equal to the width of the cabin. The location of each passenger emergency exit must be indicated by a sign visible to occupants approaching along the main passenger aisle. There must be a locating sign—

(i) Above the aisle near each over-the-wing passenger emergency exit, or at another ceiling location if it is more practical because of low headroom;

(ii) Next to each floor level passenger emergency exit, except that one sign may serve two such exits if they both can be seen readily from that sign; and

(iii) On each bulkhead or divider that prevents fore and aft vision along the passenger cabin, to indicate emergency exits beyond and obscured by it, except that if this is not possible the sign may be placed at another appropriate location.

(2) Each passenger emergency exit marking and each locating sign must meet the following:

(i) For an airplane for which the application for the type certificate was filed prior to May 1, 1972, each passenger emergency exit marking and each locating sign must be manufactured to meet the requirements of 25.812(b) of this chapter in effect on April 30, 1972. On these airplanes, no sign may continue to be used if its luminescence (brightness) decreases to below 100 microlamberts. The colors may be reversed if it increases the emergency illumination of the passenger compartment. However, the Administrator may authorize deviation from the 2-inch background requirements if the Administrator finds that special circumstances exist that make compliance impractical and that the proposed deviation provides an equivalent level of safety.

(ii) For an airplane for which the application for the type certificate was filed on or after May 1, 1972, each passenger emergency exit marking and each locating sign must be manufactured to meet the interior emergency exit marking requirements under which the airplane was type certificated. On these airplanes, no sign may continue to be used if its luminescence (brightness) decreases to below 250 microlamberts.

(c) Lighting for interior emergency exit markings. Each passenger-carrying airplane must have an emergency lighting system, independent of the main lighting system. However, sources of general cabin illumination may be common to both the emergency and the main lighting systems if the power supply to the emergency lighting system is independent of the power supply to the main lighting system. The emergency lighting system must—

(1) Illuminate each passenger exit marking and locating sign; and

(2) Provide enough general lighting in the passenger cabin so that the average illumination, when measured at 40-inch intervals at seat armrest height, on the centerline of the main passenger aisle, is at least 0.05 foot-candles.

(d) Emergency light operation. Except for lights forming part of emergency lighting subsystems provided in compliance with 25.812(g) of this chapter (as prescribed in paragraph (h) of this section) that serve no more than one assist means, are independent of the airplane's main emergency lighting systems, and are automatically activated when the assist means is deployed, each light required by paragraphs (c) and (h) must comply with the following:

(1) Each light must be operable manually and must operate automatically from the independent lighting system—

(i) In a crash landing; or

(ii) Whenever the airplane's normal electric power to the light is interrupted.

(2) Each light must—

(i) Be operable manually from the flightcrew station and from a point in the passenger compartment that is readily accessible to a normal flight attendant seat;

(ii) Have a means to prevent inadvertent operation of the manual controls; and

(iii) When armed or turned on at either station, remain lighted or become lighted upon interruption of the airplane's normal electric power.

Each light must be armed or turned on during taxiing, takeoff, and landing. In showing compliance with this paragraph, a transverse vertical separation of the fuselage need not be considered.

(3) Each light must provide the required level of illumination for at least 10 minutes at the critical ambient conditions after emergency landing.

(e) Emergency exit operating handles.

(1) For a passenger-carrying airplane for which the application for the type certificate was filed prior to May 1, 1972, the location of each passenger emergency exit operating handle and instructions for opening the exit must be shown by a marking on or near the exit that is readable from a distance of 30 inches. In addition, for each Type I and Type II emergency exit with a locking mechanism released by rotary motion of the handle, the instructions for opening must be shown by—

(i) A red arrow with a shaft at least 3/4 inch wide and a head twice the width of the shaft, extending along at least 70 degrees of arc at a radius approximately equal to 3/4 of the handle length; and

(ii) The word "open" in red letters 1 inch high placed horizontally near the head of the arrow.

(2) For a passenger-carrying airplane for which the application for the type certificate was filed on or after May 1, 1972, the location of each passenger emergency exit operating handle and instructions for opening the exit must be shown in accordance with the requirements under which the airplane was type certificated. On these airplanes, no operating handle or operating handle cover may continue to be used if its luminescence (brightness) decreases to below 100 microlamberts.

(f) Emergency exit access. Access to emergency exits must be provided as follows for each passenger-carrying airplane:

(1) Each passageway between individual passenger areas, or leading to a Type I or Type II emergency exit, must be unobstructed and at least 20 inches wide.

(2) There must be enough space next to each Type I or Type II emergency exit to allow a crewmember to assist in the evacuation of passengers without reducing the unobstructed width of the passageway below that required in paragraph (f)(1) of this section. However, the Administrator may authorize deviation from this requirement for an airplane certificated under the provisions of part 4b of the Civil Air Regulations in effect before December 20, 1951, if the Administrator finds that special circumstances exist that provide an equivalent level of safety.

(3) There must be access from the main aisle to each Type III and Type IV exit. The access from the aisle to these exits must not be obstructed by seats, berths, or other protrusions in a manner that would reduce the effectiveness of the exit. In addition—

(i) For an airplane for which the application for the type certificate was filed prior to May 1, 1972, the access must meet the requirements of 25.813(c) of this chapter in effect on April 30, 1972; and

(ii) For an airplane for which the application for the type certificate was filed on or after May 1, 1972, the access must meet the emergency exit access requirements under which the airplane was certificated.

(4) If it is necessary to pass through a passageway between passenger compartments to reach any required emergency exit from any seat in the passenger cabin, the passageway must not be obstructed. However, curtains may be used if they allow free entry through the passageway.

(5) No door may be installed in any partition between passenger compartments.

(6) If it is necessary to pass through a doorway separating the passenger cabin from other areas to reach any required emergency exit from any passenger seat, the door must have a means to latch it in open position, and the door must be latched open during each takeoff and landing. The latching means must be able to withstand the loads imposed upon it when the door is subjected to the ultimate interia forces, relative to the surrounding structure, listed in 25.561(b) of this chapter.

(g) Exterior exit markings. Each passenger emergency exit and the means of opening that exit from the outside must be marked on the outside of the airplane. There must be a 2-inch colored band outlining each passenger emergency exit on the side of the fuselage. Each outside marking, including the band, must be readily distinguishable from the surrounding fuselage area by contrast in color. The markings must comply with the following:

(1) If the reflectance of the darker color is 15 percent or less, the reflectance of the lighter color must be at least 45 percent. "Reflectance" is the ratio of the luminous flux reflected by a body to the luminous flux it receives.

(2) If the reflectance of the darker color is greater than 15 percent, at least a 30 percent difference between its reflectance and the reflectance of the lighter color must be provided.

(3) Exits that are not in the side of the fuselage must have the external means of opening and applicable instructions marked conspicuously in red or, if red is inconspicuous against the background color, in bright chrome yellow and, when the opening means for such an exit is located on only one side of the fuselage, a conspicuous marking to that effect must be provided on the other side.

(h) Exterior emergency lighting and escape route.

(1) Each passenger-carrying airplane must be equipped with exterior lighting that meets the following requirements:

(i) For an airplane for which the application for the type certificate was filed prior to May 1, 1972, the requirements of 25.812(f) and (g) of this chapter in effect on April 30, 1972.

(ii) For an airplane for which the application for the type certificate was filed on or after May 1, 1972, the exterior emergency lighting requirements under which the airplane was type certificated.

(2) Each passenger-carrying airplane must be equipped with a slip-resistant escape route that meets the following requirements:

(i) For an airplane for which the application for the type certificate was filed prior to May 1, 1972, the requirements of 25.803(e) of this chapter in effect on April 30, 1972.

(ii) For an airplane for which the application for the type certificate was filed on or after May 1, 1972, the slip-resistant escape route requirements under which the airplane was type certificated.

(i) Floor level exits. Each floor level door or exit in the side of the fuselage (other than those leading into a cargo or baggage compartment that is not accessible from the passenger cabin) that is 44 or more inches high and 20 or more inches wide, but not wider than 46 inches, each passenger ventral exit (except the ventral exits on M–404 and CV–240 airplanes) and each tail cone exit must meet the requirements of this section for floor level emergency exits. However, the Administrator may grant a deviation from this paragraph if the Administrator finds that circumstances make full compliance impractical and that an acceptable level of safety has been achieved.

(j) Additional emergency exits. Approved emergency exits in the passenger compartments that are in excess of the minimum num-

FAR 125

ber of required emergency exits must meet all of the applicable provisions of this section except paragraph (f), (1), (2), and (3) and must be readily accessible.

(k) On each large passenger-carrying turbojet-powered airplane, each ventral exit and tailcone exit must be—

(1) Designed and constructed so that it cannot be opened during flight; and

(2) Marked with a placard readable from a distance of 30 inches and installed at a conspicuous location near the means of opening the exit, stating that the exit has been designed and constructed so that it cannot be opened during flight.

Appendix B to Part 125 — Criteria for Demonstration of Emergency Evacuation Procedures Under 125.189

(a) Aborted takeoff demonstration.

(1) The demonstration must be conducted either during the dark of the night or during daylight with the dark of the night simulated. If the demonstration is conducted indoors during daylight hours, it must be conducted with each window covered and each door closed to minimize the daylight effect. Illumination on the floor or ground may be used, but it must be kept low and shielded against shining into the airplane's windows or doors.

(2) The airplane must be in a normal ground attitude with landing gear extended.

(3) Stands or ramps may be used for descent from the wing to the ground. Safety equipment such as mats or inverted life rafts may be placed on the ground to protect participants. No other equipment that is not part of the airplane's emergency evacuation equipment may be used to aid the participants in reaching the ground.

(4) The airplane's normal electric power sources must be de-energized.

(5) All emergency equipment for the type of passenger-carrying operation involved must be installed in accordance with the certificate holder's manual.

(6) Each external door and exit and each internal door or curtain must be in position to simulate a normal takeoff.

(7) A representative passenger load of persons in normal health must be used. At least 30 percent must be females. At least 5 percent must be over 60 years of age with a proportionate number of females. At least 5 percent, but not more than 10 percent, must be children under 12 years of age, prorated through that age group. Three life-size dolls, not included as part of the total passenger load, must be carried by passengers to simulate live infants 2 years old or younger. Crewmembers, mechanics, and training personnel who maintain or operate the airplane in the normal course of their duties may not be used as passengers.

(8) No passenger may be assigned a specific seat except as the Administrator may require. Except as required by item (12) of this paragraph, no employee of the certificate holder may be seated next to an emergency exit.

(9) Seat belts and shoulder harnesses (as required) must be fastened.

(10) Before the start of the demonstration, approximately one-half of the total average amount of carry-on baggage, blankets, pillows, and other similar articles must be distributed at several locations in the aisles and emergency exit access ways to create minor obstructions.

(11) The seating density and arrangement of the airplane must be representative of the highest capacity passenger version of that airplane the certificate holder operates or proposes to operate.

(12) Each crewmember must be a member of a regularly scheduled line crew, must be seated in that crewmember's normally assigned seat for takeoff, and must remain in that seat until the signal for commencement of the demonstration received.

(13) No crewmember or passenger may be given prior knowledge of the emergency exits available for the demonstration.

(14) The certificate holder may not practice, rehearse, or describe the demonstration for the participants nor may a participant have taken part in this type of demonstration within the preceding 6 months.

(15) The pretakeoff passenger briefing required by 125.327 may be given in accordance with the certificate holder's manual. The passengers may also be warned to follow directions of crewmembers, but may not be instructed on the procedures to be followed in the demonstration.

(16) If safety equipment as allowed by item (3) of this section provided, either all passenger and cockpit windows must be blacked out or all of the emergency exits must have safety equipment to prevent disclosure of the available emergency exits.

(17) Not more than 50 percent of the emergency exits in the sides of the fuselage of an airplane that meet all of the requirements applicable to the required emergency exits for that airplane may be used for the demonstration. Exits that are not to be used in the demonstration must have the exit handle deactivated or must be indicated by red lights, red tape or other acceptable means, placed outside the exits to indicate fire or other reason that they are unusable. The exits to be used must be representative of all of the emergency exits on the airplane and must be designated by the certificate holder, subject to approval by the Administrator. At least one floor level exit must be used.

(18) All evacuees, except those using an over-the-wing exit must leave the airplane by a means provided as part of the airplane's equipment.

(19) The certificate holder's approved procedures and all of the emergency equipment that is normally available, including slides, ropes, lights, and megaphones, must be fully utilized during the demonstration.

(20) The evacuation time period is completed when the last occupant has evacuated the airplane and is on the ground. Evacuees using stands or ramps allowed by item (3) above are considered to be on the ground when they are on the stand or ramp: Provided, That the acceptance rate of the stand or ramp is no greater than the acceptance rate of the means available on the airplane for descent from the wing during an actual crash situation.

(b) Ditching demonstration. The demonstration must assume that daylight hours exist outside the airplane and that all required crewmembers are available for the demonstration.

(1) If the certificate holder's manual requires the use of passengers to assist in the launching of liferafts, the needed passengers must be aboard the airplane and participate in the demonstration according to the manual.

(2) A stand must be placed at each emergency exit and wing with the top of the platform at a height simulating the water level of the airplane following a ditching.

(3) After the ditching signal has been received, each evacuee must don a life vest according to the certificate holder's manual.

(4) Each liferaft must be launched and inflated according to the certificate holder's manual and all other required emergency equipment must be placed in rafts.

(5) Each evacuee must enter a liferaft and the crewmembers assigned to each liferaft must indicate the location of emergency equipment aboard the raft and describe its use.

(6) Either the airplane, a mockup of the airplane, or a floating device simulating a passenger compartment must be used.

    (i) If a mockup of the airplane is used, it must be a life-size mockup of the interior and representative of the airplane currently used by or proposed to be used by the certificate holder and must contain adequate seats for use of the evacuees. Operation of the emergency exits and the doors must closely simulate that on the airplane. Sufficient wing area must be installed outside the over-the-wing exits to demonstrate the evacuation.

    (ii) If a floating device simulating a passenger compartment is used, it must be representative, to the extent possible, of the passenger compartment of the airplane used in operations. Operation of the emergency exits and the doors must closely simulate operation on that airplane. Sufficient wing area must be installed outside the over-the-wing exits to demonstrate the evacuation. The device must be equipped with the same survival equipment as is installed on the airplane, to accommodate all persons participating in the demonstration.

Appendix C to Part 125 — Ice Protection

If certification with ice protection provisions is desired, compliance with the following must be shown:

(a) The recommended procedures for the use of the ice protection equipment must be set forth in the Airplane Flight Manual.

(b) An analysis must be performed to establish, on the basis of the airplane's operational needs, the adequacy of the ice protection system for the various components of the airplane. In addition, tests of the ice protection system must be conducted to demonstrate that the airplane is capable of operating safely in continuous maximum and intermittent maximum icing conditions as described in appendix C of part 25 of this chapter.

(c) Compliance with all or portions of this section may be accomplished by reference, where applicable because of similarity of the designs, to analyses and tests performed by the applicant for a type certificated model.

Appendix D to Part 125 — Airplane Flight Recorder Specification

AIRPLANE FLIGHT RECORDER SPECIFICATION				
Parameters	Range	Accuracy (Sensor Input) TO DFDR Readout	Sampling Internal (Per Second)	Resolution Readout
Time (GMT or Frame Counter) (range 0 to 4095, sampled 1 per frame).	24 Hrs.	+/-0.125% Per Hour	0.25 (1 per 4 seconds)	1 sec
Altitude	-1,000 ft to max certificated altitude or aircraft	+/- 100 to +/-700 ft (See Table, 1 TSO-C51a).	1	5 ft to 35 ft[1]
Airspeed	50 KIAS to V_{SO} and V_{SO} to $1.2V_D$	+/-5%, +/-3%	1	1kt
Heading	360°	+/-2°	1	0.5°
Normal Acceleration (Vertical).	-3g to +6g	+/-1% of max range excluding datum error of +/- 5%	8	0.01g
Pitch Attitude	+/-75°	+/-2°	1	0.5°
Roll Attitude	+/-180°	+/-2°	1	0.5°
Radio Transmitter Keying	On-off (Discrete)		1	
Thrust /Power on Each Engine.	Full range forward	+/-2°	1	0.2%[2]
Trailing Edge Flap or Cockpit Control Selection.	Full range or each discrete position.	+/-3° or as pilot's indicator.	0.5	0.5%[2]
Leading Edge Flap or Cockpit Control Selection.	Full range or each discrete position.	+/-3° or as pilot's indicator.	0.5	0.5%[2]
Thrust Reverser Position.	Stowed, in transit, and reverse (Discrete).		1 (per 4 seconds per engine).	
Ground Spoiler Position/Speed Brake Selection.	Full range or each discrete position.	+/-2% unless higher accuracy uniquely required.	1	0.2%[2]
Marker Beacon Passage	Discrete		1	
Autopilot Engagement	Discrete		1	
Longitudinal Acceleration	+/-1g	+/-1.5% max range excluding datum error of +/-5%.	4	0.01g
Pilot Input and/or Surface Position-Primary Controls (Pitch, Roll, Yaw)[3]	Full range	+/-2° unless higher accuracy uniquely required.	1	
Lateral Acceleration	+/-1g	+/-1.5% max range excluding datum error of +/-5%	4	0.01g
Pitch Trim Position	Full range	+/-3% unless higher accuracy uniquely required.	1	0.3%[2]
Glideslope Deviation	+/-400 Microamps	+/-3%	1	0.3%[2]

Appendix D to Part 125 (Continued) — Airplane Flight Recorder Specification

AIRPLANE FLIGHT RECORDER SPECIFICATION				
Parameters	Range	Accuracy (Sensor Input) TO DFDR Readout	Sampling Internal (Per Second)	Resolution Readout
Localizer Deviation	+/-400 Microamps	+/-3%	1	0.3%[2]
AFCS Mode and Engagement Status.	Discrete		1	
Radio Altitude	-20 ft to 2,500 ft	+/-2 Ft or +/-3% Whichever is Greater Below 500 Ft and +/-5% Above 500 Ft.		1 ft +5%[2] above 500 ft
Master Warning	Discrete		1	
Main Gear Squat Switch Status.	Discrete		1	
Angle of Attack (if recorded directly).	As installed	As installed	2	0.3%[2]
Outside Air Temperature or Total Air Temperature.	-50°C to +90°C	+/- 2°C	0.5	0.3°C
Hydraulics, Each System Low Pressure.	Discrete		0.5	or 0.5%[2]
Groundspeed	As installed	Most Accurate systems Installed (IMS Equipped Aircraft Only).	1	0.2%[2]
Drift Angle	When available. As installed.	As installed	4	
Wind Speed and Direction.	When available. As installed.	As installed	4	
Latitude and Longitude	When available. As installed.	As installed	4	
Brake pressure/Brake pedal position.	As installed.	As installed	1	
Additional engine parameters: EPR N[1] N[2] EGT	As installed As installed As installed As installed	As installed As installed As installed As installed	1 (per engine) 1 (per engine) 1 (per engine) 1 (per engine)	
Throttle Lever Position	As installed	As installed	1 (per engine)	
Fuel Flow	As installed	As installed	1 (per engine)	
TCAS: TA RA Sensitivity level (as selected by crew).	As installed As installed As installed	As installed As installed As installed	1 1 2	
GPWS (ground proximity warning system).	Discrete			
Landing gear or gear selector position	Discrete		0.25 (1 per 4 seconds)	
DME 1 and 2 Distance	0-200 NM	As installed	0.25	1 mi
Nav 1 and 2 Frequency Selection	Full range	As installed	0.25	

[1] When altitude rate is recorded. Altitude rate must have sufficient resolution and sampling to permit the derivation of altitude to 5 feet.
[2] Percent of full range.
[3] For airplanes that can demonstrate the capability of deriving either the control input on control movement (one from the other) for all modes of operation and flight regimes, the "or" applies. For airplanes with non-mechanical control systems (fly-by-wire) the "and" applies. In airplanes with split surfaces, suitable combination of inputs is acceptable in lieu of recording each surface separately.
[4] this column applies to aircraft manufactured after October 11,1991.

[Doc. No. 25530, 53 FR 26150, July 11, 1988; 53 FR 30906, Aug. 16, 1988]

Appendix E to Part 125 — Airplane Flight Recorder Specifications

Tables on following pages.

The recorded values must meet the designated range, resolution and accuracy requirements during static and dynamic conditions. Dynamic condition means the parameter is experiencing change at the maximum rate attainable, including the maximum rate of reversal. All data recorded must be correlated in time to within one second.

[Doc. No. 28109, 62 FR 38390, July 17, 1997; 62 FR 48135, Sept. 12, 1997, as amended by Amdt. 125–32, 64 FR 46121, Aug. 24, 1999; 65 FR 2295, Jan. 14, 2000; Amdt. 125–32, 65 FR 2295, Jan. 14, 2000; Amdt. 125–34, 65 FR 51745, Aug. 24, 2000; 65 FR 81735, Dec. 27, 2000; Amdt. 125–39, 67 FR 54323, Aug. 21, 2002; Amdt. 125–42, 68 FR 42937, July 18, 2003; 68 FR 50069, Aug. 20, 2003; 68 FR 53877, Sept. 15, 2003; Amdt. 125–54, 73 FR 12568, Mar. 7, 2008; Amdt. 125-60, 75 FR 17046, Apr. 5, 2010; Amdt. 125-57, 75 FR 7357, Feb. 19, 2010]

Appendix E to Part 125 (Continued)

PARAMETERS	RANGE	ACCURACY (SENSOR INPUT)	SECONDS PER SAMPLING INTERVAL	RESOLUTION	REMARKS
		AIRPLANE FLIGHT RECORDER SPECIFICATIONS			
2. Pressure Altitude	-1000 ft to max certificated altitude of aircraft. +5000 ft.	+/-100 to +/-700ft (see table, TSO C124a or TSO C51a).	1	5 ft to 35 ft	Data should be obtained from the air data computer when practicable.
3. Indicated airspeed or Calibrated airspeed	50 KIAS or minimum value to Max V_{SO} to $1.2V_D$	+/-5% and +/-3%	1	1 kt	Data should be obtained from the air data computer when practicable.
4. Heading (Primary flight crew reference)	0-360° and Discrete "true" or "mag."	+/-2°	1	0.5°	When true or magnetic heading can be selected as the primary heading reference, a discrete indicating selection must be recorded.
5. Normal Acceleration (Vertical)	-3g to +6g	+/-1% of max range excluding datum error of +/-5%	0.125	0.004g	
6. Pitch Attitude	+/-75°	+/-2°	1 or 0.25 for airplanes operated under 125.226(f)	0.5°	A sampling rate of 0.25 is recommended.
7. Roll Attitude[2]	+/-180°	+/-2°	1 or 0.5 for airplanes operated under 121.344(f)	0.5°	A sampling rate of 0.5 is recommended.
8. Manual Radio Transmitter Keying CVR/DFDR synchronization reference	On-Off (Discrete) None		1		Preferably each crew member but one discrete acceptable for all transmission provided the CVR/FDR system complies with TSO C124a CVR synchronization (paragraph 4.2.1 ED-55).
9. Thrust/Power on each engine—primary flight crew reference[14]	Full Range Forward	+/-2%	1 (per engine)	0.2% of full range	Sufficient parameters (e.g. EPR, N1 or Torque, NP) as appropriate to the particular engine be recorded to determine power in forward and reverse thrust, including potential overspeed condition.
10. Autopilot Engagement.	Discrete "on" or "off"		1		
11. Longitudinal Acceleration	+/-1g	+/-1.5% max. range excluding datum error of +/-5%	0.25	0.004g	
12 a. Pitch Control(s) position (non-fly-by-wire systems)	Full Range	+/-2° Unless Higher Accuracy Uniquely Required	0.5 or 0.25 for airplanes operated under 125.226(f)	0.2% of full range	For airplanes that have a flight control break away capability that allows either pilot to operate the controls independently, record both control inputs. The control inputs may be sampled alternately once per second to produce the sampling interval of 0.5 or 0.25, as applicable.
12b. Pitch Control(s) Position (fly-by-wire systems)[3]	Full Range	+/-2° Unless Higher Accuracy Uniquely Required	0.5 or 0.25 for airplanes operated under 121.344(f)	0.2% of full range	
13a. Lateral Control position(s) (non-fly-by-wire)	Full Range	+/-2° Unless Higher Accuracy Uniquely Required	0.5 or 0.25 for airplanes operated under 125.226(f)	0.2% of full range	For airplanes that have a flight control break away capability that allows either pilot to operate the controls independently, record both control inputs. The control inputs may be sampled alternately once per second to produce the sampling interval of 0.5 or 0.25, as applicable.
13b. Lateral Control position(s) (fly-by-wire)	Full Range	+/-2° Unless Higher Accuracy Uniquely Required	0.5 or 0.25 for airplanes operated under 121.344(f)	0.2% of full range	

FAR
125

Appendix E to Part 125 (Continued)

AIRPLANE FLIGHT RECORDER SPECIFICATIONS					
PARAMETERS	RANGE	ACCURACY (SENSOR INPUT)	SECONDS PER SAMPLING INTERVAL	RESOLUTION	REMARKS
14a. Yaw Control position(s) (non-fly-by-wire)[5]	Full Range	+/-2° Unless Higher Accuracy Uniquely Required	0.5	0.2% of full range	For airplanes that have a flight control break away capability that allows either pilot to operate the controls independently, record both control inputs. The control inputs may be sampled alternately once per second to produce the sampling interval of 0.5.
14b. Yaw Control position(s) (fly-by-wire)	Full Range	+/-2° Unless Higher Accuracy Uniquely Required	0.5	0.2% of full range	
15. Pitch Control Surface(s) Position[6]	Full Range	+/-2° Unless Higher Accuracy Uniquely Required	0.5 or 0.25 for airplanes operated under 121.344(f)	0.2% of full range	For airplanes fitted with multiple or split surfaces, a suitable combination of inputs is acceptable in lieu of recording each surface separately. The control surfaces may be sampled alernately to produce the sampling interval of 0.5 or 0.25.
16 Lateral Control Surface(s) Position[7]	Full Range	+/-2° Unless Higher Accuracy Uniquely Required	0.5 or 0.25 for airplanes operated under 121.344(f)	0.2% of full range	A suitable combination of surface position sensors is acceptable in lieu of recording each surface separately. The control surfaces may be sampled alternately to produce the sampling interval of 0.5 or 0.25.
17. Yaw Control Surface(s) Position[8]	Full Range	+/-2° Unless Higher Accuracy Uniquely Required	0.5	0.2% of full range	For airplanes with multiple or split surfaces, a suitable combination of surface position sensors is acceptable in lieu of recording each surface separately. The control surfaces may be sampled alternately to produce the sampling interval of 0.5.
18. Lateral Acceleration	+/- 1g	+/-1.5% max. range excluding datum error of +/-5%	0.25	0.004g	
19. Pitch Trim Surface Position[8]	Full Range	+/-3 deg. Unless Higher Accuracy Uniquely Required	1	0.3% of full range	
20. Trailing Edge Flap or Cockpit Control Selection[10]	Full Range of Each position (discrete)	+/-3 deg. or as Pilot's Indicator	2	0.5% of full range	Flap position and cockpit control may each be sampled alternately at 4 second intervals, to give a data point every 2 seconds.
21. Leading Edge Flap or Cockpit Control Selection[11]	Full Range of Each Discrete Position	+/-3° or as Pilot's indicator and sufficient to determine each discrete position	2	0.5% of full range	Left and right sides, or flap position and cockpit control may each be sampled at 4 second intervals so as to give a data point every 2 seconds.
22. Each Thrust Reverser Position (or equivalent for propeller airplane)	Stowed, In Transit, and Reverse (Discrete)		1 (per engine)		Turbo-jet — 2 discretes enable the 3 states to be determined. Turbo-prop 1 discrete.
23. Ground Spoiler Position or Speed Brake Selection[12]	Full Range or Each Position. (discrete)	+/-2° Unless Higher Accuracy Uniquely Required.	1 or 0.5 for airplanes operated under 121.344(f)	0.2% of full range	
24. Outside Air Temperature or Total Air Temperature[13]	-50°C to +90° C	+/-2°C	2	+/-3°C	

Appendix E to Part 125 (Continued)

AIRPLANE FLIGHT RECORDER SPECIFICATIONS					
PARAMETERS	RANGE	ACCURACY (SENSOR INPUT)	SECONDS PER SAMPLING INTERVAL	RESOLUTION	REMARKS
25. Autopilot/ Autothrottle/AFCS Mode and Engagement Status	A suitable combination of discretes		1		Discretes should show which systems are engaged and which primary modes are controlling the flight path and speed of the aircraft.
26. Radio Altitude	-20 ft to 2,500 ft	+/-2 ft or +/- 3% Whichever is Greater Below 500 ft and +/-5% Above 500 ft.	1	1 ft +5% above 500 ft	For autoland/category 3 operations, each radio altimeter should be recorded, but arranged so that at least one is recorded each second.
27. Localizer Deviation, MLS Azimuth, or GPS Lateral Deviation	+/-400 Microamps or available sensor range as installed. +/-62°	As installed +/-3% recommended.	1	0.3% of full range	For autoland/category 3 operations, each radio altimeter should be recorded, but arranged so that at least one is recorded each second. It is not necessary to record ILS and MLS at the same time, only the approach aid in use need be recorded.
28. Glideslope Deviation, MLS Elevation, or GPS Vertical Deviation	+/-400 Microamps or available sensor range as installed. 0.9 to +30°	As installed +/-3% recommended	1	0.3% of full range	For autoland/category 3 operations, each radio altimeter should be recorded, but arranged so that at least one is recorded each second. It is not necessary to record ILS and MLS at the same time, only the approach aid in use need be recorded.
29. Marker Beacon Passage	Discrete "on" or "off"		1		A single discrete is acceptable for all markers
30. Master Warning	Discrete		1		Record the master warning and record each 'red' warning that connot be determined from other parameters or from the cockpit voice recorder.
31. Air/ground sensor (primary airplane system reference nose or main gear)	Discrete "air" or "ground"		1 (0.25 recommended.)		
32. Angle of Attack (If measured directly)	As installed	As Installed	2 or 0.5 for airplanes operated under §125.226(f)	0.3% of full range	If left and right sensors are available, each may be recorded at 4 or 1 second intervals, as appropriate, so as to give a data point at 2 seconds or 0.5 second, as required.
33.Hydraulic Pressure Low, Each System	Discrete or available sensor range, "low" or "normal"	+/-5%	2	0.5% of full range	
34. Groundspeed	As Installed	Most Accurate Systems Installed	1	0.2% of full range	
35.GPWS (ground proximity warning system)	Discrete "warning" or "off"		1		A suitable combination of discretes unless recorder capicaity is limited in which case a single discrete for all modes is acceptable.
36. Landing Gear Position or Landing gear cockpit control selection	Discrete		4		A suitable combination of discretes should be recorded.
37. Drift Angle[15]	As installed	As installed	4	0.1°	
38. Wind Speed and Direction	As installed	As installed	4	1 knot, and 1.0°	
39.Latitude and Longitude	As installed	As installed	4	0.002°, or as installed	Provided by the Primary Navigation System Reference. Where capacity permits Latitude/longitude resolution should be 0.0002°.

FAR
125

Appendix E to Part 125 (Continued)

AIRPLANE FLIGHT RECORDER SPECIFICATIONS					
PARAMETERS	RANGE	ACCURACY (SENSOR INPUT)	SECONDS PER SAMPLING INTERVAL	RESOLUTION	REMARKS
40. Stick shaker and pusher activation	Discrete(s) "on" or "off"		1		A suitable combination of discretes to determine activation.
41. Windshear Detection	Discrete "warning" or "off"		1		
42. Throttle/Power Lever Position[16]	Full Range	+/-2%	1 for each lever	2% of full range	For airplanes with non-mechanically linked cockpit engine controls.
43. Additional Engine Parameters	As installed	As installed	Each engine each second	2% of full range	Where capacity permits, the preferred priority is indicated vibration level, N2, EGT, Fuel Flow, Fuel Cut-off lever position and N3, unless engine manufacturer recommends otherwise.
44. Traffic Alert and Collision Avoidance System (TCAS)	Discretes	As installed	1		A suitable combination of discretes should be recorded to determine the status of—Combined Control, Vertical Control, Up Advisory, and Down Advisory. (ref. ARINC Characteristic 735 Attachment 6E, TCAS VERTICAL RA DATA OUTPUT WORD.)
45. DME 1 and 2 Distance	0-200 NM	As installed	4	1NM	1 mile
46. Nav 1 and 2 Selected Frequency	Full Range	As installed	4		Sufficient to determine selected frequency
47. Selected barometric setting	Full Range	+/-5%	(1 per 64 sec.)	0.2% of full range	
48. Selected Altitude	Full Range	+/-5%	1	100 ft	
49. Selected speed	Full Range	+/-5%	1	1 knot	
35. GPWS (ground proximity warning system)	Discrete "warning" or "off"		1		A suitable combination of discretes unless recorder capicaity is limited in which case a single discrete for all modes is acceptable.
50. Selected Mach	Full Range	+/-5%	1	.01	
51. Selected vertical speed	Full Range	+/-5%	1	100 ft/min	
52. Selected heading	Full Range	+/-5%	1	1°	
53. Selected flight path	Full Range	+/-5%	1	1°	
54. Selected decision height	Full Range	+/-5%	64	1 ft	
55. EFIS display format	Discrete(s)		4		Discretes should show the display system status (e.g. off, normal, fail, composite, sector, plan nav aids, weather radar, range, copy.
56. Multi-function Engine Alerts Display format	Discrete(s)		4		Discretes should show the display system status (e.g. off, normal, fail, and the identity of display pages for emergency procedures, need not be recorded.
57. Thrust command[17]	Full Range	+/-2%	2	2% of full range	
58. Thrust target	Full Range	+/-2%	4	2% of full range	
59. Fuel quantity in CG trim tank	Full Range	+/-5%	(1 per 64 sec.)	1% of full range	
60. Primary Navigation System Reference	Discrete GPS, INS, VOR/DME, MLS, Localizer Glideslope		4		A suitable combination of discretes to determine the Primary Navigation System reference.

Appendix E to Part 125 (Continued)

			AIRPLANE FLIGHT RECORDER SPECIFICATIONS		
PARAMETERS	RANGE	ACCURACY (SENSOR INPUT)	SECONDS PER SAMPLING INTERVAL	RESOLUTION	REMARKS
61. Ice Detection	Discrete "ice" or "no ice"		4		
62. Engine warning each engine vibration	Discrete		1		
63. Engine warning each engine over temp	Discrete		1		
64. Engine warning each engine oil pressure low	Discrete		1		
65. Engine warning each engine over speed	Discrete		1		
66. Yaw Trim Surface Position	Full Range	+/-3% Unless Higher Accuracy Uniquely Required	2	0.3% of full range	
67. Roll Trim Surface Position	Full Range	+/-3% Unless Higher Accuracy Uniquely Required	2	0.3% of full range	
68. Brake Pressure (left and right	As installed	+/-5%	1		To determine braking effort applied by pilots or by autobrakes
69. Brake Pedal Application (left and right)	Discrete or Analog "applied" or "off"	+/-5% (Analog)	1		To determine braking applied by pilots.
70. Yaw or sideslip angle	Full Range	+/-5%	1	0.5°	
71. Engine bleed valve position	Discrete "open" or "closed"		4		
72. De-icing or anti-icing system selection	Discrete "on" or "off"		4		
73. Computed center of gravity	Full Range	+/-5%	(1 per 64 sec.)	1% of full range	
74. AC electrical bus status.	Discrete "power" or "off"		4		Each bus.
75. DC electrical bus status.	Discrete "power" or "off"		4		Each bus.
76. APU bleed valve position.	Discrete "open" or "closed"		4		
77. Hydraulic Pressure (each system)	Full Range	+/-5%	2	100 psi	
78. Loss of cabin pressure	Discrete "loss" or "normal"		1		
79. Computer failure (critical flight and engine control systems)	Discrete "fail" or "normal"		4		
80. Heads -up display (when an information source is installed)	Discrete(s) "on" or "off"		4		
81. Para-visual display (when an information source is installed)	Discrete(s) "on" or "off"		1		

FAR 125

Appendix E to Part 125 (Continued)

AIRPLANE FLIGHT RECORDER SPECIFICATIONS					
PARAMETERS	RANGE	ACCURACY (SENSOR INPUT)	SECONDS PER SAMPLING INTERVAL	RESOLUTION	REMARKS
82. Cockpit trim control input position - pitch	Full Range	+/-5%	1	0.2% of full range	Where mechanical means for control inputs are not available, cockpit display trim positions should be recorded.
83. Cockpit trim control input position - roll	Full Range	+/-5%	1	0.7% of full range	Where mechanical means for control inputs are not available, cockpit display trim positions should be recorded.
84. Cockpit trim control input position - yaw	Full Range	+/-5%	1	0.3% of full range	Where mechanical means for control inputs are not available, cockpit display trim positions should be recorded.
85. Trailing edge flap and cockpit flap control position	Full Range	+/-5%	2	0.5% of full range	Trailing edge flaps and cockpit flap control position may each be sampled alternately at 4 second intervals to provide a sample each 0.5 second.
86. Leading edge flap and cockpit flap control position	Full Range or Discrete	+/-5%	1	0.5% of full range	
87. Ground spoiler position and speed brake selection	Full Range or Discrete	+/-5%	0.5	0.2% of full range	
88. All cockpit flight control input forces (control wheel, control column, rudder pedal)	Full Range Control wheel +/- 70 lbs Control Column +/-85 lbs Rudder pedal +/- 165 lbs	+/-5%	1	0.2% of full range	For fly-by-wire flight control systems, where flight control surface position is a function of the control input device only, it is not necessary to record this parameter. For airplanes that have a flight control breakaway capability that allows either pilot to operate the control independently, record both control force inputs. The control force inputs may be sampled alternately once per 2 seconds to produce the sampling interval of 1.

[1]For A300 B2/B4 airplanes, resolution = 6 seconds.
[2]For A330/A340 series airplanes, resolution = 0.703 deg.
[3]For A318/A319/A320/A321 series airplanes, resolution = 0.275% (0.088 deg.>0.064 deg.).
For A330/A340 series airplanes, resolution = 2.20% (0.703 deg. >0.064 deg.).
[4]For A318/A319/A320/A321 series airplanes, resolution = 0.22% (0.088 deg. >0.080 deg.).
For A330/A340 series airplanes, resolution = 1.76% (0.703 deg. >0.080 deg.).
[5]For A330/A340 series airplanes, resolution = 1.18% (0.703° >0.120°).
For A330/A340 series airplanes, seconds per sampling interval = 1.
[6]For A330/A340 series airplanes, resolution = 0.783% (0.352 deg. >0.090 deg.).
[7]For A330/A340 series airplanes, aileron resolution = 0.704% (0.352 deg. >0.100 deg.).
For A330/A340 series airplanes, spoiler resolution = 1.406% (0.703 deg. >0.100 deg.).
[8]For A330/A340 series airplanes, resolution = 0.30% (0.176 deg. >0.12 deg.).
For A330/A340 series airplanes, seconds per sampling interval = 1.
[9]For all Airbus airplanes , resolution = 0.518% (0.088 deg. >0.051 deg.).
[10]For A330/340 series airplanes, resolution = 1.05% (0.250 deg. >0.120 deg.).
[11]For A330/A340 series airplanes, resolution = 1.05% (0.250 deg. >0.120 deg.).
For A300 B2/B4 series airplanes, resolution = 0.92% (0.230 deg. >0.125 deg.).
[12]For A300-600/A310 series airplanes, speed brake resolution = 0.224% (0.112 deg. >0.100 deg.).
For A330/A340 series airplanes, spoiler resolution = 1.406% (0.703 deg. >0.100 deg.).
[13]For A330/A340 series airplanes = 0.5 deg. C.).
[14]For A330 airplanes with PW or RR engines, resolution = .29%
[15]For A330/A340 series airplanes, resolution = 0.352 deg.
[16]For A318/319/A320/A321 series airplanes, resolution = 4.32%. F or A330/A340 series airplanes, resolution is 3.27% of full range for throttle lever angle (TLA; for reverse thrust, reverse throttle lever angle (RLA) resolution is nonlinear over the active reverse thrust range, which is 51.54 deg. to 96.14 deg. The resolved element is 2.8 deg. uniformly over the entire active reverse thrust range, or 2.9% of the full range value of 96.14 deg.
[17]For A318/A319/A320/A321 series airplanes, with IAE engines. resolution = 2.58%.
[18]For all aircraft manufactured on or after December 6, 2010, the seconds per sampling interval is 0.125. Each input must be recorded at this rate. Alternately sampling inputs (interleaving) to meet this sampling interval is prohibited.

[Doc. No. 28109, 62 FR 38390, July 17, 1997; 62 FR 48135, Sept. 12, 1997, as amended by Amdt. 125-32, 64 FR 46121, Aug. 24, 1999; 65 FR 2295, Jan. 14, 2000; Amdt. 125-32, 65 FR 2295, Jan. 14, 2000; Amdt. 125-34, 65 FR 51745, Aug. 24, 2000; 65 FR 81735, Dec. 27, 2000; Amdt. 125-39, 67 FR 54323, Aug. 21, 2002; Amdt. 125-42, 68 FR 42937, July 18, 2003; 68 FR 50069, Aug. 20, 2003; 68 FR 53877, Sept. 15, 2003; Amdt. 125-54, 73 FR 12568, Mar. 7, 2008; Amdt. 125-56, 73 FR 73180, Dec. 2, 2008; Amdt. 125-60, 75 FR 17046, Apr. 5, 2010; Amdt. 125-59, 75 FR 7357, Feb. 19, 2010; Amdt. 125-62, 78 FR 39971, July 3, 2013; Docket FAA-2017-0733, Amdt. 125-67, 82 FR 34399, July 25, 2017]

PART 135 — OPERATING REQUIREMENTS: COMMUTER AND ON-DEMAND OPERATIONS AND RULES GOVERNING PERSONS ON BOARD SUCH AIRCRAFT

Authority: 49 U.S.C. 106(f), 106(g), 40113, 41706, 44701-44702, 44705, 44709, 44711-44713, 44715-44717, 44722, 44730, 45101-45105; Pub. L. 112-95, 126 Stat. 58 (49 U.S.C. 44730).

Source: Docket No. 16097, 43 FR 46783, Oct. 10, 1978, unless otherwise noted.

Special Federal Aviation Regulation No. 50–2

Editorial Note: For the text of SFAR No. 50–2, see part 91 of this book.

Special Federal Aviation Regulation No. 97

Editorial Note: For the text of SFAR No. 97, see part 91 of this book.

FAR 135

Subpart A — General

Authority: 49 U.S.C. 106(f), 106(g), 40113, 41706, 44701-44702, 44705, 44709, 44711-44713, 44715-44717, 44722, 44730, 45101-45105; Pub. L. 112-95, 126 Stat. 58 (49 U.S.C. 44730).

Source: Docket No. 16097, 43 FR 46783, Oct. 10, 1978, unless otherwise noted.

135.1   Applicability

(a) This part prescribes rules governing—

(1) The commuter or on-demand operations of each person who holds or is required to hold an Air Carrier Certificate or Operating Certificate under part 119 of this chapter.

(2) Each person employed or used by a certificate holder conducting operations under this part including the maintenance, preventative maintenance and alteration of an aircraft.

(3) The transportation of mail by aircraft conducted under a postal service contract awarded under 39 U.S.C. 5402c.

(4) Each person who applies for provisional approval of an Advanced Qualification Program curriculum, curriculum segment, or portion of a curriculum segment under subpart Y of part 121 of this chapter of 14 CFR part 121 and each person employed or used by an air carrier or commercial operator under this part to perform training, qualification, or evaluation functions under an Advanced Qualification Program under subpart Y of part 121 of this chapter of 14 CFR part 121.

(5) Nonstop Commercial Air Tour flights conducted for compensation or hire in accordance with 119.1(e)(2) of this chapter that begin and end at the same airport and are conducted within a 25-statute-mile radius of that airport; provided further that these operations must comply only with the drug and alcohol testing requirements in 120.31, 120.33, 120.35, 120.37, and 120.39 of this chapter; and with the provisions of part 136, subpart A, and 91.147 of this chapter by September 11, 2007.

(6) Each person who is on board an aircraft being operated under this part.

(7) Each person who is an applicant for an Air Carrier Certificate or an Operating Certificate under 119 of this chapter, when conducting proving tests.

(8) Commercial Air tours conducted by holders of operations specifications issued under this part must comply with the provisions of part 136, Subpart A of this chapter by September 11, 2007.

(9) Helicopter air ambulance operations as defined in §135.601(b)(1).

(b) [Reserved]

(c) An operator who does not hold a part 119 certificate and who operates under the provisions of 91.147 of this chapter is permitted to use a person who is otherwise authorized to perform aircraft maintenance or preventive maintenance duties and who is not subject to anti-drug and alcohol misuse prevent programs to perform—

(1) Aircraft maintenance or preventive maintenance on the operator's aircraft if the operator would otherwise be required to transport the aircraft more than 50 nautical miles further than the repair point closest to operator's principal place of operation to obtain these services; or

(2) Emergency repairs on the operator's aircraft if the aircraft cannot be safely operated to a location where an employee subject to FAA-approved programs can perform the repairs.

[Doc. No. 16097, 43 FR 46783, Oct. 10, 1978]

Editorial Note: ForFederal Registercitations affecting 135.1, see the List of CFR Sections Affected, which appears in the Finding Aids section of the printed volume and on GPO Access.

FAR 135

135.2 Compliance schedule for operators that transition to part 121 of this chapter; certain new entrant operators

(a) Applicability. This section applies to the following:

(1) Each certificate holder that was issued an air carrier or operating certificate and operations specifications under the requirements of part 135 of this chapter or under SFAR No. 38–2 of 14 CFR part 121 before January 19, 1996, and that conducts scheduled passenger-carrying operations with:

    (i) Nontransport category turbopropeller powered airplanes type certificated after December 31, 1964, that have a passenger seat configuration of 10–19 seats;

    (ii) Transport category turbopropeller powered airplanes that have a passenger seat configuration of 20–30 seats; or

    (iii) Turbojet engine powered airplanes having a passenger seat configuration of 1–30 seats.

(2) Each person who, after January 19, 1996, applies for or obtains an initial air carrier or operating certificate and operations specifications to conduct scheduled passenger-carrying operations in the kinds of airplanes described in paragraphs (a)(1)(i), (a)(1)(ii), or paragraph (a)(1)(iii) of this section.

(b) Obtaining operations specifications. A certificate holder described in paragraph (a)(1) of this section may not, after March 20, 1997, operate an airplane described in paragraphs (a)(1)(i), (a)(1)(ii), or (a)(1)(iii) of this section in scheduled passenger-carrying operations, unless it obtains operations specifications to conduct its scheduled operations under part 121 of this chapter on or before March 20, 1997.

(c) Regular or accelerated compliance. Except as provided in paragraphs (d), and (e) of this section, each certificate holder described in paragraph (a)(1) of this section shall comply with each applicable requirement of part 121 of this chapter on and after March 20, 1997 or on and after the date on which the certificate holder is issued operations specifications under this part, whichever occurs first. Except as provided in paragraphs (d) and (e) of this section, each person described in paragraph (a)(2) of this section shall comply with each applicable requirement of part 121 of this chapter on and after the date on which that person is issued a certificate and operations specifications under part 121 of this chapter.

(d) Delayed compliance dates. Unless paragraph (e) of this section specifies an earlier compliance date, no certificate holder that is covered by paragraph (a) of this section may operate an airplane in 14 CFR part 121 operations on or after a date listed in this paragraph unless that airplane meets the applicable requirement of this paragraph:

(1) Nontransport category turbopropeller powered airplanes type certificated after December 31, 1964, that have a passenger seat configuration of 10–19 seats. No certificate holder may operate under this part an airplane that is described in paragraph (a)(1)(i) of this section on or after a date listed in paragraph (d)(1) of this section unless that airplane meets the applicable requirement listed in paragraph (d)(1) of this section:

    (i) December 20, 1997:

      (A) Section 121.289, Landing gear aural warning.

      (B) Section 121.308, Lavatory fire protection.

      (C) Section 121.310(e), Emergency exit handle illumination.

      (D) Section 121.337(b)(8), Protective breathing equipment.

      (E) Section 121.340, Emergency flotation means.

    (ii) December 20, 1999: Section 121.342, Pitot heat indication system.

    (iii) December 20, 2010:

      (A) For airplanes described in 121.157(f), the Airplane Performance Operating Limitations in 121.189 through 121.197.

      (B) Section 121.161(b), Ditching approval.

      (C) Section 121.305(j), Third attitude indicator.

      (D) Section 121.312(c), Passenger seat cushion flammability.

    (iv) March 12, 1999: Section 121.310(b)(1), Interior emergency exit locating sign.

(2) Transport category turbopropeller powered airplanes that have a passenger seat configuration of 20–30 seats. No certificate holder may operate under this part an airplane that is described in paragraph (a)(1)(ii) of this section on or after a date listed in paragraph (d)(2) of this section unless that airplane meets the applicable requirement listed in paragraph (d)(2) of this section:

    (i) December 20, 1997:

      (A) Section 121.308, Lavatory fire protection.

      (B) Section 121.337(b) (8) and (9), Protective breathing equipment.

      (C) Section 121.340, Emergency flotation means.

    (ii) December 20, 2010: Section 121.305(j), Third attitude indicator.

(e) Newly manufactured airplanes. No certificate holder that is described in paragraph (a) of this section may operate under part 121 of this chapter an airplane manufactured on or after a date listed in this paragraph (e) unless that airplane meets the applicable requirement listed in this paragraph (e).

(1) For nontransport category turbopropeller powered airplanes type certificated after December 31, 1964, that have a passenger seat configuration of 10–19 seats:

    (i) Manufactured on or after March 20, 1997:

      (A) Section 121.305(j), Third attitude indicator.

      (B) Section 121.311(f), Safety belts and shoulder harnesses.

    (ii) Manufactured on or after December 20, 1997: Section 121.317(a), Fasten seat belt light.

    (iii) Manufactured on or after December 20, 1999: Section 121.293, Takeoff warning system.

    (iv) Manufactured on or after March 12, 1999: Section 121.310(b)(1), Interior emergency exit locating sign.

(2) For transport category turbopropeller powered airplanes that have a passenger seat configuration of 20–30 seats manufactured on or after March 20, 1997: Section 121.305(j), Third attitude indicator.

(f) New type certification requirements. No person may operate an airplane for which the application for a type certificate was filed after March 29, 1995, in 14 CFR part 121 operations unless that airplane is type certificated under part 25 of this chapter.

(g) Transition plan. Before March 19, 1996 each certificate holder described in paragraph (a)(1) of this section must submit to the FAA a transition plan (containing a calendar of events) for moving from conducting its scheduled operations under the commuter requirements of part 135 of this chapter to the requirements for domestic or flag operations under part 121 of this chapter. Each transition plan must contain details on the following:

(1) Plans for obtaining new operations specifications authorizing domestic or flag operations;

(2) Plans for being in compliance with the applicable requirements of part 121 of this chapter on or before March 20, 1997; and

(3) Plans for complying with the compliance date schedules contained in paragraphs (d) and (e) of this section.

[Doc. No. 28154, 60 FR 65938, Dec. 20, 1995, as amended by Amdt. 135–65, 61 FR 30435, June 14, 1996; Amdt. 135–66, 62 FR 13257, Mar. 19, 1997]

135.3 Rules applicable to operations subject to this part

(a) Each person operating an aircraft in operations under this part shall—

(1) While operating inside the United States, comply with the applicable rules of this chapter; and

(2) While operating outside the United States, comply with Annex 2, Rules of the Air, to the Convention on International Civil Aviation or the regulations of any foreign country, whichever applies, and with any rules of parts 61 and 91 of this chapter and this part that are more restrictive than that Annex or those regulations and that can be complied with without violating that Annex or those regulations. Annex 2 is incorporated by reference in 91.703(b) of this chapter.

(b) Each certificate holder that conducts commuter operations under this part with airplanes in which two pilots are required by the type certification rules of this chapter shall comply with subparts N and O of part 121 of this chapter instead of the requirements of subparts E, G, and H of this part. Notwithstanding the requirements of this paragraph, a pilot serving under this part as second in command in a commuter operation with airplanes in which two pilots are required by the type certification rules of this chapter may meet the requirements of 135.245 instead of the requirements of 121.436.

(c) If authorized by the Administrator upon application, each certificate holder that conducts operations under this part to which paragraph (b) of this section does not apply, may comply with the applicable sections of subparts N and O of part 121 instead of the requirements of subparts E, G, and H of this part, except that those authorized certificate holders may choose to comply with the operating experience requirements of 135.244, instead of the requirements of 121.434 of this chapter. Notwithstanding the requirements of this paragraph, a pilot serving under this part as second in command may meet the requirements of 135.245 instead of the requirements of 121.436.

(d) Additional limitations applicable to certificate holders that are required by paragraph (b) of this section or authorized in accordance with paragraph (c) of this section, to comply with part 121, subparts N and O of this chapter instead of subparts E, G, and H of this part.

(1) Upgrade training.

(i) Each certificate holder must include in upgrade ground training for pilots, instruction in at least the subjects identified in 121.419(a) of this chapter, as applicable to their assigned duties; and, for pilots serving in crews of two or more pilots, beginning on April 27, 2022, instruction and facilitated discussion in the subjects identified in §121.419(c) of this chapter.

(ii) Each certificate holder must include in upgrade flight training for pilots, flight training for the maneuvers and procedures required in 121.424(a), (c), (e), and (f) of this chapter; and, for pilots serving in crews of two or more pilots, beginning on April 27, 2022, the flight training required in 121.424(b) of this chapter.

(2) Initial and recurrent leadership and command and mentoring training. Certificate holders are not required to include leadership and command training in 121.409(b)(2)(ii)(B)(6), 121.419(c)(1), 121.424(b) and 121.427(d)(1) of this chapter and mentoring training in 121.419(c)(2) and 121.427(d)(1) of this chapter in initial and recurrent training for pilots in command who serve in operations that use only one pilot.

(3) One-time leadership and command and mentoring training. Section 121.429 of this chapter does not apply to certificate holders conducting operations under this part when those operations use only one pilot.

[Doc. No. 27993, 60 FR 65949, Dec. 20, 1995, as amended by Amdt. 135-65, 61 FR 30435, June 14, 1996; Amdt. 135-127A, 78 FR 77574, Dec. 24, 2013; Docket FAA-2010-0100, Amdt. 135-127B, 81 FR 2, Jan. 4, 2016; Amdt. 135-142, 85 FR 10935, Feb. 25, 2020]

135.4 Applicability of rules for eligible on-demand operations

(a) An "eligible on-demand operation" is an on-demand operation conducted under this part that meets the following requirements:

(1) Two-pilot crew. The flightcrew must consist of at least two qualified pilots employed or contracted by the certificate holder.

(2) Flight crew experience. The crewmembers must have met the applicable requirements of part 61 of this chapter and have the following experience and ratings:

(i) Total flight time for all pilots:

(A) Pilot in command—A minimum of 1,500 hours.

(B) Second in command—A minimum of 500 hours.

(ii) For multi-engine turbine-powered fixed-wing and powered lift aircraft, the following FAA certification and ratings requirements:

(A) Pilot in command—Airline transport pilot and applicable type ratings.

(B) Second in command—Commercial pilot and instrument ratings.

(iii) For all other aircraft, the following FAA certification and rating requirements:

(A) Pilot in command—Commercial pilot and instrument ratings.

(B) Second in command—Commercial pilot and instrument ratings.

(3) Pilot operating limitations. If the second in command of a fixed-wing aircraft has fewer than 100 hours of flight time as second in command flying in the aircraft make and model and, if a type rating is required, in the type aircraft being flown, and the pilot in command is not an appropriately qualified check pilot, the pilot in command shall make all takeoffs and landings in any of the following situations:

(i) Landings at the destination airport when a Destination Airport Analysis is required by 135.385(f); and

(ii) In any of the following conditions:

(A) The prevailing visibility for the airport is at or below 3/4 mile.

(B) The runway visual range for the runway to be used is at or below 4,000 feet.

(C) The runway to be used has water, snow, slush, ice, or similar contamination that may adversely affect aircraft performance.

(D) The braking action on the runway to be used is reported to be less than "good."

(E) The crosswind component for the runway to be used is in excess of 15 knots.

(F) Windshear is reported in the vicinity of the airport.

(G) Any other condition in which the pilot in command determines it to be prudent to exercise the pilot in command's authority.

(4) Crew pairing. Either the pilot in command or the second in command must have at least 75 hours of flight time in that aircraft make or model and, if a type rating is required, for that type aircraft, either as pilot in command or second in command.

(b) The Administrator may authorize deviations from paragraphs (a)(2)(i) or (a)(4) of this section if the responsible Flight Standards office that issued the certificate holder's operations specifications finds that the crewmember has comparable experience, and can effectively perform the functions associated with the position in accordance with the requirements of this chapter. The Administrator may, at any time, terminate any grant of deviation authority issued under this paragraph. Grants of deviation under this paragraph may be granted after consideration of the size and scope of the operation, the qualifications of the intended personnel and the following circumstances:

(1) A newly authorized certificate holder does not employ any pilots who meet the minimum requirements of paragraphs (a)(2)(i) or (a)(4) of this section.

(2) An existing certificate holder adds to its fleet a new category and class aircraft not used before in its operation.

(3) An existing certificate holder establishes a new base to which it assigns pilots who will be required to become qualified on the aircraft operated from that base.

(c) An eligible on-demand operation may comply with alternative requirements specified in 135.225(b), 135.385(f), and 135.387(b) instead of the requirements that apply to other on-demand operations.

[Doc. No. FAA-2001-10047, 68 FR 54585, Sept. 17, 2003, as amended by Docket FAA-2018-0119, Amdt. 135-139, 83 FR 9175, Mar. 5, 2018]

135.7   Applicability of rules to unauthorized operators

The rules in this part which apply to a person certificated under part 119 of this chapter also apply to a person who engages in any operation governed by this part without an appropriate certificate and operations specifications required by part 119 of this chapter.

[Doc. No. 16097, 43 FR 46783, Oct. 10, 1978, as amended by Amdt. 135–58, 60 FR 65939, Dec. 20, 1995]

135.12   Previously trained crewmembers

A certificate holder may use a crewmember who received the certificate holder's training in accordance with subparts E, G, and H of this part before March 19, 1997 without complying with initial training and qualification requirements of subparts N and O of part 121 of this chapter. The crewmember must comply with the applicable recurrent training requirements of part 121 of this chapter.

[Doc. No. 27993, 60 FR 65950, Dec. 20, 1995]

135.19   Emergency operations

(a) In an emergency involving the safety of persons or property, the certificate holder may deviate from the rules of this part relating to aircraft and equipment and weather minimums to the extent required to meet that emergency.

(b) In an emergency involving the safety of persons or property, the pilot in command may deviate from the rules of this part to the extent required to meet that emergency.

(c) Each person who, under the authority of this section, deviates from a rule of this part shall, within 10 days, excluding Saturdays, Sundays, and Federal holidays, after the deviation, send to the responsible Flight Standards office charged with the overall inspection of the certificate holder a complete report of the aircraft operation involved, including a description of the deviation and reasons for it.

[Docket No. 16097, 43 FR 46783, Oct. 10, 1978, as amended by Docket FAA-2018-0119, Amdt. 135-139, 83 FR 9175, Mar. 5, 2018]

135.21   Manual requirements

(a) Each certificate holder, other than one who uses only one pilot in the certificate holder's operations, shall prepare and keep current a manual setting forth the certificate holder's procedures and policies acceptable to the Administrator. This manual must be used by the certificate holder's flight, ground, and maintenance personnel in conducting its operations. However, the Administrator may authorize a deviation from this paragraph if the Administrator finds that, because of the limited size of the operation, all or part of the manual is not necessary for guidance of flight, ground, or maintenance personnel.

(b) Each certificate holder shall maintain at least one copy of the manual at its principal base of operations.

(c) The manual must not be contrary to any applicable Federal regulations, foreign regulation applicable to the certificate holder's operations in foreign countries, or the certificate holder's operating certificate or operations specifications.

(d) A copy of the manual, or appropriate portions of the manual (and changes and additions) shall be made available to maintenance and ground operations personnel by the certificate holder and furnished to—

(1) Its flight crewmembers; and

(2) Representatives of the Administrator assigned to the certificate holder.

(e) Each employee of the certificate holder to whom a manual or appropriate portions of it are furnished under paragraph (d)(1) of this section shall keep it up to date with the changes and additions furnished to them.

(f) Except as provided in paragraph (h) of this section, each certificate holder must carry appropriate parts of the manual on each aircraft when away from the principal operations base. The appropriate parts must be available for use by ground or flight personnel.

(g) For the purpose of complying with paragraph (d) of this section, a certificate holder may furnish the persons listed therein with all or part of its manual in printed form or other form, acceptable to the Administrator, that is retrievable in the English language. If the certificate holder furnishes all or part of the manual in other than printed form, it must ensure there is a compatible reading device available to those persons that provides a legible image of the information and instructions, or a system that is able to retrieve the information and instructions in the English language.

(h) If a certificate holder conducts aircraft inspections or maintenance at specified stations where it keeps the approved inspection program manual, it is not required to carry the manual aboard the aircraft en route to those stations.

[Doc. No. 16097, 43 FR 46783, Oct. 10, 1978, as amended by Amdt. 135–18, 47 FR 33396, Aug. 2, 1982; Amdt. 135–58, 60 FR 65939, Dec. 20, 1995; Amdt. 135–66, 62 FR 13257, Mar. 19, 1997; Amdt. 135–91, 68 FR 54585, Sept. 17, 2003]

135.23   Manual contents

Each manual shall have the date of the last revision on each revised page. The manual must include—

(a) The name of each management person required under 119.69(a) of this chapter who is authorized to act for the certificate holder, the person's assigned area of responsibility, the person's duties, responsibilities, and authority, and the name and title of each person authorized to exercise operational control under 135.77;

(b) Procedures for ensuring compliance with aircraft weight and balance limitations and, for multiengine aircraft, for determining compliance with 135.185;

(c) Copies of the certificate holder's operations specifications or appropriate extracted information, including area of operations authorized, category and class of aircraft authorized, crew complements, and types of operations authorized;

(d) Procedures for complying with accident notification requirements;

(e) Procedures for ensuring that the pilot in command knows that required airworthiness inspections have been made and that the aircraft has been approved for return to service in compliance with applicable maintenance requirements;

(f) Procedures for reporting and recording mechanical irregularities that come to the attention of the pilot in command before, during, and after completion of a flight;

(g) Procedures to be followed by the pilot in command for determining that mechanical irregularities or defects reported for previous flights have been corrected or that correction has been deferred;

(h) Procedures to be followed by the pilot in command to obtain maintenance, preventive maintenance, and servicing of the aircraft at a place where previous arrangements have not been made by the operator, when the pilot is authorized to so act for the operator;

(i) Procedures under 135.179 for the release for, or continuation of, flight if any item of equipment required for the particular type of operation becomes inoperative or unserviceable en route;

(j) Procedures for refueling aircraft, eliminating fuel contamination, protecting from fire (including electrostatic protection), and supervising and protecting passengers during refueling;

(k) Procedures to be followed by the pilot in command in the briefing under 135.117;

(l) Flight locating procedures, when applicable;

(m) Procedures for ensuring compliance with emergency procedures, including a list of the functions assigned each category of required crewmembers in connection with an emergency and emergency evacuation duties under 135.123;

(n) En route qualification procedures for pilots, when applicable;

(o) The approved aircraft inspection program, when applicable;

(p)

(1) Procedures and information, as described in paragraph (p)(2) of this section, to assist each crewmember and person performing or directly supervising the following job functions involving items for transport on an aircraft:

(i) Acceptance;

(ii) Rejection;

(iii) Handling;

(iv) Storage incidental to transport;

(v) Packaging of company material; or

(vi) Loading.

(2) Ensure that the procedures and information described in this paragraph are sufficient to assist a person in identifying packages that are marked or labeled as containing hazardous materials or that show signs of containing undeclared hazardous materials. The procedures and information must include:

(i) Procedures for rejecting packages that do not conform to the Hazardous Materials Regulations in 49 CFR parts 171 through 180 or that appear to contain undeclared hazardous materials;

(ii) Procedures for complying with the hazardous materials incident reporting requirements of 49 CFR 171.15 and 171.16 and discrepancy reporting requirements of 49 CFR 175.31.

(iii) The certificate holder's hazmat policies and whether the certificate holder is authorized to carry, or is prohibited from carrying, hazardous materials; and

(iv) If the certificate holder's operations specifications permit the transport of hazardous materials, procedures and information to ensure the following:

(A) That packages containing hazardous materials are properly offered and accepted in compliance with 49 CFR parts 171 through 180;

(B) That packages containing hazardous materials are properly handled, stored, packaged, loaded and carried on board an aircraft in compliance with 49 CFR parts 171 through 180;

(C) That the requirements for Notice to the Pilot in Command (49 CFR 175.33) are complied with; and

(D) That aircraft replacement parts, consumable materials or other items regulated by 49 CFR parts 171 through 180 are properly handled, packaged, and transported.

(q) Procedures for the evacuation of persons who may need the assistance of another person to move expeditiously to an exit if an emergency occurs; and

(r) If required by 135.385, an approved Destination Airport Analysis establishing runway safety margins at destination airports, taking into account the following factors as supported by published aircraft performance data supplied by the aircraft manufacturer for the appropriate runway conditions—

(1) Pilot qualifications and experience;

(2) Aircraft performance data to include normal, abnormal and emergency procedures as supplied by the aircraft manufacturer;

(3) Airport facilities and topography;

(4) Runway conditions (including contamination);

(5) Airport or area weather reporting;

(6) Appropriate additional runway safety margins, if required;

(7) Airplane inoperative equipment;

(8) Environmental conditions; and

(9) Other criteria affecting aircraft performance.

(s) Other procedures and policy instructions regarding the certificate holder's operations issued by the certificate holder.

[Doc. No. 16097, 43 FR 46783, Oct. 10, 1978, as amended by Amdt. 135–20, 51 FR 40709, Nov. 7, 1986; Amdt. 135–58, 60 FR 65939, Dec. 20, 1995; Amdt. 135–91, 68 FR 54586, Sept. 17, 2003; Amdt. 135–101, 70 FR 58829, Oct. 7, 2005]

135.25 Aircraft requirements

(a) Except as provided in paragraph (d) of this section, no certificate holder may operate an aircraft under this part unless that aircraft—

(1) Is registered as a civil aircraft of the United States and carries an appropriate and current airworthiness certificate issued under this chapter; and

(2) Is in an airworthy condition and meets the applicable airworthiness requirements of this chapter, including those relating to identification and equipment.

(b) Each certificate holder must have the exclusive use of at least one aircraft that meets the requirements for at least one kind of operation authorized in the certificate holder's operations specifications. In addition, for each kind of operation for which the certificate holder does not have the exclusive use of an aircraft, the certificate holder must have available for use under a written agreement (including arrangements for performing required maintenance) at least one aircraft that meets the requirements for that kind of operation. However, this paragraph does not prohibit the operator from using or authorizing the use of the aircraft for other than operations under this part and does not require the certificate holder to have exclusive use of all aircraft that the certificate holder uses.

(c) For the purposes of paragraph (b) of this section, a person has exclusive use of an aircraft if that person has the sole possession, control, and use of it for flight, as owner, or has a written agreement (including arrangements for performing required maintenance), in effect when the aircraft is operated, giving the person that possession, control, and use for at least 6 consecutive months.

(d) A certificate holder may operate in common carriage, and for the carriage of mail, a civil aircraft which is leased or chartered to it without crew and is registered in a country which is a party to the Convention on International Civil Aviation if—

(1) The aircraft carries an appropriate airworthiness certificate issued by the country of registration and meets the registration and identification requirements of that country;

(2) The aircraft is of a type design which is approved under a U.S. type certificate and complies with all of the requirements of this chapter (14 CFR chapter I) that would be applicable to that aircraft were it registered in the United States, including the requirements which must be met for issuance of a U.S. standard airworthiness certificate (including type design conformity, condition for safe operation, and the noise, fuel venting, and engine emission requirements of this chapter), except that a U.S. registration certificate and a U.S. standard airworthiness certificate will not be issued for the aircraft;

(3) The aircraft is operated by U.S.-certificated airmen employed by the certificate holder; and

FAR 135

(4) The certificate holder files a copy of the aircraft lease or charter agreement with the FAA Aircraft Registry, Department of Transportation, 6400 South MacArthur Boulevard, Oklahoma City, OK (Mailing address: P.O. Box 25504, Oklahoma City, OK 73125).

[Doc. No. 16097, 43 FR 46783, Oct. 10, 1978, as amended by Amdt. 135–8, 45 FR 68649, Oct. 16, 1980; Amdt. 135–66, 62 FR 13257, Mar. 19, 1997]

135.41   Carriage of narcotic drugs, marihuana, and depressant or stimulant drugs or substances

If the holder of a certificate operating under this part allows any aircraft owned or leased by that holder to be engaged in any operation that the certificate holder knows to be in violation of 91.19(a) of this chapter, that operation is a basis for suspending or revoking the certificate.

[Doc. No. 28154, 60 FR 65939, Dec. 20, 1995]

135.43   Crewmember certificates: International operations

(a) This section describes the certificates that were issued to United States citizens who were employed by air carriers at the time of issuance as flight crewmembers on United States registered aircraft engaged in international air commerce. The purpose of the certificate is to facilitate the entry and clearance of those crewmembers into ICAO contracting states. They were issued under Annex 9, as amended, to the Convention on International Civil Aviation.

(b) The holder of a certificate issued under this section, or the air carrier by whom the holder is employed, shall surrender the certificate for cancellation at the responsible Flight Standards office at the termination of the holder's employment with that air carrier.

[Doc. No. 28154, 61 FR 30435, June 14, 1996, as amended by Docket FAA-2018-0119, Amdt. 135-139, 83 FR 9175, Mar. 5, 2018]

Subpart B — Flight Operations

135.61   General

This subpart prescribes rules, in addition to those in part 91 of this chapter, that apply to operations under this part.

135.63   Recordkeeping requirements

(a) Each certificate holder shall keep at its principal business office or at other places approved by the Administrator, and shall make available for inspection by the Administrator the following—

   (1) The certificate holder's operating certificate;

   (2) The certificate holder's operations specifications;

   (3) A current list of the aircraft used or available for use in operations under this part and the operations for which each is equipped;

   (4) An individual record of each pilot used in operations under this part, including the following information:

     (i) The full name of the pilot.

     (ii) The pilot certificate (by type and number) and ratings that the pilot holds.

     (iii) The pilot's aeronautical experience in sufficient detail to determine the pilot's qualifications to pilot aircraft in operations under this part.

     (iv) The pilot's current duties and the date of the pilot's assignment to those duties.

     (v) The effective date and class of the medical certificate that the pilot holds.

     (vi) The date and result of each of the initial and recurrent competency tests and proficiency and route checks required by this part and the type of aircraft flown during that test or check.

     (vii) The pilot's flight time in sufficient detail to determine compliance with the flight time limitations of this part.

     (viii) The pilot's check pilot authorization, if any.

     (ix) Any action taken concerning the pilot's release from employment for physical or professional disqualification.

     (x) The date of the completion of the initial phase and each recurrent phase of the training required by this part; and

   (5) An individual record for each flight attendant who is required under this part, maintained in sufficient detail to determine compliance with the applicable portions of 135.273 of this part.

(b) Each certificate holder must keep each record required by paragraph (a)(3) of this section for at least 6 months, and must keep each record required by paragraphs (a)(4) and (a)(5) of this section for at least 12 months.

(c) For multiengine aircraft, each certificate holder is responsible for the preparation and accuracy of a load manifest in duplicate containing information concerning the loading of the aircraft. The manifest must be prepared before each takeoff and must include

   (1) The number of passengers;

   (2) The total weight of the loaded aircraft;

   (3) The maximum allowable takeoff weight for that flight;

   (4) The center of gravity limits;

   (5) The center of gravity of the loaded aircraft, except that the actual center of gravity need not be computed if the aircraft is loaded according to a loading schedule or other approved method that ensures that the center of gravity of the loaded aircraft is within approved limits. In those cases, an entry shall be made on the manifest indicating that the center of gravity is within limits according to a loading schedule or other approved method;

   (6) The registration number of the aircraft or flight number;

   (7) The origin and destination; and

   (8) Identification of crew members and their crew position assignments.

(d) The pilot in command of an aircraft for which a load manifest must be prepared shall carry a copy of the completed load manifest in the aircraft to its destination. The certificate holder shall keep copies of completed load manifests for at least 30 days at its principal operations base, or at another location used by it and approved by the Administrator.

[Doc. No. 16097, 43 FR 46783, Oct. 10, 1978, as amended by Amdt. 135–52, 59 FR 42993, Aug. 19, 1994]

135.64   Retention of contracts and amendments: Commercial operators who conduct intrastate operations for compensation or hire

Each commercial operator who conducts intrastate operations for compensation or hire shall keep a copy of each written contract under which it provides services as a commercial operator for a period of at least one year after the date of execution of the contract. In the case of an oral contract, it shall keep a memorandum stating its elements and of any amendments to it, for a period of at least one year after the execution of that contract or change.

[Doc. No. 28154, 60 FR 65939, Dec. 20, 1995, as amended by Amdt. 135–65, 61 FR 30435, June 14, 1996; Amdt. 135–66, 62 FR 13257, Mar. 19, 1997]

135.65   Reporting mechanical irregularities

(a) Each certificate holder shall provide an aircraft maintenance log to be carried on board each aircraft for recording or deferring mechanical irregularities and their correction.

(b) The pilot in command shall enter or have entered in the aircraft maintenance log each mechanical irregularity that comes to the pilot's attention during flight time. Before each flight, the pilot in command shall, if the pilot does not already know, determine the status of each irregularity entered in the maintenance log at the end of the preceding flight.

(c) Each person who takes corrective action or defers action concerning a reported or observed failure or malfunction of an airframe, powerplant, propeller, rotor, or applicance, shall record the action taken in the aircraft maintenance log under the applicable maintenance requirements of this chapter.

(d) Each certificate holder shall establish a procedure for keeping copies of the aircraft maintenance log required by this section in the aircraft for access by appropriate personnel and shall include that procedure in the manual required by 135.21.

135.67 Reporting potentially hazardous meteorological conditions and irregularities of ground facilities or navigation aids

Whenever a pilot encounters a potentially hazardous meteorological condition or an irregularity in a ground facility or navigation aid in flight, the knowledge of which the pilot considers essential to the safety of other flights, the pilot shall notify an appropriate ground radio station as soon as practicable.

[Doc. No. 16097, 43 FR 46783, Oct. 1, 1978, as amended at Amdt. 135–1, 44 FR 26737, May 7, 1979; Amdt. 135–110, 72 FR 31684, June 7, 2007]

135.69 Restriction or suspension of operations: Continuation of flight in an emergency

(a) During operations under this part, if a certificate holder or pilot in command knows of conditions, including airport and runway conditions, that are a hazard to safe operations, the certificate holder or pilot in command, as the case may be, shall restrict or suspend operations as necessary until those conditions are corrected.

(b) No pilot in command may allow a flight to continue toward any airport of intended landing under the conditions set forth in paragraph (a) of this section, unless, in the opinion of the pilot in command, the conditions that are a hazard to safe operations may reasonably be expected to be corrected by the estimated time of arrival or, unless there is no safer procedure. In the latter event, the continuation toward that airport is an emergency situation under 135.19.

135.71 Airworthiness check

The pilot in command may not begin a flight unless the pilot determines that the airworthiness inspections required by 91.409 of this chapter, or 135.419, whichever is applicable, have been made.

[Doc. No. 16097, 43 FR 46783, Oct. 10, 1978, as amended by Amdt. 135–32, 54 FR 34332, Aug. 18, 1989]

135.73 Inspections and tests

Each certificate holder and each person employed by the certificate holder shall allow the Administrator, at any time or place, to make inspections or tests (including en route inspections) to determine the holder's compliance with the Federal Aviation Act of 1958, applicable regulations, and the certificate holder's operating certificate, and operations specifications.

135.75 Inspectors credentials: Admission to pilots' compartment: Forward observer's seat

(a) Whenever, in performing the duties of conducting an inspection, an FAA inspector presents an Aviation Safety Inspector credential, FAA Form 110A, to the pilot in command of an aircraft operated by the certificate holder, the inspector must be given free and uninterrupted access to the pilot compartment of that aircraft. However, this paragraph does not limit the emergency authority of the pilot in command to exclude any person from the pilot compartment in the interest of safety.

(b) A forward observer's seat on the flight deck, or forward passenger seat with headset or speaker must be provided for use by the Administrator while conducting en route inspections. The suitability of the location of the seat and the headset or speaker for use in conducting en route inspections is determined by the Administrator.

135.76 DOD Commercial Air Carrier Evaluator's Credentials: Admission to pilots compartment: Forward observer's seat

(a) Whenever, in performing the duties of conducting an evaluation, a DOD commercial air carrier evaluator presents S&A Form 110B, "DOD Commercial Air Carrier Evaluator's Credential," to the pilot in command of an aircraft operated by the certificate holder, the evaluator must be given free and uninterrupted access to the pilot's compartment of that aircraft. However, this paragraph does not limit the emergency authority of the pilot in command to exclude any person from the pilot compartment in the interest of safety.

(b) A forward observer's seat on the flight deck or forward passenger seat with headset or speaker must be provided for use by the evaluator while conducting en route evaluations. The suitability of the location of the seat and the headset or speaker for use in conducting en route evaluations is determined by the FAA.

[Doc. No. FAA–2003–15571, 68 FR 41218, July 10, 2003]

135.77 Responsibility for operational control

Each certificate holder is responsible for operational control and shall list, in the manual required by 135.21, the name and title of each person authorized by it to exercise operational control.

135.78 Instrument approach procedures and IFR landing minimums

No person may make an instrument approach at an airport except in accordance with IFR weather minimums and instrument approach procedures set forth in the certificate holder's operations specifications.

[Doc. No. FAA–2002–14002, 72 FR 31684, June 7, 2007]

135.79 Flight locating requirements

(a) Each certificate holder must have procedures established for locating each flight, for which an FAA flight plan is not filed, that—

   (1) Provide the certificate holder with at least the information required to be included in a VFR flight plan;

   (2) Provide for timely notification of an FAA facility or search and rescue facility, if an aircraft is overdue or missing; and

   (3) Provide the certificate holder with the location, date, and estimated time for reestablishing communications, if the flight will operate in an area where communications cannot be maintained.

(b) Flight locating information shall be retained at the certificate holder's principal place of business, or at other places designated by the certificate holder in the flight locating procedures, until the completion of the flight.

(c) Each certificate holder shall furnish the representative of the Administrator assigned to it with a copy of its flight locating procedures and any changes or additions, unless those procedures are included in a manual required under this part.

[Doc. No. 16097, 43 FR 46783, Oct. 10, 1978, as amended by Amdt. 135–110, 72 FR 31684, June 7, 2007]

135.81 Informing personnel of operational information and appropriate changes

Each certificate holder shall inform each person in its employment of the operations specifications that apply to that person's duties and responsibilities and shall make available to each pilot in the certificate holder's employ the following materials in current form:

(a) Airman's Information Manual (Alaska Supplement in Alaska and Pacific Chart Supplement in Pacific-Asia Regions) or a commercial publication that contains the same information.

(b) This part and part 91 of this chapter.

(c) Aircraft Equipment Manuals, and Aircraft Flight Manual or equivalent.

(d) For foreign operations, the International Flight Information Manual or a commercial publication that contains the same information concerning the pertinent operational and entry requirements of the foreign country or countries involved.

135.83   Operating information required

(a) The operator of an aircraft must provide the following materials, in current and appropriate form, accessible to the pilot at the pilot station, and the pilot shall use them:

(1) A cockpit checklist.

(2) For multiengine aircraft or for aircraft with retractable landing gear, an emergency cockpit checklist containing the procedures required by paragraph (c) of this section, as appropriate.

(3) Pertinent aeronautical charts.

(4) For IFR operations, each pertinent navigational en route, terminal area, and approach and letdown chart.

(5) For multiengine aircraft, one-engine-inoperative climb performance data and if the aircraft is approved for use in IFR or over-the-top operations, that data must be sufficient to enable the pilot to determine compliance with 135.181(a)(2).

(b) Each cockpit checklist required by paragraph (a)(1) of this section must contain the following procedures:

(1) Before starting engines;

(2) Before takeoff;

(3) Cruise;

(4) Before landing;

(5) After landing;

(6) Stopping engines.

(c) Each emergency cockpit checklist required by paragraph (a)(2) of this section must contain the following procedures, as appropriate:

(1) Emergency operation of fuel, hydraulic, electrical, and mechanical systems.

(2) Emergency operation of instruments and controls.

(3) Engine inoperative procedures.

(4) Any other emergency procedures necessary for safety.

135.85   Carriage of persons without compliance with the passenger-carrying provisions of this part

The following persons may be carried aboard an aircraft without complying with the passenger-carrying requirements of this part:

(a) A crewmember or other employee of the certificate holder.

(b) A person necessary for the safe handling of animals on the aircraft.

(c) A person necessary for the safe handling of hazardous materials (as defined in subchapter C of title 49 CFR).

(d) A person performing duty as a security or honor guard accompanying a shipment made by or under the authority of the U.S. Government.

(e) A military courier or a military route supervisor carried by a military cargo contract air carrier or commercial operator in operations under a military cargo contract, if that carriage is specifically authorized by the appropriate military service.

(f) An authorized representative of the Administrator conducting an en route inspection.

(g) A person, authorized by the Administrator, who is performing a duty connected with a cargo operation of the certificate holder.

(h) A DOD commercial air carrier evaluator conducting an en route evaluation.

[Docket No. 16097, 43 FR 46783, Oct. 10, 1978, as amended by Amdt. 135–88, 68 FR 41218, July 10, 2003]

135.87   Carriage of cargo including carry-on baggage

No person may carry cargo, including carry-on baggage, in or on any aircraft unless—

(a) It is carried in an approved cargo rack, bin, or compartment installed in or on the aircraft;

(b) It is secured by an approved means; or

(c) It is carried in accordance with each of the following:

(1) For cargo, it is properly secured by a safety belt or other tie down having enough strength to eliminate the possibility o: shifting under all normally anticipated flight and ground conditions, or for carry-on baggage, it is restrained so as to prevent its movement during air turbulence.

(2) It is packaged or covered to avoid possible injury to occupants.

(3) It does not impose any load on seats or on the floor structure that exceeds the load limitation for those components.

(4) It is not located in a position that obstructs the access to, o: use of, any required emergency or regular exit, or the use o the aisle between the crew and the passenger compartment, o: located in a position that obscures any passenger's view of the "seat belt" sign, "no smoking" sign, or any required exit sign unless an auxiliary sign or other approved means for proper notification of the passengers is provided.

(5) It is not carried directly above seated occupants.

(6) It is stowed in compliance with this section for takeoff and landing.

(7) For cargo only operations, paragraph (c)(4) of this section does not apply if the cargo is loaded so that at least one emergency or regular exit is available to provide all occupants o: the aircraft a means of unobstructed exit from the aircraft if an emergency occurs.

(d) Each passenger seat under which baggage is stowed shall be fitted with a means to prevent articles of baggage stowed under it from sliding under crash impacts severe enough to induce the ultimate inertia forces specified in the emergency landing condition regulations under which the aircraft was type certificated.

(e) When cargo is carried in cargo compartments that are designed to require the physical entry of a crewmember to extinguish any fire that may occur during flight, the cargo must be loaded so as to allow a crewmember to effectively reach all parts of the compartment with the contents of a hand fire extinguisher.

135.89   Pilot requirements: Use of oxygen

(a) Unpressurized aircraft. Each pilot of an unpressurized aircraft shall use oxygen continuously when flying—

(1) At altitudes above 10,000 feet through 12,000 feet MSL for that part of the flight at those altitudes that is of more than 30 minutes duration; and

(2) Above 12,000 feet MSL.

(b) Pressurized aircraft.

(1) Whenever a pressurized aircraft is operated with the cabin pressure altitude more than 10,000 feet MSL, each pilot shall comply with paragraph (a) of this section.

(2) Whenever a pressurized aircraft is operated at altitudes above 25,000 feet through 35,000 feet MSL, unless each pilot has an approved quick-donning type oxygen mask—

(i) At least one pilot at the controls shall wear, secured and sealed, an oxygen mask that either supplies oxygen at all times or automatically supplies oxygen whenever the cabin pressure altitude exceeds 12,000 feet MSL; and

(ii) During that flight, each other pilot on flight deck duty shall have an oxygen mask, connected to an oxygen supply, located so as to allow immediate placing of the mask on the pilot's face sealed and secured for use.

(3) Whenever a pressurized aircraft is operated at altitudes above 35,000 feet MSL, at least one pilot at the controls shall wear secured and sealed, an oxygen mask required by paragraph (b)(2)(i) of this section.

(4) If one pilot leaves a pilot duty station of an aircraft when operating at altitudes above 25,000 feet MSL, the remaining

pilot at the controls shall put on and use an approved oxygen mask until the other pilot returns to the pilot duty station of the aircraft.

135.91 Oxygen and portable oxygen concentrators for medical use by passengers

(a) Except as provided in paragraphs (d) and (e) of this section, no certificate holder may allow the carriage or operation of equipment for the storage, generation or dispensing of medical oxygen unless the conditions in paragraphs (a) through (c) of this section are satisfied. Beginning August 22, 2016, a certificate holder may allow a passenger to carry and operate a portable oxygen concentrator when the conditions in paragraphs (b) and (f) of this section are satisfied.

(1) The equipment must be—

(i) Of an approved type or in conformity with the manufacturing, packaging, marking, labeling, and maintenance requirements of title 49 CFR parts 171, 172, and 173, except 173.24(a)(1);

(ii) When owned by the certificate holder, maintained under the certificate holder's approved maintenance program;

(iii) Free of flammable contaminants on all exterior surfaces;

(iv) Constructed so that all valves, fittings, and gauges are protected from damage during carriage or operation; and

(v) Appropriately secured.

(2) When the oxygen is stored in the form of a liquid, the equipment must have been under the certificate holder's approved maintenance program since its purchase new or since the storage container was last purged.

(3) When the oxygen is stored in the form of a compressed gas as defined in title 49 CFR 173.115(b)—

(i) When owned by the certificate holder, it must be maintained under its approved maintenance program; and

(ii) The pressure in any oxygen cylinder must not exceed the rated cylinder pressure.

(4) The pilot in command must be advised when the equipment is on board, and when it is intended to be used.

(5) The equipment must be stowed, and each person using the equipment must be seated, so as not to restrict access to or use of any required emergency or regular exit, or of the aisle in the passenger compartment.

(b) No person may smoke or create an open flame and no certificate holder may allow any person to smoke or create an open flame within 10 feet of oxygen storage and dispensing equipment carried under paragraph (a) of this section or a portable oxygen concentrator carried and operated under paragraph (f) of this section.

(c) No certificate holder may allow any person other than a person trained in the use of medical oxygen equipment to connect or disconnect oxygen bottles or any other ancillary component while any passenger is aboard the aircraft.

(d) Paragraph (a)(1)(i) of this section does not apply when that equipment is furnished by a professional or medical emergency service for use on board an aircraft in a medical emergency when no other practical means of transportation (including any other properly equipped certificate holder) is reasonably available and the person carried under the medical emergency is accompanied by a person trained in the use of medical oxygen.

(e) Each certificate holder who, under the authority of paragraph (d) of this section, deviates from paragraph (a)(1)(i) of this section under a medical emergency shall, within 10 days, excluding Saturdays, Sundays, and Federal holidays, after the deviation, send to the responsible Flight Standards office a complete report of the operation involved, including a description of the deviation and the reasons for it.

(f) Portable oxygen concentrators—(1) Acceptance criteria. A passenger may carry or operate a portable oxygen concentrator for personal use on board an aircraft and a certificate holder may allow a passenger to carry or operate a portable oxygen concentrator on board an aircraft operated under this part during all phases of flight if the portable oxygen concentrator satisfies all of the requirements of this paragraph (f):

(i) Is legally marketed in the United States in accordance with Food and Drug Administration requirements in title 21 of the CFR;

(ii) Does not radiate radio frequency emissions that interfere with aircraft systems;

(iii) Generates a maximum oxygen pressure of less than 200 kPa gauge (29.0 psig/43.8 psia) at 20 °C (68 °F);

(iv) Does not contain any hazardous materials subject to the Hazardous Materials Regulations (49 CFR parts 171 through 180) except as provided in 49 CFR 175.10 for batteries used to power portable electronic devices and that do not require aircraft operator approval; and

(v) Bears a label on the exterior of the device applied in a manner that ensures the label will remain affixed for the life of the device and containing the following certification statement in red lettering: "The manufacturer of this POC has determined this device conforms to all applicable FAA acceptance criteria for POC carriage and use on board aircraft." The label requirements in this paragraph (f)(1)(v) do not apply to the following portable oxygen concentrators approved by the FAA for use on board aircraft prior to May 24, 2016:

(A) AirSep Focus;
(B) AirSep FreeStyle;
(C) AirSep FreeStyle 5;
(D) AirSep LifeStyle;
(E) Delphi RS-00400;
(F) DeVilbiss Healthcare iGo;
(G) Inogen One;
(H) Inogen One G2;
(I) Inogen One G3;
(J) Inova Labs LifeChoice;
(K) Inova Labs LifeChoice Activox;
(L) International Biophysics LifeChoice;
(M) Invacare Solo2;
(N) Invacare XPO2;
(O) Oxlife Independence Oxygen Concentrator;
(P) Oxus RS-00400;
(Q) Precision Medical EasyPulse;
(R) Respironics EverGo;
(S) Respironics SimplyGo;
(T) SeQual Eclipse;
(U) SeQual eQuinox Oxygen System (model 4000);
(V) SeQual Oxywell Oxygen System (model 4000);
(W) SeQual SAROS; and
(X) VBox Trooper Oxygen Concentrator.

(2) Operating requirements. Portable oxygen concentrators that satisfy the acceptance criteria identified in paragraph (f)(1) of this section may be carried on or operated by a passenger on board an aircraft provided the aircraft operator ensures that all of the conditions in this paragraph (f)(2) are satisfied:

(i) Exit seats. No person operating a portable oxygen concentrator is permitted to occupy an exit seat.

(ii) Stowage of device. During movement on the surface, takeoff and landing, the device must be stowed under the seat in front of the user, or in another approved stowage location so that it does not block the aisle way or the entryway to the row. If the device is to be operated by the user, it must be operated only at a seat location that does not restrict any passenger's access to, or use of, any required emergency or regular exit, or the aisle(s) in the passenger compartment.

[Doc. No. 16097, 43 FR 46783, Oct. 10, 1978, as amended by Amdt. 135-60, 61 FR 2616, Jan. 26, 1996; Docket FAA-2014-0554, Amdt. 135-133, 81 FR 33119, May 24, 2016; Docket FAA-2018-0119, Amdt. 135-139, 83 FR 9175, Mar. 5, 2018]

135.93 Minimum altitudes for use of autopilot.

(a) Definitions. For purpose of this section—

  (1) Altitudes for takeoff/initial climb and go-around/missed approach are defined as above the airport elevation.

  (2) Altitudes for enroute operations are defined as above terrain elevation.

  (3) Altitudes for approach are defined as above the touchdown zone elevation (TDZE), unless the altitude is specifically in reference to DA (H) or MDA, in which case the altitude is defined by reference to the DA(H) or MDA itself.

(b) Takeoff and initial climb. No person may use an autopilot for takeoff or initial climb below the higher of 500 feet or an altitude that is no lower than twice the altitude loss specified in the Airplane Flight Manual (AFM), except as follows—

  (1) At a minimum engagement altitude specified in the AFM; or

  (2) At an altitude specified by the Administrator, whichever is greater.

(c) Enroute. No person may use an autopilot enroute, including climb and descent, below the following—

  (1) 500 feet;

  (2) At an altitude that is no lower than twice the altitude loss specified in the AFM for an autopilot malfunction in cruise conditions; or

  (3) At an altitude specified by the Administrator, whichever is greater.

(d) Approach. No person may use an autopilot at an altitude lower than 50 feet below the DA(H) or MDA for the instrument procedure being flown, except as follows—

  (1) For autopilots with an AFM specified altitude loss for approach operations—

    (i) An altitude no lower than twice the specified altitude loss if higher than 50 feet below the MDA or DA(H);

    (ii) An altitude no lower than 50 feet higher than the altitude loss specified in the AFM, when the following conditions are met—

      (A) Reported weather conditions are less than the basic VFR weather conditions in 91.155 of this chapter;

      (B) Suitable visual references specified in 91.175 of this chapter have been established on the instrument approach procedure; and

      (C) The autopilot is coupled and receiving both lateral and vertical path references;

    (iii) An altitude no lower than the higher of the altitude loss specified in the AFM or 50 feet above the TDZE, when the following conditions are met—

      (A) Reported weather conditions are equal to or better than the basic VFR weather conditions in 91.155 of this chapter; and

      (B) The autopilot is coupled and receiving both lateral and vertical path references; or

    (iv) A greater altitude specified by the Administrator.

  (2) For autopilots with AFM specified approach altitude limitations, the greater of—

    (i) The minimum use altitude specified for the coupled approach mode selected;

    (ii) 50 feet; or

    (iii) An altitude specified by Administrator.

  (3) For autopilots with an AFM specified negligible or zero altitude loss for an autopilot approach mode malfunction, the greater of—

    (i) 50 feet; or

    (ii) An altitude specified by Administrator.

  (4) If executing an autopilot coupled go-around or missed approach using a certificated and functioning autopilot in accordance with paragraph (e) in this section.

(e) Go-Around/Missed Approach. No person may engage an autopilot during a go-around or missed approach below the minimum engagement altitude specified for takeoff and initial climb in paragraph (b) in this section. An autopilot minimum use altitude does not apply to a go-around/missed approach initiated with an engaged autopilot. Performing a go-around or missed approach with an engaged autopilot must not adversely affect safe obstacle clearance.

(f) Landing. Notwithstanding paragraph (d) of this section, autopilot minimum use altitudes do not apply to autopilot operations when an approved automatic landing system mode is being used for landing. Automatic landing systems must be authorized in an operations specification issued to the operator.

(g) This section does not apply to operations conducted in rotorcraft.

[Doc. No. FAA-2012-1059, 79 FR 6088, Feb. 3, 2014]

135.95 Airmen: Limitations on use of services

(a) No certificate holder may use the services of any person as an airman unless the person performing those services—

  (1) Holds an appropriate and current airman certificate; and

  (2) Is qualified, under this chapter, for the operation for which the person is to be used.

(b) A certificate holder may obtain approval to provide a temporary document verifying a flightcrew member's airman certificate and medical certificate privileges under an approved certificate verification plan set forth in the certificate holder's operations specifications. A document provided by the certificate holder may be carried as an airman certificate or medical certificate on flights within the United States for up to 72 hours.

[Amdt. No. 135-140, 83 FR 30282, June 27, 2018]

135.97 Aircraft and facilities for recent flight experience

Each certificate holder shall provide aircraft and facilities to enable each of its pilots to maintain and demonstrate the pilot's ability to conduct all operations for which the pilot is authorized.

135.98 Operations in the North Polar Area

After August 13, 2008, no certificate holder may operate an aircraft in the region north of 78°N latitude ("North Polar Area"), other than intrastate operations wholly within the state of Alaska, unless authorized by the FAA. The certificate holder's operation specifications must include the following:

(a) The designation of airports that may be used for en-route diversions and the requirements the airports must meet at the time of diversion.

(b) Except for all-cargo operations, a recovery plan for passengers at designated diversion airports.

(c) A fuel-freeze strategy and procedures for monitoring fuel freezing for operations in the North Polar Area.

(d) A plan to ensure communication capability for operations in the North Polar Area.

(e) An MEL for operations in the North Polar Area.

(f) A training plan for operations in the North Polar Area.

(g) A plan for mitigating crew exposure to radiation during solar flare activity.

(h) A plan for providing at least two cold weather anti-exposure suits in the aircraft, to protect crewmembers during outside activity at a diversion airport with extreme climatic conditions. The FAA may relieve the certificate holder from this requirement if the season of the year makes the equipment unnecessary.

[Doc. No. FAA–2002–6717, 72 FR 1885, Jan. 16, 2007, as amended by Amdt. 135–112, 73 FR 8798, Feb. 15, 2008]

135.99 Composition of flight crew.

(a) No certificate holder may operate an aircraft with less than the minimum flight crew specified in the aircraft operating limitations or the Aircraft Flight Manual for that aircraft and required by this part for the kind of operation being conducted.

(b) No certificate holder may operate an aircraft without a second in command if that aircraft has a passenger seating configuration, excluding any pilot seat, of ten seats or more.

(c) Except as provided in paragraph (d) of this section, a certificate holder authorized to conduct operations under instrument flight rules may receive authorization from the Administrator through its operations specifications to establish a second-in-command professional development program. As part of that program, a pilot employed by the certificate holder may log time as second in command in operations conducted under this part and part 91 of this chapter that do not require a second pilot by type certification of the aircraft or the regulation under which the flight is being conducted, provided the flight operation is conducted in accordance with the certificate holder's operations specifications for second-in-command professional development program; and—

(1) The certificate holder:

(i) Maintains records for each assigned second in command consistent with the requirements in 135.63;

(ii) Provides a copy of the records required by 135.63(a)(4) (vi) and (x) to the assigned second in command upon request and within a reasonable time; and

(iii) Establishes and maintains a data collection and analysis process that will enable the certificate holder and the FAA to determine whether the second-in-command professional development program is accomplishing its objectives.

(2) The aircraft is a multiengine airplane or a single-engine turbine-powered airplane. The aircraft must have an independent set of controls for a second pilot flightcrew member, which may not include a throwover control wheel. The aircraft must also have the following equipment and independent instrumentation for a second pilot:

(i) An airspeed indicator;

(ii) Sensitive altimeter adjustable for barometric pressure;

(iii) Gyroscopic bank and pitch indicator;

(iv) Gyroscopic rate-of-turn indicator combined with an integral slip-skid indicator;

(v) Gyroscopic direction indicator;

(vi) For IFR operations, a vertical speed indicator;

(vii) For IFR operations, course guidance for en route navigation and instrument approaches; and

(viii) A microphone, transmit switch, and headphone or speaker.

(3) The pilot assigned to serve as second in command satisfies the following requirements:

(i) The second in command qualifications in 135.245;

(ii) The flight time and duty period limitations and rest requirements in subpart F of this part;

(iii) The crewmember testing requirements for second in command in subpart G of this part; and

(iv) The crewmember training requirements for second in command in subpart H of this part.

(4) The pilot assigned to serve as pilot in command satisfies the following requirements:

(i) Has been fully qualified to serve as a pilot in command for the certificate holder for at least the previous 6 calendar months; and

(ii) Has completed mentoring training, including techniques for reinforcing the highest standards of technical performance, airmanship and professionalism within the preceding 36 calendar months.

(d) The following certificate holders are not eligible to receive authorization for a second-in-command professional development program under paragraph (c) of this section:

(1) A certificate holder that uses only one pilot in its operations; and

(2) A certificate holder that has been approved to deviate from the requirements in 135.21(a), 135.341(a), or 119.69(a) of this chapter.

135.100 Flight crewmember duties

(a) No certificate holder shall require, nor may any flight crewmember perform, any duties during a critical phase of flight except those duties required for the safe operation of the aircraft. Duties such as company required calls made for such nonsafety related purposes as ordering galley supplies and confirming passenger connections, announcements made to passengers promoting the air carrier or pointing out sights of interest, and filling out company payroll and related records are not required for the safe operation of the aircraft.

(b) No flight crewmember may engage in, nor may any pilot in command permit, any activity during a critical phase of flight which could distract any flight crewmember from the performance of his or her duties or which could interfere in any way with the proper conduct of those duties. Activities such as eating meals, engaging in nonessential conversations within the cockpit and nonessential communications between the cabin and cockpit crews, and reading publications not related to the proper conduct of the flight are not required for the safe operation of the aircraft.

(c) For the purposes of this section, critical phases of flight includes all ground operations involving taxi, takeoff and landing, and all other flight operations conducted below 10,000 feet, except cruise flight.

NOTE: *Taxi is defined as "movement of an airplane under its own power on the surface of an airport."*

[Doc. No. 20661, 46 FR 5502, Jan. 19, 1981]

135.101 Second in command required under IFR

Except as provided in 135.105, no person may operate an aircraft carrying passengers under IFR unless there is a second in command in the aircraft.

[Doc. No. 28743, 62 FR 42374, Aug. 6, 1997]

135.103 [Reserved]

135.105 Exception to second in command requirement: Approval for use of autopilot system

(a) Except as provided in 135.99 and 135.111, unless two pilots are required by this chapter for operations under VFR, a person may operate an aircraft without a second in command, if it is equipped with an operative approved autopilot system and the use of that system is authorized by appropriate operations specifications. No certificate holder may use any person, nor may any person serve, as a pilot in command under this section of an aircraft operated in a commuter operation, as defined in part 119 of this chapter unless that person has at least 100 hours pilot in command flight time in the make and model of aircraft to be flown and has met all other applicable requirements of this part.

(b) The certificate holder may apply for an amendment of its operations specifications to authorize the use of an autopilot system in place of a second in command.

(c) The Administrator issues an amendment to the operations specifications authorizing the use of an autopilot system, in place of a second in command, if—

(1) The autopilot is capable of operating the aircraft controls to maintain flight and maneuver it about the three axes; and

(2) The certificate holder shows, to the satisfaction of the Administrator, that operations using the autopilot system can be conducted safely and in compliance with this part.

The amendment contains any conditions or limitations on the use of the autopilot system that the Administrator determines are needed in the interest of safety.

[Doc. No. 16097, 43 FR 46783, Oct. 10, 1978, as amended by Amdt. 135–3, 45 FR 7542, Feb. 4, 1980; Amdt. 135–58, 60 FR 65939, Dec. 20, 1995]

135.107　Flight attendant crewmember requirement

No certificate holder may operate an aircraft that has a passenger seating configuration, excluding any pilot seat, of more than 19 unless there is a flight attendant crewmember on board the aircraft.

135.109　Pilot in command or second in command: Designation required

(a) Each certificate holder shall designate a—

(1) Pilot in command for each flight; and

(2) Second in command for each flight requiring two pilots.

(b) The pilot in command, as designated by the certificate holder, shall remain the pilot in command at all times during that flight.

135.111　Second in command required in Category II operations

No person may operate an aircraft in a Category II operation unless there is a second in command of the aircraft.

135.113　Passenger occupancy of pilot seat

No certificate holder may operate an aircraft type certificated after October 15, 1971, that has a passenger seating configuration, excluding any pilot seat, of more than eight seats if any person other than the pilot in command, a second in command, a company check airman, or an authorized representative of the Administrator, the National Transportation Safety Board, or the United States Postal Service occupies a pilot seat.

135.115　Manipulation of controls

No pilot in command may allow any person to manipulate the flight controls of an aircraft during flight conducted under this part, nor may any person manipulate the controls during such flight unless that person is—

(a) A pilot employed by the certificate holder and qualified in the aircraft; or

(b) An authorized safety representative of the Administrator who has the permission of the pilot in command, is qualified in the aircraft, and is checking flight operations.

135.117　Briefing of passengers before flight

(a) Before each takeoff each pilot in command of an aircraft carrying passengers shall ensure that all passengers have been orally briefed on—

(1) Smoking. Each passenger shall be briefed on when, where, and under what conditions smoking is prohibited (including, but not limited to, any applicable requirements of part 252 of this title). This briefing shall include a statement that the Federal Aviation Regulations require passenger compliance with the lighted passenger information signs (if such signs are required), posted placards, areas designated for safety purposes as no smoking areas, and crewmember instructions with regard to these items. The briefing shall also include a statement (if the aircraft is equipped with a lavatory) that Federal law prohibits: tampering with, disabling, or destroying any smoke detector installed in an aircraft lavatory; smoking in lavatories; and, when applicable, smoking in passenger compartments.

(2) The use of safety belts, including instructions on how to fasten and unfasten the safety belts. Each passenger shall be briefed on when, where, and under what conditions the safety belt must be fastened about that passenger. This briefing shall include a statement that the Federal Aviation Regulations require passenger compliance with lighted passenger information signs and crewmember instructions concerning the use of safety belts.

(3) The placement of seat backs in an upright position before takeoff and landing;

(4) Location and means for opening the passenger entry door and emergency exits;

(5) Location of survival equipment;

(6) If the flight involves extended overwater operation, ditching procedures and the use of required flotation equipment;

(7) If the flight involves operations above 12,000 feet MSL, the normal and emergency use of oxygen; and

(8) Location and operation of fire extinguishers.

(9) If a rotorcraft operation involves flight beyond autorotational distance from the shoreline, as defined in 135.168(a), use of life preservers, ditching procedures and emergency exit from the rotorcraft in the event of a ditching; and the location and use of life rafts and other life preserver devices if applicable.

(b) Before each takeoff the pilot in command shall ensure that each person who may need the assistance of another person to move expeditiously to an exit if an emergency occurs and that person's attendant, if any, has received a briefing as to the procedures to be followed if an evacuation occurs. This paragraph does not apply to a person who has been given a briefing before a previous leg of a flight in the same aircraft.

(c) The oral briefing required by paragraph (a) of this section shall be given by the pilot in command or a crewmember.

(d) Notwithstanding the provisions of paragraph (c) of this section, for aircraft certificated to carry 19 passengers or less, the oral briefing required by paragraph (a) of this section shall be given by the pilot in command, a crewmember, or other qualified person designated by the certificate holder and approved by the Administrator.

(e) The oral briefing required by paragraph (a) of this section must be supplemented by printed cards which must be carried in the aircraft in locations convenient for the use of each passenger. The cards must—

(1) Be appropriate for the aircraft on which they are to be used;

(2) Contain a diagram of, and method of operating, the emergency exits;

(3) Contain other instructions necessary for the use of emergency equipment on board the aircraft; and

(4) No later than June 12, 2005, for scheduled Commuter passenger-carrying flights, include the sentence, "Final assembly of this aircraft was completed in [INSERT NAME OF COUNTRY]."

(f) The briefing required by paragraph (a) may be delivered by means of an approved recording playback device that is audible to each passenger under normal noise levels.

[Doc. No. 16097, 43 FR 46783, Oct. 10, 1978, as amended by Amdt. 135–9, 51 FR 40709, Nov. 7, 1986; Amdt. 135–25, 53 FR 12362, Apr. 13, 1988; Amdt. 135–44, 57 FR 42675, Sept. 15, 1992; 57 FR 43776, Sept. 22, 1992; 69 FR 39294, June 29, 2004]

135.119　Prohibition against carriage of weapons

No person may, while on board an aircraft being operated by a certificate holder, carry on or about that person a deadly or dangerous weapon, either concealed or unconcealed. This section does not apply to—

(a) Officials or employees of a municipality or a State, or of the United States, who are authorized to carry arms; or

(b) Crewmembers and other persons authorized by the certificate holder to carry arms.

135.120 Prohibition on interference with crewmembers

No person may assault, threaten, intimidate, or interfere with a crewmember in the performance of the crewmember's duties aboard an aircraft being operated under this part.

[Doc. No. FAA–1998–4954, 64 FR 1080, Jan. 7, 1999]

135.121 Alcoholic beverages

(a) No person may drink any alcoholic beverage aboard an aircraft unless the certificate holder operating the aircraft has served that beverage.

(b) No certificate holder may serve any alcoholic beverage to any person aboard its aircraft if that person appears to be intoxicated.

(c) No certificate holder may allow any person to board any of its aircraft if that person appears to be intoxicated.

135.122 Stowage of food, beverage, and passenger service equipment during aircraft movement on the surface, takeoff, and landing

(a) No certificate holder may move an aircraft on the surface, take off, or land when any food, beverage, or tableware furnished by the certificate holder is located at any passenger seat.

(b) No certificate holder may move an aircraft on the surface, take off, or land unless each food and beverage tray and seat back tray table is secured in its stowed position.

(c) No certificate holder may permit an aircraft to move on the surface, take off, or land unless each passenger serving cart is secured in its stowed position.

(d) Each passenger shall comply with instructions given by a crewmember with regard to compliance with this section.

[Doc. No. 26142, 57 FR 42675, Sept. 15, 1992]

135.123 Emergency and emergency evacuation duties

(a) Each certificate holder shall assign to each required crewmember for each type of aircraft as appropriate, the necessary functions to be performed in an emergency or in a situation requiring emergency evacuation. The certificate holder shall ensure that those functions can be practicably accomplished, and will meet any reasonably anticipated emergency including incapacitation of individual crewmembers or their inability to reach the passenger cabin because of shifting cargo in combination cargo-passenger aircraft.

(b) The certificate holder shall describe in the manual required under 135.21 the functions of each category of required crewmembers assigned under paragraph (a) of this section.

135.125 Aircraft security

Certificate holders conducting operators conducting operations under this part must comply with the applicable security requirements in 49 CFR chapter XII.

[67 FR 8350, Feb. 22, 2002]

135.127 Passenger information requirements and smoking prohibitions

(a) No person may conduct a scheduled flight on which smoking is prohibited by part 252 of this title unless the "No Smoking" passenger information signs are lighted during the entire flight, or one or more "No Smoking" placards meeting the requirements of 25.1541 of this chapter are posted during the entire flight. If both the lighted signs and the placards are used, the signs must remain lighted during the entire flight segment.

(b) No person may smoke while a "No Smoking" sign is lighted or while "No Smoking" placards are posted, except as follows:

(1) On-demand operations. The pilot in command of an aircraft engaged in an on-demand operation may authorize smoking on the flight deck (if it is physically separated from any passenger compartment), except in any of the following situations:

(i) During aircraft movement on the surface or during takeoff or landing;

(ii) During scheduled passenger-carrying public charter operations conducted under part 380 of this title;

(iii) During on-demand operations conducted interstate that meet paragraph (2) of the definition "On-demand operation" in 110.2 of this chapter, unless permitted under paragraph (b)(2) of this section; or

(iv) During any operation where smoking is prohibited by part 252 of this title or by international agreement.

(2) Certain intrastate commuter operations and certain intrastate on-demand operations. Except during aircraft movement on the surface or during takeoff or landing, a pilot in command of an aircraft engaged in a commuter operation or an on-demand operation that meets paragraph (2) of the definition of "On-demand operation" in 110.2 of this chapter may authorize smoking on the flight deck (if it is physically separated from the passenger compartment, if any) if—

(i) Smoking on the flight deck is not otherwise prohibited by part 252 of this title;

(ii) The flight is conducted entirely within the same State of the United States (a flight from one place in Hawaii to another place in Hawaii through the airspace over a place outside Hawaii is not entirely within the same State); and

(iii) The aircraft is either not turbojet-powered or the aircraft is not capable of carrying at least 30 passengers.

(c) No person may smoke in any aircraft lavatory.

(d) No person may operate an aircraft with a lavatory equipped with a smoke detector unless there is in that lavatory a sign or placard which reads: "Federal law provides for a penalty of up to $2,000 for tampering with the smoke detector installed in this lavatory."

(e) No person may tamper with, disable, or destroy any smoke detector installed in any aircraft lavatory.

(f) On flight segments other than those described in paragraph (a) of this section, the "No Smoking" sign required by 135.177(a)(3) of this part must be turned on during any movement of the aircraft on the surface, for each takeoff or landing, and at any other time considered necessary by the pilot in command.

(g) The passenger information requirements prescribed in 91.517 (b) and (d) of this chapter are in addition to the requirements prescribed in this section.

(h) Each passenger shall comply with instructions given him or her by crewmembers regarding compliance with paragraphs (b), (c), and (e) of this section.

[Doc. No. 25590, 55 FR 8367, Mar. 7, 1990, as amended by Amdt. 135–35, 55 FR 20135, May 15, 1990; Amdt. 135–44, 57 FR 42675, Sept. 15, 1992; Amdt. 135–60, 61 FR 2616, Jan. 26, 1996; Amdt. 135–76, 65 FR 36780, June 9, 2000; Amdt. 135–124, 76 FR 7491, Feb. 10, 2011]

135.128 Use of safety belts and child restraint systems

(a) Except as provided in this paragraph, each person on board an aircraft operated under this part shall occupy an approved seat or berth with a separate safety belt properly secured about him or her during movement on the surface, takeoff, and landing. For seaplane and float equipped rotorcraft operations during movement on the surface, the person pushing off the seaplane or rotorcraft from the dock and the person mooring the seaplane or rotorcraft at the dock are excepted from the preceding seating and safety belt requirements. A safety belt provided for the occupant of a seat may not be used by more than one person who has reached his or her second birthday. Notwithstanding the preceding requirements, a child may:

(1) Be held by an adult who is occupying an approved seat or berth, provided the child has not reached his or her second birthday and the child does not occupy or use any restraining device; or

(2) Notwithstanding any other requirement of this chapter, occupy an approved child restraint system furnished by the certificate holder or one of the persons described in paragraph (a)

FAR 135

(2)(i) of this section, provided:

(i) The child is accompanied by a parent, guardian, or attendant designated by the child's parent or guardian to attend to the safety of the child during the flight;

(ii) Except as provided in paragraph (a)(2)(ii)(D) of this section, the approved child restraint system bears one or more labels as follows:

(A) Seats manufactured to U.S. standards between January 1, 1981, and February 25, 1985, must bear the label: "This child restraint system conforms to all applicable Federal motor vehicle safety standards";

(B) Seats manufactured to U.S. standards on or after February 26, 1985, must bear two labels:

(1) "This child restraint system conforms to all applicable Federal motor vehicle safety standards"; and

(2) "THIS RESTRAINT IS CERTIFIED FOR USE IN MOTOR VEHICLES AND AIRCRAFT" in red lettering;

(C) Seats that do not qualify under paragraphs (a)(2)(ii)(A) and (a)(2)(ii)(B) of this section must bear a label or markings showing:

(1) That the seat was approved by a foreign government;

(2) That the seat was manufactured under the standards of the United Nations;

(3) That the seat or child restraint device furnished by the certificate holder was approved by the FAA through Type Certificate or Supplemental Type Certificate; or

(4) That the seat or child restraint device furnished by the certificate holder, or one of the persons described in paragraph (a)(2)(i) of this section, was approved by the FAA in accordance with 21.8(d) of this chapter or Technical Standard Order C-100b, or a later version. The child restraint device manufactured by AmSafe, Inc. (CARES, Part No. 4082) and approved by the FAA in accordance with 21.305(d) (2010 ed.) of this chapter may continue to bear a label or markings showing FAA approval in accordance with 21.305(d) (2010 ed.) of this chapter.

(D) Except as provided in 135.128(a)(2)(ii)(C)(3) and 135.128(a)(2)(ii)(C)(4), booster-type child restraint systems (as defined in Federal Motor Vehicle Safety Standard No. 213 (49 CFR 571.213)), vest- and harness-type child restraint systems, and lap held child restraints are not approved for use in aircraft; and

(iii) The certificate holder complies with the following requirements:

(A) The restraint system must be properly secured to an approved forward-facing seat or berth;

(B) The child must be properly secured in the restraint system and must not exceed the specified weight limit for the restraint system; and

(C) The restraint system must bear the appropriate label(s).

(b) Except as provided in paragraph (b)(3) of this section, the following prohibitions apply to certificate holders:

(1) Except as provided in 135.128 (a)(2)(ii)(C)(3) and 135.128 (a)(2)(ii)(C)(4), no certificate holder may permit a child, in an aircraft, to occupy a booster-type child restraint system, a vest-type child restraint system, a harness-type child restraint system, or a lap held child restraint system during take off, landing, and movement on the surface.

(2) Except as required in paragraph (b)(1) of this section, no certificate holder may prohibit a child, if requested by the child's parent, guardian, or designated attendant, from occupying a child restraint system furnished by the child's parent, guardian, or designated attendant provided:

(i) The child holds a ticket for an approved seat or berth or such seat or berth is otherwise made available to the certificate holder for the child's use;

(ii) The requirements of paragraph (a)(2)(i) of this section are met;

(iii) The requirements of paragraph (a)(2)(iii) of this section are met; and

(iv) The child restraint system has one or more of the labels described in paragraphs (a)(2)(ii)(A) through (a)(2)(ii)(C) of this section.

(3) This section does not prohibit the certificate holder from providing child restraint systems authorized by this or, consistent with safe operating practices, determining the most appropriate passenger seat location for the child restraint system.

[Doc. No. 26142, 57 FR 42676, Sept. 15, 1992, as amended by Amdt. 135-62, 61 FR 28422, June 4, 1996; Amdt. 135-100, 70 FR 50907, Aug. 26, 2005; Amdt. 135-106, 71 FR 40010, July 14, 2006; 71 FR 59374, Oct. 10, 2006; Amdt. 135-130, 79 FR 28812, May 20, 2014]

135.129   Exit seating

(a)

(1) *Applicability.* This section applies to all certificate holders operating under this part, except for on-demand operations with aircraft having 19 or fewer passenger seats and commuter operations with aircraft having 9 or fewer passenger seats.

(2) *Duty to make determination of suitability.* Each certificate holder shall determine, to the extent necessary to perform the applicable functions of paragraph (d) of this section, the suitability of each person it permits to occupy an exit seat. For the purpose of this section—

(i) Exit seat means—

(A) Each seat having direct access to an exit; and

(B) Each seat in a row of seats through which passengers would have to pass to gain access to an exit, from the first seat inboard of the exit to the first aisle inboard of the exit.

(ii) A passenger seat having direct access means a seat from which a passenger can proceed directly to the exit without entering an aisle or passing around an obstruction.

(3) *Persons designated to make determination.* Each certificate holder shall make the passenger exit seating determinations required by this paragraph in a non-discriminatory manner consistent with the requirements of this section, by persons designated in the certificate holder's required operations manual.

(4) *Submission of designation for approval.* Each certificate holder shall designate the exit seats for each passenger seating configuration in its fleet in accordance with the definition in this paragraph and submit those designations for approval as part of the procedures required to be submitted for approval under paragraphs (n) and (p) of this section.

(b) No certificate holder may seat a person in a seat affected by this section if the certificate holder determines that it is likely that the person would be unable to perform one or more of the applicable functions listed in paragraph (d) of this section because—

(1) The person lacks sufficient mobility, strength, or dexterity in both arms and hands, and both legs:

(i) To reach upward, sideways, and downward to the location of emergency exit and exit-slide operating mechanisms;

(ii) To grasp and push, pull, turn, or otherwise manipulate those mechanisms;

(iii) To push, shove, pull, or otherwise open emergency exits;

(iv) To lift out, hold, deposit on nearby seats, or maneuver over the seatbacks to the next row objects the size and weight of over-wing window exit doors;

(v) To remove obstructions of size and weight similar over-wing exit doors;

(vi) To reach the emergency exit expeditiously;

(vii) To maintain balance while removing obstructions;

(viii) To exit expeditiously;

(ix) To stabilize an escape slide after deployment; or

(x) To assist others in getting off an escape slide;

(2) The person is less than 15 years of age or lacks the capacity to perform one or more of the applicable functions listed in paragraph (d) of this section without the assistance of an adult companion, parent, or other relative;

(3) The person lacks the ability to read and understand instructions required by this section and related to emergency evacuation provided by the certificate holder in printed or graphic form or the ability to understand oral crew commands.

(4) The person lacks sufficient visual capacity to perform one or more of the applicable functions in paragraph (d) of this section without the assistance of visual aids beyond contact lenses or eyeglasses;

(5) The person lacks sufficient aural capacity to hear and understand instructions shouted by flight attendants, without assistance beyond a hearing aid;

(6) The person lacks the ability adequately to impart information orally to other passengers; or,

(7) The person has:

(i) A condition or responsibilities, such as caring for small children, that might prevent the person from performing one or more of the applicable functions listed in paragraph (d) of this section; or

(ii) A condition that might cause the person harm if he or she performs one or more of the applicable functions listed in paragraph (d) of this section.

(c) Each passenger shall comply with instructions given by a crewmember or other authorized employee of the certificate holder implementing exit seating restrictions established in accordance with this section.

(d) Each certificate holder shall include on passenger information cards, presented in the language in which briefings and oral commands are given by the crew, at each exit seat affected by this section, information that, in the event of an emergency in which a crewmember is not available to assist, a passenger occupying an exit seat may use if called upon to perform the following functions:

(1) Locate the emergency exit;

(2) Recognize the emergency exit opening mechanism;

(3) Comprehend the instructions for operating the emergency exit;

(4) Operate the emergency exit;

(5) Assess whether opening the emergency exit will increase the hazards to which passengers may be exposed;

(6) Follow oral directions and hand signals given by a crewmember;

(7) Stow or secure the emergency exit door so that it will not impede use of the exit;

(8) Assess the condition of an escape slide, activate the slide, and stabilize the slide after deployment to assist others in getting off the slide;

(9) Pass expeditiously through the emergency exit; and

(10) Assess, select, and follow a safe path away from the emergency exit.

(e) Each certificate holder shall include on passenger information cards, at each exit seat—

(1) In the primary language in which emergency commands are given by the crew, the selection criteria set forth in paragraph (b) of this section, and a request that a passenger identify himself or herself to allow reseating if he or she—

(i) Cannot meet the selection criteria set forth in paragraph (b) of this section;

(ii) Has a nondiscernible condition that will prevent him or her from performing the applicable functions listed in paragraph (d) of this section;

(iii) May suffer bodily harm as the result of performing one or more of those functions; or

(iv) Does not wish to perform those functions; and,

(2) In each language used by the certificate holder for passenger information cards, a request that a passenger identify himself or herself to allow reseating if he or she lacks the ability to read, speak, or understand the language or the graphic form in which instructions required by this section and related to emergency evacuation are provided by the certificate holder, or the ability to understand the specified language in which crew commands will be given in an emergency;

(3) May suffer bodily harm as the result of performing one or more of those functions; or,

(4) Does not wish to perform those functions.

A certificate holder shall not require the passenger to disclose his or her reason for needing reseating.

(f) Each certificate holder shall make available for inspection by the public at all passenger loading gates and ticket counters at each airport where it conducts passenger operations, written procedures established for making determinations in regard to exit row seating.

(g) No certificate holder may allow taxi or pushback unless at least one required crewmember has verified that no exit seat is occupied by a person the crewmember determines is likely to be unable to perform the applicable functions listed in paragraph (d) of this section.

(h) Each certificate holder shall include in its passenger briefings a reference to the passenger information cards, required by paragraphs (d) and (e), the selection criteria set forth in paragraph (b), and the functions to be performed, set forth in paragraph (d) of this section.

(i) Each certificate holder shall include in its passenger briefings a request that a passenger identify himself or herself to allow reseating if he or she—

(1) Cannot meet the selection criteria set forth in paragraph (b) of this section;

(2) Has a nondiscernible condition that will prevent him or her from performing the applicable functions listed in paragraph (d) of this section;

(3) May suffer bodily harm as the result of performing one or more of those functions; or,

(4) Does not wish to perform those functions.

A certificate holder shall not require the passenger to disclose his or her reason for needing reseating.

(j) [Reserved]

(k) In the event a certificate holder determines in accordance with this section that it is likely that a passenger assigned to an exit seat would be unable to perform the functions listed in paragraph (d) of this section or a passenger requests a non-exit seat, the certificate holder shall expeditiously relocate the passenger to a non-exit seat.

(l) In the event of full booking in the non-exit seats and if necessary to accommodate a passenger being relocated from an exit seat, the

FAR 135

certificate holder shall move a passenger who is willing and able to assume the evacuation functions that may be required, to an exit seat.

(m) A certificate holder may deny transportation to any passenger under this section only because—

(1) The passenger refuses to comply with instructions given by a crewmember or other authorized employee of the certificate holder implementing exit seating restrictions established in accordance with this section, or

(2) The only seat that will physically accommodate the person's handicap is an exit seat.

(n) In order to comply with this section certificate holders shall—

(1) Establish procedures that address:

(i) The criteria listed in paragraph (b) of this section;

(ii) The functions listed in paragraph (d) of this section;

(iii) The requirements for airport information, passenger information cards, crewmember verification of appropriate seating in exit seats, passenger briefings, seat assignments, and denial of transportation as set forth in this section;

(iv) How to resolve disputes arising from implementation of this section, including identification of the certificate holder employee on the airport to whom complaints should be addressed for resolution; and,

(2) Submit their procedures for preliminary review and approval to the principal operations inspectors assigned to them at the responsible Flight Standards office.

(o) Certificate holders shall assign seats prior to boarding consistent with the criteria listed in paragraph (b) and the functions listed in paragraph (d) of this section, to the maximum extent feasible.

(p) The procedures required by paragraph (n) of this section will not become effective until final approval is granted by the Executive Director, Flight Standards Service, Washington, DC. Approval will be based solely upon the safety aspects of the certificate holder's procedures.

[Doc. No. 25821, 55 FR 8073, Mar. 6, 1990, as amended by Amdt. 135-45, 57 FR 48664, Oct. 27, 1992; Amdt. 135-50, 59 FR 33603, June 29, 1994; Amdt. 135-60, 61 FR 2616, Jan. 26, 1996; Docket FAA-2018-0119, Amdt. 135-139, 83 FR 9175, Mar. 5, 2018]

Subpart C — Aircraft and Equipment

135.141   Applicability

This subpart prescribes aircraft and equipment requirements for operations under this part. The requirements of this subpart are in addition to the aircraft and equipment requirements of part 91 of this chapter. However, this part does not require the duplication of any equipment required by this chapter.

135.143   General requirements

(a) No person may operate an aircraft under this part unless that aircraft and its equipment meet the applicable regulations of this chapter.

(b) Except as provided in 135.179, no person may operate an aircraft under this part unless the required instruments and equipment in it have been approved and are in an operable condition.

(c) ATC transponder equipment installed within the time periods indicated below must meet the performance and environmental requirements of the following TSO's:

(1) Through January 1, 1992:

(i) Any class of TSO-C74b or any class of TSO-C74c as appropriate, provided that the equipment was manufactured before January 1, 1990; or

(ii) The appropriate class of TSO-C112 (Mode S).

(2) After January 1, 1992: The appropriate class of TSO-C112 (Mode S). For purposes of paragraph (c)(2) of this section, "installation" does not include—

(i) Temporary installation of TSO-C74b or TSO-C74c substitute equipment, as appropriate, during maintenance of the permanent equipment;

(ii) Reinstallation of equipment after temporary removal for maintenance; or

(iii) For fleet operations, installation of equipment in a fleet aircraft after removal of the equipment for maintenance from another aircraft in the same operator's fleet.

[Doc. No. 16097, 43 FR 46783, Oct. 10, 1978, as amended by Amdt. 135-22, 52 FR 3392, Feb. 3, 1987]

135.144   Portable electronic devices

(a) Except as provided in paragraph (b) of this section, no person may operate, nor may any operator or pilot in command of an aircraft allow the operation of, any portable electronic device on any U.S.-registered civil aircraft operating under this part.

(b) Paragraph (a) of this section does not apply to—

(1) Portable voice recorders;

(2) Hearing aids;

(3) Heart pacemakers;

(4) Electric shavers;

(5) Portable oxygen concentrators that comply with the requirements in 135.91; or

(6) Any other portable electronic device that the part 119 certificate holder has determined will not cause interference with the navigation or communication system of the aircraft on which it is to be used.

(c). The determination required by paragraph (b)(6) of this section shall be made by that part 119 certificate holder operating the aircraft on which the particular device is to be used.

[Doc. No. FAA-1998-4954, 64 FR 1080, Jan. 7, 1999, as amended by Docket FAA-2014-0554, Amdt. 135-133, 81 FR 33120, May 24, 2016]

135.145   Aircraft proving and validation tests

(a) No certificate holder may operate an aircraft, other than a turbojet aircraft, for which two pilots are required by this chapter for operations under VFR, if it has not previously proved such an aircraft in operations under this part in at least 25 hours of proving tests acceptable to the Administrator including—

(1) Five hours of night time, if night flights are to be authorized;

(2) Five instrument approach procedures under simulated or actual conditions, if IFR flights are to be authorized; and

(3) Entry into a representative number of en route airports as determined by the Administrator.

(b) No certificate holder may operate a turbojet airplane if it has not previously proved a turbojet airplane in operations under this part in at least 25 hours of proving tests acceptable to the Administrator including—

(1) Five hours of night time, if night flights are to be authorized;

(2) Five instrument approach procedures under simulated or actual conditions, if IFR flights are to be authorized; and

(3) Entry into a representative number of en route airports as determined by the Administrator.

(c) No certificate holder may carry passengers in an aircraft during proving tests, except those needed to make the tests and those designated by the Administrator to observe the tests. However, pilot flight training may be conducted during the proving tests.

(d) Validation testing is required to determine that a certificate holder is capable of conducting operations safely and in compliance with applicable regulatory standards. Validation tests are required for the following authorizations:

(1) The addition of an aircraft for which two pilots are required for operations under VFR or a turbojet airplane, if that aircraft or an aircraft of the same make or similar design has not been previously proved or validated in operations under this part.

(2) Operations outside U.S. airspace.

(3) Class II navigation authorizations.

(4) Special performance or operational authorizations.

(e) Validation tests must be accomplished by test methods acceptable to the Administrator. Actual flights may not be required when an applicant can demonstrate competence and compliance with appropriate regulations without conducting a flight.

(f) Proving tests and validation tests may be conducted simultaneously when appropriate.

(g) The Administrator may authorize deviations from this section if the Administrator finds that special circumstances make full compliance with this section unnecessary.

[Doc. No. FAA–2001–10047, 68 FR 54586, Sept. 17, 2003]

135.147   Dual controls required

No person may operate an aircraft in operations requiring two pilots unless it is equipped with functioning dual controls. However, if the aircraft type certification operating limitations do not require two pilots, a throwover control wheel may be used in place of two control wheels.

135.149   Equipment requirements: General

No person may operate an aircraft unless it is equipped with—

(a) A sensitive altimeter that is adjustable for barometric pressure;

(b) Heating or deicing equipment for each carburetor or, for a pressure carburetor, an alternate air source;

(c) For turbojet airplanes, in addition to two gyroscopic bank-and-pitch indicators (artificial horizons) for use at the pilot stations, a third indicator that is installed in accordance with the instrument requirements prescribed in 121.305(j) of this chapter.

(d) [Reserved]

(e) For turbine powered aircraft, any other equipment as the Administrator may require.

[Doc. No. 16097, 43 FR 46783, Oct. 10, 1978, as amended at Amdt. 135–1, 44 FR 26737, May 7, 1979; Amdt. 135–34, 54 FR 43926, Oct. 27, 1989; Amdt. 135–38, 55 FR 43310, Oct. 26, 1990]

135.150   Public address and crewmember interphone systems

No person may operate an aircraft having a passenger seating configuration, excluding any pilot seat, of more than 19 unless it is equipped with—

(a) A public address system which—

(1) Is capable of operation independent of the crewmember interphone system required by paragraph (b) of this section, except for handsets, headsets, microphones, selector switches, and signaling devices;

(2) Is approved in accordance with 21.305 of this chapter;

(3) Is accessible for immediate use from each of two flight crewmember stations in the pilot compartment;

(4) For each required floor-level passenger emergency exit which has an adjacent flight attendant seat, has a microphone which is readily accessible to the seated flight attendant, except that one microphone may serve more than one exit, provided the proximity of the exits allows unassisted verbal communication between seated flight attendants;

(5) Is capable of operation within 10 seconds by a flight attendant at each of those stations in the passenger compartment from which its use is accessible;

(6) Is audible at all passenger seats, lavatories, and flight attendant seats and work stations; and

(7) For transport category airplanes manufactured on or after November 27, 1990, meets the requirements of 25.1423 of this chapter.

(b) A crewmember interphone system which—

(1) Is capable of operation independent of the public address system

required by paragraph (a) of this section, except for handsets, headsets, microphones, selector switches, and signaling devices;

(2) Is approved in accordance with 21.305 of this chapter;

(3) Provides a means of two-way communication between the pilot compartment and—

(i)   Each passenger compartment; and

(ii)   Each galley located on other than the main passenger deck level;

(4) Is accessible for immediate use from each of two flight crewmember stations in the pilot compartment;

(5) Is accessible for use from at least one normal flight attendant station in each passenger compartment;

(6) Is capable of operation within 10 seconds by a flight attendant at each of those stations in each passenger compartment from which its use is accessible; and

(7) For large turbojet-powered airplanes—

(i)   Is accessible for use at enough flight attendant stations so that all floor-level emergency exits (or entryways to those exits in the case of exits located within galleys) in each passenger compartment are observable from one or more of those stations so equipped;

(ii)   Has an alerting system incorporating aural or visual signals for use by flight crewmembers to alert flight attendants and for use by flight attendants to alert flight crewmembers;

(iii)   For the alerting system required by paragraph (b)(7)(ii) of this section, has a means for the recipient of a call to determine whether it is a normal call or an emergency call; and

(iv)   When the airplane is on the ground, provides a means of two-way communication between ground personnel and either of at least two flight crewmembers in the pilot compartment. The interphone system station for use by ground personnel must be so located that personnel using the system may avoid visible detection from within the airplane.

[Doc. No. 24995, 54 FR 43926, Oct. 27, 1989]

135.151   Cockpit voice recorders

(a) No person may operate a multiengine, turbine-powered airplane or rotorcraft having a passenger seating configuration of six or more and for which two pilots are required by certification or operating rules unless it is equipped with an approved cockpit voice recorder that:

(1) Is installed in compliance with 23.1457(a)(1) and (2), (b), (c), (d)(1)(i), (2), and (3), (e), (f), and (g); 25.1457(a)(1) and (2), (b), (c), (d)(1)(i), (2) and (3), (e), (f), and (g); 27.1457(a) (1) and (2), (b), (c), (d)(1)(i), (2) and (3), (e), (f), and (g); or 29.1457(a)(1) and (2), (b), (c), (d)(1)(i), (2) and (3), (e), (f), and (g) of this chapter, as applicable; and

(2) Is operated continuously from the use of the check list before the flight to completion of the final check list at the end of the flight.

(b) No person may operate a multiengine, turbine-powered airplane or rotorcraft having a passenger seating configuration of 20 or more seats unless it is equipped with an approved cockpit voice recorder that—

(1) Is installed in accordance with requirements of 23.1457 (except paragraphs (a)(6), (d)(1)(ii), (4), and (5)); 25.1457 (except paragraphs (a)(6), (d) (1)(ii), (4), and (5)); 27.1457 (except paragraphs (a)(6), (d)(1)(ii), (4), and (5)); or 29.1457 (except paragraphs (a)(6), (d)(1)(ii), (4), and (5)) of this chapter, as applicable; and

(2) Is operated continuously from the use of the check list before the flight to completion of the final check list at the end of the flight.

(c) In the event of an accident, or occurrence requiring immediate notification of the National Transportation Safety Board which results in termination of the flight, the certificate holder shall keep the recorded information for at least 60 days or, if requested by the Administrator or the Board, for a longer period. Information obtained from the record may be used to assist in determining the cause of accidents or occurrences in connection with investigations. The Administrator does not use the record in any civil penalty or certificate action.

(d) For those aircraft equipped to record the uninterrupted audio signals received by a boom or a mask microphone the flight crewmembers are required to use the boom microphone below 18,000 feet mean sea level. No person may operate a large turbine engine powered airplane manufactured after October 11, 1991, or on which a cockpit voice recorder has been installed after October 11, 1991, unless it is equipped to record the uninterrupted audio signal received by a boom or mask microphone in accordance with 25.1457(c)(5) of this chapter.

(e) In complying with this section, an approved cockpit voice recorder having an erasure feature may be used, so that during the operation of the recorder, information:

(1) Recorded in accordance with paragraph (a) of this section and recorded more than 15 minutes earlier; or

(2) Recorded in accordance with paragraph (b) of this section and recorded more than 30 minutes earlier; may be erased or otherwise obliterated.

(f) By April 7, 2012, all airplanes subject to paragraph (a) or paragraph (b) of this section that are manufactured before April 7, 2010, and that are required to have a flight data recorder installed in accordance with 135.152, must have a cockpit voice recorder installed that also—

(1) Meets the requirements in 23.1457(d)(6) or 25.1457(d)(6) of this chapter, as applicable; and

(2) If transport category, meet the requirements in 25.1457(a)(3), (a)(4), and (a)(5) of this chapter.

(g)

(1) No person may operate a multiengine, turbine-powered airplane or rotorcraft that is manufactured on or after April 7, 2010, that has a passenger seating configuration of six or more seats, for which two pilots are required by certification or operating rules, and that is required to have a flight data recorder under 135.152, unless it is equipped with an approved cockpit voice recorder that also—

   (i) Is installed in accordance with the requirements of 23.1457 (except for paragraph (a)(6)); 25.1457 (except for paragraph (a)(6)); 27.1457 (except for paragraph (a)(6)) of this chapter, as applicable; and

   (ii) Is operated continuously from the use of the check list before the flight, to completion of the final check list at the end of the flight; and

   (iii) Retains at least the last 2 hours of recorded information using a recorder that meets the standards of TSO–C123a, or later revision.

   (iv) For all airplanes or rotorcraft manufactured on or after December 6, 2010, also meets the requirements of 23.1457 (a)(6); 25.1457 (a)(6); 27.1457 (a)(6); or 29.1457 (a)(6) of this chapter, as applicable

(2) No person may operate a multiengine, turbine-powered airplane or rotorcraft that is manufactured on or after April 7, 2010, has a passenger seating configuration of 20 or more seats, and that is required to have a flight data recorder under 135.152, unless it is equipped with an approved cockpit voice recorder that also—

   (i) Is installed in accordance with the requirements of 23.1457 (except for paragraph (a)(6)) 25.1457 (except for paragraph (a)(6)) 27.1457 (except for paragraph (a)(6)); or 29.1457 (a)(6)) of this chapter, as applicable; and

   (ii) Is operated continuously from the use of the check list before the flight, to completion of the final check list at the end of the flight; and

   (iii) Retains at least the last 2 hours of recorded information using a recorder that meets the standards of TSO–C123a, or later revision.

   (iv) For all airplanes or rotorcraft manufactured on or after December 6, 2010, also meets the requirements of 23.1457 (a)(6); 25.1457 (a)(6); 27.1457 (a)(6); or 29.1457 (a)(6) of this chapter, as applicable.

(h) All airplanes or rotorcraft required by this part to have a cockpit voice recorder and a flight data recorder, that install datalink communication equipment on or after December 6, 2010, must record all datalink messages as required by the certification rule applicable to the aircraft.

[Doc. No. 16097, 43 FR 46783, Oct. 10, 1978, as amended by Amdt. 135–23, 52 FR 9637, Mar. 25, 1987; Amdt. 135–26, 53 FR 26151, July 11, 1988; Amdt. 135–60, 61 FR 2616, Jan. 26, 1996; Amdt. 135–113, 73 FR 12570, Mar. 7, 2008; Amdt. 135–113, 74 FR 32801, July 9, 2009; Amdt 135-121, 75 FR 17046, Apr. 5, 2010]

135.152 Flight data recorders

(a) Except as provided in paragraph (k) of this section, no person may operate under this part a multi-engine, turbine-engine powered airplane or rotorcraft having a passenger seating configuration, excluding any required crewmember seat, of 10 to 19 seats, that was either brought onto the U.S. register after, or was registered outside the United States and added to the operator's U.S. operations specifications after, October 11, 1991, unless it is equipped with one or more approved flight recorders that use a digital method of recording and storing data and a method of readily retrieving that data from the storage medium. The parameters specified in either Appendix B or C of this part, as applicable must be recorded within the range, accuracy, resolution, and recording intervals as specified. The recorder shall retain no less than 25 hours of aircraft operation.

(b) After October 11, 1991, no person may operate a multiengine, turbine-powered airplane having a passenger seating configuration of 20 to 30 seats or a multiengine, turbine-powered rotorcraft having a passenger seating configuration of 20 or more seats unless it is equipped with one or more approved flight recorders that utilize a digital method of recording and storing data, and a method of readily retrieving that data from the storage medium. The parameters in appendix D or E of this part, as applicable, that are set forth below, must be recorded within the ranges, accuracies, resolutions, and sampling intervals as specified.

(1) Except as provided in paragraph (b)(3) of this section for aircraft type certificated before October 1, 1969, the following parameters must be recorded:

   (i) Time;

   (ii) Altitude;

   (iii) Airspeed;

   (iv) Vertical acceleration;

   (v) Heading;

   (vi) Time of each radio transmission to or from air traffic control;

   (vii) Pitch attitude;

   (viii) Roll attitude;

   (ix) Longitudinal acceleration;

   (x) Control column or pitch control surface position; and

   (xi) Thrust of each engine.

(2) Except as provided in paragraph (b)(3) of this section for aircraft type certificated after September 30, 1969, the following parameters must be recorded:

   (i) Time;

   (ii) Altitude;

(iii) Airspeed;

(iv) Vertical acceleration;

(v) Heading;

(vi) Time of each radio transmission either to or from air traffic control;

(vii) Pitch attitude;

(viii) Roll attitude;

(ix) Longitudinal acceleration;

(x) Pitch trim position;

(xi) Control column or pitch control surface position;

(xii) Control wheel or lateral control surface position;

(xiii) Rudder pedal or yaw control surface position;

(xiv) Thrust of each engine;

(xv) Position of each thrust reverser;

(xvi) Trailing edge flap or cockpit flap control position; and

(xvii) Leading edge flap or cockpit flap control position.

(3) For aircraft manufactured after October 11, 1991, all of the parameters listed in appendix D or E of this part, as applicable, must be recorded.

(c) Whenever a flight recorder required by this section is installed, it must be operated continuously from the instant the airplane begins the takeoff roll or the rotorcraft begins the lift-off until the airplane has completed the landing roll or the rotorcraft has landed at its destination.

(d) Except as provided in paragraph (c) of this section, and except for recorded data erased as authorized in this paragraph, each certificate holder shall keep the recorded data prescribed in paragraph (a) of this section until the aircraft has been operating for at least 25 hours of the operating time specified in paragraph (c) of this section. In addition, each certificate holder shall keep the recorded data prescribed in paragraph (b) of this section for an airplane until the airplane has been operating for at least 25 hours, and for a rotorcraft until the rotorcraft has been operating for at least 10 hours, of the operating time specified in paragraph (c) of this section. A total of 1 hour of recorded data may be erased for the purpose of testing the flight recorder or the flight recorder system. Any erasure made in accordance with this paragraph must be of the oldest recorded data accumulated at the time of testing. Except as provided in paragraph (c) of this section, no record need be kept more than 60 days.

(e) In the event of an accident or occurrence that requires the immediate notification of the National Transportation Safety Board under 49 CFR part 830 of its regulations and that results in termination of the flight, the certificate holder shall remove the recording media from the aircraft and keep the recorded data required by paragraphs (a) and (b) of this section for at least 60 days or for a longer period upon request of the Board or the Administrator.

(f)

(1) For airplanes manufactured on or before August 18, 2000, and all other aircraft, each flight recorder required by this section must be installed in accordance with the requirements of 23.1459 (except paragraphs (a)(3)(ii) and (6)), 25.1459 (except paragraphs (a)(3)(ii) an d(7)), 27.1459 (except paragraphs (a)(3)(ii) and (6)), or 29.1459 (except paragraphs (a)(3)(ii) and (6)), as appropriate, of this chapter. The correlation required by paragraph (c) of 23.1459, 25.1459, 27.1459, or 29.1459 of this chapter, as appropriate, need be established only on one aircraft of a group of aircraft:

(i) That are of the same type;

(ii) On which the flight recorder models and their installations are the same; and

(iii) On which there are no differences in the type designs with respect to the installation of the first pilot's instruments associated with the flight recorder. The most recent instrument calibration, including the recording medium from which this calibration is derived, and the recorder correlation must be retained by the certificate holder.

(2) For airplanes manufactured after August 18, 2000, each flight data recorder system required by this section must be installed in accordance with the requirements of 23.1459 (a) (except paragraphs (a)(3)(ii) and (6)), (b), (d) and (e), or 25.1459 (a) (except paragraphs (a)(3)(ii) and (7)), (b), (d), and (e) of this chapter. A correlation must be established between the values recorded by the flight data recorder and the corresponding values being measured. The correlation must contain a sufficient number of correlation points to accurately establish the conversion from the recorded values to engineering units or discrete state over the full operating range of the parameter. Except for airplanes having separate altitude and airspeed sensors that are an integral part of the flight data recorder system, a single correlation may be established for any group of airplanes—

(i) That are of the same type;

(ii) On which the flight recorder system and its installation are the same; and

(iii) On which there is no difference in the type design with respect to the installation of those sensors associated with the flight data recorder system. Documentation sufficient to convert recorded data into the engineering units and discrete values specified in the applicable appendix must be maintained by the certificate holder.

(g) Each flight recorder required by this section that records the data specified in paragraphs (a) and (b) of this section must have an approved device to assist in locating that recorder under water.

(h) The operational parameters required to be recorded by digital flight data recorders required by paragraphs (i) and (j) of this section are as follows, the phrase "when an information source is installed" following a parameter indicates that recording of that parameter is not intended to require a change in installed equipment.

(1) Time;

(2) Pressure altitude;

(3) Indicated airspeed;

(4) Heading—primary flight crew reference (if selectable, record discrete, true or magnetic);

(5) Normal acceleration (Vertical);

(6) Pitch attitude;

(7) Roll attitude;

(8) Manual radio transmitter keying, or CVR/DFDR synchronization reference;

(9) Thrust/power of each engine—primary flight crew reference;

(10) Autopilot engagement status;

(11) Longitudinal acceleration;

(12) Pitch control input;

(13) Lateral control input;

(14) Rudder pedal input;

(15) Primary pitch control surface position;

(16) Primary lateral control surface position;

(17) Primary yaw control surface position;

(18) Lateral acceleration;

(19) Pitch trim surface position or parameters of paragraph (h)(82) of this section if currently recorded;

(20) Trailing edge flap or cockpit flap control selection (except when parameters of paragraph (h)(85) of this section apply);

(21) Leading edge flap or cockpit flap control selection (except when parameters of paragraph (h)(86) of this section apply);

(22) Each Thrust reverser position (or equivalent for propeller airplane);

(23) Ground spoiler position or speed brake selection (except when parameters of paragraph (h)(87) of this section apply);

(24) Outside or total air temperature;

(25) Automatic Flight Control System (AFCS) modes and engagement status, including autothrottle;

(26) Radio altitude (when an information source is installed);

(27) Localizer deviation, MLS Azimuth;

(28) Glideslope deviation, MLS Elevation;

(29) Marker beacon passage;

(30) Master warning;

(31) Air/ground sensor (primary airplane system reference nose or main gear);

(32) Angle of attack (when information source is installed);

(33) Hydraulic pressure low (each system);

(34) Ground speed (when an information source is installed);

(35) Ground proximity warning system;

(36) Landing gear position or landing gear cockpit control selection;

(37) Drift angle (when an information source is installed);

(38) Wind speed and direction (when an information source is installed);

(39) Latitude and longitude (when an information source is installed);

(40) Stick shaker/pusher (when an information source is installed);

(41) Windshear (when an information source is installed);

(42) Throttle/power lever position;

(43) Additional engine parameters (as designated in appendix F of this part);

(44) Traffic alert and collision avoidance system;

(45) DME 1 and 2 distances;

(46) Nav 1 and 2 selected frequency;

(47) Selected barometric setting (when an information source is installed);

(48) Selected altitude (when an information source is installed);

(49) Selected speed (when an information source is installed);

(50) Selected mach (when an information source is installed);

(51) Selected vertical speed (when an information source is installed);

(52) Selected heading (when an information source is installed);

(53) Selected flight path (when an information source is installed);

(54) Selected decision height (when an information source is installed);

(55) EFIS display format;

(56) Multi-function/engine/alerts display format;

(57) Thrust command (when an information source is installed);

(58) Thrust target (when an information source is installed);

(59) Fuel quantity in CG trim tank (when an information source is installed);

(60) Primary Navigation System Reference;

(61) Icing (when an information source is installed);

(62) Engine warning each engine vibration (when an information source is installed);

(63) Engine warning each engine over temp. (when an information source is installed);

(64) Engine warning each engine oil pressure low (when an information source is installed);

(65) Engine warning each engine over speed (when an information source is installed;

(66) Yaw trim surface position;

(67) Roll trim surface position;

(68) Brake pressure (selected system);

(69) Brake pedal application (left and right);

(70) Yaw or sideslip angle (when an information source is installed);

(71) Engine bleed valve position (when an information source is installed);

(72) De-icing or anti-icing system selection (when an information source is installed);

(73) Computed center of gravity (when an information source is installed);

(74) AC electrical bus status;

(75) DC electrical bus status;

(76) APU bleed valve position (when an information source is installed);

(77) Hydraulic pressure (each system);

(78) Loss of cabin pressure;

(79) Computer failure;

(80) Heads-up display (when an information source is installed);

(81) Para-visual display (when an information source is installed);

(82) Cockpit trim control input position—pitch;

(83) Cockpit trim control input position—roll;

(84) Cockpit trim control input position—yaw;

(85) Trailing edge flap and cockpit flap control position;

(86) Leading edge flap and cockpit flap control position;

(87) Ground spoiler position and speed brake selection; and

(88) All cockpit flight control input forces (control wheel, control column, rudder pedal).

(i) For all turbine-engine powered airplanes with a seating configuration, excluding any required crewmember seat, of 10 to 30 passenger seats, manufactured after August 18, 2000—

   (1) The parameters listed in paragraphs (h)(1) through (h)(57) of this section must be recorded within the ranges, accuracies, resolutions, and recording intervals specified in Appendix F of this part.

   (2) Commensurate with the capacity of the recording system, all additional parameters for which information sources are installed and which are connected to the recording system must be recorded within the ranges, accuracies, resolutions, and sampling intervals specified in Appendix F of this part.

(j) For all turbine-engine-powered airplanes with a seating configuration, excluding any required crewmember seat, of 10 to 30 passenger seats, that are manufactured after August 19, 2002 the parameters listed in paragraph (a)(1) through (a)(88) of this section must be recorded within the ranges, accuracies, resolutions, and recording intervals specified in Appendix F of this part.

(k) For aircraft manufactured before August 18, 1997, the following aircraft types need not comply with this section: Bell 212, Bell 214ST, Bell 412, Bell 412SP, Boeing Chinook (BV–234), Boeing/Kawasaki Vertol 107 (BV/KV–107–II), deHavilland DHC–6, Eurocopter Puma 330J, Sikorsky 58, Sikorsky 61N, Sikorsky 76A.

(l) By April 7, 2012, all aircraft manufactured before April 7, 2010, must also meet the requirements in 23.1459(a)(7), 25.1459(a)(8), 27.1459(e), or 29.1459(e) of this chapter, as applicable.

(m) All aircraft manufactured on or after April 7, 2010, must have a flight data recorder installed that also—

(1) Meets the requirements of 23.1459(a)(3), (a)(6), and (a)(7), 25.1459(a)(3), (a)(7), and (a)(8), 27.1459(a)(3), (a)(6), and (e), or 29.1459(a)(3), (a)(6), and (e) of this chapter, as applicable; and

(2) Retains the 25 hours of recorded information required in paragraph (d) of this section using a recorder that meets the standards of TSO–C124a, or later revision.

[Doc. No. 25530, 53 FR 26151, July 11, 1988, as amended by Amdt. 135–69, 62 FR 38396, July 17, 1997; 62 FR 48135, Sept. 12, 1997; Amdt. 135–89, 68 FR 42939, July 18, 2003; Amdt. 135–113, 73 FR 12570, Mar. 7, 2008; AMdt. 135-113, 74 FR 32801, July 9, 2009]

135.153   [Reserved]

135.154   Terrain awareness and warning system

(a) Airplanes manufactured after March 29, 2002:

(1) No person may operate a turbine-powered airplane configured with 10 or more passenger seats, excluding any pilot seat, unless that airplane is equipped with an approved terrain awareness and warning system that meets the requirements for Class A equipment in Technical Standard Order (TSO)–C151. The airplane must also include an approved terrain situational awareness display.

(2) No person may operate a turbine-powered airplane configured with 6 to 9 passenger seats, excluding any pilot seat, unless that airplane is equipped with an approved terrain awareness and warning system that meets as a minimum the requirements for Class B equipment in Technical Standard Order (TSO)–C151.

(b) Airplanes manufactured on or before March 29, 2002:

(1) No person may operate a turbine-powered airplane configured with 10 or more passenger seats, excluding any pilot seat, after March 29, 2005, unless that airplane is equipped with an approved terrain awareness and warning system that meets the requirements for Class A equipment in Technical Standard Order (TSO)–C151. The airplane must also include an approved terrain situational awareness display.

(2) No person may operate a turbine-powered airplane configured with 6 to 9 passenger seats, excluding any pilot seat, after March 29, 2005, unless that airplane is equipped with an approved terrain awareness and warning system that meets as a minimum the requirements for Class B equipment in Technical Standard Order (TSO)–C151.

(Approved by the Office of Management and Budget under control number 2120–0631)

(c) Airplane Flight Manual. The Airplane Flight Manual shall contain appropriate procedures for—

(1) The use of the terrain awareness and warning system; and

(2) Proper flight crew reaction in response to the terrain awareness and warning system audio and visual warnings.

[Doc. No. 29312, 65 FR 16755, Mar. 29, 2000]

135.155   Fire extinguishers: Passenger-carrying aircraft

No person may operate an aircraft carrying passengers unless it is equipped with hand fire extinguishers of an approved type for use in crew and passenger compartments as follows—

(a) The type and quantity of extinguishing agent must be suitable for the kinds of fires likely to occur;

(b) At least one hand fire extinguisher must be provided and conveniently located on the flight deck for use by the flight crew; and

(c) At least one hand fire extinguisher must be conveniently located in the passenger compartment of each aircraft having a passenger seating configuration, excluding any pilot seat, of at least 10 seats but less than 31 seats.

135.156   Flight data recorders: filtered data

(a) A flight data signal is filtered when an original sensor signal has been changed in any way, other than changes necessary to:

(1) Accomplish analog to digital conversion of the signal;

(2) Format a digital signal to be DFDR compatible; or

(3) Eliminate a high frequency component of a signal that is outside the operational bandwidth of the sensor.

(b) An original sensor signal for any flight recorder parameter required to be recorded under 135.152 may be filtered only if the recorded signal value continues to meet the requirements of Appendix D or F of this part, as applicable.

(c) For a parameter described in 135.152(h)(12) through (17), (42), or (88), or the corresponding parameter in Appendix D of this part, if the recorded signal value if filtered and does not meet the requirements of Appendix D or F of this part, as applicable, the certificate holder must:

(1) Remove the filtering and ensure that the recorded signal value meets the requirements of Appendix D or F of this part, as applicable; or

(2) Demonstrate by test and analysis that the original sensor signal value can be reconstructed from the recorded data. This demonstration requires that:

(i) The FAA determine that the procedure and test results submitted by the certificate holder as its compliance with paragraph (c)(2) of this section are repeatable; and

(ii) The certificate holder maintains documentation of the procedure required to reconstruct the original sensor signal value. This documentation is also subject to the requirements of 135.152(e).

(d) Compliance. Compliance is required as follows:

(1) No later than October 20, 2011, each operator must determine, for each aircraft on its operations specifications, whether the aircraft's DFDR system is filtering any of the parameters listed in paragraph (c) of this section. The operator must create a record of this determination for each aircraft it operates, and maintain it as part of the correlation documentation required by 135.152 (f)(1)(iii) or (f)(2)(iii) of this part as applicable.

(2) For aircraft that are not filtering any listed parameter, no further action is required unless the aircraft's DFDR system is modified in a manner that would cause it to meet the definition of filtering on any listed parameter.

(3) For aircraft found to be filtering a parameter listed in paragraph (c) of this section the operator must either:

(i) No later than April 21, 2014, remove the filtering; or

(ii) No later than April 22, 2013, submit the necessary procedure and test results required by paragraph (c)(2) of this section.

(4) After April 21, 2014, no aircraft flight data recording system may filter any parameter listed in paragraph (c) of this section that does not meet the requirements of Appendix D or F of this part, unless the certificate holder possesses test and analysis procedures and the test results that have been approved by the FAA. All records of tests, analysis and procedures used to comply with this section must be maintained as part of the correlation documentation required by 135.152 (f)(1)(iii) of (f)(2)(iii) as applicable.

[Doc. No. FAA–2006–26135, 75 FR 7357, Feb. 19, 2010]

135.157   Oxygen equipment requirements

(a) Unpressurized aircraft. No person may operate an unpressurized aircraft at altitudes prescribed in this section unless it is equipped with enough oxygen dispensers and oxygen to supply the pilots under 135.89(a) and to supply, when flying—

(1) At altitudes above 10,000 feet through 15,000 feet MSL, oxygen to at least 10 percent of the occupants of the aircraft, other than the pilots, for that part of the flight at those altitudes that is of more than 30 minutes duration; and

(2) Above 15,000 feet MSL, oxygen to each occupant of the aircraft other than the pilots.

FAR 135

(b) Pressurized aircraft. No person may operate a pressurized aircraft—

(1) At altitudes above 25,000 feet MSL, unless at least a 10-minute supply of supplemental oxygen is available for each occupant of the aircraft, other than the pilots, for use when a descent is necessary due to loss of cabin pressurization; and

(2) Unless it is equipped with enough oxygen dispensers and oxygen to comply with paragraph (a) of this section whenever the cabin pressure altitude exceeds 10,000 feet MSL and, if the cabin pressurization fails, to comply with 135.89 (a) or to provide a 2-hour supply for each pilot, whichever is greater, and to supply when flying—

(i) At altitudes above 10,000 feet through 15,000 feet MSL, oxygen to at least 10 percent of the occupants of the aircraft, other than the pilots, for that part of the flight at those altitudes that is of more than 30 minutes duration; and

(ii) Above 15,000 feet MSL, oxygen to each occupant of the aircraft, other than the pilots, for one hour unless, at all times during flight above that altitude, the aircraft can safely descend to 15,000 feet MSL within four minutes, in which case only a 30-minute supply is required.

(c) The equipment required by this section must have a means—

(1) To enable the pilots to readily determine, in flight, the amount of oxygen available in each source of supply and whether the oxygen is being delivered to the dispensing units; or

(2) In the case of individual dispensing units, to enable each user to make those determinations with respect to that person's oxygen supply and delivery; and

(3) To allow the pilots to use undiluted oxygen at their discretion at altitudes above 25,000 feet MSL.

135.158   Pitot heat indication systems

(a) Except as provided in paragraph (b) of this section, after April 12, 1981, no person may operate a transport category airplane equipped with a flight instrument pitot heating system unless the airplane is also equipped with an operable pitot heat indication system that complies with 25.1326 of this chapter in effect on April 12, 1978.

(b) A certificate holder may obtain an extension of the April 12, 1981, compliance date specified in paragraph (a) of this section, but not beyond April 12, 1983, from the Executive Director, Flight Standards Service if the certificate holder—

(1) Shows that due to circumstances beyond its control it cannot comply by the specified compliance date; and

(2) Submits by the specified compliance date a schedule for compliance, acceptable to the Executive Director, indicating that compliance will be achieved at the earliest practicable date.

[Doc. No. 18094, Amdt. 135-17, 46 FR 48306, Aug. 31, 1981, as amended by Amdt. 135-33, 54 FR 39294, Sept. 25, 1989; Docket FAA-2018-0119, Amdt. 135-139, 83 FR 9175, Mar. 5, 2018]

135.159   Equipment requirements: Carrying passengers under VFR at night or under VFR over-the-top conditions

No person may operate an aircraft carrying passengers under VFR at night or under VFR over-the-top, unless it is equipped with—

(a) A gyroscopic rate-of-turn indicator except on the following aircraft:

(1) Airplanes with a third attitude instrument system usable through flight attitudes of 360 degrees of pitch-and-roll and installed in accordance with the instrument requirements prescribed in 121.305(j) of this chapter.

(2) Helicopters with a third attitude instrument system usable through flight attitudes of ±80 degrees of pitch and ±120 degrees of roll and installed in accordance with 29.1303(g) of this chapter.

(3) Helicopters with a maximum certificated takeoff weight of 6,000 pounds or less.

(b) A slip skid indicator.

(c) A gyroscopic bank-and-pitch indicator.

(d) A gyroscopic direction indicator.

(e) A generator or generators able to supply all probable combinations of continuous in-flight electrical loads for required equipment and for recharging the battery.

(f) For night flights—

(1) An anticollision light system;

(2) Instrument lights to make all instruments, switches, and gauges easily readable, the direct rays of which are shielded from the pilots' eyes; and

(3) A flashlight having at least two size "D" cells or equivalent.

(g) For the purpose of paragraph (e) of this section, a continuous in-flight electrical load includes one that draws current continuously during flight, such as radio equipment and electrically driven instruments and lights, but does not include occasional intermittent loads.

(h) Notwithstanding provisions of paragraphs (b), (c), and (d), helicopters having a maximum certificated takeoff weight of 6,000 pounds or less may be operated until January 6, 1988, under visual flight rules at night without a slip skid indicator, a gyroscopic bank-and-pitch indicator, or a gyroscopic direction indicator.

[Doc. No. 24550, 51 FR 40709, Nov. 7, 1986, as amended by Amdt. 135-38, 55 FR 43310, Oct. 26, 1990]

135.160   Radio altimeters for rotorcraft operations

(a) After April 24, 2017, no person may operate a rotorcraft unless that rotorcraft is equipped with an operable FAA-approved radio altimeter, or an FAA-approved device that incorporates a radio altimeter, unless otherwise authorized in the certificate holder's approved minimum equipment list.

(b) Deviation authority. The Administrator may authorize deviations from paragraph (a) of this section for rotorcraft that are unable to incorporate a radio altimeter. This deviation will be issued as a Letter of Deviation Authority. The deviation may be terminated or amended at any time by the Administrator. The request for deviation authority is applicable to rotorcraft with a maximum gross takeoff weight no greater than 2,950 pounds. The request for deviation authority must contain a complete statement of the circumstances and justification, and must be submitted to the responsible Flight Standards office, not less than 60 days prior to the date of intended operations.

[Doc. No. FAA-2010-0982, 79 FR 9973, Feb. 21, 2014, as amended by Docket FAA-2018-0119, Amdt. 135-139, 83 FR 9175, Mar. 5, 2018]

135.161   Communication and navigation equipment for aircraft operations under VFR over routes navigated by pilotage

(a) No person may operate an aircraft under VFR over routes that can be navigated by pilotage unless the aircraft is equipped with the two-way radio communication equipment necessary under normal operating conditions to fulfill the following:

(1) Communicate with at least one appropriate station from any point on the route, except in remote locations and areas of mountainous terrain where geographical constraints make such communication impossible.

(2) Communicate with appropriate air traffic control facilities from any point within Class B, Class C, or Class D airspace, or within a Class E surface area designated for an airport in which flights are intended; and

(3) Receive meteorological information from any point en route, except in remote locations and areas of mountainous terrain where geographical constraints make such communication impossible.

(b) No person may operate an aircraft at night under VFR over routes that can be navigated by pilotage unless that aircraft is equipped with—

(1) Two-way radio communication equipment necessary under normal operating conditions to fulfill the functions specified in paragraph (a) of this section; and

(2) Navigation equipment suitable for the route to be flown.

[Doc. No. FAA–2002–14002, 72 FR 31684, June 7, 2007; as amended by Amdt.135-116, 74 FR 20205, May 1, 2009]

135.163 Equipment requirements: Aircraft carrying passengers under IFR

No person may operate an aircraft under IFR, carrying passengers, unless it has—

(a) A vertical speed indicator;

(b) A free-air temperature indicator;

(c) A heated pitot tube for each airspeed indicator;

(d) A power failure warning device or vacuum indicator to show the power available for gyroscopic instruments from each power source;

(e) An alternate source of static pressure for the altimeter and the airspeed and vertical speed indicators;

(f) For a single-engine aircraft:

(1) Two independent electrical power generating sources each of which is able to supply all probable combinations of continuous inflight electrical loads for required instruments and equipment; or

(2) In addition to the primary electrical power generating source, a standby battery or an alternate source of electric power that is capable of supplying 150% of the electrical loads of all required instruments and equipment necessary for safe emergency operation of the aircraft for at least one hour;

(g) For multi-engine aircraft, at least two generators or alternators each of which is on a separate engine, of which any combination of one-half of the total number are rated sufficiently to supply the electrical loads of all required instruments and equipment necessary for safe emergency operation of the aircraft except that for multi-engine helicopters, the two required generators may be mounted on the main rotor drive train; and

(h) Two independent sources of energy (with means of selecting either) of which at least one is an engine-driven pump or generator, each of which is able to drive all required gyroscopic instruments powered by, or to be powered by, that particular source and installed so that failure of one instrument or source, does not interfere with the energy supply to the remaining instruments or the other energy source unless, for single-engine aircraft in all cargo operations only, the rate of turn indicator has a source of energy separate from the bank and pitch and direction indicators. For the purpose of this paragraph, for multi-engine aircraft, each engine-driven source of energy must be on a different engine.

(i) For the purpose of paragraph (f) of this section, a continuous inflight electrical load includes one that draws current continuously during flight, such as radio equipment, electrically driven instruments, and lights, but does not include occasional intermittent loads.

[Doc. No. 16097, 43 FR 46783, Oct. 10, 1978, as amended by Amdt. 135–70, 62 FR 42374, Aug. 6, 1997; Amdt. 135–72, 63 FR 25573, May 8, 1998]

135.165 Communication and navigation equipment: Extended over-water or IFR operations

(a) Aircraft navigation equipment requirements — General . Except as provided in paragraph (g) of this section, no person may conduct operations under IFR or extended over-water unless—

(1) The en route navigation aids necessary for navigating the aircraft along the route (e.g., ATS routes, arrival and departure routes, and instrument approach procedures, including missed approach procedures if a missed approach routing is specified in the procedure) are available and suitable for use by the navigation systems required by this section;

(2) The aircraft used in extended over-water operations is equipped with at least two-approved independent navigation systems suitable for navigating the aircraft along the route to be flown within the degree of accuracy required for ATC.

(3) The aircraft used for IFR operations is equipped with at least—

(i) One marker beacon receiver providing visual and aural signals; and

(ii) One ILS receiver.

(4) Any RNAV system used to meet the navigation equipment requirements of this section is authorized in the certificate holder's operations specifications.

(b) Use of a single independent navigation system for IFR operations. The aircraft may be equipped with a single independent navigation system suitable for navigating the aircraft along the route to be flown within the degree of accuracy required for ATC if:

(1) It can be shown that the aircraft is equipped with at least one other independent navigation system suitable, in the event of loss of the navigation capability of the single independent navigation system permitted by this paragraph at any point along the route, for proceeding safely to a suitable airport and completing an instrument approach; and

(2) The aircraft has sufficient fuel so that the flight may proceed safely to a suitable airport by use of the remaining navigation system, and complete an instrument approach and land.

(c) VOR navigation equipment. Whenever VOR navigation equipment is required by paragraph (a) or (b) of this section, no person may operate an aircraft unless it is equipped with at least one approved DME or suitable RNAV system.

(d) Airplane communication equipment requirements. Except as permitted in paragraph (e) of this section, no person may operate a turbojet airplane having a passenger seat configuration, excluding any pilot seat, of 10 seats or more, or a multiengine airplane in a commuter operation, as defined in part 119 of this chapter, under IFR or in extended over-water operations unless the airplane is equipped with—

(1) At least two independent communication systems necessary under normal operating conditions to fulfill the functions specified in 121.347(a) of this chapter; and

(2) At least one of the communication systems required by paragraph (d)(1) of this section must have two-way voice communication capability.

(e) IFR or extended over-water communications equipment requirements. A person may operate an aircraft other than that specified in paragraph (d) of this section under IFR or in extended over-water operations if it meets all of the requirements of this section, with the exception that only one communication system transmitter is required for operations other than extended over-water operations.

(f) Additional aircraft communication equipment requirements. In addition to the requirements in paragraphs (d) and (e) of this section, no person may operate an aircraft under IFR or in extended over-water operations unless it is equipped with at least:

(1) Two microphones; and

(2) Two headsets or one headset and one speaker.

(g) Extended over-water exceptions. Notwithstanding the requirements of paragraphs (a), (d), and (e) of this section, installation and use of a single long-range navigation system and a single long-range communication system for extended over-water operations in certain geographic areas may be authorized by the Administrator and approved in the certificate holder's operations specifications. The following are among the operational factors the Administrator may consider in granting an authorization:

(1) The ability of the flight crew to navigate the airplane along the route within the degree of accuracy required for ATC;

(2) The length of the route being flown; and

(3) The duration of the very high frequency communications gap.

[Doc. No. FAA–2002–14002, 72 FR 31684, June 7, 2007]

FAR 135

135.167 Emergency equipment: Extended overwater operations

(a) Except where the Administrator, by amending the operations specifications of the certificate holder, requires the carriage of all or any specific items of the equipment listed below for any overwater operation, or, upon application of the certificate holder, the Administrator allows deviation for a particular extended overwater operation, no person may operate an aircraft in extended overwater operations unless it carries, installed in conspicuously marked locations easily accessible to the occupants if a ditching occurs, the following equipment:

(1) An approved life preserver equipped with an approved survivor locator light for each occupant of the aircraft. The life preserver must be easily accessible to each seated occupant.

(2) Enough approved liferafts of a rated capacity and buoyancy to accommodate the occupants of the aircraft.

(b) Each liferaft required by paragraph (a) of this section must be equipped with or contain at least the following:

(1) One approved survivor locator light.

(2) One approved pyrotechnic signaling device.

(3) Either—

   (i) One survival kit, appropriately equipped for the route to be flown; or

   (ii) One canopy (for sail, sunshade, or rain catcher);

   (iii) One radar reflector;

   (iv) One liferaft repair kit;

   (v) One bailing bucket;

   (vi) One signaling mirror;

   (vii) One police whistle;

   (viii) One raft knife;

   (ix) One CO_2 bottle for emergency inflation;

   (x) One inflation pump;

   (xi) Two oars;

   (xii) One 75-foot retaining line;

   (xiii) One magnetic compass;

   (xiv) One dye marker;

   (xv) One flashlight having at least two size "D" cells or equivalent;

   (xvi) A 2-day supply of emergency food rations supplying at least 1,000 calories per day for each person;

   (xvii) For each two persons the raft is rated to carry, two pints of water or one sea water desalting kit;

   (xviii) One fishing kit; and

   (xix) One book on survival appropriate for the area in which the aircraft is operated.

(c) No person may operate an airplane in extended overwater operations unless there is attached to one of the life rafts required by paragraph (a) of this section, an approved survival type emergency locator transmitter. Batteries used in this transmitter must be replaced (or recharged, if the batteries are rechargeable) when the transmitter has been in use for more than 1 cumulative hour, or, when 50 percent of their useful life (or for rechargeable batteries, 50 percent of their useful life of charge) has expired, as established by the transmitter manufacturer under its approval. The new expiration date for replacing (or recharging) the battery must be legibly marked on the outside of the transmitter. The battery useful life (or useful life of charge) requirements of this paragraph do not apply to batteries (such as water-activated batteries) that are essentially unaffected during probable storage intervals.

[Doc. No. 16097, 43 FR 46783, Oct. 10, 1978, as amended by Amdt. 135–4, 45 FR 38348, June 30, 1980; Amdt. 135–20, 51 FR 40710, Nov. 7, 1986; Amdt. 135–49, 59 FR 32058, June 21, 1994; Amdt. 135–91, 68 FR 54586, Sept. 17, 2003]

135.168 Emergency equipment: Overwater rotorcraft operations

(a) *Definitions.* For the purposes of this section, the following definitions apply—

Autorotational distance refers to the distance a rotorcraft can travel in autorotation as described by the manufacturer in the approved Rotorcraft Flight Manual.

Shoreline means that area of the land adjacent to the water of an ocean, sea, lake, pond, river, or tidal basin that is above the high-water mark at which a rotorcraft could be landed safely. This does not include land areas which are unsuitable for landing such as vertical cliffs or land intermittently under water.

(b) *Required equipment.* Except when authorized by the certificate holder's operations specifications, or when necessary only for takeoff or landing, no person may operate a rotorcraft beyond autorotational distance from the shoreline unless it carries:

(1) An approved life preserver equipped with an approved survivor locator light for each occupant of the rotorcraft. The life preserver must be worn by each occupant while the rotorcraft is beyond autorotational distance from the shoreline, except for a patient transported during a helicopter air ambulance operation, as defined in 135.601(b)(1), when wearing a life preserver would be inadvisable for medical reasons; and

(2) An approved and installed 406 MHz emergency locator transmitter (ELT) with 121.5 MHz homing capability. Batteries used in ELTs must be maintained in accordance with the following—

   (i) Non-rechargeable batteries must be replaced when the transmitter has been in use for more than 1 cumulative hour or when 50% of their useful lives have expired, as established by the transmitter manufacturer under its approval. The new expiration date for replacing the batteries must be legibly marked on the outside of the transmitter. The battery useful life requirements of this paragraph (b)(2) do not apply to batteries (such as water-activated batteries) that are essentially unaffected during probable storage intervals; or

   (ii) Rechargeable batteries used in the transmitter must be recharged when the transmitter has been in use for more than 1 cumulative hour or when 50% of their useful-life-of-charge has expired, as established by the transmitter manufacturer under its approval. The new expiration date for recharging the batteries must be legibly marked on the outside of the transmitter. The battery useful-life-of-charge requirements of this paragraph (b)(2) do not apply to batteries (such as water-activated batteries) that are essentially unaffected during probable storage intervals.

(c) [Reserved].

(d) *ELT standards.* The ELT required by paragraph (b)(2) of this section must meet the requirements in:

(1) TSO-C126, TSO-C126a, or TSO-C126b; and

(2) Section 2 of either RTCA DO-204 or RTCA DO-204A, as specified by the TSO complied with in paragraph (d)(1) of this section.

(e) *ELT alternative compliance.* Operators with an ELT required by paragraph (b)(2) of this section, or an ELT with an approved deviation under 21.618 of this chapter, are in compliance with this section.

(f) *Incorporation by reference.* The standards required in this section are incorporated by reference into this section with the approval of the Director of the Federal Register under 5 U.S.C. 552(a) and 1 CFR part 51. To enforce any edition other than that specified in this section, the FAA must publish notice of change in the Federal Register and the material must be available to the public. All approved material is available for inspection at the FAA's Office of Rulemaking (ARM-1), 800 Independence Avenue SW., Washington, DC 20591 (telephone (202) 267-9677) and from the sources indicated below. It is also available for inspection at the National

Archives and Records Administration (NARA). For information on the availability of this material at NARA, call (202) 741-6030 or go to http://www.archives.gov/federal_register/code_of_federal_regulations/ibr_locations.html.

(1) U.S. Department of Transportation, Subsequent Distribution Office, DOT Warehouse M30, Ardmore East Business Center, 3341 Q 75th Avenue, Landover, MD 20785; telephone (301) 322-5377. Copies are also available on the FAA's Web site. Use the following link and type the TSO number in the search box: http://www.airweb.faa.gov/Regulatory_and_Guidance_Library/rgTSO.nsf/Frameset?OpenPage.

   (i) TSO-C126, 406 MHz Emergency Locator Transmitter (ELT), Dec. 23, 1992,

   (ii) TSO-C126a, 406 MHz Emergency Locator Transmitter (ELT), Dec. 17, 2008, and

   (iii) TSO-C126b, 406 MHz Emergency Locator Transmitter (ELT), Nov. 26, 2012.

(2) RTCA, Inc., 1150 18th Street NW., Suite 910, Washington, DC 20036, telephone (202) 833-9339, and are also available on RTCA's Web site at http://www.rtca.org/onlinecart/index.cfm.

   (i) RTCA DO-204, Minimum Operational Performance Standards (MOPS) 406 MHz Emergency Locator Transmitters (ELTs), Sept. 29, 1989, and

   (ii) RTCA DO-204A, Minimum Operational Performance Standards (MOPS) 406 MHz Emergency Locator Transmitters (ELT), Dec. 6, 2007.

[Doc. No. FAA-2010-0982, 79 FR 9973, Feb. 21, 2014, as amended by Amdt. 135-138, 83 FR 1189, Jan. 10, 2018]

135.169 Additional airworthiness requirements

(a) Except for commuter category airplanes, no person may operate a large airplane unless it meets the additional airworthiness requirements of 121.213 through 121.283 and 121.307 of this chapter.

(b) No person may operate a small airplane that has a passenger-seating configuration, excluding pilot seats, of 10 seats or more unless it is type certificated—

(1) In the transport category;

(2) Before July 1, 1970, in the normal category and meets special conditions issued by the Administrator for airplanes intended for use in operations under this part;

(3) Before July 19, 1970, in the normal category and meets the additional airworthiness standards in Special Federal Aviation Regulation No. 23;

(4) In the normal category and meets the additional airworthiness standards in appendix A;

(5) In the normal category and complies with section 1.(a) of Special Federal Aviation Regulation No. 41;

(6) In the normal category and complies with section 1.(b) of Special Federal Aviation Regulation No. 41;

(7) In the commuter category; or

(8) In the normal category, as a multi-engine certification level 4 airplane as defined in part 23 of this chapter.

(c) No person may operate a small airplane with a passenger seating configuration, excluding any pilot seat, of 10 seats or more, with a seating configuration greater than the maximum seating configuration used in that type airplane in operations under this part before August 19, 1977. This paragraph does not apply to—

(1) An airplane that is type certificated in the transport category; or

(2) An airplane that complies with—

   (i) Appendix A of this part provided that its passenger seating configuration, excluding pilot seats, does not exceed 19 seats; or

   (ii) Special Federal Aviation Regulation No. 41.

(d) Cargo or baggage compartments:

(1) After March 20, 1991, each Class C or D compartment, as defined in 25.857 of part 25 of this chapter, greater than 200 cubic feet in volume in a transport category airplane type certificated after January 1, 1958, must have ceiling and sidewall panels which are constructed of:

   (i) Glass fiber reinforced resin;

   (ii) Materials which meet the test requirements of part 25, appendix F, part III of this chapter; or

   (iii) In the case of liner installations approved prior to March 20, 1989, aluminum.

(2) For compliance with this paragraph, the term "liner" includes any design feature, such as a joint or fastener, which would affect the capability of the liner to safely contain a fire.

[Doc. No. 16097, 43 FR 46783, Oct. 10, 1978, as amended by Amdt. 135-2, 44 FR 53731, Sept. 17, 1979; Amdt. 135-21, 52 FR 1836, Jan. 15, 1987; 52 FR 34745, Sept. 14, 1987; Amdt. 135-31, 54 FR 7389, Feb. 17, 1989; Amdt. 135-55, 60 FR 6628, Feb. 2, 1995; Docket FAA-2015-1621, Amdt. 135-136, 81 FR 96701, Dec. 30, 2016]

135.170 Materials for compartment interiors

(a) No person may operate an airplane that conforms to an amended or supplemental type certificate issued in accordance with SFAR No. 41 for a maximum certificated takeoff weight in excess of 12,500 pounds unless within one year after issuance of the initial airworthiness certificate under that SFAR, the airplane meets the compartment interior requirements set forth in 25.853(a) in effect March 6, 1995 (formerly 25.853 (a), (b), (b–1), (b–2), and (b–3) of this chapter in effect on September 26, 1978).

(b) Except for commuter category airplanes and airplanes certificated under Special Federal Aviation Regulation No. 41, no person may operate a large airplane unless it meets the following additional airworthiness requirements:

(1) Except for those materials covered by paragraph (b)(2) of this section, all materials in each compartment used by the crewmembers or passengers must meet the requirements of 25.853 of this chapter in effect as follows or later amendment thereto:

   (i) Except as provided in paragraph (b)(1)(iv) of this section, each airplane with a passenger capacity of 20 or more and manufactured after August 19, 1988, but prior to August 20, 1990, must comply with the heat release rate testing provisions of 25.853(d) in effect March 6, 1995 (formerly 25.853(a–1) in effect on August 20, 1986), except that the total heat release over the first 2 minutes of sample exposure rate must not exceed 100 kilowatt minutes per square meter and the peak heat release rate must not exceed 100 kilowatts per square meter.

   (ii) Each airplane with a passenger capacity of 20 or more and manufactured after August 19, 1990, must comply with the heat release rate and smoke testing provisions of 25.853(d) in effect March 6, 1995 (formerly 25.83(a–1) in effect on September 26, 1988).

   (iii) Except as provided in paragraph (b)(1) (v) or (vi) of this section, each airplane for which the application for type certificate was filed prior to May 1, 1972, must comply with the provisions of 25.853 in effect on April 30, 1972, regardless of the passenger capacity, if there is a substantially complete replacement of the cabin interior after April 30, 1972.

   (iv) Except as provided in paragraph (b)(1) (v) or (vi) of this section, each airplane for which the application for type certificate was filed after May 1, 1972, must comply with the material requirements under which the airplane was type certificated regardless of the passenger capacity if there is a substantially complete replacement of the cabin interior after that date.

(v) Except as provided in paragraph (b)(1)(vi) of this section, each airplane that was type certificated after January 1, 1958, must comply with the heat release testing provisions of 25.853(d) in effect March 6, 1995 (formerly 25.853(a–1) in effect on August 20, 1986), if there is a substantially complete replacement of the cabin interior components identified in that paragraph on or after that date, except that the total heat release over the first 2 minutes of sample exposure shall not exceed 100 kilowatt-minutes per square meter and the peak heat release rate shall not exceed 100 kilowatts per square meter.

(vi) Each airplane that was type certificated after January 1, 1958, must comply with the heat release rate and smoke testing provisions of 25.853(d) in effect March 6, 1995 (formerly 25.853(a–1) in effect on August 20, 1986), if there is a substantially complete replacement of the cabin interior components identified in that paragraph after August 19, 1990.

(vii) Contrary provisions of this section notwithstanding, the Director of the division of the Aircraft Certification Service responsible for the airworthiness rules may authorize deviation from the requirements of paragraph (b)(1)(i), (b)(1)(ii), (b)(1)(v), or (b)(1)(vi) of this section for specific components of the cabin interior that do not meet applicable flammability and smoke emission requirements, if the determination is made that special circumstances exist that make compliance impractical. Such grants of deviation will be limited to those airplanes manufactured within 1 year after the applicable date specified in this section and those airplanes in which the interior is replaced within 1 year of that date. A request for such grant of deviation must include a thorough and accurate analysis of each component subject to §25.853(d) in effect March 6, 1995 (formerly §25.853(a-1) in effect on August 20, 1986), the steps being taken to achieve compliance, and, for the few components for which timely compliance will not be achieved, credible reasons for such noncompliance.

(viii) Contrary provisions of this section notwithstanding, galley carts and standard galley containers that do not meet the flammability and smoke emission requirements of 25.853(d) in effect March 6, 1995 (formerly 25.853(a–1) in effect on August 20, 1986), may be used in airplanes that must meet the requirements of paragraph (b)(1)(i), (b)(1)(ii), (b)(1)(iv) or (b)(1)(vi) of this section provided the galley carts or standard containers were manufactured prior to March 6, 1995.

(2) For airplanes type certificated after January 1, 1958, seat cushions, except those on flight crewmember seats, in any compartment occupied by crew or passengers must comply with the requirements pertaining to fire protection of seat cushions in 25.853(c) effective November 26, 1984.

(c) Thermal/acoustic insulation materials. For transport category airplanes type certificated after January 1, 1958:

(1) For airplanes manufactured before September 2, 2005, when thermal/acoustic insulation is installed in the fuselage as replacements after September 2, 2005, the insulation must meet the flame propagation requirements of 25.856 of this chapter, effective September 2, 2003, if it is:

(i) Of a blanket construction, or

(ii) Installed around air ducting.

(2) For airplanes manufactured after September 2, 2005, thermal/acoustic insulation materials installed in the fuselage must meet the flame propagation requirements of 25.856 of this chapter, effective September 2, 2003.

[Doc. No. 26192, 60 FR 6628, Feb. 2, 1995; Amdt. 135-55, 60 FR 11194, Mar. 1, 1995; Amdt. 135-56, 60 FR 13011, Mar. 9, 1995; Amdt. 135-90, 68 FR 45084, July 31, 2003; Amdt. 135-103, 70 FR 77752, Dec. 30, 2005; Docket FAA-2018-0119, Amdt. 135-139, 83 FR 9175, Mar. 5, 2018]

135.171 Shoulder harness installation at flight crewmember stations

(a) No person may operate a turbojet aircraft or an aircraft having a passenger seating configuration, excluding any pilot seat, of 10 seats or more unless it is equipped with an approved shoulder harness installed for each flight crewmember station.

(b) Each flight crewmember occupying a station equipped with a shoulder harness must fasten the shoulder harness during takeoff and landing, except that the shoulder harness may be unfastened if the crewmember cannot perform the required duties with the shoulder harness fastened.

135.173 Airborne thunderstorm detection equipment requirements

(a) No person may operate an aircraft that has a passenger seating configuration, excluding any pilot seat, of 10 seats or more in passenger-carrying operations, except a helicopter operating under day VFR conditions, unless the aircraft is equipped with either approved thunderstorm detection equipment or approved airborne weather radar equipment.

(b) No person may operate a helicopter that has a passenger seating configuration, excluding any pilot seat, of 10 seats or more in passenger-carrying operations, under night VFR when current weather reports indicate that thunderstorms or other potentially hazardous weather conditions that can be detected with airborne thunderstorm detection equipment may reasonably be expected along the route to be flown, unless the helicopter is equipped with either approved thunderstorm detection equipment or approved airborne weather radar equipment.

(c) No person may begin a flight under IFR or night VFR conditions when current weather reports indicate that thunderstorms or other potentially hazardous weather conditions that can be detected with airborne thunderstorm detection equipment, required by paragraph (a) or (b) of this section, may reasonably be expected along the route to be flown, unless the airborne thunderstorm detection equipment is in satisfactory operating condition.

(d) If the airborne thunderstorm detection equipment becomes inoperative en route, the aircraft must be operated under the instructions and procedures specified for that event in the manual required by 135.21.

(e) This section does not apply to aircraft used solely within the State of Hawaii, within the State of Alaska, within that part of Canada west of longitude 130 degrees W, between latitude 70 degrees N, and latitude 53 degrees N, or during any training, test, or ferry flight.

(f) Without regard to any other provision of this part, an alternate electrical power supply is not required for airborne thunderstorm detection equipment.

[Doc. No. 16097, 43 FR 46783, Oct. 10, 1978, as amended by Amdt. 135–20, 51 FR 40710, Nov. 7, 1986; Amdt. 135–60, 61 FR 2616, Jan. 26, 1996]

135.175 Airborne weather radar equipment requirements

(a) No person may operate a large, transport category aircraft in passenger-carrying operations unless approved airborne weather radar equipment is installed in the aircraft.

(b) No person may begin a flight under IFR or night VFR conditions when current weather reports indicate that thunderstorms, or other potentially hazardous weather conditions that can be detected with airborne weather radar equipment, may reasonably be expected along the route to be flown, unless the airborne weather radar equipment required by paragraph (a) of this section is in satisfactory operating condition.

(c) If the airborne weather radar equipment becomes inoperative en route, the aircraft must be operated under the instructions and procedures specified for that event in the manual required by 135.21.

(d) This section does not apply to aircraft used solely within the State of Hawaii, within the State of Alaska, within that part of Canada west of longitude 130 degrees W, between latitude 70 degrees N, and latitude 53 degrees N, or during any training, test, or ferry flight.

(e) Without regard to any other provision of this part, an alternate electrical power supply is not required for airborne weather radar equipment.

135.177 Emergency equipment requirements for aircraft having a passenger seating configuration of more than 19 passengers

(a) No person may operate an aircraft having a passenger seating configuration, excluding any pilot seat, of more than 19 seats unless it is equipped with the following emergency equipment:

(1) At least one approved first-aid kit for treatment of injuries likely to occur in flight or in a minor accident that must:

    (i) Be readily accessible to crewmembers.

    (ii) Be stored securely and kept free from dust, moisture, and damaging temperatures.

    (iii) Contain at least the following appropriately maintained contents in the specified quantities:

CONTENTS	QUANTITY
Adhesive bandage compresses, 1-inch	16
Antiseptic swabs	20
Ammonia inhalants	10
Bandage compresses, 4-inch	8
Triangular bandage compresses, 40-inch	5
Arm splint, noninflatable	1
Leg splint, noninflatable	1
Roller bandage, 4-inch	4
Adhesive tape, 1-inch standard roll	2
Bandage scissors	1
Protective nonpermeable gloves or equivalent	1 pair

(2) A crash axe carried so as to be accessible to the crew but inaccessible to passengers during normal operations.

(3) Signs that are visible to all occupants to notify them when smoking is prohibited and when safety belts must be fastened. The signs must be constructed so that they can be turned on during any movement of the aircraft on the surface, for each takeoff or landing, and at other times considered necessary by the pilot in command. "No smoking" signs shall be turned on when required by 135.127.

(4) [Reserved]

(b) Each item of equipment must be inspected regularly under inspection periods established in the operations specifications to ensure its condition for continued serviceability and immediate readiness to perform its intended emergency purposes.

[Doc. No. 16097, 43 FR 46783, Oct. 10, 1978, as amended by Amdt. 135–25, 53 FR 12362, Apr. 13, 1988; Amdt. 135–43, 57 FR 19245, May 4, 1992; Amdt. 135–44, 57 FR 42676, Sept. 15, 1992; Amdt. 135–47, 59 FR 1781, Jan. 12, 1994; Amdt. 135–53, 59 FR 52643, Oct. 18, 1994; 59 FR 55208, Nov. 4, 1994; Amdt. 121–281, 66 FR 19045, Apr. 12, 2001]

135.178 Additional emergency equipment

No person may operate an airplane having a passenger seating configuration of more than 19 seats, unless it has the additional emergency equipment specified in paragraphs (a) through (l) of this section.

(a) Means for emergency evacuation. Each passenger-carrying land-plane emergency exit (other than over-the-wing) that is more than 6 feet from the ground, with the airplane on the ground and the landing gear extended, must have an approved means to assist the occupants in descending to the ground. The assisting means for a floor-level emergency exit must meet the requirements of 25.809(f)(1) of this chapter in effect on April 30, 1972, except that, for any airplane for which the application for the type certificate was filed after that date, it must meet the requirements under which the airplane was type certificated. An assisting means that deploys automatically must be armed during taxiing, takeoffs, and landings; however, the Administrator may grant a deviation from the requirement of automatic deployment if he finds that the design of the exit makes compliance impractical, if the assisting means automatically erects upon deployment and, with respect to required emergency exits, if an emergency evacuation demonstration is conducted in accordance with 121.291(a) of this chapter. This paragraph does not apply to the rear window emergency exit of Douglas DC–3 airplanes operated with fewer than 36 occupants, including crewmembers, and fewer than five exits authorized for passenger use.

(b) Interior emergency exit marking. The following must be complied with for each passenger-carrying airplane:

(1) Each passenger emergency exit, its means of access, and its means of opening must be conspicuously marked. The identity and locating of each passenger emergency exit must be recognizable from a distance equal to the width of the cabin. The location of each passenger emergency exit must be indicated by a sign visible to occupants approaching along the main passenger aisle. There must be a locating sign—

    (i) Above the aisle near each over-the-wing passenger emergency exit, or at another ceiling location if it is more practical because of low headroom;

    (ii) Next to each floor level passenger emergency exit, except that one sign may serve two such exits if they both can be seen readily from that sign; and

    (iii) On each bulkhead or divider that prevents fore and aft vision along the passenger cabin, to indicate emergency exits beyond and obscured by it, except that if this is not possible, the sign may be placed at another appropriate location.

(2) Each passenger emergency exit marking and each locating sign must meet the following:

    (i) For an airplane for which the application for the type certificate was filed prior to May 1, 1972, each passenger emergency exit marking and each locating sign must be manufactured to meet the requirements of 25.812(b) of this chapter in effect on April 30, 1972. On these airplanes, no sign may continue to be used if its luminescence (brightness) decreases to below 100 microlamberts. The colors may be reversed if it increases the emergency illumination of the passenger compartment. However, the Administrator may authorize deviation from the 2-inch background requirements if he finds that special circumstances exist that make compliance impractical and that the proposed deviation provides an equivalent level of safety.

    (ii) For an airplane for which the application for the type certificate was filed on or after May 1, 1972, each passenger emergency exit marking and each locating sign must be manufactured to meet the interior emergency exit marking requirements under which the airplane was type certificated. On these airplanes, no sign may continue to be used if its luminescence (brightness) decreases to below 250 microlamberts.

(c) Lighting for interior emergency exit markings. Each passenger-carrying airplane must have an emergency lighting system, independent of the main lighting system; however, sources of general cabin illumination may be common to both the emergency and

FAR 135

the main lighting systems if the power supply to the emergency lighting system is independent of the power supply to the main lighting system. The emergency lighting system must—

(1) Illuminate each passenger exit marking and locating sign;

(2) Provide enough general lighting in the passenger cabin so that the average illumination when measured at 40-inch intervals at seat armrest height, on the centerline of the main passenger aisle, is at least 0.05 foot-candles; and

(3) For airplanes type certificated after January 1, 1958, include floor proximity emergency escape path marking which meets the requirements of 25.812(e) of this chapter in effect on November 26, 1984.

(d) *Emergency light operation.* Except for lights forming part of emergency lighting subsystems provided in compliance with 25.812(h) of this chapter (as prescribed in paragraph (h) of this section) that serve no more than one assist means, are independent of the airplane's main emergency lighting systems, and are automatically activated when the assist means is deployed, each light required by paragraphs (c) and (h) of this section must:

(1) Be operable manually both from the flightcrew station and from a point in the passenger compartment that is readily accessible to a normal flight attendant seat;

(2) Have a means to prevent inadvertent operation of the manual controls;

(3) When armed or turned on at either station, remain lighted or become lighted upon interruption of the airplane's normal electric power;

(4) Be armed or turned on during taxiing, takeoff, and landing. In showing compliance with this paragraph, a transverse vertical separation of the fuselage need not be considered;

(5) Provide the required level of illumination for at least 10 minutes at the critical ambient conditions after emergency landing; and

(6) Have a cockpit control device that has an "on," "off," and "armed" position.

(e) *Emergency exit operating handles.*

(1) For a passenger-carrying airplane for which the application for the type certificate was filed prior to May 1, 1972, the location of each passenger emergency exit operating handle, and instructions for opening the exit, must be shown by a marking on or near the exit that is readable from a distance of 30 inches. In addition, for each Type I and Type II emergency exit with a locking mechanism released by rotary motion of the handle, the instructions for opening must be shown by—

(i) A red arrow with a shaft at least three-fourths inch wide and a head twice the width of the shaft, extending along at least 70° of arc at a radius approximately equal to three-fourths of the handle length; and

(ii) The word "open" in red letters 1 inch high placed horizontally near the head of the arrow.

(2) For a passenger-carrying airplane for which the application for the type certificate was filed on or after May 1, 1972, the location of each passenger emergency exit operating handle and instructions for opening the exit must be shown in accordance with the requirements under which the airplane was type certificated. On these airplanes, no operating handle or operating handle cover may continue to be used if its luminescence (brightness) decreases to below 100 microlamberts.

(f) *Emergency exit access.* Access to emergency exits must be provided as follows for each passenger-carrying airplane:

(1) Each passageway between individual passenger areas, or leading to a Type I or Type II emergency exit, must be unobstructed and at least 20 inches wide.

(2) There must be enough space next to each Type I or Type II emergency exit to allow a crewmember to assist in the evacuation of passengers without reducing the unobstructed width of the passageway below that required in paragraph (f)(1) of

this section; however, the Administrator may authorize deviation from this requirement for an airplane certificated under the provisions of part 4b of the Civil Air Regulations in effect before December 20, 1951, if he finds that special circumstances exist that provide an equivalent level of safety.

(3) There must be access from the main aisle to each Type III and Type IV exit. The access from the aisle to these exits must not be obstructed by seats, berths, or other protrusions in a manner that would reduce the effectiveness of the exit. In addition, for a transport category airplane type certificated after January 1, 1958, there must be placards installed in accordance with 25.813(c)(3) of this chapter for each Type III exit after December 3, 1992.

(4) If it is necessary to pass through a passageway between passenger compartments to reach any required emergency exit from any seat in the passenger cabin, the passageway must not be obstructed. Curtains may, however, be used if they allow free entry through the passageway.

(5) No door may be installed in any partition between passenger compartments.

(6) If it is necessary to pass through a doorway separating the passenger cabin from other areas to reach a required emergency exit from any passenger seat, the door must have a means to latch it in the open position, and the door must be latched open during each takeoff and landing. The latching means must be able to withstand the loads imposed upon it when the door is subjected to the ultimate inertia forces, relative to the surrounding structure, listed in 25.561(b) of this chapter.

(g) *Exterior exit markings.* Each passenger emergency exit and the means of opening that exit from the outside must be marked on the outside of the airplane. There must be a 2-inch colored band outlining each passenger emergency exit on the side of the fuselage. Each outside marking, including the band, must be readily distinguishable from the surrounding fuselage area by contrast in color. The markings must comply with the following:

(1) If the reflectance of the darker color is 15 percent or less, the reflectance of the lighter color must be at least 45 percent.

(2) If the reflectance of the darker color is greater than 15 percent, at least a 30 percent difference between its reflectance and the reflectance of the lighter color must be provided.

(3) Exits that are not in the side of the fuselage must have the external means of opening and applicable instructions marked conspicuously in red or, if red is inconspicuous against the background color, in bright chrome yellow and, when the opening means for such an exit is located on only one side of the fuselage, a conspicuous marking to that effect must be provided on the other side. "Reflectance" is the ratio of the luminous flux reflected by a body to the luminous flux it receives.

(h) *Exterior emergency lighting and escape route.*

(1) Each passenger-carrying airplane must be equipped with exterior lighting that meets the following requirements:

(i) For an airplane for which the application for the type certificate was filed prior to May 1, 1972, the requirements of 25.812 (f) and (g) of this chapter in effect on April 30, 1972.

(ii) For an airplane for which the application for the type certificate was filed on or after May 1, 1972, the exterior emergency lighting requirements under which the airplane was type certificated.

(2) Each passenger-carrying airplane must be equipped with a slip-resistant escape route that meets the following requirements:

(i) For an airplane for which the application for the type certificate was filed prior to May 1, 1972, the requirements of 25.803(e) of this chapter in effect on April 30, 1972.

(ii) For an airplane for which the application for the type certificate was filed on or after May 1, 1972, the slip-resistant escape route requirements under which the airplane was type certificated.

(i) Floor level exits. Each floor level door or exit in the side of the fuselage (other than those leading into a cargo or baggage compartment that is not accessible from the passenger cabin) that is 44 or more inches high and 20 or more inches wide, but not wider than 46 inches, each passenger ventral exit (except the ventral exits on Martin 404 and Convair 240 airplanes), and each tail cone exit, must meet the requirements of this section for floor level emergency exits. However, the Administrator may grant a deviation from this paragraph if he finds that circumstances make full compliance impractical and that an acceptable level of safety has been achieved.

(j) Additional emergency exits. Approved emergency exits in the passenger compartments that are in excess of the minimum number of required emergency exits must meet all of the applicable provisions of this section, except paragraphs (f) (1), (2), and (3) of this section, and must be readily accessible.

(k) On each large passenger-carrying turbojet-powered airplane, each ventral exit and tailcone exit must be—

(1) Designed and constructed so that it cannot be opened during flight; and

(2) Marked with a placard readable from a distance of 30 inches and installed at a conspicuous location near the means of opening the exit, stating that the exit has been designed and constructed so that it cannot be opened during flight.

(l) Portable lights. No person may operate a passenger-carrying airplane unless it is equipped with flashlight stowage provisions accessible from each flight attendant seat.

[Doc. No. 26530, 57 FR 19245, May 4, 1992; 57 FR 29120, June 30, 1992, as amended at 57 FR 34682, Aug. 6, 1992]

135.179 Inoperable instruments and equipment

(a) No person may take off an aircraft with inoperable instruments or equipment installed unless the following conditions are met:

(1) An approved Minimum Equipment List exists for that aircraft.

(2) The responsible Flight Standards office has issued the certificate holder operations specifications authorizing operations in accordance with an approved Minimum Equipment List. The flight crew shall have direct access at all times prior to flight to all of the information contained in the approved Minimum Equipment List through printed or other means approved by the Administrator in the certificate holders operations specifications. An approved Minimum Equipment List, as authorized by the operations specifications, constitutes an approved change to the type design without requiring recertification.

(3) The approved Minimum Equipment List must:

(i) Be prepared in accordance with the limitations specified in paragraph (b) of this section.

(ii) Provide for the operation of the aircraft with certain instruments and equipment in an inoperable condition.

(4) Records identifying the inoperable instruments and equipment and the information required by (a)(3)(ii) of this section must be available to the pilot.

(5) The aircraft is operated under all applicable conditions and limitations contained in the Minimum Equipment List and the operations specifications authorizing use of the Minimum Equipment List.

(b) The following instruments and equipment may not be included in the Minimum Equipment List:

(1) Instruments and equipment that are either specifically or otherwise required by the airworthiness requirements under which the airplane is type certificated and which are essential for safe operations under all operating conditions.

(2) Instruments and equipment required by an airworthiness directive to be in operable condition unless the airworthiness directive provides otherwise.

(3) Instruments and equipment required for specific operations by this part.

(c) Notwithstanding paragraphs (b)(1) and (b)(3) of this section, an aircraft with inoperable instruments or equipment may be operated under a special flight permit under 21.197 and 21.199 of this chapter.

[Doc. No. 25780, 56 FR 12311, Mar. 22, 1991; 56 FR 14920, Apr. 8, 1991, as amended by Amdt. 135-60, 61 FR 2616, Jan. 26, 1996; Amdt. 135-91, 68 FR 54586, Sept. 17, 2003; Docket FAA-2018-0119, Amdt. 135-139, 83 FR 9175, Mar. 5, 2018]

135.180 Traffic Alert and Collision Avoidance System

(a) Unless otherwise authorized by the Administrator, after December 31, 1995, no person may operate a turbine powered airplane that has a passenger seat configuration, excluding any pilot seat, of 10 to 30 seats unless it is equipped with an approved traffic alert and collision avoidance system. If a TCAS II system is installed, it must be capable of coordinating with TCAS units that meet TSO C–119.

(b) The airplane flight manual required by 135.21 of this part shall contain the following information on the TCAS I system required by this section:

(1) Appropriate procedures for—

(i) The use of the equipment; and

(ii) Proper flightcrew action with respect to the equipment operation.

(2) An outline of all input sources that must be operating for the TCAS to function properly.

[Doc. No. 25355, 54 FR 951, Jan. 10, 1989, as amended by Amdt. 135–54, 59 FR 67587, Dec. 29, 1994]

135.181 Performance requirements: Aircraft operated over-the-top or in IFR conditions

(a) Except as provided in paragraphs (b) and (c) of this section, no person may—

(1) Operate a single-engine aircraft carrying passengers over-the-top; or

(2) Operate a multiengine aircraft carrying passengers over-the-top or in IFR conditions at a weight that will not allow it to climb, with the critical engine inoperative, at least 50 feet a minute when operating at the MEAs of the route to be flown or 5,000 feet MSL, whichever is higher.

(b) Notwithstanding the restrictions in paragraph (a)(2) of this section, multiengine helicopters carrying passengers offshore may conduct such operations in over-the-top or in IFR conditions at a weight that will allow the helicopter to climb at least 50 feet per minute with the critical engine inoperative when operating at the MEA of the route to be flown or 1,500 feet MSL, whichever is higher.

(c) Without regard to paragraph (a) of this section, if the latest weather reports or forecasts, or any combination of them, indicate that the weather along the planned route (including takeoff and landing) allows flight under VFR under the ceiling (if a ceiling exists) and that the weather is forecast to remain so until at least 1 hour after the estimated time of arrival at the destination, a person may operate an aircraft over-the-top.

(d) Without regard to paragraph (a) of this section, a person may operate an aircraft over-the-top under conditions allowing—

(1) For multiengine aircraft, descent or continuance of the flight under VFR if its critical engine fails; or

(2) For single-engine aircraft, descent under VFR if its engine fails.

[Doc. No. 16097, 43 FR 46783, Oct. 10, 1978, as amended by Amdt. 135–20, 51 FR 40710, Nov. 7, 1986; Amdt. 135–70, 62 FR 42374, Aug. 6, 1997]

135.183 Performance requirements: Land aircraft operated over water

No person may operate a land aircraft carrying passengers over water unless—

(a) It is operated at an altitude that allows it to reach land in the case of engine failure;

(b) It is necessary for takeoff or landing;

(c) It is a multiengine aircraft operated at a weight that will allow it to climb, with the critical engine inoperative, at least 50 feet a minute, at an altitude of 1,000 feet above the surface; or

(d) It is a helicopter equipped with helicopter flotation devices.

135.185 Empty weight and center of gravity: Currency requirement

(a) No person may operate a multiengine aircraft unless the current empty weight and center of gravity are calculated from values established by actual weighing of the aircraft within the preceding 36 calendar months.

(b) Paragraph (a) of this section does not apply to—

(1) Aircraft issued an original airworthiness certificate within the preceding 36 calendar months; and

(2) Aircraft operated under a weight and balance system approved in the operations specifications of the certificate holder.

Subpart D — VFR/IFR Operating Limitations and Weather Requirements

135.201 Applicability

This subpart prescribes the operating limitations for VFR/IFR flight operations and associated weather requirements for operations under this part.

135.203 VFR: Minimum altitudes

Except when necessary for takeoff and landing, no person may operate under VFR—

(a) An airplane—

(1) During the day, below 500 feet above the surface or less than 500 feet horizontally from any obstacle; or

(2) At night, at an altitude less than 1,000 feet above the highest obstacle within a horizontal distance of 5 miles from the course intended to be flown or, in designated mountainous terrain, less than 2,000 feet above the highest obstacle within a horizontal distance of 5 miles from the course intended to be flown; or

(b) A helicopter over a congested area at an altitude less than 300 feet above the surface.

135.205 VFR: Visibility requirements

(a) No person may operate an airplane under VFR in uncontrolled airspace when the ceiling is less than 1,000 feet unless flight visibility is at least 2 miles.

(b) No person may operate a helicopter under VFR in Class G airspace at an altitude of 1,200 feet or less above the surface or within the lateral boundaries of the surface areas of Class B, Class C, Class D, or Class E airspace designated for an airport unless the visibility is at least—

(1) During the day—1/2 mile; or

(2) At night—1 mile.

[Doc. No. 16097, 43 FR 46783, Oct. 10, 1978, as amended by Amdt. 135–41, 56 FR 65663, Dec. 17, 1991]

135.207 VFR: Helicopter surface reference requirements

No person may operate a helicopter under VFR unless that person has visual surface reference or, at night, visual surface light reference, sufficient to safely control the helicopter.

135.209 VFR: Fuel supply

(a) No person may begin a flight operation in an airplane under VFR unless, considering wind and forecast weather conditions, it has enough fuel to fly to the first point of intended landing and, assuming normal cruising fuel consumption—

(1) During the day, to fly after that for at least 30 minutes; or

(2) At night, to fly after that for at least 45 minutes.

(b) No person may begin a flight operation in a helicopter under VFR unless, considering wind and forecast weather conditions, it has enough fuel to fly to the first point of intended landing and, assuming normal cruising fuel consumption, to fly after that for at least 20 minutes.

135.211 VFR: Over-the-top carrying passengers: Operating limitations

Subject to any additional limitations in 135.181, no person may operate an aircraft under VFR over-the-top carrying passengers, unless—

(a) Weather reports or forecasts, or any combination of them, indicate that the weather at the intended point of termination of over-the-top flight—

(1) Allows descent to beneath the ceiling under VFR and is forecast to remain so until at least 1 hour after the estimated time of arrival at that point; or

(2) Allows an IFR approach and landing with flight clear of the clouds until reaching the prescribed initial approach altitude over the final approach facility, unless the approach is made with the use of radar under 91.175(i) of this chapter; or

(b) It is operated under conditions allowing—

(1) For multiengine aircraft, descent or continuation of the flight under VFR if its critical engine fails; or

(2) For single-engine aircraft, descent under VFR if its engine fails.

[Doc. No. 16097, 43 FR 46783, Oct. 10, 1978, as amended by Amdt. 135–32, 54 FR 34332, Aug. 18, 1989; 73 FR 20164, Apr. 15, 2008]

135.213 Weather reports and forecasts

(a) Whenever a person operating an aircraft under this part is required to use a weather report or forecast, that person shall use that of the U.S. National Weather Service, a source approved by the U.S. National Weather Service, or a source approved by the Administrator. However, for operations under VFR, the pilot in command may, if such a report is not available, use weather information based on that pilot's own observations or on those of other persons competent to supply appropriate observations.

(b) For the purposes of paragraph (a) of this section, weather observations made and furnished to pilots to conduct IFR operations at an airport must be taken at the airport where those IFR operations are conducted, unless the Administrator issues operations specifications allowing the use of weather observations taken at a location not at the airport where the IFR operations are conducted. The Administrator issues such operations specifications when, after investigation by the U.S. National Weather Service and the responsible Flight Standards office, it is found that the standards of safety for that operation would allow the deviation from this paragraph for a particular operation for which an air carrier operating certificate or operating certificate has been issued.

[Doc. No. 16097, 43 FR 46783, Oct. 10, 1978, as amended by Amdt. 135–60, 61 FR 2616, Jan. 26, 1996; Docket FAA-2018-0119, Amdt. 135-139, 83 FR 9175, Mar. 5, 2018]

135.215 IFR: Operating limitations

(a) Except as provided in paragraphs (b), (c) and (d) of this section, no person may operate an aircraft under IFR outside of controlled airspace or at any airport that does not have an approved standard instrument approach procedure.

(b) The Administrator may issue operations specifications to the certificate holder to allow it to operate under IFR over routes outside controlled airspace if—

(1) The certificate holder shows the Administrator that the flight crew is able to navigate, without visual reference to the ground, over an intended track without deviating more than 5 degrees or 5 miles, whichever is less, from that track; and

(2) The Administrator determines that the proposed operations can be conducted safely.

(c) A person may operate an aircraft under IFR outside of controlled airspace if the certificate holder has been approved for the operations and that operation is necessary to—

(1) Conduct an instrument approach to an airport for which there is in use a current approved standard or special instrument approach procedure; or

(2) Climb into controlled airspace during an approved missed approach procedure; or

(3) Make an IFR departure from an airport having an approved instrument approach procedure.

(d) The Administrator may issue operations specifications to the certificate holder to allow it to depart at an airport that does not have an approved standard instrument approach procedure when the Administrator determines that it is necessary to make an IFR departure from that airport and that the proposed operations can be conducted safely. The approval to operate at that airport does not include an approval to make an IFR approach to that airport.

135.217   IFR: Takeoff limitations

No person may takeoff an aircraft under IFR from an airport where weather conditions are at or above takeoff minimums but are below authorized IFR landing minimums unless there is an alternate airport within 1 hour's flying time (at normal cruising speed, in still air) of the airport of departure.

135.219   IFR: Destination airport weather minimums

No person may take off an aircraft under IFR or begin an IFR or over-the-top operation unless the latest weather reports or forecasts, or any combination of them, indicate that weather conditions at the estimated time of arrival at the next airport of intended landing will be at or above authorized IFR landing minimums.

135.221   IFR: Alternate airport weather minimums

(a) *Aircraft other than rotorcraft.* No person may designate an alternate airport unless the weather reports or forecasts, or any combination of them, indicate that the weather conditions will be at or above authorized alternate airport landing minimums for that airport at the estimated time of arrival.

(b) *Rotorcraft.* Unless otherwise authorized by the Administrator, no person may include an alternate airport in an IFR flight plan unless appropriate weather reports or weather forecasts, or a combination of them, indicate that, at the estimated time of arrival at the alternate airport, the ceiling and visibility at that airport will be at or above the following weather minimums—

(1) If, for the alternate airport, an instrument approach procedure has been published in part 97 of this chapter or a special instrument approach procedure has been issued by the FAA to the certificate holder, the ceiling is 200 feet above the minimum for the approach to be flown, and visibility is at least 1 statute mile but never less than the minimum visibility for the approach to be flown.

(2) If, for the alternate airport, no instrument approach procedure has been published in part 97 of this chapter and no special instrument approach procedure has been issued by the FAA to the certificate holder, the ceiling and visibility minimums are those allowing descent from the minimum enroute altitude (MEA), approach, and landing under basic VFR.

[Doc. No. FAA-2010-0982, 79 FR 9974, Feb. 21, 2014]

135.223   IFR: Alternate airport requirements

(a) Except as provided in paragraph (b) of this section, no person may operate an aircraft in IFR conditions unless it carries enough fuel (considering weather reports or forecasts or any combination of them) to—

(1) Complete the flight to the first airport of intended landing;

(2) Fly from that airport to the alternate airport; and

(3) Fly after that for 45 minutes at normal cruising speed or, for helicopters, fly after that for 30 minutes at normal cruising speed.

(b) Paragraph (a)(2) of this section does not apply if part 97 of this chapter prescribes a standard instrument approach procedure for the first airport of intended landing and, for at least one hour before and after the estimated time of arrival, the appropriate weather reports or forecasts, or any combination of them, indicate that—

(1) The ceiling will be at least 1,500 feet above the lowest circling approach MDA; or

(2) If a circling instrument approach is not authorized for the airport, the ceiling will be at least 1,500 feet above the lowest published minimum or 2,000 feet above the airport elevation, whichever is higher; and

(3) Visibility for that airport is forecast to be at least three miles, or two miles more than the lowest applicable visibility minimums, whichever is the greater, for the instrument approach procedure to be used at the destination airport.

[Doc. No. 16097, 43 FR 46783, Oct. 10, 1978, as amended by Amdt. 135–20, 51 FR 40710, Nov. 7, 1986]

135.225   IFR: Takeoff, approach and landing minimums

(a) Except to the extent permitted by paragraphs (b) and (j) of this section, no pilot may begin an instrument approach procedure to an airport unless—

(1) That airport has a weather reporting facility operated by the U.S. National Weather Service, a source approved by U.S. National Weather Service, or a source approved by the Administrator; and

(2) The latest weather report issued by that weather reporting facility indicates that weather conditions are at or above the authorized IFR landing minimums for that airport.

(b) A pilot conducting an eligible on-demand operation may begin and conduct an instrument approach procedure to an airport that does not have a weather reporting facility operated by the U.S. National Weather Service, a source approved by the U.S. National Weather Service, or a source approved by the Administrator if—

(1) The alternate airport has a weather reporting facility operated by the U.S. National Weather Service, a source approved by the U.S. National Weather Service, or a source approved by the Administrator; and

(2) The latest weather report issued by the weather reporting facility includes a current local altimeter setting for the destination airport. If no local altimeter setting for the destination airport is available, the pilot may use the current altimeter setting provided by the facility designated on the approach chart for the destination airport.

(c) Except as provided in paragraph (j) of this section, no pilot may begin the final approach segment of an instrument approach procedure to an airport unless the latest weather reported by the facility described in paragraph (a)(1) of this section indicates that weather conditions are at or above the authorized IFR landing minimums for that procedure.

(d) Except as provided in paragraph (j) of this section, a pilot who has begun the final approach segment of an instrument approach to an airport under paragraph (c) of this section, and receives a later weather report indicating that conditions have worsened to below the minimum requirements, may continue the approach only if the following conditions are met—

(1) The later weather report is received when the aircraft is in one of the following approach phases:

    (i)   The aircraft is on an ILS final approach and has passed the final approach fix;

    (ii) The aircraft is on an ASR or PAR final approach and has been turned over to the final approach controller; or

428 Part 135—Operating Requirements: Commuter and On-Demand Operation.

(iii) The aircraft is on a non-precision final approach and the aircraft—

(A) Has passed the appropriate facility or final approach fix; or

(B) Where a final approach fix is not specified, has completed the procedure turn and is established inbound toward the airport on the final approach course within the distance prescribed in the procedure; and

(2) The pilot in command finds, on reaching the authorized MDA or DA/DH, that the actual weather conditions are at or above the minimums prescribed for the procedure being used.

(e) The MDA or DA/DH and visibility landing minimums prescribed in part 97 of this chapter or in the operator's operations specifications are increased by 100 feet and 1/2 mile respectively, but not to exceed the ceiling and visibility minimums for that airport when used as an alternate airport, for each pilot in command of a turbine-powered airplane who has not served at least 100 hours as pilot in command in that type of airplane.

(f) Each pilot making an IFR takeoff or approach and landing at a military or foreign airport shall comply with applicable instrument approach procedures and weather minimums prescribed by the authority having jurisdiction over that airport. In addition, unless authorized by the certificate holder's operations specifications, no pilot may, at that airport—

(1) Take off under IFR when the visibility is less than 1 mile; or

(2) Make an instrument approach when the visibility is less than $^1/_2$ mile.

(g) If takeoff minimums are specified in part 97 of this chapter for the take-off airport, no pilot may take off an aircraft under IFR when the weather conditions reported by the facility described in paragraph (a)(1) of this section are less than the takeoff minimums specified for the takeoff airport in part 97 or in the certificate holder's operations specifications.

(h) Except as provided in paragraph (i) of this section, if takeoff minimums are not prescribed in part 97 of this chapter for the take-off airport, no pilot may takeoff an aircraft under IFR when the weather conditions reported by the facility described in paragraph (a)(1) of this section are less than that prescribed in part 91 of this chapter or in the certificate holder's operations specifications.

(i) At airports where straight-in instrument approach procedures are authorized, a pilot may takeoff an aircraft under IFR when the weather conditions reported by the facility described in paragraph (a)(1) of this section are equal to or better than the lowest straight-in landing minimums, unless otherwise restricted, if—

(1) The wind direction and velocity at the time of takeoff are such that a straight-in instrument approach can be made to the runway served by the instrument approach;

(2) The associated ground facilities upon which the landing minimums are predicated and the related airborne equipment are in normal operation; and

(3) The certificate holder has been approved for such operations.

(j) A pilot may begin an instrument approach procedure, or continue an approach, at an airport when the visibility is reported to be less than the visibility minimums prescribed for that procedure if the pilot uses an operable EFVS in accordance with §91.176 of this chapter and the certificate holder's operations specifications for EFVS operations.

[Doc. No. 16097, 43 FR 46783, Oct. 10, 1978, as amended by Amdt. 135-91, 68 FR 54586, Sept. 17, 2003; Amdt. 135-93, 69 FR 1641, Jan. 9, 2004; Amdt. 135-110, 72 FR 31685, June 7, 2007; Amdt. 135-126, 77 FR 1632, Jan. 11, 2012; Docket FAA-2013-0485, Amdt. 135-135, 81 FR 90177, Dec. 13, 2016]

135.227 Icing conditions: Operating limitations

(a) No pilot may take off an aircraft that has frost, ice, or snow adhering to any rotor blade, propeller, windshield, stabilizing or control surface; to a powerplant installation; or to an airspeed, altimeter, rate of climb, flight attitude instrument system, or wing except that takeoffs may be made with frost under the wing in the area of the fuel tanks if authorized by the FAA.

(1) Takeoffs may be made with frost adhering to the wings, or stabilizing or control surfaces, if the frost has been polished to make it smooth.

(2) Takeoffs may be made with frost under the wing in the area of the fuel tanks if authorized by the Administrator.

(b) No certificate holder may authorize an airplane to take off and no pilot may take off an airplane any time conditions are such that frost, ice, or snow may reasonably be expected to adhere to the airplane unless the pilot has completed all applicable training as required by 135.341 and unless one of the following requirements is met:

(1) A pretakeoff contamination check, that has been established by the certificate holder and approved by the Administrator for the specific airplane type, has been completed within 5 minutes prior to beginning takeoff. A pretakeoff contamination check is a check to make sure the wings and control surfaces are free of frost, ice, or snow.

(2) The certificate holder has an approved alternative procedure and under that procedure the airplane is determined to be free of frost, ice, or snow.

(3) The certificate holder has an approved deicing/anti-icing program that complies with 121.629(c) of this chapter and the takeoff complies with that program.

(c) No pilot may fly under IFR into known or forecast light or moderate icing conditions or under VFR into known light or moderate icing conditions, unless—

(1) The aircraft has functioning deicing or anti-icing equipment protecting each rotor blade, propeller, windshield, wing, stabilizing or control surface, and each airspeed, altimeter, rate of climb, or flight attitude instrument system;

(2) The airplane has ice protection provisions that meet section 34 of appendix A of this part; or

(3) The airplane meets transport category airplane type certification provisions, including the requirements for certification for flight in icing conditions.

(d) No pilot may fly a helicopter under IFR into known or forecast icing conditions or under VFR into known icing conditions unless it has been type certificated and appropriately equipped for operations in icing conditions.

(e) Except for an airplane that has ice protection provisions that meet section 34 of appendix A, or those for transport category airplane type certification, no pilot may fly an aircraft into known or forecast severe icing conditions.

(f) If current weather reports and briefing information relied upon by the pilot in command indicate that the forecast icing conditions that would otherwise prohibit the flight will not be encountered during the flight because of changed weather conditions since the forecast, the restrictions in paragraphs (c), (d), and (e) of this section based on forecast conditions do not apply.

[Doc. No. 16097, 43 FR 46783, Oct. 10, 1978, as amended by Amdt. 133–20, 51 FR 40710, Nov. 7, 1986; Amdt. 135–46, 58 FR 69629, Dec. 30, 1993; Amdt. 135–60, 61 FR 2616, Jan. 26, 1996; Amdt. 135-119, 74 FR 62696, Dec. 1, 2009]

135.229 Airport requirements

(a) No certificate holder may use any airport unless it is adequate for the proposed operation, considering such items as size, surface obstructions, and lighting.

(b) No pilot of an aircraft carrying passengers at night may takeoff from, or land on, an airport unless—

(1) That pilot has determined the wind direction from an illuminated wind direction indicator or local ground communications or, in the case of takeoff, that pilot's personal observations; and

(2) The limits of the area to be used for landing or takeoff are clearly shown—

   (i)   For airplanes, by boundary or runway marker lights;

   (ii) For helicopters, by boundary or runway marker lights or reflective material.

(c) For the purpose of paragraph (b) of this section, if the area to be used for takeoff or landing is marked by flare pots or lanterns, their use must be approved by the Administrator.

Subpart E — Flight Crewmember Requirements

135.241 Applicability

Except as provided in 135.3, this subpart prescribes the flight crewmember requirements for operations under this part.

[Doc. No. 16097, 43 FR 46783, Oct. 10, 1978, as amended by Amdt. 121–250, 60 FR 65950, Dec. 20, 1995]

135.243 Pilot in command qualifications

(a) No certificate holder may use a person, nor may any person serve, as pilot in command in passenger-carrying operations—

  (1) Of a turbojet airplane, of an airplane having a passenger-seat configuration, excluding each crewmember seat, of 10 seats or more, or of a multiengine airplane in a commuter operation as defined in part 119 of this chapter, unless that person holds an airline transport pilot certificate with appropriate category and class ratings and, if required, an appropriate type rating for that airplane.

  (2) Of a helicopter in a scheduled interstate air transportation operation by an air carrier within the 48 contiguous states unless that person holds an airline transport pilot certificate, appropriate type ratings, and an instrument rating.

(b) Except as provided in paragraph (a) of this section, no certificate holder may use a person, nor may any person serve, as pilot in command of an aircraft under VFR unless that person—

  (1) Holds at least a commercial pilot certificate with appropriate category and class ratings and, if required, an appropriate type rating for that aircraft; and

  (2) Has had at least 500 hours time as a pilot, including at least 100 hours of cross-country flight time, at least 25 hours of which were at night; and

  (3) For an airplane, holds an instrument rating or an airline transport pilot certificate with an airplane category rating; or

  (4) For helicopter operations conducted VFR over-the-top, holds a helicopter instrument rating, or an airline transport pilot certificate with a category and class rating for that aircraft, not limited to VFR.

(c) Except as provided in paragraph (a) of this section, no certificate holder may use a person, nor may any person serve, as pilot in command of an aircraft under IFR unless that person—

  (1) Holds at least a commercial pilot certificate with appropriate category and class ratings and, if required, an appropriate type rating for that aircraft; and

  (2) Has had at least 1,200 hours of flight time as a pilot, including 500 hours of cross country flight time, 100 hours of night flight time, and 75 hours of actual or simulated instrument time at least 50 hours of which were in actual flight; and

  (3) For an airplane, holds an instrument rating or an airline transport pilot certificate with an airplane category rating; or

  (4) For a helicopter, holds a helicopter instrument rating, or an airline transport pilot certificate with a category and class rating for that aircraft, not limited to VFR.

(d) Paragraph (b)(3) of this section does not apply when—

  (1) The aircraft used is a single reciprocating-engine-powered airplane;

  (2) The certificate holder does not conduct any operation pursuant to a published flight schedule which specifies five or more round trips a week between two or more points and places between which the round trips are performed, and does not transport mail by air under a contract or contracts with the United States Postal Service having total amount estimated at the beginning of any semiannual reporting period (January 1–June 30; July 1–December 31) to be in excess of $20,000 over the 12 months commencing with the beginning of the reporting period;

  (3) The area, as specified in the certificate holder's operations specifications, is an isolated area, as determined by the Flight Standards office, if it is shown that—

    (i) The primary means of navigation in the area is by pilotage, since radio navigational aids are largely ineffective; and

    (ii) The primary means of transportation in the area is by air;

  (4) Each flight is conducted under day VFR with a ceiling of not less than 1,000 feet and visibility not less than 3 statute miles;

  (5) Weather reports or forecasts, or any combination of them, indicate that for the period commencing with the planned departure and ending 30 minutes after the planned arrival at the destination the flight may be conducted under VFR with a ceiling of not less than 1,000 feet and visibility of not less than 3 statute miles, except that if weather reports and forecasts are not available, the pilot in command may use that pilot's observations or those of other persons competent to supply weather observations if those observations indicate the flight may be conducted under VFR with the ceiling and visibility required in this paragraph;

  (6) The distance of each flight from the certificate holder's base of operation to destination does not exceed 250 nautical miles for a pilot who holds a commercial pilot certificate with an airplane rating without an instrument rating, provided the pilot's certificate does not contain any limitation to the contrary; and

  (7) The areas to be flown are approved by the responsible Flight Standards office and are listed in the certificate holder's operations specifications.

[Doc. No. 16097, 43 FR 46783, Oct. 10, 1978; Amdt. 135-1, 43 FR 49975, Oct. 26, 1978, as amended by Amdt. 135-15, 46 FR 30971, June 11, 1981; Amdt. 135-58, 60 FR 65939, Dec. 20, 1995; Docket FAA-2018-0119, Amdt. 135-139, 83 FR 9175, Mar. 5, 2018]

135.244 Operating experience

(a) No certificate holder may use any person, nor may any person serve, as a pilot in command of an aircraft operated in a commuter operation, as defined in part 119 of this chapter unless that person has completed, prior to designation as pilot in command, on that make and basic model aircraft and in that crewmember position, the following operating experience in each make and basic model of aircraft to be flown:

  (1) Aircraft, single engine—10 hours.

  (2) Aircraft multiengine, reciprocating engine-powered—15 hours.

  (3) Aircraft multiengine, turbine engine-powered—20 hours.

  (4) Airplane, turbojet-powered—25 hours.

(b) In acquiring the operating experience, each person must comply with the following:

  (1) The operating experience must be acquired after satisfactory completion of the appropriate ground and flight training for the aircraft and crewmember position. Approved provisions for the operating experience must be included in the certificate holder's training program.

  (2) The experience must be acquired in flight during commuter passenger-carrying operations under this part. However, in the case of an aircraft not previously used by the certificate holder in operations under this part, operating experience acquired in the aircraft during proving flights or ferry flights may be used to meet this requirement.

  (3) Each person must acquire the operating experience while performing the duties of a pilot in command under the supervision of a qualified check pilot.

(4) The hours of operating experience may be reduced to not less than 50 percent of the hours required by this section by the substitution of one additional takeoff and landing for each hour of flight.

[Doc. No. 20011, 45 FR 7541, Feb. 4, 1980, as amended by Amdt. 135–9, 45 FR 80461, Dec. 14, 1980; Amdt. 135–58, 60 FR 65940, Dec. 20, 1995]

135.245   Second in command qualifications

(a) Except as provided in paragraph (b) of this section, no certificate holder may use any person, nor may any person serve, as second in command of an aircraft unless that person holds at least a commercial pilot certificate with appropriate category and class ratings and an instrument rating.

(b) A second in command of a helicopter operated under VFR, other than over-the-top, must have at least a commercial pilot certificate with an appropriate aircraft category and class rating.

(c) No certificate holder may use any person, nor may any person serve, as second in command under IFR unless that person meets the following instrument experience requirements:

(1) Use of an airplane or helicopter for maintaining instrument experience. Within the 6 calendar months preceding the month of the flight, that person performed and logged at least the following tasks and iterations in-flight in an airplane or helicopter, as appropriate, in actual weather conditions, or under simulated instrument conditions using a view-limiting device:

(i)   Six instrument approaches;

(ii)   Holding procedures and tasks; and

(iii) Intercepting and tracking courses through the use of navigational electronic systems.

(2) Use of an FSTD for maintaining instrument experience. A person may accomplish the requirements in paragraph (c)(1) of this section in an approved FSTD, or a combination of aircraft and FSTD, provided:

(i)   The FSTD represents the category of aircraft for the instrument rating privileges to be maintained;

(ii)   The person performs the tasks and iterations in simulated instrument conditions; and

(iii) A flight instructor qualified under 135.338 or a check pilot qualified under 135.337 observes the tasks and iterations and signs the person's logbook or training record to verify the time and content of the session.

(d) A second in command who has failed to meet the instrument experience requirements of paragraph (c) of this section for more than six calendar months must reestablish instrument recency under the supervision of a flight instructor qualified under 135.338 or a check pilot qualified under 135.337. To reestablish instrument recency, a second in command must complete at least the following areas of operation required for the instrument rating practical test in an aircraft or FSTD that represents the category of aircraft for the instrument experience requirements to be reestablished:

(1) Air traffic control clearances and procedures;

(2) Flight by reference to instruments;

(3) Navigation systems;

(4) Instrument approach procedures;

(5) Emergency operations; and

(6) Postflight procedures.

[44 FR 26738, May 7, 1979, as amended at 83 FR 30283, June 27, 2018]

135.247   Pilot qualifications: Recent experience

(a) No certificate holder may use any person, nor may any person serve, as pilot in command of an aircraft carrying passengers unless, within the preceding 90 days, that person has—

(1) Made three takeoffs and three landings as the sole manipulator of the flight controls in an aircraft of the same category

and class and, if a type rating is required, of the same type in which that person is to serve; or

(2) For operation during the period beginning 1 hour after sunset and ending 1 hour before sunrise (as published in the Air Almanac), made three takeoffs and three landings during that period as the sole manipulator of the flight controls in an aircraft of the same category and class and, if a type rating is required, of the same type in which that person is to serve.

A person who complies with paragraph (a)(2) of this section need not comply with paragraph (a)(1) of this section.

(3) Paragraph (a)(2) of this section does not apply to a pilot in command of a turbine-powered airplane that is type certificated for more than one pilot crewmember, provided that pilot has complied with the requirements of paragraph (a)(3)(i) or (ii) of this section:

(i)   The pilot in command must hold at least a commercial pilot certificate with the appropriate category, class, and type rating for each airplane that is type certificated for more than one pilot crewmember that the pilot seeks to operate under this alternative, and:

(A) That pilot must have logged at least 1,500 hours of aeronautical experience as a pilot;

(B) In each airplane that is type certificated for more than one pilot crewmember that the pilot seeks to operate under this alternative, that pilot must have accomplished and logged the daytime takeoff and landing recent flight experience of paragraph (a) of this section, as the sole manipulator of the flight controls;

(C) Within the preceding 90 days prior to the operation of that airplane that is type certificated for more than one pilot crewmember, the pilot must have accomplished and logged at least 15 hours of flight time in the type of airplane that the pilot seeks to operate under this alternative; and

(D) That pilot has accomplished and logged at least 3 takeoffs and 3 landings to a full stop, as the sole manipulator of the flight controls, in a turbine-powered airplane that requires more than one pilot crewmember. The pilot must have performed the takeoffs and landings during the period beginning 1 hour after sunset and ending 1 hour before sunrise within the preceding 6 months prior to the month of the flight.

(ii)   The pilot in command must hold at least a commercial pilot certificate with the appropriate category, class, and type rating for each airplane that is type certificated for more than one pilot crewmember that the pilot seeks to operate under this alternative, and:

(A) That pilot must have logged at least 1,500 hours of aeronautical experience as a pilot;

(B) In each airplane that is type certificated for more than one pilot crewmember that the pilot seeks to operate under this alternative, that pilot must have accomplished and logged the daytime takeoff and landing recent flight experience of paragraph (a) of this section, as the sole manipulator of the flight controls;

(C) Within the preceding 90 days prior to the operation of that airplane that is type certificated for more than one pilot crewmember, the pilot must have accomplished and logged at least 15 hours of flight time in the type of airplane that the pilot seeks to operate under this alternative; and

(D) Within the preceding 12 months prior to the month of the flight, the pilot must have completed a training program that is approved under part 142 of this chapter. The approved training program must have required and the pilot must have performed, at least 6 takeoffs and 6 landings to a full stop as the sole manipulator of the controls in a flight simulator that is representative of a turbine-powered airplane that requires more than one pilot crewmember. The flight simulator's visual system must have been adjusted to represent the period beginning 1 hour after sunset and ending 1 hour before sunrise.

(b) For the purpose of paragraph (a) of this section, if the aircraft is a tailwheel airplane, each takeoff must be made in a tailwheel airplane and each landing must be made to a full stop in a tailwheel airplane.

[Doc. No. 16097, 43 FR 46783, Oct. 10, 1978, as amended by Amdt. 135–91, 68 FR 54587, Sept. 17, 2003]

135.249   [Reserved]

135.251   [Reserved]

135.253   [Reserved]

135.255   [Reserved]

Subpart F — Crewmember Flight Time and Duty Period Limitations and Rest Requirements

Source: Docket No. 23634, 50 FR 29320, July 18, 1985, unless otherwise noted.

135.261   Applicability

Sections 135.263 through 135.273 of this part prescribe flight time limitations, duty period limitations, and rest requirements for operations conducted under this part as follows:

(a) Section 135.263 applies to all operations under this subpart.

(b) Section 135.265 applies to:

(1) Scheduled passenger-carrying operations except those conducted solely within the state of Alaska. "Scheduled passenger-carrying operations" means passenger-carrying operations that are conducted in accordance with a published schedule which covers at least five round trips per week on at least one route between two or more points, includes dates or times (or both), and is openly advertised or otherwise made readily available to the general public, and

(2) Any other operation under this part, if the operator elects to comply with 135.265 and obtains an appropriate operations specification amendment.

(c) Sections 135.267 and 135.269 apply to any operation that is not a scheduled passenger-carrying operation and to any operation conducted solely within the State of Alaska, unless the operator elects to comply with 135.265 as authorized under paragraph (b)(2) of this section.

(d) Section 135.271 contains special daily flight time limits for operations conducted under the helicopter emergency medical evacuation service (HEMES).

(e) Section 135.273 prescribes duty period limitations and rest requirements for flight attendants in all operations conducted under this part.

[Doc. No. 23634, 50 FR 29320, July 18, 1985, as amended by Amdt. 135–52, 59 FR 42993, Aug. 19, 1994]

135.263   Flight time limitations and rest requirements: All certificate holders

(a) A certificate holder may assign a flight crewmember and a flight crewmember may accept an assignment for flight time only when the applicable requirements of 135.263 through 135.271 are met.

(b) No certificate holder may assign any flight crewmember to any duty with the certificate holder during any required rest period.

(c) Time spent in transportation, not local in character, that a certificate holder requires of a flight crewmember and provides to transport the crewmember to an airport at which he is to serve on a flight as a crewmember, or from an airport at which he was relieved from duty to return to his home station, is not considered part of a rest period.

(d) A flight crewmember is not considered to be assigned flight time in excess of flight time limitations if the flights to which he is assigned normally terminate within the limitations, but due to circumstances beyond the control of the certificate holder or flight crewmember (such as adverse weather conditions), are not at the time of departure expected to reach their destination within the planned flight time.

135.265   Flight time limitations and rest requirements: Scheduled operations

(a) No certificate holder may schedule any flight crewmember, and no flight crewmember may accept an assignment, for flight time in scheduled operations or in other commercial flying if that crewmember's total flight time in all commercial flying will exceed—

(1) 1,200 hours in any calendar year.

(2) 120 hours in any calendar month.

(3) 34 hours in any 7 consecutive days.

(4) 8 hours during any 24 consecutive hours for a flight crew consisting of one pilot.

(5) 8 hours between required rest periods for a flight crew consisting of two pilots qualified under this part for the operation being conducted.

(b) Except as provided in paragraph (c) of this section, no certificate holder may schedule a flight crewmember, and no flight crewmember may accept an assignment, for flight time during the 24 consecutive hours preceding the scheduled completion of any flight segment without a scheduled rest period during that 24 hours of at least the following:

(1) 9 consecutive hours of rest for less than 8 hours of scheduled flight time.

(2) 10 consecutive hours of rest for 8 or more but less than 9 hours of scheduled flight time.

(3) 11 consecutive hours of rest for 9 or more hours of scheduled flight time.

(c) A certificate holder may schedule a flight crewmember for less than the rest required in paragraph (b) of this section or may reduce a scheduled rest under the following conditions:

(1) A rest required under paragraph (b)(1) of this section may be scheduled for or reduced to a minimum of 8 hours if the flight crewmember is given a rest period of at least 10 hours that must begin no later than 24 hours after the commencement of the reduced rest period.

(2) A rest required under paragraph (b)(2) of this section may be scheduled for or reduced to a minimum of 8 hours if the flight crewmember is given a rest period of at least 11 hours that must begin no later than 24 hours after the commencement of the reduced rest period.

(3) A rest required under paragraph (b)(3) of this section may be scheduled for or reduced to a minimum of 9 hours if the flight crewmember is given a rest period of at least 12 hours that must begin no later than 24 hours after the commencement of the reduced rest period.

(d) Each certificate holder shall relieve each flight crewmember engaged in scheduled air transportation from all further duty for at least 24 consecutive hours during any 7 consecutive days.

135.267   Flight time limitations and rest requirements: Unscheduled one- and two-pilot crews

(a) No certificate holder may assign any flight crewmember, and no flight crewmember may accept an assignment, for flight time as a member of a one- or two-pilot crew if that crewmember's total flight time in all commercial flying will exceed—

(1) 500 hours in any calendar quarter.

FAR 135

(2) 800 hours in any two consecutive calendar quarters.

(3) 1,400 hours in any calendar year.

(b) Except as provided in paragraph (c) of this section, during any 24 consecutive hours the total flight time of the assigned flight when added to any other commercial flying by that flight crewmember may not exceed—

(1) 8 hours for a flight crew consisting of one pilot; or

(2) 10 hours for a flight crew consisting of two pilots qualified under this part for the operation being conducted.

(c) A flight crewmember's flight time may exceed the flight time limits of paragraph (b) of this section if the assigned flight time occurs during a regularly assigned duty period of no more than 14 hours and—

(1) If this duty period is immediately preceded by and followed by a required rest period of at least 10 consecutive hours of rest;

(2) If flight time is assigned during this period, that total flight time when added to any other commercial flying by the flight crewmember may not exceed—

(i)   8 hours for a flight crew consisting of one pilot; or

(ii)   10 hours for a flight crew consisting of two pilots; and

(3) If the combined duty and rest periods equal 24 hours.

(d) Each assignment under paragraph (b) of this section must provide for at least 10 consecutive hours of rest during the 24-hour period that precedes the planned completion time of the assignment.

(e) When a flight crewmember has exceeded the daily flight time limitations in this section, because of circumstances beyond the control of the certificate holder or flight crewmember (such as adverse weather conditions), that flight crewmember must have a rest period before being assigned or accepting an assignment for flight time of at least—

(1) 11 consecutive hours of rest if the flight time limitation is exceeded by not more than 30 minutes;

(2) 12 consecutive hours of rest if the flight time limitation is exceeded by more than 30 minutes, but not more than 60 minutes; and

(3) 16 consecutive hours of rest if the flight time limitation is exceeded by more than 60 minutes.

(f) The certificate holder must provide each flight crewmember at least 13 rest periods of at least 24 consecutive hours each in each calendar quarter.

[Doc. No. 23634, 50 FR 29320, July 18, 1985, as amended by Amdt. 135–33, 54 FR 39294, Sept. 25, 1989; Amdt. 135–60, 61 FR 2616, Jan. 26, 1996]

135.269   Flight time limitations and rest requirements: Unscheduled three- and four-pilot crews

(a) No certificate holder may assign any flight crewmember, and no flight crewmember may accept an assignment, for flight time as a member of a three- or four-pilot crew if that crewmember's total flight time in all commercial flying will exceed—

(1) 500 hours in any calendar quarter.

(2) 800 hours in any two consecutive calendar quarters.

(3) 1,400 hours in any calendar year.

(b) No certificate holder may assign any pilot to a crew of three or four pilots, unless that assignment provides—

(1) At least 10 consecutive hours of rest immediately preceding the assignment;

(2) No more than 8 hours of flight deck duty in any 24 consecutive hours;

(3) No more than 18 duty hours for a three-pilot crew or 20 duty hours for a four-pilot crew in any 24 consecutive hours;

(4) No more than 12 hours aloft for a three-pilot crew or 16 hours aloft for a four-pilot crew during the maximum duty hours specified in paragraph (b)(3) of this section;

(5) Adequate sleeping facilities on the aircraft for the relief pilot;

(6) Upon completion of the assignment, a rest period of at least 12 hours;

(7) For a three-pilot crew, a crew which consists of at least the following:

(i)   A pilot in command (PIC) who meets the applicable flight crewmember requirements of subpart E of part 135;

(ii)   A PIC who meets the applicable flight crewmember requirements of subpart E of part 135, except those prescribed in 135.244 and 135.247; and

(iii) A second in command (SIC) who meets the SIC qualifications of 135.245.

(8) For a four-pilot crew, at least three pilots who meet the conditions of paragraph (b)(7) of this section, plus a fourth pilot who meets the SIC qualifications of 135.245.

(c) When a flight crewmember has exceeded the daily flight deck duty limitation in this section by more than 60 minutes, because of circumstances beyond the control of the certificate holder or flight crewmember, that flight crewmember must have a rest period before the next duty period of at least 16 consecutive hours.

(d) A certificate holder must provide each flight crewmember at least 13 rest periods of at least 24 consecutive hours each in each calendar quarter.

135.271   Helicopter hospital emergency medical evacuation service (HEMES)

(a) No certificate holder may assign any flight crewmember, and no flight crewmember may accept an assignment for flight time if that crewmember's total flight time in all commercial flight will exceed—

(1) 500 hours in any calendar quarter.

(2) 800 hours in any two consecutive calendar quarters.

(3) 1,400 hours in any calendar year.

(b) No certificate holder may assign a helicopter flight crewmember, and no flight crewmember may accept an assignment, for hospital emergency medical evacuation service helicopter operations unless that assignment provides for at least 10 consecutive hours of rest immediately preceding reporting to the hospital for availability for flight time.

(c) No flight crewmember may accrue more than 8 hours of flight time during any 24-consecutive hour period of a HEMES assignment, unless an emergency medical evacuation operation is prolonged. Each flight crewmember who exceeds the daily 8 hour flight time limitation in this paragraph must be relieved of the HEMES assignment immediately upon the completion of that emergency medical evacuation operation and must be given a rest period in compliance with paragraph (h) of this section.

(d) Each flight crewmember must receive at least 8 consecutive hours of rest during any 24 consecutive hour period of a HEMES assignment. A flight crewmember must be relieved of the HEMES assignment if he or she has not or cannot receive at least 8 consecutive hours of rest during any 24 consecutive hour period of a HEMES assignment.

(e) A HEMES assignment may not exceed 72 consecutive hours at the hospital.

(f) An adequate place of rest must be provided at, or in close proximity to, the hospital at which the HEMES assignment is being performed.

(g) No certificate holder may assign any other duties to a flight crewmember during a HEMES assignment.

(h) Each pilot must be given a rest period upon completion of the HEMES assignment and prior to being assigned any further duty with the certificate holder of—

(1) At least 12 consecutive hours for an assignment of less than 48 hours.

(2) At least 16 consecutive hours for an assignment of more than 48 hours.

) The certificate holder must provide each flight crewmember at least 13 rest periods of at least 24 consecutive hours each in each calendar quarter.

35.273 Duty period limitations and rest time requirements

a) For purposes of this section—

Calendar day means the period of elapsed time, using Coordinated Universal Time or local time, that begins at midnight and ends 24 hours later at the next midnight.

Duty period means the period of elapsed time between reporting for n assignment involving flight time and release from that assignment y the certificate holder. The time is calculated using either Coordinated Universal Time or local time to reflect the total elapsed time.

Flight attendant means an individual, other than a flight crewmember, who is assigned by the certificate holder, in accordance with the required minimum crew complement under the certificate holder's operations specifications or in addition to that minimum complement, to duty in an aircraft during flight time and whose duties include but are not necessarily limited to cabin-safety-related responsibilities.

Rest period means the period free of all responsibility for work or duty should the occasion arise.

b) Except as provided in paragraph (c) of this section, a certificate holder may assign a duty period to a flight attendant only when the applicable duty period limitations and rest requirements of this paragraph are met.

(1) Except as provided in paragraphs (b)(4), (b)(5), and (b)(6) of this section, no certificate holder may assign a flight attendant to a scheduled duty period of more than 14 hours.

(2) Except as provided in paragraph (b)(3) of this section, a flight attendant scheduled to a duty period of 14 hours or less as provided under paragraph (b)(1) of this section must be given a scheduled rest period of at least 9 consecutive hours. This rest period must occur between the completion of the scheduled duty period and the commencement of the subsequent duty period.

(3) The rest period required under paragraph (b)(2) of this section may be scheduled or reduced to 8 consecutive hours if the flight attendant is provided a subsequent rest period of at least 10 consecutive hours; this subsequent rest period must be scheduled to begin no later than 24 hours after the beginning of the reduced rest period and must occur between the completion of the scheduled duty period and the commencement of the subsequent duty period.

(4) A certificate holder may assign a flight attendant to a scheduled duty period of more than 14 hours, but no more than 16 hours, if the certificate holder has assigned to the flight or flights in that duty period at least one flight attendant in addition to the minimum flight attendant complement required for the flight or flights in that duty period under the certificate holder's operations specifications.

(5) A certificate holder may assign a flight attendant to a scheduled duty period of more than 16 hours, but no more than 18 hours, if the certificate holder has assigned to the flight or flights in that duty period at least two flight attendants in addition to the minimum flight attendant complement required for the flight or flights in that duty period under the certificate holder's operations specifications.

(6) A certificate holder may assign a flight attendant to a scheduled duty period of more than 18 hours, but no more than 20 hours, if the scheduled duty period includes one or more flights that land or take off outside the 48 contiguous states and the District of Columbia, and if the certificate holder has assigned to the flight or flights in that duty period at least three flight attendants in addition to the minimum flight attendant

complement required for the flight or flights in that duty period under the certificate holder's operations specifications.

(7) Except as provided in paragraph (b)(8) of this section, a flight attendant scheduled to a duty period of more than 14 hours but no more than 20 hours, as provided in paragraphs (b)(4), (b)(5), and (b)(6) of this section, must be given a scheduled rest period of at least 12 consecutive hours. This rest period must occur between the completion of the scheduled duty period and the commencement of the subsequent duty period.

(8) The rest period required under paragraph (b)(7) of this section may be scheduled or reduced to 10 consecutive hours if the flight attendant is provided a subsequent rest period of at least 14 consecutive hours; this subsequent rest period must be scheduled to begin no later than 24 hours after the beginning of the reduced rest period and must occur between the completion of the scheduled duty period and the commencement of the subsequent duty period.

(9) Notwithstanding paragraphs (b)(4), (b)(5), and (b)(6) of this section, if a certificate holder elects to reduce the rest period to 10 hours as authorized by paragraph (b)(8) of this section, the certificate holder may not schedule a flight attendant for a duty period of more than 14 hours during the 24-hour period commencing after the beginning of the reduced rest period.

(10) No certificate holder may assign a flight attendant any duty period with the certificate holder unless the flight attendant has had at least the minimum rest required under this section.

(11) No certificate holder may assign a flight attendant to perform any duty with the certificate holder during any required rest period.

(12) Time spent in transportation, not local in character, that a certificate holder requires of a flight attendant and provides to transport the flight attendant to an airport at which that flight attendant is to serve on a flight as a crewmember, or from an airport at which the flight attendant was relieved from duty to return to the flight attendant's home station, is not considered part of a rest period.

(13) Each certificate holder must relieve each flight attendant engaged in air transportation from all further duty for at least 24 consecutive hours during any 7 consecutive calendar days.

(14) A flight attendant is not considered to be scheduled for duty in excess of duty period limitations if the flights to which the flight attendant is assigned are scheduled and normally terminate within the limitations but due to circumstances beyond the control of the certificate holder (such as adverse weather conditions) are not at the time of departure expected to reach their destination within the scheduled time.

(c) Notwithstanding paragraph (b) of this section, a certificate holder may apply the flight crewmember flight time and duty limitations and rest requirements of this part to flight attendants for all operations conducted under this part provided that—

(1) The certificate holder establishes written procedures that—

(i) Apply to all flight attendants used in the certificate holder's operation;

(ii) Include the flight crewmember requirements contained in subpart F of this part, as appropriate to the operation being conducted, except that rest facilities on board the aircraft are not required; and

(iii) Include provisions to add one flight attendant to the minimum flight attendant complement for each flight crewmember who is in excess of the minimum number required in the aircraft type certificate data sheet and who is assigned to the aircraft under the provisions of subpart F of this part, as applicable.

(iv) Are approved by the Administrator and described or referenced in the certificate holder's operations specifications; and

(2) Whenever the Administrator finds that revisions are necessary for the continued adequacy of duty period limitation and rest

FAR 135

requirement procedures that are required by paragraph (c)(1) of this section and that had been granted final approval, the certificate holder must, after notification by the Administrator, make any changes in the procedures that are found necessary by the Administrator. Within 30 days after the certificate holder receives such notice, it may file a petition to reconsider the notice with the responsible Flight Standards office. The filing of a petition to reconsider stays the notice, pending decision by the Administrator. However, if the Administrator finds that there is an emergency that requires immediate action in the interest of safety, the Administrator may, upon a statement of the reasons, require a change effective without stay.

[Amdt. 135-52, 59 FR 42993, Aug. 19, 1994, as amended by Amdt. 135-60, 61 FR 2616, Jan. 26, 1996; Docket FAA-2018-0119, Amdt. 135-139, 83 FR 9175, Mar. 5, 2018]

Subpart G — Crewmember Testing Requirements

135.291   Applicability

Except as provided in 135.3, this subpart—

(a) Prescribes the tests and checks required for pilot and flight attendant crewmembers and for the approval of check pilots in operations under this part; and

(b) Permits training center personnel authorized under part 142 of this chapter who meet the requirements of 135.337 and 135.339 to conduct training, testing, and checking under contract or other arrangement to those persons subject to the requirements of this subpart.

[Doc. No. 26933, 61 FR 34561, July 2, 1996, as amended by Amdt. 135–91, 68 FR 54587, Sept. 17, 2003]

135.293   Initial and recurrent pilot testing requirements

(a) No certificate holder may use a pilot, nor may any person serve as a pilot, unless, since the beginning of the 12th calendar month before that service, that pilot has passed a written or oral test, given by the Administrator or an authorized check pilot, on that pilot's knowledge in the following areas—

(1) The appropriate provisions of parts 61, 91, and 135 of this chapter and the operations specifications and the manual of the certificate holder;

(2) For each type of aircraft to be flown by the pilot, the aircraft powerplant, major components and systems, major appliances, performance and operating limitations, standard and emergency operating procedures, and the contents of the approved Aircraft Flight Manual or equivalent, as applicable;

(3) For each type of aircraft to be flown by the pilot, the method of determining compliance with weight and balance limitations for takeoff, landing and en route operations;

(4) Navigation and use of air navigation aids appropriate to the operation or pilot authorization, including, when applicable, instrument approach facilities and procedures;

(5) Air traffic control procedures, including IFR procedures when applicable;

(6) Meteorology in general, including the principles of frontal systems, icing, fog, thunderstorms, and windshear, and, if appropriate for the operation of the certificate holder, high altitude weather;

(7) Procedures for—

(i) Recognizing and avoiding severe weather situations;

(ii) Escaping from severe weather situations, in case of inadvertent encounters, including low-altitude windshear (except that rotorcraft pilots are not required to be tested on escaping from low-altitude windshear); and

(iii) Operating in or near thunderstorms (including best penetrating altitudes), turbulent air (including clear air turbulence), icing, hail, and other potentially hazardous meteorological conditions;

(8) New equipment, procedures, or techniques, as appropriate; an

(9) For rotorcraft pilots, procedures for aircraft handling in fla light, whiteout, and brownout conditions, including metho for recognizing and avoiding those conditions.

(b) No certificate holder may use a pilot, nor may any person serv as a pilot, in any aircraft unless, since the beginning of the 12 calendar month before that service, that pilot has passed a cor petency check given by the Administrator or an authorized chec pilot in that class of aircraft, if single-engine airplane other tha turbojet, or that type of aircraft, if helicopter, multiengine ai plane, or turbojet airplane, to determine the pilot's competen in practical skills and techniques in that aircraft or class of ai craft. The extent of the competency check shall be determine by the Administrator or authorized check pilot conducting t competency check. The competency check may include any the maneuvers and procedures currently required for the origin issuance of the particular pilot certificate required for the oper tions authorized and appropriate to the category, class and ty of aircraft involved. For the purposes of this paragraph, type, to an airplane, means any one of a group of airplanes determine by the Administrator to have a similar means of propulsion, th same manufacturer, and no significantly different handling flight characteristics. For the purposes of this paragraph, type, to a helicopter, means a basic make and model.

(c) Each competency check given in a rotorcraft must include demonstration of the pilot's ability to maneuver the rotorcra solely by reference to instruments. The check must determine th pilot's ability to safely maneuver the rotorcraft into visual me teorological conditions following an inadvertent encounter wit instrument meteorological conditions. For competency checks i non-IFR-certified rotorcraft, the pilot must perform such maneu vers as are appropriate to the rotorcraft's installed equipment, th certificate holder's operations specifications, and the operatin environment.

(d) The instrument proficiency check required by 135.297 may b substituted for the competency check required by this section fo the type of aircraft used in the check.

(e) For the purpose of this part, competent performance of a proce dure or maneuver by a person to be used as a pilot requires tha the pilot be the obvious master of the aircraft, with the successfu outcome of the maneuver never in doubt.

(f) The Administrator or authorized check pilot certifies the compe tency of each pilot who passes the knowledge or flight check i the certificate holder's pilot records.

(g) Portions of a required competency check may be given in an ai craft simulator or other appropriate training device, if approve by the Administrator.

(h) Rotorcraft pilots must be tested on the subjects in paragraph (a (9) of this section when taking a written or oral knowledge tes after April 22, 2015. Rotorcraft pilots must be checked on th maneuvers and procedures in paragraph (c) of this section whe taking a competency check after April 22, 2015.

(i) If the certificate holder is authorized to conduct EFVS opera tions, the competency check in paragraph (b) of this section mus include tasks appropriate to the EFVS operations the certificate holder is authorized to conduct.

[Doc. No. 16097, 43 FR 46783, Oct. 10, 1978, as amended by Amdt 135-27, 53 FR 37697, Sept. 27, 1988; Amdt. 135-129, 79 FR 9974 Feb. 21, 2014; 79 FR 22012, Apr. 21, 2014; Docket FAA-2013-0485 Amdt. 135-135, 81 FR 90177, Dec. 13, 2016]

135.295   Initial and recurrent flight attendant crewmember testing requirements

No certificate holder may use a flight attendant crewmember, no may any person serve as a flight attendant crewmember unless, since the beginning of the 12th calendar month before that service, the certificate holder has determined by appropriate initial and recurren testing that the person is knowledgeable and competent in the fol lowing areas as appropriate to assigned duties and responsibilities—

a) Authority of the pilot in command;

b) Passenger handling, including procedures to be followed in handling deranged persons or other persons whose conduct might jeopardize safety;

c) Crewmember assignments, functions, and responsibilities during ditching and evacuation of persons who may need the assistance of another person to move expeditiously to an exit in an emergency;

d) Briefing of passengers;

e) Location and operation of portable fire extinguishers and other items of emergency equipment;

f) Proper use of cabin equipment and controls;

g) Location and operation of passenger oxygen equipment;

h) Location and operation of all normal and emergency exits, including evacuation chutes and escape ropes; and

i) Seating of persons who may need assistance of another person to move rapidly to an exit in an emergency as prescribed by the certificate holder's operations manual.

135.297 Pilot in command: Instrument proficiency check requirements

(a) No certificate holder may use a pilot, nor may any person serve, as a pilot in command of an aircraft under IFR unless, since the beginning of the 6th calendar month before that service, that pilot has passed an instrument proficiency check under this section administered by the Administrator or an authorized check pilot.

(b) No pilot may use any type of precision instrument approach procedure under IFR unless, since the beginning of the 6th calendar month before that use, the pilot satisfactorily demonstrated that type of approach procedure. No pilot may use any type of nonprecision approach procedure under IFR unless, since the beginning of the 6th calendar month before that use, the pilot has satisfactorily demonstrated either that type of approach procedure or any other two different types of nonprecision approach procedures. The instrument approach procedure or procedures must include at least one straight-in approach, one circling approach, and one missed approach. Each type of approach procedure demonstrated must be conducted to published minimums for that procedure.

(c) The instrument proficiency check required by paragraph (a) of this section consists of an oral or written equipment test and a flight check under simulated or actual IFR conditions. The equipment test includes questions on emergency procedures, engine operation, fuel and lubrication systems, power settings, stall speeds, best engine-out speed, propeller and supercharger operations, and hydraulic, mechanical, and electrical systems, as appropriate. The flight check includes navigation by instruments, recovery from simulated emergencies, and standard instrument approaches involving navigational facilities which that pilot is to be authorized to use. Each pilot taking the instrument proficiency check must show that standard of competence required by 135.293(e).

(1) The instrument proficiency check must—

    (i) For a pilot in command of an airplane under 135.243(a), include the procedures and maneuvers for an airline transport pilot certificate in the particular type of airplane, if appropriate; and

    (ii) For a pilot in command of an airplane or helicopter under 135.243(c), include the procedures and maneuvers for a commercial pilot certificate with an instrument rating and, if required, for the appropriate type rating.

(2) The instrument proficiency check must be given by an authorized check airman or by the Administrator.

(d) If the pilot in command is assigned to pilot only one type of aircraft, that pilot must take the instrument proficiency check required by paragraph (a) of this section in that type of aircraft.

(e) If the pilot in command is assigned to pilot more than one type of aircraft, that pilot must take the instrument proficiency check required by paragraph (a) of this section in each type of aircraft to which that pilot is assigned, in rotation, but not more than one flight check during each period described in paragraph (a) of this section.

(f) If the pilot in command is assigned to pilot both single-engine and multiengine aircraft, that pilot must initially take the instrument proficiency check required by paragraph (a) of this section in a multiengine aircraft, and each succeeding check alternately in single-engine and multiengine aircraft, but not more than one flight check during each period described in paragraph (a) of this section. Portions of a required flight check may be given in an aircraft simulator or other appropriate training device, if approved by the Administrator.

(g) If the pilot in command is authorized to use an autopilot system in place of a second in command, that pilot must show, during the required instrument proficiency check, that the pilot is able (without a second in command) both with and without using the autopilot to—

(1) Conduct instrument operations competently; and

(2) Properly conduct air-ground communications and comply with complex air traffic control instructions.

(3) Each pilot taking the autopilot check must show that, while using the autopilot, the airplane can be operated as proficiently as it would be if a second in command were present to handle air-ground communications and air traffic control instructions. The autopilot check need only be demonstrated once every 12 calendar months during the instrument proficiency check required under paragraph (a) of this section.

[Doc. No. 16097, 43 FR 46783, Oct. 10, 1978, as amended by Amdt. 135–15, 46 FR 30971, June 11, 1981]

135.299 Pilot in command: Line checks: Routes and airports

(a) No certificate holder may use a pilot, nor may any person serve, as a pilot in command of a flight unless, since the beginning of the 12th calendar month before that service, that pilot has passed a flight check in one of the types of aircraft which that pilot is to fly. The flight check shall—

(1) Be given by an approved check pilot or by the Administrator;

(2) Consist of at least one flight over one route segment; and

(3) Include takeoffs and landings at one or more representative airports. In addition to the requirements of this paragraph, for a pilot authorized to conduct IFR operations, at least one flight shall be flown over a civil airway, an approved off-airway route, or a portion of either of them.

(b) The pilot who conducts the check shall determine whether the pilot being checked satisfactorily performs the duties and responsibilities of a pilot in command in operations under this part, and shall so certify in the pilot training record.

(c) Each certificate holder shall establish in the manual required by 135.21 a procedure which will ensure that each pilot who has not flown over a route and into an airport within the preceding 90 days will, before beginning the flight, become familiar with all available information required for the safe operation of that flight.

135.301 Crewmember: Tests and checks, grace provisions, training to accepted standards

(a) If a crewmember who is required to take a test or a flight check under this part, completes the test or flight check in the calendar month before or after the calendar month in which it is required, that crewmember is considered to have completed the test or check in the calendar month in which it is required.

(b) If a pilot being checked under this subpart fails any of the required maneuvers, the person giving the check may give additional training to the pilot during the course of the check. In addition to repeating the maneuvers failed, the person giving the check may require the pilot being checked to repeat any other maneuvers that are necessary to determine the pilot's proficiency. If the pilot being checked is unable to demonstrate satisfactory performance to the person conducting the check, the certificate holder may not use the pilot, nor may the pilot serve, as a flight crewmember in operations under this part until the pilot has satisfactorily completed the check.

Subpart H — Training

135.321 Applicability and terms used

(a) Except as provided in 135.3, this subpart prescribes the requirements applicable to—

(1) A certificate holder under this part which contracts with, or otherwise arranges to use the services of a training center certificated under part 142 to perform training, testing, and checking functions;

(2) Each certificate holder for establishing and maintaining an approved training program for crewmembers, check airmen and instructors, and other operations personnel employed or used by that certificate holder; and

(3) Each certificate holder for the qualification, approval, and use of aircraft simulators and flight training devices in the conduct of the program.

(b) For the purposes of this subpart, the following terms and definitions apply:

(1) Initial training. The training required for crewmembers who have not qualified and served in the same capacity on an aircraft.

(2) Transition training. The training required for crewmembers who have qualified and served in the same capacity on another aircraft.

(3) Upgrade training. The training required for crewmembers who have qualified and served as second in command on a particular aircraft type, before they serve as pilot in command on that aircraft.

(4) Differences training. The training required for crewmembers who have qualified and served on a particular type aircraft, when the Administrator finds differences training is necessary before a crewmember serves in the same capacity on a particular variation of that aircraft.

(5) Recurrent training. The training required for crewmembers to remain adequately trained and currently proficient for each aircraft, crewmember position, and type of operation in which the crewmember serves.

(6) In flight. The maneuvers, procedures, or functions that must be conducted in the aircraft.

(7) Training center. An organization governed by the applicable requirements of part 142 of this chapter that conducts training, testing, and checking under contract or other arrangement to certificate holders subject to the requirements of this part.

(8) Requalification training. The training required for crewmembers previously trained and qualified, but who have become unqualified due to not having met within the required period the—

(i) Recurrent pilot testing requirements of 135.293;

(ii) Instrument proficiency check requirements of 135.297; or

(iii) Line checks required by 135.299.

[Doc. No. 16097, 43 FR 46783, Oct. 10, 1978, as amended by Amdt. 121–250, 60 FR 65950, Dec. 20, 1995; Amdt. 135–63, 61 FR 34561, July 2, 1996; Amdt. 135–91, 68 FR 54588, Sept. 17, 2003]

135.323 Training program: General

(a) Each certificate holder required to have a training program under 135.341 shall:

(1) Establish and implement a training program that satisfies the requirements of this subpart and that ensures that each crewmember, aircraft dispatcher, flight instructor and check airman is adequately trained to perform his or her assigned duties. Prior to implementation, the certificate holder must obtain initial and final FAA approval of the training program.

(2) Provide adequate ground and flight training facilities and properly qualified ground instructors for the training required by this subpart.

(3) Provide and keep current for each aircraft type used and, if applicable, the particular variations within the aircraft type appropriate training material, examinations, forms, instructions, and procedures for use in conducting the training and checks required by this subpart.

(4) Provide enough flight instructors, check airmen, and simulator instructors to conduct required flight training and flight checks and simulator training courses allowed under this subpart.

(b) Whenever a crewmember who is required to take recurrent training under this subpart completes the training in the calendar month before, or the calendar month after, the month in which that training is required, the crewmember is considered to have completed it in the calendar month in which it was required.

(c) Each instructor, supervisor, or check airman who is responsible for a particular ground training subject, segment of flight training, course of training, flight check, or competence check under this part shall certify as to the proficiency and knowledge of the crewmember, flight instructor, or check airman concerned upon completion of that training or check. That certification shall be made a part of the crewmember's record. When the certification required by this paragraph is made by an entry in a computerized recordkeeping system, the certifying instructor, supervisor, or check airman, must be identified with that entry. However, the signature of the certifying instructor, supervisor, or check airman is not required for computerized entries.

(d) Training subjects that apply to more than one aircraft or crewmember position and that have been satisfactorily completed during previous training while employed by the certificate holder for another aircraft or another crewmember position, need not be repeated during subsequent training other than recurrent training.

(e) Aircraft simulators and other training devices may be used in the certificate holder's training program if approved by the Administrator.

[Doc. No. 16097, 43 FR 46783, Oct. 10, 1978, as amended by Amdt. 135–101, 70 FR 58829, Oct. 7, 2005]

135.324 Training program: Special rules

(a) Other than the certificate holder, only another certificate holder certificated under this part or a training center certificated under part 142 of this chapter is eligible under this subpart to conduct training, testing, and checking under contract or other arrangement to those persons subject to the requirements of this subpart.

(b) A certificate holder may contract with, or otherwise arrange to use the services of, a training center certificated under part 142 of this chapter to conduct training, testing, and checking required by this part only if the training center—

(1) Holds applicable training specifications issued under part 142 of this chapter;

(2) Has facilities, training equipment, and courseware meeting the applicable requirements of part 142 of this chapter;

(3) Has approved curriculums, curriculum segments, and portions of curriculum segments applicable for use in training courses required by this subpart; and

(4) Has sufficient instructor and check airmen qualified under the applicable requirements of 135.337 through 135.340 to provide training, testing, and checking to persons subject to the requirements of this subpart.

[Doc. No. 26933, 61 FR 34562, July 2, 1996, as amended by Amdt. 135–67, 62 FR 13791, Mar. 21, 1997; Amdt. 135–91, 68 FR 54588, Sept. 17, 2003]

135.325 Training program and revision: Initial and final approval

(a) To obtain initial and final approval of a training program, or a revision to an approved training program, each certificate holder must submit to the Administrator—

(1) An outline of the proposed or revised curriculum, that provides enough information for a preliminary evaluation of the proposed training program or revision; and

(2) Additional relevant information that may be requested by the Administrator.

(b) If the proposed training program or revision complies with this subpart, the Administrator grants initial approval in writing after which the certificate holder may conduct the training under that program. The Administrator then evaluates the effectiveness of the training program and advises the certificate holder of deficiencies, if any, that must be corrected.

(c) The Administrator grants final approval of the proposed training program or revision if the certificate holder shows that the training conducted under the initial approval in paragraph (b) of this section ensures that each person who successfully completes the training is adequately trained to perform that person's assigned duties.

(d) Whenever the Administrator finds that revisions are necessary for the continued adequacy of a training program that has been granted final approval, the certificate holder shall, after notification by the Administrator, make any changes in the program that are found necessary by the Administrator. Within 30 days after the certificate holder receives the notice, it may file a petition to reconsider the notice with the Administrator. The filing of a petition to reconsider stays the notice pending a decision by the Administrator. However, if the Administrator finds that there is an emergency that requires immediate action in the interest of safety, the Administrator may, upon a statement of the reasons, require a change effective without stay.

135.327 Training program: Curriculum

(a) Each certificate holder must prepare and keep current a written training program curriculum for each type of aircraft for each crewmember required for that type aircraft. The curriculum must include ground and flight training required by this subpart.

(b) Each training program curriculum must include the following:

(1) A list of principal ground training subjects, including emergency training subjects, that are provided.

(2) A list of all the training devices, mockups, systems trainers, procedures trainers, or other training aids that the certificate holder will use.

(3) Detailed descriptions or pictorial displays of the approved normal, abnormal, and emergency maneuvers, procedures and functions that will be performed during each flight training phase or flight check, indicating those maneuvers, procedures and functions that are to be performed during the in-flight portions of flight training and flight checks.

135.329 Crewmember training requirements

(a) Each certificate holder must include in its training program the following initial and transition ground training as appropriate to the particular assignment of the crewmember:

(1) Basic indoctrination ground training for newly hired crewmembers including instruction in at least the—

   (i) Duties and responsibilities of crewmembers as applicable;

   (ii) Appropriate provisions of this chapter;

   (iii) Contents of the certificate holder's operating certificate and operations specifications (not required for flight attendants); and

   (iv) Appropriate portions of the certificate holder's operating manual.

(2) The initial and transition ground training in 135.345 and 135.349, as applicable.

(3) Emergency training in 135.331.

(4) Crew resource management training in 135.330.

(b) Each training program must provide the initial and transition flight training in 135.347, as applicable.

(c) Each training program must provide recurrent ground and flight training in 135.351.

(d) Upgrade training in 135.345 and 135.347 for a particular type aircraft may be included in the training program for crewmembers who have qualified and served as second in command on that aircraft.

(e) In addition to initial, transition, upgrade and recurrent training, each training program must provide ground and flight training, instruction, and practice necessary to ensure that each crewmember—

(1) Remains adequately trained and currently proficient for each aircraft, crewmember position, and type of operation in which the crewmember serves; and

(2) Qualifies in new equipment, facilities, procedures, and techniques, including modifications to aircraft.

Docket No. 16097, 43 FR 46783, Oct. 10, 1978, as amended by Amdt. 135–122, 76 FR 3837, Jan. 21, 2011]

135.330 Crew resource management training

(a) Each certificate holder must have an approved crew resource management training program that includes initial and recurrent training. The training program must include at least the following:

(1) Authority of the pilot in command;

(2) Communication processes, decisions, and coordination, to include communication with Air Traffic Control, personnel performing flight locating and other operational functions, and passengers;

(3) Building and maintenance of a flight team;

(4) Workload and time management;

(5) Situational awareness;

(6) Effects of fatigue on performance, avoidance strategies and countermeasures;

(7) Effects of stress and stress reduction strategies; and

(8) Aeronautical decision-making and judgment training tailored to the operator's flight operations and aviation environment.

(b) After March 22, 2013, no certificate holder may use a person as a flightcrew member or flight attendant unless that person has completed approved crew resource management initial training with that certificate holder.

(c) For flightcrew members and flight attendants, the Administrator, at his or her discretion, may credit crew resource management training completed with that certificate holder before March 22, 2013, toward all or part of the initial CRM training required by this section.

(d) In granting credit for initial CRM training, the Administrator considers training aids, devices, methods and procedures used by the certificate holder in a voluntary CRM program included in a training program required by 135.341, 135.345, or 135.349.

[Docket No. FAA–2009–0023, 76 FR 3837, Jan. 21, 2011]

135.331 Crewmember emergency training

(a) Each training program must provide emergency training under this section for each aircraft type, model, and configuration, each crewmember, and each kind of operation conducted, as appropriate for each crewmember and the certificate holder.

(b) Emergency training must provide the following:

(1) Instruction in emergency assignments and procedures, including coordination among crewmembers.

(2) Individual instruction in the location, function, and operation of emergency equipment including—

   (i) Equipment used in ditching and evacuation;

(ii) First aid equipment and its proper use; and

(iii) Portable fire extinguishers, with emphasis on the type of extinguisher to be used on different classes of fires.

(3) Instruction in the handling of emergency situations including—

    (i) Rapid decompression;

    (ii) Fire in flight or on the surface and smoke control procedures with emphasis on electrical equipment and related circuit breakers found in cabin areas;

    (iii) Ditching and evacuation;

    (iv) Illness, injury, or other abnormal situations involving passengers or crewmembers; and

    (v) Hijacking and other unusual situations.

(4) Review of the certificate holder's previous aircraft accidents and incidents involving actual emergency situations.

(c) Each crewmember must perform at least the following emergency drills, using the proper emergency equipment and procedures, unless the Administrator finds that, for a particular drill, the crewmember can be adequately trained by demonstration:

(1) Ditching, if applicable.

(2) Emergency evacuation.

(3) Fire extinguishing and smoke control.

(4) Operation and use of emergency exits, including deployment and use of evacuation chutes, if applicable.

(5) Use of crew and passenger oxygen.

(6) Removal of life rafts from the aircraft, inflation of the life rafts, use of life lines, and boarding of passengers and crew, if applicable.

(7) Donning and inflation of life vests and the use of other individual flotation devices, if applicable.

(d) Crewmembers who serve in operations above 25,000 feet must receive instruction in the following:

(1) Respiration.

(2) Hypoxia.

(3) Duration of consciousness without supplemental oxygen at altitude.

(4) Gas expansion.

(5) Gas bubble formation.

(6) Physical phenomena and incidents of decompression.

135.335 Approval of aircraft simulators and other training devices

(a) Training courses using aircraft simulators and other training devices may be included in the certificate holder's training program if approved by the Administrator.

(b) Each aircraft simulator and other training device that is used in a training course or in checks required under this subpart must meet the following requirements:

(1) It must be specifically approved for—

    (i) The certificate holder; and

    (ii) The particular maneuver, procedure, or crewmember function involved.

(2) It must maintain the performance, functional, and other characteristics that are required for approval.

(3) Additionally, for aircraft simulators, it must be—

    (i) Approved for the type aircraft and, if applicable, the particular variation within type for which the training or check is being conducted; and

    (ii) Modified to conform with any modification to the aircraft being simulated that changes the performance, functional, or other characteristics required for approval.

(c) A particular aircraft simulator or other training device may be used by more than one certificate holder.

(d) In granting initial and final approval of training programs or revisions to them, the Administrator considers the training devices, methods and procedures listed in the certificate holder's curriculum under 135.327.

[Doc. No. 16907, 43 FR 46783, Oct. 10, 1978, as amended by Amdt. 135–1, 44 FR 26738, May 7, 1979]

135.336 Airline transport pilot certification training program

(a) A certificate holder may obtain approval to establish and implement a training program to satisfy the requirements of 61.156 of this chapter. The training program must be separate from the air carrier training program required by this part.

(b) No certificate holder may use a person nor may any person serve as an instructor in a training program approved to meet the requirements of 61.156 of this chapter unless the instructor:

(1) Holds an airline transport pilot certificate with an airplane category multiengine class rating;

(2) Has at least 2 years of experience as a pilot in command in operations conducted under 91.1053(a)(2)(i) of this chapter, 135.243(a)(1) of this part, or as a pilot in command or second in command in any operation conducted under part 121 of this chapter;

(3) Except for the holder of a flight instructor certificate, receives nitial training on the following topics:

    (i) The fundamental principles of the learning process;

    (ii) Elements of effective teaching, instruction methods, and techniques;

    (iii) Instructor duties, privileges, responsibilities, and limitations;

    (iv) Training policies and procedures; and

    (v) Evaluation.

(4) If providing training in a flight simulation training device, holds an aircraft type rating for the aircraft represented by the flight simulation training device utilized in the training program and have received training and evaluation within the preceding 12 months from the certificate holder on:

    (i) Proper operation of flight simulator and flight training device controls and systems;

    (ii) Proper operation of environmental and fault panels;

    (iii) Data and motion limitations of simulation;

    (iv) Minimum equipment requirements for each curriculum; and

    (v) The maneuvers that will be demonstrated in the flight simulation training device.

(c) A certificate holder may not issue a graduation certificate to a student unless that student has completed all the curriculum requirements of the course.

(d) A certificate holder must conduct evaluations to ensure that training techniques, procedures, and standards are acceptable to the Administrator.

[Doc. No. FAA-2010-0100, 78 FR 42379, July 15, 2013]

135.337 Qualifications: Check airmen (aircraft) and check airmen (simulator)

(a) For the purposes of this section and 135.339:

(1) A check airman (aircraft) is a person who is qualified to conduct flight checks in an aircraft, in a flight simulator, or in a flight training device for a particular type aircraft.

(2) A check airman (simulator) is a person who is qualified to conduct flight checks, but only in a flight simulator, in a flight training device, or both, for a particular type aircraft.

(3) Check airmen (aircraft) and check airmen (simulator) are those check airmen who perform the functions described in 135.321 (a) and 135.323(a)(4) and (c).

(b) No certificate holder may use a person, nor may any person serve as a check airman (aircraft) in a training program established under this subpart unless, with respect to the aircraft type involved, that person—

(1) Holds the airman certificates and ratings required to serve as a pilot in command in operations under this part;

(2) Has satisfactorily completed the training phases for the aircraft, including recurrent training, that are required to serve as a pilot in command in operations under this part;

(3) Has satisfactorily completed the proficiency or competency checks that are required to serve as a pilot in command in operations under this part;

(4) Has satisfactorily completed the applicable training requirements of 135.339;

(5) Holds at least a Class III medical certificate unless serving as a required crewmember, in which case holds a Class I or Class II medical certificate as appropriate.

(6) Has satisfied the recency of experience requirements of 135.247; and

(7) Has been approved by the Administrator for the check airman duties involved.

(c) No certificate holder may use a person, nor may any person serve as a check airman (simulator) in a training program established under this subpart unless, with respect to the aircraft type involved, that person meets the provisions of paragraph (b) of this section, or—

(1) Holds the applicable airman certificates and ratings, except medical certificate, required to serve as a pilot in command in operations under this part;

(2) Has satisfactorily completed the appropriate training phases for the aircraft, including recurrent training, that are required to serve as a pilot in command in operations under this part;

(3) Has satisfactorily completed the appropriate proficiency or competency checks that are required to serve as a pilot in command in operations under this part;

(4) Has satisfactorily completed the applicable training requirements of 135.339; and

(5) Has been approved by the Administrator for the check airman (simulator) duties involved.

(d) Completion of the requirements in paragraphs (b) (2), (3), and (4) or (c) (2), (3), and (4) of this section, as applicable, shall be entered in the individual's training record maintained by the certificate holder.

(e) Check airmen who do not hold an appropriate medical certificate may function as check airmen (simulator), but may not serve as flightcrew members in operations under this part.

(f) A check airman (simulator) must accomplish the following—

(1) Fly at least two flight segments as a required crewmember for the type, class, or category aircraft involved within the 12-month preceding the performance of any check airman duty in a flight simulator; or

(2) Satisfactorily complete an approved line-observation program within the period prescribed by that program and that must precede the performance of any check airman duty in a flight simulator.

(g) The flight segments or line-observation program required in paragraph (f) of this section are considered to be completed in the month required if completed in the calendar month before or the calendar month after the month in which they are due.

[Doc. No. 28471, 61 FR 30744, June 17, 1996]

135.338 Qualifications: Flight instructors (aircraft) and flight instructors (simulator)

(a) For the purposes of this section and 135.340:

(1) A flight instructor (aircraft) is a person who is qualified to instruct in an aircraft, in a flight simulator, or in a flight training device for a particular type, class, or category aircraft.

(2) A flight instructor (simulator) is a person who is qualified to instruct in a flight simulator, in a flight training device, or in both, for a particular type, class, or category aircraft.

(3) Flight instructors (aircraft) and flight instructors (simulator) are those instructors who perform the functions described in 135.321(a) and 135.323 (a)(4) and (c).

(b) No certificate holder may use a person, nor may any person serve as a flight instructor (aircraft) in a training program established under this subpart unless, with respect to the type, class, or category aircraft involved, that person—

(1) Holds the airman certificates and ratings required to serve as a pilot in command in operations under this part;

(2) Has satisfactorily completed the training phases for the aircraft, including recurrent training, that are required to serve as a pilot in command in operations under this part;

(3) Has satisfactorily completed the proficiency or competency checks that are required to serve as a pilot in command in operations under this part;

(4) Has satisfactorily completed the applicable training requirements of 135.340;

(5) Holds at least a Class III medical certificate; and

(6) Has satisfied the recency of experience requirements of 135.247.

(c) No certificate holder may use a person, nor may any person serve as a flight instructor (simulator) in a training program established under this subpart, unless, with respect to the type, class, or category aircraft involved, that person meets the provisions of paragraph (b) of this section, or—

(1) Holds the airman certificates and ratings, except medical certificate, required to serve as a pilot in command in operations under this part except before March 19, 1997 that person need not hold a type rating for the type, class, or category of aircraft involved.

(2) Has satisfactorily completed the appropriate training phases for the aircraft, including recurrent training, that are required to serve as a pilot in command in operations under this part;

(3) Has satisfactorily completed the appropriate proficiency or competency checks that are required to serve as a pilot in command in operations under this part; and

(4) Has satisfactorily completed the applicable training requirements of 135.340.

(d) Completion of the requirements in paragraphs (b) (2), (3), and (4) or (c) (2), (3), and (4) of this section, as applicable, shall be entered in the individual's training record maintained by the certificate holder.

(e) An airman who does not hold a medical certificate may function as a flight instructor in an aircraft if functioning as a non-required crewmember, but may not serve as a flightcrew member in operations under this part.

(f) A flight instructor (simulator) must accomplish the following—

(1) Fly at least two flight segments as a required crewmember for the type, class, or category aircraft involved within the 12-month period preceding the performance of any flight instructor duty in a flight simulator; or

(2) Satisfactorily complete an approved line-observation program within the period prescribed by that program preceding the performance of any flight instructor duty in a flight simulator.

(g) The flight segments or line-observation program required in paragraph (f) of this section are considered completed in the month required if completed in the calendar month before, or in the calendar month after, the month in which they are due.

[Doc. No. 28471, 61 FR 30744, June 17, 1996; 62 FR 3739, Jan. 24, 1997, as amended by Amdt. 135–125, 76 FR , June 16, 2011]

FAR 135

135.339   Initial and transition training and checking: Check airmen (aircraft), check airmen (simulator)

(a) No certificate holder may use a person nor may any person serve as a check airman unless—

(1) That person has satisfactorily completed initial or transition check airman training; and

(2) Within the preceding 24 calendar months, that person satisfactorily conducts a proficiency or competency check under the observation of an FAA inspector or an aircrew designated examiner employed by the operator. The observation check may be accomplished in part or in full in an aircraft, in a flight simulator, or in a flight training device. This paragraph applies after March 19, 1997.

(b) The observation check required by paragraph (a)(2) of this section is considered to have been completed in the month required if completed in the calendar month before or the calendar month after the month in which it is due.

(c) The initial ground training for check airmen must include the following:

(1) Check airman duties, functions, and responsibilities.

(2) The applicable Code of Federal Regulations and the certificate holder's policies and procedures.

(3) The applicable methods, procedures, and techniques for conducting the required checks.

(4) Proper evaluation of student performance including the detection of—

(i) Improper and insufficient training; and

(ii) Personal characteristics of an applicant that could adversely affect safety.

(5) The corrective action in the case of unsatisfactory checks.

(6) The approved methods, procedures, and limitations for performing the required normal, abnormal, and emergency procedures in the aircraft.

(d) The transition ground training for check airmen must include the approved methods, procedures, and limitations for performing the required normal, abnormal, and emergency procedures applicable to the aircraft to which the check airman is in transition.

(e) The initial and transition flight training for check airmen (aircraft) must include the following—

(1) The safety measures for emergency situations that are likely to develop during a check;

(2) The potential results of improper, untimely, or nonexecution of safety measures during a check;

(3) Training and practice in conducting flight checks from the left and right pilot seats in the required normal, abnormal, and emergency procedures to ensure competence to conduct the pilot flight checks required by this part; and

(4) The safety measures to be taken from either pilot seat for emergency situations that are likely to develop during checking.

(f) The requirements of paragraph (e) of this section may be accomplished in full or in part in flight, in a flight simulator, or in a flight training device, as appropriate.

(g) The initial and transition flight training for check airmen (simulator) must include the following:

(1) Training and practice in conducting flight checks in the required normal, abnormal, and emergency procedures to ensure competence to conduct the flight checks required by this part. This training and practice must be accomplished in a flight simulator or in a flight training device.

(2) Training in the operation of flight simulators, flight training devices, or both, to ensure competence to conduct the flight checks required by this part.

[Doc. No. 28471, 61 FR 30745, June 17, 1996; 62 FR 3739, Jan. 24, 1997]

135.340   Initial and transition training and checking: Flight instructors (aircraft), flight instructors (simulator)

(a) No certificate holder may use a person nor may any person serve as a flight instructor unless—

(1) That person has satisfactorily completed initial or transition flight instructor training; and

(2) Within the preceding 24 calendar months, that person satisfactorily conducts instruction under the observation of an FAA inspector, an operator check airman, or an aircrew designated examiner employed by the operator. The observation check may be accomplished in part or in full in an aircraft, in a flight simulator, or in a flight training device. This paragraph applies after March 19, 1997.

(b) The observation check required by paragraph (a)(2) of this section is considered to have been completed in the month required if completed in the calendar month before, or the calendar month after, the month in which it is due.

(c) The initial ground training for flight instructors must include the following:

(1) Flight instructor duties, functions, and responsibilities.

(2) The applicable Code of Federal Regulations and the certificate holder's policies and procedures.

(3) The applicable methods, procedures, and techniques for conducting flight instruction.

(4) Proper evaluation of student performance including the detection of—

(i) Improper and insufficient training; and

(ii) Personal characteristics of an applicant that could adversely affect safety.

(5) The corrective action in the case of unsatisfactory training progress.

(6) The approved methods, procedures, and limitations for performing the required normal, abnormal, and emergency procedures in the aircraft.

(7) Except for holders of a flight instructor certificate—

(i) The fundamental principles of the teaching-learning process;

(ii) Teaching methods and procedures; and

(iii) The instructor-student relationship.

(d) The transition ground training for flight instructors must include the approved methods, procedures, and limitations for performing the required normal, abnormal, and emergency procedures applicable to the type, class, or category aircraft to which the flight instructor is in transition.

(e) The initial and transition flight training for flight instructors (aircraft) must include the following—

(1) The safety measures for emergency situations that are likely to develop during instruction;

(2) The potential results of improper or untimely safety measures during instruction;

(3) Training and practice from the left and right pilot seats in the required normal, abnormal, and emergency maneuvers to ensure competence to conduct the flight instruction required by this part; and

(4) The safety measures to be taken from either the left or right pilot seat for emergency situations that are likely to develop during instruction.

(f) The requirements of paragraph (e) of this section may be accomplished in full or in part in flight, in a flight simulator, or in a flight training device, as appropriate.

(g) The initial and transition flight training for a flight instructor (simulator) must include the following:

(1) Training and practice in the required normal, abnormal, and emergency procedures to ensure competence to conduct the

flight instruction required by this part. These maneuvers and procedures must be accomplished in full or in part in a flight simulator or in a flight training device.

(2) Training in the operation of flight simulators, flight training devices, or both, to ensure competence to conduct the flight instruction required by this part.

[Doc. No. 28471, 61 FR 30745, June 17, 1996; 61 FR 34927, July 3, 1996; 62 FR 3739, Jan. 24, 1997]

135.341 Pilot and flight attendant crewmember training programs

(a) Each certificate holder, other than one who uses only one pilot in the certificate holder's operations, shall establish and maintain an approved pilot training program, and each certificate holder who uses a flight attendant crewmember shall establish and maintain an approved flight attendant training program, that is appropriate to the operations to which each pilot and flight attend- ant is to be assigned, and will ensure that they are adequately trained to meet the applicable knowledge and practical testing requirements of 135.293 through 135.301. However, the Administrator may authorize a deviation from this section if the Administrator finds that, because of the limited size and scope of the operation, safety will allow a deviation from these requirements. This deviation authority does not extend to the training provided under 135.336.

(b) Each certificate holder required to have a training program by paragraph (a) of this section shall include in that program ground and flight training curriculums for—

(1) Initial training;

(2) Transition training;

(3) Upgrade training;

(4) Differences training; and

(5) Recurrent training.

(c) Each certificate holder required to have a training program by paragraph (a) of this section shall provide current and appropriate study materials for use by each required pilot and flight attendant.

(d) The certificate holder shall furnish copies of the pilot and flight attendant crewmember training program, and all changes and additions, to the assigned representative of the Administrator. If the certificate holder uses training facilities of other persons, a copy of those training programs or appropriate portions used for those facilities shall also be furnished. Curricula that follow FAA published curricula may be cited by reference in the copy of the training program furnished to the representative of the Administrator and need not be furnished with the program.

[Doc. No. 16097, 43 FR 46783, Oct. 10, 1978, as amended by Amdt. 135–18, 47 FR 33396, Aug. 2, 1982]

135.343 Crewmember initial and recurrent training requirements

No certificate holder may use a person, nor may any person serve, as a crewmember in operations under this part unless that crewmember has completed the appropriate initial or recurrent training phase of the training program appropriate to the type of operation in which the crewmember is to serve since the beginning of the 12th calendar month before that service. This section does not apply to a certificate holder that uses only one pilot in the certificate holder's operations.

[Doc. No. 16097, 43 FR 46783, Oct. 10, 1978, as amended by Amdt. 135–18, 47 FR 33396, Aug. 2, 1982]

135.345 Pilots: Initial, transition, and upgrade ground training

Initial, transition, and upgrade ground training for pilots must include instruction in at least the following, as applicable to their duties:

(a) General subjects—

(1) The certificate holder's flight locating procedures;

(2) Principles and methods for determining weight and balance, and runway limitations for takeoff and landing;

(3) Enough meteorology to ensure a practical knowledge of weather phenomena, including the principles of frontal systems, icing, fog, thunderstorms, windshear and, if appropriate, high altitude weather situations;

(4) Air traffic control systems, procedures, and phraseology;

(5) Navigation and the use of navigational aids, including instrument approach procedures;

(6) Normal and emergency communication procedures;

(7) Visual cues before and during descent below DA/DH or MDA;

(8) ETOPS, if applicable;

(9) After August 13, 2008, passenger recovery plan for any passenger-carrying operation (other than intrastate operations wholly within the state of Alaska) in the North Polar area; and

(10) Other instructions necessary to ensure the pilot's competence.

(b) For each aircraft type—

(1) A general description;

(2) Performance characteristics;

(3) Engines and propellers;

(4) Major components;

(5) Major aircraft systems (i.e., flight controls, electrical, and hydraulic), other systems, as appropriate, principles of normal, abnormal, and emergency operations, appropriate procedures and limitations;

(6) Knowledge and procedures for—

(i) Recognizing and avoiding severe weather situations;

(ii) Escaping from severe weather situations, in case of inadvertent encounters, including low-altitude windshear (except that rotorcraft pilots are not required to be trained in escaping from low-altitude windshear);

(iii) Operating in or near thunderstorms (including best penetrating altitudes), turbulent air (including clear air turbulence), icing, hail, and other potentially hazardous meteorological conditions; and

(iv) Operating airplanes during ground icing conditions, (i.e., any time conditions are such that frost, ice, or snow may reasonably be expected to adhere to the airplane), if the certificate holder expects to authorize takeoffs in ground icing conditions, including:

(A) The use of holdover times when using deicing/anti-icing fluids;

(B) Airplane deicing/anti-icing procedures, including inspection and check procedures and responsibilities;

(C) Communications;

(D) Airplane surface contamination (i.e., adherence of frost, ice, or snow) and critical area identification, and knowledge of how contamination adversely affects airplane performance and flight characteristics;

(E) Types and characteristics of deicing/anti-icing fluids, if used by the certificate holder;

(F) Cold weather preflight inspection procedures;

(G) Techniques for recognizing contamination on the airplane;

(7) Operating limitations;

(8) Fuel consumption and cruise control;

(9) Flight planning;

(10) Each normal and emergency procedure; and

(11) The approved Aircraft Flight Manual, or equivalent.

[Doc. No. 16097, 43 FR 46783, Oct. 10, 1978, as amended by Amdt. 135–27, 53 FR 37697, Sept. 27, 1988; Amdt. 135–46, 58 FR 69630,

Dec. 30, 1993; Amdt. 135–108, 72 FR 1885, Jan. 16, 2007; Amdt. 135–110, 72 FR 31685, June 7, 2007; Amdt. 135–112, 73 FR 8798, Feb. 15, 2008]

135.347   Pilots: Initial, transition, upgrade, and differences flight training

(a) Initial, transition, upgrade, and differences training for pilots must include flight and practice in each of the maneuvers and procedures in the approved training program curriculum.

(b) The maneuvers and procedures required by paragraph (a) of this section must be performed in flight, except to the extent that certain maneuvers and procedures may be performed in an aircraft simulator, or an appropriate training device, as allowed by this subpart.

(c) If the certificate holder's approved training program includes a course of training using an aircraft simulator or other training device, each pilot must successfully complete—

  (1) Training and practice in the simulator or training device in at least the maneuvers and procedures in this subpart that are capable of being performed in the aircraft simulator or training device; and

  (2) A flight check in the aircraft or a check in the simulator or training device to the level of proficiency of a pilot in command or second in command, as applicable, in at least the maneuvers and procedures that are capable of being performed in an aircraft simulator or training device.

135.349   Flight attendants: Initial and transition ground training

Initial and transition ground training for flight attendants must include instruction in at least the following—

(a) General subjects—

  (1) The authority of the pilot in command; and

  (2) Passenger handling, including procedures to be followed in handling deranged persons or other persons whose conduct might jeopardize safety.

(b) For each aircraft type—

  (1) A general description of the aircraft emphasizing physical characteristics that may have a bearing on ditching, evacuation, and inflight emergency procedures and on other related duties;

  (2) The use of both the public address system and the means of communicating with other flight crewmembers, including emergency means in the case of attempted hijacking or other unusual situations; and

  (3) Proper use of electrical galley equipment and the controls for cabin heat and ventilation.

135.351   Recurrent training

(a) Each certificate holder must ensure that each crewmember receives recurrent training and is adequately trained and currently proficient for the type aircraft and crewmember position involved.

(b) Recurrent ground training for crewmembers must include at least the following:

  (1) A quiz or other review to determine the crewmember's knowledge of the aircraft and crewmember position involved.

  (2) Instruction as necessary in the subjects required for initial ground training by this subpart, as appropriate, including low-altitude windshear training and training on operating during ground icing conditions as prescribed in 135.341 and described in 135.345, crew resource management training as prescribed in 135.330, and emergency training as prescribed in 135.331.

(c) Recurrent flight training for pilots must include, at least, flight training in the maneuvers or procedures in this subpart, except

that satisfactory completion of the check required by 135.293 within the preceding 12 calendar months may be substituted for recurrent flight training.

[Doc. No. 16097, 43 FR 46783, Oct. 10, 1978, as amended by Amdt. 135–27, 53 FR 37698, Sept. 27, 1988; Amdt. 135–46, 58 FR 69630, Dec. 30, 1993; Amdt. 135–122, 76 FR 3837, Jan. 21, 2011]

135.353   [Reserved]

Subpart I — Airplane Performance Operating Limitations

135.361   Applicability

(a) This subpart prescribes airplane performance operating limitations applicable to the operation of the categories of airplanes listed in 135.363 when operated under this part.

(b) For the purpose of this subpart, effective length of the runway, for landing means the distance from the point at which the obstruction clearance plane associated with the approach end of the runway intersects the centerline of the runway to the far end of the runway.

(c) For the purpose of this subpart, obstruction clearance plane means a plane sloping upward from the runway at a slope of 1:20 to the horizontal, and tangent to or clearing all obstructions within a specified area surrounding the runway as shown in a profile view of that area. In the plan view, the centerline of the specified area coincides with the centerline of the runway, beginning at the point where the obstruction clearance plane intersects the centerline of the runway and proceeding to a point at least 1,500 feet from the beginning point. After that the centerline coincides with the take-off path over the ground for the runway (in the case of takeoffs) or with the instrument approach counterpart (for landings), or, where the applicable one of these paths has not been established, it proceeds consistent with turns of at least 4,000-foot radius until a point is reached beyond which the obstruction clearance plane clears all obstructions. This area extends laterally 200 feet on each side of the centerline at the point where the obstruction clearance plane intersects the runway and continues at this width to the end of the runway; then it increases uniformly to 500 feet on each side of the centerline at a point 1,500 feet from the intersection of the obstruction clearance plane with the runway; after that it extends laterally 500 feet on each side of the centerline.

135.363   General

(a) Each certificate holder operating a reciprocating engine powered large transport category airplane shall comply with 135.365 through 135.377.

(b) Each certificate holder operating a turbine engine powered large transport category airplane shall comply with 135.379 through 135.387, except that when it operates a turbopropeller-powered large transport category airplane certificated after August 29, 1959, but previously type certificated with the same number of reciprocating engines, it may comply with 135.365 through 135.377.

(c) Each certificate holder operating a large nontransport category airplane shall comply with 135.389 through 135.395 and any determination of compliance must be based only on approved performance data. For the purpose of this subpart, a large nontransport category airplane is an airplane that was type certificated before July 1, 1942.

(d) Each certificate holder operating a small transport category airplane shall comply with 135.397.

(e) Each certificate holder operating a small nontransport category airplane shall comply with 135.399.

(f) The performance data in the Airplane Flight Manual applies in determining compliance with 135.365 through 135.387. Where conditions are different from those on which the performance data is based, compliance is determined by interpolation or by computing the effects of change in the specific variables, if the results of the interpolation or computations are substantially as accurate as the results of direct tests.

(g) No person may take off a reciprocating engine powered large transport category airplane at a weight that is more than the allowable weight for the runway being used (determined under the runway takeoff limitations of the transport category operating rules of this subpart) after taking into account the temperature operating correction factors in section 4a.749a-T or section 4b.117 of the Civil Air Regulations in effect on January 31, 1965, and in the applicable Airplane Flight Manual.

(h) The Administrator may author- ize in the operations specifications deviations from this subpart if special circumstances make a literal observ- ance of a requirement unnecessary for safety.

(i) The 10-mile width specified in 135.369 through 135.373 may be reduced to 5 miles, for not more than 20 miles, when operating under VFR or where navigation facilities furnish reliable and accurate identification of high ground and obstructions located outside of 5 miles, but within 10 miles, on each side of the intended track.

(j) Each certificate holder operating a commuter category airplane shall comply with 135.398.

[Doc. No. 16097, 43 FR 46783, Oct. 10, 1978, as amended by Amdt. 135–21, 52 FR 1836, Jan. 15, 1987]

135.364 Maximum flying time outside the United States

After August 13, 2008, no certificate holder may operate an airplane, other than an all-cargo airplane with more than two engines, on a planned route that exceeds 180 minutes flying time (at the one-engine-inoperative cruise speed under standard conditions in still air) from an Adequate Airport outside the continental United States unless the operation is approved by the FAA in accordance with Appendix G of this part, Extended Operations (ETOPS).

[Doc. No. FAA–1999–6717, 73 FR 8798, Feb. 15, 2008]

135.365 Large transport category airplanes: Reciprocating engine powered: Weight limitations

(a) No person may take off a reciprocating engine powered large transport category airplane from an airport located at an elevation outside of the range for which maximum takeoff weights have been determined for that airplane.

(b) No person may take off a reciprocating engine powered large transport category airplane for an airport of intended destination that is located at an elevation outside of the range for which maximum landing weights have been determined for that airplane.

(c) No person may specify, or have specified, an alternate airport that is located at an elevation outside of the range for which maximum landing weights have been determined for the reciprocating engine powered large transport category airplane concerned.

(d) No person may take off a reciprocating engine powered large transport category airplane at a weight more than the maximum authorized takeoff weight for the elevation of the airport.

(e) No person may take off a reciprocating engine powered large transport category airplane if its weight on arrival at the airport of destination will be more than the maximum authorized landing weight for the elevation of that airport, allowing for normal consumption of fuel and oil en route.

135.367 Large transport category airplanes: Reciprocating engine powered: Takeoff limitations

(a) No person operating a reciprocating engine powered large transport category airplane may take off that airplane unless it is possible—

(1) To stop the airplane safely on the runway, as shown by the accelerate-stop distance data, at any time during takeoff until reaching critical-engine failure speed;

(2) If the critical engine fails at any time after the airplane reaches critical-engine failure speed V_1, to continue the takeoff and reach a height of 50 feet, as indicated by the takeoff path data, before passing over the end of the runway; and

(3) To clear all obstacles either by at least 50 feet vertically (as shown by the takeoff path data) or 200 feet horizontally within the airport boundaries and 300 feet horizontally beyond the boundaries, without banking before reaching a height of 50 feet (as shown by the takeoff path data) and after that without banking more than 15 degrees.

(b) In applying this section, corrections must be made for any runway gradient .To allow forwind effect, takeoff data based on still air may be corrected by taking into account not more than 50 percent of any reported headwind component and not less than 150 percent of any reported tailwind component.

135.369 Large transport category airplanes: Reciprocating engine powered: En route limitations: All engines operating

(a) No person operating a reciprocating engine powered large transport category airplane may take off that airplane at a weight, allowing for normal consumption of fuel and oil, that does not allow a rate of climb (in feet per minute), with all engines operating, of at least 6.90 V_{SO} (that is, the number of feet per minute obtained by multiplying the number of knots by 6.90) at an altitude of a least 1,000 feet above the highest ground or obstruction within ten miles of each side of the intended track.

(b) This section does not apply to large transport category airplanes certificated under part 4a of the Civil Air Regulations.

135.371 Large transport category airplanes: Reciprocating engine powered: En route limitations: One engine inoperative

(a) Except as provided in paragraph (b) of this section, no person operating a reciprocating engine powered large transport category airplane may take off that airplane at a weight, allowing for normal consumption of fuel and oil, that does not allow a rate of climb (in feet per minute), with one engine inoperative, of at least $(0.079-0.106/N)$ V_{SO2} (where N is the number of engines installed and Vsois expressed in knots) at an altitude of least 1,000 feet above the highest ground or obstruction within 10 miles of each side of the intended track. However, for the purposes of this paragraph the rate of climb for transport category airplanes certificated under part 4a of the Civil Air Regulations is 0.026 V_{SO2}.

(b) In place of the requirements of paragraph (a) of this section, a person may, under an approved procedure, operate a reciprocating engine powered large transport category airplane at an all-engines-operating altitude that allows the airplane to continue, after an engine failure, to an alternate airport where a landing can be made under 135.377, allowing for normal consumption of fuel and oil. After the assumed failure, the flight path must clear the ground and any obstruction within five miles on each side of the intended track by at least 2,000 feet.

(c) If an approved procedure under paragraph (b) of this section is used, the certificate holder shall comply with the following:

(1) The rate of climb (as prescribed in the Airplane Flight Manual for the appropriate weight and altitude) used in calculating the airplane's flight path shall be diminished by an amount in feet per minute, equal to $(0.079-0.106/N)$ V_{SO2} (when N is the number of engines installed and Vsois expressed in knots) for airplanes certificated under part 25 of this chapter and by 0.026 V_{SO2} for airplanes certificated under part 4a of the Civil Air Regulations.

(2) The all-engines-operating altitude shall be sufficient so that in the event the critical engine becomes inoperative at any point along the route, the flight will be able to proceed to a predetermined alternate airport by use of this procedure. In determining the takeoff weight, the airplane is assumed to pass over the critical obstruction following engine failure at a point no closer to the critical obstruction than the nearest approved navigational fix, unless the Administrator approves a procedure established on a different basis upon finding that adequate operational safeguards exist.

(3) The airplane must meet the provisions of paragraph (a) of this section at 1,000 feet above the airport used as an alternate in this procedure.

FAR 135

(4) The procedure must include an approved method of accounting for winds and temperatures that would otherwise adversely affect the flight path.

(5) In complying with this procedure, fuel jettisoning is allowed if the certificate holder shows that it has an adequate training program, that proper instructions are given to the flight crew, and all other precautions are taken to ensure a safe procedure.

(6) The certificate holder and the pilot in command shall jointly elect an alternate airport for which the appropriate weather reports or forecasts, or any combination of them, indicate that weather conditions will be at or above the alternate weather minimum specified in the certificate holder's operations specifications for that airport when the flight arrives.

[Docket No. 16097, 43 FR 46783, Oct. 10, 1978, as amended by Amdt. 135–110, 72 FR 31685, June 7, 2007]

135.373 Part 25 transport category airplanes with four or more engines: Reciprocating engine powered: En route limitations: Two engines inoperative

(a) No person may operate an airplane certificated under part 25 and having four or more engines unless—

(1) There is no place along the intended track that is more than 90 minutes (with all engines operating at cruising power) from an airport that meets 135.377; or

(2) It is operated at a weight allowing the airplane, with the two critical engines inoperative, to climb at 0.013 Vso2 feet per minute (that is, the number of feet per minute obtained by multiplying the number of knots squared by 0.013) at an altitude of 1,000 feet above the highest ground or obstruction within 10 miles on each side of the intended track, or at an altitude of 5,000 feet, whichever is higher.

(b) For the purposes of paragraph (a)(2) of this section, it is assumed that—

(1) The two engines fail at the point that is most critical with respect to the takeoff weight;

(2) Consumption of fuel and oil is normal with all engines operating up to the point where the two engines fail with two engines operating beyond that point;

(3) Where the engines are assumed to fail at an altitude above the prescribed minimum altitude, compliance with the prescribed rate of climb at the prescribed minimum altitude need not be shown during the descent from the cruising altitude to the prescribed minimum altitude, if those requirements can be met once the prescribed minimum altitude is reached, and assuming descent to be along a net flight path and the rate of descent to be 0.013 V_{so2} greater than the rate in the approved performance data; and

(4) If fuel jettisoning is provided, the airplane's weight at the point where the two engines fail is considered to be not less than that which would include enough fuel to proceed to an airport meeting 135.377 and to arrive at an altitude of at least 1,000 feet directly over that airport.

135.375 Large transport category airplanes: Reciprocating engine powered: Landing limitations: Destination airports

(a) Except as provided in paragraph (b) of this section, no person operating a reciprocating engine powered large transport category airplane may take off that airplane, unless its weight on arrival, allowing for normal consumption of fuel and oil in flight, would allow a full stop landing at the intended destination within 60 percent of the effective length of each runway described below from a point 50 feet directly above the intersection of the obstruction clearance plane and the runway. For the purposes of determining the allowable landing weight at the destination airport the following is assumed:

(1) The airplane is landed on the most favorable runway and in the most favorable direction in still air.

(2) The airplane is landed on the most suitable runway considering the probable wind velocity and direction (forecast for the expected time of arrival), the ground handling characteristics of the type of airplane, and other conditions such as landing aids and terrain, and allowing for the effect of the landing path and roll of not more than 50 percent of the headwind component or not less than 150 percent of the tailwind component.

(b) An airplane that would be prohibited from being taken off because it could not meet paragraph (a)(2) of this section may be taken off if an alternate airport is selected that meets all of this section except that the airplane can accomplish a full stop landing within 70 percent of the effective length of the runway.

135.377 Large transport category airplanes: Reciprocating engine powered: Landing limitations: Alternate airports

No person may list an airport as an alternate airport in a flight plan unless the airplane (at the weight anticipated at the time of arrival at the airport), based on the assumptions in 135.375(a) (1) and (2), can be brought to a full stop landing within 70 percent of the effective length of the runway.

135.379 Large transport category airplanes: Turbine engine powered: Takeoff limitations

(a) No person operating a turbine engine powered large transport category airplane may take off that airplane at a weight greater than that listed in the Airplane Flight Manual for the elevation of the airport and for the ambient temperature existing at take- off.

(b) No person operating a turbine engine powered large transport category airplane certificated after August 26, 1957, but before August 30, 1959 (SR422, 422A), may take off that airplane at a weight greater than that listed in the Airplane Flight Manual for the minumum distance required for takeoff. In the case of an airplane certificated after September 30, 1958 (SR422A, 422B), the takeoff distance may include a clearway distance but the clearway distance included may notbegreaterthanone-halfofthe takeoff run.

(c) No person operating a turbine engine powered large transport category airplane certificated after August 29, 1959 (SR422B), may take off that airplane at a weight greater than that listed in the Airplane Flight Manual at which compliance with the following may be shown:

(1) The accelerate-stop distance, as defined in 25.109 of this chapter, must not exceed the length of the runway plus the length of any stopway.

(2) The takeoff distance must not exceed the length of the runway plus the length of any clearway except that the length of any clearway included must not be greater than one-half the length of the runway.

(3) The takeoff run must not be greater than the length of the runway.

(d) No person operating a turbine engine powered large transport category airplane may take off that airplane at a weight greater than that listed in the Airplane Flight Manual—

(1) For an airplane certificated after August 26, 1957, but before October 1, 1958 (SR422), that allows a takeoff path that clears all obstacles either by at least (35+0.01 D) feet vertically (D is the distance along the intended flight path from the end of the runway in feet), or by at least 200 feet horizontally within the airport boundaries and by at least 300 feet horizontally after passing the boundaries; or

(2) For an airplane certificated after September 30, 1958 (SR422A, 422B), that allows a net takeoff flight path that clears all obstacles either by a height of at least 35 feet vertically, or by at least 200 feet horizontally within the airport boundaries and by at least 300 feet horizontally after passing the boundaries.

(e) In determining maximum weights, minimum distances, and flight paths under paragraphs (a) through (d) of this section, correction must be made for the runway to be used, the elevation of the airport, the effective runway gradient, the ambient temperature and wind component at the time of takeoff, and, if operating limitations exist for the minimum distances required for takeoff from wet runways, the runway surface condition (dry or wet). Wet runway distances associated with grooved or porous friction course runways, if provided in the Airplane Flight Manual, may be used only for runways that are grooved or treated with a porous friction course (PFC) overlay, and that the operator determines are designed, constructed, and maintained in a manner acceptable to the Administrator.

(f) For the purposes of this section, it is assumed that the airplane is not banked before reaching a height of 50 feet, as shown by the takeoff path or net takeoff flight path data (as appropriate) in the Airplane Flight Manual, and after that the maximum bank is not more than 15 degrees.

(g) For the purposes of this section, the terms, takeoff distance, takeoff run, net takeoff flight path, have the same meanings as set forth in the rules under which the airplane was certificated.

[Doc. No. 16097, 43 FR 46783, Oct. 10, 1978, as amended by Amdt. 135–71, 63 FR 8321, Feb. 18, 1998]

135.381 Large transport category airplanes: Turbine engine powered: En route limitations: One engine inoperative

(a) No person operating a turbine engine powered large transport category airplane may take off that airplane at a weight, allowing for normal consumption of fuel and oil, that is greater than that which (under the approved, one engine inoperative, en route net flight path data in the Airplane Flight Manual for that airplane) will allow compliance with paragraph (a) (1) or (2) of this section, based on the ambient temperatures expected en route.

(1) There is a positive slope at an altitude of at least 1,000 feet above all terrain and obstructions within five statute miles on each side of the intended track, and, in addition, if airplane was certificated after August 29, 1958 (SR422B), there is a positive slope at 1,500 feet above the airport where the airplane is assumed to land after an engine fails.

(2) The net flight path allows the airplane to continue flight from the cruising altitude to an airport where a landing can be made under 135.387 clearing all terrain and obstructions within five statute miles of the intended track by at least 2,000 feet vertically and with a positive slope at 1,000 feet above the airport where the airplane lands after an engine fails, or, if that airplane was certificated after September 30, 1958 (SR422A, 422B), with a positive slope at 1,500 feet above the airport where the airplane lands after an engine fails.

(b) For the purpose of paragraph (a)(2) of this section, it is assumed that—

(1) The engine fails at the most critical point en route;

(2) The airplane passes over the critical obstruction, after engine failure at a point that is no closer to the obstruction than the approved navigation fix, unless the Administrator authorizes a different procedure based on adequate operational safeguards;

(3) An approved method is used to allow for adverse winds;

(4) Fuel jettisoning will be allowed if the certificate holder shows that the crew is properly instructed, that the training program is adequate, and that all other precautions are taken to ensure a safe procedure;

(5) The alternate airport is selected and meets the prescribed weather minimums; and

(6) The consumption of fuel and oil after engine failure is the same as the consumption that is allowed for in the approved net flight path data in the Airplane Flight Manual.

[Docket No. 16097, 43 FR 46783, Oct. 10, 1978, as amended by Amdt. 135–110, 72 FR 31685, June 7, 2007]

135.383 Large transport category airplanes: Turbine engine powered: En route limitations: Two engines inoperative

(a) Airplanes certificated after August 26, 1957, but before October 1, 1958 (SR422). No person may operate a turbine engine powered large transport category airplane along an intended route unless that person complies with either of the following:

(1) There is no place along the intended track that is more than 90 minutes (with all engines operating at cruising power) from an airport that meets 135.387.

(2) Its weight, according to the two-engine-inoperative, en route, net flight path data in the Airplane Flight Manual, allows the airplane to fly from the point where the two engines are assumed to fail simultaneously to an airport that meets 135.387, with a net flight path (considering the ambient temperature anticipated along the track) having a positive slope at an altitude of at least 1,000 feet above all terrain and obstructions within five statute miles on each side of the intended track, or at an altitude of 5,000 feet, whichever is higher.

For the purposes of paragraph (a)(2) of this section, it is assumed that the two engines fail at the most critical point en route, that if fuel jettisoning is provided, the airplane's weight at the point where the engines fail includes enough fuel to continue to the airport and to arrive at an altitude of at least 1,000 feet directly over the airport, and that the fuel and oil consumption after engine failure is the same as the consumption allowed for in the net flight path data in the Airplane Flight Manual.

(b) Airplanes certificated after September 30, 1958, but before August 30, 1959 (SR422A). No person may operate a turbine engine powered large transport category airplane along an intended route unless that person complies with either of the following:

(1) There is no place along the intended track that is more than 90 minutes (with all engines operating at cruising power) from an airport that meets 135.387.

(2) Its weight, according to the two-engine-inoperative, en route, net flight path data in the Airplane Flight Manual allows the airplane to fly from the point where the two engines are assumed to fail simultaneously to an airport that meets 135.387 with a net flight path (considering the ambient temperatures anticipated along the track) having a positive slope at an altitude of at least 1,000 feet above all terrain and obstructions within five statute miles on each side of the intended track, or at an altitude of 2,000 feet, whichever is higher.

For the purpose of paragraph (b)(2) of this section, it is assumed that the two engines fail at the most critical point en route, that the airplane's weight at the point where the engines fail includes enough fuel to continue to the airport, to arrive at an altitude of at least 1,500 feet directly over the airport, and after that to fly for 15 minutes at cruise power or thrust, or both, and that the consumption of fuel and oil after engine failure is the same as the consumption allowed for in the net flight path data in the Airplane Flight Manual.

(c) Aircraft certificated after August 29, 1959 (SR422B). No person may operate a turbine engine powered large transport category airplane along an intended route unless that person complies with either of the following:

(1) There is no place along the intended track that is more than 90 minutes (with all engines operating at cruising power) from an airport that meets 135.387.

(2) Its weight, according to the two-engine-inoperative, en route, net flight path data in the Airplane Flight Manual, allows the airplane to fly from the point where the two engines are assumed to fail simultaneously to an airport that meets 135.387, with the net flight path (considering the ambient temperatures anticipated along the track) clearing vertically by at least 2,000 feet all terrain and obstructions within five statute miles on each side of the intended track. For the purposes of this paragraph, it is assumed that—

(i) The two engines fail at the most critical point en route;

FAR 135

(ii) The net flight path has a positive slope at 1,500 feet above the airport where the landing is assumed to be made after the engines fail;

(iii) Fuel jettisoning will be approved if the certificate holder shows that the crew is properly instructed, that the training program is adequate, and that all other precautions are taken to ensure a safe procedure;

(iv) The airplane's weight at the point where the two engines are assumed to fail provides enough fuel to continue to the airport, to arrive at an altitude of at least 1,500 feet directly over the airport, and after that to fly for 15 minutes at cruise power or thrust, or both; and

(v) The consumption of fuel and oil after the engines fail is the same as the consumption that is allowed for in the net flight path data in the Airplane Flight Manual.

135.385   Large transport category airplanes: Turbine engine powered: Landing limitations: Destination airports

(a) No person operating a turbine engine powered large transport category airplane may take off that airplane at a weight that (allowing for normal consumption of fuel and oil in flight to the destination or alternate airport) the weight of the airplane on arrival would exceed the landing weight in the Airplane Flight Manual for the elevation of the destination or alternate airport and the ambient temperature anticipated at the time of landing.

(b) Except as provided in paragraph (c), (d), (e), or (f) of this section, no person operating a turbine engine powered large transport category airplane may take off that airplane unless its weight on arrival, allowing for normal consumption of fuel and oil in flight (in accordance with the landing distance in the Airplane Flight Manual for the elevation of the destination airport and the wind conditions expected there at the time of landing), would allow a full stop landing at the intended destination airport within 60 percent of the effective length of each runway described below from a point 50 feet above the intersection of the obstruction clearance plane and the runway. For the purpose of determining the allowable landing weight at the destination airport the following is assumed:

(1) The airplane is landed on the most favorable runway and in the most favorable direction, in still air.

(2) The airplane is landed on the most suitable runway considering the probable wind velocity and direction and the ground handling characteristics of the airplane, and considering other conditions such as landing aids and terrain.

(c) A turbopropeller powered airplane that would be prohibited from being taken off because it could not meet paragraph (b)(2) of this section, may be taken off if an alternate airport is selected that meets all of this section except that the airplane can accomplish a full stop landing within 70 percent of the effective length of the runway.

(d) Unless, based on a showing of actual operating landing techniques on wet runways, a shorter landing distance (but never less than that required by paragraph (b) of this section) has been approved for a specific type and model airplane and included in the Airplane Flight Manual, no person may take off a turbojet airplane when the appropriate weather reports or forecasts, or any combination of them, indicate that the runways at the destination airport may be wet or slippery at the estimated time of arrival unless the effective runway length at the destination airport is at least 115 percent of the runway length required under paragraph (b) of this section.

(e) A turbojet airplane that would be prohibited from being taken off because it could not meet paragraph (b)(2) of this section may be taken off if an alternate airport is selected that meets all of paragraph (b) of this section.

(f) An eligible on-demand operator may take off a turbine engine powered large transport category airplane on an on-demand flight if all of the following conditions exist:

(1) The operation is permitted by an approved Destination Airport Analysis in that person's operations manual.

(2) The airplane's weight on arrival, allowing for normal consumption of fuel and oil in flight (in accordance with the landing distance in the Airplane Flight Manual for the elevation of the destination airport and the wind conditions expected there at the time of landing), would allow a full stop landing at the intended destination airport within 80 percent of the effective length of each runway described below from a point 50 feet above the intersection of the obstruction clearance plane and the runway. For the purpose of determining the allowable landing weight at the destination airport, the following is assumed:

(i) The airplane is landed on the most favorable runway and in the most favorable direction, in still air.

(ii) The airplane is landed on the most suitable runway considering the probable wind velocity and direction and the ground handling characteristics of the airplane, and considering other conditions such as landing aids and terrain.

(3) The operation is authorized by operations specifications.

[Doc. No. 16097, 43 FR 46783, Oct. 10, 1978, as amended by Amdt. 135–91, 68 FR 54588, Sept. 17, 2003]

135.387   Large transport category airplanes: Turbine engine powered: Landing limitations: Alternate airports

(a) Except as provided in paragraph (b) of this section, no person may select an airport as an alternate airport for a turbine engine powered large transport category airplane unless (based on the assumptions in 135.385(b)) that airplane, at the weight expected at the time of arrival, can be brought to a full stop landing within 70 percent of the effective length of the runway for turbo-propeller-powered airplanes and 60 percent of the effective length of the runway for turbojet airplanes, from a point 50 feet above the intersection of the obstruction clearance plane and the runway.

(b) Eligible on-demand operators may select an airport as an alternate airport for a turbine engine powered large transport category airplane if (based on the assumptions in 135.385(f)) that airplane, at the weight expected at the time of arrival, can be brought to a full stop landing within 80 percent of the effective length of the runway from a point 50 feet above the intersection of the obstruction clearance plane and the runway.

[Doc. No. FAA–2001–10047, 68 FR 54588, Sept. 17, 2003]

135.389   Large nontransport category airplanes: Takeoff limitations

(a) No person operating a large nontransport category airplane may take off that airplane at a weight greater than the weight that would allow the airplane to be brought to a safe stop within the effective length of the runway, from any point during the takeoff before reaching 105 percent of minimum control speed (the minimum speed at which an airplane can be safely controlled in flight after an engine becomes inoperative) or 115 percent of the power off stalling speed in the takeoff configuration, whichever is greater.

(b) For the purposes of this section—

(1) It may be assumed that takeoff power is used on all engines during the acceleration;

(2) Not more than 50 percent of the reported headwind component, or not less than 150 percent of the reported tailwind component, may be taken into account;

(3) The average runway gradient (the difference between the elevations of the endpoints of the runway divided by the total length) must be considered if it is more than one-half of one percent;

(4) It is assumed that the airplane is operating in standard atmosphere; and

(5) For takeoff, effective length of the runway means the distance from the end of the runway at which the takeoff is started to a point at which the obstruction clearance plane associated with the other end of the runway intersects the runway centerline.

135.391 Large nontransport category airplanes: En route limitations: One engine inoperative

(a) Except as provided in paragraph (b) of this section, no person operating a large nontransport category airplane may take off that airplane at a weight that does not allow a rate of climb of at least 50 feet a minute, with the critical engine inoperative, at an altitude of at least 1,000 feet above the highest obstruction within five miles on each side of the intended track, or 5,000 feet, whichever is higher.

(b) Without regard to paragraph (a) of this section, if the Administrator finds that safe operations are not impaired, a person may operate the airplane at an altitude that allows the airplane, in case of engine failure, to clear all obstructions within five miles on each side of the intended track by 1,000 feet. If this procedure is used, the rate of descent for the appropriate weight and altitude is assumed to be 50 feet a minute greater than the rate in the approved performance data. Before approving such a procedure, the Administrator considers the following for the route, route segement, or area concerned:

(1) The reliability of wind and weather forecasting.

(2) The location and kinds of navigation aids.

(3) The prevailing weather conditions, particularly the frequency and amount of turbulence normally encountered.

(4) Terrain features.

(5) Air traffic problems.

(6) Any other operational factors that affect the operations.

(c) For the purposes of this section, it is assumed that—

(1) The critical engine is inoperative;

(2) The propeller of the inoperative engine is in the minimum drag position;

(3) The wing flaps and landing gear are in the most favorable position;

(4) The operating engines are operating at the maximum continuous power available;

(5) The airplane is operating in standard atmosphere; and

(6) The weight of the airplane is progressively reduced by the anticipated consumption of fuel and oil.

135.393 Large nontransport category airplanes: Landing limitations: Destination airports

(a) No person operating a large nontransport category airplane may take off that airplane at a weight that—

(1) Allowing for anticipated consumption of fuel and oil, is greater than the weight that would allow a full stop landing within 60 percent of the effective length of the most suitable runway at the destination airport; and

(2) Is greater than the weight allowable if the landing is to be made on the runway—

(i) With the greatest effective length in still air; and

(ii) Required by the probable wind, taking into account not more than 50 percent of the headwind component or not less than 150 percent of the tailwind component.

(b) For the purpose of this section, it is assumed that—

(1) The airplane passes directly over the intersection of the obstruction clearance plane and the runway at a height of 50 feet in a steady gliding approach at a true indicated airspeed of at least 1.3 V_{so};

(2) The landing does not require exceptional pilot skill; and

(3) The airplane is operating in standard atmosphere.

135.395 Large nontransport category airplanes: Landing limitations: Alternate airports

No person may select an airport as an alternate airport for a large nontransport category airplane unless that airplane (at the weight anticipated at the time of arrival), based on the assumptions in 135.393(b), can be brought to a full stop landing within 70 percent of the effective length of the runway.

135.397 Small transport category airplane performance operating limitations

(a) No person may operate a reciprocating engine powered small trans-port category airplane unless that person complies with the weight limitations in 135.365, the takeoff limitations in 135.367 (except paragraph (a)(3)), and the landing limitations in 135.375 and 135.377.

(b) No person may operate a turbine engine powered small transport category airplane unless that person complies with the takeoff limitations in 135.379 (except paragraphs (d) and (f)) and the landing limitations in 135.385 and 135.387.

135.398 Commuter category airplanes performance operating limitations

(a) No person may operate a commuter category airplane unless that person complies with the takeoff weight limitations in the approved Airplane Flight Manual.

(b) No person may take off an airplane type certificated in the commuter category at a weight greater than that listed in the Airplane Flight Manual that allows a net takeoff flight path that clears all obstacles either by a height of at least 35 feet vertically, or at least 200 feet horizontally within the airport boundaries and by at least 300 feet horizontally after passing the boundaries.

(c) No person may operate a commuter category airplane unless that person complies with the landing limitations prescribed in 135.385 and 135.387 of this part. For purposes of this paragraph, 135.385 and 135.387 are applicable to all commuter category airplanes notwithstanding their stated applicability to turbine-engine-powered large transport category airplanes.

(d) In determining maximum weights, minimum distances and flight paths under paragraphs (a) through (c) of this section, correction must be made for the runway to be used, the elevation of the airport, the effective runway gradient, and ambient temperature, and wind component at the time of takeoff.

(e) For the purposes of this section, the assumption is that the airplane is not banked before reaching a height of 50 feet as shown by the net takeoff flight path data in the Airplane Flight Manual and thereafter the maximum bank is not more than 15 degrees.

[Doc. No. 23516, 52 FR 1836, Jan. 15, 1987]

135.399 Small nontransport category airplane performance operating limitations

(a) No person may operate a reciprocating engine or turbopropeller-powered small airplane that is certificated under 135.169(b) (2), (3), (4), (5), or (6) unless that person complies with the takeoff weight limitations in the approved Airplane Flight Manual or equivalent for operations under this part, and, if the airplane is certificated under 135.169(b) (4) or (5) with the landing weight limitations in the Approved Airplane Flight Manual or equivalent for operations under this part.

(b) No person may operate an airplane that is certificated under 135.169(b)(6) unless that person complies with the landing limitations prescribed in 135.385 and 135.387 of this part. For purposes of this paragraph, 135.385 and 135.387 are applicable to reciprocating and turbopropeller-powered small airplanes notwithstanding their stated applicability to turbine engine powered large transport category airplanes.

[44 FR 53731, Sept. 17, 1979]

Subpart J — Maintenance, Preventive Maintenance, and Alterations

135.411 Applicability

(a) This subpart prescribes rules in addition to those in other parts of this chapter for the maintenance, preventive maintenance, and alterations for each certificate holder as follows:

(1) Aircraft that are type certificated for a passenger seating configuration, excluding any pilot seat, of nine seats or less, shall be maintained under parts 91 and 43 of this chapter and 135.415, 135.417, 135.421 and 135.422. An approved aircraft inspection program may be used under 135.419.

(2) Aircraft that are type certificated for a passenger seating configuration, excluding any pilot seat, of ten seats or more, shall be maintained under a maintenance program in 135.415, 135.417, 135.423 through 135.443.

(b) A certificate holder who is not otherwise required, may elect to maintain its aircraft under paragraph (a)(2) of this section.

(c) Single engine aircraft used in passenger-carrying IFR operations shall also be maintained in accordance with 135.421 (c), (d), and (e).

(d) A certificate holder who elects to operate in accordance with 135.364 must maintain its aircraft under paragraph (a)(2) of this section and the additional requirements of Appendix G of this part.

[Doc. No. 16097, 43 FR 46783, Oct. 10, 1978, as amended by Amdt. 135–70, 62 FR 42374, Aug. 6, 1997; Amdt. 135–78, 65 FR 60556, Oct. 11, 2000; Amdt. 135–92, 68 FR 69308, Dec. 12, 2003; Amdt. 135–81, 70 FR 5533, Feb. 2, 2005; Amdt. 135–108, 72 FR 1885, Jan. 16, 2007; 72 FR 53114, Sept. 18, 2007]

135.413 Responsibility for airworthiness

(a) Each certificate holder is primarily responsible for the airworthiness of its aircraft, including airframes, aircraft engines, propellers, rotors, appliances, and parts, and shall have its aircraft maintained under this chapter, and shall have defects repaired between required maintenance under part 43 of this chapter.

(b) Each certificate holder who maintains its aircraft under 135.411(a)(2) shall—

(1) Perform the maintenance, preventive maintenance, and alteration of its aircraft, including airframe, aircraft engines, propellers, rotors, appliances, emergency equipment and parts, under its manual and this chapter; or

(2) Make arrangements with another person for the performance of maintenance, preventive maintenance, or alteration. However, the certificate holder shall ensure that any maintenance, preventive maintenance, or alteration that is performed by another person is performed under the certificate holder's manual and this chapter.

135.415 Service difficulty reports

(a) Each certificate holder shall report the occurrence or detection of each failure, malfunction, or defect in an aircraft concerning—

(1) Fires during flight and whether the related fire-warning system functioned properly;

(2) Fires during flight not protected by related fire-warning system;

(3) False fire-warning during flight;

(4) An exhaust system that causes damage during flight to the engine, adjacent structure, equipment, or components;

(5) An aircraft component that causes accumulation or circulation of smoke, vapor, or toxic or noxious fumes in the crew compartment or passenger cabin during flight;

(6) Engine shutdown during flight because of flameout;

(7) Engine shutdown during flight when external damage to the engine or aircraft structure occurs;

(8) Engine shutdown during flight due to foreign object ingestion or icing;

(9) Shutdown of more than one engine during flight;

(10) A propeller feathering system or ability of the system to control overspeed during flight;

(11) A fuel or fuel-dumping system that affects fuel flow or causes hazardous leakage during flight;

(12) An unwanted landing gear extension or retraction or opening or closing of landing gear doors during flight;

(13) Brake system components that result in loss of brake actuating force when the aircraft is in motion on the ground;

(14) Aircraft structure that requires major repair;

(15) Cracks, permanent deformation, or corrosion of aircraft structures, if more than the maximum acceptable to the manufacturer or the FAA; and

(16) Aircraft components or systems that result in taking emergency actions during flight (except action to shut-down an engine).

(b) For the purpose of this section, during flight means the period from the moment the aircraft leaves the surface of the earth on takeoff until it touches down on landing.

(c) In addition to the reports required by paragraph (a) of this section, each certificate holder shall report any other failure, malfunction, or defect in an aircraft that occurs or is detected at any time if, in its opinion, the failure, malfunction, or defect has endangered or may endanger the safe operation of the aircraft.

(d) Each certificate holder shall submit each report required by this section, covering each 24-hour period beginning at 0900 local time of each day and ending at 0900 local time on the next day, to the FAA offices in Oklahoma City, Oklahoma. Each report of occurrences during a 24-hour period shall be submitted to the collection point within the next 96 hours. However, a report due on Saturday or Sunday may be submitted on the following Monday, and a report due on a holiday may be submitted on the next workday.

(e) The certificate holder shall transmit the reports required by this section on a form and in a manner prescribed by the Administrator, and shall include as much of the following as is available:

(1) The type and identification number of the aircraft.

(2) The name of the operator.

(3) The date.

(4) The nature of the failure, malfunction, or defect.

(5) Identification of the part and system involved, including available information pertaining to type designation of the major component and time since last overhaul, if known.

(6) Apparent cause of the failure, malfunction or defect (e.g., wear, crack, design deficiency, or personnel error).

(7) Other pertinent information necessary for more complete identification, determination of seriousness, or corrective action.

(f) A certificate holder that is also the holder of a type certificate (including a supplemental type certificate), a Parts Manufacturer Approval, or a Technical Standard Order Authorization, or that is the licensee of a type certificate need not report a failure, malfunction, or defect under this section if the failure, malfunction, or defect has been reported by it under 21.3 or 37.17 of this chapter or under the accident reporting provisions of part 830 of the regulations of the National Transportation Safety Board.

(g) No person may withhold a report required by this section even though all information required by this section is not available.

(h) When the certificate holder gets additional information, including information from the manufacturer or other agency, concerning a report required by this section, it shall expeditiously submit it as a supplement to the first report and reference the date and place of submission of the first report.

[Doc. No. 16097, 43 FR 46783, Oct. 10, 1978, as amended by Amdt. 135–102, 70 FR 76979, Dec. 29, 2005]

135.417 Mechanical interruption summary report

Each certificate holder shall mail or deliver, before the end of the

10th day of the following month, a summary report of the following occurrences in multiengine aircraft for the preceding month to the responsible Flight Standards office:

(a) Each interruption to a flight, unscheduled change of aircraft en route, or unscheduled stop or diversion from a route, caused by known or suspected mechanical difficulties or malfunctions that are not required to be reported under 135.415.

(b) The number of propeller featherings in flight, listed by type of propeller and engine and aircraft on which it was installed. Propeller featherings for training, demonstration, or flight check purposes need not be reported.

[Doc. No. 16097, 43 FR 46783, Oct. 10, 1978, as amended by Amdt. 135–60, 61 FR 2616, Jan. 26, 1996]

135.419   Approved aircraft inspection program

(a) Whenever the Administrator finds that the aircraft inspections required or allowed under part 91 of this chapter are not adequate to meet this part, or upon application by a certificate holder, the Administrator may amend the certificate holder's operations specifications under 119.51, to require or allow an approved aircraft inspection program for any make and model aircraft of which the certificate holder has the exclusive use of at least one aircraft (as defined in 135.25(b)).

(b) A certificate holder who applies for an amendment of its operations specifications to allow an approved aircraft inspection program must submit that program with its application for approval by the Administrator.

(c) Each certificate holder who is required by its operations specifications to have an approved aircraft inspection program shall submit a program for approval by the Administrator within 30 days of the amendment of its operations specifications or within any other period that the Administrator may prescribe in the operations specifications.

(d) The aircraft inspection program submitted for approval by the Administrator must contain the following:

(1) Instructions and procedures for the conduct of aircraft inspections (which must include necessary tests and checks), setting forth in detail the parts and areas of the airframe, engines, propellers, rotors, and appliances, including emergency equipment, that must be inspected.

(2) A schedule for the performance of the aircraft inspections under paragraph (d)(1) of this section expressed in terms of the time in service, calendar time, number of system operations, or any combination of these.

(3) Instructions and procedures for recording discrepancies found during inspections and correction or deferral of discrepancies including form and disposition of records.

(e) After approval, the certificate holder shall include the approved aircraft inspection program in the manual required by 135.21.

(f) Whenever the Administrator finds that revisions to an approved aircraft inspection program are necessary for the continued adequacy of the program, the certificate holder shall, after notification by the Administrator, make any changes in the program found by the Administrator to be necessary. The certificate holder may petition the Administrator to reconsider the notice to make any changes in a program. The petition must be filed with the representatives of the Administrator assigned to it within 30 days after the certificate holder receives the notice. Except in the case of an emergency requiring immediate action in the interest of safety, the filing of the petition stays the notice pending a decision by the Administrator.

(g) Each certificate holder who has an approved aircraft inspection program shall have each aircraft that is subject to the program inspected in accordance with the program.

(h) The registration number of each aircraft that is subject to an approved aircraft inspection program must be included in the operations specifications of the certificate holder.

[Doc. No. 16097, 43 FR 46783, Oct. 10, 1978, as amended by Amdt. 135–104, 71 FR 536, Jan. 4, 2006]

135.421   Additional maintenance requirements

(a) Each certificate holder who operates an aircraft type certificated for a passenger seating configuration, excluding any pilot seat, of nine seats or less, must comply with the manufacturer's recommended maintenance programs, or a program approved by the Administrator, for each aircraft engine, propeller, rotor, and each item of emergency equipment required by this chapter.

(b) For the purpose of this section, a manufacturer's maintenance program is one which is contained in the maintenance manual or maintenance instructions set forth by the manufacturer as required by this chapter for the aircraft, aircraft engine, propeller, rotor or item of emergency equipment.

(c) For each single engine aircraft to be used in passenger-carrying IFR operations, each certificate holder must incorporate into its maintenance program either:

(1) The manufacturer's recommended engine trend monitoring program, which includes an oil analysis, if appropriate, or

(2) An FAA approved engine trend monitoring program that includes an oil analysis at each 100 hour interval or at the manufacturer's suggested interval, whichever is more frequent.

(d) For single engine aircraft to be used in passenger-carrying IFR operations, written maintenance instructions containing the methods, techniques, and practices necessary to maintain the equipment specified in 135.105, and 135.163 (f) and (h) are required.

(e) No certificate holder may operate a single engine aircraft under IFR, carrying passengers, unless the certificate holder records and maintains in the engine maintenance records the results of each test, observation, and inspection required by the applicable engine trend monitoring program specified in (c) (1) and (2) of this section.

[Doc. No. 16097, 43 FR 46783, Oct. 10, 1978, as amended by Amdt. 135–70, 62 FR 42374, Aug. 6, 1997]

135.422   Aging airplane inspections and records reviews for multiengine airplanes certificated with nine or fewer passenger seats

(a) Applicability. This section applies to multiengine airplanes certificated with nine or fewer passenger seats, operated by a certificate holder in a scheduled operation under this part, except for those airplanes operated by a certificate holder in a scheduled operation between any point within the State of Alaska and any other point within the State of Alaska.

(b) Operation after inspections and records review. After the dates specified in this paragraph, a certificate holder may not operate a multiengine airplane in a scheduled operation under this part unless the Administrator has notified the certificate holder that the Administrator has completed the aging airplane inspection and records review required by this section. During the inspection and records review, the certificate holder must demonstrate to the Administrator that the maintenance of age-sensitive parts and components of the airplane has been adequate and timely enough to ensure the highest degree of safety.

(1) Airplanes exceeding 24 years in service on December 8, 2003; initial and repetitive inspections and records reviews. For an airplane that has exceeded 24 years in service on December 8, 2003, no later than December 5, 2007, and thereafter at intervals not to exceed 7 years.

(2) Airplanes exceeding 14 years in service but not 24 years in service on December 8, 2003; initial and repetitive inspections and records reviews. For an airplane that has exceeded 14 years in service, but not 24 years in service, on December 8, 2003, no later than December 4, 2008, and thereafter at intervals not to exceed 7 years.

(3) Airplanes not exceeding 14 years in service on December 8, 2003; initial and repetitive inspections and records reviews. For an airplane that has not exceeded 14 years in service on December 8, 2003, no later than 5 years after the start of the airplane's 15th year in service and thereafter at intervals not to exceed 7 years.

(c) Unforeseen schedule conflict. In the event of an unforeseen scheduling conflict for a specific airplane, the Administrator may approve an extension of up to 90 days beyond an interval specified in paragraph (b) of this section.

(d) Airplane and records availability. The certificate holder must make available to the Administrator each airplane for which an inspection and records review is required under this section, in a condition for inspection specified by the Administrator, together with the records containing the following information:

(1) Total years in service of the airplane;

(2) Total time in service of the airframe;

(3) Date of the last inspection and records review required by this section;

(4) Current status of life-limited parts of the airframe;

(5) Time since the last overhaul of all structural components required to be overhauled on a specific time basis;

(6) Current inspection status of the airplane, including the time since the last inspection required by the inspection program under which the airplane is maintained;

(7) Current status of applicable airworthiness directives, including the date and methods of compliance, and, if the airworthiness directive involves recurring action, the time and date when the next action is required;

(8) A list of major structural alterations; and

(9) A report of major structural repairs and the current inspection status for these repairs.

(e) Notification to the Administrator. Each certificate holder must notify the Administrator at least 60 days before the date on which the airplane and airplane records will be made available for the inspection and records review.

[Doc. No. FAA–1999–5401, 70 FR 5533, Feb. 2, 2005]

135.423   Maintenance, preventive maintenance, and alteration organization

(a) Each certificate holder that performs any of its maintenance (other than required inspections), preventive maintenance, or alterations, and each person with whom it arranges for the performance of that work, must have an organization adequate to perform the work.

(b) Each certificate holder that performs any inspections required by its manual under 135.427(b) (2) or (3), (in this subpart referred to as required inspections), and each person with whom it arranges for the performance of that work, must have an organization adequate to perform that work.

(c) Each person performing required inspections in addition to other maintenance, preventive maintenance, or alterations, shall organize the performance of those functions so as to separate the required inspection functions from the other maintenance, preventive maintenance, and alteration functions. The separation shall be below the level of administrative control at which overall responsibility for the required inspection functions and other maintenance, preventive maintenance, and alteration functions is exercised.

[Doc. No. 16097, 43 FR 46783, Oct. 10, 1978. Redesignated by Amdt. 135–81, 67 FR 72765, Dec. 6, 2002. Redesignated by Amdt. 135–81, 70 FR 5533, Feb. 2, 2005]

135.425   Maintenance, preventive maintenance, and alteration programs

Each certificate holder shall have an inspection program and a program covering other maintenance, preventive maintenance, and alterations, that ensures that—

(a) Maintenance, preventive maintenance, and alterations performed by it, or by other persons, are performed under the certificate holder's manual;

(b) Competent personnel and adequate facilities and equipment are provided for the proper performance of maintenance, preventive maintenance, and alterations; and

(c) Each aircraft released to service is airworthy and has been properly maintained for operation under this part.

135.426   Contract maintenance

(a) A certificate holder may arrange with another person for the performance of maintenance, preventive maintenance, and alterations as authorized in 135.437(a) only if the certificate holder has met all the requirements in this section. For purposes of this section—

(1) maintenance provider is any person who performs maintenance, preventive maintenance, or an alteration for a certificate holder other than a person who is trained by and employed directly by that certificate holder.

(2) Covered work means any of the following:

(i) Essential maintenance that could result in a failure, malfunction, or defect endangering the safe operation of an aircraft if not performed properly or if improper parts or materials are used;

(ii) Regularly scheduled maintenance; or

(iii) A required inspection item on an aircraft.

(3) Directly in charge means having responsibility for covered work performed by a maintenance provider. A representative of the certificate holder directly in charge of covered work does not need to physically observe and direct each maintenance provider constantly, but must be available for consultation on matters requiring instruction or decision.

(b) Each certificate holder must be directly in charge of all covered work done for it by a maintenance provider.

(c) Each maintenance provider must perform all covered work in accordance with the certificate holder's maintenance manual.

(d) No maintenance provider may perform covered work unless that work is carried out under the supervision and control of the certificate holder.

(e) Each certificate holder who contracts for maintenance, preventive maintenance, or alterations must develop and implement policies, procedures, methods, and instructions for the accomplishment of all contracted maintenance, preventive maintenance, and alterations. These policies, procedures, methods, and instructions must provide for the maintenance, preventive maintenance, and alterations to be performed in accordance with the certificate holder's maintenance program and maintenance manual.

(f) Each certificate holder who contracts for maintenance, preventive maintenance, or alterations must ensure that its system for the continuing analysis and surveillance of the maintenance preventive maintenance, and alterations carried out by a maintenance provider, as required by 135.431(a), contains procedures for oversight of all contracted covered work.

(g) The policies, procedures, methods, and instructions required by paragraphs (e) and (f) of this section must be acceptable to the FAA and included in the certificate holder's maintenance manual as required by 135.427(b)(10).

(h) Each certificate holder who contracts for maintenance, preventive maintenance, or alterations must provide to its responsible Flight Standards office, in a format acceptable to the FAA, a list that includes the name and physical (street) address, or addresses where the work is carried out for each maintenance provider that performs work for the certificate holder, and a description of the type of maintenance, preventive maintenance, or alteration that is to be performed at each location. The list must be updated with any changes, including additions or deletions, and the updated list provided to the FAA in a format acceptable to the FAA by the last day of each calendar month.

[Docket FAA-2011-1136, Amdt. 135-132, 80 FR 11547, Mar. 4 2015, as amended by Docket FAA-2018-0119, Amdt. 135-139, 83 FR 9175, Mar. 5, 2018]

135.427 Manual requirements

a) Each certificate holder shall put in its manual the chart or description of the certificate holder's organization required by 135.423 and a list of persons with whom it has arranged for the performance of any of its required inspections, other maintenance, preventive maintenance, or alterations, including a general description of that work.

b) Each certificate holder shall put in its manual the programs required by 135.425 that must be followed in performing maintenance, preventive maintenance, and alterations of that certificate holder's aircraft, including airframes, aircraft engines, propellers, rotors, appliances, emergency equipment, and parts, and must include at least the following:

(1) The method of performing routine and nonroutine maintenance (other than required inspections), preventive maintenance, and alterations.

(2) A designation of the items of maintenance and alteration that must be inspected (required inspections) including at least those that could result in a failure, malfunction, or defect endangering the safe operation of the aircraft, if not performed properly or if improper parts or materials are used.

(3) The method of performing required inspections and a designation by occupational title of personnel authorized to perform each required inspection.

(4) Procedures for the reinspection of work performed under previous required inspection findings (buy-back procedures).

(5) Procedures, standards, and limits necessary for required inspections and acceptance or rejection of the items required to be inspected and for periodic inspection and calibration of precision tools, measuring devices, and test equipment.

(6) Procedures to ensure that all required inspections are performed.

(7) Instructions to prevent any person who performs any item of work from performing any required inspection of that work.

(8) Instructions and procedures to prevent any decision of an inspector regarding any required inspection from being countermanded by persons other than supervisory personnel of the inspection unit, or a person at the level of administrative control that has overall responsibility for the management of both the required inspection functions and the other maintenance, preventive maintenance, and alterations functions.

(9) Procedures to ensure that required inspections, other maintenance, preventive maintenance, and alterations that are not completed as a result of work interruptions are properly completed before the aircraft is released to service.

(10) Policies, procedures, methods, and instructions for the accomplishment of all maintenance, preventive maintenance, and alterations carried out by a maintenance provider. These policies, procedures, methods, and instructions must be acceptable to the FAA and ensure that, when followed by the maintenance provider, the maintenance, preventive maintenance, and alterations are performed in accordance with the certificate holder's maintenance program and maintenance manual.

c) Each certificate holder shall put in its manual a suitable system (which may include a coded system) that provides for the retention of the following information—

(1) A description (or reference to data acceptable to the Administrator) of the work performed;

(2) The name of the person performing the work if the work is performed by a person outside the organization of the certificate holder; and

(3) The name or other positive identification of the individual approving the work.

d) For the purposes of this part, the certificate holder must prepare that part of its manual containing maintenance information and instructions, in whole or in part, in printed form or other form, acceptable to the Administrator, that is retrievable in the English language.

[Doc. No. 16097, 43 FR 46783, Oct. 10, 1978, as amended by Amdt. 135-66, 62 FR 13257, Mar. 19, 1997; 69 FR 18472, Apr. 8, 2004; Amdt. 135-118, 74 FR 38522, Aug. 4, 2009; Docket FAA-2011-1136, Amdt. 135-132, 80 FR 11547, Mar. 4, 2015]

135.429 Required inspection personnel

(a) No person may use any person to perform required inspections unless the person performing the inspection is appropriately certificated, properly trained, qualified, and authorized to do so.

(b) No person may allow any person to perform a required inspection unless, at the time, the person performing that inspection is under the supervision and control of an inspection unit.

(c) No person may perform a required inspection if that person performed the item of work required to be inspected.

(d) In the case of rotorcraft that operate in remote areas or sites, the Administrator may approve procedures for the performance of required inspection items by a pilot when no other qualified person is available, provided—

(1) The pilot is employed by the certificate holder;

(2) It can be shown to the satisfaction of the Administrator that each pilot authorized to perform required inspections is properly trained and qualified;

(3) The required inspection is a result of a mechanical interruption and is not a part of a certificate holder's continuous airworthiness maintenance program;

(4) Each item is inspected after each flight until the item has been inspected by an appropriately certificated mechanic other than the one who originally performed the item of work; and

(5) Each item of work that is a required inspection item that is part of the flight control system shall be flight tested and reinspected before the aircraft is approved for return to service.

(e) Each certificate holder shall maintain, or shall determine that each person with whom it arranges to perform its required inspections maintains, a current listing of persons who have been trained, qualified, and authorized to conduct required inspections. The persons must be identified by name, occupational title and the inspections that they are authorized to perform. The certificate holder (or person with whom it arranges to perform its required inspections) shall give written information to each person so authorized, describing the extent of that person's responsibilities, authorities, and inspectional limitations. The list shall be made available for inspection by the Administrator upon request.

[Doc. No. 16097, 43 FR 46783, Oct. 10, 1978, as amended by Amdt. 135–20, 51 FR 40710, Nov. 7, 1986]

135.431 Continuing analysis and surveillance

(a) Each certificate holder shall establish and maintain a system for the continuing analysis and surveillance of the performance and effectiveness of its inspection program and the program covering other maintenance, preventive maintenance, and alterations and for the correction of any deficiency in those programs, regardless of whether those programs are carried out by the certificate holder or by another person.

(b) Whenever the Administrator finds that either or both of the programs described in paragraph (a) of this section does not contain adequate procedures and standards to meet this part, the certificate holder shall, after notification by the Administrator, make changes in those programs requested by the Administrator.

(c) A certificate holder may petition the Administrator to reconsider the notice to make a change in a program. The petition must be filed with the responsible Flight Standards office within 30 days after the certificate holder receives the notice. Except in the case of an emergency requiring immediate action in the interest of safety, the filing of the petition stays the notice pending a decision by the Administrator.

[Doc. No. 16097, 43 FR 46783, Oct. 10, 1978, as amended by Amdt. 135-60, 61 FR 2617, Jan. 26, 1996; Docket FAA-2018-0119, Amdt. 135-139, 83 FR 9175, Mar. 5, 2018]

FAR 135

135.433 Maintenance and preventive maintenance training program

Each certificate holder or a person performing maintenance or preventive maintenance functions for it shall have a training program to ensure that each person (including inspection personnel) who determines the adequacy of work done is fully informed about procedures and techniques and new equipment in use and is competent to perform that person's duties.

135.435 Certificate requirements

(a) Except for maintenance, preventive maintenance, alterations, and required inspections performed by a certificated repair station that is located outside the United States, each person who is directly in charge of maintenance, preventive maintenance, or alterations, and each person performing required inspections must hold an appropriate airman certificate.

(b) For the purpose of this section, a person directly in charge is each person assigned to a position in which that person is responsible for the work of a shop or station that performs maintenance, preventive maintenance, alterations, or other functions affecting airworthiness. A person who is directly in charge need not physically observe and direct each worker constantly but must be available for consultation and decision on matters requiring instruction or decision from higher authority than that of the person performing the work.

[Doc. No. 16097, 43 FR 46783, Oct. 10, 1978, as amended by Amdt. 135–82, 66 FR 41117, Aug. 6, 2001]

135.437 Authority to perform and approve maintenance, preventive maintenance, and alterations

(a) A certificate holder may perform or make arrangements with other persons to perform maintenance, preventive maintenance, and alterations as provided in its maintenance manual. In addition, a certificate holder may perform these functions for another certificate holder as provided in the maintenance manual of the other certificate holder.

(b) A certificate holder may approve any airframe, aircraft engine, propeller, rotor, or appliance for return to service after maintenance, preventive maintenance, or alterations that are performed under paragraph (a) of this section. However, in the case of a major repair or alteration, the work must have been done in accordance with technical data approved by the Administrator.

135.439 Maintenance recording requirements

(a) Each certificate holder shall keep (using the system specified in the manual required in 135.427) the following records for the periods specified in paragraph (b) of this section:

(1) All the records necessary to show that all requirements for the issuance of an airworthiness release under 135.443 have been met.

(2) Records containing the following information:

    (i)   The total time in service of the airframe, engine, propeller, and rotor.

    (ii)   The current status of life-limited parts of each airframe, engine, propeller, rotor, and appliance.

    (iii)   The time since last overhaul of each item installed on the aircraft which are required to be overhauled on a specified time basis.

    (iv)   The identification of the current inspection status of the aircraft, including the time since the last inspections required by the inspection program under which the aircraft and its appliances are maintained.

    (v)   The current status of applicable airworthiness directives, including the date and methods of compliance, and, if the airworthiness directive involves recurring action, the time and date when the next action is required.

    (vi)   A list of current major alterations and repairs to each airframe, engine, propeller, rotor, and appliance.

(b) Each certificate holder shall retain the records required to be kept by this section for the following periods:

(1) Except for the records of the last complete overhaul of each airframe, engine, propeller, rotor, and appliance the records specified in paragraph (a)(1) of this section shall be retained until the work is repeated or superseded by other work or for one year after the work is performed.

(2) The records of the last complete overhaul of each airframe, engine, propeller, rotor, and appliance shall be retained until the work is superseded by work of equivalent scope and detail.

(3) The records specified in paragraph (a)(2) of this section shall be retained and transferred with the aircraft at the time the aircraft is sold.

(c) The certificate holder shall make all maintenance records required to be kept by this section available for inspection by the Administrator or any representative of the National Transportation Safety Board.

[Doc. No. 16097, 43 FR 46783, Oct. 10, 1978; 43 FR 49975, Oct. 26, 1978]

135.441 Transfer of maintenance records

Each certificate holder who sells a United States registered aircraft shall transfer to the purchaser, at the time of the sale, the following records of that aircraft, in plain language form or in coded form which provides for the preservation and retrieval of information in a manner acceptable to the Administrator:

(a) The records specified in 135.439(a)(2).

(b) The records specified in 135.439(a)(1) which are not included in the records covered by paragraph (a) of this section, except that the purchaser may allow the seller to keep physical custody of such records. However, custody of records by the seller does not relieve the purchaser of its responsibility under 135.439(c) to make the records available for inspection by the Administrator or any representative of the National Transportation Safety Board.

135.443 Airworthiness release or aircraft maintenance log entry

(a) No certificate holder may operate an aircraft after maintenance, preventive maintenance, or alterations are performed on the aircraft unless the certificate holder prepares, or causes the person with whom the certificate holder arranges for the performance of the maintenance, preventive maintenance, or alterations, to prepare—

(1) An airworthiness release; or

(2) An appropriate entry in the aircraft maintenance log.

(b) The airworthiness release or log entry required by paragraph (a) of this section must—

(1) Be prepared in accordance with the procedure in the certificate holder's manual;

(2) Include a certification that—

    (i)   The work was performed in accordance with the require-ments of the certificate holder's manual;

    (ii)   All items required to be inspected were inspected by an authorized person who determined that the work was satisfactorily completed;

    (iii)   No known condition exists that would make the aircraft unairworthy; and

    (iv)   So far as the work performed is concerned, the aircraft is in condition for safe operation; and

(3) Be signed by an authorized certificated mechanic or repairman, except that a certificated repairman may sign the release or entry only for the work for which that person is employed and for which that person is certificated.

(c) Notwithstanding paragraph (b)(3) of this section, after maintenance, preventive maintenance, or alterations performed by a repair station located outside the United States , the airworthiness release or log entry required by paragraph (a) of this section may be signed by a person authorized by that repair station.

(d) Instead of restating each of the conditions of the certification required by paragraph (b) of this section, the certificate holder may state in its manual that the signature of an authorized certificated mechanic or repairman constitutes that certification.

[Doc. No. 16097, 43 FR 46783, Oct. 10, 1978, as amended by Amdt. 135–29, 53 FR 47375, Nov. 22, 1988; Amdt. 135–82, 66 FR 41117, Aug. 6, 2001]

Subpart K — Hazardous Materials Training Program

Source: Doc. No. FAA–2003–15085, 70 FR 58829, Oct. 7, 2005, unless otherwise noted.

135.501　Applicability and definitions

(a) This subpart prescribes the requirements applicable to each certificate holder for training each crewmember and person performing or directly supervising any of the following job functions involving any item for transport on board an aircraft:

(1) Acceptance;

(2) Rejection;

(3) Handling;

(4) Storage incidental to transport;

(5) Packaging of company material; or

(6) Loading.

(b) Definitions. For purposes of this subpart, the following definitions apply:

(1) Company material (COMAT) —Material owned or used by a certificate holder.

(2) Initial hazardous materials training —The basic training required for each newly hired person, or each person changing job functions, who performs or directly supervises any of the job functions specified in paragraph (a) of this section.

(3) Recurrent hazardous materials training —The training required every 24 months for each person who has satisfactorily completed the certificate holder's approved initial hazardous materials training program and performs or directly supervises any of the job functions specified in paragraph (a) of this section.

135.503　Hazardous materials training: General

(a) Each certificate holder must establish and implement a hazardous materials training program that:

(1) Satisfies the requirements of Appendix O of part 121 of this book.

Editor's Note: Appendix O is not included in part 121 of this book.

(2) Ensures that each person performing or directly supervising any of the job functions specified in 135.501(a) is trained to comply with all applicable parts of 49 CFR parts 171 through 180 and the requirements of this subpart; and

(3) Enables the trained person to recognize items that contain, or may contain, hazardous materials regulated by 49 CFR parts 171 through 180.

(b) Each certificate holder must provide initial hazardous materials training and recurrent hazardous materials training to each crewmember and person performing or directly supervising any of the job functions specified in 135.501(a).

(c) Each certificate holder's hazardous materials training program must be approved by the FAA prior to implementation.

135.505　Hazardous materials training required

(a) Training requirement. Except as provided in paragraphs (b), (c) and (f) of this section, no certificate holder may use any crewmember or person to perform any of the job functions or direct supervisory responsibilities, and no person may perform any of the job functions or direct supervisory responsibilities, specified in 135.501(a) unless that person has satisfactorily completed the certificate holder's FAA-approved initial or recurrent hazardous materials training program within the past 24 months.

(b) New hire or new job function. A person who is a new hire and has not yet satisfactorily completed the required initial hazardous materials training, or a person who is changing job functions and has not received initial or recurrent training for a job function involving storage incidental to transport, or loading of items for transport on an aircraft, may perform those job functions for not more than 30 days from the date of hire or a change in job function, if the person is under the direct visual supervision of a person who is authorized by the certificate holder to supervise that person and who has successfully completed the certificate holder's FAA-approved initial or recurrent training program within the past 24 months.

(c) Persons who work for more than one certificate holder. A certificate holder that uses or assigns a person to perform or directly supervise a job function specified in 135.501(a), when that person also performs or directly supervises the same job function for another certificate holder, need only train that person in its own policies and procedures regarding those job functions, if all of the following are met:

(1) The certificate holder using this exception receives written verification from the person designated to hold the training records representing the other certificate holder that the person has satisfactorily completed hazardous materials training for the specific job function under the other certificate holder's FAA approved hazardous material training program under appendix O of part 121 of this chapter; and

(2) The certificate holder who trained the person has the same operations specifications regarding the acceptance, handling, and transport of hazardous materials as the certificate holder using this exception.

(d) Recurrent hazardous materials training—Completion date. A person who satisfactorily completes recurrent hazardous materials training in the calendar month before, or the calendar month after, the month in which the recurrent training is due, is considered to have taken that training during the month in which it is due. If the person completes this training earlier than the month before it is due, the month of the completion date becomes his or her new anniversary month.

(e) Repair stations. A certificate holder must ensure that each repair station performing work for, or on the certificate holder's behalf is notified in writing of the certificate holder's policies and operations specification authorization permitting or prohibition against the acceptance, rejection, handling, storage incidental to transport, and transportation of hazardous materials, including company material. This notification requirement applies only to repair stations that are regulated by 49 CFR parts 171 through 180.

(f) Certificate holders operating at foreign locations. This exception applies if a certificate holder operating at a foreign location where the country requires the certificate holder to use persons working in that country to load aircraft. In such a case, the certificate holder may use those persons even if they have not been trained in accordance with the certificate holder's FAA approved hazardous materials training program. Those persons, however, must be under the direct visual supervision of someone who has successfully completed the certificate holder's approved initial or recurrent hazardous materials training program in accordance with this part. This exception applies only to those persons who load aircraft.

135.507　Hazardous materials training records

(a) General requirement. Each certificate holder must maintain a record of all training required by this part received within the preceding three years for each person who performs or directly supervises a job function specified in 135.501(a). The record must be maintained during the time that the person performs or directly supervises any of those job functions, and for 90 days

FAR 135

thereafter. These training records must be kept for direct employees of the certificate holder, as well as independent contractors, subcontractors, and any other person who performs or directly supervises these job functions for the certificate holder.

(b) Location of records. The certificate holder must retain the training records required by paragraph (a) of this section for all initial and recurrent training received within the preceding 3 years for all persons performing or directly supervising the job functions listed in Appendix O of part 121 of this chapter at a designated location. The records must be available upon request at the location where the trained person performs or directly supervises the job function specified in 135.501(a). Records may be maintained electronically and provided on location electronically. When the person ceases to perform or directly supervise a hazardous materials job function, the certificate holder must retain the hazardous materials training records for an additional 90 days and make them available upon request at the last location where the person worked.

(c) Content of records. Each record must contain the following:

(1) The individual's name;

(2) The most recent training completion date;

(3) A description, copy or reference to training materials used to meet the training requirement;

(4) The name and address of the organization providing the training; and

(5) A copy of the certification issued when the individual was trained, which shows that a test has been completed satisfactorily.

(d) New hire or new job function. Each certificate holder using a person under the exception in 135.505(b) must maintain a record for that person. The records must be available upon request at the location where the trained person performs or directly supervises the job function specified in 135.501(a). Records may be maintained electronically and provided on location electronically. The record must include the following:

(1) A signed statement from an authorized representative of the certificate holder authorizing the use of the person in accordance with the exception;

(2) The date of hire or change in job function;

(3) The person's name and assigned job function;

(4) The name of the supervisor of the job function; and

(5) The date the person is to complete hazardous materials training in accordance with Appendix O of part 121 of this chapter.

Subpart L — Helicopter Air Ambulance Equipment, Operations, and Training Requirements

Source: Doc. No. FAA-2010-0982, 79 FR 9975, Feb. 21, 2014, unless otherwise noted.

135.601 Applicability and definitions

(a) **Applicability.** This subpart prescribes the requirements applicable to each certificate holder conducting helicopter air ambulance operations.

(b) **Definitions.** For purposes of this subpart, the following definitions apply:

(1) *Helicopter air ambulance operation* means a flight, or sequence of flights, with a patient or medical personnel on board, for the purpose of medical transportation, by a part 135 certificate holder authorized by the Administrator to conduct helicopter air ambulance operations. A helicopter air ambulance operation includes, but is not limited to—

 (i) Flights conducted to position the helicopter at the site at which a patient or donor organ will be picked up.

 (ii) Flights conducted to reposition the helicopter after completing the patient, or donor organ transport.

 (iii) Flights initiated for the transport of a patient or donor organ that are terminated due to weather or other reasons.

(2) **Medical personnel** means a person or persons with medical training, including but not limited to flight physicians, flight nurses, or flight paramedics, who are carried aboard a helicopter during helicopter air ambulance operations in order to provide medical care.

(3) **Mountainous** means designated mountainous areas as listed in part 95 of this chapter.

(4) **Nonmountainous** means areas other than mountainous areas as listed in part 95 of this chapter.

135.603 Pilot-in-command instrument qualifications.

After April 24, 2017, no certificate holder may use, nor may any person serve as, a pilot in command of a helicopter air ambulance operation unless that person meets the requirements of 135.243 and holds a helicopter instrument rating or an airline transport pilot certificate with a category and class rating for that aircraft, that is not limited to VFR.

135.605 Helicopter terrain awareness and warning system (HTAWS)

(a) After April 24, 2017, no person may operate a helicopter in helicopter air ambulance operations unless that helicopter is equipped with a helicopter terrain awareness and warning system (HTAWS) that meets the requirements in TSO-C194 and Section 2 of RTCA DO-309.

(b) The certificate holder's Rotorcraft Flight Manual must contain appropriate procedures for—

(1) The use of the HTAWS; and

(2) Proper flight crew response to HTAWS audio and visual warnings.

(c) Certificate holders with HTAWS required by this section with an approved deviation under 21.618 of this chapter are in compliance with this section.

(d) The standards required in this section are incorporated by reference into this section with the approval of the Director of the Federal Register under 5 U.S.C. 552(a) and 1 CFR part 51. To enforce any edition other than that specified in this section, the FAA must publish notice of change in the Federal Register and the material must be available to the public. All approved material is available for inspection at the FAA's Office of Rulemaking (ARM-1), 800 Independence Avenue SW., Washington, DC 20591 (telephone (202) 267-9677) and from the sources indicated below. It is also available for inspection at the National Archives and Records Administration (NARA). For information on the availability of this material at NARA, call (202) 741-6030 or go to http://www.archives.gov/federal_register/code_of_federal_regulations/ibr_locations.html.

(1) U.S. Department of Transportation, Subsequent Distribution Office, DOT Warehouse M30, Ardmore East Business Center, 3341 Q 75th Avenue, Landover, MD 20785; telephone (301) 322-5377. Copies are also available on the FAA's Web site. Use the following link and type the TSO number in the search box: http://rgl.faa.gov/Regulatory_and_Guidance_Library/rgTSO.nsf/Frameset?OpenPage.

 (i) TSO C-194, Helicopter Terrain Awareness and Warning System (HTAWS), Dec. 17, 2008.

 (ii) [Reserved]

(2) RTCA, Inc., 1150 18th Street NW., Suite 910, Washington, DC 20036, telephone (202) 833-9339, and are also available on RTCA's Web site at http://www.rtca.org/onlinecart/index.cfm.

 (i) RTCA DO-309, Minimum Operational Performance Standards (MOPS) for Helicopter Terrain Awareness and Warning System (HTAWS) Airborne Equipment, Mar. 13, 2008.

 (ii) [Reserved]

135.607 Flight Data Monitoring System

After April 23, 2018, no person may operate a helicopter in air ambulance operations unless it is equipped with an approved flight data monitoring system capable of recording flight performance data. This system must:

(a) Receive electrical power from the bus that provides the maximum reliability for operation without jeopardizing service to essential or emergency loads, and

(b) Be operated from the application of electrical power before takeoff until the removal of electrical power after termination of flight.

135.609 VFR ceiling and visibility requirements for Class G airspace

(a) Unless otherwise specified in the certificate holder's operations specifications, when conducting VFR helicopter air ambulance operations in Class G airspace, the weather minimums in the following table apply:

LOCATION	DAY		NIGHT		NIGHT USING AN APPROVED NVIS OR HTAWS	
	Ceiling	Flight Visibility	Ceiling	Flight Visibility	Ceiling	Flight Visibility
Nonmountainous local flying areas	800 feet	2 statute miles	1,000 feet	3 statute miles	800 feet	3 statute miles
Nonmountainous nonlocal flying areas	800 feet	3 statute miles	1,000 feet	5 statute miles	1,000 feet	3 statute miles
Mountainous local flying areas	800 feet	3 statute miles	1,500 feet	3 statute miles	1,000 feet	3 statute miles
Mountainous nonlocal flying areas	1,000 feet	3 statute miles	1,500 feet	5 statute miles	1,000 feet	5 statute miles

(b) A certificate holder may designate local flying areas in a manner acceptable to the Administrator, that must—

(1) Not exceed 50 nautical miles in any direction from each designated location;

(2) Take into account obstacles and terrain features that are easily identifiable by the pilot in command and from which the pilot in command may visually determine a position; and

(3) Take into account the operating environment and capabilities of the certificate holder's helicopters.

(c) A pilot must demonstrate a level of familiarity with the local flying area by passing an examination given by the certificate holder within the 12 calendar months prior to using the local flying area.

[Doc. No. FAA-2010-0982, 79 FR 9975, Feb. 2, 2014; Amdt. 135-129A, 79 FR 41126, July 15, 2014]

135.611 IFR operations at locations without weather reporting

(a) If a certificate holder is authorized to conduct helicopter IFR operations, the Administrator may authorize the certificate holder to conduct IFR helicopter air ambulance operations at airports with an instrument approach procedure and at which a weather report is not available from the U.S. National Weather Service (NWS), a source approved by the NWS, or a source approved by the FAA, subject to the following limitations:

(1) The certificate holder must obtain a weather report from a weather reporting facility operated by the NWS, a source approved by the NWS, or a source approved by the FAA, that is located within 15 nautical miles of the airport. If a weather report is not available, the certificate holder may obtain weather reports, forecasts, or any combination of them from the NWS, a source approved by the NWS, or a source approved by the FAA, for information regarding the weather observed in the vicinity of the airport;

(2) Flight planning for IFR flights conducted under this paragraph must include selection of an alternate airport that meets the requirements of 135.221 and 135.223;

(3) In Class G airspace, IFR departures with visual transitions are authorized only after the pilot in command determines that the weather conditions at the departure point are at or above takeoff minimums depicted in a published departure procedure or VFR minimum ceilings and visibilities in accordance with 135.609.

(4) All approaches must be conducted at Category A approach speeds as established in part 97 or those required for the type of approach being used.

(b) Each helicopter air ambulance operated under this section must be equipped with functioning severe weather detection equipment, unless the pilot in command reasonably determines severe weather will not be encountered at the destination, the alternate destination, or along the route of flight.

(c) Pilots conducting operations pursuant to this section may use the weather information obtained in paragraph (a) to satisfy the weather report and forecast requirements of 135.213 and 135.225(a).

(d) After completing a landing at the airport at which a weather report is not available, the pilot in command is authorized to determine if the weather meets the takeoff requirements of part 97 of this chapter or the certificate holder's operations specification, as applicable.

[Doc. No. FAA-2010-0982, 79 FR 9975, Feb. 21, 2014, as amended by Amdt. 135-131, 79 FR 43622, July 28, 2014; Amdt. 135-141, 84 FR 35823, July 25, 2019]

135.613 Approach/departure IFR transitions

(a) **Approaches.** When conducting an authorized instrument approach and transitioning from IFR to VFR flight, upon transitioning to VFR flight the following weather minimums apply—

(1) For Point-in-Space (PinS) Copter Instrument approaches annotated with a "Proceed VFR" segment, if the distance from the missed approach point to the landing area is 1 NM or less, flight visibility must be at least 1 statute mile and the ceiling on the approach chart applies;

(2) For all instrument approaches, including PinS when paragraph (a)(1) of this section does not apply, if the distance from the missed approach point to the landing area is 3 NM or less, the applicable VFR weather minimums are—

　　(i) For Day Operations: No less than a 600-foot ceiling and 2 statute miles flight visibility;

　　(ii) For Night Operations: No less than a 600-foot ceiling and 3 statute miles flight visibility; or

(3) For all instrument approaches, including PinS, if the distance from the missed approach point to the landing area is greater than 3 NM, the VFR weather minimums required by the class of airspace.

(b) **Departures.** For transitions from VFR to IFR upon departure—

(1) The VFR weather minimums of paragraph (a) of this section apply if—

　　(i) An FAA-approved obstacle departure procedure is followed; and

  (ii) An IFR clearance is obtained on or before reaching a predetermined location that is not more than 3 NM from the departure location.

 (2) If the departure does not meet the requirements of paragraph (b)(1) of this section, the VFR weather minimums required by the class of airspace apply.

135.615　VFR flight planning

(a) **Pre-flight**. Prior to conducting VFR operations, the pilot in command must—

 (1) Determine the minimum safe cruise altitude by evaluating the terrain and obstacles along the planned route of flight;

 (2) Identify and document the highest obstacle along the planned route of flight; and

 (3) Using the minimum safe cruise altitudes in paragraphs (b)(1)-(2) of this section, determine the minimum required ceiling and visibility to conduct the planned flight by applying the weather minimums appropriate to the class of airspace for the planned flight.

(b) **Enroute**. While conducting VFR operations, the pilot in command must ensure that all terrain and obstacles along the route of flight are cleared vertically by no less than the following:

 (1) 300 feet for day operations.

 (2) 500 feet for night operations.

(c) **Rerouting the planned flight path**. A pilot in command may deviate from the planned flight path for reasons such as weather conditions or operational considerations. Such deviations do not relieve the pilot in command of the weather requirements or the requirements for terrain and obstacle clearance contained in this part and in part 91 of this chapter. Rerouting, change in destination, or other changes to the planned flight that occur while the helicopter is on the ground at an intermediate stop require evaluation of the new route in accordance with paragraph (a) of this section.

(d) **Operations manual**. Each certificate holder must document its VFR flight planning procedures in its operations manual.

135.617　Pre-flight risk analysis

(a) Each certificate holder conducting helicopter air ambulance operations must establish, and document in its operations manual, an FAA-approved preflight risk analysis that includes at least the following—

 (1) Flight considerations, to include obstacles and terrain along the planned route of flight, landing zone conditions, and fuel requirements;

 (2) Human factors, such as crew fatigue, life events, and other stressors;

 (3) Weather, including departure, en route, destination, and forecasted;

 (4) A procedure for determining whether another helicopter air ambulance operator has refused or rejected a flight request; and

 (5) Strategies and procedures for mitigating identified risks, including procedures for obtaining and documenting approval of the certificate holder's management personnel to release a flight when a risk exceeds a level predetermined by the certificate holder.

(b) Each certificate holder must develop a preflight risk analysis worksheet to include, at a minimum, the items in paragraph (a) of this section.

(c) Prior to the first leg of each helicopter air ambulance operation, the pilot in command must conduct a preflight risk analysis and complete the preflight risk analysis worksheet in accordance with the certificate holder's FAA-approved procedures. The pilot in command must sign the preflight risk analysis worksheet and specify the date and time it was completed.

(d) The certificate holder must retain the original or a copy of each completed preflight risk analysis worksheet at a location speci-

fied in its operations manual for at least 90 days from the date of the operation.

135.619　Operations control centers

(a) **Operations control center**. After April 22, 2016, certificate holders authorized to conduct helicopter air ambulance operations, with 10 or more helicopter air ambulances assigned to the certificate holder's operations specifications, must have an operations control center. The operations control center must be staffed by operations control specialists who, at a minimum—

 (1) Provide two-way communications with pilots;

 (2) Provide pilots with weather briefings, to include current and forecasted weather along the planned route of flight;

 (3) Monitor the progress of the flight; and

 (4) Participate in the preflight risk analysis required under 135.617 to include the following:

  (i) Ensure the pilot has completed all required items on the preflight risk analysis worksheet;

  (ii) Confirm and verify all entries on the preflight risk analysis worksheet;

  (iii) Assist the pilot in mitigating any identified risk prior to takeoff; and

  (iv) Acknowledge in writing, specifying the date and time, that the preflight risk analysis worksheet has been accurately completed and that, according to their professional judgment, the flight can be conducted safely.

(b) **Operations control center staffing**. Each certificate holder conducting helicopter air ambulance operations must provide enough operations control specialists at each operations control center to ensure the certificate holder maintains operational control of each flight.

(c) **Documentation of duties and responsibilities**. Each certificate holder must describe in its operations manual the duties and responsibilities of operations control specialists, including preflight risk mitigation strategies and control measures, shift change checklist, and training and testing procedures to hold the position, including procedures for retesting.

(d) **Training requirements**. No certificate holder may use, nor may any person perform the duties of, an operations control specialist unless the operations control specialist has satisfactorily completed the training requirements of this paragraph.

 (1) **Initial training**. Before performing the duties of an operations control specialist, each person must satisfactorily complete the certificate holder's FAA-approved operations control specialist initial training program and pass an FAA-approved knowledge and practical test given by the certificate holder. Initial training must include a minimum of 80 hours of training on the topics listed in paragraph (f) of this section. A certificate holder may reduce the number of hours of initial training to a minimum of 40 hours for persons who have obtained, at the time of beginning initial training, a total of at least 2 years of experience during the last 5 years in any one or in any combination of the following areas—

  (i) In military aircraft operations as a pilot, flight navigator, or meteorologist;

  (ii) In air carrier operations as a pilot, flight engineer, certified aircraft dispatcher, or meteorologist; or

  (iii) In aircraft operations as an air traffic controller or a flight service specialist.

 (2) **Recurrent training**. Every 12 months after satisfactory completion of the initial training, each operations control specialist must complete a minimum of 40 hours of recurrent training on the topics listed in paragraph (f) of this section and pass an FAA-approved knowledge and practical test given by the certificate holder on those topics.

(e) **Training records**. The certificate holder must maintain a training record for each operations control specialist employed by the certificate holder for the duration of that individual's employment and for 90 days thereafter. The training record must include a chronological log for each training course, including the number of training hours and the examination dates and results.

(f) **Training topics.** Each certificate holder must have an FAA-approved operations control specialist training program that covers at least the following topics—

(1) Aviation weather, including:

(i) General meteorology;

(ii) Prevailing weather;

(iii) Adverse and deteriorating weather;

(iv) Windshear;

(v) Icing conditions;

(vi) Use of aviation weather products;

(vii) Available sources of information; and

(viii) Weather minimums;

(2) Navigation, including:

(i) Navigation aids;

(ii) Instrument approach procedures;

(iii) Navigational publications; and

(iv) Navigation techniques;

(3) Flight monitoring, including:

(i) Available flight-monitoring procedures; and

(ii) Alternate flight-monitoring procedures;

(4) Air traffic control, including:

(i) Airspace;

(ii) Air traffic control procedures;

(iii) Aeronautical charts; and

(iv) Aeronautical data sources;

(5) Aviation communication, including:

(i) Available aircraft communications systems;

(ii) Normal communication procedures;

(iii) Abnormal communication procedures; and

(iv) Emergency communication procedures;

(6) Aircraft systems, including:

(i) Communications systems;

(ii) Navigation systems;

(iii) Surveillance systems;

(iv) Fueling systems;

(v) Specialized systems;

(vi) General maintenance requirements; and

(vii) Minimum equipment lists;

(7) Aircraft limitations and performance, including:

(i) Aircraft operational limitations;

(ii) Aircraft performance;

(iii) Weight and balance procedures and limitations; and

(iv) Landing zone and landing facility requirements;

(8) Aviation policy and regulations, including:

(i) 14 CFR Parts 1, 27, 29, 61, 71, 91, and 135;

(ii) 49 CFR Part 830;

(iii) Company operations specifications;

(iv) Company general operations policies;

(v) Enhanced operational control policies;

(vi) Aeronautical decision making and risk management;

(vii) Lost aircraft procedures; and

(viii) Emergency and search and rescue procedures, including plotting coordinates in degrees, minutes, seconds format, and degrees, decimal minutes format;

(9) Crew resource management, including:

(i) Concepts and practical application;

(ii) Risk management and risk mitigation; and

(iii) Pre-flight risk analysis procedures required under 135.617;

(10) Local flying area orientation, including:

(i) Terrain features;

(ii) Obstructions;

(iii) Weather phenomena for local area;

(iv) Airspace and air traffic control facilities;

(v) Heliports, airports, landing zones, and fuel facilities;

(vi) Instrument approaches;

(vii) Predominant air traffic flow;

(viii) Landmarks and cultural features, including areas prone to flat-light, whiteout, and brownout conditions; and

(ix) Local aviation and safety resources and contact information; and

(11) Any other requirements as determined by the Administrator to ensure safe operations.

(g) **Operations control specialist duty time limitations.** (1) Each certificate holder must establish the daily duty period for an operations control specialist so that it begins at a time that allows that person to become thoroughly familiar with operational considerations, including existing and anticipated weather conditions in the area of operations, helicopter operations in progress, and helicopter maintenance status, before performing duties associated with any helicopter air ambulance operation. The operations control specialist must remain on duty until relieved by another qualified operations control specialist or until each helicopter air ambulance monitored by that person has completed its flight or gone beyond that person's jurisdiction.

(2) Except in cases where circumstances or emergency conditions beyond the control of the certificate holder require otherwise—

(i) No certificate holder may schedule an operations control specialist for more than 10 consecutive hours of duty;

(ii) If an operations control specialist is scheduled for more than 10 hours of duty in 24 consecutive hours, the certificate holder must provide that person a rest period of at least 8 hours at or before the end of 10 hours of duty;

(iii) If an operations control specialist is on duty for more than 10 consecutive hours, the certificate holder must provide that person a rest period of at least 8 hours before that person's next duty period;

(iv) Each operations control specialist must be relieved of all duty with the certificate holder for at least 24 consecutive hours during any 7 consecutive days.

(h) **Drug and alcohol testing.** Operations control specialists must be tested for drugs and alcohol according to the certificate holder's Drug and Alcohol Testing Program administered under part 120 of this chapter.

135.621 Briefing of medical personnel

(a) Except as provided in paragraph (b) of this section, prior to each helicopter air ambulance operation, each pilot in command, or other flight crewmember designated by the certificate holder, must ensure that all medical personnel have been briefed on the following—

FAR
135

(1) Passenger briefing requirements in 135.117(a) and (b); and

(2) Physiological aspects of flight;

(3) Patient loading and unloading;

(4) Safety in and around the helicopter;

(5) In-flight emergency procedures;

(6) Emergency landing procedures;

(7) Emergency evacuation procedures;

(8) Efficient and safe communications with the pilot; and

(9) Operational differences between day and night operations, if appropriate.

(b) The briefing required in paragraphs (a)(2) through (9) of this section may be omitted if all medical personnel on board have satisfactorily completed the certificate holder's FAA-approved medical personnel training program within the preceding 24 calendar months. Each training program must include a minimum of 4 hours of ground training, and 4 hours of training in and around an air ambulance helicopter, on the topics set forth in paragraph (a)(2) through (9) of this section.

(c) Each certificate holder must maintain a record for each person trained under this section that—

(1) Contains the individual's name, the most recent training completion date, and a description, copy, or reference to training materials used to meet the training requirement.

(2) Is maintained for 24 calendar months following the individual's completion of training.

[Doc. No. FAA-2010-0982, 79 FR 9975, Feb. 2, 2014; Amdt. 135-129A, 79 FR 41126, July 15, 2014]

Appendix A to Part 135 — Additional Airworthiness Standards for 10 or More Passenger Airplanes

Applicability

1. Applicability

This appendix prescribes the additional airworthiness standards required by 135.169.

2. References

Unless otherwise provided, references in this appendix to specific sections of part 23 of the Federal Aviation Regulations (FAR part 23) are to those sections of part 23 in effect on March 30, 1967.

Flight Requirements

3. General

Compliance must be shown with the applicable requirements of subpart B of FAR part 23, as supplemented or modified in 4 through 10.

Performance

4. General

(a) Unless otherwise prescribed in this appendix, compliance with each applicable performance requirement in sections 4 through 7 must be shown for ambient atmospheric conditions and still air.

(b) The performance must correspond to the propulsive thrust available under the particular ambient atmospheric conditions and the particular flight condition. The available propulsive thrust must correspond to engine power or thrust, not exceeding the approved power or thrust less—

(1) Installation losses; and

(2) The power or equivalent thrust absorbed by the accessories and services appropriate to the particular ambient atmospheric conditions and the particular flight condition.

(c) Unless otherwise prescribed in this appendix, the applicant must select the take-off, en route, and landing configurations for the airplane.

(d) The airplane configuration may vary with weight, altitude, and temperature, to the extent they are compatible with the operating procedures required by paragraph (e) of this section.

(e) Unless otherwise prescribed in this appendix, in determining the critical engine inoperative takeoff performance, the accelerate-stop distance, takeoff distance, changes in the airplane's configuration, speed, power, and thrust must be made under procedures established by the applicant for operation in service.

(f) Procedures for the execution of balked landings must be established by the applicant and included in the Airplane Flight Manual.

(g) The procedures established under paragraphs (e) and (f) of this section must—

(1) Be able to be consistently executed in service by a crew of average skill;

(2) Use methods or devices that are safe and reliable; and

(3) Include allowance for any time delays, in the execution of the procedures, that may reasonably be expected in service.

5. Takeoff

(a) General. Takeoff speeds, the accelerate-stop distance, the takeoff distance, and the one-engine-inoperative takeoff flight path data (described in paragraphs (b), (c), (d), and (f) of this section), must be determined for—

(1) Each weight, altitude, and ambient temperature within the operational limits selected by the applicant;

(2) The selected configuration for takeoff;

(3) The center of gravity in the most unfavorable position;

(4) The operating engine within approved operating limitations and

(5) Takeoff data based on smooth, dry, hard-surface runway.

(b) Takeoff speeds.

(1) The decision speed V_1 is the calibrated airspeed on the ground at which, as a result of engine failure or other reasons, the pilot is assumed to have made a decision to continue or discontinue the takeoff. The speed V_1 must be selected by the applicant but may not be less than—

    (i) $1.10\ V_{S1}$;

    (ii) $1.10\ V_{MC}$;

    (iii) A speed that allows acceleration to V_1 and stop under paragraph (c) of this section; or

    (iv) A speed at which the airplane can be rotated for takeoff and shown to be adequate to safely continue the takeoff, using normal piloting skill, when the critical engine is suddenly made inoperative.

(2) The initial climb out speed V_2, in terms of calibrated airspeed, must be selected by the applicant so as to allow the gradient of climb required in section 6(b)(2), but it must not be less than V_1 or less than $1.2\ V_{S1}$.

(3) Other essential take off speeds necessary for safe operation of the airplane.

(c) Accelerate-stop distance.

(1) The accelerate-stop distance is the sum of the distances necessary to—

    (i)   Accelerate the airplane from a standing start to V_1; and

    (ii)   Come to a full stop from the point at which V_1 is reached assuming that in the case of engine failure, failure of the critical engine is recognized by the pilot at the speed V_1.

(2) Means other than wheel brakes may be used to determine the accelerate-stop distance if that means is available with the critical engine inoperative and—

    (i)   Is safe and reliable;

    (ii)   Is used so that consistent results can be expected under normal operating conditions; and

(iii) Is such that exceptional skill is not required to control the airplane.

(d) All engines operating takeoff distance. The all engine operating takeoff distance is the horizontal distance required to takeoff and climb to a height of 50 feet above the takeoff surface under the procedures in FAR 23.51(a).

(e) One-engine-inoperative takeoff. Determine the weight for each altitude and temperature within the operational limits established for the airplane, at which the airplane has the capability, after failure of the critical engine at V_1 determined under paragraph (b) of this section, to take off and climb at not less than V_2, to a height 1,000 feet above the takeoff surface and attain the speed and configuration at which compliance is shown with the en route one-engine-inoperative gradient of climb specified in section 6(c).

(f) One-engine-inoperative takeoff flight path data. The one-engine-inoperative takeoff flight path data consist of takeoff flight paths extending from a standing start to a point in the takeoff at which the airplane reaches a height 1,000 feet above the takeoff surface under paragraph (e) of this section.

6. Climb

(a) Landing climb: All-engines-operating. The maximum weight must be determined with the airplane in the landing configuration, for each altitude, and ambient temperature within the operational limits established for the airplane, with the most unfavorable center of gravity, and out-of-ground effect in free air, at which the steady gradient of climb will not be less than 3.3 percent, with:

(1) The engines at the power that is available 8 seconds after initiation of movement of the power or thrust controls from the minimum flight idle to the takeoff position.

(2) A climb speed not greater than the approach speed established under section 7 and not less than the greater of 1.05 V_{MC} or 1.10 V_{S1}.

(b) Takeoff climb: one-engine-inoperative. The maximum weight at which the airplane meets the minimum climb performance specified in paragraphs (1) and (2) of this paragraph must be determined for each altitude and ambient temperature within the operational limits established for the airplane, out of ground effect in free air, with the airplane in the takeoff configuration, with the most unfavorable center of gravity, the critical engine inoperative, the remaining engines at the maximum takeoff power or thrust, and the propeller of the inoperative engine windmilling with the propeller controls in the normal position except that, if an approved automatic feathering system is installed, the propellers may be in the feathered position:

(1) Takeoff: landing gear extended. The minimum steady gradient of climb must be measurably positive at the speed V_1.

(2) Takeoff: landing gear retracted. The minimum steady gradient of climb may not be less than 2 percent at speed V_2. For airplanes with fixed landing gear this requirement must be met with the landing gear extended.

(c) En route climb: one-engine-inoperative. The maximum weight must be determined for each altitude and ambient temperature within the operational limits established for the airplane, at which the steady gradient of climb is not less 1.2 percent at an altitude 1,000 feet above the takeoff surface, with the airplane in the en route configuration, the critical engine inoperative, the remaining engine at the maximum continuous power or thrust, and the most unfavorable center of gravity.

7. Landing

(a) The landing field length described in paragraph (b) of this section must be determined for standard atmosphere at each weight and altitude within the operational limits established by the applicant.

(b) The landing field length is equal to the landing distance determined under FAR 23.75(a) divided by a factor of 0.6 for the destination airport and 0.7 for the alternate airport. Instead of the gliding approach specified in FAR 23.75(a)(1), the landing may be preceded by a steady approach down to the 50-foot height at a gradient of descent not greater than 5.2 percent (3°) at a calibrated airspeed not less than 1.3 V_{S1}.

Trim

8. Trim

(a) Lateral and directional trim. The airplane must maintain lateral and directional trim in level flight at a speed of V Hor V_{MO}/M_{MO}, whichever is lower, with landing gear and wing flaps retracted.

(b) Longitudinal trim. The airplane must maintain longitudinal trim during the following conditions, except that it need not maintain trim at a speed greater than V_{MO}/M_{MO}:

(1) In the approach conditions specified in FAR 23.161(c) (3) through (5), except that instead of the speeds specified in those paragraphs, trim must be maintained with a stick force of not more than 10 pounds down to a speed used in showing compliance with section 7 or 1.4 V S1whichever is lower.

(2) In level flight at any speed from V_H or V_{MO}/M_{MO}, whichever is lower, to either V_x or 1.4 V_{S1}, with the landing gear and wing flaps retracted.

Stability

9. Static longitudinal stability

(a) In showing compliance with FAR 23.175(b) and with paragraph (b) of this section, the airspeed must return to within ±7 1/2 percent of the trim speed.

(b) Cruise stability. The stick force curve must have a stable slope for a speed range of ±50 knots from the trim speed except that the speeds need not exceed V_{FC}/M_{FC} or be less than 1.4 V_{S1}. This speed range will be considered to begin at the outer extremes of the friction band and the stick force may not exceed 50 pounds with—

(1) Landing gear retracted;

(2) Wing flaps retracted;

(3) The maximum cruising power as selected by the applicant as an operating limitation for turbine engines or 75 percent of maximum continuous power for reciprocating engines except that the power need not exceed that required at V_{MO}/M_{MO};

(4) Maximum takeoff weight; and

(5) The airplane trimmed for level flight with the power specified in paragraph (3) of this paragraph.

V_{FC}/M_{FC} may not be less than a speed midway between V_{MO}/M_{MO} and V_{DF}/M_{DF}, except that, for altitudes where Mach number is the limiting factor, M_{FC} need not exceed the Mach number at which effective speed warning occurs.

(c) Climb stability (turbopropeller powered airplanes only). In showing compliance with FAR 23.175(a), an applicant must, instead of the power specified in FAR 23.175(a)(4), use the maximum power or thrust selected by the applicant as an operating limitation for use during climb at the best rate of climb speed, except that the speed need not be less than 1.4 V_{S1}.

Stalls

10. Stall warning

If artificial stall warning is required to comply with FAR 23.207, the warning device must give clearly distinguishable indications under expected conditions of flight. The use of a visual warning device that requires the attention of the crew within the cockpit is not acceptable by itself.

Control Systems

11. Electric trim tabs

The airplane must meet FAR 23.677 and in addition it must be shown

FAR
135

that the airplane is safely controllable and that a pilot can perform all the maneuvers and operations necessary to effect a safe landing following any probable electric trim tab runaway which might be reasonably expected in service allowing for appropriate time delay after pilot recognition of the runaway. This demonstration must be conducted at the critical airplane weights and center of gravity positions.

Instruments: Installation

12. Arrangement and visibility

Each instrument must meet FAR 23.1321 and in addition:

(a) Each flight, navigation, and powerplant instrument for use by any pilot must be plainly visible to the pilot from the pilot's station with the minimum practicable deviation from the pilot's normal position and line of vision when the pilot is looking forward along the flight path.

(b) The flight instruments required by FAR 23.1303 and by the applicable operating rules must be grouped on the instrument panel and centered as nearly as practicable about the vertical plane of each pilot's forward vision. In addition—

    (1) The instrument that most effectively indicates the attitude must be in the panel in the top center position;

    (2) The instrument that most effectively indicates the airspeed must be on the panel directly to the left of the instrument in the top center position;

    (3) The instrument that most effectively indicates altitude must be adjacent to and directly to the right of the instrument in the top center position; and

    (4) The instrument that most effectively indicates direction of flight must be adjacent to and directly below the instrument in the top center position.

13. Airspeed indicating system

Each airspeed indicating system must meet FAR 23.1323 and in addition:

(a) Airspeed indicating instruments must be of an approved type and must be calibrated to indicate true airspeed at sea level in the standard atmosphere with a minimum practicable instrument calibration error when the corresponding pitot and static pressures are supplied to the instruments.

(b) The airspeed indicating system must be calibrated to determine the system error, i.e., the relation between IAS and CAS, in flight and during the accelerate-takeoff ground run. The ground run calibration must be obtained between 0.8 of the minimum value of V_1 and 1.2 times the maximum value of V_1, considering the approved ranges of altitude and weight. The ground run calibration is determined assuming an engine failure at the minimum value of V_1.

(c) The airspeed error of the installation excluding the instrument calibration error, must not exceed 3 percent or 5 knots whichever is greater, throughout the speed range from V_{MO} to 1.3 V_{S1} with flaps retracted and from 1.3 V_{SO} to V_{FE} with flaps in the landing position.

(d) Information showing the relationship between IAS and CAS must be shown in the Airplane Flight manual.

14. Static air vent system

The static air vent system must meet FAR 23.1325. The altimeter system calibration must be determined and shown in the Airplane Flight Manual.

Operating Limitations and Information

15. Maximum operating limit speed V_{MO}/ M_{MO}

Instead of establishing operating limitations based on V_{NE} and V_{NO}, the applicant must establish a maximum operating limit speed V_{MO}/ M_{MO} as follows:

(a) The maximum operating limit speed must not exceed the design cruising speed V_C and must be sufficiently below V_D/ M_D or V_{DF}/

M_{DF} to make it highly improbable that the latter speeds will be inadvertently exceeded in flight.

(b) The speed V_{MO} must not exceed 0.8 V_D/ M_D or 0.8 V_{DF}/ M_{DF} unless flight demonstrations involving upsets as specified by the Administrator indicates a lower speed margin will not result in speeds exceeding V_D/ M_D or V_{DF}. Atmospheric variations, horizontal gusts, system and equipment errors, and airframe production variations are taken into account.

16. Minimum flight crew

In addition to meeting FAR 23.1523, the applicant must establish the minimum number and type of qualified flight crew personnel sufficient for safe operation of the airplane considering—

(a) Each kind of operation for which the applicant desires approval;

(b) The workload on each crewmember considering the following:

    (1) Flight path control.

    (2) Collision avoidance.

    (3) Navigation.

    (4) Communications.

    (5) Operation and monitoring of all essential aircraft systems.

    (6) Command decisions; and

(c) The accessibility and ease of operation of necessary controls by the appropriate crewmember during all normal and emergency operations when at the crewmember flight station.

17. Airspeed indicator

The airspeed indicator must meet FAR 23.1545 except that, the airspeed notations and markings in terms of V_{NO} and V_{NH} must be replaced by the V_{MO}/ M_{MO} notations. The airspeed indicator markings must be easily read and understood by the pilot. A placard adjacent to the airspeed indicator is an acceptable means of showing compliance with FAR 23.1545(c).

Airplane Flight Manual

18. General

The Airplane Flight Manual must be prepared under FARs 23.1583 and 23.1587, and in addition the operating limitations and performance information in sections 19 and 20 must be included.

19. Operating limitations

The Airplane Flight Manual must include the following limitations—

(a) Airspeed limitations.

    (1) The maximum operating limit speed V_{MO}/ M_{MO} and a statement that this speed limit may not be deliberately exceeded in any regime of flight (climb, cruise, or descent) unless a higher speed is authorized for flight test or pilot training;

    (2) If an airspeed limitation is based upon compressibility effects, a statement to this effect and information as to any symptoms, the probable behavior of the airplane, and the recommended recovery procedures; and

    (3) The airspeed limits, shown in terms of V_{MO} /M_{MO} instead of V_{NO} and V_{NE}.

(b) Takeoff weight limitations. The maximum takeoff weight for each airport elevation, ambient temperature, and available takeoff runway length within the range selected by the applicant may not exceed the weight at which—

    (1) The all-engine-operating takeoff distance determined under section 5(b) or the accelerate-stop distance determined under section 5(c), whichever is greater, is equal to the available runway length;

    (2) The airplane complies with the one-engine-inoperative takeoff requirements specified in section 5(e); and

    (3) The airplane complies with the one-engine-inoperative takeoff and en route climb requirements specified in sections 6 (b) and (c).

(c) Landing weight limitations. The maximum landing weight for each airport elevation (standard temperature) and available landing runway length, within the range selected by the applicant. This weight may not exceed the weight at which the landing field length determined under section 7(b) is equal to the available runway length. In showing compliance with this operating limitation, it is acceptable to assume that the landing weight at the destination will be equal to the takeoff weight reduced by the normal consumption of fuel and oil en route.

20. Performance information

The Airplane Flight Manual must contain the performance information determined under the performance requirements of this appendix. The information must include the following:

(a) Sufficient information so that the takeoff weight limits specified in section 19(b) can be determined for all temperatures and altitudes within the operation limitations selected by the applicant.

(b) The conditions under which the performance information was obtained, including the airspeed at the 50-foot height used to determine landing distances.

(c) The performance information (determined by extrapolation and computed for the range of weights between the maximum landing and takeoff weights) for—

(1) Climb in the landing configuration; and

(2) Landing distance.

(d) Procedure established under section 4 related to the limitations and information required by this section in the form of guidance material including any relevant limitations or information.

(e) An explanation of significant or unusual flight or ground handling characteristics of the airplane.

(f) Airspeeds, as indicated airspeeds, corresponding to those determined for takeoff under section 5(b).

21. Maximum operating altitudes

The maximum operating altitude to which operation is allowed, as limited by flight, structural, powerplant, functional, or equipment characteristics, must be specified in the Airplane Flight Manual.

22. Stowage provision for airplane flight manual

Provision must be made for stowing the Airplane Flight Manual in a suitable fixed container which is readily accessible to the pilot.

23. Operating procedures

Procedures for restarting turbine engines in flight (including the effects of altitude) must be set forth in the Airplane Flight Manual.

Airframe Requirements

Flight Loads

24. Engine torque

(a) Each turbopropeller engine mount and its supporting structure must be designed for the torque effects of:

(1) The conditions in FAR 23.361(a).

(2) The limit engine torque corresponding to takeoff power and propeller speed multiplied by a factor accounting for propeller control system malfunction, including quick feathering action, simultaneously with 1 g level flight loads. In the absence of a ration- al analysis, a factor of 1.6 must be used.

(b) The limit torque is obtained by multiplying the mean torque by a factor of 1.25.

25. Turbine engine gyroscopic loads

Each turbopropeller engine mount and its supporting structure must be designed for the gyroscopic loads that result, with the engines at maximum continuous r.p.m., under either—

(a) The conditions in FARs 23.351 and 23.423; or

(b) All possible combinations of the following:

(1) A yaw velocity of 2.5 radians per second.

(2) A pitch velocity of 1.0 radians per second.

(3) A normal load factor of 2.5.

(4) Maximum continuous thrust.

26. Unsymmetrical loads due to engine failure

(a) Turbopropeller powered airplanes must be designed for the unsymmetrical loads resulting from the failure of the critical engine including the following conditions in combination with a single malfunction of the propeller drag limiting system, considering the probable pilot corrective action on the flight controls:

(1) At speeds between V_{MO} and V_D, the loads resulting from power failure because of fuel flow interruption are considered to be limit loads.

(2) At speeds between V_{MO} and V_C, the loads resulting from the disconnection of the engine compressor from the turbine or from loss of the turbine blades are considered to be ultimate loads.

(3) The time history of the thrust decay and drag buildup occurring as a result of the prescribed engine failures must be substantiated by test or other data applicable to the particular engine-propeller combination.

(4) The timing and magnitude of the probable pilot corrective action must be conservatively estimated, considering the characteristics of the particular engine-propeller-airplane combination.

(b) Pilot corrective action may be assumed to be initiated at the time maximum yawing velocity is reached, but not earlier than 2 seconds after the engine failure. The magnitude of the corrective action may be based on the control forces in FAR 23.397 except that lower forces may be assumed where it is shown by analysis or test that these forces can control the yaw and roll resulting from the prescribed engine failure conditions.

Ground Loads

27. Dual wheel landing gear units

Each dual wheel landing gear unit and its supporting structure must be shown to comply with the following:

(a) Pivoting. The airplane must be assumed to pivot about one side of the main gear with the brakes on that side locked. The limit vertical load factor must be 1.0 and the coefficient of friction 0.8. This condition need apply only to the main gear and its supporting structure.

(b) Unequal tire inflation. A 60–40 percent distribution of the loads established under FAR 23.471 through FAR 23.483 must be applied to the dual wheels.

(c) Flat tire.

(1) Sixty percent of the loads in FAR 23.471 through FAR 23.483 must be applied to either wheel in a unit.

(2) Sixty percent of the limit drag and side loads and 100 percent of the limit vertical load established under FARs 23.493 and 23.485 must be applied to either wheel in a unit except that the vertical load need not exceed the maximum vertical load in paragraph (c)(1) of this section.

Fatigue Evaluation

28. Fatigue evaluation of wing and associated structure

Unless it is shown that the structure, operating stress levels, materials and expected use are comparable from a fatigue standpoint to a similar design which has had substantial satisfactory service experience, the strength, detail design, and the fabrication of those parts of the wing, wing carrythrough, and attaching structure whose failure would be catastrophic must be evaluated under either—

(a) A fatigue strength investigation in which the structure is shown by analysis, tests, or both to be able to withstand the repeated loads of variable magnitude expected in service; or

FAR 135

(b) A fail-safe strength investigation in which it is shown by analysis, tests, or both that catastrophic failure of the structure is not probable after fatigue, or obvious partial failure, of a principal structural element, and that the remaining structure is able to withstand a static ultimate load factor of 75 percent of the critical limit load factor at V C.These loads must be multiplied by a factor of 1.15 unless the dynamic effects of failure under static load are otherwise considered.

Design and Construction

29. Flutter

For multiengine turbopropeller powered airplanes, a dynamic evaluation must be made and must include—

(a) The significant elastic, inertia, and aerodynamic forces associated with the rotations and displacements of the plane of the propeller; and

(b) Engine-propeller-nacelle stiffness and damping variations appropriate to the particular configuration.

Landing Gear

30. Flap operated landing gear warning device

Airplanes having retractable landing gear and wing flaps must be equipped with a warning device that functions continuously when the wing flaps are extended to a flap position that activates the warning device to give adequate warning before landing, using normal landing procedures, if the landing gear is not fully extended and locked. There may not be a manual shut off for this warning device. The flap position sensing unit may be installed at any suitable location. The system for this device may use any part of the system (including the aural warning device) provided for other landing gear warning devices.

Personnel and Cargo Accommodations

31. Cargo and baggage compartments

Cargo and baggage compartments must be designed to meet FAR 23.787 (a) and (b), and in addition means must be provided to protect passengers from injury by the contents of any cargo or baggage compartment when the ultimate forward inertia force is 9 g.

32. Doors and exits

The airplane must meet FAR 23.783 and FAR 23.807 (a)(3), (b), and (c), and in addition:

(a) There must be a means to lock and safeguard each external door and exit against opening in flight either inadvertently by persons, or as a result of mechanical failure. Each external door must be operable from both the inside and the outside.

(b) There must be means for direct visual inspection of the locking mechanism by crewmembers to determine whether external doors and exits, for which the initial opening movement is outward, are fully locked. In addition, there must be a visual means to signal to crewmembers when normally used external doors are closed and fully locked.

(c) The passenger entrance door must qualify as a floor level emergency exit. Each additional required emergency exit except floor level exits must be located over the wing or must be provided with acceptable means to assist the occupants in descending to the ground. In addition to the passenger entrance door:

(1) For a total seating capacity of 15 or less, an emergency exit as defined in FAR 23.807(b) is required on each side of the cabin.

(2) For a total seating capacity of 16 through 23, three emergency exits as defined in FAR 23.807(b) are required with one on the same side as the door and two on the side opposite the door.

(d) An evacuation demonstration must be conducted utilizing the maximum number of occupants for which certification is desired. It must be conducted under simulated night conditions utilizing only the emergency exits on the most critical side of the aircraft. The participants must be representative of average airline passengers with no previous practice or rehearsal for the demonstration. Evacuation must be completed within 90 seconds.

(e) Each emergency exit must be marked with the word "Exit" by a sign which has white letters 1 inch high on a red background 2 inches high, be self-illuminated or independently internally electrically illuminated, and have a minimum luminescence (brightness) of at least 160 microlamberts. The colors may be reversed if the passenger compartment illumination is essentially the same.

(f) Access to window type emergency exits must not be obstructed by seats or seat backs.

(g) The width of the main passenger aisle at any point between seats must equal or exceed the values in the following table:

	MINIMUM MAIN PASSENGER AISLE WIDTH	
Total seating capacity	Less than 25 inches from floor	25 inches and more from floor
10 through 23	9 inches	15 inches

Miscellaneous

33. Lightning strike protection

Parts that are electrically insulated from the basic airframe must be connected to it through lightning arrestors unless a lightning strike on the insulated part—

(a) Is improbable because of shielding by other parts; or

(b) Is not hazardous.

34. Ice protection

If certification with ice protection provisions is desired, compliance with the following must be shown:

(a) The recommended procedures for the use of the ice protection equipment must be set forth in the Airplane Flight Manual.

(b) An analysis must be performed to establish, on the basis of the airplane's operational needs, the adequacy of the ice protection system for the various components of the airplane. In addition, tests of the ice protection system must be conducted to demonstrate that the airplane is capable of operating safely in continuous maximum and intermittent maximum icing conditions as described in appendix C of part 25 of this chapter.

(c) Compliance with all or portions of this section may be accomplished by reference, where applicable because of similarity of the designs, to analysis and tests performed by the applicant for a type certificated model.

35. Maintenance information

The applicant must make available to the owner at the time of delivery of the airplane the information the applicant considers essential for the proper maintenance of the airplane. That information must include the following:

(a) Description of systems, including electrical, hydraulic, and fuel controls.

(b) Lubrication instructions setting forth the frequency and the lubricants and fluids which are to be used in the various systems.

(c) Pressures and electrical loads applicable to the various systems.

(d) Tolerances and adjustments necessary for proper functioning.

(e) Methods of leveling, raising, and towing.

(f) Methods of balancing control surfaces.

(g) Identification of primary and secondary structures.

(h) Frequency and extent of inspections necessary to the proper operation of the airplane.

(i) Special repair methods applicable to the airplane.

(j) Special inspection techniques, such as X-ray, ultrasonic, and magnetic particle inspection.

(k) List of special tools.

Propulsion

General

36. Vibration characteristics

For turbopropeller powered airplanes, the engine installation must not result in vibration characteristics of the engine exceeding those established during the type certification of the engine.

37. In flight restarting of engine

If the engine on turbopropeller powered airplanes cannot be restarted at the maximum cruise altitude, a determination must be made of the altitude below which restarts can be consistently accomplished. Restart information must be provided in the Airplane Flight Manual.

38. Engines

(a) For turbopropeller powered airplanes. The engine installation must comply with the following:

  (1) Engine isolation. The powerplants must be arranged and isolated from each other to allow operation, in at least one configuration, so that the failure or malfunction of any engine, or of any system that can affect the engine, will not—

    (i) Prevent the continued safe operation of the remaining engines; or

    (ii) Require immediate action by any crewmember for continued safe operation.

  (2) Control of engine rotation. There must be a means to individually stop and restart the rotation of any engine in flight except that engine rotation need not be stopped if continued rotation could not jeopardize the safety of the airplane. Each component of the stopping and restarting system on the engine side of the firewall, and that might be exposed to fire, must be at least fire resistant. If hydraulic propeller feathering systems are used for this purpose, the feathering lines must be at least fire resistant under the operating conditions that may be expected to exist during feathering.

  (3) Engine speed and gas temperature control devices. The powerplant systems associated with engine control devices, systems, and instrumentation must provide reasonable assurance that those engine operating limitations that adversely affect turbine rotor structural integrity will not be exceeded in service.

(b) For reciprocating engine powered airplanes. To provide engine isolation, the powerplants must be arranged and isolated from each other to allow operation, in at least one configuration, so that the failure or malfunction of any engine, or of any system that can affect that engine, will not—

  (1) Prevent the continued safe operation of the remaining engines; or

  (2) Require immediate action by any crewmember for continued safe operation.

39. Turbopropeller reversing systems

(a) Turbopropeller reversing systems intended for ground operation must be designed so that no single failure or malfunction of the system will result in unwanted reverse thrust under any expected operating condition. Failure of structural elements need not be considered if the probability of this kind of failure is extremely remote.

(b) Turbopropeller reversing systems intended for in flight use must be designed so that no unsafe condition will result during normal operation of the system, or from any failure (or reasonably likely combination of failures) of the reversing system, under any antic-

ipated condition of operation of the airplane. Failure of structural elements need not be considered if the probability of this kind of failure is extremely remote.

(c) Compliance with this section may be shown by failure analysis, testing, or both for propeller systems that allow propeller blades to move from the flight low-pitch position to a position that is substantially less than that at the normal flight low-pitch stop position. The analysis may include or be supported by the analysis made to show compliance with the type certification of the propeller and associated installation components. Credit will be given for pertinent analysis and testing completed by the engine and propeller manufacturers.

40. Turbopropeller drag-limiting systems

Turbopropeller drag-limiting systems must be designed so that no single failure or malfunction of any of the systems during normal or emergency operation results in propeller drag in excess of that for which the airplane was designed. Failure of structural elements of the drag-limiting systems need not be considered if the probability of this kind of failure is extremely remote.

41. Turbine engine powerplant operating characteristics

For turbopropeller powered airplanes, the turbine engine powerplant operating characteristics must be investigated in flight to determine that no adverse characteristics (such as stall, surge, or flameout) are present to a hazardous degree, during normal and emergency operation within the range of operating limitations of the airplane and of the engine.

42. Fuel flow

(a) For turbopropeller powered airplanes—

  (1) The fuel system must provide for continuous supply of fuel to the engines for normal operation without interruption due to depletion of fuel in any tank other than the main tank; and

  (2) The fuel flow rate for turbopropeller engine fuel pump systems must not be less than 125 percent of the fuel flow required to develop the standard sea level atmospheric conditions takeoff power selected and included as an operating limitation in the Airplane Flight Manual.

(b) For reciprocating engine powered airplanes, it is acceptable for the fuel flow rate for each pump system (main and reserve supply) to be 125 percent of the takeoff fuel consumption of the engine.

Fuel System Components

43. Fuel pumps

For turbopropeller powered airplanes, a reliable and independent power source must be provided for each pump used with turbine engines which do not have provisions for mechanically driving the main pumps. It must be demonstrated that the pump installations provide a reliability and durability equivalent to that in FAR 23.991(a).

44. Fuel strainer or filter

For turbopropeller powered airplanes, the following apply:

(a) There must be a fuel strainer or filter between the tank outlet and the fuel metering device of the engine. In addition, the fuel strainer or filter must be—

  (1) Between the tank outlet and the engine-driven positive displacement pump inlet, if there is an engine-driven positive displacement pump;

  (2) Accessible for drainage and cleaning and, for the strainer screen, easily removable; and

  (3) Mounted so that its weight is not supported by the connecting lines or by the inlet or outlet connections of the strainer or filter itself.

(b) Unless there are means in the fuel system to prevent the accumulation of ice on the filter, there must be means to automatically maintain the fuel-flow if ice-clogging of the filter occurs; and

FAR 135

(c) The fuel strainer or filter must be of adequate capacity (for operating limitations established to ensure proper service) and of appropriate mesh to insure proper engine operation, with the fuel contaminated to a degree (for particle size and density) that can be reasonably expected in service. The degree of fuel filtering may not be less than that established for the engine type certification.

45. Lightning strike protection

Protection must be provided against the ignition of flammable vapors in the fuel vent system due to lightning strikes.

Cooling

46. Cooling test procedures for turbopropeller powered airplanes

(a) Turbopropeller powered airplanes must be shown to comply with FAR 23.1041 during takeoff, climb, en route, and landing stages of flight that correspond to the applicable performance requirements. The cooling tests must be conducted with the airplane in the configuration, and operating under the conditions that are critical relative to cooling during each stage of flight. For the cooling tests a temperature is "stabilized" when its rate of change is less than 2° F. per minute.

(b) Temperatures must be stabilized under the conditions from which entry is made into each stage of flight being investigated unless the entry condition is not one during which component and engine fluid temperatures would stabilize, in which case, operation through the full entry condition must be conducted before entry into the stage of flight being investigated to allow temperatures to reach their natural levels at the time of entry. The takeoff cooling test must be preceded by a period during which the powerplant component and engine fluid temperatures are stabilized with the engines at ground idle.

(c) Cooling tests for each stage of flight must be continued until—

(1) The component and engine fluid temperatures stabilize;

(2) The stage of flight is completed; or

(3) An operating limitation is reached.

Induction System

47. Air induction

For turbopropeller powered airplanes—

(a) There must be means to prevent hazardous quantities of fuel leakage or overflow from drains, vents, or other components of flammable fluid systems from entering the engine intake systems; and

(b) The air inlet ducts must be located or protected so as to minimize the ingestion of foreign matter during takeoff, landing, and taxiing.

48. Induction system icing protection

For turbopropeller powered airplanes, each turbine engine must be able to operate throughout its flight power range without adverse effect on engine operation or serious loss of power or thrust, under the icing conditions specified in appendix C of part 25 of this chapter. In addition, there must be means to indicate to appropriate flight crewmembers the functioning of the powerplant ice protection system.

49. Turbine engine bleed air systems

Turbine engine bleed air systems of turbopropeller powered airplanes must be investigated to determine—

(a) That no hazard to the airplane will result if a duct rupture occurs. This condition must consider that a failure of the duct can occur anywhere between the engine port and the airplane bleed service; and

(b) That, if the bleed air system is used for direct cabin pressurization, it is not possible for hazardous contamination of the cabin air system to occur in event of lubrication system failure.

Exhaust System

50. Exhaust system drains

Turbopropeller engine exhaust systems having low spots or pockets must incorporate drains at those locations. These drains must discharge clear of the airplane in normal and ground attitudes to prevent the accumulation of fuel after the failure of an attempted engine start.

Powerplant Controls and Accessories

51. Engine controls

If throttles or power levers for turbopropeller powered airplanes are such that any position of these controls will reduce the fuel flow to the engine(s) below that necessary for satisfactory and safe idle operation of the engine while the airplane is in flight, a means must be provided to prevent inadvertent movement of the control into this position. The means provided must incorporate a positive lock or stop at this idle position and must require a separate and distinct operation by the crew to displace the control from the normal engine operating range.

52. Reverse thrust controls

For turbopropeller powered airplanes, the propeller reverse thrust controls must have a means to prevent their inadvertent operation. The means must have a positive lock or stop at the idle position and must require a separate and distinct operation by the crew to displace the control from the flight regime.

53. Engine ignition systems

Each turbopropeller airplane ignition system must be considered an essential electrical load.

54. Powerplant accessories

The powerplant accessories must meet FAR 23.1163, and if the continued rotation of any accessory remotely driven by the engine is hazardous when malfunctioning occurs, there must be means to prevent rotation without interfering with the continued operation of the engine.

Powerplant Fire Protection

55. Fire detector system

For turbopropeller powered airplanes, the following apply:

(a) There must be a means that ensures prompt detection of fire in the engine compartment. An overtemperature switch in each engine cooling air exit is an acceptable method of meeting this requirement.

(b) Each fire detector must be constructed and installed to withstand the vibration, inertia, and other loads to which it may be subjected in operation.

(c) No fire detector may be affected by any oil, water, other fluids, or fumes that might be present.

(d) There must be means to allow the flight crew to check, in flight, the functioning of each fire detector electric circuit.

(e) Wiring and other components of each fire detector system in a fire zone must be at least fire resistant.

56. Fire protection, cowling and nacelle skin

For reciprocating engine powered airplanes, the engine cowling must be designed and constructed so that no fire originating in the engine compartment can enter either through openings or by burn through, any other region where it would create additional hazards.

57. Flammable fluid fire protection

If flammable fluids or vapors might be liberated by the leakage of fluid systems in areas other than engine compartments, there must be means to—

(a) Prevent the ignition of those fluids or vapors by any other equipment; or

(b) Control any fire resulting from that ignition.

Equipment

58. Powerplant instruments

(a) The following are required for turbopropeller airplanes:

(1) The instruments required by FAR 23.1305 (a) (1) through (4), (b) (2) and (4).

(2) A gas temperature indicator for each engine.

(3) Free air temperature indicator.

(4) A fuel flowmeter indicator for each engine.

(5) Oil pressure warning means for each engine.

(6) A torque indicator or adequate means for indicating power output for each engine.

(7) Fire warning indicator for each engine.

(8) A means to indicate when the propeller blade angle is below the low-pitch position corresponding to idle operation in flight.

(9) A means to indicate the functioning of the ice protection system for each engine.

(b) For turbopropeller powered airplanes, the turbopropeller blade position indicator must begin indicating when the blade has moved below the flight low-pitch position.

(c) The following instruments are required for reciprocating engine powered airplanes:

(1) The instruments required by FAR 23.1305.

(2) A cylinder head temperature indicator for each engine.

(3) A manifold pressure indicator for each engine.

Systems and Equipments

General

59. Function and installation

The systems and equipment of the airplane must meet FAR 23.1301, and the following:

(a) Each item of additional installed equipment must—

(1) Be of a kind and design appropriate to its intended function;

(2) Be labeled as to its identification, function, or operating limitations, or any applicable combination of these factors, unless misuse or inadvertent actuation cannot create a hazard;

(3) Be installed according to limitations specified for that equipment; and

(4) Function properly when installed.

(b) Systems and installations must be designed to safeguard against hazards to the aircraft in the event of their malfunction or failure.

(c) Where an installation, the functioning of which is necessary in showing compliance with the applicable requirements, requires a power supply, that installation must be considered an essential load on the power supply, and the power sources and the distribution system must be capable of supplying the following power loads in probable operation combinations and for probable durations:

(1) All essential loads after failure of any prime mover, power converter, or energy storage device.

(2) All essential loads after failure of any one engine on two-engine airplanes.

(3) In determining the probable operating combinations and durations of essential loads for the power failure conditions described in paragraphs (1) and (2) of this paragraph, it is permissible to assume that the power loads are reduced in accordance with a monitoring procedure which is consistent with safety in the types of operations authorized.

60. Ventilation

The ventilation system of the airplane must meet FAR 23.831, and in addition, for pressurized aircraft, the ventilating air in flight crew and passenger compartments must be free of harmful or hazardous concentrations of gases and vapors in normal operation and in the event of reasonably probable failures or malfunctioning of the ventilating, heating, pressurization, or other systems, and equipment. If accumulation of hazardous quantities of smoke in the cockpit area is reasonably probable, smoke evacuation must be readily accomplished.

Electrical Systems and Equipment

61. General

The electrical systems and equipment of the airplane must meet FAR 23.1351, and the following:

(a) Electrical system capacity. The required generating capacity, and number and kinds of power sources must—

(1) Be determined by an electrical load analysis; and

(2) Meet FAR 23.1301.

(b) Generating system. The generating system includes electrical power sources, main power busses, transmission cables, and associated control, regulation and protective devices. It must be designed so that—

(1) The system voltage and frequency (as applicable) at the terminals of all essential load equipment can be maintained within the limits for which the equipment is designed, during any probable operating conditions;

(2) System transients due to switching, fault clearing, or other causes do not make essential loads inoperative, and do not cause a smoke or fire hazard;

(3) There are means, accessible in flight to appropriate crewmembers, for the individual and collective disconnection of the electrical power sources from the system; and

(4) There are means to indicate to appropriate crewmembers the generating system quantities essential for the safe operation of the system, including the voltage and current supplied by each generator.

62. Electrical equipment and installation

Electrical equipment, controls, and wiring must be installed so that operation of any one unit or system of units will not adversely affect the simultaneous operation of any other electrical unit or system essential to the safe operation.

63. Distribution system

(a) For the purpose of complying with this section, the distribution system includes the distribution busses, their associated feeders, and each control and protective device.

(b) Each system must be designed so that essential load circuits can be supplied in the event of reasonably probable faults or open circuits, including faults in heavy current carrying cables.

(c) If two independent sources of electrical power for particular equipment or systems are required under this appendix, their electrical energy supply must be ensured by means such as duplicate electrical equipment, throwover switching, or multichannel or loop circuits separately routed.

64. Circuit protective devices

The circuit protective devices for the electrical circuits of the airplane must meet FAR 23.1357, and in addition circuits for loads which are essential to safe operation must have individual and exclusive circuit protection.

Appendix B to Part 135 — Airplane Flight Recorder Specifications

PARAMETERS	RANGE	INSTALLED SYSTEM[1] MINIMUM ACCURACY (TO RECOVERED DATA)	SAMPLING INTERVAL (PER SECOND)	RESOLUTION[4] READOUT
Relative time (from recorded on prior to takeoff)	25hr minimum	±0.125% per hour	1	1 sec
Indicated airspeed	V_{SO} to V_D (KIAS)	±5% or ±10 kts., whichever is greater. Resolution 2 kts. below 175 KIAS	1	1%[3]
Altitude	-1,000 ft to max cert. alt. of A/C	±100 to ±700 ft. (see Table 1, TSO C51-a)	1	25 to 150
Magnetic heading	360°	±-5°	1	1°
Vertical acceleration	-3g to +6g	±0.2g in addition to ±0.3g maximum datum	4 (or 1 per second where peaks, ref. to 1g are recorded)	0.03g
Longitudinal acceleration	±1.0g	±1.5% max. range excluding datum error of ±5%	2	0.01g
Pitch attitude	100% of usable	±2°	1	0.8°
Roll attitude	±60° or 100% of usable range, whichever is greater	±2°	1	0.8°
Stabilizer trim position Or	Full range	±3% unless higher uniquely required	1	1%[3]
Pitch control position	Full range	±3% unless higher uniquely required	1	1%[3]
Engine Power, Each Engine				
Fan or N_1 speed or EPR or cockpit indications used for aircraft certification Or	Maximum range	±5%	1	1%[3]
Prop. speed and torque (sample once/sec as close together as practicable)			1 (prop speed), 1 (torque)	
Altitude rate[2] (need depends on altitude resolution)	±8,000 fpm	±10%. Resolution 250 fpm below 12,000 ft. indicated	1	250 fpm Below 12,000
Angle of attack[2] (need depends on altitude resolution)	-20° to 40° or of usable range	±2 °	1	0.8%[3]
Radio transmitter keying (discrete)	On/off		1	
TE flaps (discrete or analog)	Each discrete position (U, D, T/O, AAP) Or		1	
	Analog 0-100% range	±3 °	1	1%[3]
LE flaps (discrete or analog)	Each discrete position (U, D, T/O, AAP) Or		1	
	Analog 0-100% range	±3 °	1	1%[3]
Thrust reverser, each engine (Discrete)	Stowed or full reverse		1	
Spoiler/speedbrake (discrete)	Stowed or out		1	
Autopilot engaged (discrete)	Engaged or disengaged		1	

[1] When data sources are aircraft instruments (except altimeters) of acceptable quality to fly the aircraft the recording system excluding these sensors (but including all other characteristics of the recording system) shall contribute no more than half of the values in this column.

[2] If data from the altitude encoding altimeter (100ft resolution) is used, the either one of these parameters should also be recorded. If however, altitude is recorded at a minimum resolution of 25 feet, then these two parameters can be omitted.

[3] Percent of full range.

[4] This column applies to aircraft manufactured after October 11, 1991.

[Doc. No. 25530, 53 FR 26152, July 11, 1988; 53 FR 30906, Aug. 16, 1988, as amended by Amdt. 135–69, 62 FR 38397, July 17, 1997]

Appendix C to Part 135 — Helicopter Flight Recorder Specifications

PARAMETERS	RANGE	INSTALLED SYSTEM[1] MINIMUM ACCURACY (TO RECOVERED DATA)	SAMPLING INTERVAL (PER SECOND)	RESOLUTION[3] READOUT
Relative time (from recorded on prior to takeoff)	25 hr minimum	±0.125% per hour	1	1 sec
Indicated airspeed	V_{MIN} to V_D (KIAS) (minimum airspeed signal attainable with installed pitot-static system)	±5% or ±10 kts., whichever is greater.	1	1 kt
Altitude	-1,000 ft. to 20,000 ft. pressure altitude	±100 to ±700 ft. (see Table 1, TSO C51-a).	1	25 to 150 ft
Magnetic heading	360 °	±5°	1	1°
Vertical acceleration	-3g to +6g	±0.2g in addition to ± 0.3g maximum datum	4 (or 1 per second where peaks, ref. to 1g are recorded)	0.05g
Longitudinal acceleration	±1.0g	±1.5% max. range excluding datum error of ±5%	2	0.03g
Pitch attitude	100% of usable range	±2°	1	0.8°
Roll attitude	±60° or 100% of usable range, whichever is greater	±2°	1	0.8°
Altitude rate	±8,000 fpm	±10% Resolution 250 fpm below 12,000 ft. indicated	1	250 fpm below 12,000
ENGINE POWER, EACH ENGINE Main rotor speed	Maximum range	±5%	1	1%[2]
Free or power turbine	Maximum range	±5%	1	1%[2]
Engine torque	Maximum range	±5%	1	1%[2]
FLIGHT CONTROL — HYDRAULIC PRESSURE Primary (discrete)	High/low		1	
Secondary - if applicable (discrete)	High/low		1	
Radio transmitter keying (discrete)	On/off		1	
Autopilot engaged (discrete)	Engaged or disengaged		1	
SAS status - engaged (discrete)	Engaged/disengaged		1	
SAS fault status (discrete) Flight Controls	Fault/OK		1	
Collective	Full range	±3%	2	1%[2]
Pedal position	Full range	±3%	2	1%[2]
Lat. cyclic	Full range	±3%	2	1%[2]
Long. cyclic	Full range	±3%	2	1%[2]
Controllable stabilator position	Full range	±3%	2	1%[2]

[1] When data sources are aircraft instruments (except altimeters) of acceptable quality to fly the aircraft the recording system excluding these sensors (but including all other characteristics of the recording system) shall contribute no more than half of the values in this column.
[2] Percent of full range.
[3] This column applies to aircraft manufactured after October 11, 1991.
[4] For all aircraft manufactured on or after December 6, 2010, the sampling interval per second is 4.

[Doc. No. 25530, 53 FR 26152, July 11, 1988; 53 FR 30906, Aug. 16, 1988, as amended by Amdt. 135–69, 62 FR 38397, July 17, 1997; Amdt. 135–113, 73 FR 12570, Mar. 7, 2008; 73 FR 15281, Mar. 21, 2008; Amdt. 135–121, 75 FR 17047, Apr. 5, 2010]

Appendix D to Part 135 — Airplane Flight Recorder Specification

PARAMETERS	RANGE	ACCURACY SENSOR INPUT TO DFDR READOUT	SAMPLING IINTERVAL (PER SECOND)	RESOLUTION[4] READOUT
Time (GMT or Frame Counter) (range 0 to 4095, sampled 1 per frame)	24 Hrs	±0.125% per hour	0.25 (1 per 4 seconds)	1 sec
Altitude	-1,000 ft. to max certificated altitude of aircraft.	±100 to ±700 ft. (see Table 1, TSO C51a).	1	5 to 35 ft[1]
Airspeed	50 KIAS to V_{SO}, and V_{SO} to 1.2 V_D.	±5% or ±3%	1	1 kt
Heading	360 °	±2°	1	0.5°
Normal Acceleration (Vertical)	-3g to +6g	±1% of max range excluding datum error of ±5%	8	0.01g
Pitch attitude	±75°	±2°	1	0.5°
Roll attitude	±180°	±2°.	1	0.5°
Radio transmitter keying	On/Off (Discrete)		1	
Thrust/Power on Each Engine.	Full range forward	±2%	1 (per engine)	0.2%[2]
Trailing Edge Flap or Cockpit Control Selection	Full range or each discrete position.	±3 ° or as pilot's indicator	0.5	0.5%[2]
Leading Edge Flap on or Cockpit Control Selection	Full range or each discrete position.	±3 ° or as pilot's indicator	0.5	0.5%[2]
Thrust Reverser Position	Stowed, in transit, and reverse (discretion).		1 (per 4 seconds per engine)	
Ground Spoiler Position/Speed Brake Selection	Full range or each discrete position.	±2% unless higher accuracy uniquely required	1	0.22[2]
Marker Beacon Passage	Discrete		1	
Autopilot Engagement	Discrete		1	
Longitudinal Acceleration	±1g	±1.5% max range excluding datum error of ±5%	4	0.01g
Pilot Input And/or Surface Position - Primary Controls (Pitch, Roll, Yaw)[3]	Full range	±2 ° unless higher accuracy uniquely required	1	0.2%[2]
Lateral Acceleration	±1g	±1.5% max range excluding datum error of ±5%	4	0.01g
Pitch Trim Position	Full range	± 3% unless higher accuracy uniquely required	1	0.3%[2]
Glideslope Deviation	± 400 Microamps	±3%	1	0.3%[2]
Localizer Deviation	±400 Microamps	±3%	1	0.3%[2]
AFCS Mode and Engagement Status	Discrete		1	0.3%[2]
Radio Altitude	-20 ft to 2,500 ft	±2 ft or ±3% whichever is greater below 500 ft and ±5% above 500 ft	1	1 ft +5%[2] above 500 ft
Master Warning	Discrete		1	
Main Gear Squat Switch Status	Discrete		1	
Angle of Attack (if recorded directly)	As installed	As installed	2	0.3%[2]
Outside Air Temperature or Total Air Temperature	-50° C to +90° C	±2 deg C.	0.5	0.3° C
Hydraulics, Each System Low Pressure	Discrete		0.5	or 0.5%[2]
Groundspeed	As installed	Most accurate systems installed (IMS equipped aircraft only).	1	0.2%[2]

Appendix D to Part 135 — Airplane Flight Recorder Specification (Continued)

If additional recording capacity is available, recording of the following parameters is recommended.
The parameters are listed in the order of significance:

PARAMETERS	RANGE	ACCURACY SENSOR INPUT TO DFDR READOUT	SAMPLING IINTERVAL (PER SECOND)	RESOLUTION[4] READOUT
Drift Angle	When available. As installed.	As installed	4	
Wind Speed and Direction	When available. As installed.	As installed	4	
Latitude and Longitude	When available. As installed.	As installed	4	
Brake pressure/Brake pedal position.	As installed	As installed	1	
Additional engine parameters:	As installed			
EPR	As installed	As installed	1 (per engine)	
N[1]	As installed	As installed	1 (per engine)	
N[2]	As installed	As installed	1 (per engine)	
EGT	As installed	As installed	1 (per engine)	
Throttle Lever Position	As installed	As installed	1 (per engine)	
Fuel Flow	As installed	As installed	1 (per engine)	
TCAS:				
TA	As installed	As installed	1	
RA	As installed	As installed	1	
Sensitivity level (as selected by crew).	As installed	As installed	2	
GPWS (ground proximity warning system).	Discrete		1	
Landing gear or gear selector position.	Discrete		0.25 (1 per 4 seconds)	
DME 1 and 2 Distance	0-200 NM;	As installed	0.25	1 mi
Nav 1 and 2 Frequency Selection	Full range	As installed	0.25	

[1] When altititude rate is recorded. Altitude rate must have sufficient resolution and sampling to permit the derivation of altitude to 5 feet.
[2] Percent of full range.
[3] For airplanes that can demonstrate the capability of deriving either the control input on control movement (one from the other) for all modes of operation and flight regimes, the "or" applies. For airplanes with non-mechanical control systems (fly-by-wire) the "and" applies. In airplanes with split surfaces, suitable combination of inputs is acceptable in lieu of recording each surface separately.
[4] This column applies to aircraft manufactured after October 11, 1991.

[Doc. No. 25530, 53 FR 26153, July 11, 1988; 53 FR 30906, Aug. 16, 1988]

Appendix E to Part 135 — Helicopter Flight Recorder Specifications

PARAMETERS	RANGE	ACCURACY SENSOR INPUT TO DFDR READOUT	SAMPLING INTERVAL (PER SECOND)	RESOLUTION[2] READ-OUT
Time (GMT)	24 Hrs	±0.125% per hour	0.25 (1 per 4 seconds)	1 sec
Altitude	-1,000 ft. to max certificated altitude of aircraft.	±100 to ±700 ft. (see Table 1, TSO C51-a).	1	5 to 30 ft
Airspeed	As the installed measuring system.	±3%	1	1 kt
Heading	360 °	±2 °	1	0.5 °
Normal Acceleration (Vertical)	-3g to +6g	±1% of max range excluding datum error of ±5%	8	0.01g
Pitch attitude	±75 °	±2 °	2	0.5 °
Roll attitude	±180 °	±2 °	2	0.5 °
Radio Transmitter Keying	On/Off (Discrete)		1	0.25 sec
Power in Each Engine: Free Power Turbine Speed and Engine Torque	0-130% (power Turbine Speed) Full range (Torque)	±2%	1 speed 1 torque (per engine)	0.2%[1] to 0.4%[1]
Main Rotor Speed	0-130%	±2%	2	0.3%[1]
Altitude Rate	±6,000 ft/min	As installed	2	0.2%[1]
Pilot Input - Primary Controls (Collective, Longitudinal Cyclic, Lateral Cyclic, Pedal).	Full range	±3%	2	0.5%[1]
Flight Control Hydraulic Pressure Low.	Discrete, each circuit		1	
Flight Control Hydraulic Pressure Selector Switch Position, 1st and 2nd stage.	Discrete		1	
Afcs Mode and Engagement Status.	Discrete, (5 bits necessary)		1	
Stability Augmentation System Engage.	Discrete		1	
Sas Fault Status	Discrete		0.25	
Main Gearbox Temperature Low.	As installed	As installed	0.25	0.5%[1]
Main Gearbox Temperature High.	As installed	As installed	0.5	0.5%[1]
Controllable Stabilator Position.	Full Range	±3%	2	0.4%[1]
Longitudinal Acceleration	±1g	±1.5% max range excluding datum error of ±5%	4	0.01g
Lateral Acceleration	±1g	±1.5% max range excluding datum of ±5%	4	0.01g
Master Warning	Discrete		1	
Nav 1 and 2 Frequency Selection.	Full Range	As installed	0.25	
Outside Air Temperature	-50 ° C to +90 ° C	±2 ° C	0.5	0.3 ° C

[1] Percent of full range.
[2] This column applies to aircraft manufactured after October 11, 1991.
[3] For all aircraft manufactured on or after December 6, 2010, the sampling interval per second is 4.

[Doc. No. 25530, 53 FR 26154, July 11, 1988; 53 FR 30906, Aug. 16, 1988; Amdt. 135–113, 73 FR 12571, Mar. 7, 2008; 73 FR 15281, Mar. 21, 2008; Amdt. 135–121, 75 FR 17047, Apr. 5, 2010]

Appendix F to Part 135 — Airplane Flight Recorder Specification

The recorded values must meet the designated range, resolution and accuracy requirements during static and dynamic conditions. Dynamic condition means the parameter is experiencing change at the maximum rate attainable, including the maximum rate of reversal. All data recorded must be correlated in time to within one second.

PARAMETERS	RANGE	ACCURACY (SENSOR INPUT)	SECONDS PER SAMPLING INTERVAL	RESOLUTION	REMARKS
1. Time or Relative Times Counts[1]	24 Hrs. 0 to 4095	±0.125% Per Hour	4	1 sec	UTC time preferred when available. Counter increments each 4 seconds of system operation.
2. Pressure Altitude	-1000 ft to max certificated altitude of aircraft. +5000 ft.	±100 to ±700ft (see table, TSO C124a or TSO C51a).	1	5 feet to 35 feet	Data should be obtained from the air data computer when practicable.
3. Indicated airspeed or Calibrated airspeed	50 KIAS or minimum value to Mas V_{so}[1] to 1.2 V_D	±5% and ±3%	1	1 kt	Data should be obtained from the air data computer when practicable.
4. Heading (Primary flight crew reference)	0-360 ° and Discrete "true" or "mag."	±2 °	1	0.5 °	When true or magnetic heading can be selected as the primary heading reference, a discrete indicating selection must be recorded.
5. Normal Acceleration (Vertical)[9]	-3g to +6g	±1% of max range excluding datum error of ±5%	0.125	0.004g	
6. Pitch Attitude	±75 °	±2 °	1 or 0.25 for airplanes operated under 135.152(j)	0.5 °	A sampling rate of 0.25 is recommended.
7. Roll Attitude[2]	±180 ° 0	±2 °	1 or 0.5 for airplanes operated under 135.152(j)	0.5 °	A sampling rate of 0.5 is recommended.
8. Manual Radio Transmitter Keying CVR/DFDR synchronization reference	On-Off (Discrete) None		1		Preferably each crew member but one discrete acceptable for all transmission provided the CVR/FDR system complies with TSO C124a CVR synchronization (paragraph 4.2.1 ED-55).
9. Thrust/Power on each engine—primary flight crew reference	Full Range Forward	±2%	1 (per engine)	0.2% of full range	Sufficient parameters (e.g. EPR, N1 or Torque, NP) as appropriate to the particular engine be recorded to determine power in forward and reverse thrust, including potential overspeed conditions.
10. Autopilot Engagement	Discrete "on" or "off"		1		
11. Longitudinal Acceleration	±1g	±1.5% max. range excluding datum error of ±5%	0.25	0.004g	
12 a. Pitch Control(s) position (non-fly-by-wire systems)	Full Range	±2 ° Unless Higher Accuracy Uniquely Required	0.5 or 0.25 for airplanes operated under 135.152(j)	0.2% of full range	For airplanes that have a flight control break away capability that allows either pilot to operate the controls independently, record both control inputs. The control inputs may be sampled alternately once per second to produce the sampling interval of 0.5 or 0.25, as applicable.
12b. Pitch Control(s) Position (fly-by-wire systems)[3]	Full Range	±2 ° Unless Higher Accuracy Uniquely Required	0.5 or 0.25 for airplanes operated under 135.152(j)	0.2% of full range	
13a. Lateral Control position(s) (non-fly-by-wire)	Full Rangew	±2 ° Unless Higher Accuracy Uniquely Required	0.5 or 0.25 for airplanes operated under 135.152(j)	0.2% of full range	For airplanes that have a flight control break away capability that allows either pilot to operate the controls independently, record both control inputs. The control inputs may be sampled alternately once per second to produce the sampling interval of 0.5 or 0.25, as applicable.
13b. Lateral Control position(s) (fly-by-wire)[4]	Full Range	±2 ° Unless Higher Accuracy Uniquely Required	0.5 or 0.25 for airplanes operated under 135.152(j)	0.2% of full range	

Appendix F to Part 135 — Airplane Flight Recorder Specification (Continued)

PARAMETERS	RANGE	ACCURACY (SENSOR INPUT)	SECONDS PER SAMPLING INTERVAL	RESOLUTION	REMARKS
14a. Yaw Control position(s) (non-fly-by-wire)[5]	Full Range	±2 ° Unless Higher Accuracy Uniquely Required	0.5 or 0.25 for airplanes operated under 135.152(j)	0.2% of full range	For airplanes that have a flight control break away capability that allows either pilot to operate the controls independently, record both control inputs. The control inputs may be sampled alternately once per second to produce the sampling interval of 0.5.
14b. Yaw Control position(s) (fly-by-wire)	Full Range	±2 ° Unless Higher Accuracy Uniquely Required	0.5	0.2% of full range	
15. Pitch Control Surface(s) Position[6]	Full Range	±2 ° Unless Higher Accuracy Uniquely Required	0.5 or 0.25 for airplanes operated under 135.152(j)	0.2% of full range	For airplanes fitted with multiple or split surfaces, a suitable combination of inputs is acceptable in lieu of recording each surface separately. The control surfaces may be sampled alernately to produce the sampling interval of 0.5 or 0.25.
16 Lateral Control Surface(s) Position[7]	Full Range	±2 ° Unless Higher Accuracy Uniquely Required	0.5 or 0.25 for airplanes operated under 135.152(j)	0.2% of full range	A suitable combination of surface position sensors is acceptable in lieu of recording each surface separately. The control surfaces may be sampled alternately to produce the sampling interval of 0.5 or 0.25.
17. Yaw Control Surface(s) Position[8]	Full Range	±2 ° Unless Higher Accuracy Uniquely Required	0.5	0.2% of full range	For airplanes fitted with multiple or split surfaces, a suitable combination of inputs is acceptable in lieu of recording each surface separately. The control surfaces may be sampled alernately to produce the sampling interval of 0.5.
18. Lateral Acceleration	± 1g	±1.55% max. range excluding datum error of ±5%	0.25	0.004g	
19. Pitch Trim Surface Position	Full Range	±3% Unless Higher Accuracy Uniquely Required	1	0.3% of full range	
20. Trailing Edge Flap or Cockpit Control Selection[10]	Full Range of Each position (discrete)	±3 ° or as Pilot's Indicator	2	0.5% of full range	Flap position and cockpit control may each be sampled alternately at 4 second intervals, to give a data point every 2 seconds.
21. Leading Edge Flap or Cockpit Control Selection[11]	Full Range of Each Discrete Position	±3 ° or as Pilot's indicator and sufficient to determine each discrete position	2	0.5% of full range	Left and right sides, or flap position and cockpit control may each be sampled at 4 second intervals so as to give a data point every 2 seconds.
22. Each Thrust Reverser Position (or equivalent for propeller airplane)	Stowed, In Transit, and Reverse (Discrete)		1 (per engine)		Turbo-jet—2 discretes enable the 3 states to be determined. Turbo-prop 1 discrete.
23. Ground Spoiler Position or Speed Brake Selection[12]	Full Range or Each Position. (discrete)	±2 ° Unless Higher Accuracy Uniquely Required.	1 0.5 for airplanes operated under 135.152(j)	0.2% of full range	
24. Outside Air Temperature or Total Air Temperature[13]	-50 °C to +90° C	±2 °C	2	0.3 °C	
25. Autopilot/Autothrottle/AFCS Mode and Engagement Status	A suitable combination of discretes		1		Discretes should show which systems are engaged and which primary modes are controlling the flight path and speed of the aircraft.
26. Radio Altitude[14]	-20 ft to 2,500 ft	±2 ft or ±3% Whichever is Greater Below 500 ft and ±5% Above 500 ft.	1	1 ft +5% above 500 ft	For autoland/category 3 operations, each radio altimeter should be recorded, but arranged so that at least one is recorded each second.
27. Localizer Deviation, MLS Azimuth, or GPS Lateral Deviation	±400 Microamps or available sensor range as installed. ±62 °	As installed ±3% recommended.	1	0.3% of full range	For autoland/category 3 operations, each radio altimeter should be recorded, but arranged so that at least one is recorded each second. It is not necessary to record ILS and MLS at the same time, only the approach aid in use need be recorded.

Appendix F to Part 135 — Airplane Flight Recorder Specification (Continued)

PARAMETERS	RANGE	ACCURACY (SENSOR INPUT)	SECONDS PER SAMPLING INTERVAL	RESOLUTION	REMARKS
28. Glideslope Deviation, MLS Elevation, or GPS Vertical Deviation	±400 Microamps or available sensor range as installed. 0.9 to +30 °	As installed ±3% recommended	1	0.3% of full range	For autoland/category 3 operations. Each system should be recorded, but arranged so that at least one is recorded each second. It is not necessary to record ILS and MLS at the same time, only the approach aid in use need be recorded.
29. Marker Beacon Passage	Discrete "on" or "off"		1		A single discrete is acceptable for all markers
30. Master Warning	Discrete		1		Record the master warning and record each 'red' warning that cannot be determined from other parameters or from the cockpit voice recorder.
31. Air/ground sensor (primary airplane system reference nose or main gear)	Discrete "air" or "ground"		1 (0.25 recommended.)		
32. Angle of Attack (If measured directly)	As installed	As installed	2 or 0.5 for airplanes operated under 135.152(j)	0.3% of full range	If left and right sensors are available, each may be recorded at 4 or 1 second intervals, as appropriate, so as to give a data point at 2 seconds or 0.5 second, as required.
33.Hydraulic Pressure Low, Each System	Discrete or available sensor range, "low" or "normal"	±5%	2	0.5% of full range	
34. Groundspeed	As installed	Most Accurate Systems Installed	1	0.2% of full range	
35.GPWS (ground proximity warning system)	Discrete "warning" or "off"		1		A suitable combination of discretes unless recorder capicaity is limited in which case a single discrete for all modes is acceptable.
36. Landing Gear Position or Landing gear cockpit control selection	Discrete		4		A suitable combination of discretes should be recorded.
37. Drift Angle[15]	As installed	As installed	4	0.1 °	
38. Wind Speed and Direction	As installed	As installed	4	1 knot, and 1.0 °	
39.Latitude and Longitude	As installed	As installed	4	0.002 °, or as installed	Provided by the Primary Navigation System Reference. Where capacity permits Latitude/longitude resolution should be 0.0002 °.
40. Stick shaker and pusher activation	Discrete(s) "on" or "off"		1		A suitable combination of discretes to determine activation.
41. Windshear Detection	Discrete "warning" or "off"		1		
42. Throttle/Power Lever Position[16]	Full range	±2%	1 for each lever	2% of full range	For airplanes with non-mechanically linked cockpit engine controls.
43. Additional Engine Parameters	As installed	As installed	Each engine each second	2% of full range	Where capacity permits, the preferred priority is indicated vibration level, N2, EGT, Fuel Flow, Fuel Cut-off lever position and N3, unless engine manufacturer recommends otherwise.
44. Traffic Alert and Collision Avoidance System (TCAS)	Discretes	As installed	1		A suitable combination of discretes should be recorded to determine the status of— Combined Control, Vertical Control, Up Advisory, and Down Advisory. (ref. ARINC Characteristic 735 Attachment 6E, TCAS VERTICAL RA DATA OUTPUT WORD.)
45. DME 1 and 2 Distance	0-200 NM;	As installed	4	1NM	1 mile.
46. Nav 1 and 2 Selected Frequency	Full Range	As installed	4		Sufficient to determine selected frequency.
47. Selected barometric setting	Full Range	±5%	(1 per 64 sec.)	0.2% of full range	
48. Selected Altitude	Full Range	±5%	1	100 ft.	
49. Selected speed	Full Range	±5%	1	1 knot.	
50. Selected Mach	Full Range	±5%	1	.01	

FAR 135

Appendix F to Part 135 — Airplane Flight Recorder Specification (Continued)

PARAMETERS	RANGE	ACCURACY (SENSOR INPUT)	SECONDS PER SAMPLING INTERVAL	RESOLUTION	REMARKS
51. Selected vertical speed	Full Range	±5%	1	100 ft/min.	
52. Selected heading	Full Range	±5%	1	1 °	
53. Selected flight path	Full Range	±5%	1	1 °	
54. Selected decision height	Full Range	±5%	64	1 ft	
55. EFIS display format	Discrete(s)		4		Discretes should show the display system status (e.g. off, normal, fail, composite, sector, plan nav aids, weather radar, range, copy.
56. Multi-function Engine Alerts Display format	Discrete(s)		4		Discretes should show the display system status (e.g. off, normal, fail, and the identity of display pages for emergency procedures, need not be recorded.
57. Thrust command[17]	Full Range	±2%	2	2% of full range	
58. Thrust target	Full Range	±2%	4	2% of full range	
59. Fuel quantity in CG trim tank	Full Range	±5%	(1 per 64 sec.)	1% of full range	
60. Primary Navigation System Reference	Discrete GPS, INS, VOR/DME, MLS, Localizer Glideslope		4		A suitable combination of discretes to determine the Primary Navigation System reference.
61. Ice Detection	Discrete "ice" or "no ice"		4		
62. Engine warning each engine vibration	Discrete		1		
63. Engine warning each engine over temp	Discrete		1		
64. Engine warning each engine oil pressure low	Discrete		1		
65. Engine warning each engine over speed	Discrete		1		
66. Yaw Trim Surface Position	Full Range	±3% Unless Higher Accuracy Uniquely Required	2	0.3% of full range	
67. Roll Trim Surface Position	Full Range	±3% Unless Higher Accuracy Uniquely Required	2	0.3% of full range	
68. Brake Pressure (left and right	As installed	±5%	1		To determine braking effort applied by pilots or by autobrakes
69. Brake Pedal Application (left and right)	Discrete or Analog "applied" or "off"	±5% (analog)	1		To determine braking applied by pilots.
70. Yaw or sideslip angle	Full Range	±5%	1	0.5 °	
71. Engine bleed valve position	Discrete "open" or "closed"		4		
72. De-icing or anti-icing system selection	Discrete "on" or "off"		4		
73. Computed center of gravity	Full Range	±5%	(1 per 64 sec.)	1% of full range	
74. AC electrical bus status.	Discrete "power" or "off"		4		Each bus.
75. DC electrical bus status.	Discrete "power" or "off"		4		Each bus.
76. APU bleed valve position.	Discrete "open" or "closed"		4		
77. Hydraulic Pressure (each system)	Full Range	±5%	2	100 psi	
78. Loss of cabin pressure	Discrete "loss" or "normal"		1		

Appendix F to Part 135 — Airplane Flight Recorder Specification (Continued)

PARAMETERS	RANGE	ACCURACY (SENSOR INPUT)	SECONDS PER SAMPLING INTERVAL	RESOLUTION	REMARKS
79. Computer failure (critical flight and engine control systems)	Discrete(s) "fail" or "normal"		4		
80. Heads -up display (when an information source is installed)	Discrete(s) "on" or "off"		4		
81. Para-visual display (when an information source is installed)	Discrete(s) "on" or "off"		1		
82. Cockpit trim control input position - pitch	Full Range	±5%	1	0.2% of full range	
83. Cockpit trim control input position - roll	Full Range	±5%	1	0.7% of full range	Where mechanical means for control inputs are not available, cockpit display trim positions should be recorded.
84. Cockpit trim control input position - yaw	Full Range	±5%	1	0.3% of full range	Where mechanical means for control inputs are not available, cockpit display trim positions should be recorded.
85. Trailing edge flap and cockpit flap control position	Full Range	±5%	2	0.5% of full range	Trailing edge flaps and cockpit flap control position may each be sampled alternately at 4 second intervals to provide a sample each 0.5 second.
86. Leading edge flap and cockpit flap control position	Full Range or Discrete	±5%	1	0.5% of full range	
87. Ground spoiler position and speed brake selection	Full Range or Discrete	±5%	0.5	0.2% of full range	
88. All cockpit flight control input forces (control wheel, control column, rudder pedal)	Full Range Control wheel ±70 lbs Control Column ±85 lbs Rudder pedal ± 165 lbs	±5%	1	0.2% of full range	For fly-by-wire flight control systems, where flight control surface position is a function of the displacement of the control input device only, it is not necessary to record this parameter. For airplanes that have a flight control breakaway capability that allows either pilot to operate the control independently, record both control force inputs. The control force inputs may be sampled alternately once per 2 seconds to produce the sampling interval of 1.

[1] For A300 B2/B4 airplanes, resolution = 6 seconds.
[2] For A330/A340 series airplanes, resolution = 0.703°.
[3] For A318/A319/A320/A321 series airplanes, resolution = 0.275% (0.088°>0.064°). For A330/A340 series airplanes, resolution = 2.20% (0.703°>0.064°).
[4] For A318/A319/A320/A321 series airplanes, resolution = 0.22% (0.088°>0.080°). For A330/A340 series airplanes, resolution = 1.76% (0.703°>0.080°).
[5] For A330/A340 series airplanes, resolution = 1.18% (0.703°>0.120°).
[6] For A330/A340 series airplanes, resolution = 0.783% (0.352°>0.090°).
[7] For A330/A340 series airplanes, aileron resolution = 0.704% (0.352°>0.100°). For A330/A340 series airplanes, spoiler resolution = 1.406% (0.703°>0.100°).
[8] For A330/A340 series airplanes, resolution = 0.30% (0.176°>0.12°). For A330/A340 series airplanes, seconds per sampling interval = 1.
[9] For B-717 series airplanes, resolution = .005g. For Dassault F900C/F900EX airplanes, resolution = .007g.
[10] For A330/A340 series airplanes, resolution = 1.05% (0.250°>0.120°).
[11] For A330/A340 series airplanes, resolution = 1.05% (0.250°>0.120°). For A300 B2/B4 series airplanes, resolution = 0.92% (0.230°>0.125°).
[12] For A330/A340 series airplanes, spoiler resolution = 1.406% (0.703°>0.100°).
[13] For A330/A340 series airplanes, resolution = 0.5 °C.
[14] For Dassault F900C/F900EX airplanes, Radio Altitude resolution = 1.25 ft.
[15] For A330/A340 series airplanes, resolution = 0.352 degrees.
[16] For A318/A319/A320/A321 series airplanes, resolution = 4.32%. For A330/A340 series airplanes, resolution is 3.27% of full range for throttle lever angle (TLA); for reverse thrust, reverse throttle lever angle (RLA) resolution is nonlinear over the active reverse thrust range, which is 51.54 degrees to 96.14 degrees. The resolved element is 2.8 degrees uniformly over the entire active reverse thrust range, or 2.9% of the full range value of 96.14 degrees.
[17] For A318/A319/A320/A321 series airplanes, with IAE engines, resolution = 2.58%.
[18] For all aircraft manufactured on or after December 6, 2010, the seconds per sampling interval is 0.125. Each input must be recorded at this rate. Alternately sampling inputs (interleaving) to meet this sampling interval is prohibited.

[Doc. No. 28109, 62 FR 38398, July 17, 1997; 62 FR 48135, Sept. 12, 1997; Amdt. 135-85, 67 FR 54323, Aug. 21, 2002; Amdt. 135-89, 68 FR 42939, July 18, 2003; 68 FR 50069, Aug. 20, 2003; Amdt. 135-113, 73 FR 12570, Mar. 7, 2008; Amdt. 135-121, 75 FR 17047, Apr. 5, 2010; Amdt. 135-120, 75 FR 7357, Feb. 19, 2010; Docket FAA-2017-0733, Amdt. 135-137, 82 FR 34399, July 25, 2017]

Appendix G to Part 135 — Extended Operations (ETOPS)

G135.1 Definitions

G135.1.1

Adequate Airport means an airport that an airplane operator may list with approval from the FAA because that airport meets the landing limitations of 135.385 or is a military airport that is active and operational.

G135.1.2

ETOPS Alternate Airport means an adequate airport that is designated in a dispatch or flight release for use in the event of a diversion during ETOPS. This definition applies to flight planning and does not in any way limit the authority of the pilot in command during flight.

G135.1.3

ETOPS Entry Point means the first point on the route of an ETOPS flight, determined using a one-engine inoperative cruise speed under standard conditions in still air, that is more than 180 minutes from an adequate airport.

G135.1.4

ETOPS Qualified Person means a person, performing maintenance for the certificate holder, who has satisfactorily completed the certificate holder's ETOPS training program.

G135.2 Requirements

G135.2.1 General

After August 13, 2008, no certificate holder may operate an airplane, other than an all-cargo airplane with more than two engines, outside the continental United States more than 180 minutes flying time (at the one-engine-inoperative cruise speed under standard conditions in still air) from an airport described in 135.364 unless—

(a) The certificate holder receives ETOPS approval from the FAA;

(b) The operation is conducted in a multi-engine transport category turbine-powered airplane;

(c) The operation is planned to be no more than 240 minutes flying time (at the one engine inoperative cruise speed under standard conditions in still air) from an airport described in 135.364; and

(d) The certificate holder meets the requirements of this appendix.

G135.2.2 Required certificate holder experience prior to conducting ETOPS

Before applying for ETOPS approval, the certificate holder must have at least 12 months experience conducting international operations (excluding Canada and Mexico) with multi-engine transport category turbine-engine powered airplanes. The certificate holder may consider the following experience as international operations:

(a) Operations to or from the State of Hawaii.

(b) For certificate holders granted approval to operate under part 135 or part 121 before February 15, 2007, up to 6 months of domestic operating experience and operations in Canada and Mexico in multi-engine transport category turbojet-powered airplanes may be credited as part of the required 12 months of international experience required by paragraph G135.2.2(a) of this appendix.

(c) ETOPS experience with other aircraft types to the extent authorized by the FAA.

G135.2.3 Airplane requirements

No certificate holder may conduct ETOPS in an airplane that was manufactured after February 17, 2015 unless the airplane meets the standards of 25.1535.

G135.2.4 Crew information requirements

The certificate holder must ensure that flight crews have in-flight access to current weather and operational information needed to comply with 135.83, 135.225, and 135.229. This includes information on all ETOPS Alternate Airports, all destination alternates, and the destination airport proposed for each ETOPS flight.

G135.2.5 Operational Requirements

(a) No person may allow a flight to continue beyond its ETOPS Entry Point unless—

(1) The weather conditions at each ETOPS Alternate Airport are forecast to be at or above the operating minima in the certificate holder's operations specifications for that airport when it might be used (from the earliest to the latest possible landing time), and

(2) All ETOPS Alternate Airports within the authorized ETOPS maximum diversion time are reviewed for any changes in conditions that have occurred since dispatch.

(b) In the event that an operator cannot comply with paragraph G135.2.5(a)(1) of this appendix for a specific airport, another ETOPS Alternate Airport must be substituted within the maximum ETOPS diversion time that could be authorized for that flight with weather conditions at or above operating minima.

(c) Pilots must plan and conduct ETOPS under instrument flight rules.

(d) Time-Limited Systems.

(1) Except as provided in paragraph G135.2.5(d)(3) of this appendix, the time required to fly the distance to each ETOPS Alternate Airport (at the all-engines-operating cruise speed corrected for wind and temperature) may not exceed the time specified in the Airplane Flight Manual for the airplane's most limiting fire suppression system time required by regulation for any cargo or baggage compartments (if installed), minus 15 minutes.

(2) Except as provided in G135.2.5(d)(3) of this appendix, the time required to fly the distance to each ETOPS Alternate Airport (at the approved one-engine-inoperative cruise speed corrected for wind and temperature) may not exceed the time specified in the Airplane Flight Manual for the airplane's most time limited system time (other than the airplane's most limiting fire suppression system time required by regulation for any cargo or baggage compartments), minus 15 minutes.

(3) A certificate holder operating an airplane without the Airplane Flight Manual information needed to comply with paragraphs G135.2.5(d)(1) and (d)(2) of this appendix, may continue ETOPS with that airplane until February 17, 2015.

G135.2.6 Communications Requirements

(a) No person may conduct an ETOPS flight unless the following communications equipment, appropriate to the route to be flown is installed and operational:

(1) Two independent communication transmitters, at least one of which allows voice communication.

(2) Two independent communication receivers, at least one of which allows voice communication.

(3) Two headsets, or one headset and one speaker.

(b) In areas where voice communication facilities are not available or are of such poor quality that voice communication is not possible, communication using an alternative system must be substituted.

G135.2.7 Fuel Requirements

No person may dispatch or release for flight an ETOPS flight unless, considering wind and other weather conditions expected, it has the fuel otherwise required by this part and enough fuel to satisfy each of the following requirements:

(a) Fuel to fly to an ETOPS Alternate Airport.

(1) Fuel to account for rapid decompression and engine failure The airplane must carry the greater of the following amounts of fuel:

(i) Fuel sufficient to fly to an ETOPS Alternate Airport

assuming a rapid decompression at the most critical point followed by descent to a safe altitude in compliance with the oxygen supply requirements of 135.157;

(ii) Fuel sufficient to fly to an ETOPS Alternate Airport (at the one-engine-inoperative cruise speed under standard conditions in still air) assuming a rapid decompression and a simultaneous engine failure at the most critical point followed by descent to a safe altitude in compliance with the oxygen requirements of 135.157; or

(iii) Fuel sufficient to fly to an ETOPS Alternate Airport (at the one-engine-inoperative cruise speed under standard conditions in still air) assuming an engine failure at the most critical point followed by descent to the one engine inoperative cruise altitude.

(2) Fuel to account for errors in wind forecasting. In calculating the amount of fuel required by paragraph G135.2.7(a)(1) of this appendix, the certificate holder must increase the actual forecast wind speed by 5% (resulting in an increase in headwind or a decrease in tailwind) to account for any potential errors in wind forecasting. If a certificate holder is not using the actual forecast wind based on a wind model accepted by the FAA, the airplane must carry additional fuel equal to 5% of the fuel required by paragraph G135.2.7(a) of this appendix, as reserve fuel to allow for errors in wind data.

(3) Fuel to account for icing. In calculating the amount of fuel required by paragraph G135.2.7(a)(1) of this appendix, (after completing the wind calculation in G135.2.7(a)(2) of this appendix), the certificate holder must ensure that the airplane carries the greater of the following amounts of fuel in anticipation of possible icing during the diversion:

(i) Fuel that would be burned as a result of airframe icing during 10 percent of the time icing is forecast (including the fuel used by engine and wing anti-ice during this period).

(ii) Fuel that would be used for engine anti-ice, and if appropriate wing anti-ice, for the entire time during which icing is forecast.

(4) Fuel to account for engine deterioration. In calculating the amount of fuel required by paragraph G135.2.7(a)(1) of this appendix (after completing the wind calculation in paragraph G135.2.7(a)(2) of this appendix), the certificate holder must ensure the airplane also carries fuel equal to 5% of the fuel specified above, to account for deterioration in cruise fuel burn performance unless the certificate holder has a program to monitor airplane in-service deterioration to cruise fuel burn performance.

(b) Fuel to account for holding, approach, and landing. In addition to the fuel required by paragraph G135.2.7 (a) of this appendix, the airplane must carry fuel sufficient to hold at 1500 feet above field elevation for 15 minutes upon reaching the ETOPS Alternate Airport and then conduct an instrument approach and land.

(c) Fuel to account for APU use. If an APU is a required power source, the certificate holder must account for its fuel consumption during the appropriate phases of flight.

G135.2.8 Maintenance Program Requirements

In order to conduct an ETOPS flight under 135.364, each certificate holder must develop and comply with the ETOPS maintenance program as authorized in the certificate holder's operations specifications for each two-engine airplane-engine combination used in ETOPS. This provision does not apply to operations using an airplane with more than two engines. The certificate holder must develop this ETOPS maintenance program to supplement the maintenance program currently approved for the operator. This ETOPS maintenance program must include the following elements:

(a) ETOPS maintenance document. The certificate holder must have an ETOPS maintenance document for use by each person involved in ETOPS. The document must—

(1) List each ETOPS Significant System,

(2) Refer to or include all of the ETOPS maintenance elements in this section,

(3) Refer to or include all supportive programs and procedures,

(4) Refer to or include all duties and responsibilities, and

(5) Clearly state where referenced material is located in the certificate holder's document system.

(b) ETOPS pre-departure service check. The certificate holder must develop a pre-departure check tailored to their specific operation.

(1) The certificate holder must complete a pre-departure service check immediately before each ETOPS flight.

(2) At a minimum, this check must:

(i) Verify the condition of all ETOPS Significant Systems;

(ii) Verify the overall status of the airplane by reviewing applicable maintenance records; and

(iii) Include an interior and exterior inspection to include a determination of engine and APU oil levels and consumption rates.

(3) An appropriately trained maintenance person, who is ETOPS qualified must accomplish and certify by signature ETOPS specific tasks. Before an ETOPS flight may commence, an ETOPS pre-departure service check (PDSC) Signatory Person, who has been authorized by the certificate holder, must certify by signature, that the ETOPS PDSC has been completed.

(4) For the purposes of this paragraph (b) only, the following definitions apply:

(i) ETOPS qualified person: A person is ETOPS qualified when that person satisfactorily completes the operator's ETOPS training program and is authorized by the certificate holder.

(ii) ETOPS PDSC Signatory Person: A person is an ETOPS PDSC Signatory Person when that person is ETOPS Qualified and that person:

(A) When certifying the completion of the ETOPS PDSC in the United States:

(1) Works for an operator authorized to engage in part 135 or 121 operation or works for a part 145 repair station; and

(2) Holds a U.S. Mechanic's Certificate with airframe and powerplant ratings.

(B) When certifying the completion of the ETOPS PDSC outside of the U.S. holds a certificate in accordance with 43.17(c)(1) of this chapter; or

(C) When certifying the completion of the ETOPS PDSC outside the U.S. holds the certificates needed or has the requisite experience or training to return aircraft to service on behalf of an ETOPS maintenance entity.

(iii) ETOPS maintenance entity: An entity authorized to perform ETOPS maintenance and complete ETOPS pre-departure service checks and that entity is:

(A) Certificated to engage in part 135 or 121 operations;

(B) Repair station certificated under part 145 of this title; or

(C) Entity authorized pursuant to 43.17(c)(2) of this chapter.

(c) Limitations on dual maintenance.

(1) Except as specified in paragraph G135.2.8(c)(2) of this appendix, the certificate holder may not perform scheduled or unscheduled dual maintenance during the same maintenance visit on the same or a substantially similar ETOPS Significant System listed in the ETOPS maintenance document, if the improper maintenance could result in the failure of an ETOPS Significant System.

(2) In the event dual maintenance as defined in paragraph G135.2.8(c)(1) of this appendix cannot be avoided, the certificate holder may perform maintenance provided:

    (i) The maintenance action on each affected ETOPS Significant System is performed by a different technician, or

    (ii) The maintenance action on each affected ETOPS Significant System is performed by the same technician under the direct supervision of a second qualified individual; and

    (iii) For either paragraph G135.2.8(c)(2)(i) or (ii) of this appendix, a qualified individual conducts a ground verification test and any in-flight verification test required under the program developed pursuant to paragraph G135.2.8(d) of this appendix.

(d) Verification program. The certificate holder must develop a program for the resolution of discrepancies that will ensure the effectiveness of maintenance actions taken on ETOPS Significant Systems. The verification program must identify potential problems and verify satisfactory corrective action. The verification program must include ground verification and in-flight verification policy and procedures. The certificate holder must establish procedures to clearly indicate who is going to initiate the verification action and what action is necessary. The verification action may be performed on an ETOPS revenue flight provided the verification action is documented as satisfactorily completed upon reaching the ETOPS entry point.

(e) Task identification. The certificate holder must identify all ETOPS-specific tasks. An ETOPS qualified person must accomplish and certify by signature that the ETOPS-specific task has been completed.

(f) Centralized maintenance control procedures. The certificate holder must develop procedures for centralized maintenance control for ETOPS.

(g) ETOPS parts control program. The certificate holder must develop an ETOPS parts control program to ensure the proper identification of parts used to maintain the configuration of airplanes used in ETOPS.

(h) Each certificate holder who contracts for maintenance, preventive maintenance, or alterations must provide to its responsible Flight Standards office, in a format acceptable to the FAA, a list that includes the name and physical (street) address, or addresses, where the work is carried out for each maintenance provider that performs work for the certificate holder, and a description of the type of maintenance, preventive maintenance, or alteration that is to be performed at each location. The list must be updated with any changes, including additions or deletions, and the updated list provided to the FAA in a format acceptable to the FAA by the last day of each calendar month.

    (1) IFSDs, except planned IFSDs performed for flight training.

    (2) Diversions and turnbacks for failures, malfunctions, or defects associated with any airplane or engine system.

    (3) Uncommanded power or thrust changes or surges.

    (4) Inability to control the engine or obtain desired power or thrust.

    (5) Inadvertent fuel loss or unavailability, or uncorrectable fuel imbalance in flight.

    (6) Failures, malfunctions or defects associated with ETOPS Significant Systems.

    (7) Any event that would jeopardize the safe flight and landing of the airplane on an ETOPS flight.

(i) Propulsion system monitoring.

The certificate holder, in coordination with the responsible Flight Standards office, must—

    (1) Establish criteria as to what action is to be taken when adverse trends in propulsion system conditions are detected, and

    (2) Investigate common cause effects or systemic errors and submit the findings to the responsible Flight Standards office within 30 days.

(j) Engine condition monitoring.

    (1) The certificate holder must establish an engine-condition monitoring program to detect deterioration at an early stage and to allow for corrective action before safe operation is affected.

    (2) This program must describe the parameters to be monitored, the method of data collection, the method of analyzing data, and the process for taking corrective action.

    (3) The program must ensure that engine limit margins are maintained so that a prolonged engine-inoperative diversion may be conducted at approved power levels and in all expected environmental conditions without exceeding approved engine limits. This includes approved limits for items such as rotor speeds and exhaust gas temperatures.

(k) Oil consumption monitoring. The certificate holder must develop an engine oil consumption monitoring program to ensure that there is enough oil to complete each ETOPS flight. APU oil consumption must be included if an APU is required for ETOPS. The operator's consumption limit may not exceed the manufacturer's recommendation. Monitoring must be continuous and include oil added at each ETOPS departure point. The program must compare the amount of oil added at each ETOPS departure point with the running average consumption to identify sudden increases.

(l) APU in-flight start program. If an APU is required for ETOPS, but is not required to run during the ETOPS portion of the flight, the certificate holder must have a program acceptable to the FAA for cold soak in-flight start and run reliability.

(m) Maintenance training. For each airplane-engine combination, the certificate holder must develop a maintenance training program to ensure that it provides training adequate to support ETOPS. It must include ETOPS specific training for all persons involved in ETOPS maintenance that focuses on the special nature of ETOPS. This training must be in addition to the operator's maintenance training program used to qualify individuals for specific airplanes and engines.

(n) Configuration, maintenance, and procedures (CMP) document. The certificate holder must use a system to ensure compliance with the minimum requirements set forth in the current version of the CMP document for each airplane-engine combination that has a CMP.

(o) Reporting. The certificate holder must report quarterly to the responsible Flight Standards office and the airplane and engine manufacturer for each airplane authorized for ETOPS. The report must provide the operating hours and cycles for each airplane.

G135.2.9   Delayed compliance date for all airplanes

A certificate holder need not comply with this appendix for any airplane until August 13, 2008.

[Docket FAA-2011-1136, Amdt. 135-132, 80 FR 11547, Mar. 4, 2015, as amended by Docket FAA-2018-0119, Amdt. 135-139, 83 FR 9175, Mar. 5, 2018]

PART 145 — REPAIR STATIONS

Authority: 49 U.S.C. 106(g), 40113, 44701–44702, 44707, 44709, 44717.

Subpart A — General

Source: Docket No. FAA–1999–5836, 66 FR 41117, Aug. 6, 2001, unless otherwise noted.

145.1 Applicability

This part describes how to obtain a repair station certificate. This part also contains the rules a certificated repair station must follow related to its performance of maintenance, preventive maintenance, or alterations of an aircraft, airframe, aircraft engine, propeller, appliance, or component part to which part 43 applies. It also applies to any person who holds, or is required to hold, a repair station certificate issued under this part.

145.3 Definition of terms

For the purposes of this part, the following definitions apply:

(a) Accountable manager means the person designated by the certificated repair station who is responsible for and has the authority over all repair station operations that are conducted under part 145, including ensuring that repair station personnel follow the regulations and serving as the primary contact with the FAA.

(b) Article means an aircraft, airframe, aircraft engine, propeller, appliance, or component part.

(c) Directly in charge means having the responsibility for the work of a certificated repair station that performs maintenance, preventive maintenance, alterations, or other functions affecting aircraft airworthiness. A person directly in charge does not need to physically observe and direct each worker constantly but must be available for consultation on matters requiring instruction or decision from higher authority.

(d) Line maintenance means —

(1) Any unscheduled maintenance resulting from unforeseen events; or

(2) Scheduled checks that contain servicing and/or inspections that do not require specialized training, equipment, or facilities.

145.5 Certificate and operations specifications requirements

(a) No person may operate as a certificated repair station without, or in violation of, a repair station certificate, ratings, or operations specifications issued under this part.

(b) The certificate and operations specifications issued to a certificated repair station must be available on the premises for inspection by the public and the FAA.

145.12 Repair station records: Falsification, reproduction, alteration, or omission.

(a) No person may make or cause to be made:

(1) Any fraudulent or intentionally false entry in:

(i) Any application for a repair station certificate or rating (including in any document used in support of that application); or

(ii) Any record or report that is made, kept, or used to show compliance with any requirement under this part;

(2) Any reproduction, for fraudulent purpose, of any application (including any document used in support of that application), record, or report under this part; or

(3) Any alteration, for fraudulent purpose, of any application (including any document used in support of that application), record, or report under this part.

(b) No person may, by omission, knowingly conceal or cause to be concealed, a material fact in:

(1) Any application for a repair station certificate or rating (including in any document used in support of that application); or

(2) Any record or report that is made, kept, or used to show compliance with any requirement under this part.

(c) The commission by any person of an act prohibited under paragraphs (a) or (b) of this section is a basis for any one or any combination of the following:

(1) Suspending or revoking the repair station certificate and any certificate, approval, or authorization issued by the FAA and held by that person.

(2) A civil penalty.

(3) The denial of an application under this part.

[Doc. No. FAA-2006-26408, 79 FR 46984, Aug. 12, 2014]

Subpart B — Certification

Source: Docket No. FAA–1999–5836, 66 FR 41117, Aug. 6, 2001, unless otherwise noted.

145.51   Application for certificate

(a) An application for a repair station certificate and rating must be made in a format acceptable to the FAA and must include the following:

    (1) A repair station manual acceptable to the FAA as required by 145.207;

    (2) A quality control manual acceptable to the FAA as required by 145.211(c);

    (3) A list by type, make, or model, as appropriate, of each article for which the application is made;

    (4) An organizational chart of the repair station and the names and titles of managing and supervisory personnel;

    (5) A description of the housing and facilities, including the physical address, in accordance with 145.103;

    (6) A list of the maintenance functions, for approval by the FAA, to be performed for the repair station under contract by another person in accordance with 145.217; and

    (7) A training program for approval by the FAA in accordance with 145.163.

(b) The equipment, personnel, technical data, and housing and facilities required for the certificate and rating, or for an additional rating, must be in place for inspection at the time of certification or rating approval by the FAA. However, the requirement to have the equipment in place at the time of initial certification or rating approval may be met if the applicant has a contract acceptable to the FAA with another person to make the equipment available to the repair station at any time it is necessary when the relevant work is being performed.

(c) In addition to meeting the other applicable requirements for a repair station certificate and rating, an applicant for a repair station certificate and rating located outside the United States must meet the following requirements:

    (1) The applicant must show that the repair station certificate and/or rating is necessary for maintaining or altering the following:

        (i)   U.S.-registered aircraft and articles for use on U.S.-registered aircraft, or

        (ii) Foreign-registered aircraft operated under the provisions of part 121 or part 135, and articles for use on these aircraft.

    (2) The applicant must show that the fee prescribed by the FAA has been paid.

(d) An application for an additional rating, amended repair station certificate, or renewal of a repair station certificate must be made in a format acceptable to the FAA. The application must include only that information necessary to substantiate the change or renewal of the certificate.

(e) The FAA may deny an application for a repair station certificate if the FAA finds that:

    (1) The applicant holds a repair station certificate in the process of being revoked, or previously held a repair station certificate that was revoked;

    (2) The applicant intends to fill or fills a management position with an individual who exercised control over or who held the same or a similar position with a certificate holder whose repair station certificate was revoked, or is in the process of being revoked, and that individual materially contributed to the circumstances causing the revocation or causing the revocation process; or

    (3) An individual who will have control over or substantial ownership interest in the applicant had the same or similar control or interest in a certificate holder whose repair station certificate was revoked, or is in the process of being revoked, and that individual materially contributed to the circumstances causing the revocation or causing the revocation process.

(f) If the FAA revokes a repair station certificate, an individual described in paragraphs (e)(2) and (3) of this section is subject to an order under the procedures set forth in 14 CFR 13.20, finding that the individual materially contributed to the circumstances causing the revocation or causing the revocation process.

[Docket No. FAA-1999-5836, 66 FR 41117, Aug. 6, 2001, as amended by Amdt. 145-30, 79 FR 46984, Aug. 12, 2014]

145.53   Issue of certificate

(a) Except as provided in 145.51(e) or paragraph (b), (c), or (d) of this section, a person who meets the requirements of subparts A through E of this part is entitled to a repair station certificate with appropriate ratings prescribing such operations specifications and limitations as are necessary in the interest of safety.

(b) If the person is located in a country with which the United States has a bilateral aviation safety agreement, the FAA may find that the person meets the requirements of this part based on a certification from the civil aviation authority of that country. This certification must be made in accordance with implementation procedures signed by the Administrator or the Administrator's designee.

(c) Before a repair station certificate can be issued for a repair station that is located within the United States, the applicant shall certify in writing that all "hazmat employees" (see 49 CFR 171.8) for the repair station, its contractors, or subcontractors are trained as required in 49 CFR part 172 subpart H.

(d) Before a repair station certificate can be issued for a repair station that is located outside the United States, the applicant shall certify in writing that all employees for the repair station, its contractors, or subcontractors performing a job function concerning the transport of dangerous goods (hazardous material) are trained as outlined in the most current edition of the International Civil Aviation Organization Technical Instructions for the Safe Transport of Dangerous Goods by Air.

[Doc. No. FAA-2003-15085, 70 FR 58831, Oct. 7, 2005, as amended by Amdt. 145-30, 79 FR 46984, Aug. 12, 2014]

145.55   Duration and renewal of certificate

(a) A certificate or rating issued to a repair station located in the United States is effective from the date of issue until the repair station surrenders the certificate and the FAA accepts it for cancellation, or the FAA suspends or revokes it.

(b) A certificate or rating issued to a repair station located outside the United States is effective from the date of issue until the last day of the 12th month after the date of issue unless the repair station surrenders the certificate and the FAA accepts it for cancellation, or the FAA suspends or revokes it. The FAA may renew the certificate or rating for 24 months if the repair station has operated in compliance with the applicable requirements of part 145 within the preceding certificate duration period.

(c) A certificated repair station located outside the United States that applies for a renewal of its repair station certificate must—

    (1) Submit its request for renewal no later than 30 days before the repair station's current certificate expires. If a request for renewal is not made within this period, the repair station must follow the application procedures in 145.51.

    (2) Send its request for renewal to the FAA office that has jurisdiction over the certificated repair station.

    (3) Show that the fee prescribed by the FAA has been paid.

(d) The holder of an expired, surrendered, suspended, or revoked certificate must return it to the FAA.

[Docket No. FAA-1999-5836, 66 FR 41117, Aug. 6, 2001, as amended by Amdt. 145-30, 79 FR 46984, Aug. 12, 2014]

45.57 Amendment to or transfer of certificate

a) A repair station certificate holder applying for a change to its certificate must submit a request in a format acceptable to the Administrator. A change to the certificate must include certification in compliance with 145.53(c) or (d), if not previously submitted. A certificate change is necessary if the certificate holder—

(1) Changes the name or location of the repair station, or

(2) Requests to add or amend a rating.

b) If the holder of a repair station certificate sells or transfers its assets and the new owner chooses to operate as a repair station, the new owner must apply for an amended or new certificate in accordance with 145.51.

[Docket No. FAA-2006-26408, 79 FR 46984, Aug. 12, 2014]

45.59 Ratings

The following ratings are issued under this subpart:

a) Airframe ratings.

(1) Class 1: Composite construction of small aircraft.

(2) Class 2: Composite construction of large aircraft.

(3) Class 3: All-metal construction of small aircraft.

(4) Class 4: All-metal construction of large aircraft.

b) Powerplant ratings.

(1) Class 1: Reciprocating engines of 400 horsepower or less.

(2) Class 2: Reciprocating engines of more than 400 horsepower.

(3) Class 3: Turbine engines.

c) Propeller ratings.

(1) Class 1: Fixed-pitch and ground-adjustable propellers of wood, metal, or composite construction.

(2) Class 2: Other propellers, by make.

d) Radio ratings.

(1) Class 1: Communication equipment. Radio transmitting and/or receiving equipment used in an aircraft to send or receive communications in flight, regardless of carrier frequency or type of modulation used. This equipment includes auxiliary and related aircraft interphone systems, amplifier systems, electrical or electronic intercrew signaling devices, and similar equipment. This equipment does not include equipment used for navigating or aiding navigation of aircraft, equipment used for measuring altitude or terrain clearance, other measuring equipment operated on radio or radar principles, or mechanical, electrical, gyroscopic, or electronic instruments that are a part of communications radio equipment.

(2) Class 2: Navigational equipment. A radio system used in an aircraft for en route or approach navigation. This does not include equipment operated on radar or pulsed radio frequency principles, or equipment used for measuring altitude or terrain clearance.

(3) Class 3: Radar equipment. An aircraft electronic system operated on radar or pulsed radio frequency principles.

(e) Instrument ratings.

(1) Class 1: Mechanical. A diaphragm, bourdon tube, aneroid, optical, or mechanically driven centrifugal instrument used on aircraft or to operate aircraft, including tachometers, airspeed indicators, pressure gauges drift sights, magnetic compasses, altimeters, or similar mechanical instruments.

(2) Class 2: Electrical. Self-synchronous and electrical-indicating instruments and systems, including remote indicating instruments, cylinder head temperature gauges, or similar electrical instruments.

(3) Class 3: Gyroscopic. An instrument or system using gyroscopic principles and motivated by air pressure or electrical energy, including automatic pilot control units, turn and bank indicators, directional gyros, and their parts, and flux gate and gyrosyn compasses.

(4) Class 4: Electronic. An instrument whose operation depends on electron tubes, transistors, or similar devices, including capacitance type quantity gauges, system amplifiers, and engine analyzers.

(f) Accessory ratings.

(1) Class 1: A mechanical accessory that depends on friction, hydraulics, mechanical linkage, or pneumatic pressure for operation, including aircraft wheel brakes, mechanically driven pumps, carburetors, aircraft wheel assemblies, shock absorber struts and hydraulic servo units.

(2) Class 2: An electrical accessory that depends on electrical energy for its operation, and a generator, including starters, voltage regulators, electric motors, electrically driven fuel pumps magnetos, or similar electrical accessories.

(3) Class 3: An electronic accessory that depends on the use of an electron tube transistor, or similar device, including supercharger, temperature, air conditioning controls, or similar electronic controls.

145.61   Limited ratings

(a) The FAA may issue a limited rating to a certificated repair station that maintains or alters only a particular type of airframe, powerplant, propeller, radio, instrument, or accessory, or part thereof, or performs only specialized maintenance requiring equipment and skills not ordinarily performed under other repair station ratings. Such a rating may be limited to a specific model aircraft, engine, or constituent part, or to any number of parts made by a particular manufacturer.

(b) The FAA issues limited ratings for—

(1) Airframes of a particular make and model;

(2) Engines of a particular make and model;

(3) Propellers of a particular make and model;

(4) Instruments of a particular make and model;

(5) Radio equipment of a particular make and model;

(6) Accessories of a particular make and model;

(7) Landing gear components;

(8) Floats, by make;

(9) Nondestructive inspection, testing, and processing;

(10) Emergency equipment;

(11) Rotor blades, by make and model;

(12) Aircraft fabric work;

(13) Any other purpose for which the FAA finds the applicant's request is appropriate.

(c) For a limited rating for specialized services, the operations specifications of the repair station must contain the specification used to perform the specialized service. The specification may be—

(1) A civil or military specification currently used by industry and approved by the FAA, or

(2) A specification developed by the applicant and approved by the FAA.

Subpart C — Housing, Facilities, Equipment, Materials, and Data

Source: Docket No. FAA–1999–5836, 66 FR 41117, Aug. 6, 2001, unless otherwise noted.

145.101   General

A certificated repair station must provide housing, facilities, equipment, materials, and data that meet the applicable requirements for the issuance of the certificate and ratings the repair station holds.

145.103   Housing and facilities requirements

(a) Each certificated repair station must provide—

(1) Housing for the facilities, equipment, materials, and personnel consistent with its ratings and limitations.

(2) Facilities for properly performing the maintenance, preventive maintenance, or alterations of articles or the specialized service for which it is rated. Facilities must include the following:

    (i) Sufficient work space and areas for the proper segregation and protection of articles during all maintenance, preventive maintenance, or alterations.

    (ii) Segregated work areas enabling environmentally hazardous or sensitive operations such as painting, cleaning, welding, avionics work, electronic work, and machining to be done properly and in a manner that does not adversely affect other maintenance or alteration articles or activities;

    (iii) Suitable racks, hoists, trays, stands, and other segregation means for the storage and protection of all articles undergoing maintenance, preventive maintenance, or alterations, and;

    (iv) Space sufficient to segregate articles and materials stocked for installation from those articles undergoing maintenance, preventive maintenance, or alterations to the standards required by this part.

    (v) Ventilation, lighting, and control of temperature, humidity, and other climatic conditions sufficient to ensure personnel perform maintenance, preventive maintenance, or alterations to the standards required by this part.

(b) A certificated repair station may perform maintenance, preventive maintenance, or alterations on articles outside of its housing if it provides suitable facilities that are acceptable to the FAA and meet the requirements of §145.103(a) so that the work can be done in accordance with the requirements of part 43 of this chapter.

[Docket FAA-2016-8744, Amdt. 145-31, 81 FR 49163, July 27, 2016]

145.105   Change of location, housing, or facilities

(a) A certificated repair station may not change the location of its housing without written approval from the FAA.

(b) A certificated repair station may not make any changes to its housing or facilities required by 145.103 that could have a significant effect on its ability to perform the maintenance, preventive maintenance, or alterations under its repair station certificate and operations specifications without written approval from the FAA.

(c) The FAA may prescribe the conditions, including any limitations, under which a certificated repair station must operate while it is changing its location, housing, or facilities.

145.107   Satellite repair stations

(a) A certificated repair station under the managerial control of another certificated repair station may operate as a satellite repair station with its own certificate issued by the FAA. A satellite repair station—

    (1) May not hold a rating not held by the certificated repair station with managerial control;

    (2) Must meet the requirements for each rating it holds;

    (3) Must submit a repair station manual acceptable to the FAA as required by 145.207; and

    (4) Must submit a quality control manual acceptable to the FAA as required by 145.211(c).

(b) Unless the FAA indicates otherwise, personnel and equipment from the certificated repair station with managerial control and from each of the satellite repair stations may be shared. However, inspection personnel must be designated for each satellite repair station and available at the satellite repair station any time a determination of airworthiness or return to service is made. In other circumstances, inspection personnel may be away from the premises but must be available by telephone, radio, or other electronic means.

(c) A satellite repair station may not be located in a country other than the domicile country of the certificated repair station with managerial control.

145.109   Equipment, materials, and data requirements

(a) Except as otherwise prescribed by the FAA, a certificated repair station must have the equipment, tools, and materials necessary to perform the maintenance, preventive maintenance, or alterations under its repair station certificate and operations specifications in accordance with part 43. The equipment, tools, and material must be located on the premises and under the repair station's control when the work is being done.

(b) A certificated repair station must ensure all test and inspection equipment and tools used to make airworthiness determinations on articles are calibrated to a standard acceptable to the FAA.

(c) The equipment, tools, and material must be those recommended by the manufacturer of the article or must be at least equivalent to those recommended by the manufacturer and acceptable to the FAA.

(d) A certificated repair station must maintain, in a format acceptable to the FAA, the documents and data required for the performance of maintenance, preventive maintenance, or alterations under its repair station certificate and operations specifications in accordance with part 43. The following documents and data must be current and accessible when the relevant work is being done:

    (1) Airworthiness directives,

    (2) Instructions for continued airworthiness,

    (3) Maintenance manuals,

    (4) Overhaul manuals,

    (5) Standard practice manuals,

    (6) Service bulletins, and

    (7) Other applicable data acceptable to or approved by the FAA.

Subpart D — Personnel

Source: Docket No. FAA–1999–5836, 66 FR 41117, Aug. 6, 2001 unless otherwise noted.

145.151   Personnel requirements

Each certificated repair station must—

(a) Designate a repair station employee as the accountable manager;

(b) Provide qualified personnel to plan, supervise, perform, and approve for return to service the maintenance, preventive maintenance, or alterations performed under the repair station certificate and operations specifications;

(c) Ensure it has a sufficient number of employees with the training or knowledge and experience in the performance of maintenance, preventive maintenance, or alterations authorized by the repair station certificate and operations specifications to ensure all work is performed in accordance with part 43; and

(d) Determine the abilities of its noncertificated employees performing maintenance functions based on training, knowledge, experience, or practical tests.

145.153   Supervisory personnel requirements

(a) A certificated repair station must ensure it has a sufficient number of supervisors to direct the work performed under the repair station certificate and operations specifications. The supervisor must oversee the work performed by any individuals who are unfamiliar with the methods, techniques, practices, aids, equipment, and tools used to perform the maintenance, preventive maintenance, or alterations.

(b) Each supervisor must—

    (1) If employed by a repair station located inside the United States, be appropriately certificated as a mechanic or repairman under part 65 of this chapter for the work being supervised.

    (2) If employed by a repair station located outside the United States—

        (i) Have a minimum of 18 months of practical experience in the work being performed; or

(ii) Be trained in or thoroughly familiar with the methods, techniques, practices, aids, equipment, and tools used to perform the maintenance, preventive maintenance, or alterations.

(c) A certificated repair station must ensure its supervisors understand, read, and write English.

[Docket No. FAA-1999-5836, 66 FR 41117, Aug. 6, 2001, as amended by Amdt. 145-30, 79 FR 46984, Aug. 12, 2014]

145.155   Inspection personnel requirements

(a) A certificated repair station must ensure that persons performing inspections under the repair station certificate and operations specifications are—

(1) Thoroughly familiar with the applicable regulations in this chapter and with the inspection methods, techniques, practices, aids, equipment, and tools used to determine the airworthiness of the article on which maintenance, preventive maintenance, or alterations are being performed; and

(2) Proficient in using the various types of inspection equipment and visual inspection aids appropriate for the article being inspected.

(b) A certificated repair station must ensure its inspectors understand, read, and write English.

[Docket No. FAA-1999-5836, 66 FR 41117, Aug. 6, 2001, as amended by Amdt. 145-30, 79 FR 46985, Aug. 12, 2014]

145.157   Personnel authorized to approve an article for return to service

(a) A certificated repair station located inside the United States must ensure each person authorized to approve an article for return to service under the repair station certificate and operations specifications is appropriately certificated as a mechanic or repairman under part 65.

(b) A certificated repair station located outside the United States must ensure each person authorized to approve an article for return to service under the repair station certificate and operations specifications is—

(1) Trained in or has 18 months practical experience with the methods, techniques, practices, aids, equipment, and tools used to perform the maintenance, preventive maintenance, or alterations; and

(2) Thoroughly familiar with the applicable regulations in this chapter and proficient in the use of the various inspection methods, techniques, practices, aids, equipment, and tools appropriate for the work being performed and approved for return to service.

(c) A certificated repair station must ensure each person authorized to approve an article for return to service understands, reads, and writes English.

[Docket No. FAA-1999-5836, 66 FR 41117, Aug. 6, 2001, as amended by Amdt. 145-30, 79 FR 46985, Aug. 12, 2014]

145.159   Recommendation of a person for certification as a repairman

A certificated repair station that chooses to use repairmen to meet the applicable personnel requirements of this part must certify in a format acceptable to the FAA that each person recommended for certification as a repairman—

(a) Is employed by the repair station, and

(b) Meets the eligibility requirements of 65.101.

145.160   Employment of former FAA employees

(a) Except as specified in paragraph (c) of this section, no holder of a repair station certificate may knowingly employ or make a contractual arrangement which permits an individual to act as an agent or representative of the certificate holder in any matter before the Federal Aviation Administration if the individual, in the preceding 2 years—

(1) Served as, or was directly responsible for the oversight of, a Flight Standards Service aviation safety inspector; and

(2) Had direct responsibility to inspect, or oversee the inspection of, the operations of the certificate holder.

(b) For the purpose of this section, an individual shall be considered to be acting as an agent or representative of a certificate holder in a matter before the agency if the individual makes any written or oral communication on behalf of the certificate holder to the agency (or any of its officers or employees) in connection with a particular matter, whether or not involving a specific party and without regard to whether the individual has participated in, or had responsibility for, the particular matter while serving as a Flight Standards Service aviation safety inspector.

(c) The provisions of this section do not prohibit a holder of a repair station certificate from knowingly employing or making a contractual arrangement which permits an individual to act as an agent or representative of the certificate holder in any matter before the Federal Aviation Administration if the individual was employed by the certificate holder before October 21, 2011.

[Doc. No. FAA–2008–1154, 76 FR 52237, Aug. 22, 2011]

145.161   Records of management, supervisory, and inspection personnel

(a) A certificated repair station must maintain and make available in a format acceptable to the FAA the following:

(1) A roster of management and supervisory personnel that includes the names of the repair station officials who are responsible for its management and the names of its supervisors who oversee maintenance functions.

(2) A roster with the names of all inspection personnel.

(3) A roster of personnel authorized to sign a maintenance release for approving a maintained or altered article for return to service.

(4) A summary of the employment of each individual whose name is on the personnel rosters required by paragraphs (a)(1) through (a)(3) of this section. The summary must contain enough information on each individual listed on the roster to show compliance with the experience requirements of this part and must include the following:

(i) Present title,

(ii) Total years of experience and the type of maintenance work performed,

(iii) Past relevant employment with names of employers and periods of employment,

(iv) Scope of present employment, and

(v) The type of mechanic or repairman certificate held and the ratings on that certificate, if applicable.

(b) Within 5 business days of the change, the rosters required by this section must reflect changes caused by termination, reassignment, change in duties or scope of assignment, or addition of personnel.

145.163   Training requirements

(a) A certificated repair station must have and use an employee training program approved by the FAA that consists of initial and recurrent training. An applicant for a repair station certificate must submit a training program for approval by the FAA as required by 145.51(a)(7).

(1) An applicant for a repair station certificate must submit a training program for approval by the FAA as required by 145.51(a)(7).

(2) A repair station certificated before that date must submit its training program to the FAA for approval by the last day of the month in which its repair station certificate was issued.

(b) The training program must ensure each employee assigned to perform maintenance, preventive maintenance, or alterations, and inspection functions is capable of performing the assigned task.

(c) A certificated repair station must document, in a format acceptable to the FAA, the individual employee training required under paragraph (a) of this section. These training records must be retained for a minimum of 2 years.

(d) A certificated repair station must submit revisions to its training program to its responsible Flight Standards office in accordance with the procedures required by §145.209(e).

[Doc. No. FAA-1999-5836, 66 FR 41117, Aug. 6, 2001, as amended at 70 FR 15581, Mar. 28, 2005; Amdt. 145-30, 79 FR 46985, Aug. 12, 2014; Docket FAA-2018-0119, Amdt. 145-32, 83 FR 9176, Mar. 5, 2018]

145.165   Hazardous materials training

(a) Each repair station that meets the definition of a hazmat employer under 49 CFR 171.8 must have a hazardous materials training program that meets the training requirements of 49 CFR part 172 subpart H.

(b) A repair station employee may not perform or directly supervise a job function listed in 121.1001 or 135.501 for, or on behalf of the part 121 or 135 operator including loading of items for transport on an aircraft operated by a part 121 or part 135 certificate holder unless that person has received training in accordance with the part 121 or part 135 operator's FAA approved hazardous materials training program.

[Doc. No. FAA–2003–15085, 70 FR 58831, Oct. 7, 2005]

Subpart E — Operating Rules

Source: Docket No. FAA–1999–5836, 66 FR 41117, Aug. 6, 2001, unless otherwise noted.

145.201   Privileges and limitations of certificate

(a) A certificated repair station may—

(1) Perform maintenance, preventive maintenance, or alterations in accordance with part 43 on any article for which it is rated and within the limitations in its operations specifications.

(2) Arrange for another person to perform the maintenance, preventive maintenance, or alterations of any article for which the certificated repair station is rated. If that person is not certificated under part 145, the certificated repair station must ensure that the noncertificated person follows a quality control system equivalent to the system followed by the certificated repair station.

(3) Approve for return to service any article for which it is rated after it has performed maintenance, preventive maintenance, or an alteration in accordance with part 43.

(b) A certificated repair station may not maintain or alter any article for which it is not rated, and may not maintain or alter any article for which it is rated if it requires special technical data, equipment, or facilities that are not available to it.

(c) A certificated repair station may not approve for return to service'

(1) Any article unless the maintenance, preventive maintenance, or alteration was performed in accordance with the applicable approved technical data or data acceptable to the FAA.

(2) Any article after a major repair or major alteration unless the major repair or major alteration was performed in accordance with applicable approved technical data; and

(3) Any experimental aircraft after a major repair or major alteration performed under 43.1(b) unless the major repair or major alteration was performed in accordance with methods and applicable technical data acceptable to the FAA.

145.203   Work performed at another location

A certificated repair station may temporarily transport material, equipment, and personnel needed to perform maintenance, preventive maintenance, alterations, or certain specialized services on an article for which it is rated to a place other than the repair station's fixed location if the following requirements are met:

(a) The work is necessary due to a special circumstance, as determined by the FAA; or

(b) It is necessary to perform such work on a recurring basis, and the repair station's manual includes the procedures for accomplishing maintenance, preventive maintenance, alterations, or specialized services at a place other than the repair station's fixed location.

145.205   Maintenance, preventive maintenance, and alterations performed for certificate holders under parts 121, 125, and 135, and for foreign air carriers or foreign persons operating a U.S.-registered aircraft in common carriage under part 129

(a) A certificated repair station that performs maintenance, preventive maintenance, or alterations for an air carrier or commercial operator that has a continuous airworthiness maintenance program under part 121 or part 135 must follow the air carrier's or commercial operator's program and applicable sections of its maintenance manual.

(b) A certificated repair station that performs inspections for a certificate holder conducting operations under part 125 must follow the operator's FAA-approved inspection program.

(c) A certificated repair station that performs maintenance, preventive maintenance, or alterations for a foreign air carrier or foreign person operating a U.S.-registered aircraft under part 129 must follow the operator's FAA-approved maintenance program.

(d) The FAA may grant approval for a certificated repair station to perform line maintenance for an air carrier certificated under part 121 or part 135 of this chapter, or a foreign air carrier or foreign person operating a U.S.-registered aircraft in common carriage under part 129 of this chapter on any aircraft of that air carrier or person, provided-

(1) The certificated repair station performs such line maintenance in accordance with the operator's manual, if applicable, and approved maintenance program;

(2) The certificated repair station has the necessary equipment, trained personnel, and technical data to perform such line maintenance; and

(3) The certificated repair station's operations specifications include an authorization to perform line maintenance.

145.206   Notification of hazardous materials authorizations

(a) Each repair station must acknowledge receipt of the part 121 or part 135 operator notification required under 121.1005(e) and 135.505(e) of this chapter prior to performing work for, or on behalf of that certificate holder.

(b) Prior to performing work for or on behalf of a part 121 or part 135 operator, each repair station must notify its employees, contractors, or subcontractors that handle or replace aircraft components or other items regulated by 49 CFR parts 171 through 180 of each certificate holder's operations specifications authorization permitting, or prohibition against, carrying hazardous materials. This notification must be provided subsequent to the notification by the part 121 or part 135 operator of such operations specifications authorization/designation.

[Doc. No. FAA–2003–15085, 70 FR 58831, Oct. 7, 2005, as amended by Amdt. 145–25, 70 FR 75397, Dec. 20, 2005]

145.207   Repair station manual

(a) A certificated repair station must prepare and follow a repair station manual acceptable to the FAA.

(b) A certificated repair station must maintain a current repair station manual.

(c) A certificated repair station's current repair station manual must be accessible for use by repair station personnel required by subpart D of this part.

(d) A certificated repair station must provide to its responsible Flight Standards office the current repair station manual in a format acceptable to the FAA.

(e) A certificated repair station must notify its responsible Flight Standards office of each revision of its repair station manual in accordance with the procedures required by 145.209(j).

[Docket No. FAA-1999-5836, 66 FR 41117, Aug. 6, 2001, as amended by Docket FAA-2018-0119, Amdt. 145-32, 83 FR 9176, Mar. 5, 2018]

145.209 Repair station manual contents

A certificated repair station's manual must include the following:

(a) An organizational chart identifying—

    (1) Each management position with authority to act on behalf of the repair station,

    (2) The area of responsibility assigned to each management position, and

    (3) The duties, responsibilities, and authority of each management position;

(b) Procedures for maintaining and revising the rosters required by 145.161;

(c) A description of the certificated repair station's operations, including the housing, facilities, equipment, and materials as required by subpart C of this part;

(d) Procedures for—

    (1) Revising the capability list provided for in 145.215 and notifying the responsible Flight Standards office of revisions to the list, including how often the responsible Flight Standards office will be notified of revisions; and

    (2) The self-evaluation required under 145.215(c) for revising the capability list, including methods and frequency of such evaluations, and procedures for reporting the results to the appropriate manager for review and action;

(e) Procedures for revising the training program required by 145.163 and submitting revisions to the responsible Flight Standards office for approval;

(f) Procedures to govern work performed at another location in accordance with 145.203;

(g) Procedures for maintenance, preventive maintenance, or alterations performed under 145.205;

(h) Procedures for—

    (1) Maintaining and revising the contract maintenance information required by 145.217(a)(2)(i), including submitting revisions to the responsible Flight Standards office for approval; and

    (2) Maintaining and revising the contract maintenance information required by 145.217(a)(2)(ii) and notifying the responsible Flight Standards office of revisions to this information, including how often the responsible Flight Standards office will be notified of revisions;

(i) A description of the required records and the recordkeeping system used to obtain, store, and retrieve the required records;

(j) Procedures for revising the repair station's manual and notifying its responsible Flight Standards office of revisions to the manual, including how often the responsible Flight Standards office will be notified of revisions; and

(k) A description of the system used to identify and control sections of the repair station manual.

[Docket No. FAA-1999-5836, 66 FR 41117, Aug. 6, 2001, as amended by Docket FAA-2018-0119, Amdt. 145-32, 83 FR 9176, Mar. 5, 2018]

145.211 Quality control system

(a) A certificated repair station must establish and maintain a quality control system acceptable to the FAA that ensures the airworthiness of the articles on which the repair station or any of its contractors performs maintenance, preventive maintenance, or alterations.

(b) Repair station personnel must follow the quality control system when performing maintenance, preventive maintenance, or alterations under the repair station certificate and operations specifications.

(c) A certificated repair station must prepare and keep current a quality control manual in a format acceptable to the FAA that includes the following:

    (1) A description of the system and procedures used for—

        (i) Inspecting incoming raw materials to ensure acceptable quality;

        (ii) Performing preliminary inspection of all articles that are maintained;

        (iii) Inspecting all articles that have been involved in an accident for hidden damage before maintenance, preventive maintenance, or alteration is performed;

        (iv) Establishing and maintaining proficiency of inspection personnel;

        (v) Establishing and maintaining current technical data for maintaining articles;

        (vi) Qualifying and surveilling noncertificated persons who perform maintenance, prevention maintenance, or alterations for the repair station;

        (vii) Performing final inspection and return to service of maintained articles;

        (viii) Calibrating measuring and test equipment used in maintaining articles, including the intervals at which the equipment will be calibrated; and

        (ix) Taking corrective action on deficiencies;

    (2) References, where applicable, to the manufacturer's inspection standards for a particular article, including reference to any data specified by that manufacturer;

    (3) A sample of the inspection and maintenance forms and instructions for completing such forms or a reference to a separate forms manual; and

    (4) Procedures for revising the quality control manual required under this section and notifying the responsible Flight Standards office of the revisions, including how often the responsible Flight Standards office will be notified of revisions.

(d) A certificated repair station must notify its responsible Flight Standards office of revisions to its quality control manual.

[Docket No. FAA-1999-5836, 66 FR 41117, Aug. 6, 2001, as amended by Docket FAA-2018-0119, Amdt. 145-32, 83 FR 9176, Mar. 5, 2018]

145.213 Inspection of maintenance, preventive maintenance, or alterations

(a) A certificated repair station must inspect each article upon which it has performed maintenance, preventive maintenance, or alterations as described in paragraphs (b) and (c) of this section before approving that article for return to service.

(b) A certificated repair station must certify on an article's maintenance release that the article is airworthy with respect to the maintenance, preventive maintenance, or alterations performed after—

    (1) The repair station performs work on the article; and

    (2) An inspector inspects the article on which the repair station has performed work and determines it to be airworthy with respect to the work performed.

(c) For the purposes of paragraphs (a) and (b) of this section, an inspector must meet the requirements of 145.155.

(d) Except for individuals employed by a repair station located outside the United States, only an employee appropriately certificated as a mechanic or repairman under part 65 is authorized to sign off on final inspections and maintenance releases for the repair station.

[Docket No. FAA-1999-5836, 66 FR 41117, Aug. 6, 2001, as amended by Amdt. 145-30, 79 FR 46985, Aug. 12, 2014]

145.215 Capability list

(a) A certificated repair station with a limited rating may perform maintenance, preventive maintenance, or alterations on an article if the article is listed on a current capability list acceptable to the FAA or on the repair station's operations specifications.

(b) The capability list must identify each article by make and model or other nomenclature designated by the article's manufacturer and be available in a format acceptable to the FAA.

(c) An article may be listed on the capability list only if the article is within the scope of the ratings of the repair station's certificate, and only after the repair station has performed a self-evaluation in accordance with the procedures under 145.209(d)(2). The repair station must perform this self-evaluation to determine that the repair station has all of the housing, facilities, equipment, material, technical data, processes, and trained personnel in place to perform the work on the article as required by part 145. The repair station must retain on file documentation of the evaluation.

(d) Upon listing an additional article on its capability list, the repair station must provide its responsible Flight Standards office with a copy of the revised list in accordance with the procedures required in 145.209(d)(1).

[Docket No. FAA-1999-5836, 66 FR 41117, Aug. 6, 2001, as amended by Docket FAA-2018-0119, Amdt. 145-32, 83 FR 9176, Mar. 5, 2018]

145.217 Contract maintenance

(a) A certificated repair station may contract a maintenance function pertaining to an article to an outside source provided—

(1) The FAA approves the maintenance function to be contracted to the outside source; and

(2) The repair station maintains and makes available to its responsible Flight Standards office, in a format acceptable to the FAA, the following information:

(i) The maintenance functions contracted to each outside facility; and

(ii) The name of each outside facility to whom the repair station contracts maintenance functions and the type of certificate and ratings, if any, held by each facility.

(b) A certificated repair station may contract a maintenance function pertaining to an article to a noncertificated person provided—

(1) The noncertificated person follows a quality control system equivalent to the system followed by the certificated repair station;

(2) The certificated repair station remains directly in charge of the work performed by the noncertificated person; and

(3) The certificated repair station verifies, by test and/or inspection, that the work has been performed satisfactorily by the noncertificated person and that the article is airworthy before approving it for return to service.

(c) A certificated repair station may not provide only approval for return to service of a complete type-certificated product following contract maintenance, preventive maintenance, or alterations.

[Docket No. FAA-1999-5836, 66 FR 41117, Aug. 6, 2001, as amended by Docket FAA-2018-0119, Amdt. 145-32, 83 FR 9176, Mar. 5, 2018]

145.219 Recordkeeping

(a) A certificated repair station must retain records in English that demonstrate compliance with the requirements of part 43. The records must be retained in a format acceptable to the FAA.

(b) A certificated repair station must provide a copy of the maintenance release to the owner or operator of the article on which the maintenance, preventive maintenance, or alteration was performed.

(c) A certificated repair station must retain the records required by this section for at least 2 years from the date the article was approved for return to service.

(d) A certificated repair station must make all required records available for inspection by the FAA and the National Transportation Safety Board.

145.221 Service difficulty reports

(a) A certificated repair station must report to the FAA within 96 hours after it discovers any serious failure, malfunction, or defect of an article. The report must be in a format acceptable to the FAA.

(b) The report required under paragraph (a) of this section must include as much of the following information as is available:

(1) Aircraft registration number;

(2) Type, make, and model of the article;

(3) Date of the discovery of the failure, malfunction, or defect;

(4) Nature of the failure, malfunction, or defect;

(5) Time since last overhaul, if applicable;

(6) Apparent cause of the failure, malfunction, or defect; and

(7) Other pertinent information that is necessary for more complete identification, determination of seriousness, or corrective action.

(c) The holder of a repair station certificate that is also the holder of a part 121, 125, or 135 certificate; type certificate (including a supplemental type certificate); parts manufacturer approval; or technical standard order authorization, or that is the licensee of a type certificate holder, does not need to report a failure, malfunction, or defect under this section if the failure, malfunction, or defect has been reported under parts 21, 121, 125, or 135 of this chapter.

(d) A certificated repair station may submit a service difficulty report for the following:

(1) A part 121 certificate holder, provided the report meets the requirements of part 121 of this chapter, as appropriate.

(2) A part 125 certificate holder, provided the report meets the requirements of part 125 of this chapter, as appropriate.

(3) A part 135 certificate holder, provided the report meets the requirements of part 135 of the chapter, as appropriate.

(e) A certificated repair station authorized to report a failure, malfunction, or defect under paragraph (d) of this section must not report the same failure, malfunction, or defect under paragraph (a) of this section. A copy of the report submitted under paragraph (d) of this section must be forwarded to the certificate holder.

[Doc. No. FAA-1999-5836, 66 FR 41117, Aug. 6, 2001, as amended by Amdt. 22, 68 FR 75382, Dec. 30, 2003; Amdt. 145-26, 70 FR 76979, Dec. 29, 2005; Amdt. 145-30, 79 FR 46985, Aug. 12, 2014; Amdt. 145-30A, 79 FR 66607, Nov. 10, 2014]

145.223 FAA inspections

(a) A certificated repair station must allow the FAA to inspect that repair station at any time to determine compliance with this chapter.

(b) A certificated repair station may not contract for the performance of a maintenance function on an article with a noncertificated person unless it provides in its contract with the noncertificated person that the FAA may make an inspection and observe the performance of the noncertificated person's work on the article.

(c) A certificated repair station may not return to service any article on which a maintenance function was performed by a noncertificated person if the noncertificated person does not permit the FAA to make the inspection described in paragraph (b) of this section.

PART 147 — AVIATION MAINTENANCE TECHNICIAN SCHOOLS

Subpart A — General

Subpart B — Certification and Operating Requirements

Authority: 49 U.S.C. 106(g), 40113, 44701-44702, 44707-44709; Sec. 135, Public Law 116-260, 134 Stat. 1182.

Source: Docket No.: FAA-2021-0237; Amdt. No. 147-9; 87 FR 31415, May 24, 2022, unless otherwise noted.

Subpart A — General

147.1   Applicability

This part prescribes the requirements for issuing aviation maintenance technician school certificates and associated ratings and the general operating rules for the holders of those certificates and ratings.

147.3   Certificate required

No person may operate an aviation maintenance technician school without, or in violation of, an aviation maintenance technician school certificate and the operations specifications issued under this part.

147.5   Application requirements

(a) To be issued a certificate or rating under this part, an applicant must demonstrate compliance with the requirements of this part.

(b) An application for a certificate and rating to operate an aviation maintenance technician school must include the following:

(1) A description of the facilities, including the physical address of the applicant's primary location for operation of the school, and any additional fixed locations where training will be provided, and the equipment and materials to be used at each location;

(2) A description of the manner in which the school's curriculum will ensure the student has the knowledge and skills necessary for attaining a mechanic certificate and associated ratings under subpart D of part 65 of this chapter;

(3) A description of the manner in which the school will ensure it provides the necessary qualified instructors to meet the requirements of 147.19; and

(4) Any additional information necessary to demonstrate compliance with the requirements of this part.

(c) An application for an additional rating or amended certificate must include only the information required by paragraph (b) of this section that is necessary to substantiate the reason for the additional rating or change sought.

147.7   Duration of certificates

An aviation maintenance technician school certificate or rating issued under this part is effective from the date of issue until the certificate or rating is surrendered, suspended, or revoked.

147.11   Ratings

The following ratings may be issued under this part:

(a) Airframe.

(b) Powerplant.

(c) Airframe and powerplant.

Subpart B — Certification and Operating Requirements

147.13 Facilities, equipment, and material requirements

(a) Each certificated aviation maintenance technician school must provide and maintain the facilities, equipment, and materials that are appropriate to the rating or ratings held by the school and the number of students taught.

(b) For certificated aviation maintenance technician schools that provide training at more than one location in accordance with 147.15, the facilities, equipment, and materials used at each location must be appropriate to the curriculum or portion of the curriculum, and the number of students being taught, at that location.

147.15   Training provided at another location

A certificated aviation maintenance technician school may provide training at any fixed location other than its primary location, provided the additional training location meets the requirements of this part and is listed in the certificate holder's operations specifications.

147.17   Training requirements

(a) Each certificated aviation maintenance technician school must:

(1) Establish, maintain, and utilize a curriculum that is designed to continually align with the mechanic airman certification standards referenced in paragraph (b) of this section, as appropriate for the ratings held;

(2) Provide training of a quality that meets the requirements of 147.25; and

(3) Ensure students have the knowledge and skills necessary to be prepared to test for a mechanic certificate and associated ratings under subpart D of part 65 of this chapter.

(b) FAA-S-ACS-1, Aviation Mechanic General, Airframe, and Powerplant Airman Certification Standards, November 1, 2021, is incorporated by reference into this section with the approval of the Director of the Federal Register under 5 U.S.C. 552(a) and 1 CFR part 51. This material is available for inspection at the Federal Aviation Administration (FAA) and the National Archives and Records Administration (NARA). Contact FAA, Airman Testing Standards Branch/Regulatory Support Division, 405-954-4151, AFS630Comments@faa.gov. For information on the availability of this material at NARA, email: fr.inspection@nara.gov, or go to www.archives.gov/federal-register/cfr/ibr-locations.html. The material may be obtained from FAA, 800 Independence Avenue SW, Washington, DC 20591, 866-835-5322, www.faa.gov/training_testing.

147.19   Instructor requirements

Each certificated aviation maintenance technician school must:

(a) Provide qualified instructors to teach in a manner that ensures positive educational outcomes are achieved;

(b) Ensure instructors either -

(1) Hold a mechanic certificate with one or more appropriate ratings; or

(2) If they do not hold a mechanic certificate, are otherwise specifically qualified to teach their assigned content; and

(c) Ensure the student-to-instructor ratio does not exceed 25:1 for any shop class.

147.21   Certificate of completion

Each certificated aviation maintenance technician school must provide an authenticated document to each graduating student, indicating the student's date of graduation and curriculum completed.

147.23   Quality control system

(a) Each certificated aviation maintenance technician school must -

   (1) Be accredited within the meaning of 20 U.S.C. 1001(a)(5); or

   (2) Establish and maintain a quality control system that meets the requirements specified in paragraph (b) of this section, and is approved by the Administrator.

(b) The quality control system specified in paragraph (a)(2) of this section must provide procedures for recordkeeping, assessment, issuing credit, issuing of final course grades, attendance, ensuring sufficient number of instructors, granting of graduation documentation, and corrective action for addressing deficiencies.

147.25   Minimum passage rate

(a) Each certificated aviation maintenance technician school must maintain the pass rate specified in paragraph (b) of this section for the most recent 3-year period.

(b) For students who take an FAA mechanic test under part 65 of this chapter within 60 days after graduation, at least 70 percent of students must pass one of the following tests or any combination thereof:

   (1) Written test;

   (2) Oral test; or

   (3) Practical test.

(c) For students who take a combination of tests within the 60-day window specified in paragraph (b) of this section, an aviation maintenance technician school must count a failure on any one test as a student failure for purposes of determining the pass rate, unless that failed test is subsequently passed within the 60-day window.

147.27   FAA inspection

A certificated aviation maintenance technician school must allow the Administrator such access as the Administrator determines necessary to inspect the one or more locations of the school for purposes of determining the school's compliance with the requirements of this part.

147.29   Display of certificate

A certificated aviation maintenance technician school must display its aviation maintenance technician school certificate at a place in each location of the school, including the primary location and any additional fixed locations, that is visible by and normally accessible to the public.

147.31   Early testing

When a student satisfactorily completes the general portion of a certificated aviation maintenance technician school's curriculum, the school may issue an authenticated document that demonstrates the student's preparedness to take the mechanic general written test in accordance with 65.75(c) of this chapter.

PART 183—REPRESENTATIVES OF THE ADMINISTRATOR

Subpart A — General

Subpart B — Certification of Representatives

Subpart C — Kinds of Designations: Privileges

Subpart D — Organization Designation Authorization

Authority: 31 U.S.C. 9701; 49 U.S.C. 106(f), 106 (g), 40113, 44702, 45303.

Source: Docket No. 1151, 27 FR 4951, May 26, 1962, unless otherwise noted.

Editorial Note: For miscellaneous amendments to cross references in this part 183, see Amdt. 183–1, 31 FR 9211, July 6, 1966.

Subpart A — General

183.1   Scope

This part describes the requirements for designating private persons to act as representatives of the Administrator in examining, inspecting, and testing persons and aircraft for the purpose of issuing airman, operating, and aircraft certificates. In addition, this part states the privileges of those representatives and prescribes rules for the exercising of those privileges, as follows:

(a) An individual may be designated as a representative of the Administrator under subparts B or C of this part.

(b) An organization may be designated as a representative of the Administrator by obtaining an Organization Designation Authorization under subpart D of this part.

[Doc. No. FAA–2003–16685, 70 FR 59946, Oct. 13, 2005]

Subpart B — Certification of Representatives

183.11   Selection

(a) The Federal Air Surgeon, or his or her authorized representatives within the FAA, may select Aviation Medical Examiners from qualified physicians who apply. In addition, the Federal Air Surgeon may designate qualified forensic pathologists to assist in the medical investigation of aircraft accidents.

(b) Any local Flight Standards Inspector may select a pilot examiner, technical personnel examiner, or a designated aircraft maintenance inspector whenever he determines there is a need for one.

(c)

(1) The Aircraft Certification Service may select Designated Engineering Representatives from qualified persons who apply by a letter accompanied by a "Statement of Qualifications of Designated Engineering Representative."

(2) The Aircraft Certification Service may select Designated Manufacturing Inspection Representatives from qualified persons who apply by a letter accompanied by a "Statement of Qualifications of Designated Manufacturing Inspection Representative."

(d) The Associate Administrator for Air Traffic, may select Air Traffic Control Tower Operator Examiners.

(e) The Aircraft Certification Service may select Designated Airworthiness Representatives from qualified persons who apply by a letter accompanied by a "Statement of Qualifications of Designated Airworthiness Representative."

(Approved by the Office of Management and Budget under control number 2120-0035)

(Secs. 313(a), 314, 601, 603, 605, and 1102, Federal Aviation Act of 1958, as amended (49 U.S.C. 1354(a), 1355, 1421, 1423, 1425, and 1502); sec. 6(c) Department of Transportation Act (49 U.S.C. 1655(c)))

[Doc. No. 1151, 27 FR 4951, May 26, 1962, as amended by Amdt. 183-7, 45 FR 32669, May 19, 1980; Amdt. 183-8, 48 FR 16179, Apr. 14, 1983; Amdt. 183-9, 54 FR 39296, Sept. 25, 1989; Amdt. 183-13, 73 FR 43066, July 24, 2008; Docket FAA-2018-0119, Amdt. 183-17, 83 FR 9176, Mar. 5, 2018]

183.13   Certification

(a) A "Certificate of Designation" and an appropriate Identification Card is issued to each Aviation Medical Examiner and to each forensic pathologist designated under 183.11(a).

(b) A "Certificate of Authority" specifying the kinds of designation for which the person concerned is qualified and stating an expiration date is issued to each Flight Standards Designated Representative, along with a "Certificate of Designation" for display purposes, designating the holder as a Flight Standards Representative and specifying the kind of designation for which he is qualified.

(c) A "Certificate of Authority," stating the specific functions which the person concerned is authorized to perform and stating an expiration date, is issued to each Designated Airworthiness Representative, along with a "Certificate of Designation" for display purposes.

(Secs. 601 and 602, 72 Stat. 752, 49 U.S.C. 1421–1422; secs. 313(a), 314, 601, 603, 605, and 1102, Federal Aviation Act of 1958, as amended (49 U.S.C. 1354(a), 1355, 1421, 1423, 1425, and 1502); sec. 6(c) Department of Transportation Act (49 U.S.C. 1655(c)))

[Doc. No. 1151, 27 FR 4951, May 26, 1962, as amended by Amdt. 183–2, 32 FR 46, Jan. 5, 1967; Amdt. 183–8, 48 FR 16179, Apr. 14, 1983]

183.15   Duration of certificates

(a) Unless sooner terminated under paragraph (b) of this section, a designation as an Aviation Medical Examiner or as a Flight Standards or Aircraft Certification Service Designated Representative as described in 183.21, 183.23, 183.25, 183.27, 183.29, 183.31, or 183.33 is effective until the expiration date shown on the document granting the authorization.

(b) A designation made under this subpart terminates:

(1) Upon the written request of the representative;

(2) Upon the written request of the employer in any case in which the recommendation of the employer is required for the designation;

(3) Upon the representative being separated from the employment of the employer who recommended him or her for certification;

(4) Upon a finding by the Administrator that the representative has not properly performed his or her duties under the designation;

(5) Upon the assistance of the representative being no longer needed by the Administrator; or

(6) For any reason the Administrator considers appropriate.

[Doc. No. FAA–2007–27812, 73 FR 43066, July 24, 2008]

183.17   Reports

Each representative designated under this part shall make such reports as are prescribed by the Administrator.

Subpart C — Kinds of Designations: Privileges

183.21   Aviation Medical Examiners

An Aviation Medical Examiner may—

(a) Accept applications for physical examinations necessary for issuing medical certificates under part 67 of this chapter;

(b) Under the general supervision of the Federal Air Surgeon or the appropriate senior regional flight surgeon, conduct those physical examinations;

(c) Issue or deny medical certificates in accordance with part 67 of this chapter, subject to reconsideration by the Federal Air Surgeon or his or her authorized representatives within the FAA; and

(d) [Reserved.]

(e) As requested, participate in investigating aircraft accidents.

(Secs. 601 and 602, 72 Stat. 752, 49 U.S.C. 1421–1422)

[Doc. No. 1151, 27 FR 4951, May 26, 1962, as amended by Amdt. 183-2, 32 FR 46, Jan. 5, 1967; Amdt. 183-5, 38 FR 12203, May 10, 1973; Docket FAA-2010-1127, Amdt. 183-15, 81 FR 1307, Jan. 12, 2016]

183.23   Pilot examiners

Any pilot examiner, instrument rating examiner, or airline transport pilot examiner may—

(a) As authorized in his designation, accept applications for flight tests necessary for issuing pilot certificates and ratings under this chapter;

(b) Under the general supervision of the appropriate local Flight Standards Inspector, conduct those tests;

(c) In the discretion of the appropriate local Flight Standards Inspector, issue temporary pilot certificates and ratings to qualified applicants; and

(d) Accept an application for a remote pilot certificate with a small UAS rating and verify the identity of the applicant in a form and manner acceptable to the Administrator.

[Docket 1151, 27 FR 4951, May 26, 1962, as amended by Docket FAA-2015-0150, Amdt. 183-16, 81 FR 42214, June 28, 2016]

183.25   Technical personnel examiners

(a) A designated mechanic examiner (DME) (airframe and power plant) may—

(1) Accept applications for, and conduct, mechanic, oral and practical tests necessary for issuing mechanic certificates under part 65 of this chapter; and

(2) In the discretion of the appropriate local Flight Standards Inspector, issue temporary mechanic certificates to qualified applicants.

(b) A designated parachute rigger examiner (DPRE) may—

(1) Accept applications for, and conduct, oral and practical tests necessary for issuing parachute rigger certificates under part 65 of this chapter; and

(2) In the discretion of the appropriate local Flight Standards Inspector, issue temporary parachute rigger certificates to qualified applicants.

(c) An air traffic control tower operator examiner may—

(1) Accept applications for, and conduct, written and practical tests necessary for issuing control tower operator certificates under part 65 of this chapter; and

(2) In the discretion of the Associate Administrator for Air Traffic issue temporary control tower operator certificates to qualified applicants.

(d) A designated flight engineer examiner (DFEE) may—

(1) Accept applications for, and conduct, oral and practical tests necessary for issuing flight engineer certificates under part 63 of this chapter; and

(2) In the discretion of the appropriate local Flight Standards Inspector, issue temporary flight engineer certificates to qualified applicants.

(e) A designated flight navigator examiner (DFNE) may—

(1) Accept applications for, and conduct, oral and practical tests necessary for issuing flight navigator certificates under part 63 of this chapter; and

(2) In the discretion of the appropriate local Flight Standards Inspector, issue temporary flight navigator certificates to qualified applicants.

(f) A designated aircraft dispatcher examiner (DADE) may—

(1) Accept applications for, and conduct, written and practical tests necessary for issuing aircraft dispatcher certificates under part 65 of this chapter; and

(2) In the discretion of the appropriate local Flight Standards Inspector, issue temporary aircraft dispatcher certificates to qualified applicants.

[Doc. No. 1151, 27 FR 4951, May 26, 1962, as amended by Amdt. 183–9, 54 FR 39296, Sept. 25, 1989]

183.27   Designated aircraft maintenance inspectors

A designated aircraft maintenance inspector (DAMI) may approve maintenance on civil aircraft used by United States military flying clubs in foreign countries.

183.29   Designated engineering representatives

(a) A structural engineering representative may approve structural engineering information and other structural considerations within limits prescribed by and under the general supervision of the Administrator, whenever the representative determines that information and other structural considerations comply with the applicable regulations of this chapter.

(b) A power plant engineering representative may approve information relating to power plant installations within limitations prescribed by and under the general supervision of the Administrator whenever the representative determines that information complies with the applicable regulations of this chapter.

(c) A systems and equipment engineering representative may approve engineering information relating to equipment and systems, other than those of a structural, powerplant, or radio nature, within limits prescribed by and under the general supervision of the Administrator, whenever the representative determines that information complies with the applicable regulations of this chapter.

(d) A radio engineering representative may approve engineering information relating to the design and operating characteristics of radio equipment, within limits prescribed by and under the general supervision of the Administrator whenever the representative determines that information complies with the applicable regulations of this chapter.

(e) An engine engineering representative may approve engineering information relating to engine design, operation and service, within limits prescribed by and under the general supervision of the Administrator, whenever the representative determines that information complies with the applicable regulations of this chapter.

(f) A propeller engineering representative may approve engineering information relating to propeller design, operation, and maintenance, within limits prescribed by and under the general supervision of the Administrator whenever the representative determines that information complies with the applicable regulations of this chapter.

(g) A flight analyst representative may approve flight test information, within limits prescribed by and under the general supervision of the Administrator, whenever the representative determines that information complies with the applicable regulations of this chapter.

(h) A flight test pilot representative may make flight tests, and prepare and approve flight test information relating to compliance with the regulations of this chapter, within limits prescribed by and under the general supervision of the Administrator.

(i) An acoustical engineering representative may witness and approve aircraft noise certification tests and approve measured noise data and evaluated noise data analyses, within the limits prescribed by, and under the general supervision of, the Administrator, whenever the representative determines that the noise test, test data, and associated analyses are in conformity with the applicable regulations of this chapter. Those regulations include, where appropriate, the methodologies and any equivalencies previously approved by the Director of Environment and Energy, for that noise test series. No designated acoustical engineering representative may determine that a type design change is not an acoustical change, or approve equivalencies to prescribed noise procedures or standards.

[Doc. No. 1151, 27 FR 4951, May 26, 1962, as amended by Amdt. 183–7, 45 FR 32669, May 19, 1980; Amdt. 183–9, 54 FR 39296, Sept. 25, 1989]

183.31 Designated manufacturing inspection representatives

A designated manufacturing inspection representative (DMIR) may, within limits prescribed by, and under the general supervision of, the Administrator, do the following:

(a) Issue—

(1) Original airworthiness certificates for aircraft and airworthiness approvals for engines, propellers, and product parts that conform to the approved design requirements and are in a condition for safe operation;

(2) Export certificates of airworthiness and airworthiness approval tags in accordance with subpart L of part 21 of this chapter;

(3) Experimental certificates for aircraft for which the manufacturer holds the type certificate and which have undergone changes to the type design requiring a flight test; and

(4) Special flight permits to export aircraft.

(b) Conduct any inspections that may be necessary to determine that—

(1) Prototype products and related parts conform to design specifications; and

(2) Production products and related parts conform to the approved type design and are in condition for safe operation.

(c) Perform functions authorized by this section for the manufacturer, or the manufacturer's supplier, at any location authorized by the FAA.

[Doc. No. 16622, 45 FR 1416, Jan. 7, 1980]

183.33 Designated Airworthiness Representative

A Designated Airworthiness Representative (DAR) may, within limits prescribed by and under the general supervision of the Administrator, do the following:

(a) Perform examination, inspection, and testing services necessary to issue, and to determine the continuing effectiveness of, certificates, including issuing certificates, as authorized by the Executive Director, Flight Standards Service in the area of maintenance or as authorized by the Executive Director, Aircraft Certification Service in the areas of manufacturing and engineering.

(b) Charge a fee for his or her services.

(c) Perform authorized functions at any authorized location.

(Secs. 313(a), 314, 601, 603, 605, and 1102, Federal Aviation Act of 1958, as amended (49 U.S.C. 1354(a), 1355, 1421, 1423, 1425, and 1502); sec.6(c) Department of Transportation Act (49 U.S.C. 1655(c)))

[Doc. No. 23140, 48 FR 16179, Apr. 14, 1983, as amended by Amdt. 183-9, 54 FR 39296, Sept. 25, 1989; Amdt. 183-11, 67 FR 72766, Dec. 6, 2002; Docket FAA-2018-0119, Amdt. 183-17, 83 FR 9176, Mar. 5, 2018]

Subpart D — Organization Designation Authorization

Source: Doc. No. FAA–2003–16685, 70 FR 59947, Oct. 13, 2005, unless otherwise noted.

183.41 Applicability and definitions

(a) This subpart contains the procedures required to obtain an Organization Designation Authorization, which allows an organization to perform specified functions on behalf of the Administrator related to engineering, manufacturing, operations, airworthiness, or maintenance.

(b) Definitions. For the purposes of this subpart:

Organization Designation Authorization (ODA) means the authorization to perform approved functions on behalf of the Administrator.

ODA Holder means the organization that obtains the authorization from the Administrator, as identified in a Letter of Designation.

ODA Unit means an identifiable group of two or more individuals within the ODA Holder's organization that performs the authorized functions.

183.43 Application

An application for an ODA may be submitted after November 14, 2006. An application for an ODA must be submitted in a form and manner prescribed by the Administrator and must include the following:

(a) A description of the functions for which authorization is requested.

(b) A description of how the applicant satisfies the requirements of 183.47 of this part;

(c) A description of the applicant's organizational structure, including a description of the proposed ODA Unit as it relates to the applicant's organizational structure; and

(d) A proposed procedures manual as described in 183.53 of this part.

183.45 Issuance of Organization Designation Authorizations

(a) The Administrator may issue an ODA Letter of Designation if:

(1) The applicant meets the applicable requirements of this subpart; and

(2) A need exists for a delegation of the function.

(b) An ODA Holder must apply to and obtain approval from the Administrator for any proposed changes to the functions or limitations described in the ODA Holder's authorization.

183.47 Qualifications

To qualify for consideration as an ODA, the applicant must—

(a) Have sufficient facilities, resources, and personnel, to perform the functions for which authorization is requested;

(b) Have sufficient experience with FAA requirements, processes, and procedures to perform the functions for which authorization is requested; and

(c) Have sufficient, relevant experience to perform the functions for which authorization is requested.

183.49 Authorized functions

(a) Consistent with an ODA Holder's qualifications, the Administrator may delegate any function determined appropriate under 49 U.S.C. 44702(d).

(b) Under the general supervision of the Administrator, an ODA Unit may perform only those functions, and is subject to the limitations, listed in the ODA Holder's procedures manual.

183.51   ODA Unit personnel

Each ODA Holder must have within its ODA Unit—

(a) At least one qualified ODA administrator; and either

(b) A staff consisting of the engineering, flight test, inspection, or maintenance personnel needed to perform the functions authorized. Staff members must have the experience and expertise to find compliance, determine conformity, determine airworthiness, issue certificates or issue approvals; or

(c) A staff consisting of operations personnel who have the experience and expertise to find compliance with the regulations governing the issuance of pilot, crew member, or operating certificates, authorizations, or endorsements as needed to perform the functions authorized.

183.53   Procedures manual

No ODA Letter of Designation may be issued before the Administrator approves an applicant's procedures manual. The approved manual must:

(a) Be available to each member of the ODA Unit;

(b) Include a description of those changes to the manual or procedures that may be made by the ODA Holder. All other changes to the manual or procedures must be approved by the Administrator before they are implemented.

(c) Contain the following:

(1) The authorized functions and limitations, including the products, certificates, and ratings;

(2) The procedures for performing the authorized functions;

(3) Description of the ODA Holder's and the ODA Unit's organizational structure and responsibilities;

(4) A description of the facilities at which the authorized functions are performed;

(5) A process and a procedure for periodic audit by the ODA Holder of the ODA Unit and its procedures;

(6) The procedures outlining actions required based on audit results, including documentation of all corrective actions;

(7) The procedures for communicating with the appropriate FAA offices regarding administration of the delegation authorization;

(8) The procedures for acquiring and maintaining regulatory guidance material associated with each authorized function;

(9) The training requirements for ODA Unit personnel;

(10) For authorized functions, the procedures and requirements related to maintaining and submitting records;

(11) A description of each ODA Unit position, and the knowledge and experience required for each position;

(12) The procedures for appointing ODA Unit members and the means of documenting Unit membership, as required under 183.61(a)(4) of this part;

(13) The procedures for performing the activities required by 183.63 or 183.65 of this part;

(14) The procedures for revising the manual, pursuant to the limitations of paragraph (b) of this section; and

(15) Any other information required by the Administrator necessary to supervise the ODA Holder in the performance of its authorized functions.

183.55   Limitations

(a) If any change occurs that may affect an ODA Unit's qualifications or ability to perform a function (such as a change in the location of facilities, resources, personnel or the organizational structure), no Unit member may perform that function until the Administrator is notified of the change, and the change is approved and appropriately documented as required by the procedures manual.

(b) No ODA Unit member may issue a certificate, authorization, or other approval until any findings reserved for the Administrator have been made.

(c) An ODA Holder is subject to any other limitations as specified by the Administrator.

183.57   Responsibilities of an ODA Holder

The ODA Holder must—

(a) Comply with the procedures contained in its approved procedures manual;

(b) Give ODA Unit members sufficient authority to perform the authorized functions;

(c) Ensure that no conflicting non-ODA Unit duties or other interference affects the performance of authorized functions by ODA Unit members.

(d) Cooperate with the Administrator in his performance of oversight of the ODA Holder and the ODA Unit.

(e) Notify the Administrator of any change that could affect the ODA Holder's ability to continue to meet the requirements of this part within 48 hours of the change occurring.

183.59   Inspection

The Administrator, at any time and for any reason, may inspect an ODA Holder's or applicant's facilities, products, components, parts, appliances, procedures, operations, and records associated with the authorized or requested functions.

183.61   Records and reports

(a) Each ODA Holder must ensure that the following records are maintained for the duration of the authorization:

(1) [Reserved]

(2) For any approval or certificate issued by an ODA Unit member (except those airworthiness certificates and approvals not issued in support of type design approval projects):

(i)   The application and data required to be submitted under this chapter to obtain the certificate or approval; and

(ii) The data and records documenting the ODA Unit member's approval or determination of compliance.

(3) A list of the products, components, parts, or appliances for which ODA Unit members have issued a certificate or approval.

(4) The names, responsibilities, qualifications and example signature of each member of the ODA Unit who performs an authorized function.

(5) A copy of each manual approved or accepted by the ODA Unit, including all historical changes.

(6) Training records for ODA Unit members and ODA administrators.

(7) Any other records specified in the ODA Holder's procedures manual.

(8) The procedures manual required under 183.53 of this part, including all changes.

(b) Each ODA Holder must ensure that the following are maintained for five years:

(1) A record of each periodic audit and any corrective actions resulting from them; and

(2) A record of any reported service difficulties associated with approvals or certificates issued by an ODA Unit member.

(c) For airworthiness certificates and approvals not issued in support of a type design approval project, each ODA Holder must ensure the following are maintained for two years;

(1) The application and data required to be submitted under this chapter to obtain the certificate or approval; and

(2) The data and records documenting the ODA Unit member's approval or determination of compliance.

(d) For all records required by this section to be maintained, each ODA Holder must:

(1) Ensure that the records and data are available to the Administrator for inspection at any time;

(2) Submit all records and data to the Administrator upon surrender or termination of the authorization.

(e) Each ODA Holder must compile and submit any report required by the Administrator to exercise his supervision of the ODA Holder.

[Doc. No. FAA–2003–16685, 70 FR 59947, Oct. 13, 2005, as amended by Amdt. 183–14, 76 FR 8893, Feb. 16, 2011]

183.63 Continuing requirements: Products, parts or appliances

For any approval or certificate for a product, part or appliance issued under the authority of this subpart, an ODA Holder must:

(a) Monitor reported service problems related to certificates or approvals it holds;

(b) Notify the Administrator of:

(1) A condition in a product, part or appliance that could result in a finding of unsafe condition by the Administrator; or

(2) A product, part or appliance not meeting the applicable airworthiness requirements for which the ODA Holder has obtained or issued a certificate or approval.

(c) Investigate any suspected unsafe condition or finding of noncompliance with the airworthiness requirements for any product, part or appliance, as required by the Administrator, and report to the Administrator the results of the investigation and any action taken or proposed.

(d) Submit to the Administrator the information necessary to implement corrective action needed for safe operation of the product, part or appliance.

[Doc. No. FAA–2003–16685, 70 FR 59947, Oct. 13, 2005, as amended by Amdt. 183–14, 76 FR 8893, Feb. 16, 2011]

183.65 Continuing requirements: Operational approvals

For any operational authorization, airman certificate, air carrier certificate, air operator certificate, or air agency certificate issued under the authority of this subpart, an ODA Holder must:

(a) Notify the Administrator of any error that the ODA Holder finds it made in issuing an authorization or certificate;

(b) Notify the Administrator of any authorization or certificate that the ODA Holder finds it issued to an applicant not meeting the applicable requirements;

(c) When required by the Administrator, investigate any problem concerning the issuance of an authorization or certificate; and

(d) When notified by the Administrator, suspend issuance of similar authorizations or certificates until the ODA Holder implements all corrective action required by the Administrator.

183.67 Transferability and duration

(a) An ODA is effective until the date shown on the Letter of Designation, unless sooner terminated by the Administrator.

(b) No ODA may be transferred at any time.

(c) The Administrator may terminate or temporarily suspend an ODA for any reason, including that the ODA Holder:

(1) Has requested in writing that the authorization be suspended or terminated;

(2) Has not properly performed its duties;

(3) Is no longer needed; or

(4) No longer meets the qualifications required to perform authorized functions.

PART 193 — PROTECTION OF VOLUNTARILY SUBMITTED INFORMATION

193.1   What does this part cover?
193.3   Definitions.
193.5   How may I submit safety or security information and have it protected from disclosure?
193.7   What does it mean for the FAA to designate information as protected?
193.9   Will the FAA ever disclose information that is designated as protected under this part?
193.11   What is the notice procedure?
193.13   What is the no-notice procedure?
193.15   What FAA officials exercise the authority of the Administrator under this part?
193.17   How must design and production approval holders handle information they receive from the FAA under this part?

Authority: 49 U.S.C. 106(g), 40113, 40123.

Source: 66 FR 33805, June 25, 2001, unless otherwise note.

193.1   What does this part cover?

This part describes when and how the FAA protects from disclosure safety and security information that you submit voluntarily to the FAA. This part carries out 49 U.S.C. 40123, protection of voluntarily submitted information.

193.3   Definitions.

Agency means each authority of the Government of the United States, whether or not the agency is within or subject to review by another agency, but does not include—

(1) The Congress;

(2) The courts of the United States;

(3) The governments of the territories or possessions of the United States;

(4) The government of the District of Columbia;

(5) Court martial and military commissions.

De-identified means that the identity of the source of the information, and the names of persons have been removed from the information.

Disclose means to release information to a person other than another agency. Examples are disclosures under the Freedom of Information Act (5 U.S.C. 552), in rulemaking proceedings, in a press release, or to a party to a legal action.

Information includes data, reports, source, and other information. "Information" may be used to describe the whole or a portion of a submission of information.

Summarized means that individual incidents are not specifically described, but are presented in statistical or other general form.

Voluntary means that the information was not required to be submitted as part of a mandatory program, and was not submitted as a condition of doing business with the government. "Voluntarily-provided information" does not include information submitted as part of complying with statutory, regulatory, or contractual requirements, except that information submitted as part of complying with a voluntary program under this part is considered to be voluntarily provided.

193.5   How may I submit safety or security information and have it protected from disclosure?

(a) You may do so under a program under this part. The program may be developed based on your proposal, a proposal from another person, or a proposal developed by the FAA.

(b) You may be any person, including an individual, a company, or an organization.

(c) You may propose to develop a program under this part using either the notice procedure in 193.11 or the no-notice procedure in 193.13.

(d) If the FAA decides to protect the information that you propose to submit it issues an order designating the information as protected under this part.

(e) The FAA only issues an order designating information as protected if the FAA makes the findings in 193.7.

(f) The designation may be for a program in which all similar persons may participate, or for a program in which only you submit information.

(g) Even if you receive protection from disclosure under this part, this part does not establish the extent to which the FAA may or may not use the information to take enforcement action. Limits on enforcement action applicable to a program under this part will be in another policy or rule.

193.7   What does it mean for the FAA to designate information as protected?

(a) General. When the FAA issues an order designating information as protected under this part, the FAA does not disclose the information except as provided in this part.

(b) What findings does the FAA make before designating information as protected? The FAA designates information as protected under this part when the FAA finds that—

(1) The information is provided voluntarily;

(2) The information is safety or security related;

(3) The disclosure of the information would inhibit the voluntary provision of that type of information;

(4) The receipt of that type of information aids in fulfilling the FAA's safety and security responsibilities; and

(5) Withholding such information from disclosure, under the circumstances provided in this part, will be consistent with the FAA's safety and security responsibilities.

(c) How will the FAA handle requests for information under the Freedom of Information Act (FOIA)? The FAA does not disclose information that is designated as protected under this part in response to a FOIA request.

(d) What if the FAA obtains from another source the same information I submit? Only information received under a program under this part is protected from disclosure under this part. Information obtained by the FAA through another means is not protected under this part.

(e) Sharing information with other agencies. The FAA may provide information that you have submitted under this part to other agencies with safety or security responsibilities. The agencies are subject to the requirements of 49 U.S.C. 40123 regarding nondisclosure of information. The FAA will give the information to another agency only if, for each such request, the other agency provides the FAA with adequate assurance, in writing, that—

(1) The agency has a safety or security need for the information, including the general nature of the need.

(2) The agency will protect the information from disclosure as required in 49 U.S.C. 40123, this part, and the designation. This includes a commitment that the agency will mark the information as provided in the designation.

(3) The agency will limit access to those with a need to know to carry out safety or security responsibilities.

(f) What if the FAA receives a subpoena for the information I submit? When the FAA receives a subpoena for information you have submitted under this part, the FAA contacts you to determine whether you object to disclosure of the information or you wish to participate in responding to the subpoena. If both you and the FAA determine that release of the information is appropriate, the information is released. Otherwise, the FAA will not release information designated as protected under this part unless ordered to do so by a court of competent jurisdiction.

193.9 Will the FAA ever disclose information that is designated as protected under this part?

The FAA discloses information that is designated as protected under this part when withholding it would not be consistent with the FAA's safety and security responsibilities, as follows:

(a) Disclosure in all programs.

(1) The FAA may disclose de-identified, summarized information submitted under this part to explain the need for changes in policies and regulations. An example is the FAA publishing a notice of proposed rulemaking based on your information, and including a de-identified, summarized version of your information (and the information from other persons, if applicable) to explain the need for the notice of proposed rulemaking.

(2) The FAA may disclose information provided under this part to correct a condition that compromises safety or security, if that condition continues uncorrected.

(3) The FAA may disclose information provided under this part to carry out a criminal investigation or prosecution.

(4) The FAA may disclose information provided under this part to comply with 49 U.S.C. 44905, regarding information about threats to civil aviation.

(b) Additional disclosures. For each program, the FAA may find that there are additional circumstances under which withholding information provided under this part would not be consistent with the FAA's safety and security responsibilities. Those circumstances are described in the designation for that program.

193.11 What is the notice procedure?

This section states the notice procedure for the FAA to designate information as protected under this part. This procedure is used when there is not an immediate safety or security need for the information. This procedure generally is used to specify a type of information that you and others like you will provide on an on-going basis.

(a) Application. You may apply to have information designated as protected under this part by submitting an application addressed to the U.S. Department of Transportation, Docket Operations, West Building Ground Floor, Room W12–140, 1200 New Jersey Avenue, SE., Washington, DC 20590 for paper submissions, and the Federal Docket Management System (FDMS) Web page at http://www.regulations.gov for electronic submissions. Your application must include the designation described in paragraph (c) of this section that you want the FAA to issue. You should not include in your application any information that you do not want available to the public. The FAA may issue a proposed designation based on the application or may deny your application.

(b) Proposed designation. Before issuing a designation under this section, based either on your application or the FAA's own initiative, the FAA publishes a proposed designation in the Federal Register and requests comment.

(c) Designation. The FAA designates information as protected under this part if, after review of the comments, the FAA makes the findings in 193.7. The FAA publishes in the Federal Register an order designating the information provided under the program as protected under this part. The designation includes the following:

(1) A summary of why the FAA finds that you and others, if applicable, will provide the information voluntarily.

(2) A description of the type of information that you and others, if applicable, may voluntarily provide under the program and a summary of why the FAA finds that the information is safety or security related.

(3) A summary of why the FAA finds that the disclosure of the information would inhibit you and others, if applicable, from voluntarily providing of that type of information.

(4) A summary of why the receipt of that type of information aids in fulfilling the FAA's safety and security responsibilities.

(5) A summary of why withholding such information from disclosure would be consistent with the FAA's safety and security

responsibilities, including a statement as to the circumstances under which, and a summary of why, withholding such information from disclosure would not be consistent with the FAA's safety and security responsibilities, as described in 193.9.

(6) A summary of how the FAA will distinguish information protected under this part from information the FAA receives from other sources.

(7) A summary of the significant comments received and the FAA's responses.

(d) Amendment of designation. The FAA may amend a designation using the procedures in paragraphs (a), (b), and (c) of this section.

(e) Withdrawal of designation. The FAA may withdraw a designation under this section at any time the FAA finds that continuation of the designation does not meet the elements of 193.7, or if the requirements of the designation are not met. The FAA withdraws the designation by publishing a notice in the Federal Register. The withdrawal is effective on the date of publication or such later date as the notice may state. Information provided during the time the program was designated remains protected under this part and the program. Information provided after the withdrawal of the designation is effective is not protected under this part or the program.

[66 FR 33805, June 25, 2001, as amended at 72 FR 68475, Dec. 5, 2007]

193.13 What is the no-notice procedure?

This section states the no-notice procedure for the FAA to designate information as protected under this part. This procedure is used when there is an immediate safety or security need for the information. This procedure generally is used for specific information that you will provide on a short-term basis.

(a) Application. You may request that the FAA designate information you are offering as protected under this part. You must state your name, at least the general nature of information, and whether you will provide the information without the protection of this part. Your request may be verbal or writing.

(b) Designation. The FAA issues a written order designating information provided under this section as protected under this part. The FAA designates the information as protected under this part if the FAA—

(1) Makes the findings as 193.7; and

(2) Finds that there is an immediate safety or security need to obtain the information without carrying out the procedures in 193.11 of this part.

(c) Time limit. Except as provided in paragraphs (c)(1) and (c)(2) of this section, no designation under this section continues in effect for more than 60 days after the date of designation. Information provided during the time the designation was in effect remains protected under this part. Information provided that the designation ceases to be in effect is not protected under this part. The designation remains in effect for more than 60 days if—

(1) The procedures to designate such information under 193.11(a) have been initiated, or

(2) There is an ongoing enforcement or criminal investigation, in which case the designation may continue until the investigation is completed.

(d) Amendment of designation. The FAA may amend a designation under this section using the procedures in paragraphs (a) and (b) of this section.

(e) Withdrawal of designation. The FAA may withdraw a designation under this section at any time the FAA finds that continuation does not meet the elements of 193.7, or if the requirements of the designation are not met. The FAA withdraws the designation by notifying the person in writing that the designation is withdrawn. The withdrawal is effective on the date of receipt of the notice or such later date as the notice may state. Information provided during the time the designation was in effect remains protected under this part. Information provided after the withdrawal is effective is not protected under this part.

193.15 What FAA officials exercise the authority of the Administrator under this part?

(a) The authority to issue proposed and final designations, to issue proposed and final amendments of designations, and to withdraw designations under this part, and to disclose information that has been designated as protected under this part, is delegated by the Administrator to Associate Administrators and Assistant Administrators and to the Chief Counsel, their Deputies, and any individual formally designated as Acting Associate or Assistant Administrator, Acting Chief Counsel, or Acting Deputy of such offices.

(b) The officials identified in paragraph (a) of this section may further delegate the authority to issue proposed designations and proposed amendments to designations.

193.17 How must design and production approval holders handle information they receive from the FAA under this part?

(a) If the FAA discloses information under 193.9(a)(2) to the holders of design approvals of production approvals issued by the FAA, the approval holder must disclose that information only to persons who need to know the information to address the safety or security condition.

(b) Unless an emergency exists, before disclosing information to approval holders the FAA will contact the submitter of the information.

FAR
193

**U.S. Department
of Transportation**
Federal Aviation
Administration

Advisory Circular

Subject: Aviation Safety Reporting Program	**Date:** 4/2/21	**AC No:** 00-46F
	Initiated by: AFS-200	**Change:**

1 **PURPOSE OF THIS ADVISORY CIRCULAR (AC).** This advisory circular (AC) provides guidance for the submission of reports under the Federal Aviation Administration (FAA) Aviation Safety Reporting Program (ASRP). The ASRP is a cooperative safety reporting program that invites pilots, controllers, flight attendants (F/A), maintenance personnel, dispatchers, and other users of the National Airspace System (NAS), or any other person, to report to the National Aeronautics and Space Administration (NASA) actual or potential discrepancies and deficiencies in aviation safety. NASA serves as a third party to receive and process Aviation Safety Reports. Examples of operations covered by the program include departure, en route, approach, and landing operations and procedures; air traffic control (ATC) procedures and equipment; crew and ATC communications; aircraft cabin operations; aircraft movement on the airport; near midair collisions (NMAC); aircraft maintenance and recordkeeping; airport conditions or services; and unmanned aircraft operations. The effectiveness of this program in improving safety depends on the free, unrestricted flow of information from the users of the NAS. Based on information obtained from this program, the FAA will take corrective action as necessary to remedy defects or deficiencies in the NAS. The reports may also provide data for improving the current system and planning for a future system.

2 **EFFECT OF GUIDANCE.** The contents of this document do not have the force and effect of law and are not meant to bind the public in any way. This document is intended only to provide clarity to the public regarding existing requirements under the law or agency policies. This AC is not mandatory and does not constitute a regulation.

3 **AUDIENCE.** The audience for this AC includes pilots, controllers, F/As, maintenance personnel, dispatchers, and other users of the NAS, or any other person who reports either actual or potential discrepancies and deficiencies to NASA that involve the safety of aviation operations.

4 **WHERE YOU CAN FIND THIS AC.** You can find this AC on the FAA's website at https://www.faa.gov/regulations_policies/advisory_circulars.

5 **WHAT THIS AC CANCELS.** AC 00-46E, Aviation Safety Reporting Program, dated December 16, 2011, is canceled.

6 BACKGROUND.

6.1 FAA Mission. The primary mission of the FAA is to promote aviation safety. To further this mission, the FAA instituted a voluntary ASRP on April 30, 1975, designed to encourage the identification and reporting of deficiencies and discrepancies in the NAS.

6.2 NASA Partnership. The FAA determined that ASRP effectiveness would be greatly enhanced if NASA, rather than the FAA, accomplished the receipt, processing, and analysis of raw data. This would ensure the anonymity of the reporter and of all parties involved in a reported occurrence or incident and, consequently, increase the flow of information necessary for the effective evaluation of the safety and efficiency of the NAS. Accordingly, NASA designed and administers the Aviation Safety Reporting System (ASRS) to perform these functions in accordance with a Memorandum of Agreement (MOA) executed by the FAA and NASA on August 15, 1975, as modified September 30, 1983, and August 13, 1987. NASA conducts current ASRS operations in accordance with an MOA executed by the FAA and NASA on June 15, 1999.

7 NASA RESPONSIBILITIES.

7.1 General. The NASA ASRS provides for the receipt, analysis, and de-identification of Aviation Safety Reports. In addition, the ASRS publishes and distributes periodic reports of findings obtained through the reporting program to the public, the aviation community, and the FAA.

7.2 Advisory Committee. The NASA ASRS Advisory Committee, composed of representatives from the aviation community, including NASA, the FAA, and the National Transportation Safety Board (NTSB) advises NASA on the conduct of the ASRS. The Committee conducts periodic meetings to evaluate and ensure the effectiveness of the reporting system.

8 PROHIBITION AGAINST THE USE OF REPORTS FOR ENFORCEMENT PURPOSES.

8.1 Background. Designed and operated by NASA, the NASA ASRS security system ensures the confidentiality and anonymity of the reporter, and other parties as appropriate, involved in a reported occurrence or incident. The FAA will not seek, and NASA will not release or make available to the FAA, any report filed with NASA under the ASRS or any other information that might reveal the identity of any party involved in an occurrence or incident reported under the ASRS. There has been no breach of confidentiality of the ASRS under NASA management.

8.2 Use Restrictions. The FAA will not use any reports submitted to NASA under the ASRS (or information derived therefrom) in any enforcement action, except information concerning criminal offenses or accidents that are covered under paragraphs 10.1.1 and 10.1.2. Refer to Title 14 of the Code of Federal Regulations (14 CFR) part 91, § 91.25 (which prohibits the use of any reports submitted to NASA under the ASRS (or information derived therefrom) in any enforcement action within the scope of 14 CFR part 91, except information concerning criminal offenses or accidents).

8.3 **Non-ASRS Report.** When a violation of 14 CFR comes to the attention of the FAA from a source other than a report filed with NASA under the ASRS, the Administrator of the FAA will take appropriate action. See paragraph <u>12</u>.

9 **REPORTING PROCEDURES.** NASA ASRS forms have been prepared specifically for intended users (including Form 277A for air traffic use, Form 277B for general use (including pilots), Form 277C for F/As, Form 277D for maintenance personnel, and Form 277U for unmanned operations) and are preaddressed and postage free, or are available online for access and filing electronically. Additionally, organizations may elect to securely transfer copies of reports from their internal reporting system to NASA ASRS directly. Forms with a narrative report should be completed and mailed to ASRS at NASA Aviation Safety Reporting System, P.O. Box 189, Moffett Field, California 94035-0189, or filed electronically with ASRS through the NASA ASRS website at https://asrs.arc.nasa.gov/.

10 **PROCESSING OF REPORTS.**

10.1 **Processing Procedures.** NASA procedures for processing Aviation Safety Reports provide for the initial screening of reports for:

10.1.1 Information concerning criminal offenses, which will be referred promptly to the Department of Justice and the FAA;

10.1.2 Information concerning accidents, which will be referred promptly to the NTSB and the FAA; and

Note: Reports discussing criminal activities or accidents are not de-identified prior to their referral to the agencies outlined above.

10.1.3 Time-critical information that, after de-identification, will be promptly referred to the FAA and other interested parties.

10.2 **Reporter Identification (ID) Strip.** Each Aviation Safety Report, in paper or electronic format, contains an ID strip that contains the information that identifies the person submitting the report. NASA will time stamp and return the ID strip to the reporter as a receipt by NASA. This will provide the reporter with proof that he or she filed a report on a specific incident or occurrence. The ID strip section of the ASRS report form provides NASA program personnel with the means to contact the reporter if there is a need for additional information to understand more completely the report's content. Except in the case of reports describing accidents or criminal activities, NASA does not create or retain a copy of an ASRS form's ID strip for ASRS files. Prompt return of ID strips is a primary element of the ASRS program's report de-identification process and ensures the reporter's anonymity.

11 **DE-IDENTIFICATION.** All information that might assist in or establish the ID of persons filing ASRS reports and parties named in those reports will be deleted, except for reports covered under paragraphs 10.1.1 and 10.1.2. This de-identification will be accomplished within a timely manner after NASA's receipt of the reports.

12   ENFORCEMENT POLICY.

12.1   **Administrator's Responsibilities.** The Administrator of the FAA will perform his or her responsibility under Title 49 of the United States Code (49 U.S.C.) subtitle VII, and enforce the statute and the 14 CFR in a manner that will reduce or eliminate the possibility of, or recurrence of, aircraft accidents. The FAA enforcement procedures are set forth in 14 CFR part 13 and FAA policy.

12.2   **Enforcement Action.** When determining the type and extent of the enforcement action to take in a particular case, the FAA will consider the following factors:

1. Nature of the violation;

2. Whether the violation was inadvertent or deliberate;

3. The certificate holder's (CH) level of experience and responsibility;

4. Attitude of the violator;

5. The hazard to safety of others, which should have been foreseen;

6. Action taken by an employer or other government authority;

7. Length of time that has elapsed since the violation;

8. The CH's use of the certificate;

9. The need for special deterrent action in a particular regulatory area or segment of the aviation community; and

10. Presence of any factors involving national interest, such as the use of aircraft for criminal purposes.

12.3   **Waiver of Imposition of Sanction.** The FAA considers the filing of a report with NASA concerning an incident or occurrence involving a violation of 49 U.S.C. subtitle VII or the 14 CFR to be indicative of a constructive attitude. Such an attitude will tend to prevent future violations. Accordingly, although a finding of violation may be made, neither a civil penalty nor certificate suspension will be imposed if:

12.3.1   The violation was inadvertent and not deliberate;

12.3.2   The violation did not involve a criminal offense, accident, or action under 49 U.S.C. § 44709, which discloses a lack of qualification or competency, which is wholly excluded from this policy;

12.3.3   The person has not been found in any prior FAA enforcement action to have committed a violation of 49 U.S.C. subtitle VII, or any regulation promulgated there for a period of 5 years prior to the date of occurrence; and

12.3.4   The person proves that, within 10 days after the violation, or date when the person became aware or should have been aware of the violation, he or she completed and delivered or mailed a written report of the incident or occurrence to NASA.

Note: Paragraph <u>12</u> does not apply to air traffic controllers who are covered under the provisions of the Air Traffic Safety Action Program (ATSAP), as described in the ATSAP Memorandum of Understanding (MOU).

13 **OTHER REPORTS.** This program does not eliminate responsibility for reports, narratives, or forms presently required by existing directives.

14 **AVAILABILITY OF FORMS.** Electronic reporting forms (NASA ASRS Form 277-series) are available for access and secure electronic filing from the NASA ASRS website at https://asrs.arc.nasa.gov/. Alternatively, forms from this site may be accessed, printed, and completed by hand, or accessed and completed by computer and then printed. These may then be mailed to NASA Aviation Safety Reporting System, P.O. Box 189, Moffett Field, California 94035-0189.

15 **AC FEEDACK FORM.** For your convenience, the AC Feedback Form is the last page of this AC. Note any deficiencies found, clarifications needed, or suggested improvements regarding the contents of this AC on the Feedback Form.

Robert C. Carty
Deputy Executive Director, Flight Standards Service

**U.S. Department
of Transportation**
Federal Aviation
Administration

Advisory

Circular

Subject: Eligibility, Quality, and Identification of Aeronautical Replacement Parts	**Date:** 9/14/18	**AC No:** 20-62E
	Initiated by: AFS-300	**Change:** 1

1. PURPOSE OF THIS ADVISORY CIRCULAR (AC). This AC provides information and guidance for use in determining the quality, eligibility, and traceability of aeronautical parts and materials intended for installation on U.S. type certificated (TC) products and articles, and to enable compliance with the applicable regulations.

2. PRINCIPAL CHANGES. This change corrects definitions from Title 14 of the Code of Federal Regulations (14 CFR) parts 1 and 21. It also corrects the list of related reading materials and hyperlinks within the document.

PAGE CONTROL CHART

Remove Pages	Dated	Insert Pages	Dated
Pages 1 thru 7	12/23/10	Pages 1 thru 7	9/14/18
Pages 11 and 12	12/23/10	Pages 11 and 12	9/14/18

Rick Domingo
Executive Director, Flight Standards Service

**U.S. Department
of Transportation**
Federal Aviation
Administration

Advisory
Circular

Subject: Eligibility, Quality, and Identification of Aeronautical Replacement Parts	**Date:** 12/23/10 **AC No:** 20-62E **Initiated by:** AFS-300 **Change:**

1. PURPOSE OF THIS ADVISORY CIRCULAR (AC). This AC provides information and guidance for use in determining the quality, eligibility, and traceability of aeronautical parts and materials intended for installation on U.S. type certificated (TC) products and articles, and to enable compliance with the applicable regulations.

2. AUDIENCE. This AC is intended for use by aircraft operators, maintenance organizations, and maintenance personnel when determining the quality, eligibility, and traceability of aeronautical parts and materials intended for installation on U.S. TC'd products and articles, and to enable compliance with the applicable regulations.

3. WHERE YOU CAN FIND THIS AC. You can find this AC on the FAA's website at http://www.faa.gov/regulations_policies/advisory_circulars.

4. WHAT THIS AC CANCELS. AC 20-62D, Eligibility, Quality, and Identification of Approved Aeronautical Replacement Parts, dated May 24, 1996, is canceled.

5. RELATED CFR PARTS. Title 14 of the Code of Federal Regulations (14 CFR) parts 1, 21, 39, 43, 45, 91, 119, 121, 125, 129, 135, and 145.

6. DEFINITIONS. The following definitions apply to this AC:

    a. Federal Aviation Administration (FAA)-Approved Parts. Under part 21, §§ 21.8 and 21.9, articles produced under an FAA-approved production system, and which conform to FAA-approved data, may be approved under the following:

        (1) A Parts Manufacturer Approval (PMA) issued under part 21 subpart K.

        (2) A Technical Standard Order Authorization (TSOA) issued under part 21 subpart O.

        (3) In conjunction with type certification procedures for a product. In any manner approved by the Administrator, such as part 21 subparts F and G. In addition, part 21 subpart N provides for the acceptance of a new part produced in a country or jurisdiction with which the United States has an agreement for the acceptance of parts for export and import. The part is approved when the country of manufacture issues a Certificate of Airworthiness for export of the part.

    b. Acceptable Parts. The following parts may be found to be acceptable for installation on a TC'd product:

(1) Standard parts (such as nuts and bolts) conforming to an established industry or U.S. specification.

(2) Parts produced by an owner or operator for maintaining or altering their own product and which are shown to conform to FAA-approved data.

(3) Parts for which inspections and tests have been accomplished by appropriately certificated persons authorized to determine conformity to FAA-approved design.

(4) Parts fabricated by an appropriately rated certificate holder with a quality system and consumed in the repair or alteration of a product or article in accordance with part 43.

(5) A commercial part as defined in § 21.1.

c. Article. Means a material, part, component, process, or appliance.

d. Commercial Part. An article that is listed on an FAA-approved Commercial Parts List included in a design approval holder's (DAH) instructions for continued airworthiness (ICA) in accordance with § 21.50.

e. Product. An aircraft, aircraft engine, or propeller.

f. Standard Part. A part manufactured in complete compliance with an established U.S. Government or industry-accepted specification, which includes design, manufacturing, and uniform identification requirements. The specification must include all information necessary to produce and conform to the part. The specification must be published so that any party may manufacture the part. Examples include, but are not limited to, National Aerospace Standard (NAS), Air Force/Navy (AN) Aeronautical Standard, Society of Automotive Engineers (SAE), Aerospace Standard (AS), Military Standard (MS), etc.

g. Interface Component. An article that serves as a functional interface between an aircraft and an aircraft engine, an aircraft engine and a propeller, or an aircraft and a propeller. An interface component is designated by the holder of the TC or Supplemental Type Certificate (STC) who controls the approved design data for that article.

h. Surplus. Describes a product, assembly, part, or material that has been released as surplus by the military, manufacturers, owners/operators, repair facilities, or any other parts supplier. These products should show traceability to an FAA-approved manufacturing procedure.

i. Overhauled. Describes an airframe, aircraft engine, propeller, appliance, or component part using methods, techniques, and practices acceptable to the Administrator, which has undergone the following:

(1) Has been disassembled, cleaned, inspected, repaired when necessary, and reassembled to the extent possible.

(2) Has been tested in accordance with approved standards and technical data, or current standards and technical data acceptable to the Administrator (i.e., manufacturer's data), which have been developed and documented by the holder of one of the following:

- TC;
- STC, or article approval under § 21.8; or
- PMA.

j.   Rebuilt. A used product or article that has been completely disassembled, inspected, repaired as necessary, reassembled, tested, and approved in the same manner and to the same tolerances and limits as a new item with either new or used parts. However, all parts used must conform to the production drawing tolerances and limits for new parts or be of approved oversized or undersized dimensions for a new engine.

k.   Return to Service Inspection Records. The person approving or disapproving for return to service a TC'd product must ensure that the required maintenance record entries comply with part 43, and therefore must include the following information:

- Type of inspection and a brief description of the extent of the inspection;
- Date;
- Product hours, cycles, or life limits as applicable;
- Signature, certificate number, and kind of certificate held by the person approving or disapproving for return to service; and
- The appropriate certifying statement that the product or part thereof is approved or disapproved for return to service, as applicable.

l.   As Is. Describes any airframe, aircraft engine, propeller, appliance, component part, or material, the condition of which is unknown.

m.   Appropriate Certificated Person. As related to approval for return to service after maintenance, preventive maintenance, rebuilding, or alteration, it can include the holder of a:

(1) Mechanic Certificate. May perform maintenance, preventive maintenance, and alterations as provided in 14 CFR part 65.

(2) Inspection Authorization (IA). May inspect and approve for return to service any aircraft or related part or appliance (except aircraft maintained in accordance with a Continuous Airworthiness Maintenance Program (CAMP) under part 121 or 135) after a major repair or alteration as provided in part 43 if the work was done in accordance with technical data approved by the Administrator. Perform an annual inspection, or supervise a progressive inspection according to part 43, §§ 43.13 and 43.15.

(3) Repair Station Certificate Under Part 145. May perform maintenance, preventive maintenance, or alterations as provided in part 145.

(4) Air Carriers. Air carriers operating may perform maintenance, preventive maintenance, or alterations as provided under part 119, 121, 125, 129, or 135.

(5) Private Pilot Certificate (for Preventive Maintenance). May perform preventive maintenance described in part 43 appendix A on any aircraft operated by the pilot except, those aircraft operated under part 119, 121, 125, 129, or 135.

(6) Manufacturer's TC or Production Certificate (PC). May rebuild or alter any product or article which it manufactured under a TC or PC. Section 43.3(j) also allows for the rebuilding or alteration of any product or article which it manufactures under a TSOA, PMA, or Product and Process Specification issued by the Administrator. Likewise, the regulation allows the Production Approval Holder (PAH) the ability to perform any inspection required by part 91 or part 125 on aircraft it manufactured under a TC, or currently manufactures under a PC.

n. Owner/Operator Produced Part. Parts that were produced by an owner/operator for installation on their own aircraft (i.e., by a certificated air carrier). An owner/operator is considered a producer of a part, if the owner participated in controlling the design, manufacture, or quality of the part. Participating in the design of the part can include supervising the manufacture of the part or providing the manufacturer with the following: the design data, the materials with which to make the part, the fabrication processes, assembly methods, or the quality control (QC) procedures.

o. Time-Limited Part. Means any part for which a mandatory replacement limit is specified in the type design, the ICA, or the maintenance manual.

7. RELATED READING MATERIALS (current editions):

- AC 00-56, Voluntary Industry Distributor Accreditation Program.
- AC 21-2, Complying with the Requirements of Importing Countries or Jurisdictions When Exporting U.S. Products, Articles, or Parts.
- AC 21-13, Standard Airworthiness Certification of Surplus Military Aircraft and Aircraft Built from Spare and Surplus Parts.
- AC 21-18, Bilateral Airworthiness Agreements.
- AC 21-23, Airworthiness Certification of Civil Aircraft, Engines, Propellers, and Related Products Imported to the United States.
- AC 21-29, Detecting and Reporting Suspected Unapproved Parts.
- AC 43-9, Maintenance Records.
- AC 43.13-1, Acceptable Methods, Techniques, and Practices—Aircraft Inspection and Repair.
- AC 43.13-2, Acceptable Methods, Techniques, and Practices—Aircraft Alterations.
- AC 43-18, Fabrication of Aircraft Parts by Maintenance Personnel.
- AC 43-216, Software Management During Aircraft Maintenance.
- FAA Order 8120.16, Suspected Unapproved Parts Program.
- FAA Order 8130.21, Procedures for Completion and Use of the Authorized Release Certificate, FAA Form 8130-3, Airworthiness Approval Tag.

8. DISCUSSION. The FAA continues to receive reports of replacement parts being offered for sale as aircraft quality when the quality and origin of the parts are unknown or questionable. Such parts may be advertised or presented as unused, like-new, or remanufactured. These imply that the quality of the parts is equal to an acceptable part. Purchasers of these parts may not be aware of the potential hazards involved with replacement parts for which acceptability for installation on a TC'd product has not been established.

a. **Replacement of Parts and Materials.** The performance rules for replacement of parts and materials used in the maintenance, preventive maintenance, and alteration of aircraft that have (or have had) a U.S. airworthiness certificate, and components thereof, are specified in § 43.13 and part 145, § 145.201. These rules require that the installer of a part use methods, techniques, and practices acceptable to the FAA. Additionally, the installer of a part must accomplish the work in such a manner and use materials of such quality that the product or appliance worked on will be at least equal to its original or properly altered condition with respect to the qualities affecting airworthiness.

b. **Replacement of Articles.** The continued airworthiness of an aircraft, which includes the replacement of articles, is the responsibility of the owner/operator, as specified in parts 91, 119, 121, 125, 129, and 135; and §§ 91.403, 121.363, 125.243, and 135.413. These rules require that the installer determine that an article is eligible for installation on a product or component prior to returning that product or component to service with the part installed. Those rules also require that the installation of a part must be accomplished in accordance with data approved by the FAA, if the installation constitutes a major repair or alteration.

c. **Conforming to Regulations.** As part of determining whether installation of an article conforms with all applicable regulations, the installer should establish that the article was manufactured under a production approval pursuant to part 21, that an originally acceptable part has been maintained in accordance with part 43, or that the part is otherwise eligible for installation (i.e., has been found to conform to data approved by the FAA). This AC addresses means to help the installer make the required determinations.

9. **IDENTIFICATION OF REPLACEMENT PARTS.** Acceptable replacement articles should be identified using one of the following methods:

a. **Airworthiness Approval Tag.** FAA Form 8130-3, Authorized Release Certificate, Airworthiness Approval Tag, may be used when exporting products or articles to meet the requirements of bilateral agreements between the United States and other countries. This includes the shipment, not the export, of a prototype product or article to another country. It also serves as approval for return to service after maintenance or alteration by persons authorized in accordance with FAA Order 8130.21.

b. **Foreign-Manufactured Replacement Parts.** New foreign-manufactured parts for use on U.S. TC'd products may be imported when there is a Bilateral Airworthiness Agreement (BAA) between the country of manufacture and the United States, and the part meets the requirements under § 21.502.

(1) The certification may be verified on a form similar to the FAA Form 8130-3 (i.e., European Aviation Safety Agency (EASA), EASA Form One), used by European member countries of the EASA with which the United States has a BAA. The EASA is an organization of European member nations that has the responsibility to develop EASA regulations and policy.

The procedures and the countries with which the United States has a BAA, and the condition of the agreements, are contained in AC 21-13.

(2) Used parts may be identified by the records required for approval for return to service as set forth in § 43.9. FAA Form 8130-3 may be used for this purpose if the requirements of § 43.9 are contained in or attached to the form and approved for return to service by a U.S. FAA-certificated repair station or U.S. air carrier under the requirement of their CAMP. There is no set format or form required for a maintenance or alteration record. However, the data or information used to identify a part must be traceable to a person authorized to perform and approve for return to service maintenance and alterations under part 43. The records must contain a minimum that data set forth in § 43.9.

(3) The use of an authorization tag does not approve the installation of a part on a TC'd product. Additional substantiated authorization for compliance with part 43 and the FAA-approved data for major repairs and alterations may be required for installation on a TC'd product.

c. **FAA Technical Standard Order (TSO) Markings.** A TSOA is issued under § 21.611 and marked in accordance with part 45, § 45.15. A TSOA must be permanently and legibly marked with the following:

- Name and address of the manufacturer;
- The name, type, part number, or model designation of the article;
- The serial number or the date of manufacture of the article, or both; and
- The applicable TSO number.

d. **FAA-PMA Symbol.** An FAA-PMA is issued under § 21.311. Each PMA part should be marked with the letters, "FAA-PMA," in accordance with § 45.15:

- Certificate holder's name;
- Trademark, symbol, or other FAA-approved identification; and
- Part number.

NOTE: **If the FAA finds a part or article is too small or otherwise impractical to mark with any of the information required by part 45, the manufacturer must attach that information to the part or its container.**

e. **PAH's Documents or Markings.** Documents or markings such as shipping tickets and invoices may provide evidence that a part was produced by a manufacturer holding an FAA-approved manufacturing process.

f. **Direct Ship Authority.** In order for U.S. manufactured parts with direct ship authority to be recognized as being produced under a manufacturer's FAA production approval, the manufacturer must specifically authorize the shipping supplier, in writing, and must establish procedures to ensure that the shipped parts conform to the approved design and are in condition for safe operation. A statement to the supplier from the certificate holder authorizing direct shipment and date of authorization should be included on the shipping ticket, invoice, or other transfer document. It should contain a declaration that the individual part was produced under a PC.

   g.   Maintenance Release Document. A release, signed by an appropriately certificated person, qualified for the relevant function that signifies that the item has been returned to service after maintenance or test function has been completed. This type of documentation could be in the form of a repair station tag containing adequate information (§ 43.9); work order, FAA Form 337, Major Repair and/or Major Alteration; FAA Form 8130-3; or a maintenance record entry, which must include an appropriate description of the maintenance work performed, including the recording requirements of § 43.9 and part 43 appendix B.

   h.   Identification of Critical Components. Each person who produces a part for which there is a replacement time or an inspection interval must mark the part in accordance with § 45.15.

   i.   Marking of Life-Limited Parts. The TC or design holder must provide a means of marking a life-limited part when requested by a person to comply with § 43.10.

   > **NOTE: When a noncertificated person certifies that they are shipping the correct part ordered, the only thing they are stating is that the part number agrees with the purchase order, not the status of FAA-acceptability of the part.**

10. INFORMATION RELEVANT TO USED PARTS. The following information may be useful when assessing maintenance records and part status.

   a.   Documentation. If the part has been rebuilt, overhauled, inspected, modified, or repaired, the records should include a maintenance release, return to service tag, repaired parts tag, or similar documentation from an FAA-certificated person. Documentation describing the maintenance performed and parts replaced must be made for the part (i.e., FAA Form 8130-3 or FAA repair station work order). (Refer to § 43.9 and part 43 appendix B.)

   b.   Information to Obtain. The records should include information, either directly or by reference, to support documentation that may be helpful to the user or installer in making a final determination as to the airworthiness and eligibility of the part. Listed are examples of information one should obtain, as applicable:

   (1) Airworthiness Directives (AD) status.

   (2) Compliance or noncompliance with Service Bulletins (SB).

   (3) Life-limited parts status (i.e., time, time since overhaul, cycles, history) should be substantiated. If the part is serialized and life-limited, then both operational time and/or cycles (where applicable) must be indicated. Historical records that clearly establish and substantiate time and cycles must be provided as evidence.

   (4) Shelf-life data, including manufacturing date or cure date.

(5) Return to service date.

(6) Shortages applicable to assemblies or kits.

(7) Import or export certification documents.

(8) The name of the person who removed the part.

(9) FAA Form 337.

(10) Maintenance manual standards used for performing maintenance.

c. Unusual Circumstances. If a particular part was obtained from any of the following, then it should be so identified by some type of documentation (i.e., maintenance record entries, removal entries, overhaul records).

(1) Noncertificated aircraft (aircraft without airworthiness certificate; i.e., public use, non-U.S., and military surplus aircraft).

(2) Aircraft, aircraft engines, propellers, or appliances subjected to extreme stress, sudden stoppage, heat, major failure, or accident.

(3) Salvaged aircraft or aircraft components.

d. Seller's Designation. The seller may be able to provide documentation that shows traceability to an FAA-approved manufacturing procedure for one of the following:

(1) Parts produced by an FAA-PAH by TC, PC, PMA, TSOA.

(2) Parts produced by a foreign manufacturer (in accordance with part 21 subpart N).

(3) Standard parts produced by a named manufacturer.

(4) Parts distributed with direct ship authority.

(5) Parts produced, for the work being accomplished, by a repair station to accomplish a repair or alteration on a specific TC'd product.

(6) Parts produced by an owner or operator for installation on the owner's or operator's aircraft (i.e., by a certificated air carrier).

(7) Parts with removal records showing traceability to a U.S.-certificated aircraft, signed by an appropriately certificated person.

e. Manufactured. The manufacturer of the part should be identified; if not identified it may be difficult to prove that the part is acceptable for installation on a TC'd product.

f. Certificates and Approvals Held.

(1) Manufacturers. The certificate or approval held by the manufacturer, TC, PC, TSOA, or PMA may be listed; if not known, state as unknown.

(2) Air Agencies. The certificate held by the air agencies. Part 145 may be listed. If not known, state as unknown.

(3) Air Operator. The certificate held by air operators, parts 119, 121, 125, and 135.

g. Part Description. Indicate the part's physical description for positive identification.

h. Part Number. Document the manufacturer's part number or, if the part has been modified, the amended part number.

i. Serial Number. Document the specific part's serial number, if so marked. Determine if serialized part has any life or overhaul limitations.

j. Disposition of Life-Limited Aircraft Parts. After April 15, 2002, each person who removes a life-limited part from a TC'd product must ensure that the part is controlled in accordance with § 43.10.

11. SURPLUS. Many materials, parts, appliances, and components that have been released as surplus by the military service or by manufacturers may originate from obsolete or overstocked items. Parts obtained from surplus sources may be used, provided it is established that they meet the standards to which they were manufactured, interchangeability with the original part can be established, and they are in compliance with all applicable ADs. Such items, although advertised as "remanufactured", "high-quality", "like-new", "unused", or "looks good", should be carefully evaluated before they are purchased. The storage time, storage conditions, or shelf life of surplus parts and materials are not usually known.

12. CONDITIONS FOR SAFE OPERATION. Parts and materials should be properly stored, protected, and maintained to ensure airworthiness. The following factors should be considered when determining airworthiness:

a. Composite Materials. Generally, most composite materials (thermoset polymers) have a refrigeration shelf life recommended by the manufacturer. Composite materials must be kept refrigerated in accordance with the manufacturer's recommended temperature range and out of refrigeration time (out time) limitations. Records must be maintained of the cumulative total of material out time to prevent exceeding shelf life.

b. Anti-Friction Bearings. Anti-friction bearings that have been in storage for a long period of time or that have been improperly stored are subject to the deteriorating effects of time and elements, unless they were hermetically sealed. Such parts should be completely inspected and lubricated before being placed in service.

c.   Aircraft Fabric. Fabric and prefabricated covers should be used only if they are identifiable as meeting aircraft standards. All fabric should be examined or tested for freedom from deterioration, as determined by an appropriately certificated person.

d.   Dope, Paint, Sealants, and Adhesives. These items advertised as aircraft quality may have deteriorated due to age or environmental conditions, while in storage, and may require testing before use.

e.   Parts with Internal Seals. Internal seals on parts such as pumps, valves, actuators, motors, generators, and alternators are subject to deterioration from long-term storage and are susceptible to early failure in service. A procedure should be established for control of shelf-life items in order to prevent possible premature failures of the parts/components, unless other preventive procedures are in place.

f.   Rotating Components. Rotating components, such as propellers, engine parts, and rotor blades, may have a life-limit or retirement life. Maintenance records should reflect a complete continuity of service time and repair history. Information that indicates whether the component has exceeded the life limit may, in some cases, be obtained from the manufacturer or from an FAA-approved repair station that may have affixed a logo, decal, or some other identification.

g.   Heat and Fire. Parts that may have been exposed to heat or fire can be seriously affected and are likely unserviceable.

h.   Corrosives. Foreign or corrosive liquids can also be detrimental on aircraft parts. Parts, appliances, and components that have been submerged in saltwater may be unserviceable parts.

i.   Manufacturing Rejects. The manufacturers may offer parts that failed the manufacturers' quality assurance (QA) inspection criteria for conformity to type design, for sale as scrap without being mutilated or destroyed rendering them unusable, and are unacceptable for installation.

j.   Damaged Aircraft. Parts removed from an aircraft involved in an accident may have been subjected to undue stresses that may have seriously affected structural integrity and rendered them permanently unusable.

k.   Rebuilt Engines. Only engines that are rebuilt by a manufacturer holding an FAA production approval, an agency approved by the PAH, or an appropriately rated FAA-certificated agency can be considered as zero timed. (Refer to § 91.421.)

13. ELECTRICAL PARTS AND INSTRUMENTS.

a.   Electronic Kits. Kits assembled by noncertificated individuals are not eligible for installation on TC'd aircraft until the part is certified as airworthy and found eligible for installation in accordance with parts 21 and 43. During and after assembly, these kits should receive documented conformity inspections by properly certificated persons to ensure that they meet all applicable airworthiness requirements for use on the specific aircraft on which they are to be installed. The installation of these approved units should be accomplished by or under the supervision of a properly certificated person or agency in accordance with parts 21 and 43. When the installation is a major alteration, the kit data and the data used for the alteration of the product must be approved by a representative of the Administrator. An appropriately certificated person must complete the maintenance records to ensure that the aircraft is approved and airworthy for return to service.

b. Discrete Electrical and Electronic Component Parts. Electrical and electronic parts, such as resistors, capacitors, diodes, and transistors, if not specifically marked by the equipment manufacturer's part number or marking scheme, may be substituted or used as replacement parts, provided that such parts are tested or it is determined that they meet their published performance specifications and do not adversely affect the performance of the equipment or article into or onto which they are installed. The performance of such equipment or article must be equal to its original or properly altered or repaired condition. Integrated circuits such as hybrids, large scale integrated circuits (LSIC), programmable logic devices, gate arrays, application specific integrated circuits (ASIC), memories, Central Processing Units (CPU), etc., are not included because their highly specialized functionality does not readily lend itself to substitution.

c. Aircraft Software Parts. For eligibility, quality, and identification of aircraft software parts, refer to AC 43-216.

d. Aircraft Instruments. Instruments advertised as high quality, looks good, or remanufactured or that were acquired from aircraft involved in an accident should not be put in service unless they are inspected, tested, and/or overhauled as necessary, by an appropriately rated FAA-certificated repair station, and the installer establishes that (for the aircraft in which) the instrument installed will comply with the applicable regulations.

> **NOTE: Instruments are highly susceptible to hidden damage caused by rough handling or improper storage conditions; therefore, instruments that have been sitting on a shelf for a period that cannot be established should be tested by an appropriately rated FAA-certificated person.**

14. KNOW YOUR SUPPLIERS.

a. Used and Repaired Parts. In addition to unapproved parts, used or repaired parts may be offered for sale as like-new, near new, and remanufactured. Such terms do not aid the purchaser in positively determining whether the part is acceptable for installation on a TC'd product and do not constitute the legal serviceability and condition of aircraft parts.

b. Caution. It is the installer's responsibility to ensure airworthiness. Aircraft parts distributors, aircraft supply companies, or aircraft electronic parts distributors, unless they are a PAH, cannot certify the airworthiness of the parts they advertise and/or sell; therefore, it is the installer's responsibility to request documentation establishing traceability to a PAH.

15. REPORTING SUSPECTED UNAPPROVED PARTS (SUP).

a. SUPs. SUPs are parts, components, or materials that may not be approved or acceptable, as described in subparagraphs 4a and b. Some appear to be as good as the part manufactured from an FAA-approved source; however, there may be manufacturing processes that were not performed in accordance with FAA-approved data or possibly not performed at all, and that would not be readily apparent to the purchaser (i.e., heat treating, plating, or various tests and inspections).

b.   How to Report SUPs. Persons with possible knowledge of safety violations or other circumstances that may affect aviation safety are encouraged to report them in accordance with AC 21-29.

16. SUMMARY. The approval for return to service after maintenance of aircraft, engines, propellers, appliances, and materials and parts thereof is the responsibility of the person who performs the maintenance and who signs the record for approval for return to service. The owner/operator (as noted in subparagraph 6b) is responsible for the continued airworthiness of the aircraft. To ensure continued safety in civil aviation, it is essential that appropriate data is used when inspecting, testing, and determining the acceptability of all parts and materials. Particular caution should be exercised when the origin of parts, materials, and appliances cannot be established or when their origin is in doubt.

17. AC FEEDBACK FORM. For your convenience, the AC Feedback Form is the last page of this AC. Note any deficiencies found, clarifications needed, or suggested improvements regarding the contents of this AC on the Feedback Form.

Advisory Circular Feedback Form

If you find an error in this AC, have recommendations for improving it, or have suggestions for new items/subjects to be added, you may let us know by emailing the Flight Standards Directives Management Officer at 9-AWA-AFB-140-Directives@faa.gov.

Subject: AC 20-62E CHG 1, Eligibility, Quality, and Identification of Aeronautical Replacement Parts

Date: _____

Please check all appropriate line items:

An error (procedural or typographical) has been noted in paragraph _____ on page _____.

Recommend paragraph _____ on page _____ be changed as follows:

_____

_____

In a future change to this AC, please cover the following subject:
(Briefly describe what you want added.)

_____

_____

Other comments:

_____

_____

I would like to discuss the above. Please contact me.

Submitted by: _____   Date: _____

**U.S. Department
of Transportation**

**Federal Aviation
Administration**

Advisory
Circular

Subject: SERVICE DIFFICULTY PROGRAM (GENERAL AVIATION)	**Date:** 4/8/93	**AC No:** AC 20-109A
	Initiated by: AFS-640	**Change:**

1. **PURPOSE.** This advisory circular (AC) describes the Service Difficulty Program as it applies to general aviation activities. Instructions for completion of the revised FAA Form 8010-4 (10-92), Malfunction or Defect Report, are provided. This AC also solicits the participation of the aviation community in the Service Difficulty Program and their cooperation in improving the quality of FAA Form 8010-4.

2. **CANCELLATION.** AC 20-109, Service Difficulty Program (General Aviation), dated 1/8/79, is canceled.

3. **FORMS.** FAA Form 8010-4 (10-92), Malfunction or Defect Report, (National Stock Number (NSN) 0052-00-039-1005, Unit of Issue "BK" (25 forms per book), is available free from Flight Standards District Offices (FSDO's). See appendix 1 for directions on completing FAA Form 8010-4.

4. **DISCUSSION.** The Service Difficulty Program is an information system designed to provide assistance to aircraft owners, operators, maintenance organizations, manufacturers, and the Federal Aviation Administration (FAA) in identifying aircraft problems encountered during service. The Service Difficulty Program provides for the collection, organization, analysis, and dissemination of aircraft service information to improve service reliability of aeronautical products. The primary sources of this information are the aircraft maintenance facilities, owners, and operators. General aviation aircraft service difficulty information is normally submitted to the FAA by use of FAA Form 8010-4. However, information will be accepted in any form or format when FAA Form 8010-4 is not readily available for use.

5. **INPUT.** All of the FAA Forms 8010-4 are received by local FSDO's or Certificate Management Offices (CMO's). All the FAA Forms 8010-4 are reviewed for immediate impact items, and then forwarded for processing to the Flight Standards Service, Safety Data Analysis Section (AFS-643), in Oklahoma City, Oklahoma.

The information contained in the FAA Form 8010-4 is stored in a computerized data bank for retrieval and analysis. Items potentially hazardous to flight are telephoned directly to AFS-643 personnel by FAA Aviation Safety Inspectors in FSDO's. These items are immediately referred to, and expeditiously handled by, the appropriate FAA offices.

   a. **Certain owners, operators, certificate holders, and certificated repair stations are required by the Federal Aviation Regulations (FAR) to submit reports of defects, unairworthy conditions, and mechanical reliability problems to the FAA.** However, success of the Service Difficulty Program is enhanced by submission of service difficulty information by all of the aviation community regardless of whether required by regulation. Voluntary submission of service difficulty information is strongly encouraged.

   b. **Additional service difficulty information is collected by FAA Aviation Safety Inspectors** in the performance of routine aircraft and maintenance surveillance, accident and incident investigations, during the operation of rental aircraft, and during pilot certification flights.

c.   **All service difficulty information is retained in the computer data bank** for a period of 5 years providing a base for the detection of trends and failure rates. If necessary, data in excess of 5 years may be retrieved through the archives.

6.   **THE INFORMATION MANAGEMENT SECTION, AFS-624, IS AN INFORMATION CENTER.** AFS-624 personnel responds to individual requests from the aviation community concerning service difficulty information. Further details regarding computer-generated service difficulty information, may be obtained by telephoning (405) 954-4173 or by writing to:

> FAA
> Flight Standards Service
> **ATTN: Information Management Section (AFS-624)**
> P.O. Box 25082
> Oklahoma City, OK 73125-5012

7.   **PUBLICATIONS PRODUCED BY AFS-643.** Analysis of service difficulty information is primarily done by AFS-643. When trends are detected, they are made available to pertinent FAA field personnel for their information and possible investigation. AFS-643 produces the following publications.

a.   **The Flight Standards Service Difficulty Reports (General and Commercial),** known as the weekly summary, contains all information obtained from FAA Forms 8010-4 and those service difficulties which were reported by telephone. Reports of a significant nature are highlighted with a "star" border, while reports which are of an "URGENT AIRWORTHINESS CONCERN" are highlighted with a "black and white slashed" border. These highly significant items are sometimes obtained from sources other than FAA Forms 8010-4. This publication is distributed to FSDO's, Manufacturing Inspection District Offices (MIDO's), and Aircraft Certification Offices (ACO's). This publication is also made available to the public free of charge by telephoning (405) 954-4171 or by writing to AFS-643 at the following address:

> FAA
> Flight Standards Service
> **ATTN: Safety Data Analysis Section (AFS-643)**
> P.O. Box 25082
> Oklahoma City, OK 73125-5029

b.   **AC 43-16, General Aviation Airworthiness Alerts,** contains information that is of assistance to maintenance and inspection personnel in the performance of their duties. These items are developed from submitted FAA Form 8010-4 and articles pertaining to aviation. This publication is made available to the public free of charge by telephoning (405) 954-4171 or by writing to AFS-643 (see the address given in paragraph 7a).

8.   **IMPORTANCE OF REPORTING.** The FAA requests the cooperation of all aircraft owners, operators, mechanics, pilots, and others in reporting service difficulties experienced with airframes, powerplants, propellers, or appliances/components.

a.   **FAA Forms 8010-4 provide the FAA and industry with a very essential service record** of mechanical difficulties encountered in aircraft operations. Such reports contribute to the correction of conditions or situations which otherwise will continue to prove costly and/or adversely affect the airworthiness of aircraft.

b.   **When a system component or part of an aircraft (powerplants, propellers, or appliances) functions badly or fails to operate in the normal or usual manner,** it has malfunctioned and should be reported. Also, if a system, component, or part has a flaw or imperfection which impairs function or which may impair future function, it is defective and should be reported. While at first sight it appears this will generate numerous insignificant reports, the Service Difficulty Program is designed to detect trends. Any report can be very constructive in evaluating design or maintenance reliability.

c.   **When preparing FAA Form 8010-4,** furnish as much information as possible. Any attachments such as photographs and sketches of defective parts are appreciated. However, do not send parts to AFS-643. AFS-643 does not have storage facilities for defective parts.

d.   **Public cooperation in submitting service difficulty information is greatly appreciated** by the FAA and others who have an interest in safety. The quantity of service difficulty reports received precludes individual acknowledgement of each report.

Thomas C. Accardi
Director, Flight Standards Service

**Appendix 1. INSTRUCTIONS FOR COMPLETING THE REVISED
FAA FORM 8010-4 (10-92), MALFUNCTION OR DEFECT REPORT**

ITEM. **OPER. Control No.:** Primarily to be used for FAR Part 135 and 121 operators.
Example: ABCD9212345, BCDE1235436

ITEM. **ATA Code:** Four-digit code used primarily by the FAA.
Example: 7200, 8300

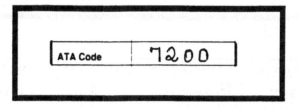

ITEM 1. **A/C Reg. No.:** Enter the complete aircraft registration number.
Example: 7523Q, 8304Q

NOTE: **The registration number is not mandatory;** however, it is of use when there is a need to trace the aircraft model by series.

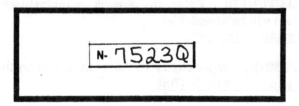

ITEM 2.   **AIRCRAFT:**

   NOTE: Always supply aircraft data if available.

   MANUFACTURER: Enter the aircraft manufacturer's name.   Any meaningful abbreviation will be acceptable.
      Example: Beech, Cessna

   MODEL/SERIES: Enter aircraft model as identified on the aircraft data plate.
      Example: 172A, 180

   SERIAL NUMBER: Enter the serial number assigned by the manufacturer.
      Example: 81RK, 94RK

Enter pertinent data	MANUFACTURER	MODEL/SERIES	SERIAL NUMBER
2. AIRCRAFT	Beech	172A	81 RK

ITEM 3.   **POWERPLANT:**

   MANUFACTURER: Enter the engine manufacturer's name.   Any meaningful abbreviation will be acceptable.
      Example: Lyc., Cont.

   MODEL/SERIES: Enter engine model as identified on the engine data plate.
      Example: IO-540, O-470R

   SERIAL NUMBER: Enter the serial number assigned by the engine manufacturer.
      Example: 4700, 2300

Enter pertinent data	MANUFACTURER	MODEL/SERIES	SERIAL NUMBER
3. POWERPLANT	Lyc.	IO-540	4700

AC 20-109A   4/8/93
Appendix 1

ITEM 4.   PROPELLER: Complete only if pertinent to the problem being reported.

> **MANUFACTURER:** Enter the manufacturer's name. Any meaningful abbreviation will be acceptable.
>   Example: Hartzl., Hamstd.

> **MODEL/SERIES:** Enter propeller model as identified in FAA type certificate data sheet/propeller specifications.
>   Example: DHCC2Y, M74CC

> **SERIAL NUMBER:** Enter the serial number assigned by the propeller manufacturer.
>   Example: D800, D900

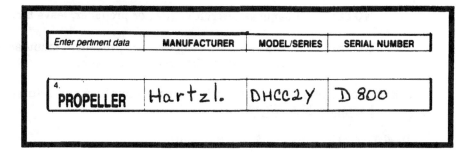

Enter pertinent data	MANUFACTURER	MODEL/SERIES	SERIAL NUMBER
4. PROPELLER	Hartzl.	DHCC2Y	D 800

ITEM 5.   SPECIFIC PART (of component) CAUSING TROUBLE:

Part Name: Enter the name of the specific part causing the problem. The appliance or component is the assembly which includes the part. For instance: When the part is a burned wire, the component would be the system using the wire, such as VHF communication system. When the part is a bearing, the appliance should be the unit using the bearing, such as starter, alternator, generator, etc. When the part is a stringer, the component name should be fuselage, wing, or stabilizer, etc.
Example: crankcase, wire

MFG. Model or Part No.: Enter the manufacturer's part number.
Example: 14542, 23893

NOTE: If same as aircraft engine, or propeller, leave blank.

NOTE: If the aircraft, engine, or propeller manufacturer is the component manufacturer, leave blank.

Serial No.: Enter the serial number assigned by the manufacturer.
Example: N/A, W5489

Part/Defect Location: Enter the location.
Example: left half, right wing

5. SPECIFIC PART *(of component)* CAUSING TROUBLE			
Part Name	MFG. Model or Part No.	Serial No.	Part Defect Location
CrankCase	14542	N/A	left half

5

ITEM 6.   APPLIANCE/COMPONENT (Assembly that includes part):

Comp/Appl Name: Enter the manufacturer's nomenclature for the component or appliance of the specific part causing the problem.
Example: engine, starter

Manufacturer: Enter the part manufacturer's name.
Example: Lyc., Lear

Model or Part No.: If supplied by the manufacturer.
Example: O-362YK-1, O-473GH-2

Serial Number: If supplied by the manufacturer.
Example: CH9693, DE8549

Part TT: Enter the service time of the part in whole hours. (If Part TT is unknown, use aircraft, engine, propeller, or appliance/component total time, whichever is applicable.)
Example: 02756, 04278

Part TSO: Enter the service time of the part since it was last overhauled, in whole hours. (If part TSO is unknown, use an aircraft, engine, propeller, or appliance/component time since last overhaul, whichever is applicable.)
Example: 00351, 00427

Part Condition: Enter the word(s) which best describe the part condition.
Example: cracked, disintegrated

6. APPLIANCE/COMPONENT *(Assembly that includes part)*			
Comp/Appl Name	Manufacturer	Model or Part No.	Serial Number
engine	Lyc.	O-362YK-1	CH9693
Part TT	Part TSO	Part Condition	
02756	00351	Cracked	

ITEM 7.   Date Sub: Enter the date of submission, day, month, year.
Example: 08/15/92, 11/15/92

7. Date Sub.
08/15/92

ITEM 8.   **Comments (Describe the malfunction or defect and the circumstances under which it occurred. State probable cause and recommendations to prevent recurrence.):** Continue on reverse side if needed. Powerplant TT and TSO should be shown in this box when it is a secondary item.

<u>Example: (See the following typed example.)</u>

NOTE: It is requested that submitters make their comments as legible as possible (preferably typed). Information vital to the FAA and the aviation industry may be lost when it is not possible to contact the submitter of an illegible report.

---

8. Comments *(Describe the malfunction or defect and the circumstances under which it occurred. State probable cause and recommendations to prevent recurrence.)*

During a scheduled inspection of the landing gear, the mechanic found the left main landing gear support was broken completely in half.

It is suspected that fatigue or an unreported hard landing could be the cause.

Optional Information:

Check a box below, if this report is related to an aircraft

☐ Accident; Date _____   ☑ Incident; Date 01/14/93

ITEM.   **Optional Information:**

Accident; Date: Accident where substantial damage to aircraft or property and/or serious injury. Enter the date of the accident (day, month, and year).
<u>Example: 01/22/93, 02/13/93</u>

Incident; Date: Anything less than an accident. Enter the date of the incident (day, month, and year).
<u>Example: 01/14/93, 02/12/93</u>

NOTE: This information may be used to trace data to accident or incident records.

ITEM.   **DISTRICT OFFICE:** District Office Flight Standards District Office Code.
                    Example: DAL, LAX

NOTE: FAA Aviation Safety Inspectors reviewing this report should show their FSDO
                    symbol in this box.

ITEM.   **SUBMITTED BY:** Enter the name (and certificate number if appropriate) of the person submitting the report. This is not mandatory, but is extremely important when further information is required. Information such as names, telephone numbers, etc., are dealt with strict confidentiality to protect the submitter. However, the report will be entered in the system even if unsigned.
                    Example: (See the following hand-written example.)

NOTE: Check the appropriate box to identify the organization/person initiating the report.

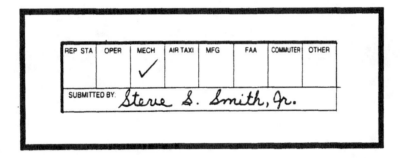

ITEM.   **TELEPHONE NUMBER:** Enter the telephone number of the person submitting the report.
                    Example: (See the following hand-written example.)

NOTE: This is not mandatory, but is of use when further information is required.

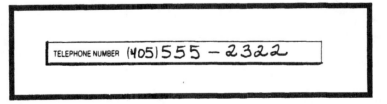

4/8/93

ITEM.   **OPERATOR DESIGNATOR:** Enter four-letter designator assigned by the FAA, as appropriate.
<u>Example: DXRA, UMNA</u>

U.S. Department
of Transportation
**Federal Aviation
Administration**

Advisory Circular

Subject: Application for U.S. Airworthiness Certificate, FAA Form 8130–6	**Date:** 9/7/2012 **AC No:** 21–12C **Initiated by:** AIR–200

1. Purpose. This advisory circular (AC) provides guidance and information needed to prepare and submit Federal Aviation Administration (FAA) Form 8130-6, Application for U.S. Airworthiness Certificate. This application is required to obtain an airworthiness certificate or to amend a current certificate. In some cases, an application may be required for the issuance of a replacement airworthiness certificate. This AC is not mandatory and does not constitute a regulation. It describes an acceptable means, but not the only means, to comply with requirements. However, if you use the means described in the AC, you must follow it in all respects.

2. Audience. This AC applies to any person applying for an FAA airworthiness certificate.

3. Effective Date. This AC is effective September 7, 2012.

4. Explanation of Changes. This revision—

    a. Updates the instructions on how to complete the current FAA Form 8130-6.

    b. Makes this AC a reference on how to properly complete FAA Form 8130-6. Form examples are found in appendix D to this AC. These examples were previously located in FAA Order 8130.2, Airworthiness Certification of Aircraft and Related Products.

5. Cancellation. This AC cancels AC 21-12B, dated November 6, 2001.

6. Where You Can Obtain FAA Form 8130-6. You can obtain FAA Form 8130-6 by downloading it from the FAA website at http://www.faa.gov, or by contacting your local FAA office. You should use the latest form version. The FAA will not accept superseded form versions.

7. How to Enter Information on FAA Form 8130-6.

    a. The FAA recommends using a fillable FAA Form 8130-6, which is available online at http://www.faa.gov. However, you may print a blank form and type or legibly print all of the required information. When handwriting in the form, you should use permanent blue or black ink. Using erasable materials such as lead/carbon pencils or erasable pens may not be acceptable.

b. All entries must be made in the English language.

c. You should not make entries in areas coded for FAA use only.

8. What Sections Should Be Completed on FAA Form 8130-6. FAA Form 8130-6 contains eight sections. Sections V and VIII are reserved for FAA or designee use only. The other sections are completed and submitted to the FAA by the registered owner or authorized agent of the registered owner. An authorized agent is someone designated by the registered owner to act on their behalf. For someone to act as an authorized agent, the FAA would accept a notarized letter of authorization signed by the registered owner. This letter should be included with the application form.

a. For standard airworthiness certificates, you should complete sections I, II, and III.

(1) You should complete section IV for applications of used aircraft and surplus U.S. military aircraft (refer to Title 14, Code of Federal Regulations (14 CFR) § 21.183(d), Used aircraft and surplus aircraft of the U.S. Armed Forces), or

(2) You should complete section IV if you have manufactured one new aircraft based on a type certificate (TC) and you meet the following two conditions:

(a) You are not the TC holder or you have a licensing agreement from the TC holder, and

(b) Evidence can be shown that the manufacture of the aircraft began before August 5, 2004 (refer to 14 CFR § 21.183(h), New aircraft manufactured under the provisions of § 21.6(b)).

b. For special airworthiness certificates except for special flight permits, you should complete sections I, II, and III.

c. For special flight permits for the purpose of production flight testing, you should complete sections II and VI, except if you are a light-sport aircraft (LSA) manufacturer. LSA manufacturers should complete sections I, II, and VI.

d. For special flight permits for purposes other than production flight testing, you should complete sections II and VII.

9. How to Complete FAA Form 8130-6. The following provides instructions and explanations on how to complete the sections that may apply to your application using paragraph 8 as a guide. Instructions and explanations have been given for all sections except V and VIII. Before starting, you may want to familiarize yourself with the form. Your review may help guide you when gathering the information requested in the blocks. Some sample airworthiness application forms have been provided in appendix D to this AC. You should contact your local FAA office if you have questions related to completing the form.

a. **Section I, Aircraft Description.** You should enter general information about the aircraft in this section of the application. Your information should include data taken from the aircraft identification (ID) plate, aircraft registration, TC data sheet (TCDS) (if applicable), aircraft specification sheet (if applicable), or aircraft listing (if applicable). In the rest of this AC, "aircraft registration" refers to the aircraft's current registration or most recent renewal.

(1) **Item #1, Registration Mark.** In this block, you should enter information about the aircraft's nationality and registration marks. This means entering the U.S. nationality designator letter "N" followed by the registration marks as shown on the aircraft registration certificate (refer to 14 CFR part 45, subpart C, Nationality and Registration Marks).

(2) **Item #2, Aircraft Builder's Name (Make).** In this block, you should enter the name of the manufacturer or builder. The following paragraphs provide additional guidance (refer to 14 CFR § 45.13(a)(1), Identification data).

(a) For standard and special airworthiness (primary, limited, provisional, and restricted categories) certificates, the manufacturer's or builder's name as it appears on the aircraft's ID plate should be used to complete the block. For former aircraft of the U.S. Armed Forces (U.S. military aircraft, not assembled from spare and/or surplus articles), the builder's name should be as listed on the TCDS.

(b) For special airworthiness certificates in the light-sport category, the builder's name is the manufacturer who is identified on FAA Form 8130-15, Light-Sport Aircraft Statement of Compliance. The builder's name, as identified on FAA Form 8130-15, should be used to complete this block and should match the aircraft's ID plate.

(c) For special airworthiness certificates in the experimental category with the purposes of operating amateur-built and operating primary kit-built aircraft, the builder's name is the person who fabricated and assembled the aircraft. To complete this block, you should enter the name of the person who fabricated and assembled the aircraft. When two or more persons are involved building the aircraft, only the person's name that is listed first on the aircraft's ID plate should be entered.

(d) For special airworthiness certificates in the experimental category for the purposes of operating LSAs, the builder's name is the manufacturer identified on the FAA Form 8130-15. Manufacturers producing LSA kits for assembly will provide a statement of compliance as evidence the design and fabrication meet applicable consensus standards. You should use the builder's name as identified on FAA Form 8130-15 to help you complete this block. The builder's name as found on the form should also match the aircraft's ID plate.

(e) For special airworthiness certificates in the experimental category (for the purposes of research and development, exhibition, air racing, crew training, and market survey, and to show compliance with regulations) or a special flight permit, the builder's name may be found on the aircraft's ID plate.

(3) **Item #3, Aircraft Model Designation.** Information about the aircraft model designation should be entered in this block. Entering trade names is not acceptable. You should refer to the additional information provided below.

(a) For standard and special airworthiness (primary, limited, provisional, or restricted category) certificates, the aircraft's model designation on the aircraft's ID plate should be used to complete the block. For surplus U.S. military aircraft, both the civil model designation and the military model designation should be used. For example, "Super King Air B200C (C-12F)" has both the civil and military model designations. However, if a U.S. military aircraft receives a TC, the military model designation becomes the civil one and should be used to complete the block (refer to 14 CFR § 21.27, Issue of type certificate: surplus aircraft of the U.S. Armed Forces). For U.S. military aircraft type certificated under the restricted category, you should use only the military designation (refer to 14 CFR § 21.25(a)(2), Issue of type certificate: restricted category aircraft).

(b) For special airworthiness certificates in the light-sport category, the aircraft's model designation can be found on the aircraft's FAA Form 8130-15. You should use the manufacturer's designation as identified on FAA Form 8130-15 to complete this block.

(c) For special airworthiness certificates in the experimental category for the purposes of operating amateur-built or operating primary kit-built aircraft, the aircraft model's designation can be an arbitrary designation. The designation can be given by the builder. If the aircraft was purchased as a kit, the model designation may be assigned by the kit manufacturer. To complete this block, you should enter the builder's designation or, if a manufacturer's kit, the assigned kit designation. The model designation should match the aircraft's ID plate.

(d) For special airworthiness certificates in the experimental category for the purposes of operating LSAs, the aircraft's model designation is identified on FAA Form 8130-15. Manufacturers producing LSA kits for assembly will provide a statement of compliance as evidence that the design and fabrication meet applicable consensus standards. You should use the aircraft's model designation as identified on FAA Form 8130-15 to complete this block.

(e) For special airworthiness certificates in the experimental category (for the purposes of research and development, exhibition, air racing, crew training, and market survey, and to show compliance with regulations) or a special flight permit, you should use the model designation found on the aircraft's ID plate to complete this block.

(4) Item #4, Year of Manufacture (Yr. Mfr.). In this block, you should enter the year the aircraft was manufactured from the aircraft's ID plate using a four-digit format (for example, "2009"). If there is a conflict between date formats outlined in this AC and the aircraft's ID plate, use the format shown on the aircraft's ID plate. For aircraft eligible for special airworthiness certificates in the light-sport category, the year of manufacture is found on the aircraft's FAA Form 8130-15.

(5) Item #5, Aircraft Serial No. (Number).

(a) For standard or special airworthiness certificates (primary, limited, provisional, and restricted categories), you should enter the manufacturer's or builder's serial number as it appears on the aircraft's ID plate. For U.S. military aircraft, you should use the manufacturer's civil serial number. The military serial number should be placed in parentheses following the civil serial number. If no civil serial number exists, you should enter the military serial number.

(b) For special airworthiness certificates in the light-sport category, the aircraft serial number is identified on the aircraft's ID plate and on FAA Form 8130-15. The ID plate and the serial numbers must match.

(c) For special airworthiness certificates in the experimental category for the purposes of operating amateur-built aircraft, the serial number is given by the builder who fabricated and assembled the aircraft. To complete this block, you should enter your designated serial number.

(d) For special airworthiness certificates in the experimental category for the purposes of operating primary kit-built aircraft, the serial number is usually given by the manufacturer of the kit. To complete this block, you should enter the kit manufacturer's designated serial number.

(e) For special airworthiness certificates in the experimental category for the purposes of operating LSAs, the serial number is assigned by the manufacturer as identified on FAA Form 8130-15. Manufacturers producing LSA kits for assembly provide a statement of compliance as evidence that the design and fabrication meet applicable consensus standards. You should use the serial number as identified on FAA Form 8130-15 to complete this block.

(f) For special airworthiness certificates in the experimental category (for the purposes of research and development, exhibition, air racing, crew training, and market survey, and to show compliance with regulations) or a special flight permit, the serial number should be found on the aircraft's ID plate.

(6) Item #6, Engine Builder's Name (Make). In this block, you should enter the aircraft engine builder's name, if applicable. The engine information in this block and the other blocks on FAA Form 8130-6 refers to engines used for aircraft propulsion (refer to 14 CFR § 1.1, General definitions).

(a) For type-certificated aircraft engines, you should enter the name of the manufacturer identified on the engine ID plate whether or not the engine conforms to type design. If a type-certificated aircraft engine no longer has an ID plate, you should enter the manufacturer's name as it is known in the marketplace or if marked on the engine. Abbreviations may be used (for example, "P&W" or "G.E.").

(b) For non-type-certificated aircraft engines, you should enter the manufacturer's name as it is known in the marketplace or if marked on the engine to complete this block (for example, Rotax). Abbreviations may be used.

(c) When no aircraft engines are installed, as in the case of a glider or balloon, enter "N/A" (not applicable) to complete this block.

(7) Item #7, Engine Model Designation. In this block, you should enter the engine model's designation.

(a) For type-certificated engines, you should enter the model designation located on the engine ID plate whether or not the engine conforms to type design. If a type-certificated aircraft engine no longer has an ID plate, you should find and use the engine manufacturer's model designation, part number, or serial number markings. Examples include "O-320-A1B," "PT6A-20A," or "CFM-56-3C-1" (refer to 14 CFR § 45.13(a)(2)).

(b) For non-type-certificated engines, you should find and use the engine manufacturer's model designation, part number, or serial number markings.

(c) When no engines are installed, as in the case of a glider or balloon, you should enter "N/A."

(8) Item #8, Number of Engines. In this block, you should enter the number (using digits) of aircraft engines installed on the aircraft if applicable. For example, an entry of "1" means that one aircraft engine is installed. For aircraft with no engines, you should enter "0."

(9) Item #9, Propeller Builder's Name (Make). You should enter the propeller builder's name if applicable. The propeller information in this block and the other blocks of FAA Form 8130-6 refers to propellers used for aircraft propulsion (refer to 14 CFR § 1.1, General definitions).

(a) For type-certificated propellers, you should enter the name of the manufacturer as shown by propeller ID markings whether or not the propeller conforms to type design. If a type-certificated propeller no longer has an ID plate, you should enter the manufacturer's name as it is known in the marketplace to complete this block.

(b) For non-type-certificated propellers, you should enter the manufacturer's name as it is known in the marketplace to complete this block.

(c) You should enter "N/A" if no propellers are installed.

(10) Item #10, Propeller Model Designation. You should enter the propeller model's designation, if applicable.

(a) For type-certificated propellers, the manufacturer is required to mark the propeller with the model designation. You should use this information to complete the block whether or not the propeller conforms to type design. If a type-certificated propeller no longer has an ID plate, you should enter the model designation as it is known in the marketplace or use the propeller diameter and pitch when a model designation is not known.

(b) For non-type-certificated propellers, you should enter the model designation as it is known in the marketplace or use the propeller diameter and pitch.

(c) When no propellers are installed, you should enter "N/A."

(11) Item #11, Aircraft Is Import. This box should be marked only when the following three conditions are met:

(a) The aircraft was manufactured outside the United States, in a country with which we have a bilateral agreement.

(b) The aircraft has been issued a U.S. TC in accordance with that agreement. Bilateral agreements can be found at http://www.faa.gov/aircraft/air_cert. Additionally, all technical data concerning noise and airworthiness has been submitted to the FAA. Manuals, placards, listings, and instrument markings required by airworthiness and noise requirements are listed in the English language (refer to 14 CFR § 21.29, Issue of type certificate: import products).

(c) The foreign aviation authority certifies the aircraft conforms to its type design and is in condition for safe operation (refer to 14 CFR § 21.183(c), Import aircraft).

b. Section II, Certification Requested. This section should help you choose which boxes to mark for the airworthiness certificate you are requesting. To clearly indicate your choices, you should use checkmarks or "x" marks in the boxes.

(1) Item A, Standard Airworthiness Certificate. A standard airworthiness certificate is issued to type-certificated aircraft in the normal, utility, acrobatic, transport, commuter, and manned free balloon categories. For a standard airworthiness certificate, you should mark the "Standard Airworthiness Certificate" box and the applicable category box. You should refer to the aircraft model TCDS to determine whether more than one category can be selected.

(a) Also included are special class aircraft such as gliders, airships, and other non-conventional aircraft. A special class aircraft may include an airframe, installed engines, and propellers for which airworthiness standards have not been issued under 14 CFR part 21, subpart B, Type Certificates. A special class should be indicated by marking the "Standard Airworthiness Certificate" box and the "Other" box. In the blank space directly above the standard category blocks, you should enter the type (for example, glider, very light aircraft, or airship).

(b) For aircraft type certificated before the adoption of categories, you should mark the "Standard Airworthiness Certificate" box and the "Other" box. You should use the blank space directly above the boxes to enter the certification basis. The certification basis can be found in the aircraft listing, specification sheet, or TCDS. Here is an example of an older certification basis entered in the blank space: "Category N/A - Certification basis CAR-04-A (Civil Air Regulations part 4a)".

(c) The following regulations may be useful when making an application for standard airworthiness:

1 Refer to 14 CFR § 21.183(a) for new aircraft manufactured under a production certificate (PC).

2 Refer to 14 CFR § 21.183(b) for new aircraft manufactured under a TC.

3 Refer to 14 CFR § 21.183(c) for import aircraft.

4 Refer to 14 CFR § 21.183(d) for used aircraft and surplus aircraft of the U.S. Armed Forces (U.S. military aircraft).

5 Refer to 14 CFR § 21.183(h) for new aircraft manufactured under the provisions of 14 CFR § 21.6(b), which allows a person to build one type-certificated aircraft without holding or licensing the TC if evidence can be shown that construction began before August 5, 2004.

(2) Item B, Special Airworthiness Certificate. This certificate is issued to aircraft not meeting the requirements for a standard airworthiness certificate. Special airworthiness certificates are identified as primary, light-sport, limited, provisional, restricted, experimental, and special flight permit.

(a) Primary Category. Special airworthiness certification in the primary category can be issued to type-certificated aircraft meeting the criteria of 14 CFR § 21.24(a)(1), Issuance of type certificate: primary category aircraft manufactured under a PC. This also includes aircraft kits provided by a PC holder to other people. However, the people who assemble these kits work under the supervision and quality control of the PC holder. To submit an application for a special airworthiness certificate in the primary category, you should mark the "Special Airworthiness Certificate" box and the "Primary" box. The following regulations may be useful when making an application of special airworthiness in the primary category:

1 Refer to 14 CFR § 21.184(a) for new primary category aircraft manufactured under a PC.

2 Refer to 14 CFR § 21.184(b) for imported aircraft in the primary category.

3 Refer to 14 CFR § 21.184(c) for aircraft having a current standard airworthiness certificate to be exchanged for a special airworthiness certificate in the primary category.

4 Refer to 14 CFR § 21.184(d) for other aircraft that may qualify for a special airworthiness certificate in the primary category.

(b) Light-Sport Category. Special airworthiness certificates in the light-sport category can be issued when your aircraft meets the requirements of 14 CFR § 21.190, Issue of airworthiness certificate for light-sport category aircraft. There are five classes in the light-sport category (airplane, powered parachute, weight-shift-control aircraft, glider, and lighter-than-air aircraft). Each class is defined by the design and manufacturing requirements of its respective consensus standard. For a special airworthiness certificate in the light-sport category, you should mark the "Special Airworthiness Certificate" box and the "Light-Sport" box, and then mark the appropriate light-sport class (for example, airplane or powered parachute). You should select only one class.

(c) Limited Category. Special airworthiness certificates in the limited category can be issued when your aircraft meets the requirements of 14 CFR § 21.189, Issue of airworthiness certificate for limited category aircraft. For a special airworthiness certificate in the limited category, you should mark the "Special Airworthiness Certificate" box and the "Limited" box.

(d) Provisional Category. Special airworthiness certificates in the provisional category can be issued when your aircraft has a provisional TC. A provisional category special airworthiness certificate is issued to conduct special purpose operations of aircraft with provisional TCs. The duration of this airworthiness certificate is limited to the duration of the provisional TC. Two classes of provisional TCs may be issued. Class I certificates may be issued for all categories and have a duration of 24 months. Class II certificates are issued for transport category aircraft only and have a duration of 12 months. When you select a special airworthiness certificate in the provisional category, you should mark the "Special Airworthiness Certificate" box and choose one of the class boxes (refer to 14 CFR § 21.221, Class I provisional airworthiness certificates, or 14 CFR § 21.223, Class II provisional airworthiness certificates).

(e) Restricted Category. Special airworthiness certificates in the restricted category can be issued when your aircraft meets the requirements in 14 CFR § 21.185, Issue of airworthiness certificate for restricted category aircraft.

1 This category includes several types of operations described in 14 CFR § 21.25(b), Issue of type certificate: Restricted category aircraft.

Form Box #	General Operations	Special Purpose
1	Agriculture and pest control operations	Spraying, dusting, seeding, and livestock and predatory animal control
2	Aerial surveying	Photography, mapping, and oil and mineral exploration
3	Aerial advertising	Skywriting, banner towing, airborne signs, and public address systems
4	Forest (wildlife conservation)	Forest and wildlife conservation
5	Patrolling operations	Patrol of pipelines, power lines, and canals
6	Weather control	Cloud seeding

2 To submit an application for a special airworthiness certificate in the restricted category, you should mark the "Special Airworthiness Certificate" box, the "Restricted" box, and the applicable operation(s). If an applicable operation is not listed, you should mark the "Other" box and provide a description of the operation in the blank space.

3 The following references may be useful when making an application of special airworthiness in the restricted category.

(aa) Refer to 14 CFR § 21.185(a) for restricted category aircraft manufactured under a PC or TC only.

(bb) Refer to 14 CFR § 21.185(b) for other aircraft (surplus U.S. military aircraft or an aircraft previously type certificated in another category).

(cc) Refer to 14 CFR § 21.185(c) for import aircraft type certificated and produced under the authority of another country with which the United States has a bilateral agreement.

(dd) Refer to FAA Order 8130.2 for procedures about restricted airworthiness certification.

(f) Experimental Category. Special airworthiness certification in the experimental category is given for aircraft with purposes defined in 14 CFR § 21.191, Experimental certificates. To submit an application for a special airworthiness certificate in the experimental category, you should mark the "Special Airworthiness Certificate" box, the "Experimental" box, and the applicable operation(s) to be conducted. Unmanned aircraft can be issued certificates for the purposes of research and development, crew training, or market survey. When making an application for an unmanned aircraft, in addition to marking the "Special Airworthiness" and "Experimental" boxes, you should mark the "Unmanned Aircraft" box. You should then mark one or more of the three listed operations boxes. The following references may be useful when making an application of special airworthiness in the experimental category.

1 Refer to 14 CFR § 21.191(a) for operations in research and development.

2 Refer to 14 CFR § 21.191(b) for operations to show compliance with regulations.

3 Refer to 14 CFR § 21.191(c) for operations related to crew training.

4 Refer to 14 CFR § 21.191(e) for operations related to exhibition.

5 Refer to 14 CFR § 21.191(e) for operations related to air racing.

6 Refer to 14 CFR § 21.191(f) for operations related to market surveys.

7 Refer to 14 CFR § 21.191(g) for operations related to amateur-built aircraft.

8 Refer to 14 CFR § 21.191(h) for operations related to kit-built aircraft (primary category aircraft assembled without the supervision and quality control of a PC holder).

9 Refer to 14 CFR § 21.191(i) for operations related to experimental LSAs.

10 Refer to FAA Order 8130.34, Airworthiness Certification of Unmanned Aircraft Systems and Optionally Piloted Aircraft.

(g) Special Flight Permit. Special flight permits are given for aircraft that may not currently meet applicable airworthiness requirements but are capable of safe flight. For a special flight permit, you should mark the "Special Airworthiness Certificate" box, the "Special Flight Permit" box, and the applicable operation to be conducted. Unmanned aircraft may be issued special flight permits for production flight testing. The following regulations may be useful reference when applying for a special flight permit.

1 Refer to 14 CFR § 21.197(a)(1) if you are flying an aircraft to a base where repairs, alterations, or maintenance are to be performed, or to a point of storage.

2 Refer to 14 CFR § 21.197(a)(2) for aircraft delivery or exports.

3 Refer to 14 CFR § 21.197(a)(3) for production flight testing of new aircraft.

4 Refer to 14 CFR § 21.197(a)(4) for evacuating aircraft from areas of impending danger.

5 Refer to 14 CFR § 21.197(a)(5) for customer demonstration flights in new aircraft that have completed production testing.

6 Refer to 14 CFR § 21.197(b) for operations of an aircraft weighing more than the maximum certificated takeoff weight.

(3) Item C, Multiple Airworthiness Certificate. Certificates can be issued to an applicant in the restricted category and one or more other categories except the primary category (refer to 14 CFR § 21.187, Issue of multiple airworthiness certificates, for additional information and requirements). For application of multiple airworthiness certificates, you should mark the "Multiple Airworthiness Certificate" box. Based upon your application, you should mark, when applicable, the "Standard Airworthiness" box with the appropriate categories and/or the "Special Airworthiness" box with the appropriate categories. On the application, you should mark only the aircraft airworthiness certificates you are requesting to hold.

c. Section III, Owner's Certification. 14 CFR part 47, Aircraft Registration, details the requirements to register aircraft.

(1) Item A, Registered Owner.

(a) Name. You should use the name as exactly shown on the aircraft registration certificate.

AC 21–12C

       (b) Address. You should use the address as exactly shown on the aircraft registration certificate.

       (c) If Dealer, Check Here. This block should be marked if the aircraft is registered under a dealer's aircraft registration certificate.

       (2) Item B, Aircraft Certification Basis. In this section, you will be asked about the aircraft specifications, airworthiness directives (AD), aircraft listing (if applicable), and supplemental TCs (STC). If your application is for multiple airworthiness certificates, the certification basis for each requested certificate should be entered. You should mark all boxes that apply to your application and complete the requested data in each block as it applies:

       (a) Aircraft Specification or Type Certificate Data Sheet. When you mark this box and complete the block, you are indicating the aircraft has a TC or aircraft specification, or complies with a consensus standard.

       1 For aircraft with TCs, you should enter the TC number (for example, "AB123"). When revisions exist, you should use the TC number plus "Rev" and the revision number (for example, "AB123 Rev 1"). The revision number is the version found on page 1 of the aircraft's TCDS.

       2 For a new aircraft or model where the TCDS or specification has been approved but not yet published, you should enter the date of approval in month/day/year format, the TC number, and the word "Preliminary" (for example, "01/02/2010 AB123 Preliminary").

       3 A special airworthiness certificate in the light-sport category or the experimental category operating light-sport requires a statement of compliance to a design consensus standard. You should mark the box and enter the applicable consensus standard for design and performance. You will find this information on the aircraft's FAA Form 8130-15. An example of an American Society for Testing and Materials design and performance standard for LSAs is "F2245-04", where "F2245" refers to the consensus standard and "-04" represents the current accepted version.

       4 For a special airworthiness certificate in the experimental category (except experimental operating light-sport), you should leave the box unmarked and enter "N/A" in the block.

       5 You should enter "N/A" in the block if you are an LSA manufacturer who has produced a first article aircraft for research and development flight testing. Before the box can be marked and the consensus standard entered in the block, the manufacturer must demonstrate compliance to the respective design and performance consensus standard. Usually when an LSA manufacturer is performing research and development, it is to demonstrate compliance to the standard. First article aircraft should not have an FAA Form 8130-15. Once flight tests show compliance to the design and performance consensus standards as well as all other applicable consensus standards, the manufacturer can create an FAA Form 8130-15 for the aircraft. When an LSA has an FAA Form 8130-15, the box should be marked and the design and performance standard entered in the block.

(b) **Airworthiness Directives.** Regardless of the type of airworthiness certificate being requested, you should review this block and indicate the aircraft is in compliance with all applicable ADs (refer to 14 CFR part 39, Airworthiness Directives, and 14 CFR § 21.99, Required design changes).

1 If all ADs are in compliance, you should check the box and then enter the latest AD biweekly supplement number published as of the date of application. You should use a four-digit year, a dash, and publication number format (for example, "2010-04"). As an example, if the day of your application is 11/28/2010, you would find 2010-24 as the latest supplement published on 11/23/2010. You would then enter "2010-24" in the block.

2 For a special airworthiness certificate in the light-sport category or the experimental category operating light-sport, you should list all applicable manufacturer safety directives available as of the date of application (for example, "SD-001"). If there are no manufacturer safety directives, "None" should be entered. This block should also contain the latest AD biweekly supplement and either the manufacturer's list of safety directives or "None" (for example, "2010-04, SD-001, SD-002" or "2010-04, None").

3 Each AD contains an applicability statement specifying the product (aircraft, aircraft engine, propeller, or appliance) to which it applies. Unless stated otherwise ADs only apply to type-certificated aircraft, including ADs issued for an engine, propeller, or appliance (refer to AC 39-7, Airworthiness Directives).

(c) **Aircraft Listing.** Older aircraft (predating TCDS) may have been originally certificated with aircraft specifications. This block should contain the page number of aircraft specification where the type or model is found. For example, a 1928 Travel Air 3000 has an aircraft specification of #31, where the aircraft type is listed on page 65 of that specification. If applicable, you should mark the box and enter the listing page number(s) as appropriate. If this block does not apply or there is no aircraft listing, you should leave the box unmarked and enter "N/A."

(d) **Supplemental Type Certificate.** This block is applicable for all standard airworthiness certifications. This block is also applicable for special airworthiness certifications in the restricted, limited, provisional, and primary categories. When one or more STCs are installed, you should mark the box and complete the block with the required information. When no STCs are installed, you should leave the box unmarked and the block blank.

1 You should enter the STC number of each STC installed. If more space is needed, you should use an attachment. When using an attachment, you should list the STCs installed by STC number only. For aircraft involved in FAA STC projects, ensure the STC number for the completed project is listed in the block at the time of application.

2 For a special airworthiness certificate in the experimental or light-sport category, you should leave the box unmarked and enter "N/A" in the block.

(3) **Item C, Aircraft Operation and Maintenance Records.**

(a) **Check if Records Are in Compliance with 14 CFR § 91.417, Maintenance Records.** Your maintenance records must comply with 14 CFR § 91.417 and be in the English language. This block is applicable to all aircraft and should be marked to indicate the recordkeeping requirements of the regulation have been met.

1 Compliance to 14 CFR § 91.417(a)(2)(i) requires the total service time of the airframe, each engine, propeller, and rotor.

2 Compliance to 14 CFR § 91.417(a)(2)(ii) requires a maintenance record of the current status of life-limited parts of each airframe, engine, propeller, rotor, and appliance.

(b) **Total Airframe Hours.** You should enter into this block the aircraft's total time in service measured in hours. Time in service should be determined from your aircraft and maintenance records.

(c) **Experimental Only.**

1 This block should only be completed when—

(aa) You are submitting an application for a new or renewed special airworthiness certificate in the experimental category (experimental certificate),

(bb) You are requesting a change from an experimental certificate back to a previously held standard airworthiness certificate, or

(cc) You are requesting a change from an experimental certificate back to a previously held special airworthiness certificate in another category.

2 You should enter "0" if you are applying for an original issuance of an experimental certificate with zero hours flown.

3 If you are renewing an experimental certificate or making an application to change back a previously held certificate, you should enter in this block the number of hours the aircraft has flown since the issue of your current experimental certificate.

(4) **Item D, Certification.** You will need to read and verify the certification statement on the application before completing this item. There are three blocks to complete:

(a) **Date of Application.** You should enter the date that you attest to the certification statement in month/day/year format (for example, "02/09/2010").

(b) **Name and Title.** You should either print or type the full name and title of the person certifying the application. A full name may include first name, a middle initial, and last name. Titles may include owner, president, director, or agent. Examples of a full name and title are "John E. Doe, Owner" and "John Doe, Director of Quality Assurance." If the signature is by the owner's agent, a notarized letter from the aircraft's registered owner authorizing the agent to act on the owner's behalf is required.

   (c) Signature. The person whose name appears in the "Name and Title" block should sign the signature block.

   d. Section IV, Inspection Agency Verification. You should only complete this section for standard airworthiness applications of used aircraft or surplus U.S. military aircraft. To qualify for a standard airworthiness certificate, you must show the aircraft conforms to a type design approved under a TC or an STC. All applicable ADs must also be in compliance. The aircraft must be inspected and found airworthy by one of four methods (refer to paragraph (1)(a) through (1)(d) of this section). Finally, the responsible person at the inspection agency will date and sign this block (refer to 14 CFR § 21.183(d), Used aircraft and surplus aircraft of the U.S. Armed Forces).

   (1) Boxes. You should mark the applicable box and provide a certificate number or aircraft manufacturer name or firm in the corresponding block.

   (a) 14 CFR part 121 Certificate Holder. You should mark this box and enter the certificate number (block 2) when the aircraft has been inspected and found airworthy by a part 121 certificate holder.

   (b) Certificated Mechanic. You should mark this box and enter the certificate number (block 3) when the aircraft has been inspected and found airworthy by a certificated mechanic.

   (c) Certificated Repair Station. You should mark this box and enter the certificate number (block 6) when the aircraft has been inspected and found airworthy by a mechanic at a certificated repair station. In the case of used aircraft and surplus aircraft of the U.S. Armed Forces, the FAA may accept a previously performed inspection in lieu of a 100-hour inspection. In this circumstance the applicant should list the foreign repair station name and number (if applicable) in block 6. Using permanent blue or black ink, the applicant should strike/draw a line through the title of block 5, initial the line-through, and provide a statement in block 5 that an equivalent inspection was performed.

   (d) Aircraft Manufacturer. You should mark this box and enter the manufacturer name (block 5) when the aircraft has been inspected and found airworthy by the manufacturer who holds the TC.

   (2) Date. You should enter the date the inspection agency attests to the verification statement. You should enter the date in month/day/year format (for example, "02/09/2010").

   (3) Title. The authorized person at the inspecting agency completes this portion. The authorized person will print or type their full name in the space. A full name may include first, middle initial as appropriate, and last name. Titles may include mechanic, technician, inspector, manager, or director. "John E. Doe, Avionics Technician" and "John Doe, Director of Quality Assurance" are some examples of a full name and title.

(4) Signature. The person whose name appears in the "Title" block should sign the signature block.

e. Section V, FAA Representative Certification. This section will be completed by the FAA inspector or designee.

f. Section VI, Production Flight Testing. You should complete this section if you are a manufacturer applying for a special flight permit with the purpose of flight testing production aircraft. If you are a manufacturer producing fully assembled aircraft in the light-sport category, you should only complete items A and C. Item B should be left blank (refer to 14 CFR § 21.197(a)(3), Special flight permits).

(1) Item A, Manufacturer.

(a) Name. You should enter the name of the manufacturer or legal name of the company.

(b) Address. You should enter the company's full physical address, which includes street address, city, state, and zip code.

(2) Item B, Production Basis.

(a) Production Certificate. You should mark this box if the manufacturer holds a PC and has produced the aircraft under this certificate. If the box is marked, a PC number should be entered in the block space.

(b) Type Certificate. You should mark this box if this aircraft was produced under a TC and not a PC.

(c) Other. This box should not be marked.

(3) Item C.

(a) Give Quantity of Certificates Required for Operating Needs. For manufacturers in serial production (except LSA manufacturers), you may request more than one certificate per application submitted. You should enter the quantity (in digits) of certificates needed for your operation. For example, entering "4" requests four certificates for use during production flight tests that can be transferred from one aircraft to another. However, for LSA production flight tests, permits are not transferable. Because each LSA is individually issued a special flight permit, you should enter "1" for one certificate.

(b) Date of Application. You should enter the current date as the special flight permit application date in the month/day/year format (for example, "02/09/2010").

(c) Name and Title. You should either print or type the full name and title. A full name usually includes first name, a middle initial, and last name. Titles may include owner, president, director, or authorized agent. "John E. Doe, Owner" and "John Doe, Director of Quality Assurance" are some examples of a full name and title.

(d) Signature. The person whose name appears in the "Name and Title" block should sign this block.

g. Section VII, Special Flight Permit Purposes Other than Production Flight Test.

(1) Item A, Description of Aircraft. Entries in this section should match the data recorded on the aircraft's registration certificate and the aircraft's ID plate as applicable.

(a) Registered Owner. You should enter the name on the aircraft's registration certificate.

(b) Address. You should enter the owner's address listed on the aircraft's registration certificate.

(c) Builder. You should enter the name of the manufacturer or builder as it appears on the aircraft's ID plate.

(d) Model. You should enter the model designation as shown on the aircraft's ID plate.

(e) Serial Number. You should enter the serial number as shown on the aircraft ID plate.

(f) Registration Mark. You should enter the U.S. nationality designator letter "N" followed by the registration marks as shown on the aircraft registration certificate.

(2) Item B, Description of Flight.

(a) Customer Demonstration Flights. You should mark this block if the special flight permit is for a customer demonstration flight.

(b) From. You should enter the aircraft's current location (for example, "Kansas City, Missouri", or the airport identifier "MCI").

(c) To. You should enter the aircraft's intended destination (for example, "Dallas, Texas", or the airport identifier "DFW").

(d) Via. This block should contain the name(s) of an airport or city at some intermediate point(s) in the flight. Entering "via" points provides a general direction of the flight route (refer to 14 CFR § 21.199(a)(2), Issue of special flight permits). For example, a flight from "Kansas City, Missouri" (or "MCI"), to "Dallas, Texas" (or "DFW"), may be flown via "Wichita, Kansas" (or "ICT"), and "Oklahoma City, Oklahoma" (or "OKC"). You should leave this block blank if there are no planned intermediate points.

(e) Departure Date. You should enter the date the flight is planned using month/day/year format (for example, "02/09/2010").

(f) Duration. The duration is the length of time needed for the special flight permit. The duration is not the same as the planned duration of the actual flight. Factors such as fueling stops, weather conditions, overnight stops, or any other reasonable condition should be given consideration when establishing the duration. The length of time needed for the aircraft to reach its intended destination should be given in whole number days or weeks (for example, "7 days" or "2 weeks") (refer to 14 CFR § 21.199).

(3) Item C, Crew Required to Operate the Aircraft and Its Equipment. In this section, you should mark the boxes of the crew required to operate the aircraft and its equipment. If additional crew members other than the ones listed in boxes are necessary, mark the "Other" box. You should then write the additional required crew member's function (for example, test engineer, avionics technician) in the space provided to the right of the "Other" box.

(4) Item D, The Aircraft Does Not Meet the Applicable Airworthiness Requirements as Follows. In the space provided, you should detail the conditions where the aircraft does not comply with the applicable airworthiness requirements. You should keep in mind this is your basis for requesting a special flight permit and will need to be specific (refer to 14 CFR § 21.199(a)(4)).

(5) Item E, The Following Restrictions Are Considered Necessary for Safe Operation. In the space provided, you should write any restrictions you consider necessary for safe operation of the aircraft (for example, reduced airspeed, operating weight, turbulence avoidance, crew limitations, or qualifications). The application will be reviewed and additional conditions and/or limitations may be prescribed for safe operation (refer to 14 CFR § 21.199(a)(5) and (6)).

(6) Item F, Certification. If this section applies to your application, you should read the certification statement and verify that you meet the requirements before completing this item. There are three blocks to complete:

(a) Date of Application. In this block, you should enter the current date using month/day/year format (for example, "02/09/2010").

(b) Name and Title. You should either print or type the full name and title. A full name usually includes first name, a middle initial, and last name. Following the full name, the block requests the title of that person. Titles may include owner, president, director, or authorized agent. "John E. Doe, Owner" or "John E. Doe, Director of Quality Assurance" are some examples of a full name and title.

(c) Signature. The person whose name appears in the "Name and Title" block should sign the block. If the signature is the owner's agent, a notarized letter from the registered owner authorizing the agent to act on the owner's behalf is required.

h. Section VIII, Airworthiness Documentation. This section will be completed by the FAA inspector or designee.

10. Submitting the Completed FAA Form 8130-6. Once you have completed the applicable sections and the FAA Form 8130-6 is signed, you should submit it to your local FAA office. Be prepared to provide additional documentation required by the regulations for final airworthiness certification. If you are an authorized agent to act in someone's behalf, a notarized letter of authority should be included with the application form. For manufacturers holding an FAA production approval, an application may be submitted to an authorized Designated Airworthiness Representative, Designated Manufacturing Inspection Representative, or Organization Designation Authorization unit member, as appropriate.

11. Where to Find This AC. You can find this AC at http://www.faa.gov/regulations_policies/advisory_circulars/.

James D. Seipel
Manager
Production and Airworthiness Division

Appendix A. Acronyms

AC   Advisory Circular
AD   Airworthiness Directive
CAR   Civil Air Regulation
CFR   Code of Federal Regulations
FAA   Federal Aviation Administration
ID   Identification
LSA   Light-Sport Aircraft
N/A   Not Applicable
PC   Production Certificate
STC   Supplemental Type Certificate
TC   Type Certificate
TCDS   Type Certificate Data Sheet

Appendix B. Related 14 CFR Parts

1. 14 CFR part 1, Definitions. 14 CFR part 1 provides definitions for terms used in the application.

2. 14 CFR part 21, Certification Procedures for Products, Articles, and Parts.
14 CFR part 21 sets forth rules for the issuance of and change to type certificates, and issuance of production certificates, airworthiness certificates, and export airworthiness approvals. It also sets forth the rules governing the holders of these certificates and the approval of certain articles.

3. 14 CFR part 39, Airworthiness Directives. 14 CFR part 39 provides a legal framework for the FAA's system of Airworthiness Directives.

4. 14 CFR part 43, Maintenance, Preventive Maintenance, Rebuilding, and Alteration.
14 CFR part 43 sets forth rules governing the maintenance, preventive maintenance, rebuilding, and alteration of aircraft having a U.S. airworthiness certificate, certain foreign-registered aircraft, and related products and articles.

5. 14 CFR part 45, Identification and Registration Marking. 14 CFR part 45 sets forth rules for display of nationality and registration marks, display of special airworthiness classification marks, identification plates for products, and identification of certain replacement and critical aircraft articles.

6. 14 CFR part 47, Aircraft Registration. 14 CFR part 47 sets forth rules for registering an aircraft.

7. 14 CFR part 91, General Operating and Flight Rules. 14 CFR part 91 sets forth rules governing the operation of most aircraft within the United States.

Appendix C. Related Publications

1. FAA Order 8130.2, Airworthiness Certification of Aircraft and Related Products.

2. FAA Order 8130.34, Airworthiness Certification of Unmanned Aircraft Systems and Optionally Piloted Aircraft.

3. AC 20-27, Certification and Operation of Amateur-Built Aircraft.

4. AC 20-65, U.S. Airworthiness Certificates and Authorizations for Operation of Domestic and Foreign Aircraft.

5. AC 21-4, Special Flight Permits for Operation of Overweight Aircraft.

6. AC 21-37, Primary Category Aircraft.

7. AC 39-7, Airworthiness Directives.

8. AC 45-2, Identification and Registration Marking.

Appendix D.
Examples of FAA Form 8130-6, Application for Airworthiness Certificate

Figure	FAA Form 8130-6 Example	Reference
D-1	Standard, Normal	14 CFR § 21.183(a)
D-2	Standard, Transport	14 CFR § 21.183(a) or (b)
D-3	Standard, Transport, Used Aircraft, No Previous U.S. Airworthiness Certificate	14 CFR § 21.183(d)
D-4	Standard, Import Glider	14 CFR § 21.183(c)
D-5	Standard, Surplus Military	14 CFR § 21.183(d)
D-6	Standard, Other, Import, JAR/VLA	14 CFR § 21.183(c)
D-7	Special, Primary	14 CFR § 21.184(a)
D-8	Special, Light-Sport (with TC installations)	14 CFR § 21.190
D-9	Special, Light-Sport (without TC installations)	14 CFR § 21.190
D-10	Special, Limited	14 CFR § 21.189
D-11	Special, Provisional, Class I	14 CFR § 21.221
D-12	Special, Restricted	14 CFR § 21.185
D-13	Special, Experimental, Research and Development	14 CFR § 21.191(a)
D-14	Special, Experimental, To Show Compliance with the CFR	14 CFR § 21.191(b)
D-15	Special, Experimental, Amateur Built (with TC installations)	14 CFR § 21.191(g)
D-16	Special, Experimental, Operating Light-Sport, Operating Light-sport Kit-Built	14 CFR § 21.191(i)
D-17	Special, Experimental, Unmanned Aircraft	14 CFR § 21.191(a),(c), or (f)
D-18A/B	Special, Special Flight Permit, Ferry flight for Repairs, Alterations, Maintenance, or Storage	14 CFR § 21.197(a)(1)
D-19A/B	Special, Special Flight Permit, Operation in Excess of Maximum Certificated Take-off Weight	14 CFR § 21.197(b)
D-20A/B	Special, Special Flight Permit, Production Flight Testing	14 CFR § 21.197(a)(3)
D-21A/B	Special, Special Flight Permit, Production Flight Testing, Light-Sport Manufacturer	14 CFR § 21.197(a)(3)
D-22A/B	Special, Special Flight Permit, Production Flight Testing, Unmanned Aircraft Manufacturer	14 CFR § 21.197(a)(3)
D-23	Multiple, Normal and Restricted	14 CFR § 21.187

AC
21-
12C

Figure D-1. Sample FAA Form 8130-6, Application for U.S. Airworthiness Certificate, Standard – Normal, Under 14 CFR § 21.183(a)
(Face Side Only)

FAA FORM 8130-6, APPLICATION FOR U.S. AIRWORTHINESS CERTIFICATE

Form Approved
O.M.B. No. 2120-0018

**U.S. Department of Transportation
Federal Aviation Administration**

APPLICATION FOR U.S. AIRWORTHINESS CERTIFICATE

INSTRUCTIONS - Print or type. Do not write in shaded areas; these are for FAA use only. Submit original only to an authorized FAA Representative. If additional space is required, use attachment. For special flight permits complete Sections II, VI, and VII as applicable.

I. AIRCRAFT DESCRIPTION

1. REGISTRATION MARK	2. AIRCRAFT BUILDER'S NAME *(Make)*	3. AIRCRAFT MODEL DESIGNATION	4. YR. MFR.	FAA CODING
N5206Q	Cessna Aircraft Company	172S	2002	

5. AIRCRAFT SERIAL NO.	6. ENGINE BUILDER'S NAME *(Make)*	7. ENGINE MODEL DESIGNATION	
17259111	Lycoming Engines	IO-360-L2A	

8. NUMBER OF ENGINES	9. PROPELLER BUILDER'S NAME *(Make)*	10. PROPELLER MODEL DESIGNATION	11. AIRCRAFT IS *(Check if applicable)*
1	McCauley Propeller Systems	1A170E/JHA7660	IMPORT

II. CERTIFICATION REQUESTED

APPLICATION IS HEREBY MADE FOR: *(Check applicable items)*

A	1	✓	STANDARD AIRWORTHINESS CERTIFICATE *(Indicate category)*	✓ NORMAL	✓ UTILITY	ACROBATIC	TRANSPORT	COMMUTER	BALLOON	OTHER

B			SPECIAL AIRWORTHINESS CERTIFICATE *(Check appropriate items)*					

	7		PRIMARY					
	9		LIGHT-SPORT *(Indicate Class)*	Airplane	Power-Parachute	Weight-Shift-Control	Glider	Lighter than Air
	2		LIMITED					

	5		PROVISIONAL *(Indicate class)*	1	CLASS I		
				2	CLASS II		

	3		RESTRICTED *(Indicate operation(s) to be conducted)*	1	AGRICULTURE AND PEST CONTROL	2	AERIAL SURVEY	3	AERIAL ADVERTISING
				4	FOREST *(Wildlife conservation)*	5	PATROLLING	8	WEATHER CONTROL
				0	OTHER *(Specify)*				

	4		EXPERIMENTAL *(Indicate operation(s) to be conducted)*	1	RESEARCH AND DEVELOPMENT	2	AMATEUR BUILT	3	EXHIBITION
				4	AIR RACING	5	CREW TRAINING	6	MARKET SURVEY
				0	TO SHOW COMPLIANCE WITH THE CFR	7	OPERATING *(Primary Category)* KIT BUILT AIRCRAFT		

				8	OPERATING LIGHT-SPORT	8A	Existing aircraft without an airworthiness certificate & do not meet § 103.1
						8B	Operating Light-Sport Kit-built
						8C	Operating light-sport previously issued special light-sport category airworthiness certificate under § 21.190

				9	UNMANNED AIRCRAFT	9A	RESEARCH AND DEVELOPMENT	9C	CREW TRAINING
						9B	MARKET SURVEY		

	8		SPECIAL FLIGHT PERMIT *(Indicate operation to be conducted, then complete Section VI or VII as applicable on reverse side)*	1	FERRY FLIGHT FOR REPAIRS, ALTERATIONS, MAINTENANCE, OR STORAGE		
				2	EVACUATE FROM AREA OF IMPENDING DANGER		
				3	OPERATION IN EXCESS OF MAXIMUM CERTIFICATED TAKE-OFF WEIGHT		
				4	DELIVERING OR EXPORTING	5	PRODUCTION FLIGHT TESTING
				6	CUSTOMER DEMONSTRATION FLIGHTS		

C	6		MULTIPLE AIRWORTHINESS CERTIFICATE *(Check ABOVE "Restricted Operation" and "Standard" or "Limited" as applicable)*

III. OWNER'S CERTIFICATION

A. REGISTERED OWNER *(As shown on certificate of aircraft registration)*   IF DEALER, CHECK HERE ➡

NAME	ADDRESS
Flight Corp.	10 Lane Ave., Doby, TX 78907

B. AIRCRAFT CERTIFICATION BASIS *(Check applicable blocks and complete items as indicated)*

✓	AIRCRAFT SPECIFICATION OR TYPE CERTIFICATE DATA SHEET *(Give No. and Revision No.)* 3A12	✓	AIRWORTHINESS DIRECTIVES *(Check if all applicable ADs are complied with and give the number of the last AD SUPPLEMENT available in the biweekly series as of the date of application)* 2002-12
	AIRCRAFT LISTING *(Give page number(s))* N/A		SUPPLEMENTAL TYPE CERTIFICATE *(List number of each STC incorporated)*

C. AIRCRAFT OPERATION AND MAINTENANCE RECORDS

✓	CHECK IF RECORDS IN COMPLIANCE WITH 14 CFR section 91.417	TOTAL AIRFRAME HOURS 10	3	EXPERIMENTAL ONLY *(Enter hours flown since last certificate issued or renewed)*

D. CERTIFICATION - I hereby certify that I am the registered owner (or his agent) of the aircraft described above, that the aircraft is registered with the Federal Aviation Administration in accordance with Title 49 of the United States Code 44101 et seq. and applicable Federal Aviation Regulations, and that the aircraft has been inspected and is airworthy and eligible for the airworthiness certificate requested.

DATE OF APPLICATION 06/20/2002	NAME AND TITLE *(Print or type)* Joe Quality, Director, QA	SIGNATURE *Joe Quality*

IV. INSPECTION AGENCY VERIFICATION

A. THE AIRCRAFT DESCRIBED ABOVE HAS BEEN INSPECTED AND FOUND AIRWORTHY BY: *(Complete the section only if 14 CFR part 21.183(d) applies)*

2	14 CFR part 121 CERTIFICATE HOLDER *(Give Certificate No.)*	3	CERTIFICATED MECHANIC *(Give Certificate No.)*	6	CERTIFICATED REPAIR STATION *(Give Certificate No.)*
5	AIRCRAFT MANUFACTURER *(Give name or firm)*				

DATE	TITLE	SIGNATURE

V. FAA REPRESENTATIVE CERTIFICATION

(Check ALL applicable block items A and B)

A. I find that the aircraft described in Section I or VII meets requirements for	4	THE CERTIFICATE REQUESTED AMENDMENT OR MODIFICATION OF CURRENT AIRWORTHINESS CERTIFICATE

B. Inspection for a special flight permit under Section VII was conducted by:	FAA INSPECTOR	FAA DESIGNEE		
	CERTIFICATE HOLDER UNDER	14 CFR part 65	14 CFR part 121 OR 135	14 CFR part 145

DATE	MIDO/FSDO OFFICE	4	FAA INSPECTOR'S SIGNATURE or DESIGNEE'S SIGNATURE AND NO.	1	FAA INSPECTOR'S CERTIFICATION FILE REVIEW SIGNATURE

FAA Form 8130-6 (04-11) All Previous Editions Superseded

Figure D-2. Sample FAA Form 8130-6, Application for U.S. Airworthiness Certificate, Standard – New Aircraft Produced in the Transport Category (Face Side Only)

FAA FORM 8130-6, APPLICATION FOR U.S. AIRWORTHINESS CERTIFICATE

Form Approved
O.M.B. No. 2120-0018

APPLICATION FOR U.S. AIRWORTHINESS CERTIFICATE

U.S. Department of Transportation
Federal Aviation Administration

INSTRUCTIONS - Print or type. Do not write in shaded areas; these are for FAA use only. Submit original only to an authorized FAA Representative. If additional space is required, use attachment. For special flight permits complete Sections II, VI, and VII as applicable.

I. AIRCRAFT DESCRIPTION

1. REGISTRATION MARK: N12345	2. AIRCRAFT BUILDER'S NAME (Make): The Boeing Company
3. AIRCRAFT MODEL DESIGNATION: 737-800	4. YR. MFR: 2010	FAA CODING
5. AIRCRAFT SERIAL NO.: 19714	6. ENGINE BUILDER'S NAME (Make): CFM International
7. ENGINE MODEL DESIGNATION: CFM56-7B26	
8. NUMBER OF ENGINES: 2	9. PROPELLER BUILDER'S NAME (Make): N/A
10. PROPELLER MODEL DESIGNATION: N/A	11. AIRCRAFT IS (Check if applicable): IMPORT

II. CERTIFICATION REQUESTED

APPLICATION IS HEREBY MADE FOR: (Check applicable items)

A 1 ✓ STANDARD AIRWORTHINESS CERTIFICATE (Indicate category): NORMAL | UTILITY | ACROBATIC | ✓ TRANSPORT | COMMUTER | BALLOON | OTHER

B SPECIAL AIRWORTHINESS CERTIFICATE (Check appropriate items)

7	PRIMARY		
9	LIGHT-SPORT (Indicate Class)	Airplane	Power-Parachute	Weight-Shift-Control	Glider	Lighter than Air
2	LIMITED		
5	PROVISIONAL (Indicate class)	1 CLASS I	2 CLASS II

3 RESTRICTED (Indicate operation(s) to be conducted)
1	AGRICULTURE AND PEST CONTROL	2	AERIAL SURVEY	3	AERIAL ADVERTISING
4	FOREST (Wildlife conservation)	5	PATROLLING	6	WEATHER CONTROL
0	OTHER (Specify)				

4 EXPERIMENTAL (Indicate operation(s) to be conducted)
1	RESEARCH AND DEVELOPMENT	2	AMATEUR BUILT	3	EXHIBITION
4	AIR RACING	5	CREW TRAINING	6	MARKET SURVEY
0	TO SHOW COMPLIANCE WITH THE CFR	7	OPERATING (Primary Category) KIT BUILT AIRCRAFT

8	OPERATING LIGHT-SPORT	8A	Existing aircraft without an airworthiness certificate & do not meet § 103.1
		8B	Operating Light-Sport Kit-built
		8C	Operating light-sport previously issued special light-sport category airworthiness certificate under § 21.190
9	UNMANNED AIRCRAFT	9A	RESEARCH AND DEVELOPMENT	9C	CREW TRAINING
		9B	MARKET SURVEY

8 SPECIAL FLIGHT PERMIT (Indicate operation to be conducted, then complete Section VI or VII as applicable on reverse side)
1	FERRY FLIGHT FOR REPAIRS, ALTERATIONS, MAINTENANCE, OR STORAGE
2	EVACUATE FROM AREA OF IMPENDING DANGER
3	OPERATION IN EXCESS OF MAXIMUM CERTIFICATED TAKE-OFF WEIGHT
4	DELIVERING OR EXPORTING	5	PRODUCTION FLIGHT TESTING
6	CUSTOMER DEMONSTRATION FLIGHTS

C 6 MULTIPLE AIRWORTHINESS CERTIFICATE (Check ABOVE "Restricted Operation" and "Standard" or "Limited" as applicable)

III. OWNER'S CERTIFICATION

A. REGISTERED OWNER (As shown on certificate of aircraft registration) | IF DEALER, CHECK HERE ➤

NAME: Shorthaul Airlines, Inc.
ADDRESS: 111 Airport Way, St. Louis MO 58010

B. AIRCRAFT CERTIFICATION BASIS (Check applicable blocks and complete items as indicated)

✓ AIRCRAFT SPECIFICATION OR TYPE CERTIFICATE DATA SHEET (Give No. and Revision No.): A16WE Rev 45	✓ AIRWORTHINESS DIRECTIVES (Check if all applicable ADs are complied with and give the number of the last AD SUPPLEMENT available in the biweekly series as of the date of application): 2010-04
AIRCRAFT LISTING (Give page number(s)): N/A	SUPPLEMENTAL TYPE CERTIFICATE (List number of each STC incorporated)

C. AIRCRAFT OPERATION AND MAINTENANCE RECORDS

| ✓ CHECK IF RECORDS IN COMPLIANCE WITH 14 CFR section 91.417 | TOTAL AIRFRAME HOURS: 80 | 3 EXPERIMENTAL ONLY (Enter hours flown since last certificate issued or renewed) |

D. CERTIFICATION - I hereby certify that I am the registered owner (or his agent) of the aircraft described above, that the aircraft is registered with the Federal Aviation Administration in accordance with Title 49 of the United States Code 44101 et seq. and applicable Federal Aviation Regulations, and that the aircraft has been inspected and is airworthy and eligible for the airworthiness certificate requested.

| DATE OF APPLICATION: 02/23/2010 | NAME AND TITLE (Print or type): John Doe, Vice President | SIGNATURE: John Doe |

IV. INSPECTION AGENCY VERIFICATION

A. THE AIRCRAFT DESCRIBED ABOVE HAS BEEN INSPECTED AND FOUND AIRWORTHY BY: (Complete this section only if 14 CFR part 21.183(d) applies)

| 2 | 14 CFR part 121 CERTIFICATE HOLDER (Give Certificate No.) | 3 | CERTIFICATED MECHANIC (Give Certificate No.) | 6 | CERTIFICATED REPAIR STATION (Give Certificate No.) |
| 5 | AIRCRAFT MANUFACTURER (Give name or firm) | | | | |

| DATE | TITLE | SIGNATURE |

V. FAA REPRESENTATIVE CERTIFICATION

(Check ALL applicable block items A and B)
A. I find that the aircraft described in Section I or VII meets requirements for | 4 | THE CERTIFICATE REQUESTED | AMENDMENT OR MODIFICATION OF CURRENT AIRWORTHINESS CERTIFICATE

B. Inspection for a special flight permit under Section VII was conducted by:
| FAA INSPECTOR | FAA DESIGNEE |
| CERTIFICATE HOLDER UNDER | 14 CFR part 65 | 14 CFR part 121 OR 135 | 14 CFR part 145 |

| DATE | MIDO/FSDO OFFICE | 4 | FAA INSPECTOR'S SIGNATURE or DESIGNEE'S SIGNATURE AND NO. | 1 | FAA INSPECTOR'S CERTIFICATION FILE REVIEW SIGNATURE |

FAA Form 8130-6 (04-11) All Previous Editions Superseded

9/7/2012

Figure D-3. Sample FAA Form 8130-6, Application for U.S. Airworthiness Certificate, Standard – Used Aircraft in the Transport Category (No Previous U.S. Airworthiness Certificate Issued) (Face Side Only)

FAA FORM 8130-6, APPLICATION FOR U.S. AIRWORTHINESS CERTIFICATE

Form Approved
O.M.B. No. 2120-0018

APPLICATION FOR U.S. AIRWORTHINESS CERTIFICATE	**INSTRUCTIONS** - Print or type. Do not write in shaded areas; these are for FAA use only. Submit original only to an authorized FAA Representative. If additional space is required, use attachment. For special flight permits complete Sections II, VI, and VII as applicable.

U.S. Department of Transportation
Federal Aviation Administration

I. AIRCRAFT DESCRIPTION

1. REGISTRATION MARK	2. AIRCRAFT BUILDER'S NAME (Make)	3. AIRCRAFT MODEL DESIGNATION	4. YR. MFR	FAA CODING
N12345	Douglas	DC-6A	1952	

5. AIRCRAFT SERIAL NO	6. ENGINE BUILDER'S NAME (Make)	7. ENGINE MODEL DESIGNATION	
43218	Pratt & Whitney	CB-16	

8. NUMBER OF ENGINES	9. PROPELLER BUILDER'S NAME (Make)	10. PROPELLER MODEL DESIGNATION	11. AIRCRAFT IS (Check if applicable)
4	Hamilton Standard	43E60-300	IMPORT

II. CERTIFICATION REQUESTED

APPLICATION IS HEREBY MADE FOR: (Check applicable items)

A 1 ✓ STANDARD AIRWORTHINESS CERTIFICATE (Indicate category) NORMAL UTILITY ACROBATIC ✓ TRANSPORT COMMUTER BALLOON OTHER

B SPECIAL AIRWORTHINESS CERTIFICATE (Check appropriate items)

	7	PRIMARY								
	9	LIGHT-SPORT (Indicate Class)		Airplane	Power-Parachute	Weight-Shift-Control	Glider	Lighter than Air		
	2	LIMITED								
	5	PROVISIONAL (Indicate class)	1	CLASS I						
			2	CLASS II						
	3	RESTRICTED (Indicate operation(s) to be conducted)	1	AGRICULTURE AND PEST CONTROL		2	AERIAL SURVEY	3	AERIAL ADVERTISING	
			4	FOREST (Wildlife conservation)		5	PATROLLING	6	WEATHER CONTROL	
			0	OTHER (Specify)						
	4	EXPERIMENTAL (Indicate operation(s) to be conducted)	1	RESEARCH AND DEVELOPMENT		2	AMATEUR BUILT	3	EXHIBITION	
			4	AIR RACING		5	CREW TRAINING	6	MARKET SURVEY	
			0	TO SHOW COMPLIANCE WITH THE CFR		7	OPERATING (Primary Category) KIT BUILT AIRCRAFT			
			8	OPERATING LIGHT-SPORT	8A	Existing aircraft without an airworthiness certificate & do not meet § 103.1				
					8B	Operating Light-Sport Kit-built				
					8C	Operating light-sport previously issued special light-sport category airworthiness certificate under § 21.190				
			9	UNMANNED AIRCRAFT	9A	RESEARCH AND DEVELOPMENT		9C	CREW TRAINING	
					9B	MARKET SURVEY				
	8	SPECIAL FLIGHT PERMIT (Indicate operation to be conducted, then complete Section VI or VII as applicable on reverse side)	1	FERRY FLIGHT FOR REPAIRS, ALTERATIONS, MAINTENANCE, OR STORAGE						
			2	EVACUATE FROM AREA OF IMPENDING DANGER						
			3	OPERATION IN EXCESS OF MAXIMUM CERTIFICATED TAKE-OFF WEIGHT						
			4	DELIVERING OR EXPORTING		5	PRODUCTION FLIGHT TESTING			
			6	CUSTOMER DEMONSTRATION FLIGHTS						

C 6 MULTIPLE AIRWORTHINESS CERTIFICATE (Check ABOVE "Restricted Operation" and "Standard" or "Limited" as applicable)

III. OWNER'S CERTIFICATION

A. REGISTERED OWNER (As shown on certificate of aircraft registration) IF DEALER, CHECK HERE ▶

NAME	ADDRESS
Tiger Aviation Corp.	234 Jane Ave., Jackson, MS 78965

B. AIRCRAFT CERTIFICATION BASIS (Check applicable blocks and complete items as indicated)

✓ AIRCRAFT SPECIFICATION OR TYPE CERTIFICATE DATA SHEET (Give No. and Revision No.) 63A Rev. 26	✓ AIRWORTHINESS DIRECTIVES (Check if all applicable ADs are complied with and give the number of the last AD SUPPLEMENT available in the biweekly series as of the date of application) 2010-02
AIRCRAFT LISTING (Give page number(s)) N/A	✓ SUPPLEMENTAL TYPE CERTIFICATE (List number of each STC incorporated) SA2-414; SA2-567; SA4-532; SA2231

C. AIRCRAFT OPERATION AND MAINTENANCE RECORDS

✓ CHECK IF RECORDS IN COMPLIANCE WITH 14 CFR section 91.417	TOTAL AIRFRAME HOURS 12347	3	EXPERIMENTAL ONLY (Enter hours flown since last certificate issued or renewed)

D. CERTIFICATION - I hereby certify that I am the registered owner (or his agent) of the aircraft described above, that the aircraft is registered with the Federal Aviation Administration in accordance with Title 49 of the United States Code 44101 et seq. and applicable Federal Aviation Regulations, and that the aircraft has been inspected and is airworthy and eligible for the airworthiness certificate requested.

DATE OF APPLICATION 01/31/2010	NAME AND TITLE (Print or type) John Doe, President	SIGNATURE John Doe

IV. INSPECTION AGENCY VERIFICATION

A. THE AIRCRAFT DESCRIBED ABOVE HAS BEEN INSPECTED AND FOUND AIRWORTHY BY: (Complete the section only if 14 CFR part 21.183(d) applies)

2	14 CFR part 121 CERTIFICATE HOLDER (Give Certificate No.)	3	CERTIFICATED MECHANIC (Give Certificate No.)	6	✓	CERTIFICATED REPAIR STATION (Give Certificate No.) AA11BB22
5	AIRCRAFT MANUFACTURER (Give name or firm)					

DATE 02/23/2010	TITLE David E. Jones, Manager	SIGNATURE David E. Jones

V. FAA REPRESENTATIVE CERTIFICATION

(Check ALL applicable block items A and B) THE CERTIFICATE REQUESTED

A. I find that the aircraft described in Section I or VII meets requirements for 4 AMENDMENT OR MODIFICATION OF CURRENT AIRWORTHINESS CERTIFICATE

B. Inspection for a special flight permit under Section VII was conducted by

		FAA INSPECTOR	FAA DESIGNEE		
		CERTIFICATE HOLDER UNDER	14 CFR part 65	14 CFR part 121 OR 135	14 CFR part 145

DATE	MIDO/FSDO OFFICE	4	FAA INSPECTOR'S SIGNATURE or DESIGNEE'S SIGNATURE AND NO.	1	FAA INSPECTOR'S CERTIFICATION FILE REVIEW SIGNATURE

FAA Form 8130-6 (04-11) All Previous Editions Superseded

Figure D-4. Sample FAA Form 8130-6, Application for U.S. Airworthiness Certificate, Standard – Import Glider
(Face Side Only)

FAA FORM 8130-6, APPLICATION FOR U.S. AIRWORTHINESS CERTIFICATE

Form Approved
O.M.B. No. 2120-0018

APPLICATION FOR U.S. AIRWORTHINESS CERTIFICATE

U.S. Department of Transportation
Federal Aviation Administration

INSTRUCTIONS - Print or type. Do not write in shaded areas; these are for FAA use only. Submit original only to an authorized FAA Representative. If additional space is required, use attachment. For special flight permits complete Sections II, VI, and VII as applicable.

I. AIRCRAFT DESCRIPTION

1. REGISTRATION MARK	2. AIRCRAFT BUILDER'S NAME *(Make)*	3. AIRCRAFT MODEL DESIGNATION	4. YR. MFR	FAA CODING
N53B	Alexander Schleicher GmbH	AS-K13	2002	

5. AIRCRAFT SERIAL NO.	6. ENGINE BUILDER'S NAME *(Make)*	7. ENGINE MODEL DESIGNATION	
501	N/A	N/A	

8. NUMBER OF ENGINES	9. PROPELLER BUILDER'S NAME *(Make)*	10. PROPELLER MODEL DESIGNATION	11. AIRCRAFT IS *(Check if applicable)*
0	N/A	N/A	✓ IMPORT

II. CERTIFICATION REQUESTED

APPLICATION IS HEREBY MADE FOR: *(Check applicable items)* **Glider**

A 1 ✓ STANDARD AIRWORTHINESS CERTIFICATE *(Indicate category)* — NORMAL · UTILITY · ACROBATIC · TRANSPORT · COMMUTER · BALLOON · ✓ OTHER

B SPECIAL AIRWORTHINESS CERTIFICATE *(Check appropriate items)*

7	PRIMARY	
9	LIGHT-SPORT *(indicate Class)*	Airplane · Power-Parachute · Weight-Shift-Control · Glider · Lighter than Air
2	LIMITED	
5	PROVISIONAL *(indicate class)*	1 CLASS I / 2 CLASS II
3	RESTRICTED *(indicate operation(s) to be conducted)*	1 AGRICULTURE AND PEST CONTROL / 2 AERIAL SURVEY / 3 AERIAL ADVERTISING / 4 FOREST *(Wildlife conservation)* / 5 PATROLLING / 6 WEATHER CONTROL / 0 OTHER *(Specify)*

EXPERIMENTAL *(indicate operation(s) to be conducted)* 4:
- 1 RESEARCH AND DEVELOPMENT / 2 AMATEUR BUILT / 3 EXHIBITION
- 4 AIR RACING / 5 CREW TRAINING / 6 MARKET SURVEY
- 0 TO SHOW COMPLIANCE WITH THE CFR / 7 OPERATING *(Primary Category)* KIT BUILT AIRCRAFT
- 8 OPERATING LIGHT-SPORT: 8A Existing aircraft without an airworthiness certificate & do not meet § 103.1 / 8B Operating Light-Sport Kit-built / 8C Operating light-sport previously issued special light-sport category airworthiness certificate under § 21.190
- 9 UNMANNED AIRCRAFT: 9A RESEARCH AND DEVELOPMENT / 9C CREW TRAINING / 9B MARKET SURVEY

SPECIAL FLIGHT PERMIT *(indicate operation to be conducted, then complete Section VI or VII as applicable on reverse side)* 8:
- 1 FERRY FLIGHT FOR REPAIRS, ALTERATIONS, MAINTENANCE, OR STORAGE
- 2 EVACUATE FROM AREA OF IMPENDING DANGER
- 3 OPERATION IN EXCESS OF MAXIMUM CERTIFICATED TAKE-OFF WEIGHT
- 4 DELIVERING OR EXPORTING / 5 PRODUCTION FLIGHT TESTING
- 6 CUSTOMER DEMONSTRATION FLIGHTS

C 6 MULTIPLE AIRWORTHINESS CERTIFICATE *(Check ABOVE "Restricted Operation" and "Standard" or "Limited" as applicable)*

III. OWNER'S CERTIFICATION

A. REGISTERED OWNER *(As shown on certificate of aircraft registration)*   IF DEALER, CHECK HERE ▶

NAME	ADDRESS
Elmer E. Jones	1601 E. 6th Street, San Diego, CA 95472

B. AIRCRAFT CERTIFICATION BASIS *(Check applicable blocks and complete items as indicated)*

✓ AIRCRAFT SPECIFICATION OR TYPE CERTIFICATE DATA SHEET *(Give No. and Revision No.)* G15EU	✓ AIRWORTHINESS DIRECTIVES *(Check if all applicable ADs are complied with and give the number of the last AD SUPPLEMENT available in the biweekly series as of the date of application)* 2002-12
AIRCRAFT LISTING *(Give page number(s))* N/A	SUPPLEMENTAL TYPE CERTIFICATE *(List number of each STC incorporated)*

C. AIRCRAFT OPERATION AND MAINTENANCE RECORDS

✓ CHECK IF RECORDS IN COMPLIANCE WITH 14 CFR section 91.417	TOTAL AIRFRAME HOURS 320	3 EXPERIMENTAL ONLY *(Enter hours flown since last certificate issued or renewed)*

D. CERTIFICATION - I hereby certify that I am the registered owner (or his agent) of the aircraft described above, that the aircraft is registered with the Federal Aviation Administration in accordance with Title 49 of the United States Code 44101 et seq. and applicable Federal Aviation Regulations, and that the aircraft has been inspected and is airworthy and eligible for the airworthiness certificate requested.

DATE OF APPLICATION	NAME AND TITLE *(Print or type)*	SIGNATURE
06/20/2002	Elmer E. Jones, Owner	*Elmer E. Jones*

IV. INSPECTION AGENCY VERIFICATION

A. THE AIRCRAFT DESCRIBED ABOVE HAS BEEN INSPECTED AND FOUND AIRWORTHY BY: *(Complete the section only if 14 CFR part 21.183(d) applies)*

2 14 CFR part 121 CERTIFICATE HOLDER *(Give Certificate No.)*	3 CERTIFICATED MECHANIC *(Give Certificate No.)*	6 CERTIFICATED REPAIR STATION *(Give Certificate No.)*
5 AIRCRAFT MANUFACTURER *(Give name or firm)*		

DATE	TITLE	SIGNATURE

V. FAA REPRESENTATIVE CERTIFICATION

(Check ALL applicable block items A and B)

A. I find that the aircraft described in Section I or VII meets requirements for 4 THE CERTIFICATE REQUESTED / AMENDMENT OR MODIFICATION OF CURRENT AIRWORTHINESS CERTIFICATE

B. Inspection for a special flight permit under Section VII was conducted by — FAA INSPECTOR / FAA DESIGNEE

CERTIFICATE HOLDER UNDER — 14 CFR part 65 / 14 CFR part 121 OR 135 / 14 CFR part 145

DATE	MIDO/FSDO OFFICE	4 FAA INSPECTOR'S SIGNATURE or DESIGNEE'S SIGNATURE AND NO.	1 FAA INSPECTOR'S CERTIFICATION FILE REVIEW SIGNATURE

FAA Form 8130-6 (04-11) All Previous Editions Superseded

Figure D-5. Sample FAA Form 8130-6, Application for U.S. Airworthiness Certificate, Standard – Surplus U.S. Military Aircraft Under § 21.183(d) (Face Side Only)

FAA FORM 8130-6, APPLICATION FOR U.S. AIRWORTHINESS CERTIFICATE

Form Approved
O.M.B. No. 2120-0018

APPLICATION FOR U.S. AIRWORTHINESS CERTIFICATE

U.S. Department of Transportation
Federal Aviation Administration

INSTRUCTIONS - Print or type. Do not write in shaded areas; these are for FAA use only. Submit original only to an authorized FAA Representative. If additional space is required, use attachment. For special flight permits complete Sections II, VI, and VII as applicable.

I. AIRCRAFT DESCRIPTION

1. REGISTRATION MARK	2. AIRCRAFT BUILDER'S NAME (Make)	3. AIRCRAFT MODEL DESIGNATION	4. YR. MFR.	FAA CODING
N34562	Hughes Aircraft Company	369A (OH-6A)	1966	

5. AIRCRAFT SERIAL NO.	6. ENGINE BUILDER'S NAME (Make)	7. ENGINE MODEL DESIGNATION	
1332	Allison Engine Company	250-C10B	

8. NUMBER OF ENGINES	9. PROPELLER BUILDER'S NAME (Make)	10. PROPELLER MODEL DESIGNATION	11. AIRCRAFT IS (Check if applicable)
1	N/A	N/A	IMPORT

II. CERTIFICATION REQUESTED

APPLICATION IS HEREBY MADE FOR: (Check applicable items)

A 1 ✓ STANDARD AIRWORTHINESS CERTIFICATE (Indicate category) ✓ NORMAL | UTILITY | ACROBATIC | TRANSPORT | COMMUTER | BALLOON | OTHER

B SPECIAL AIRWORTHINESS CERTIFICATE (Check appropriate items)

7	PRIMARY		
9	LIGHT-SPORT (Indicate Class)	Airplane	Power-Parachute	Weight-Shift-Control	Glider	Lighter than Air
2	LIMITED		
5	PROVISIONAL (Indicate class)	1 CLASS I / 2 CLASS II	
3	RESTRICTED (Indicate operation(s) to be conducted)	1 AGRICULTURE AND PEST CONTROL / 2 AERIAL SURVEY / 3 AERIAL ADVERTISING / 4 FOREST (Wildlife conservation) / 5 PATROLLING / 6 WEATHER CONTROL / 0 OTHER (Specify)	
4	EXPERIMENTAL (Indicate operation(s) to be conducted)	1 RESEARCH AND DEVELOPMENT / 2 AMATEUR BUILT / 3 EXHIBITION / 4 AIR RACING / 5 CREW TRAINING / 6 MARKET SURVEY / 0 TO SHOW COMPLIANCE WITH THE CFR / 7 OPERATING (Primary Category) KIT BUILT AIRCRAFT	
	8 OPERATING LIGHT-SPORT	8A Existing aircraft without an airworthiness certificate & do not meet § 103.1 / 8B Operating Light-Sport Kit-built / 8C Operating light-sport previously issued special light-sport category airworthiness certificate under § 21.190	
	9 UNMANNED AIRCRAFT	9A RESEARCH AND DEVELOPMENT / 9C CREW TRAINING / 9B MARKET SURVEY	
8	SPECIAL FLIGHT PERMIT (Indicate operation to be conducted, then complete Section VI or VII as applicable on reverse side)	1 FERRY FLIGHT FOR REPAIRS, ALTERATIONS, MAINTENANCE, OR STORAGE / 2 EVACUATE FROM AREA OF IMPENDING DANGER / 3 OPERATION IN EXCESS OF MAXIMUM CERTIFICATED TAKE-OFF WEIGHT / 4 DELIVERING OR EXPORTING / 5 PRODUCTION FLIGHT TESTING / 6 CUSTOMER DEMONSTRATION FLIGHTS	

C 6 MULTIPLE AIRWORTHINESS CERTIFICATE (Check ABOVE "Restricted Operation" and "Standard" or "Limited" as applicable)

III. OWNER'S CERTIFICATION

A. REGISTERED OWNER (As shown on certificate of aircraft registration) — IF DEALER, CHECK HERE ▶

NAME	ADDRESS
Helicopter Operators, Inc.	234 Perimeter Drive, Stackton CA 94044

B. AIRCRAFT CERTIFICATION BASIS (Check applicable blocks and complete items as indicated)

✓ AIRCRAFT SPECIFICATION OR TYPE CERTIFICATE DATA SHEET (Give No. and Revision No.) H3 WE Rev. 2	✓ AIRWORTHINESS DIRECTIVES (Check if all applicable ADs are complied with and give the number of the last AD SUPPLEMENT available in the biweekly series as of the date of application) 2010-02
AIRCRAFT LISTING (Give page number(s)) N/A	SUPPLEMENTAL TYPE CERTIFICATE (List number of each STC incorporated)

C. AIRCRAFT OPERATION AND MAINTENANCE RECORDS

✓ CHECK IF RECORDS IN COMPLIANCE WITH 14 CFR section 91.417	TOTAL AIRFRAME HOURS 2852	3 EXPERIMENTAL ONLY (Enter hours flown since last certificate issued or renewed)

D. CERTIFICATION - I hereby certify that I am the registered owner (or his agent) of the aircraft described above, that the aircraft is registered with the Federal Aviation Administration in accordance with Title 49 of the United States Code 44101 et seq. and applicable Federal Aviation Regulations, and that the aircraft has been inspected and is airworthy and eligible for the airworthiness certificate requested.

DATE OF APPLICATION 01/31/2010	NAME AND TITLE (Print or type) James, J. Jones, General Manager	SIGNATURE James Jones

IV. INSPECTION AGENCY VERIFICATION

A. THE AIRCRAFT DESCRIBED ABOVE HAS BEEN INSPECTED AND FOUND AIRWORTHY BY: (Complete this section only if 14 CFR part 21.183(d) applies)

2 14 CFR part 121 CERTIFICATE HOLDER (Give Certificate No.) | 3 CERTIFICATED MECHANIC (Give Certificate No.) | 6 CERTIFICATED REPAIR STATION (Give Certificate No.)

5 ✓ AIRCRAFT MANUFACTURER (Give name or firm) MD Helicopters, Inc.

DATE 02/23/2010	TITLE Richard Martin, Manager, Quality Assurance	SIGNATURE Richard Martin

V. FAA REPRESENTATIVE CERTIFICATION

(Check ALL applicable block items A and B)

THE CERTIFICATE REQUESTED

A. I find that the aircraft described in Section I or VII meets requirements for 4 AMENDMENT OR MODIFICATION OF CURRENT AIRWORTHINESS CERTIFICATE

B. Inspection for a special flight permit under Section VII was conducted by

FAA INSPECTOR	FAA DESIGNEE
CERTIFICATE HOLDER UNDER	14 CFR part 65	14 CFR part 121 OR 135	14 CFR part 145

DATE	MIDO/FSDO OFFICE	4 FAA INSPECTOR'S SIGNATURE or DESIGNEE'S SIGNATURE AND NO.	1 FAA INSPECTOR'S CERTIFICATION FILE REVIEW SIGNATURE

FAA Form 8130-6 (04-11) All Previous Editions Superseded

Figure D-6. Sample FAA Form 8130-6, Application for U.S. Airworthiness Certificate, Standard – Other, JAR/VLA
(Face Side Only)

FAA FORM 8130-6, APPLICATION FOR U.S. AIRWORTHINESS CERTIFICATE

Form Approved
O.M.B. No. 2120-0018

U.S. Department of Transportation
Federal Aviation Administration

APPLICATION FOR U.S. AIRWORTHINESS CERTIFICATE

INSTRUCTIONS - Print or type. Do not write in shaded areas; these are for FAA use only. Submit original only to an authorized FAA Representative. If additional space is required, use attachment. For special flight permits complete Sections II, VI, and VII as applicable.

I. AIRCRAFT DESCRIPTION

1. REGISTRATION MARK	2. AIRCRAFT BUILDER'S NAME (Make)	3. AIRCRAFT MODEL DESIGNATION	4. YR. MFR.	FAA CODING
N7569K	Aero Ltd	AT-3R100	2010	

5. AIRCRAFT SERIAL NO.	6. ENGINE BUILDER'S NAME (Make)	7. ENGINE MODEL DESIGNATION	
AT3-999	Bombardier-Rotax	912S2	

8. NUMBER OF ENGINES	9. PROPELLER BUILDER'S NAME (Make)	10. PROPELLER MODEL DESIGNATION	11. AIRCRAFT IS (Check if applicable)
1	GT ELICHE	GT-2/173/VRR-FW101SRTC	✓ IMPORT

II. CERTIFICATION REQUESTED

APPLICATION IS HEREBY MADE FOR: (Check applicable items)   JAR/VLA

A	1	✓	STANDARD AIRWORTHINESS CERTIFICATE (Indicate category)	NORMAL	UTILITY	ACROBATIC	TRANSPORT	COMMUTER	BALLOON	✓ OTHER

B			SPECIAL AIRWORTHINESS CERTIFICATE (Check appropriate items)

	7		PRIMARY

	9		LIGHT-SPORT (Indicate Class)		Airplane	Power-Parachute	Weight-Shift-Control	Glider	Lighter than Air

	2		LIMITED

| | 5 | | PROVISIONAL (Indicate class) | 1 | CLASS I |
| | | | | 2 | CLASS II |

	3		RESTRICTED (Indicate operation(s) to be conducted)	1	AGRICULTURE AND PEST CONTROL	2	AERIAL SURVEY	3	AERIAL ADVERTISING
				4	FOREST (Wildlife conservation)	5	PATROLLING	6	WEATHER CONTROL
				0	OTHER (Specify)				

	4		EXPERIMENTAL (Indicate operation(s) to be conducted)	1	RESEARCH AND DEVELOPMENT	2	AMATEUR BUILT	3	EXHIBITION
				4	AIR RACING	5	CREW TRAINING	6	MARKET SURVEY
				0	TO SHOW COMPLIANCE WITH THE CFR	7	OPERATING (Primary Category) KIT BUILT AIRCRAFT
				8	OPERATING LIGHT-SPORT	8A	Existing aircraft without an airworthiness certificate & do not meet § 103.1
						8B	Operating Light-Sport Kit-built
						8C	Operating light-sport previously issued special light-sport category airworthiness certificate under § 21.190
				9	UNMANNED AIRCRAFT	9A	RESEARCH AND DEVELOPMENT	9C	CREW TRAINING
						9B	MARKET SURVEY

	8		SPECIAL FLIGHT PERMIT (Indicate operation to be conducted, then complete Section VI or VII as applicable on reverse side)	1	FERRY FLIGHT FOR REPAIRS, ALTERATIONS, MAINTENANCE, OR STORAGE
				2	EVACUATE FROM AREA OF IMPENDING DANGER
				3	OPERATION IN EXCESS OF MAXIMUM CERTIFICATED TAKE-OFF WEIGHT
				4	DELIVERING OR EXPORTING	5	PRODUCTION FLIGHT TESTING
				6	CUSTOMER DEMONSTRATION FLIGHTS

C	6		MULTIPLE AIRWORTHINESS CERTIFICATE (Check ABOVE "Restricted Operation" and "Standard" or "Limited" as applicable)

III. OWNER'S CERTIFICATION

A. REGISTERED OWNER (As shown on certificate of aircraft registration)   IF DEALER, CHECK HERE ➤

NAME	ADDRESS
I. R. Applicant	14 David Rd., Nashville, TN 37243

B. AIRCRAFT CERTIFICATION BASIS (Check applicable blocks and complete items as indicated)

✓ AIRCRAFT SPECIFICATION OR TYPE CERTIFICATE DATA SHEET (Give No. and Revision No.) A61CE	✓ AIRWORTHINESS DIRECTIVES (Check if all applicable ADs are complied with and give the number of the last AD SUPPLEMENT available in the biweekly series as of the date of application) 2010-19
AIRCRAFT LISTING (Give page number(s)) N/A	SUPPLEMENTAL TYPE CERTIFICATE (List number of each STC incorporated)

C. AIRCRAFT OPERATION AND MAINTENANCE RECORDS

✓ CHECK IF RECORDS IN COMPLIANCE WITH 14 CFR section 91.417	TOTAL AIRFRAME HOURS 132	3	EXPERIMENTAL ONLY (Enter hours flown since last certificate issued or renewed)

D. CERTIFICATION - I hereby certify that I am the registered owner (or his agent) of the aircraft described above, that the aircraft is registered with the Federal Aviation Administration in accordance with Title 49 of the United States Code 44101 et seq. and applicable Federal Aviation Regulations, and that the aircraft has been inspected and is airworthy and eligible for the airworthiness certificate requested.

DATE OF APPLICATION 09/23/2010	NAME AND TITLE (Print or type) I. R. Applicant	SIGNATURE I. R. Applicant

IV. INSPECTION AGENCY VERIFICATION

A. THE AIRCRAFT DESCRIBED ABOVE HAS BEEN INSPECTED AND FOUND AIRWORTHY BY: (Complete the section only if 14 CFR part 21.183(d) applies)

2	14 CFR part 121 CERTIFICATE HOLDER (Give Certificate No.)	3	CERTIFICATED MECHANIC (Give Certificate No.)	6	CERTIFICATED REPAIR STATION (Give Certificate No.)
5	AIRCRAFT MANUFACTURER (Give name or firm)				

DATE	TITLE	SIGNATURE

V. FAA REPRESENTATIVE CERTIFICATION

(Check ALL applicable block items A and B)

A. I find that the aircraft described in Section I or VII meets requirements for		THE CERTIFICATE REQUESTED
	4	AMENDMENT OR MODIFICATION OF CURRENT AIRWORTHINESS CERTIFICATE

B. Inspection for a special flight permit under Section VII was conducted by:

	FAA INSPECTOR	FAA DESIGNEE
	CERTIFICATE HOLDER UNDER	14 CFR part 65	14 CFR part 121 OR 135	14 CFR part 145

DATE	MIDO/FSDO OFFICE	4	FAA INSPECTOR'S SIGNATURE or DESIGNEE'S SIGNATURE AND NO.	1	FAA INSPECTOR'S CERTIFICATION FILE REVIEW SIGNATURE

FAA Form 8130-6 (04-11) All Previous Editions Superseded

Figure D-7. Sample FAA Form 8130-6, Application for U.S. Airworthiness Certificate, Special - Primary Category Aircraft Certificated Under § 21.184(a) (Face Side Only)

FAA FORM 8130-6, APPLICATION FOR U.S. AIRWORTHINESS CERTIFICATE

Form Approved
O.M.B. No. 2120-0018

APPLICATION FOR U.S. AIRWORTHINESS CERTIFICATE

U.S. Department of Transportation
Federal Aviation Administration

INSTRUCTIONS - Print or type. Do not write in shaded areas; these are for FAA use only. Submit original only to an authorized FAA Representative. If additional space is required, use attachment. For special flight permits complete Sections II, VI, and VII as applicable.

I. AIRCRAFT DESCRIPTION

1. REGISTRATION MARK	2. AIRCRAFT BUILDER'S NAME (Make)	3. AIRCRAFT MODEL DESIGNATION	4. YR. MFR	FAA CODING
N2EZ	Flight Corp.	F-C-IA	1991	

5. AIRCRAFT SERIAL NO.	6. ENGINE BUILDER'S NAME (Make)	7. ENGINE MODEL DESIGNATION		
F0002	TCM	IO-360-ES		

8. NUMBER OF ENGINES	9. PROPELLER BUILDER'S NAME (Make)	10. PROPELLER MODEL DESIGNATION	11. AIRCRAFT IS (Check if applicable)
1	McCauley	2A34C209	IMPORT

II. CERTIFICATION REQUESTED

APPLICATION IS HEREBY MADE FOR: (Check applicable items)

A	1		STANDARD AIRWORTHINESS CERTIFICATE (Indicate category)			NORMAL		UTILITY		ACROBATIC		TRANSPORT		COMMUTER		BALLOON		OTHER
B		✓	SPECIAL AIRWORTHINESS CERTIFICATE (Check appropriate items)															

	7	✓	PRIMARY								
	9		LIGHT-SPORT (Indicate Class)		Airplane	Power-Parachute	Weight-Shift-Control	Glider	Lighter than Air
	2		LIMITED						

	5	PROVISIONAL (Indicate class)	1	CLASS I
			2	CLASS II

	3	RESTRICTED (Indicate operation(s) to be conducted)	1	AGRICULTURE AND PEST CONTROL	2	AERIAL SURVEY	3	AERIAL ADVERTISING
			4	FOREST (Wildlife conservation)	5	PATROLLING	8	WEATHER CONTROL
			0	OTHER (Specify)				

	4	EXPERIMENTAL (Indicate operation(s) to be conducted)	1	RESEARCH AND DEVELOPMENT		2	AMATEUR BUILT	3	EXHIBITION
			4	AIR RACING		5	CREW TRAINING	6	MARKET SURVEY
			0	TO SHOW COMPLIANCE WITH THE CFR		7	OPERATING (Primary Category) KIT BUILT AIRCRAFT		
			8	OPERATING LIGHT-SPORT	8A	Existing aircraft without an airworthiness certificate & do not meet § 103.1			
					8B	Operating Light-Sport Kit-built			
					8C	Operating light-sport previously issued special light-sport category airworthiness certificate under § 21.190			
			9	UNMANNED AIRCRAFT	9A	RESEARCH AND DEVELOPMENT	9C	CREW TRAINING	
					9B	MARKET SURVEY			

	8	SPECIAL FLIGHT PERMIT (Indicate operation to be conducted, then complete Section VI or VII as applicable on reverse side)	1	FERRY FLIGHT FOR REPAIRS, ALTERATIONS, MAINTENANCE, OR STORAGE		
			2	EVACUATE FROM AREA OF IMPENDING DANGER		
			3	OPERATION IN EXCESS OF MAXIMUM CERTIFICATED TAKE-OFF WEIGHT		
			4	DELIVERING OR EXPORTING	5	PRODUCTION FLIGHT TESTING
			6	CUSTOMER DEMONSTRATION FLIGHTS		

C	6	MULTIPLE AIRWORTHINESS CERTIFICATE (Check ABOVE "Restricted Operation" and "Standard" or "Limited" as applicable)

III. OWNER'S CERTIFICATION

A. REGISTERED OWNER (As shown on certificate of aircraft registration)   IF DEALER, CHECK HERE ➤

NAME	ADDRESS
Flight Corp.	10 Lane Ave., Doby, TX 78907

B. AIRCRAFT CERTIFICATION BASIS (Check applicable blocks and complete items as indicated)

✓	AIRCRAFT SPECIFICATION OR TYPE CERTIFICATE DATA SHEET (Give No. and Revision No.) CE785	✓	AIRWORTHINESS DIRECTIVES (Check if all applicable ADs are complied with and give the number of the last AD SUPPLEMENT available in the biweekly series as of the date of application) 2010-02
	AIRCRAFT LISTING (Give page number(s)) N/A		SUPPLEMENTAL TYPE CERTIFICATE (List number of each STC incorporated)

C. AIRCRAFT OPERATION AND MAINTENANCE RECORDS

✓	CHECK IF RECORDS IN COMPLIANCE WITH 14 CFR section 91.417	TOTAL AIRFRAME HOURS 2	3	EXPERIMENTAL ONLY (Enter hours flown since last certificate issued or renewed)

D. CERTIFICATION - I hereby certify that I am the registered owner (or his agent) of the aircraft described above, that the aircraft is registered with the Federal Aviation Administration in accordance with Title 49 of the United States Code 44101 et seq and applicable Federal Aviation Regulations, and that the aircraft has been inspected and is airworthy and eligible for the airworthiness certificate requested.

DATE OF APPLICATION	NAME AND TITLE (Print or type)	SIGNATURE
01/27/2010	Joe Quality, Director, Q.A.	Joe Quality

IV. INSPECTION AGENCY VERIFICATION

A. THE AIRCRAFT DESCRIBED ABOVE HAS BEEN INSPECTED AND FOUND AIRWORTHY BY: (Complete the section only if 14 CFR part 21.183(d) applies)

2	14 CFR part 121 CERTIFICATE HOLDER (Give Certificate No.)	3	CERTIFICATED MECHANIC (Give Certificate No.)	6	CERTIFICATED REPAIR STATION (Give Certificate No.)
5	AIRCRAFT MANUFACTURER (Give name or firm)				

DATE	TITLE	SIGNATURE

V. FAA REPRESENTATIVE CERTIFICATION

(Check ALL applicable block items A and B)

THE CERTIFICATE REQUESTED

A. I find that the aircraft described in Section I or VII meets requirements for	4	AMENDMENT OR MODIFICATION OF CURRENT AIRWORTHINESS CERTIFICATE
B. Inspection for a special flight permit under Section VII was conducted by	FAA INSPECTOR	FAA DESIGNEE
	CERTIFICATE HOLDER UNDER	14 CFR part 65	14 CFR part 121 OR 135	14 CFR part 145

DATE	MIDO/FSDO OFFICE	FAA INSPECTOR'S SIGNATURE or DESIGNEE'S SIGNATURE AND NO.	FAA INSPECTOR'S CERTIFICATION FILE REVIEW SIGNATURE

FAA Form 8130-6 (04-11) All Previous Editions Superseded

Figure D-8. Sample FAA Form 8130-6, Application for U.S. Airworthiness Certificate, Special - Light-Sport Category with Type-Certificated Installations (Face Side Only)

FAA FORM 8130-6, APPLICATION FOR U.S. AIRWORTHINESS CERTIFICATE

Form Approved
O.M.B. No. 2120-0018

APPLICATION FOR U.S. AIRWORTHINESS CERTIFICATE

U.S. Department of Transportation
Federal Aviation Administration

INSTRUCTIONS - Print or type. Do not write in shaded areas; these are for FAA use only. Submit original only to an authorized FAA Representative. If additional space is required, use attachment. For special flight permits complete Sections II, VI, and VII as applicable.

I. AIRCRAFT DESCRIPTION

1. REGISTRATION MARK	2. AIRCRAFT BUILDER'S NAME (Make)	3. AIRCRAFT MODEL DESIGNATION	4. YR MFR	FAA CODING
N12LSA	Renegade	Falcon LS	2010	

5. AIRCRAFT SERIAL NO.	6. ENGINE BUILDER'S NAME (Make)	7. ENGINE MODEL DESIGNATION	
RL 122701-001	Lycoming Engines	IO-233	

8. NUMBER OF ENGINES	9. PROPELLER BUILDER'S NAME (Make)	10. PROPELLER MODEL DESIGNATION	11. AIRCRAFT IS (Check if applicable)
1	Helix Carbon GmbH	H25F1,30mL-08-2	IMPORT

II. CERTIFICATION REQUESTED

APPLICATION IS HEREBY MADE FOR: (Check applicable items)

A 1 — STANDARD AIRWORTHINESS CERTIFICATE (Indicate category): NORMAL, UTILITY, ACROBATIC, TRANSPORT, COMMUTER, BALLOON, OTHER

B ✓ SPECIAL AIRWORTHINESS CERTIFICATE (Check appropriate items)

- 7 PRIMARY
- 9 ✓ LIGHT-SPORT (Indicate Class): ✓ Airplane, Power-Parachute, Weight-Shift-Control, Glider, Lighter than Air
- 2 LIMITED
- 5 PROVISIONAL (Indicate class): 1 CLASS I, 2 CLASS II
- 3 RESTRICTED (Indicate operation(s) to be conducted): 1 AGRICULTURE AND PEST CONTROL, 2 AERIAL SURVEY, 3 AERIAL ADVERTISING, 4 FOREST (Wildlife conservation), 5 PATROLLING, 6 WEATHER CONTROL, 0 OTHER (Specify)
- 4 EXPERIMENTAL (Indicate operation(s) to be conducted):
  - 1 RESEARCH AND DEVELOPMENT, 2 AMATEUR BUILT, 3 EXHIBITION
  - 4 AIR RACING, 5 CREW TRAINING, 6 MARKET SURVEY
  - 0 TO SHOW COMPLIANCE WITH THE CFR, 7 OPERATING (Primary Category) KIT BUILT AIRCRAFT
  - 8 OPERATING LIGHT-SPORT: 8A Existing aircraft without an airworthiness certificate & do not meet § 103.1, 8B Operating Light-Sport Kit-built, 8C Operating light-sport previously issued special light-sport category airworthiness certificate under § 21.190
  - 9 UNMANNED AIRCRAFT: 9A RESEARCH AND DEVELOPMENT, 9B MARKET SURVEY, 9C CREW TRAINING
- 8 SPECIAL FLIGHT PERMIT (Indicate operation to be conducted, then complete Section VI or VII as applicable on reverse side): 1 FERRY FLIGHT FOR REPAIRS, ALTERATIONS, MAINTENANCE, OR STORAGE, 2 EVACUATE FROM AREA OF IMPENDING DANGER, 3 OPERATION IN EXCESS OF MAXIMUM CERTIFICATED TAKE-OFF WEIGHT, 4 DELIVERING OR EXPORTING, 5 PRODUCTION FLIGHT TESTING, 6 CUSTOMER DEMONSTRATION FLIGHTS

C 6 MULTIPLE AIRWORTHINESS CERTIFICATE (Check ABOVE "Restricted Operation" and "Standard" or "Limited" as applicable)

III. OWNER'S CERTIFICATION

A. REGISTERED OWNER (As shown on certificate of aircraft registration) — IF DEALER, CHECK HERE ►

NAME	ADDRESS
Joe Quality	420 W Jackson, Unionville, MO 65265

B. AIRCRAFT CERTIFICATION BASIS (Check applicable blocks and complete items as indicated)

✓ AIRCRAFT SPECIFICATION OR TYPE CERTIFICATE DATA SHEET (Give No. and Revision No.) F2245-09

✓ AIRWORTHINESS DIRECTIVES (Check if all applicable ADs are complied with and give the number of the last AD SUPPLEMENT available in the biweekly series as of the date of application) 2010-08, NONE

AIRCRAFT LISTING (Give page number(s)) N/A

SUPPLEMENTAL TYPE CERTIFICATE (List number of each STC incorporated) N/A

C. AIRCRAFT OPERATION AND MAINTENANCE RECORDS

✓ CHECK IF RECORDS IN COMPLIANCE WITH 14 CFR section 91.417 | TOTAL AIRFRAME HOURS 25 | 3 EXPERIMENTAL ONLY (Enter hours flown since last certificate issued or renewed)

D. CERTIFICATION - I hereby certify that I am the registered owner (or his agent) of the aircraft described above, that the aircraft is registered with the Federal Aviation Administration in accordance with Title 49 of the United States Code 44101 et seq. and applicable Federal Aviation Regulations, and that the aircraft has been inspected and is airworthy and eligible for the airworthiness certificate requested.

DATE OF APPLICATION	NAME AND TITLE (Print or type)	SIGNATURE
04/15/2010	Joe Quality, Owner	Joe Quality

IV. INSPECTION AGENCY VERIFICATION

A. THE AIRCRAFT DESCRIBED ABOVE HAS BEEN INSPECTED AND FOUND AIRWORTHY BY: (Complete the section only if 14 CFR part 21.183(d) applies)

2 14 CFR part 121 CERTIFICATE HOLDER (Give Certificate No.) | 3 CERTIFICATED MECHANIC (Give Certificate No.) | 6 CERTIFICATED REPAIR STATION (Give Certificate No.)

5 AIRCRAFT MANUFACTURER (Give name or firm)

DATE	TITLE	SIGNATURE

V. FAA REPRESENTATIVE CERTIFICATION

(Check ALL applicable block items A and B)

A. I find that the aircraft described in Section I or VII meets requirements for 4 — THE CERTIFICATE REQUESTED — AMENDMENT OR MODIFICATION OF CURRENT AIRWORTHINESS CERTIFICATE

B. Inspection for a special flight permit under Section VII was conducted by FAA INSPECTOR / FAA DESIGNEE

CERTIFICATE HOLDER UNDER | 14 CFR part 65 | 14 CFR part 121 OR 135 | 14 CFR part 145

DATE	MIDO/FSDO OFFICE 4	FAA INSPECTOR'S SIGNATURE or DESIGNEE'S SIGNATURE AND NO.	FAA INSPECTOR'S CERTIFICATION FILE REVIEW 1 SIGNATURE

FAA Form 8130-6 (04-11) All Previous Editions Superseded

Figure D-9. Sample FAA Form 8130-6, Application for U.S. Airworthiness Certificate, Special - Light-Sport Category Without Type-Certificated Installations (Face Side Only)

FAA FORM 8130-6, APPLICATION FOR U.S. AIRWORTHINESS CERTIFICATE

Form Approved
O.M.B. No. 2120-0018

| U.S. Department of Transportation Federal Aviation Administration | APPLICATION FOR U.S. AIRWORTHINESS CERTIFICATE | INSTRUCTIONS - Print or type. Do not write in shaded areas; these are for FAA use only. Submit original only to an authorized FAA Representative. If additional space is required, use attachment. For special flight permits complete Sections II, VI, and VII as applicable. |

I. AIRCRAFT DESCRIPTION

1. REGISTRATION MARK	2. AIRCRAFT BUILDER'S NAME *(Make)*	3. AIRCRAFT MODEL DESIGNATION	4. YR. MFR	FAA CODING
N118GX	Remos Aircraft GmbH	GX	2009	
5. AIRCRAFT SERIAL NO.	6. ENGINE BUILDER'S NAME *(Make)*	7. ENGINE MODEL DESIGNATION		
340	Rotax Aircraft Engines	912UL		
8. NUMBER OF ENGINES	9. PROPELLER BUILDER'S NAME *(Make)*	10. PROPELLER MODEL DESIGNATION		11. AIRCRAFT IS *(Check if applicable)*
1	Neuform	CR3-65		IMPORT

II. CERTIFICATION REQUESTED

APPLICATION IS HEREBY MADE FOR: *(Check applicable items)*

A	1		STANDARD AIRWORTHINESS CERTIFICATE *(Indicate category)*	NORMAL	UTILITY	ACROBATIC	TRANSPORT	COMMUTER	BALLOON	OTHER

| B | ✓ | SPECIAL AIRWORTHINESS CERTIFICATE *(Check appropriate items)* |

	7	PRIMARY					
	9 ✓	LIGHT-SPORT *(Indicate Class)*	✓ Airplane	Power-Parachute	Weight-Shift-Control	Glider	Lighter than Air
	2	LIMITED					

| | 5 | PROVISIONAL *(Indicate class)* | 1 | CLASS I |
| | | | 2 | CLASS II |

	3	RESTRICTED *(Indicate operation(s) to be conducted)*	1	AGRICULTURE AND PEST CONTROL	2	AERIAL SURVEY	3	AERIAL ADVERTISING
			4	FOREST *(Wildlife conservation)*	5	PATROLLING	6	WEATHER CONTROL
			0	OTHER *(Specify)*				

	4	EXPERIMENTAL *(Indicate operation(s) to be conducted)*	1	RESEARCH AND DEVELOPMENT	2	AMATEUR BUILT	3	EXHIBITION
			4	AIR RACING	5	CREW TRAINING	6	MARKET SURVEY
			0	TO SHOW COMPLIANCE WITH THE CFR	7	OPERATING *(Primary Category)* KIT BUILT AIRCRAFT
			8	OPERATING LIGHT-SPORT	8A	Existing aircraft without an airworthiness certificate & do not meet § 103.1
					8B	Operating Light-Sport Kit-built
					8C	Operating light-sport previously issued special light-sport category airworthiness certificate under § 21.190
			9	UNMANNED AIRCRAFT	9A	RESEARCH AND DEVELOPMENT	9C	CREW TRAINING
					9B	MARKET SURVEY

	8	SPECIAL FLIGHT PERMIT *(Indicate operation to be conducted, then complete Section VI or VII as applicable on reverse side)*	1	FERRY FLIGHT FOR REPAIRS, ALTERATIONS, MAINTENANCE, OR STORAGE
			2	EVACUATE FROM AREA OF IMPENDING DANGER
			3	OPERATION IN EXCESS OF MAXIMUM CERTIFICATED TAKE-OFF WEIGHT
			4	DELIVERING OR EXPORTING	5	PRODUCTION FLIGHT TESTING
			6	CUSTOMER DEMONSTRATION FLIGHTS

| C | 6 | MULTIPLE AIRWORTHINESS CERTIFICATE *(Check ABOVE "Restricted Operation" and "Standard" or "Limited" as applicable)* |

III. OWNER'S CERTIFICATION

A. REGISTERED OWNER *(As shown on certificate of aircraft registration)*		IF DEALER, CHECK HERE ▶
NAME		ADDRESS
Remos Aircraft, Inc.		997 Happy Trails Dr, Ste D-1, Rogers, AR 72756

B. AIRCRAFT CERTIFICATION BASIS *(Check applicable blocks and complete items as indicated)*

✓ AIRCRAFT SPECIFICATION OR TYPE CERTIFICATE DATA SHEET *(Give No. and Revision No.)*	✓ AIRWORTHINESS DIRECTIVES *(Check if all applicable ADs are complied with and give the number of the last AD SUPPLEMENT available in the biweekly series as of the date of application)*
F2245-07a	2009-21, SD-001, SD-002, SD-003, SD-004, SD-005
AIRCRAFT LISTING *(Give page number(s))*	SUPPLEMENTAL TYPE CERTIFICATE *(List number of each STC incorporated)*
N/A	N/A

C. AIRCRAFT OPERATION AND MAINTENANCE RECORDS

✓ CHECK IF RECORDS IN COMPLIANCE WITH 14 CFR section 91.417	TOTAL AIRFRAME HOURS	3	EXPERIMENTAL ONLY *(Enter hours flown since last certificate issued or renewed)*
	10		

D. CERTIFICATION - I hereby certify that I am the registered owner (or his agent) of the aircraft described above, that the aircraft is registered with the Federal Aviation Administration in accordance with Title 49 of the United States Code 44101 et seq. and applicable Federal Aviation Regulations, and that the aircraft has been inspected and is airworthy and eligible for the airworthiness certificate requested.

DATE OF APPLICATION	NAME AND TITLE *(Print or type)*	SIGNATURE
10/22/2009	Bill Brown, Agent	*Bill Brown*

IV. INSPECTION AGENCY VERIFICATION

A. THE AIRCRAFT DESCRIBED ABOVE HAS BEEN INSPECTED AND FOUND AIRWORTHY BY: *(Complete the section only if 14 CFR part 21.183(d) applies)*

2	14 CFR part 121 CERTIFICATE HOLDER *(Give Certificate No.)*	3	CERTIFICATED MECHANIC *(Give Certificate No.)*	6	CERTIFICATED REPAIR STATION *(Give Certificate No.)*
5	AIRCRAFT MANUFACTURER *(Give name or firm)*				

DATE	TITLE	SIGNATURE

V. FAA REPRESENTATIVE CERTIFICATION

(Check ALL applicable block items A and B)

A. I find that the aircraft described in Section I or VII meets requirements for	4	THE CERTIFICATE REQUESTED
		AMENDMENT OR MODIFICATION OF CURRENT AIRWORTHINESS CERTIFICATE

B. Inspection for a special flight permit under Section VII was conducted by:	FAA INSPECTOR	FAA DESIGNEE
	CERTIFICATE HOLDER UNDER	14 CFR part 65	14 CFR part 121 OR 135	14 CFR part 145

DATE	MIDO/FSDO OFFICE	4	FAA INSPECTOR'S SIGNATURE or DESIGNEE'S SIGNATURE AND NO.	1	FAA INSPECTOR'S CERTIFICATION FILE REVIEW SIGNATURE

FAA Form 8130-6 (04-11) All Previous Editions Superseded

Figure D-10. Sample FAA Form 8130-6, Application for U.S. Airworthiness Certificate, Special – Limited Category
(Face Side Only)

FAA FORM 8130-6, APPLICATION FOR U.S. AIRWORTHINESS CERTIFICATE

Form Approved
O.M.B. No. 2120-0018

APPLICATION FOR U.S. AIRWORTHINESS CERTIFICATE

U.S. Department of Transportation
Federal Aviation Administration

INSTRUCTIONS - Print or type. Do not write in shaded areas; these are for FAA use only. Submit original only to an authorized FAA Representative. If additional space is required, use attachment. For special flight permits complete Sections II, VI, and VII as applicable.

I. AIRCRAFT DESCRIPTION

1. REGISTRATION MARK	2. AIRCRAFT BUILDER'S NAME (Make)	3. AIRCRAFT MODEL DESIGNATION	4. YR. MFR	FAA CODING
N1256	Glenn L. Martin Company	B-26C	1943	

5. AIRCRAFT SERIAL NO.	6. ENGINE BUILDER'S NAME (Make)	7. ENGINE MODEL DESIGNATION	
2256	P&W	R-2800-83AMB	

8. NUMBER OF ENGINES	9. PROPELLER BUILDER'S NAME (Make)	10. PROPELLER MODEL DESIGNATION	11. AIRCRAFT IS (Check if applicable)
2	Hamilton Standard	42E60-7/669-5-8	IMPORT

II. CERTIFICATION REQUESTED

APPLICATION IS HEREBY MADE FOR: (Check applicable items)

| A | 1 | | STANDARD AIRWORTHINESS CERTIFICATE (Indicate category) | | | NORMAL | UTILITY | ACROBATIC | TRANSPORT | COMMUTER | BALLOON | OTHER |

| B | ✓ | SPECIAL AIRWORTHINESS CERTIFICATE (Check appropriate items) |

	7	PRIMARY
	9	LIGHT-SPORT (Indicate Class)		Airplane	Power-Parachute	Weight-Shift-Control	Glider	Lighter than Air
	2 ✓	LIMITED

| | 5 | PROVISIONAL (Indicate class) | 1 | CLASS I |
| | | | 2 | CLASS II |

	3	RESTRICTED (Indicate operation(s) to be conducted)	1	AGRICULTURE AND PEST CONTROL	2	AERIAL SURVEY	3	AERIAL ADVERTISING
			4	FOREST (Wildlife conservation)	5	PATROLLING	6	WEATHER CONTROL
			0	OTHER (Specify)				

	4	EXPERIMENTAL (Indicate operation(s) to be conducted)	1	RESEARCH AND DEVELOPMENT	2	AMATEUR BUILT	3	EXHIBITION
			4	AIR RACING	5	CREW TRAINING	6	MARKET SURVEY
			0	TO SHOW COMPLIANCE WITH THE CFR	7	OPERATING (Primary Category) KIT BUILT AIRCRAFT
			8 OPERATING LIGHT-SPORT	8A	Existing aircraft without an airworthiness certificate & do not meet § 103.1
				8B	Operating Light-Sport Kit-built
				8C	Operating light-sport previously issued special light-sport category airworthiness certificate under § 21.190
			9 UNMANNED AIRCRAFT	9A	RESEARCH AND DEVELOPMENT	9C	CREW TRAINING
				9B	MARKET SURVEY

	8	SPECIAL FLIGHT PERMIT (Indicate operation to be conducted, then complete Section VI or VII as applicable on reverse side)	1	FERRY FLIGHT FOR REPAIRS, ALTERATIONS, MAINTENANCE, OR STORAGE
			2	EVACUATE FROM AREA OF IMPENDING DANGER
			3	OPERATION IN EXCESS OF MAXIMUM CERTIFICATED TAKE-OFF WEIGHT
			4	DELIVERING OR EXPORTING	5	PRODUCTION FLIGHT TESTING
			6	CUSTOMER DEMONSTRATION FLIGHTS

| C | 6 | MULTIPLE AIRWORTHINESS CERTIFICATE (Check ABOVE "Restricted Operation" and "Standard" or "Limited" as applicable) |

III. OWNER'S CERTIFICATION

A. REGISTERED OWNER (As shown on certificate of aircraft registration)   IF DEALER, CHECK HERE ➝

NAME	ADDRESS
Gas Transmission Company	1216W 48th Street, Dallas TX 64072

B. AIRCRAFT CERTIFICATION BASIS (Check applicable blocks and complete items as indicated)

✓ AIRCRAFT SPECIFICATION OR TYPE CERTIFICATE DATA SHEET (Give No. and Revision No.) AL-33 Rev 1	✓ AIRWORTHINESS DIRECTIVES (Check if all applicable ADs are complied with and give the number of the last AD SUPPLEMENT available in the biweekly series as of the date of application) 2010-02
AIRCRAFT LISTING (Give page number(s)) N/A	SUPPLEMENTAL TYPE CERTIFICATE (List number of each STC incorporated)

C. AIRCRAFT OPERATION AND MAINTENANCE RECORDS

✓ CHECK IF RECORDS IN COMPLIANCE WITH 14 CFR section 91.417	TOTAL AIRFRAME HOURS 12632	3	EXPERIMENTAL ONLY (Enter hours flown since last certificate issued or renewed)

D. CERTIFICATION - I hereby certify that I am the registered owner (or his agent) of the aircraft described above, that the aircraft is registered with the Federal Aviation Administration in accordance with Title 49 of the United States Code 44101 et seq. and applicable Federal Aviation Regulations, and that the aircraft has been inspected and is airworthy and eligible for the airworthiness certificate requested.

DATE OF APPLICATION 01/27/2010	NAME AND TITLE (Print or type) George Brown, President	SIGNATURE George Brown

IV. INSPECTION AGENCY VERIFICATION

A. THE AIRCRAFT DESCRIBED ABOVE HAS BEEN INSPECTED AND FOUND AIRWORTHY BY: (Complete the section only if 14 CFR part 21.183(d) applies)

2	14 CFR part 121 CERTIFICATE HOLDER (Give Certificate No.)	3	CERTIFICATED MECHANIC (Give Certificate No.)	6	CERTIFICATED REPAIR STATION (Give Certificate No.)
5	AIRCRAFT MANUFACTURER (Give name or firm)				

DATE	TITLE	SIGNATURE

V. FAA REPRESENTATIVE CERTIFICATION

(Check ALL applicable block items A and B)

A. I find that the aircraft described in Section I or VII meets requirements for 4 THE CERTIFICATE REQUESTED / AMENDMENT OR MODIFICATION OF CURRENT AIRWORTHINESS CERTIFICATE

B. Inspection for a special flight permit under Section VII was conducted by

	FAA INSPECTOR	FAA DESIGNEE
	CERTIFICATE HOLDER UNDER	14 CFR part 65	14 CFR part 121 OR 135	14 CFR part 145

DATE	MIDO/FSDO OFFICE	4 FAA INSPECTOR'S SIGNATURE or DESIGNEE'S SIGNATURE AND NO.	1 FAA INSPECTOR'S CERTIFICATION FILE REVIEW SIGNATURE

FAA Form 8130-6 (04-11) All Previous Editions Superseded

Figure D-11. Sample FAA Form 8130-6, Application for U.S. Airworthiness Certificate, Special – Provisional Category
(Face Side Only)

FAA FORM 8130-6, APPLICATION FOR U.S. AIRWORTHINESS CERTIFICATE

Form Approved
O.M.B. No. 2120-0018

APPLICATION FOR U.S. AIRWORTHINESS CERTIFICATE	INSTRUCTIONS - Print or type. Do not write in shaded areas; these are for FAA use only. Submit original only to an authorized FAA Representative. If additional space is required, use attachment. For special flight permits complete Sections II, VI, and VII as applicable.

U.S. Department of Transportation
Federal Aviation Administration

I. AIRCRAFT DESCRIPTION

1. REGISTRATION MARK	2. AIRCRAFT BUILDER'S NAME (Make)	3. AIRCRAFT MODEL DESIGNATION	4. YR. MFR.	FAA CODING
N502A	Lock heed -Georgia Co.	382G	1996	

5. AIRCRAFT SERIAL NO.	6. ENGINE BUILDER'S NAME (Make)	7. ENGINE MODEL DESIGNATION	
4387	Allison	501-D22A	

8. NUMBER OF ENGINES	9. PROPELLER BUILDER'S NAME (Make)	10. PROPELLER MODEL DESIGNATION	11. AIRCRAFT IS (Check if applicable)
4	Hamilton- Standard	54H60-91/54H 60-117	IMPORT

II. CERTIFICATION REQUESTED

APPLICATION IS HEREBY MADE FOR: (Check applicable items)

A	1		STANDARD AIRWORTHINESS CERTIFICATE (Indicate category)			NORMAL	UTILITY	ACROBATIC	TRANSPORT	COMMUTER	BALLOON	OTHER
B		✓	SPECIAL AIRWORTHINESS CERTIFICATE (Check appropriate items)									

	7	PRIMARY							
	9	LIGHT-SPORT (Indicate class)			Airplane	Power-Parachute	Weight-Shift-Control	Glider	Lighter than Air
	2	LIMITED							
	5 ✓	PROVISIONAL (Indicate class)	1 ✓	CLASS I					
			2	CLASS II					
	3	RESTRICTED (Indicate operation(s) to be conducted)	1	AGRICULTURE AND PEST CONTROL	2	AERIAL SURVEY	3	AERIAL ADVERTISING
			4	FOREST (Wildlife conservation)	5	PATROLLING	6	WEATHER CONTROL
			0	OTHER (Specify)				
	4	EXPERIMENTAL (Indicate operation(s) to be conducted)	1	RESEARCH AND DEVELOPMENT	2	AMATEUR BUILT	3	EXHIBITION
			4	AIR RACING	5	CREW TRAINING	6	MARKET SURVEY
			0	TO SHOW COMPLIANCE WITH THE CFR	7	OPERATING (Primary Category) KIT BUILT AIRCRAFT		
			8 OPERATING LIGHT-SPORT	8A	Existing aircraft without an airworthiness certificate & do not meet § 103.1				
				8B	Operating Light-Sport Kit-built				
				8C	Operating light-sport previously issued special light-sport category airworthiness certificate under § 21.190				
			9 UNMANNED AIRCRAFT	9A	RESEARCH AND DEVELOPMENT	9C	CREW TRAINING		
				9B	MARKET SURVEY				
	8	SPECIAL FLIGHT PERMIT (Indicate operation to be conducted, then complete Section VI or VII as applicable on reverse side)	1	FERRY FLIGHT FOR REPAIRS, ALTERATIONS, MAINTENANCE, OR STORAGE				
			2	EVACUATE FROM AREA OF IMPENDING DANGER				
			3	OPERATION IN EXCESS OF MAXIMUM CERTIFICATED TAKE-OFF WEIGHT				
			4	DELIVERING OR EXPORTING	5	PRODUCTION FLIGHT TESTING		
			6	CUSTOMER DEMONSTRATION FLIGHTS				

C	6	MULTIPLE AIRWORTHINESS CERTIFICATE (Check ABOVE "Restricted Operation" and "Standard" or "Limited" as applicable)	IF DEALER, CHECK HERE ➤

III. OWNER'S CERTIFICATION

A. REGISTERED OWNER (As shown on certificate of aircraft registration)	
NAME	ADDRESS
Lockheed Georgia Co.	Marietta, GA 30060

B. AIRCRAFT CERTIFICATION BASIS (Check applicable blocks and complete items as indicated)

✓ AIRCRAFT SPECIFICATION OR TYPE CERTIFICATE DATA SHEET (Give No. and Revision No.) A1SO	✓ AIRWORTHINESS DIRECTIVES (Check if all applicable ADs are complied with and give the number of the last AD SUPPLEMENT available in the biweekly series as of the date of application) 2010-07
AIRCRAFT LISTING (Give page number(s)) N/A	SUPPLEMENTAL TYPE CERTIFICATE (List number of each STC incorporated)

C. AIRCRAFT OPERATION AND MAINTENANCE RECORDS

✓ CHECK IF RECORDS IN COMPLIANCE WITH 14 CFR section 91.417	TOTAL AIRFRAME HOURS 12632	3	EXPERIMENTAL ONLY (Enter hours flown since last certificate issued or renewed)

D. CERTIFICATION - I hereby certify that I am the registered owner (or his agent) of the aircraft described above, that the aircraft is registered with the Federal Aviation Administration in accordance with Title 49 of the United States Code 44101 et seq. and applicable Federal Aviation Regulations, and that the aircraft has been inspected and is airworthy and eligible for the airworthiness certificate requested

DATE OF APPLICATION	NAME AND TITLE (Print or type)	SIGNATURE
04/10/2010	George Brown, President	George Brown

IV. INSPECTION AGENCY VERIFICATION

A. THE AIRCRAFT DESCRIBED ABOVE HAS BEEN INSPECTED AND FOUND AIRWORTHY BY: (Complete this section only if 14 CFR part 21.183(d) applies)

2	14 CFR part 121 CERTIFICATE HOLDER (Give Certificate No.)	3	CERTIFICATED MECHANIC (Give Certificate No.)	6	CERTIFICATED REPAIR STATION (Give Certificate No.)
5	AIRCRAFT MANUFACTURER (Give name or firm)				

DATE	TITLE	SIGNATURE

V. FAA REPRESENTATIVE CERTIFICATION

(Check ALL applicable block items A and B)

A. I find that the aircraft described in Section I or VII meets requirements for

4	AMENDMENT OR MODIFICATION OF CURRENT AIRWORTHINESS CERTIFICATE

B. Inspection for a special flight permit under Section VII was conducted by:

THE CERTIFICATE REQUESTED			
FAA INSPECTOR	FAA DESIGNEE		
CERTIFICATE HOLDER UNDER	14 CFR part 65	14 CFR part 121 OR 135	14 CFR part 145

DATE	MIDO/FSDO OFFICE	4	FAA INSPECTOR'S SIGNATURE or DESIGNEE'S SIGNATURE AND NO.	1	FAA INSPECTOR'S CERTIFICATION FILE REVIEW SIGNATURE

FAA Form 8130-6 (04-11) All Previous Editions Superseded

Figure D-12. Sample FAA Form 8130-6, Application for U.S. Airworthiness Certificate, Special – Restricted Category
(Face Side Only)

FAA FORM 8130-6, APPLICATION FOR U.S. AIRWORTHINESS CERTIFICATE

Form Approved
O.M.B. No. 2120-0018

APPLICATION FOR U.S. AIRWORTHINESS CERTIFICATE

U.S. Department of Transportation
Federal Aviation Administration

INSTRUCTIONS - Print or type. Do not write in shaded areas; these are for FAA use only. Submit original only to an authorized FAA Representative. If additional space is required, use attachment. For special flight permits complete Sections II, VI, and VII as applicable.

I. AIRCRAFT DESCRIPTION

1. REGISTRATION MARK	2. AIRCRAFT BUILDER'S NAME (Make)	3. AIRCRAFT MODEL DESIGNATION	4. YR. MFR	FAA CODING
N7777	North American Rockwell	S2R	1950	
5. AIRCRAFT SERIAL NO.	6. ENGINE BUILDER'S NAME (Make)	7. ENGINE MODEL DESIGNATION		
1916R	P&W	R1340AN1(S 3H1)		
8. NUMBER OF ENGINES	9. PROPELLER BUILDER'S NAME (Make)	10. PROPELLER MODEL DESIGNATION	11. AIRCRAFT IS (Check if applicable)	
1	Hamilton Standard	12D40-305/EAC/AG 100-2	IMPORT	

II. CERTIFICATION REQUESTED

APPLICATION IS HEREBY MADE FOR: (Check applicable items)

A	1	STANDARD AIRWORTHINESS CERTIFICATE (Indicate category)		NORMAL	UTILITY	ACROBATIC	TRANSPORT	COMMUTER	BALLOON	OTHER

B	✓	SPECIAL AIRWORTHINESS CERTIFICATE (Check appropriate items)								
	7	PRIMARY								
	9	LIGHT-SPORT (Indicate Class)		Airplane	Power-Parachute	Weight-Shift-Control	Glider	Lighter than Air		
	2	LIMITED								
	5	PROVISIONAL (Indicate class)	1	CLASS I						
			2	CLASS II						
	3 ✓	RESTRICTED (Indicate operation(s) to be conducted)	1 ✓	AGRICULTURE AND PEST CONTROL	2	AERIAL SURVEY	3	AERIAL ADVERTISING		
			4	FOREST (Wildlife conservation)	5	PATROLLING	6	WEATHER CONTROL		
			0	OTHER (Specify)						

	4	EXPERIMENTAL (Indicate operation(s) to be conducted)	1	RESEARCH AND DEVELOPMENT	2	AMATEUR BUILT	3	EXHIBITION	
			4	AIR RACING	5	CREW TRAINING	6	MARKET SURVEY	
			0	TO SHOW COMPLIANCE WITH THE CFR	7	OPERATING (Primary Category) KIT BUILT AIRCRAFT		
			8	OPERATING LIGHT-SPORT	8A	Existing aircraft without an airworthiness certificate & do not meet § 103.1		
					8B	Operating Light-Sport Kit-built		
					8C	Operating light-sport previously issued special light-sport category airworthiness certificate under § 21.190		
			9	UNMANNED AIRCRAFT	9A	RESEARCH AND DEVELOPMENT	9C	CREW TRAINING
					9B	MARKET SURVEY		

	8	SPECIAL FLIGHT PERMIT (Indicate operation to be conducted, then complete Section VI or VII as applicable on reverse side)	1	FERRY FLIGHT FOR REPAIRS, ALTERATIONS, MAINTENANCE, OR STORAGE	
			2	EVACUATE FROM AREA OF IMPENDING DANGER	
			3	OPERATION IN EXCESS OF MAXIMUM CERTIFICATED TAKE-OFF WEIGHT	
			4	DELIVERING OR EXPORTING	5	PRODUCTION FLIGHT TESTING
			6	CUSTOMER DEMONSTRATION FLIGHTS	

C	6	MULTIPLE AIRWORTHINESS CERTIFICATE (Check ABOVE "Restricted Operation" and "Standard" or "Limited" as applicable)

III. OWNER'S CERTIFICATION

A. REGISTERED OWNER (As shown on certificate of aircraft registration)		IF DEALER, CHECK HERE ▶	
NAME		ADDRESS	
DBA Crop Dusters, Inc.		105 Airport Rd., Greenville, MI 38701	

B. AIRCRAFT CERTIFICATION BASIS (Check applicable blocks and complete items as indicated)

✓ AIRCRAFT SPECIFICATION OR TYPE CERTIFICATE DATA SHEET (Give No. and Revision No.) A4SW Rev 5	✓ AIRWORTHINESS DIRECTIVES (Check if all applicable ADs are complied with and give the number of the last AD SUPPLEMENT available in the biweekly series as of the date of application) 2010-07
AIRCRAFT LISTING (Give page number(s))	SUPPLEMENTAL TYPE CERTIFICATE (List number of each STC incorporated)

C. AIRCRAFT OPERATION AND MAINTENANCE RECORDS			
✓ CHECK IF RECORDS IN COMPLIANCE WITH 14 CFR section 91.417	TOTAL AIRFRAME HOURS 2105	3	EXPERIMENTAL ONLY (Enter hours flown since last certificate issued or renewed)

D. CERTIFICATION - I hereby certify that I am the registered owner (or his agent) of the aircraft described above, that the aircraft is registered with the Federal Aviation Administration in accordance with Title 49 of the United States Code 44101 et seq. and applicable Federal Aviation Regulations, and that the aircraft has been inspected and is airworthy and eligible for the airworthiness certificate requested.

DATE OF APPLICATION 04/10/2010	NAME AND TITLE (Print or type) John J. Jones, Co-Owner	SIGNATURE John J. Jones

IV. INSPECTION AGENCY VERIFICATION

A. THE AIRCRAFT DESCRIBED ABOVE HAS BEEN INSPECTED AND FOUND AIRWORTHY BY: (Complete the section only if 14 CFR part 21.183(d) applies)

2	14 CFR part 121 CERTIFICATE HOLDER (Give Certificate No.)	3	CERTIFICATED MECHANIC (Give Certificate No.)	6	CERTIFICATED REPAIR STATION (Give Certificate No.)
5	AIRCRAFT MANUFACTURER (Give name or firm)				

DATE	TITLE	SIGNATURE

V. FAA REPRESENTATIVE CERTIFICATION

(Check ALL applicable block items A and B)

A. I find that the aircraft described in Section I or VII meets requirements for	4	THE CERTIFICATE REQUESTED AMENDMENT OR MODIFICATION OF CURRENT AIRWORTHINESS CERTIFICATE

B. Inspection for a special flight permit under Section VII was conducted by	FAA INSPECTOR	FAA DESIGNEE		
	CERTIFICATE HOLDER UNDER	14 CFR part 65	14 CFR part 121 OR 135	14 CFR part 145

DATE	MIDO/FSDO OFFICE	4	FAA INSPECTOR'S SIGNATURE or DESIGNEE'S SIGNATURE AND NO.		FAA INSPECTOR'S CERTIFICATION FILE REVIEW SIGNATURE	1

FAA Form 8130-6 (04-11) All Previous Editions Superseded

Figure D-13. Sample FAA Form 8130-6, Application for U.S. Airworthiness Certificate, Special – Experimental Category, Research and Development (Face Side Only)

FAA FORM 8130-6, APPLICATION FOR U.S. AIRWORTHINESS CERTIFICATE

Form Approved
O.M.B. No. 2120-0018

APPLICATION FOR U.S. AIRWORTHINESS CERTIFICATE

U.S. Department of Transportation
Federal Aviation Administration

INSTRUCTIONS - Print or type. Do not write in shaded areas; these are for FAA use only. Submit original only to an authorized FAA Representative. If additional space is required, use attachment. For special flight permits complete Sections II, VI, and VII as applicable.

I. AIRCRAFT DESCRIPTION

1. REGISTRATION MARK	2. AIRCRAFT BUILDER'S NAME (Make)	3. AIRCRAFT MODEL DESIGNATION	4. YR. MFR	FAA CODING
N51CA	Cessna Aircraft Company	551	1992	
5. AIRCRAFT SERIAL NO.	6. ENGINE BUILDER'S NAME (Make)	7. ENGINE MODEL DESIGNATION		
551-0004	UACL	JT15D-4		
8. NUMBER OF ENGINES	9. PROPELLER BUILDER'S NAME (Make)	10. PROPELLER MODEL DESIGNATION		11. AIRCRAFT IS (Check if applicable)
2	N/A	N/A		IMPORT

II. CERTIFICATION REQUESTED

APPLICATION IS HEREBY MADE FOR: (Check applicable items)

A	1	STANDARD AIRWORTHINESS CERTIFICATE (Indicate category)			NORMAL	UTILITY	ACROBATIC	TRANSPORT	COMMUTER	BALLOON	OTHER

B	✓	SPECIAL AIRWORTHINESS CERTIFICATE (Check appropriate items)

	7	PRIMARY						
	9	LIGHT-SPORT (Indicate Class)		Airplane	Power-Parachute	Weight-Shift-Control	Glider	Lighter than Air
	2	LIMITED						

PROVISIONAL (Indicate class): 5
| 1 | CLASS I |
| 2 | CLASS II |

RESTRICTED (Indicate operation(s) to be conducted): 3
1	AGRICULTURE AND PEST CONTROL	2	AERIAL SURVEY	3	AERIAL ADVERTISING
4	FOREST (Wildlife conservation)	5	PATROLLING	6	WEATHER CONTROL
0	OTHER (Specify)				

EXPERIMENTAL (Indicate operation(s) to be conducted): 4 ✓
1 ✓	RESEARCH AND DEVELOPMENT	2	AMATEUR BUILT	3	EXHIBITION
4	AIR RACING	5	CREW TRAINING	6	MARKET SURVEY
0	TO SHOW COMPLIANCE WITH THE CFR	7	OPERATING (Primary Category) KIT BUILT AIRCRAFT		
8 OPERATING LIGHT-SPORT	8A	Existing aircraft without an airworthiness certificate & do not meet § 103.1
	8B	Operating Light-Sport Kit-built
	8C	Operating light-sport previously issued special light-sport category airworthiness certificate under § 21.190
9 UNMANNED AIRCRAFT	9A	RESEARCH AND DEVELOPMENT	9C	CREW TRAINING
	9B	MARKET SURVEY		

SPECIAL FLIGHT PERMIT (Indicate operation to be conducted, then complete Section VI or VII as applicable on reverse side): 8
1	FERRY FLIGHT FOR REPAIRS, ALTERATIONS, MAINTENANCE, OR STORAGE
2	EVACUATE FROM AREA OF IMPENDING DANGER
3	OPERATION IN EXCESS OF MAXIMUM CERTIFICATED TAKE-OFF WEIGHT
4	DELIVERING OR EXPORTING	5	PRODUCTION FLIGHT TESTING
6	CUSTOMER DEMONSTRATION FLIGHTS

C	6	MULTIPLE AIRWORTHINESS CERTIFICATE (Check ABOVE "Restricted Operation" and "Standard" or "Limited" as applicable)

III. OWNER'S CERTIFICATION

A. REGISTERED OWNER (As shown on certificate of aircraft registration) — IF DEALER, CHECK HERE ►

NAME	ADDRESS
Cessna Aircraft Company	1 Airport Road, Wichita, KS 67277-7704

B. AIRCRAFT CERTIFICATION BASIS (Check applicable blocks and complete items as indicated)

AIRCRAFT SPECIFICATION OR TYPE CERTIFICATE DATA SHEET (Give No. and Revision No.) N/A	AIRWORTHINESS DIRECTIVES (Check if all applicable ADs are complied with and give the number of the last AD SUPPLEMENT available in the biweekly series as of the date of application) ✓ 2008-23
AIRCRAFT LISTING (Give page number(s)) N/A	SUPPLEMENTAL TYPE CERTIFICATE (List number of each STC incorporated) N/A

C. AIRCRAFT OPERATION AND MAINTENANCE RECORDS

CHECK IF RECORDS IN ✓ COMPLIANCE WITH 14 CFR section 91.417	TOTAL AIRFRAME HOURS 2509	3	EXPERIMENTAL ONLY (Enter hours flown since last certificate issued or renewed) 22

D. CERTIFICATION - I hereby certify that I am the registered owner (or his agent) of the aircraft described above, that the aircraft is registered with the Federal Aviation Administration in accordance with Title 49 of the United States Code 44101 et seq. and applicable Federal Aviation Regulations, and that the aircraft has been inspected and is airworthy and eligible for the airworthiness certificate requested.

DATE OF APPLICATION 11/15/2008	NAME AND TITLE (Print or type) A.D. Smith, Director of Total Quality	SIGNATURE A.D. Smith

IV. INSPECTION AGENCY VERIFICATION

A. THE AIRCRAFT DESCRIBED ABOVE HAS BEEN INSPECTED AND FOUND AIRWORTHY BY: (Complete this section only if 14 CFR part 21.183(d) applies)

2	14 CFR part 121 CERTIFICATE HOLDER (Give Certificate No.)	3	CERTIFICATED MECHANIC (Give Certificate No.)	6	CERTIFICATED REPAIR STATION (Give Certificate No.)
5	AIRCRAFT MANUFACTURER (Give name or firm)				

DATE	TITLE	SIGNATURE

V. FAA REPRESENTATIVE CERTIFICATION

(Check ALL applicable block items A and B)

A. I find that the aircraft described in Section I or VII meets requirements for | 4 | THE CERTIFICATE REQUESTED / AMENDMENT OR MODIFICATION OF CURRENT AIRWORTHINESS CERTIFICATE

B. Inspection for a special flight permit under Section VII was conducted by:

	FAA INSPECTOR	FAA DESIGNEE
	CERTIFICATE HOLDER UNDER	14 CFR part 65	14 CFR part 121 OR 135	14 CFR part 145

DATE	MIDO/FSDO OFFICE	4	FAA INSPECTOR'S SIGNATURE or DESIGNEE'S SIGNATURE AND NO.	1	FAA INSPECTOR'S CERTIFICATION FILE REVIEW SIGNATURE

FAA Form 8130-6 (04-11) All Previous Editions Superseded

Figure D-14. Sample FAA Form 8130-6, Application for U.S. Airworthiness Certificate, Special – Experimental Category, To Show Compliance with CFR (Face Side Only)

FAA FORM 8130-6, APPLICATION FOR U.S. AIRWORTHINESS CERTIFICATE

Form Approved
O.M.B. No. 2120-0018

U.S. Department of Transportation
Federal Aviation Administration

APPLICATION FOR U.S. AIRWORTHINESS CERTIFICATE

INSTRUCTIONS - Print or type. Do not write in shaded areas; these are for FAA use only. Submit original only to an authorized FAA Representative. If additional space is required, use attachment. For special flight permits complete Sections II, VI, and VII as applicable.

I. AIRCRAFT DESCRIPTION

1. REGISTRATION MARK	2. AIRCRAFT BUILDER'S NAME (Make)	3. AIRCRAFT MODEL DESIGNATION	4. YR MFR	FAA CODING
N654GL	Night Aircraft, LLC	N7-Xray	2009	

5. AIRCRAFT SERIAL NO.	6. ENGINE BUILDER'S NAME (Make)	7. ENGINE MODEL DESIGNATION
NX09	TCM	IO-360-ES

8. NUMBER OF ENGINES	9. PROPELLER BUILDER'S NAME (Make)	10. PROPELLER MODEL DESIGNATION	11. AIRCRAFT IS (Check if applicable)
1	McCauley Propeller Systems	2A34C209	IMPORT

II. CERTIFICATION REQUESTED

APPLICATION IS HEREBY MADE FOR: (Check applicable items)

A	1		STANDARD AIRWORTHINESS CERTIFICATE (Indicate category)	NORMAL	UTILITY	ACROBATIC	TRANSPORT	COMMUTER	BALLOON	OTHER

B	✓	SPECIAL AIRWORTHINESS CERTIFICATE (Check appropriate items)

	7	PRIMARY

	9	LIGHT-SPORT (Indicate Class)	Airplane	Power-Parachute	Weight-Shift-Control	Glider	Lighter than Air

	2	LIMITED

| | 5 | PROVISIONAL (Indicate class) | 1 | CLASS I |
| | | | 2 | CLASS II |

	3	RESTRICTED (Indicate operation(s) to be conducted)	1	AGRICULTURE AND PEST CONTROL	2	AERIAL SURVEY	3	AERIAL ADVERTISING
			4	FOREST (Wildlife conservation)	5	PATROLLING	6	WEATHER CONTROL
			0	OTHER (Specify)				

	4 ✓	EXPERIMENTAL (Indicate operation(s) to be conducted)	1		RESEARCH AND DEVELOPMENT	2	AMATEUR BUILT	3	EXHIBITION
			4		AIR RACING	5	CREW TRAINING	6	MARKET SURVEY
			0	✓	TO SHOW COMPLIANCE WITH THE CFR	7	OPERATING (Primary Category) KIT BUILT AIRCRAFT		
			8	8A	Existing aircraft without an airworthiness certificate & do not meet § 103.1				
			OPERATING LIGHT-SPORT	8B	Operating Light-Sport Kit-built				
				8C	Operating light-sport previously issued special light-sport category airworthiness certificate under § 21.190				
			9 UNMANNED AIRCRAFT	9A	RESEARCH AND DEVELOPMENT	9C	CREW TRAINING		
				9B	MARKET SURVEY				

	8	SPECIAL FLIGHT PERMIT (Indicate operation to be conducted, then complete Section VI or VII as applicable on reverse side)	1	FERRY FLIGHT FOR REPAIRS, ALTERATIONS, MAINTENANCE, OR STORAGE
			2	EVACUATE FROM AREA OF IMPENDING DANGER
			3	OPERATION IN EXCESS OF MAXIMUM CERTIFICATED TAKE-OFF WEIGHT
			4	DELIVERING OR EXPORTING	5	PRODUCTION FLIGHT TESTING
			6	CUSTOMER DEMONSTRATION FLIGHTS

C	6	MULTIPLE AIRWORTHINESS CERTIFICATE (Check ABOVE "Restricted Operation" and "Standard" or "Limited" as applicable)

III. OWNER'S CERTIFICATION

A. REGISTERED OWNER (As shown on certificate of aircraft registration)		IF DEALER, CHECK HERE ➤

NAME	ADDRESS
Mary Test	78 China Drive, Jumping, TX 89765

B. AIRCRAFT CERTIFICATION BASIS (Check applicable blocks and complete items as indicated)

AIRCRAFT SPECIFICATION OR TYPE CERTIFICATE DATA SHEET (Give No. and Revision No.) N/A	✓	AIRWORTHINESS DIRECTIVES (Check if all applicable ADs are complied with and give the number of the last AD SUPPLEMENT available in the biweekly series as of the date of application) 2010-02

AIRCRAFT LISTING (Give page number(s)) N/A	SUPPLEMENTAL TYPE CERTIFICATE (List number of each STC incorporated) N/A

C. AIRCRAFT OPERATION AND MAINTENANCE RECORDS

✓	CHECK IF RECORDS IN COMPLIANCE WITH 14 CFR section 91.417	TOTAL AIRFRAME HOURS 0	3	EXPERIMENTAL ONLY (Enter hours flown since last certificate issued or renewed) 0

D. CERTIFICATION - I hereby certify that I am the registered owner (or his agent) of the aircraft described above, that the aircraft is registered with the Federal Aviation Administration in accordance with Title 49 of the United States Code 44101 et seq. and applicable Federal Aviation Regulations, and that the aircraft has been inspected and is airworthy and eligible for the airworthiness certificate requested.

DATE OF APPLICATION 01/27/2010	NAME AND TITLE (Print or type) Mary Test, President	SIGNATURE Mary Test

IV. INSPECTION AGENCY VERIFICATION

A. THE AIRCRAFT DESCRIBED ABOVE HAS BEEN INSPECTED AND FOUND AIRWORTHY BY: (Complete the section only if 14 CFR part 21.183(d) applies)

2	14 CFR part 121 CERTIFICATE HOLDER (Give Certificate No.)	3	CERTIFICATED MECHANIC (Give Certificate No.)	6	CERTIFICATED REPAIR STATION (Give Certificate No.)
5	AIRCRAFT MANUFACTURER (Give name or firm)				

DATE	TITLE	SIGNATURE

V. FAA REPRESENTATIVE CERTIFICATION

(Check ALL applicable block items A and B)

A. I find that the aircraft described in Section I or VII meets requirements for	4	THE CERTIFICATE REQUESTED
		AMENDMENT OR MODIFICATION OF CURRENT AIRWORTHINESS CERTIFICATE

B. Inspection for a special flight permit under Section VII was conducted by:

	FAA INSPECTOR	FAA DESIGNEE			
	CERTIFICATE HOLDER UNDER	14 CFR part 65	14 CFR part 121 OR 135	14 CFR part 145

DATE	MIDO/FSDO OFFICE	4	FAA INSPECTOR'S SIGNATURE or DESIGNEE'S SIGNATURE AND NO.	1	FAA INSPECTOR'S CERTIFICATION FILE REVIEW SIGNATURE

FAA Form 8130-6 (04-11) All Previous Editions Superseded

Figure D-15. Sample FAA Form 8130-6, Application for U.S. Airworthiness Certificate, Special - Experimental Category, Amateur-Built, with Type-Certificated Installations (Face Side Only)

FAA FORM 8130-6, APPLICATION FOR U.S. AIRWORTHINESS CERTIFICATE

Form Approved
O.M.B. No. 2120-0018

U.S. Department of Transportation — Federal Aviation Administration

APPLICATION FOR U.S. AIRWORTHINESS CERTIFICATE

INSTRUCTIONS - Print or type. Do not write in shaded areas; these are for FAA use only. Submit original only to an authorized FAA Representative. If additional space is required, use attachment. For special flight permits complete Sections II, VI, and VII as applicable.

I. AIRCRAFT DESCRIPTION

1. REGISTRATION MARK	2. AIRCRAFT BUILDER'S NAME (Make)	3. AIRCRAFT MODEL DESIGNATION	4. YR. MFR.	FAA CODING
N12345	Bill Jones	Lancair IV-P	2001	

5. AIRCRAFT SERIAL NO.	6. ENGINE BUILDER'S NAME (Make)	7. ENGINE MODEL DESIGNATION
0098	Teledyne Continental Motors	TSIO-550-B(1)

8. NUMBER OF ENGINES	9. PROPELLER BUILDER'S NAME (Make)	10. PROPELLER MODEL DESIGNATION	11. AIRCRAFT IS (Check if applicable)
1	Hartzell Propeller, Inc.	PHCHYF 1RF	IMPORT

II. CERTIFICATION REQUESTED

APPLICATION IS HEREBY MADE FOR: (Check applicable items)

A. 1 STANDARD AIRWORTHINESS CERTIFICATE (Indicate category) NORMAL UTILITY ACROBATIC TRANSPORT COMMUTER BALLOON OTHER

B. ✓ SPECIAL AIRWORTHINESS CERTIFICATE (Check appropriate items)

7	PRIMARY	
9	LIGHT-SPORT (Indicate Class)	Airplane — Power-Parachute — Weight-Shift-Control — Glider — Lighter than Air
2	LIMITED	
5	PROVISIONAL (Indicate class)	1 CLASS I / 2 CLASS II

RESTRICTED (Indicate operation(s) to be conducted) — 3

1	AGRICULTURE AND PEST CONTROL	2	AERIAL SURVEY	3	AERIAL ADVERTISING
4	FOREST (Wildlife conservation)	5	PATROLLING	6	WEATHER CONTROL
0	OTHER (Specify)				

EXPERIMENTAL (Indicate operation(s) to be conducted) — 4 ✓

1	RESEARCH AND DEVELOPMENT	2 ✓	AMATEUR BUILT	3	EXHIBITION
4	AIR RACING	5	CREW TRAINING	6	MARKET SURVEY
0	TO SHOW COMPLIANCE WITH THE CFR	7	OPERATING (Primary Category) KIT BUILT AIRCRAFT		

OPERATING LIGHT-SPORT — 8	8A	Existing aircraft without an airworthiness certificate & do not meet § 103.1
	8B	Operating Light-Sport Kit-built
	8C	Operating light-sport previously issued special light-sport category airworthiness certificate under § 21.190

UNMANNED AIRCRAFT — 9	9A	RESEARCH AND DEVELOPMENT	9C	CREW TRAINING
	9B	MARKET SURVEY		

SPECIAL FLIGHT PERMIT (Indicate operation to be conducted, then complete Section VI or VII as applicable on reverse side) — 8

1	FERRY FLIGHT FOR REPAIRS, ALTERATIONS, MAINTENANCE, OR STORAGE		
2	EVACUATE FROM AREA OF IMPENDING DANGER		
3	OPERATION IN EXCESS OF MAXIMUM CERTIFICATED TAKE-OFF WEIGHT		
4	DELIVERING OR EXPORTING	5	PRODUCTION FLIGHT TESTING
6	CUSTOMER DEMONSTRATION FLIGHTS		

C. 6 MULTIPLE AIRWORTHINESS CERTIFICATE (Check ABOVE "Restricted Operation" and "Standard" or "Limited" as applicable)

III. OWNER'S CERTIFICATION

A. REGISTERED OWNER (As shown on certificate of aircraft registration)   IF DEALER, CHECK HERE ▶

NAME	ADDRESS
Bill Jones	10405 E. Mary Street, Daytona Beach, FL 32114

B. AIRCRAFT CERTIFICATION BASIS (Check applicable blocks and complete items as indicated)

AIRCRAFT SPECIFICATION OR TYPE CERTIFICATE DATA SHEET (Give No. and Revision No.)	AIRWORTHINESS DIRECTIVES (Check if all applicable ADs are complied with and give the number of the last AD SUPPLEMENT available in the biweekly series as of the date of application)
N/A	✓ 2001-12

AIRCRAFT LISTING (Give page number(s))	SUPPLEMENTAL TYPE CERTIFICATE (List number of each STC incorporated)
N/A	N/A

C. AIRCRAFT OPERATION AND MAINTENANCE RECORDS

CHECK IF RECORDS IN COMPLIANCE WITH 14 CFR section 91.417	TOTAL AIRFRAME HOURS	EXPERIMENTAL ONLY (Enter hours flown since last certificate issued or renewed)
✓	0	3 0

D. CERTIFICATION - I hereby certify that I am the registered owner (or his agent) of the aircraft described above, that the aircraft is registered with the Federal Aviation Administration in accordance with Title 49 of the United States Code 44101 *et seq* and applicable Federal Aviation Regulations, and that the aircraft has been inspected and is airworthy and eligible for the airworthiness certificate requested.

DATE OF APPLICATION	NAME AND TITLE (Print or type)	SIGNATURE
07/16/2001	Bill Jones, Owner	*Bill Jones*

IV. INSPECTION AGENCY VERIFICATION

A. THE AIRCRAFT DESCRIBED ABOVE HAS BEEN INSPECTED AND FOUND AIRWORTHY BY: (Complete the section only if 14 CFR part 21.183(d) applies)

2	14 CFR part 121 CERTIFICATE HOLDER (Give Certificate No.)	3	CERTIFICATED MECHANIC (Give Certificate No.)	6	CERTIFICATED REPAIR STATION (Give Certificate No.)
5	AIRCRAFT MANUFACTURER (Give name or firm)				

DATE	TITLE	SIGNATURE

V. FAA REPRESENTATIVE CERTIFICATION

(Check ALL applicable block items A and B)

	THE CERTIFICATE REQUESTED
A. I find that the aircraft described in Section I or VII meets requirements for — 4	AMENDMENT OR MODIFICATION OF CURRENT AIRWORTHINESS CERTIFICATE

B. Inspection for a special flight permit under Section VII was conducted by:

	FAA INSPECTOR	FAA DESIGNEE			
	CERTIFICATE HOLDER UNDER	14 CFR part 65	14 CFR part 121 OR 135	14 CFR part 145

DATE	MIDO/FSDO OFFICE — 4	FAA INSPECTOR'S SIGNATURE or DESIGNEE'S SIGNATURE AND NO.	1	FAA INSPECTOR'S CERTIFICATION FILE REVIEW SIGNATURE

FAA Form 8130-6 (04-11) All Previous Editions Superseded

Figure D-16. Sample FAA Form 8130-6, Application for U.S. Airworthiness Certificate, Special – Experimental Category, Operating Light-Sport, Operating Light-Sport Kit-Built Under §21.191(i) (Face Side Only)

FAA FORM 8130-6, APPLICATION FOR U.S. AIRWORTHINESS CERTIFICATE

Form Approved
O.M.B. No. 2120-0018

U.S. Department of Transportation
Federal Aviation Administration

APPLICATION FOR U.S. AIRWORTHINESS CERTIFICATE

INSTRUCTIONS - Print or type. Do not write in shaded areas; these are for FAA use only. Submit original only to an authorized FAA Representative. If additional space is required, use attachment. For special flight permits complete Sections II, VI, and VII as applicable.

I. AIRCRAFT DESCRIPTION

1. REGISTRATION MARK	2. AIRCRAFT BUILDER'S NAME (Make)	3. AIRCRAFT MODEL DESIGNATION	4. YR. MFR.	FAA CODING
N8514U	P&M Aviation LTD	Quik GT450	2007	

5. AIRCRAFT SERIAL NO.	6. ENGINE BUILDER'S NAME (Make)	7. ENGINE MODEL DESIGNATION	
8114	Rotax	912 ULS	

9. NUMBER OF ENGINES	9. PROPELLER BUILDER'S NAME (Make)	10. PROPELLER MODEL DESIGNATION	11. AIRCRAFT IS (Check if applicable)
1	Warp Drive	68L3HPL	IMPORT

II. CERTIFICATION REQUESTED

APPLICATION IS HEREBY MADE FOR: (Check applicable items)

A 1 STANDARD AIRWORTHINESS CERTIFICATE (Indicate category) — NORMAL, UTILITY, ACROBATIC, TRANSPORT, COMMUTER, BALLOON, OTHER

B ✓ SPECIAL AIRWORTHINESS CERTIFICATE (Check appropriate items)

7	PRIMARY						
9	LIGHT-SPORT (Indicate Class)		Airplane	Power-Parachute ✓	Weight-Shift-Control	Glider	Lighter than Air
2	LIMITED						

| 5 | PROVISIONAL (Indicate class) | 1 | CLASS I | | | | |
| | | 2 | CLASS II | | | | |

3	RESTRICTED (Indicate operation(s) to be conducted)	1	AGRICULTURE AND PEST CONTROL	2	AERIAL SURVEY	3	AERIAL ADVERTISING
		4	FOREST (Wildlife conservation)	5	PATROLLING	6	WEATHER CONTROL
		0	OTHER (Specify)				

4 ✓	EXPERIMENTAL (Indicate operation(s) to be conducted)	1	RESEARCH AND DEVELOPMENT	2	AMATEUR BUILT	3	EXHIBITION
		4	AIR RACING	5	CREW TRAINING	6	MARKET SURVEY
		0	TO SHOW COMPLIANCE WITH THE CFR	7	OPERATING (Primary Category) KIT BUILT AIRCRAFT

8 ✓	OPERATING LIGHT-SPORT	8A	Existing aircraft without an airworthiness certificate & do not meet § 103.1
		8B ✓	Operating Light-Sport Kit-built
		8C	Operating light-sport previously issued special light-sport category airworthiness certificate under § 21.190

| 9 | UNMANNED AIRCRAFT | 9A | RESEARCH AND DEVELOPMENT | 9C | CREW TRAINING |
| | | 9B | MARKET SURVEY | | |

8	SPECIAL FLIGHT PERMIT (Indicate operation to be conducted, then complete Section VI or VII as applicable on reverse side)	1	FERRY FLIGHT FOR REPAIRS, ALTERATIONS, MAINTENANCE, OR STORAGE
		2	EVACUATE FROM AREA OF IMPENDING DANGER
		3	OPERATION IN EXCESS OF MAXIMUM CERTIFICATED TAKE-OFF WEIGHT
		4	DELIVERING OR EXPORTING	5	PRODUCTION FLIGHT TESTING
		6	CUSTOMER DEMONSTRATION FLIGHTS

C 6 MULTIPLE AIRWORTHINESS CERTIFICATE (Check ABOVE "Restricted Operation" and "Standard" or "Limited" as applicable)

III. OWNER'S CERTIFICATION

A. REGISTERED OWNER (As shown on certificate of aircraft registration)   IF DEALER, CHECK HERE ▶

NAME	ADDRESS
Dean Wermer	2907 N 78 Place, Bethel, KS 66109

B. AIRCRAFT CERTIFICATION BASIS (Check applicable blocks and complete items as indicated)

✓ AIRCRAFT SPECIFICATION OR TYPE CERTIFICATE DATA SHEET (Give No. and Revision No.) F2317/F2317M-05	✓ AIRWORTHINESS DIRECTIVES (Check if all applicable ADs are complied with and give the number of the last AD SUPPLEMENT available in the biweekly series as of the date of application) 2007-17, NONE
AIRCRAFT LISTING (Give page number(s)) N/A	SUPPLEMENTAL TYPE CERTIFICATE (List number of each STC incorporated) N/A

C. AIRCRAFT OPERATION AND MAINTENANCE RECORDS

✓ CHECK IF RECORDS IN COMPLIANCE WITH 14 CFR section 91.417	TOTAL AIRFRAME HOURS 0	3 EXPERIMENTAL ONLY (Enter hours flown since last certificate issued or renewed) 0

D. CERTIFICATION - I hereby certify that I am the registered owner (or his agent) of the aircraft described above, that the aircraft is registered with the Federal Aviation Administration in accordance with Title 49 of the United States Code 44101 et seq. and applicable Federal Aviation Regulations, and that the aircraft has been inspected and is airworthy and eligible for the airworthiness certificate requested.

DATE OF APPLICATION 09/01/2007	NAME AND TITLE (Print or type) Dean Wermer, Owner	SIGNATURE Dean Wermer

IV. INSPECTION AGENCY VERIFICATION

A. THE AIRCRAFT DESCRIBED ABOVE HAS BEEN INSPECTED AND FOUND AIRWORTHY BY: (Complete the section only if 14 CFR part 21.183(d) applies)

2	14 CFR part 121 CERTIFICATE HOLDER (Give Certificate No.)	3	CERTIFICATED MECHANIC (Give Certificate No.)	6	CERTIFICATED REPAIR STATION (Give Certificate No.)
5	AIRCRAFT MANUFACTURER (Give name or firm)				

DATE	TITLE	SIGNATURE

V. FAA REPRESENTATIVE CERTIFICATION

(Check ALL applicable block items A and B)

A. I find that the aircraft described in Section I or VII meets requirements for   THE CERTIFICATE REQUESTED
4   AMENDMENT OR MODIFICATION OF CURRENT AIRWORTHINESS CERTIFICATE

B. Inspection for a special flight permit under Section VII was conducted by:

FAA INSPECTOR	FAA DESIGNEE

CERTIFICATE HOLDER UNDER	14 CFR part 65	14 CFR part 121 OR 135	14 CFR part 145

DATE	MIDO/FSDO OFFICE 4	FAA INSPECTOR'S SIGNATURE or DESIGNEE'S SIGNATURE AND NO.	1	FAA INSPECTOR'S CERTIFICATION FILE REVIEW SIGNATURE

FAA Form 8130-6 (04-11) All Previous Editions Superseded

Figure D-17. Sample FAA Form 8130-6, Application for U.S. Airworthiness Certificate, Special – Experimental Category, Unmanned Aircraft (Face Side Only)

FAA FORM 8130-6, APPLICATION FOR U.S. AIRWORTHINESS CERTIFICATE

Form Approved
O.M.B. No. 2120-0018

APPLICATION FOR U.S. AIRWORTHINESS CERTIFICATE

U.S. Department of Transportation
Federal Aviation Administration

INSTRUCTIONS - Print or type. Do not write in shaded areas; these are for FAA use only. Submit original only to an authorized FAA Representative. If additional space is required, use attachment. For special flight permits complete Sections II, VI, and VII as applicable.

I. AIRCRAFT DESCRIPTION

1. REGISTRATION MARK	2. AIRCRAFT BUILDER'S NAME (Make)	3. AIRCRAFT MODEL DESIGNATION	4. YR. MFR.	FAA CODING
N9876	General Atomics	Altair	2003	
5. AIRCRAFT SERIAL NO.	6. ENGINE BUILDER'S NAME (Make)	7. ENGINE MODEL DESIGNATION		
AA001	Honeywell International	TPE33-10T		
8. NUMBER OF ENGINES	9. PROPELLER BUILDER'S NAME (Make)	10. PROPELLER MODEL DESIGNATION	11. AIRCRAFT IS (Check if applicable)	
1	McCauley Propeller Systems	3GFR36C606-B	IMPORT	

II. CERTIFICATION REQUESTED

APPLICATION IS HEREBY MADE FOR: (Check applicable items)

A	1		STANDARD AIRWORTHINESS CERTIFICATE (Indicate category)	NORMAL	UTILITY	ACROBATIC	TRANSPORT	COMMUTER	BALLOON	OTHER
B	✓		SPECIAL AIRWORTHINESS CERTIFICATE (Check appropriate items)							

	7	PRIMARY						
	9	LIGHT-SPORT (Indicate Class)		Airplane	Power-Parachute	Weight-Shift-Control	Glider	Lighter than Air
	2	LIMITED						

	5	PROVISIONAL (Indicate class)	1	CLASS I				
			2	CLASS II				

	3	RESTRICTED (Indicate operation(s) to be conducted)	1	AGRICULTURE AND PEST CONTROL	2	AERIAL SURVEY	3	AERIAL ADVERTISING
			4	FOREST (Wildlife conservation)	5	PATROLLING	6	WEATHER CONTROL
			0	OTHER (Specify)				

	4 ✓	EXPERIMENTAL (Indicate operation(s) to be conducted)	1	RESEARCH AND DEVELOPMENT	2	AMATEUR BUILT	3	EXHIBITION
			4	AIR RACING	5	CREW TRAINING	6	MARKET SURVEY
			0	TO SHOW COMPLIANCE WITH THE CFR	7	OPERATING (Primary Category) KIT BUILT AIRCRAFT		

			8	OPERATING LIGHT-SPORT	8A	Existing aircraft without an airworthiness certificate & do not meet § 103.1
					8B	Operating Light-Sport Kit-built
					8C	Operating light-sport previously issued special light-sport category airworthiness certificate under § 21.190

			9 ✓	UNMANNED AIRCRAFT	9A ✓	RESEARCH AND DEVELOPMENT	9C ✓	CREW TRAINING
					9B ✓	MARKET SURVEY		

	8	SPECIAL FLIGHT PERMIT (Indicate operation to be conducted, then complete Section VI or VII as applicable on reverse side)	1	FERRY FLIGHT FOR REPAIRS, ALTERATIONS, MAINTENANCE, OR STORAGE		
			2	EVACUATE FROM AREA OF IMPENDING DANGER		
			3	OPERATION IN EXCESS OF MAXIMUM CERTIFICATED TAKE-OFF WEIGHT		
			4	DELIVERING OR EXPORTING	5	PRODUCTION FLIGHT TESTING
			6	CUSTOMER DEMONSTRATION FLIGHTS		

C	6		MULTIPLE AIRWORTHINESS CERTIFICATE (Check ABOVE "Restricted Operation" and "Standard" or "Limited" as applicable)

III. OWNER'S CERTIFICATION

A. REGISTERED OWNER (As shown on certificate of aircraft registration)   IF DEALER, CHECK HERE ►

NAME	ADDRESS
General Atomics Corp.	P.O. Box 138, San Diego, CA 90804

B. AIRCRAFT CERTIFICATION BASIS (Check applicable blocks and complete items as indicated)

AIRCRAFT SPECIFICATION OR TYPE CERTIFICATE DATA SHEET (Give No. and Revision No.) N/A	✓ AIRWORTHINESS DIRECTIVES (Check if all applicable ADs are complied with and give the number of the last AD SUPPLEMENT available in the biweekly series as of the date of application) 2010-25
AIRCRAFT LISTING (Give page number(s)) N/A	SUPPLEMENTAL TYPE CERTIFICATE (List number of each STC incorporated) N/A

C. AIRCRAFT OPERATION AND MAINTENANCE RECORDS

✓ CHECK IF RECORDS IN COMPLIANCE WITH 14 CFR section 91.417	TOTAL AIRFRAME HOURS 505	3 EXPERIMENTAL ONLY (Enter hours flown since last certificate issued or renewed) 58

D. CERTIFICATION - I hereby certify that I am the registered owner (or his agent) of the aircraft described above, that the aircraft is registered with the Federal Aviation Administration in accordance with Title 49 of the United States Code 44101 et seq. and applicable Federal Aviation Regulations, and that the aircraft has been inspected and is airworthy and eligible for the airworthiness certificate requested.

DATE OF APPLICATION 12/15/2010	NAME AND TITLE (Print or type) R.L. Brown, Operations Manager	SIGNATURE R.L. Brown

IV. INSPECTION AGENCY VERIFICATION

A. THE AIRCRAFT DESCRIBED ABOVE HAS BEEN INSPECTED AND FOUND AIRWORTHY BY: (Complete this section only if 14 CFR part 21.183(d) applies)

2	14 CFR part 121 CERTIFICATE HOLDER (Give Certificate No.)	3	CERTIFICATED MECHANIC (Give Certificate No.)	6	CERTIFICATED REPAIR STATION (Give Certificate No.)
5	AIRCRAFT MANUFACTURER (Give name or firm)				

DATE	TITLE	SIGNATURE

V. FAA REPRESENTATIVE CERTIFICATION

(Check ALL applicable block items A and B)

A. I find that the aircraft described in Section I or VII meets requirements for | 4 | THE CERTIFICATE REQUESTED AMENDMENT OR MODIFICATION OF CURRENT AIRWORTHINESS CERTIFICATE |

B. Inspection for a special flight permit under Section VII was conducted by

FAA INSPECTOR	FAA DESIGNEE			
CERTIFICATE HOLDER UNDER	14 CFR part 65	14 CFR part 121 OR 135	14 CFR part 145

DATE	MIDO/FSDO OFFICE	4	FAA INSPECTOR'S SIGNATURE or DESIGNEE'S SIGNATURE AND NO.	1	FAA INSPECTOR'S CERTIFICATION FILE REVIEW SIGNATURE

FAA Form 8130-6 (04-11) All Previous Editions Superseded

9/7/2012

Figure D-18a. Sample FAA Form 8130-6, Application for U.S. Airworthiness Certificate, Special – Special Flight Permit for Ferry Flight for Repairs, Alterations, Maintenance, or Storage
(Face Side)

FAA FORM 8130-6, APPLICATION FOR U.S. AIRWORTHINESS CERTIFICATE

Form Approved
O.M.B. No. 2120-0018

FAA Form 8130-6 (04-11) All Previous Editions Superseded

Figure D-18b. Sample FAA Form 8130-6, Application for U.S. Airworthiness Certificate, Special – Special Flight Permit for Ferry Flight for Repairs, Alterations, Maintenance, or Storage (Reverse Side) (cont'd.)

VI. PRODUCTION FLIGHT TESTING

A. MANUFACTURER

NAME | ADDRESS

B. PRODUCTION BASIS (Check applicable item)
- PRODUCTION CERTIFICATE (Give production certificate number)
- TYPE CERTIFICATE
- OTHER:

C. GIVE QUANTITY OF CERTIFICATES REQUIRED FOR OPERATING NEEDS

DATE OF APPLICATION | NAME AND TITLE (Print or type) | SIGNATURE

VII. SPECIAL FLIGHT PERMIT PURPOSES OTHER THAN PRODUCTION FLIGHT TEST

A. DESCRIPTION OF AIRCRAFT

REGISTERED OWNER: Robert F. Turner
ADDRESS: 4623 Mountainview Drive, Waterloo, IA 50701
BUILDER (Make): Bellanca
MODEL: 14-19-2
SERIAL NUMBER: 4099
REGISTRATION MARK: N254B

B. DESCRIPTION OF FLIGHT CUSTOMER DEMONSTRATION FLIGHTS ☐ (Check if applicable)
FROM: Waterloo, IA
TO: Des Moines, IA
VIA:
DEPARTURE DATE: 11/20/2009
DURATION: 1 day

C. CREW REQUIRED TO OPERATE THE AIRCRAFT AND ITS EQUIPMENT
✓ PILOT | CO-PILOT | FLIGHT ENGINEER | OTHER (Specify)

D. THE AIRCRAFT DOES NOT MEET THE APPLICABLE AIRWORTHINESS REQUIREMENTS AS FOLLOWS:

Aircraft damaged in landing accident. Temporary repairs have been made for one flight to repair shop at Des Moines - Dodge Airport, where permanent repairs will be made.

E. THE FOLLOWING RESTRICTIONS ARE CONSIDERED NECESSARY FOR SAFE OPERATION (Use attachment if necessary)
1. Airspeed should not exceed 115 MPH
2. Landing gear should not be retracted.
3. No passengers or cargo should be carried.

F. CERTIFICATION - I hereby certify that I am the registered owner (or his agent) of the aircraft described above, that the aircraft is registered with the Federal Aviation Administration in accordance with Title 49 of the United States Code 44101 et seq. and applicable Federal Aviation Regulations; and that the aircraft has been inspected and is safe for the flight described.

DATE: 11/10/2009 | NAME AND TITLE (Print or type): Robert F. Turner, Owner | SIGNATURE: Robert F. Turner

VIII. AIRWORTHINESS DOCUMENTATION (FAA/DESIGNEE use only)

A. Operating Limitations and Markings in Compliance With 14 CFR Section 91.9, As Applicable

B. Current Operating Limitations Attached

C. Data, Drawings, Photographs, etc. (Attach when required)

D. Current Weight and Balance Information Available in Aircraft

E. Major Repair and Alteration, FAA Form 337 (Attach when required)

F. This inspection Recorded in Aircraft Records

G. Statement of Conformity, FAA Form 8130-9 (Attach when required)

H. Foreign Airworthiness Certification for Import Aircraft (Attach when required)

I. Previous Airworthiness Certificate Issued in Accordance With 14 CFR Section _____ CAR _____ (Original attached)

J. Current Airworthiness Certificate Issued in Accordance With 14 CFR Section _____ (Copy attached)

K. Light-Sport Aircraft Statement of Compliance, FAA Form 8130-15 (Attach when required)

FAA Form 8130-6 (04-11) All Previous Editions Superseded

Figure D-19a. Sample FAA Form 8130-6, Application for U.S. Airworthiness Certificate, Special – Special Flight Permit for Ferry Flight in Excess of Maximum Take-Off Weight (Face Side)

FAA FORM 8130-6, APPLICATION FOR U.S. AIRWORTHINESS CERTIFICATE

Form Approved
O.M.B. No. 2120-0018

	APPLICATION FOR U.S. AIRWORTHINESS CERTIFICATE	INSTRUCTIONS - Print or type. Do not write in shaded areas; these are for FAA use only. Submit original only to an authorized FAA Representative. If additional space is required, use attachment. For special flight permits complete Sections II, VI, and VII as applicable.

U.S. Department of Transportation
Federal Aviation Administration

I. AIRCRAFT DESCRIPTION

1. REGISTRATION MARK	2. AIRCRAFT BUILDER'S NAME *(Make)*	3. AIRCRAFT MODEL DESIGNATION	4. YR. MFR.	FAA CODING
5. AIRCRAFT SERIAL NO.	6. ENGINE BUILDER'S NAME *(Make)*	7. ENGINE MODEL DESIGNATION		
8. NUMBER OF ENGINES	9. PROPELLER BUILDER'S NAME *(Make)*	10. PROPELLER MODEL DESIGNATION	11. AIRCRAFT IS *(Check if applicable)* IMPORT	

II. CERTIFICATION REQUESTED

APPLICATION IS HEREBY MADE FOR: *(Check applicable items)*

A	1		STANDARD AIRWORTHINESS CERTIFICATE *(Indicate category)*		NORMAL		UTILITY		ACROBATIC		TRANSPORT		COMMUTER		BALLOON		OTHER

B	✓		SPECIAL AIRWORTHINESS CERTIFICATE *(Check appropriate items)*											

		7		PRIMARY							
		9		LIGHT-SPORT *(Indicate Class)*		Airplane	Power-Parachute	Weight-Shift-Control	Glider	Lighter than Air
		2		LIMITED						

| | | 5 | PROVISIONAL *(Indicate class)* | 1 | CLASS I |
| | | | | 2 | CLASS II |

		3	RESTRICTED *(Indicate operation(s) to be conducted)*	1	AGRICULTURE AND PEST CONTROL	2	AERIAL SURVEY	3	AERIAL ADVERTISING
				4	FOREST *(Wildlife conservation)*	5	PATROLLING	6	WEATHER CONTROL
				0	OTHER *(Specify)*				

		4	EXPERIMENTAL *(Indicate operation(s) to be conducted)*	1	RESEARCH AND DEVELOPMENT	2	AMATEUR BUILT	3	EXHIBITION
				4	AIR RACING	5	CREW TRAINING	6	MARKET SURVEY
				0	TO SHOW COMPLIANCE WITH THE CFR	7	OPERATING *(Primary Category)* KIT BUILT AIRCRAFT		
				8	OPERATING LIGHT-SPORT	8A	Existing aircraft without an airworthiness certificate & do not meet § 103.1
						8B	Operating Light-Sport Kit-built
						8C	Operating light-sport previously issued special light-sport category airworthiness certificate under § 21.190
				9	UNMANNED AIRCRAFT	9A	RESEARCH AND DEVELOPMENT	9C	CREW TRAINING
						9B	MARKET SURVEY		

		8	✓	SPECIAL FLIGHT PERMIT *(Indicate operation to be conducted, then complete Section VI or VII as applicable on reverse side)*	1	FERRY FLIGHT FOR REPAIRS, ALTERATIONS, MAINTENANCE, OR STORAGE
					2	EVACUATE FROM AREA OF IMPENDING DANGER
					3	✓	OPERATION IN EXCESS OF MAXIMUM CERTIFICATED TAKE-OFF WEIGHT
					4	DELIVERING OR EXPORTING	5	PRODUCTION FLIGHT TESTING
					6	CUSTOMER DEMONSTRATION FLIGHTS

C	6		MULTIPLE AIRWORTHINESS CERTIFICATE *(Check ABOVE "Restricted Operation" and "Standard" or "Limited" as applicable)*

III. OWNER'S CERTIFICATION

A. REGISTERED OWNER *(As shown on certificate of aircraft registration)*   IF DEALER, CHECK HERE ———▶

NAME   ADDRESS

B. AIRCRAFT CERTIFICATION BASIS *(Check applicable blocks and complete items as indicated)*

AIRCRAFT SPECIFICATION OR TYPE CERTIFICATE DATA SHEET *(Give No. and Revision No.)*	AIRWORTHINESS DIRECTIVES *(Check if all applicable ADs are complied with and give the number of the last AD SUPPLEMENT available in the biweekly series as of the date of application)*
AIRCRAFT LISTING *(Give page number(s))*	SUPPLEMENTAL TYPE CERTIFICATE *(List number of each STC incorporated)*

C. AIRCRAFT OPERATION AND MAINTENANCE RECORDS

CHECK IF RECORDS IN COMPLIANCE WITH 14 CFR section 91.417	TOTAL AIRFRAME HOURS	3	EXPERIMENTAL ONLY *(Enter hours flown since last certificate issued or renewed)*

D. CERTIFICATION - I hereby certify that I am the registered owner (or his agent) of the aircraft described above, that the aircraft is registered with the Federal Aviation Administration in accordance with Title 49 of the United States Code 44101 *et seq.* and applicable Federal Aviation Regulations, and that the aircraft has been inspected and is airworthy and eligible for the airworthiness certificate requested.

DATE OF APPLICATION	NAME AND TITLE *(Print or type)*	SIGNATURE

IV. INSPECTION AGENCY VERIFICATION

A. THE AIRCRAFT DESCRIBED ABOVE HAS BEEN INSPECTED AND FOUND AIRWORTHY BY: *(Complete the section only if 14 CFR part 21.183(d) applies)*

2	14 CFR part 121 CERTIFICATE HOLDER *(Give Certificate No.)*	3	CERTIFICATED MECHANIC *(Give Certificate No.)*	6	CERTIFICATED REPAIR STATION *(Give Certificate No.)*
5	AIRCRAFT MANUFACTURER *(Give name or firm)*				

DATE	TITLE	SIGNATURE

V. FAA REPRESENTATIVE CERTIFICATION

(Check ALL applicable block items A and B)
A. I find that the aircraft described in Section I or VII meets requirements for

	THE CERTIFICATE REQUESTED
4	AMENDMENT OR MODIFICATION OF CURRENT AIRWORTHINESS CERTIFICATE

B. Inspection for a special flight permit under Section VII was conducted by:

	FAA INSPECTOR	FAA DESIGNEE		
	CERTIFICATE HOLDER UNDER	14 CFR part 65	14 CFR part 121 OR 135	14 CFR part 145

DATE	MIDO/FSDO OFFICE	4	FAA INSPECTOR'S SIGNATURE or DESIGNEE'S SIGNATURE AND NO.	1	FAA INSPECTOR'S CERTIFICATION FILE REVIEW SIGNATURE

FAA Form 8130-6 (04-11) All Previous Editions Superseded

Figure D-19b. Sample FAA Form 8130-6, Application for U.S. Airworthiness Certificate, Special – Special Flight Permit for Ferry Flight in Excess of Maximum Take-Off Weight (Reverse Side) (cont'd.)

VI. PRODUCTION FLIGHT TESTING

A. MANUFACTURER

NAME ___ ADDRESS ___

B. PRODUCTION BASIS (Check applicable item)

PRODUCTION CERTIFICATE (Give production certificate number) ___
TYPE CERTIFICATE
OTHER:

C. GIVE QUANTITY OF CERTIFICATES REQUIRED FOR OPERATING NEEDS

DATE OF APPLICATION ___ NAME AND TITLE (Print or type) ___ SIGNATURE ___

VII. SPECIAL FLIGHT PERMIT PURPOSES OTHER THAN PRODUCTION FLIGHT TEST

A. DESCRIPTION OF AIRCRAFT

REGISTERED OWNER: Weldon H. Jackson
ADDRESS: P.O. Box 945, Maui, HI 96782
BUILDER (Make): Piper
MODEL: PA 23-250F
SERIAL NUMBER: 27-4173
REGISTRATION MARK: N4588P

B. DESCRIPTION OF FLIGHT — CUSTOMER DEMONSTRATION FLIGHTS ☐ (Check if applicable)

FROM: ELP
TO: HNL
VIA: SJC
DEPARTURE DATE: 11/20/2009
DURATION: 10 days

C. CREW REQUIRED TO OPERATE THE AIRCRAFT AND ITS EQUIPMENT

✓ PILOT | CO-PILOT | FLIGHT ENGINEER | OTHER (Specify)

D. THE AIRCRAFT DOES NOT MEET THE APPLICABLE AIRWORTHINESS REQUIREMENTS AS FOLLOWS:

Temporary Ferry Fuel System installed in accordance with FAA Form 337, "Major Repair and Alteration" dated 11/5/2009.
Gross weight not to exceed 110% of certified takeoff weight.

E. THE FOLLOWING RESTRICTIONS ARE CONSIDERED NECESSARY FOR SAFE OPERATION. (Use attachment if necessary)
1. When the aircraft is in an overweight condition, the design cruise speed should not exceed 162 MPH.
2. The fuel quantity should not exceed 120 gallons in the forward tank and 35 gallons in the aft tank.
3. The sequence of use of the ferry tanks shall be as shown by a temporary placard installed in full view of the pilot.

F. CERTIFICATION - I hereby certify that I am the registered owner (or his agent) of the aircraft described above; that the aircraft is registered with the Federal Aviation Administration in accordance with Title 49 of the United States Code 44101 et seq. and applicable Federal Aviation Regulations; and that the aircraft has been inspected and is safe for the flight described.

DATE: 11/10/2009
NAME AND TITLE (Print or type): Dan Brown, Agent
SIGNATURE: Dan Brown

VIII. AIRWORTHINESS DOCUMENTATION (FAA/DESIGNEE use only)

A. Operating Limitations and Markings in Compliance With 14 CFR Section 91.9, As Applicable
B. Current Operating Limitations Attached
C. Data, Drawings, Photographs, etc. (Attach when required)
D. Current Weight and Balance Information Available in Aircraft
E. Major Repair and Alteration, FAA Form 337 (Attach when required)
F. This inspection Recorded in Aircraft Records

G. Statement of Conformity, FAA Form 8130-9 (Attach when required)
H. Foreign Airworthiness Certification for Import Aircraft (Attach when required)
I. Previous Airworthiness Certificate Issued in Accordance With 14 CFR Section ___ CAR ___ (Original attached)
J. Current Airworthiness Certificate Issued in Accordance With 14 CFR Section ___ (Copy attached)
K. Light-Sport Aircraft Statement of Compliance, FAA Form 8130-15 (Attach when required)

FAA Form 8130-6 (04-11) All Previous Editions Superseded

Figure D-20a. Sample FAA Form 8130-6, Application for U.S. Airworthiness Certificate, Special – Special Flight Permit for Production Flight Testing
(Face Side)

FAA FORM 8130-6, APPLICATION FOR U.S. AIRWORTHINESS CERTIFICATE

Form Approved
O.M.B. No. 2120-0018

U.S. Department of Transportation Federal Aviation Administration	APPLICATION FOR U.S. AIRWORTHINESS CERTIFICATE	INSTRUCTIONS - Print or type. Do not write in shaded areas; these are for FAA use only. Submit original only to an authorized FAA Representative. If additional space is required, use attachment. For special flight permits complete Sections II, VI, and VII as applicable.

I. AIRCRAFT DESCRIPTION

1. REGISTRATION MARK	2. AIRCRAFT BUILDER'S NAME (Make)	3. AIRCRAFT MODEL DESIGNATION	4. YR MFR.	FAA CODING
5. AIRCRAFT SERIAL NO.	6. ENGINE BUILDER'S NAME (Make)	7. ENGINE MODEL DESIGNATION		
8. NUMBER OF ENGINES	9. PROPELLER BUILDER'S NAME (Make)	10. PROPELLER MODEL DESIGNATION		11. AIRCRAFT IS (Check if applicable) IMPORT

II. CERTIFICATION REQUESTED

APPLICATION IS HEREBY MADE FOR: (Check applicable items)

A	1	STANDARD AIRWORTHINESS CERTIFICATE (Indicate category)	NORMAL	UTILITY	ACROBATIC	TRANSPORT	COMMUTER	BALLOON	OTHER
B	✓	SPECIAL AIRWORTHINESS CERTIFICATE (Check appropriate items)							

	7	PRIMARY						
	9	LIGHT-SPORT (Indicate Class)		Airplane	Power-Parachute	Weight-Shift-Control	Glider	Lighter than Air
	2	LIMITED						

	5	PROVISIONAL (Indicate class)	1	CLASS I
			2	CLASS II

	3	RESTRICTED (Indicate operation(s) to be conducted)	1	AGRICULTURE AND PEST CONTROL	2	AERIAL SURVEY	3	AERIAL ADVERTISING
			4	FOREST (Wildlife conservation)	5	PATROLLING	6	WEATHER CONTROL
			0	OTHER (Specify)				

	4	EXPERIMENTAL (indicate operation(s) to be conducted)	1	RESEARCH AND DEVELOPMENT		2	AMATEUR BUILT		3	EXHIBITION
			4	AIR RACING		5	CREW TRAINING		6	MARKET SURVEY
			0	TO SHOW COMPLIANCE WITH THE CFR		7	OPERATING (Primary Category) KIT BUILT AIRCRAFT			
			8	OPERATING LIGHT-SPORT	8A	Existing aircraft without an airworthiness certificate & do not meet § 103.1				
					8B	Operating Light-Sport Kit-built				
					8C	Operating light-sport previously issued special light-sport category airworthiness certificate under § 21.190				
			9	UNMANNED AIRCRAFT	9A	RESEARCH AND DEVELOPMENT	9C	CREW TRAINING		
					9B	MARKET SURVEY				

	8 ✓	SPECIAL FLIGHT PERMIT (Indicate operation to be conducted, then complete Section VI or VII as applicable on reverse side)	1	FERRY FLIGHT FOR REPAIRS, ALTERATIONS, MAINTENANCE, OR STORAGE		
			2	EVACUATE FROM AREA OF IMPENDING DANGER		
			3	OPERATION IN EXCESS OF MAXIMUM CERTIFICATED TAKE-OFF WEIGHT		
			4	DELIVERING OR EXPORTING	5 ✓	PRODUCTION FLIGHT TESTING
			6	CUSTOMER DEMONSTRATION FLIGHTS		

C	6	MULTIPLE AIRWORTHINESS CERTIFICATE (Check ABOVE "Restricted Operation" and "Standard" or "Limited" as applicable)

III. OWNER'S CERTIFICATION

A. REGISTERED OWNER (As shown on certificate of aircraft registration)		IF DEALER, CHECK HERE ►	
NAME		ADDRESS	

B. AIRCRAFT CERTIFICATION BASIS (Check applicable blocks and complete items as indicated)

AIRCRAFT SPECIFICATION OR TYPE CERTIFICATE DATA SHEET (Give No. and Revision No.)	AIRWORTHINESS DIRECTIVES (Check if all applicable ADs are complied with and give the number of the last AD SUPPLEMENT available in the biweekly series as of the date of application)
AIRCRAFT LISTING (Give page number(s))	SUPPLEMENTAL TYPE CERTIFICATE (List number of each STC incorporated)

C. AIRCRAFT OPERATION AND MAINTENANCE RECORDS

CHECK IF RECORDS IN COMPLIANCE WITH 14 CFR section 91.417	TOTAL AIRFRAME HOURS	3	EXPERIMENTAL ONLY (Enter hours flown since last certificate issued or renewed)

D. CERTIFICATION - I hereby certify that I am the registered owner (or his agent) of the aircraft described above, that the aircraft is registered with the Federal Aviation Administration in accordance with Title 49 of the United States Code 44101 et seq. and applicable Federal Aviation Regulations, and that the aircraft has been inspected and is airworthy and eligible for the airworthiness certificate requested.

DATE OF APPLICATION	NAME AND TITLE (Print or type)	SIGNATURE

IV. INSPECTION AGENCY VERIFICATION

A. THE AIRCRAFT DESCRIBED ABOVE HAS BEEN INSPECTED AND FOUND AIRWORTHY BY: (Complete the section only if 14 CFR part 21.183(d) applies)

2	14 CFR part 121 CERTIFICATE HOLDER (Give Certificate No.)	3	CERTIFICATED MECHANIC (Give Certificate No.)	6	CERTIFICATED REPAIR STATION (Give Certificate No.)
5	AIRCRAFT MANUFACTURER (Give name or firm)				

DATE	TITLE	SIGNATURE

V. FAA REPRESENTATIVE CERTIFICATION

(Check ALL applicable block items A and B)

A. I find that the aircraft described in Section I or VII meets requirements for	4	THE CERTIFICATE REQUESTED
		AMENDMENT OR MODIFICATION OF CURRENT AIRWORTHINESS CERTIFICATE

B. Inspection for a special flight permit under Section VII was conducted by:	FAA INSPECTOR	FAA DESIGNEE		
	CERTIFICATE HOLDER UNDER	14 CFR part 65	14 CFR part 121 OR 135	14 CFR part 145

DATE	MIDO/FSDO OFFICE	4	FAA INSPECTOR'S SIGNATURE or DESIGNEE'S SIGNATURE AND NO.	1	FAA INSPECTOR'S CERTIFICATION FILE REVIEW SIGNATURE

FAA Form 8130-6 (04-11) All Previous Editions Superseded

Figure D-20b. Sample FAA Form 8130-6, Application for U.S. Airworthiness Certificate, Special – Special Flight Permit for Production Flight Testing (Reverse Side) (cont'd)

VI. PRODUCTION FLIGHT TESTING	A. MANUFACTURER		

A. MANUFACTURER

NAME
Cessna Aircraft Company

ADDRESS
1 Cessna Boulevard, Witchita, KS 67215

B. PRODUCTION BASIS (Check applicable item)

✓ PRODUCTION CERTIFICATE (Give production certificate number) 123
TYPE CERTIFICATE
OTHER:

C. GIVE QUANTITY OF CERTIFICATES REQUIRED FOR OPERATING NEEDS 10

DATE OF APPLICATION
06/01/2002

NAME AND TITLE (Print or type)
Joe Quality, Manager

SIGNATURE
Joe Quality

VII. SPECIAL FLIGHT PERMIT PURPOSES OTHER THAN PRODUCTION FLIGHT TEST

A. DESCRIPTION OF AIRCRAFT

REGISTERED OWNER | ADDRESS

BUILDER (Make) | MODEL

SERIAL NUMBER | REGISTRATION MARK

B. DESCRIPTION OF FLIGHT   CUSTOMER DEMONSTRATION FLIGHTS ☐ (Check if applicable)

FROM | TO

VIA | DEPARTURE DATE | DURATION

C. CREW REQUIRED TO OPERATE THE AIRCRAFT AND ITS EQUIPMENT

PILOT | CO-PILOT | FLIGHT ENGINEER | OTHER (Specify)

D. THE AIRCRAFT DOES NOT MEET THE APPLICABLE AIRWORTHINESS REQUIREMENTS AS FOLLOWS:

E. THE FOLLOWING RESTRICTIONS ARE CONSIDERED NECESSARY FOR SAFE OPERATION: (Use attachment if necessary)

F. CERTIFICATION - I hereby certify that I am the registered owner (or his agent) of the aircraft described above, that the aircraft is registered with the Federal Aviation Administration in accordance with Title 49 of the United States Code 44101 et seq and applicable Federal Aviation Regulations; and that the aircraft has been inspected and is safe for the flight described.

DATE | NAME AND TITLE (Print or type) | SIGNATURE

VIII. AIRWORTHINESS DOCUMENTATION (FAA/DESIGNEE use only)

A. Operating Limitations and Markings in Compliance With 14 CFR Section 91.9, As Applicable
B. Current Operating Limitations Attached
C. Data, Drawings, Photographs, etc. (Attach when required)
D. Current Weight and Balance Information Available in Aircraft
E. Major Repair and Alteration, FAA Form 337 (Attach when required)
F. This Inspection Recorded in Aircraft Records

G. Statement of Conformity, FAA Form 8130-9 (Attach when required)
H. Foreign Airworthiness Certification for Import Aircraft (Attach when required)
I. Previous Airworthiness Certificate Issued in Accordance With 14 CFR Section _____ CAR _____ (Original attached)
J. Current Airworthiness Certificate Issued in Accordance With 14 CFR Section _____ (Copy attached)
K. Light-Sport Aircraft Statement of Compliance, FAA Form 8130-15 (Attach when required)

FAA Form 8130-6 (04-11) All Previous Editions Superseded

Figure D-21a. Sample FAA Form 8130-6, Application for U.S. Airworthiness Certificate, Special – Special Flight Permit for Production Flight Testing, Light-Sport Aircraft Manufacturer (Face Side)

FAA FORM 8130-6, APPLICATION FOR U.S. AIRWORTHINESS CERTIFICATE

Form Approved
O.M.B. No. 2120-0018

APPLICATION FOR U.S. AIRWORTHINESS CERTIFICATE	INSTRUCTIONS - Print or type. Do not write in shaded areas; these are for FAA use only. Submit original only to an authorized FAA Representative. If additional space is required, use attachment. For special flight permits complete Sections II, VI, and VII as applicable.

U.S. Department of Transportation
Federal Aviation Administration

I. AIRCRAFT DESCRIPTION

1. REGISTRATION MARK	2. AIRCRAFT BUILDER'S NAME *(Make)*	3. AIRCRAFT MODEL DESIGNATION	4. YR. MFR	FAA CODING
N1234LS	Acme Company	Pegasus	2010	
5. AIRCRAFT SERIAL NO.	6. ENGINE BUILDER'S NAME *(Make)*	7. ENGINE MODEL DESIGNATION		
0007	Rotax	912UL		
8. NUMBER OF ENGINES	9. PROPELLER BUILDER'S NAME *(Make)*	10. PROPELLER MODEL DESIGNATION		11. AIRCRAFT IS *(Check if applicable)*
1	IVO	3 blade		IMPORT

II. CERTIFICATION REQUESTED

APPLICATION IS HEREBY MADE FOR *(Check applicable items)*

A	1		STANDARD AIRWORTHINESS CERTIFICATE *(Indicate category)*	NORMAL	UTILITY	ACROBATIC	TRANSPORT	COMMUTER	BALLOON	OTHER

B	✓	SPECIAL AIRWORTHINESS CERTIFICATE *(Check appropriate items)*

	7	PRIMARY					
	9	LIGHT-SPORT *(Indicate Class)*	Airplane	Power-Parachute	Weight-Shift-Control	Glider	Lighter than Air
	2	LIMITED					

	5	PROVISIONAL *(Indicate class)*	1	CLASS I
			2	CLASS II

	3	RESTRICTED *(Indicate operation(s) to be conducted)*	1	AGRICULTURE AND PEST CONTROL	2	AERIAL SURVEY	3	AERIAL ADVERTISING
			4	FOREST *(Wildlife conservation)*	5	PATROLLING	6	WEATHER CONTROL
			0	OTHER *(Specify)*				

	4	EXPERIMENTAL *(Indicate operation(s) to be conducted)*	1	RESEARCH AND DEVELOPMENT			2	AMATEUR BUILT	3	EXHIBITION
			4	AIR RACING			5	CREW TRAINING	6	MARKET SURVEY
			0	TO SHOW COMPLIANCE WITH THE CFR			7	OPERATING *(Primary Category)* KIT BUILT AIRCRAFT		
			8	OPERATING LIGHT-SPORT	8A	Existing aircraft without an airworthiness certificate & do not meet § 103.1				
					8B	Operating Light-Sport Kit-built				
					8C	Operating light-sport previously issued special light-sport category airworthiness certificate under § 21.190				
			9	UNMANNED AIRCRAFT	9A	RESEARCH AND DEVELOPMENT	9C	CREW TRAINING		
					9B	MARKET SURVEY				

	8	✓	SPECIAL FLIGHT PERMIT *(Indicate operation to be conducted, then complete Section VI or VII as applicable on reverse side)*	1	FERRY FLIGHT FOR REPAIRS, ALTERATIONS, MAINTENANCE, OR STORAGE		
				2	EVACUATE FROM AREA OF IMPENDING DANGER		
				3	OPERATION IN EXCESS OF MAXIMUM CERTIFICATED TAKE-OFF WEIGHT		
				4	DELIVERING OR EXPORTING	5 ✓	PRODUCTION FLIGHT TESTING
				6	CUSTOMER DEMONSTRATION FLIGHTS		

C	8	MULTIPLE AIRWORTHINESS CERTIFICATE *(Check ABOVE "Restricted Operation" and "Standard" or "Limited" as applicable)*

III. OWNER'S CERTIFICATION

A. REGISTERED OWNER *(As shown on certificate of aircraft registration)* — IF DEALER, CHECK HERE ➤

NAME — ADDRESS

B. AIRCRAFT CERTIFICATION BASIS *(Check applicable blocks and complete items as indicated)*

AIRCRAFT SPECIFICATION OR TYPE CERTIFICATE DATA SHEET *(Give No. and Revision No.)*	AIRWORTHINESS DIRECTIVES *(Check if all applicable ADs are complied with and give the number of the last AD SUPPLEMENT available in the biweekly series as of the date of application)*
AIRCRAFT LISTING *(Give page number(s))*	SUPPLEMENTAL TYPE CERTIFICATE *(List number of each STC incorporated)*

C. AIRCRAFT OPERATION AND MAINTENANCE RECORDS

CHECK IF RECORDS IN COMPLIANCE WITH 14 CFR section 91.417	TOTAL AIRFRAME HOURS		3	EXPERIMENTAL ONLY *(Enter hours flown since last certificate issued or renewed)*

D. CERTIFICATION - I hereby certify that I am the registered owner (or his agent) of the aircraft described above, that the aircraft is registered with the Federal Aviation Administration in accordance with Title 49 of the United States Code 44101 *et seq.* and applicable Federal Aviation Regulations, and that the aircraft has been inspected and is airworthy and eligible for the airworthiness certificate requested.

DATE OF APPLICATION	NAME AND TITLE *(Print or type)*	SIGNATURE

IV. INSPECTION AGENCY VERIFICATION

A. THE AIRCRAFT DESCRIBED ABOVE HAS BEEN INSPECTED AND FOUND AIRWORTHY BY: *(Complete the section only if 14 CFR part 21.183(d) applies)*

2	14 CFR part 121 CERTIFICATE HOLDER *(Give Certificate No.)*	3	CERTIFICATED MECHANIC *(Give Certificate No.)*	6	CERTIFICATED REPAIR STATION *(Give Certificate No.)*
5	AIRCRAFT MANUFACTURER *(Give name or firm)*				

DATE	TITLE	SIGNATURE

V. FAA REPRESENTATIVE CERTIFICATION

(Check ALL applicable block items A and B)

A. I find that the aircraft described in Section I or VII meets requirements for ... | 4 | THE CERTIFICATE REQUESTED — AMENDMENT OR MODIFICATION OF CURRENT AIRWORTHINESS CERTIFICATE

B. Inspection for a special flight permit under Section VII was conducted by:	FAA INSPECTOR	FAA DESIGNEE			
	CERTIFICATE HOLDER UNDER	14 CFR part 65	14 CFR part 121 OR 135	14 CFR part 145	

DATE	MIDO/FSDO OFFICE	4	FAA INSPECTOR'S SIGNATURE or DESIGNEE'S SIGNATURE AND NO.	1	FAA INSPECTOR'S CERTIFICATION FILE REVIEW SIGNATURE

FAA Form 8130-6 (04-11) All Previous Editions Superseded

Figure D-21b. Sample FAA Form 8130-6, Application for U.S. Airworthiness Certificate, Special – Special Flight Permit for Production Flight Testing, Light-Sport Aircraft Manufacturer (Reverse Side) (cont'd.)

VI. PRODUCTION FLIGHT TESTING	A. MANUFACTURER		

NAME
ACME Co.

ADDRESS
420 W Jackson, Mexico, MO 65265

B. PRODUCTION BASIS *(Check applicable item)*

	PRODUCTION CERTIFICATE *(Give production certificate number)* ⟶
	TYPE CERTIFICATE
	OTHER:

C. GIVE QUANTITY OF CERTIFICATES REQUIRED FOR OPERATING NEEDS 1

DATE OF APPLICATION 09/01/2010	NAME AND TITLE *(Print or type)* Joseph Quality, Manager, Q.A	SIGNATURE *Joseph Quality*

VII. SPECIAL FLIGHT PERMIT PURPOSES OTHER THAN PRODUCTION FLIGHT TEST

A. DESCRIPTION OF AIRCRAFT

REGISTERED OWNER	ADDRESS
BUILDER *(Make)*	MODEL
SERIAL NUMBER	REGISTRATION MARK

B. DESCRIPTION OF FLIGHT   CUSTOMER DEMONSTRATION FLIGHTS ☐   *(Check if applicable)*

FROM	TO	
VIA	DEPARTURE DATE	DURATION

C. CREW REQUIRED TO OPERATE THE AIRCRAFT AND ITS EQUIPMENT

	PILOT	CO-PILOT		FLIGHT ENGINEER	OTHER *(Specify)*

D. THE AIRCRAFT DOES NOT MEET THE APPLICABLE AIRWORTHINESS REQUIREMENTS AS FOLLOWS:

E. THE FOLLOWING RESTRICTIONS ARE CONSIDERED NECESSARY FOR SAFE OPERATION: *(Use attachment if necessary)*

F. CERTIFICATION - I hereby certify that I am the registered owner (or his agent) of the aircraft described above; that the aircraft is registered with the Federal Aviation Administration in accordance with Title 49 of the United States Code 44101 et seq. and applicable Federal Aviation Regulations; and that the aircraft has been inspected and is safe for the flight described.

DATE	NAME AND TITLE *(Print or type)*	SIGNATURE

VIII. AIRWORTHINESS DOCUMENTATION (FAA/DESIGNEE use only)

A. Operating Limitations and Markings in Compliance With 14 CFR Section 91.9, As Applicable	G. Statement of Conformity, FAA Form 8130-9 *(Attach when required)*
B. Current Operating Limitations Attached	H. Foreign Airworthiness Certification for Import Aircraft *(Attach when required)*
C. Data, Drawings, Photographs, etc. *(Attach when required)*	I. Previous Airworthiness Certificate Issued in Accordance With 14 CFR Section _____ CAR _____ *(Original attached)*
D. Current Weight and Balance Information Available in Aircraft	
E. Major Repair and Alteration, FAA Form 337 *(Attach when required)*	J. Current Airworthiness Certificate Issued in Accordance With 14 CFR Section _____ *(Copy attached)*
F. This inspection Recorded in Aircraft Records	K. Light-Sport Aircraft Statement of Compliance, FAA Form 8130-15 *(Attach when required)*

FAA Form 8130-6 (04-11) All Previous Editions Superseded

Figure D-22a. Sample FAA Form 8130-6, Application for U.S. Airworthiness Certificate, Special – Special Flight Permit for Production Flight Testing, Unmanned Aircraft Manufacturer (Face Side)

FAA FORM 8130-6, APPLICATION FOR U.S. AIRWORTHINESS CERTIFICATE

Form Approved
O.M.B. No. 2120-0018

U.S. Department of Transportation — Federal Aviation Administration

APPLICATION FOR U.S. AIRWORTHINESS CERTIFICATE

INSTRUCTIONS - Print or type. Do not write in shaded areas; these are for FAA use only. Submit original only to an authorized FAA Representative. If additional space is required, use attachment. For special flight permits complete Sections II, VI, and VII as applicable.

I. AIRCRAFT DESCRIPTION

1. REGISTRATION MARK	2. AIRCRAFT BUILDER'S NAME *(Make)*	3. AIRCRAFT MODEL DESIGNATION	4. YR. MFR.	FAA CODING
N9876	General Atomics	Altair	2003	

5. AIRCRAFT SERIAL NO.	6. ENGINE BUILDER'S NAME *(Make)*	7. ENGINE MODEL DESIGNATION
AA001	Honeywell International	TPE33-10T

8. NUMBER OF ENGINES	9. PROPELLER BUILDER'S NAME *(Make)*	10. PROPELLER MODEL DESIGNATION	11. AIRCRAFT IS *(Check if applicable)*
1	McCauley Propeller Systems	3GFR36C606-B	IMPORT

II. CERTIFICATION REQUESTED

APPLICATION IS HEREBY MADE FOR: *(Check applicable items)*

A 1 — STANDARD AIRWORTHINESS CERTIFICATE *(Indicate category)* NORMAL | UTILITY | ACROBATIC | TRANSPORT | COMMUTER | BALLOON | OTHER

B ✓ — SPECIAL AIRWORTHINESS CERTIFICATE *(Check appropriate items)*

7	PRIMARY	
9	LIGHT-SPORT *(Indicate Class)*	Airplane | Power-Parachute | Weight-Shift-Control | Glider | Lighter than Air
2	LIMITED	

PROVISIONAL *(Indicate class)* — 5
- 1 CLASS I
- 2 CLASS II

RESTRICTED *(Indicate operation(s) to be conducted)* — 3
- 1 AGRICULTURE AND PEST CONTROL | 2 AERIAL SURVEY | 3 AERIAL ADVERTISING
- 4 FOREST *(Wildlife conservation)* | 5 PATROLLING | 6 WEATHER CONTROL
- 0 OTHER *(Specify)*

EXPERIMENTAL *(Indicate operation(s) to be conducted)* — 4
- 1 RESEARCH AND DEVELOPMENT | 2 AMATEUR BUILT | 3 EXHIBITION
- 4 AIR RACING | 5 CREW TRAINING | 6 MARKET SURVEY
- 0 TO SHOW COMPLIANCE WITH THE CFR | 7 OPERATING *(Primary Category)* KIT BUILT AIRCRAFT
- 8 OPERATING LIGHT-SPORT
  - 8A Existing aircraft without an airworthiness certificate & do not meet § 103.1
  - 8B Operating Light-Sport Kit-built
  - 8C Operating light-sport previously issued special light-sport category airworthiness certificate under § 21.190
- 9 UNMANNED AIRCRAFT
  - 9A RESEARCH AND DEVELOPMENT | 9C CREW TRAINING
  - 9B MARKET SURVEY

SPECIAL FLIGHT PERMIT ✓ *(Indicate operation to be conducted, then complete Section VI or VII as applicable on reverse side)* — 8
- 1 FERRY FLIGHT FOR REPAIRS, ALTERATIONS, MAINTENANCE, OR STORAGE
- 2 EVACUATE FROM AREA OF IMPENDING DANGER
- 3 OPERATION IN EXCESS OF MAXIMUM CERTIFICATED TAKE-OFF WEIGHT
- 4 DELIVERING OR EXPORTING | 5 ✓ PRODUCTION FLIGHT TESTING
- 6 CUSTOMER DEMONSTRATION FLIGHTS

C 6 — MULTIPLE AIRWORTHINESS CERTIFICATE *(Check ABOVE "Restricted Operation" and "Standard" or "Limited" as applicable)*

III. OWNER'S CERTIFICATION

A. REGISTERED OWNER *(As shown on certificate of aircraft registration)*   IF DEALER, CHECK HERE ➤

NAME   ADDRESS

B. AIRCRAFT CERTIFICATION BASIS *(Check applicable blocks and complete items as indicated)*

AIRCRAFT SPECIFICATION OR TYPE CERTIFICATE DATA SHEET *(Give No. and Revision No.)*   AIRWORTHINESS DIRECTIVES *(Check if all applicable ADs are complied with and give the number of the last AD SUPPLEMENT available in the biweekly series as of the date of application)*

AIRCRAFT LISTING *(Give page number(s))*   SUPPLEMENTAL TYPE CERTIFICATE *(List number of each STC incorporated)*

C. AIRCRAFT OPERATION AND MAINTENANCE RECORDS

CHECK IF RECORDS IN COMPLIANCE WITH 14 CFR section 91.417   TOTAL AIRFRAME HOURS   3 EXPERIMENTAL ONLY *(Enter hours flown since last certificate issued or renewed)*

D. CERTIFICATION - I hereby certify that I am the registered owner (or his agent) of the aircraft described above, that the aircraft is registered with the Federal Aviation Administration in accordance with Title 49 of the United States Code 44101 et seq. and applicable Federal Aviation Regulations, and that the aircraft has been inspected and is airworthy and eligible for the airworthiness certificate requested.

DATE OF APPLICATION   NAME AND TITLE *(Print or type)*   SIGNATURE

IV. INSPECTION AGENCY VERIFICATION

A. THE AIRCRAFT DESCRIBED ABOVE HAS BEEN INSPECTED AND FOUND AIRWORTHY BY: *(Complete the section only if 14 CFR part 21.183(d) applies)*

2 14 CFR part 121 CERTIFICATE HOLDER *(Give Certificate No.)* | 3 CERTIFICATED MECHANIC *(Give Certificate No.)* | 6 CERTIFICATED REPAIR STATION *(Give Certificate No.)*

5 AIRCRAFT MANUFACTURER *(Give name or firm)*

DATE   TITLE   SIGNATURE

V. FAA REPRESENTATIVE CERTIFICATION

(Check ALL applicable block items A and B)

A. I find that the aircraft described in Section I or VII meets requirements for — 4

THE CERTIFICATE REQUESTED
AMENDMENT OR MODIFICATION OF CURRENT AIRWORTHINESS CERTIFICATE

B. Inspection for a special flight permit under Section VII was conducted by: FAA INSPECTOR   FAA DESIGNEE

CERTIFICATE HOLDER UNDER | 14 CFR part 65 | 14 CFR part 121 OR 135 | 14 CFR part 145

DATE   MIDO/FSDO OFFICE — 4   FAA INSPECTOR'S SIGNATURE or DESIGNEE'S SIGNATURE AND NO.   1 FAA INSPECTOR'S CERTIFICATION FILE REVIEW SIGNATURE

FAA Form 8130-6 (04-11) All Previous Editions Superseded

Figure D-22b. Sample FAA Form 8130-6, Application for U.S. Airworthiness Certificate, Special – Special Flight Permit for Production Flight Testing, Unmanned Aircraft Manufacturer (Reverse Side) (cont'd.)

VI. PRODUCTION FLIGHT TESTING	A. MANUFACTURER	
	NAME: General Atomics Corp.	ADDRESS: P.O Box 138, San Diego, CA 90804

B. PRODUCTION BASIS (Check applicable item)
- PRODUCTION CERTIFICATE (Give production certificate number)
- TYPE CERTIFICATE
- OTHER:

C. GIVE QUANTITY OF CERTIFICATES REQUIRED FOR OPERATING NEEDS 1

DATE OF APPLICATION 12/15/2010	NAME AND TITLE (Print or type) R.L. Brown, Operations Manager	SIGNATURE R.L. Brown

VII. SPECIAL FLIGHT PERMIT PURPOSES OTHER THAN PRODUCTION FLIGHT TEST

A. DESCRIPTION OF AIRCRAFT

REGISTERED OWNER	ADDRESS
BUILDER (Make)	MODEL
SERIAL NUMBER	REGISTRATION MARK

B. DESCRIPTION OF FLIGHT — CUSTOMER DEMONSTRATION FLIGHTS ☐ (Check if applicable)

FROM	TO
VIA	DEPARTURE DATE	DURATION

C. CREW REQUIRED TO OPERATE THE AIRCRAFT AND ITS EQUIPMENT
PILOT | CO-PILOT | FLIGHT ENGINEER | OTHER (Specify)

D. THE AIRCRAFT DOES NOT MEET THE APPLICABLE AIRWORTHINESS REQUIREMENTS AS FOLLOWS:

E. THE FOLLOWING RESTRICTIONS ARE CONSIDERED NECESSARY FOR SAFE OPERATION: (Use attachment if necessary)

F. CERTIFICATION - I hereby certify that I am the registered owner (or his agent) of the aircraft described above; that the aircraft is registered with the Federal Aviation Administration in accordance with Title 49 of the United States Code 44101 et seq and applicable Federal Aviation Regulations; and that the aircraft has been inspected and is safe for the flight described.

DATE	NAME AND TITLE (Print or type)	SIGNATURE

VIII. AIRWORTHINESS DOCUMENTATION (FAA/DESIGNEE use only)

A. Operating Limitations and Markings in Compliance With 14 CFR Section 91.9, As Applicable
B. Current Operating Limitations Attached
C. Data, Drawings, Photographs, etc. (Attach when required)
D. Current Weight and Balance Information Available in Aircraft
E. Major Repair and Alteration, FAA Form 337 (Attach when required)
F. This inspection Recorded in Aircraft Records

G. Statement of Conformity, FAA Form 8130-9 (Attach when required)
H. Foreign Airworthiness Certification for Import Aircraft (Attach when required)
I. Previous Airworthiness Certificate Issued in Accordance With 14 CFR Section _____ CAR _____ (Original attached)
J. Current Airworthiness Certificate Issued in Accordance With 14 CFR Section _____ (Copy attached)
K. Light-Sport Aircraft Statement of Compliance, FAA Form 8130-15 (Attach when required)

FAA Form 8130-6 (04-11) All Previous Editions Superseded

9/7/2012

Figure D-23. Sample FAA Form 8130-6, Application for U.S. Airworthiness Certificate, Multiple (Face Side Only)

FAA FORM 8130-6, APPLICATION FOR U.S. AIRWORTHINESS CERTIFICATE

Form Approved
O.M.B. No. 2120-0018

| U.S. Department of Transportation Federal Aviation Administration | APPLICATION FOR U.S. AIRWORTHINESS CERTIFICATE | INSTRUCTIONS - Print or type. Do not write in shaded areas; these are for FAA use only. Submit original only to an authorized FAA Representative. If additional space is required, use attachment. For special flight permits complete Sections II, VI, and VII as applicable. |

I. AIRCRAFT DESCRIPTION

1. REGISTRATION MARK	2. AIRCRAFT BUILDER'S NAME *(Make)*	3. AIRCRAFT MODEL DESIGNATION	4. YR. MFR	FAA CODING
N54321	Piper Aircraft Company	PA18A-150	1951	

5. AIRCRAFT SERIAL NO.	6. ENGINE BUILDER'S NAME *(Make)*	7. ENGINE MODEL DESIGNATION	
18-3792	Lycoming Engines	O-320	

8. NUMBER OF ENGINES	9. PROPELLER BUILDER'S NAME *(Make)*	10. PROPELLER MODEL DESIGNATION	11. AIRCRAFT IS *(Check if applicable)*
1	Sensenich Propeller	M74DM	IMPORT

II. CERTIFICATION REQUESTED

APPLICATION IS HEREBY MADE FOR: *(Check applicable items)*

A	1		STANDARD AIRWORTHINESS CERTIFICATE *(Indicate category)*		NORMAL	UTILITY	ACROBATIC	TRANSPORT	COMMUTER	BALLOON	OTHER
B		✓	SPECIAL AIRWORTHINESS CERTIFICATE *(Check appropriate items)*								

	7		PRIMARY							
	9		LIGHT-SPORT *(Indicate class)*		Airplane	Power-Parachute	Weight-Shift-Control	Glider	Lighter than Air
	2		LIMITED						
	5		PROVISIONAL *(Indicate class)*	1	CLASS I				
				2	CLASS II				
	3	✓	RESTRICTED *(Indicate operation(s) to be conducted)*	1	AGRICULTURE AND PEST CONTROL	2 ✓	AERIAL SURVEY	3	AERIAL ADVERTISING
				4	FOREST *(Wildlife conservation)*	5	PATROLLING	6	WEATHER CONTROL
				0	OTHER *(Specify)*				

	4		EXPERIMENTAL *(Indicate operation(s) to be conducted)*	1	RESEARCH AND DEVELOPMENT	2	AMATEUR BUILT	3	EXHIBITION
				4	AIR RACING	5	CREW TRAINING	6	MARKET SURVEY
				0	TO SHOW COMPLIANCE WITH THE CFR	7	OPERATING *(Primary Category)* KIT BUILT AIRCRAFT		
				8 OPERATING LIGHT-SPORT	8A	Existing aircraft without an airworthiness certificate & do not meet § 103 1			
					8B	Operating Light-Sport Kit-built			
					8C	Operating light-sport previously issued special light-sport category airworthiness certificate under § 21.190			
				9 UNMANNED AIRCRAFT	9A	RESEARCH AND DEVELOPMENT	9C	CREW TRAINING	
					9B	MARKET SURVEY			

	8		SPECIAL FLIGHT PERMIT *(Indicate operation to be conducted, then complete Section VI or VII as applicable on reverse side)*	1	FERRY FLIGHT FOR REPAIRS, ALTERATIONS, MAINTENANCE, OR STORAGE		
				2	EVACUATE FROM AREA OF IMPENDING DANGER		
				3	OPERATION IN EXCESS OF MAXIMUM CERTIFICATED TAKE-OFF WEIGHT		
				4	DELIVERING OR EXPORTING	5	PRODUCTION FLIGHT TESTING
				6	CUSTOMER DEMONSTRATION FLIGHTS		

| C | 6 | ✓ | MULTIPLE AIRWORTHINESS CERTIFICATE *(Check ABOVE "Restricted Operation" and "Standard" or "Limited" as applicable)* |

III. OWNER'S CERTIFICATION

A. REGISTERED OWNER *(As shown on certificate of aircraft registration)*   IF DEALER, CHECK HERE ──▶

NAME	ADDRESS
North Central Airplane Corp.	1 Box 502 Cutback, MN, 43692

B. AIRCRAFT CERTIFICATION BASIS *(Check applicable blocks and complete items as indicated)*

✓ AIRCRAFT SPECIFICATION OR TYPE CERTIFICATE DATA SHEET *(Give No. and Revision No.)* 1A2 Rev. 33, AR-7 Rev. 9	✓ AIRWORTHINESS DIRECTIVES *(Check if all applicable ADs are complied with and give the number of the last AD SUPPLEMENT available in the biweekly series as of the date of application)* 2009-23
AIRCRAFT LISTING *(Give page number(s))* N/A	SUPPLEMENTAL TYPE CERTIFICATE *(List number of each STC incorporated)*

C. AIRCRAFT OPERATION AND MAINTENANCE RECORDS

✓ CHECK IF RECORDS IN COMPLIANCE WITH 14 CFR section 91.417	TOTAL AIRFRAME HOURS 12050	3	EXPERIMENTAL ONLY *(Enter hours flown since last certificate issued or renewed)*

D. CERTIFICATION - I hereby certify that I am the registered owner (or his agent) of the aircraft described above, that the aircraft is registered with the Federal Aviation Administration in accordance with Title 49 of the United States Code 44101 et seq. and applicable Federal Aviation Regulations, and that the aircraft has been inspected and is airworthy and eligible for the airworthiness certificate requested.

DATE OF APPLICATION 11/21/2009	NAME AND TITLE *(Print or type)* John Jones, President	SIGNATURE *John Jones*

IV. INSPECTION AGENCY VERIFICATION

A. THE AIRCRAFT DESCRIBED ABOVE HAS BEEN INSPECTED AND FOUND AIRWORTHY BY: *(Complete the section only if 14 CFR part 21.183(d) applies)*

2	14 CFR part 121 CERTIFICATE HOLDER *(Give Certificate No.)*	3	CERTIFICATED MECHANIC *(Give Certificate No.)*	6	CERTIFICATED REPAIR STATION *(Give Certificate No.)*
5	AIRCRAFT MANUFACTURER *(Give name or firm)*				

DATE	TITLE	SIGNATURE

V. FAA REPRESENTATIVE CERTIFICATION

(Check ALL applicable block items A and B)

A. I find that the aircraft described in Section I or VII meets requirements for	4	THE CERTIFICATE REQUESTED
		AMENDMENT OR MODIFICATION OF CURRENT AIRWORTHINESS CERTIFICATE

B. Inspection for a special flight permit under Section VII was conducted by:	FAA INSPECTOR	FAA DESIGNEE			
	CERTIFICATE HOLDER UNDER	14 CFR part 65	14 CFR part 121 OR 135	14 CFR part 145

DATE	MIDO/FSDO OFFICE 4	FAA INSPECTOR'S SIGNATURE or DESIGNEE'S SIGNATURE AND NO	1	FAA INSPECTOR'S CERTIFICATION FILE REVIEW SIGNATURE

FAA Form 8130-6 (04-11) All Previous Editions Superseded

**U.S. Department
of Transportation**
Federal Aviation
Administration

Advisory
Circular

Subject: Airworthiness Directives   **Date:** 3/2/12   **AC No:** 39-7D

Initiated by: AFS-300   **Change:**

1.   PURPOSE. This advisory circular (AC) provides guidance and information to owners and operators of aircraft concerning their responsibility for complying with Airworthiness Directives (AD) and recording AD compliance in the appropriate maintenance records.

2.   CANCELLATION. This AC cancels AC 39-7C, ADs, dated November 16, 1995.

3.   RELATED REGULATIONS. Title 14 of the Code of Federal Regulations (14 CFR):

- Part 39, Airworthiness Directives,
- Part 43, Maintenance, Preventive Maintenance, Rebuilding, and Alteration,

  - Section 43.9, Content, Form, and Disposition of Maintenance, Preventive Maintenance, Rebuilding, and Alteration Records (except inspections performed in accordance with part 91, part 125, § 135.411(a)(1), and § 135.419 of this chapter), and
  - Section 43.11, Content, Form, and Disposition of Records for Inspections Conducted Under Parts 91 and 125 and §§ 135.411(a)(1) and 135.419 of This Chapter;

- Part 91, General Operating and Flight Rules,

  - Section 91.403, General,
  - Section 91.417, Maintenance Records, and
  - Section 91.419, Transfer of Maintenance Records.

4.   RELATED READING MATERIAL (current editions).

- FAA-IR-M-8040.1, Airworthiness Directives Manual, and
- FAA Order 8110.103, Alternative Methods of Compliance (AMOC).

5.   BACKGROUND. The authority for the role of the Federal Aviation Administration (FAA) regarding the promotion of safe flight for civil aircraft may be found in Title 49 of the United State Code (49 U.S.C.) § 44701 et. seq. (formerly, Title VI of the Federal Aviation Act of 1958 and related statutes). Pursuant to 49 U.S.C. § 44709(a), the Administrator of the FAA may reinspect and reexamine, at any time, a civil aircraft, aircraft engine, propeller, or appliance. One way the FAA has implemented its authority is through part 39. Pursuant to its authority, the FAA issues ADs when an unsafe condition exists in a product (aircraft, aircraft engine, propeller, or appliance) and is likely to exist or develop in other products of the same type design. ADs are issued by the FAA to notify aircraft owners and operators of an unsafe condition and to require action(s) to resolve the unsafe condition. ADs prescribe the conditions and limitations, including inspection, repair, or alteration under which the product may continue to be operated. ADs are authorized under part 39 and issued in accordance with the public rulemaking procedures of the Administrative Procedure Act (APA), Title 5 of the United States Code (5 U.S.C.) § 553, and FAA procedures in 14 CFR part 11.

6. PRINCIPAL CHANGES. References to specific 14 CFR parts have been updated and text reworded for clarification throughout this AC.

7. AD CATEGORIES. ADs are published in the Federal Register (FR) as amendments to part 39 when an unsafe condition is found to exist in a product. Depending on the urgency, ADs are issued as follows:

   a. Notice of Proposed Rulemaking (NPRM) followed by a Final Rule. This is the most common type of AD. An NPRM is issued whenever safety considerations do not require the immediate imposition of action under an AD. Anyone is invited to comment on the NPRM by submitting written comments. After the comment period closes, the final rule is prepared, taking into account the comments received. Actions proposed in the notice may be changed or withdrawn in light of the comments. When the final rule, resulting from the NPRM, is adopted, it is published in the FR, and is also available electronically to subscribers at the FAA's Regulatory and Guidance Library (RGL) Web site, http://rgl.faa.gov.

   b. Final Rule; Request for Comment (FRC) (commonly referred to as an "Immediately Adopted Rule"). This is used in certain cases, when an unsafe condition warrants the immediate adoption of a rule without prior notice. In general, we issue an FRC only when it is impractical to complete the prior notice requirement procedure because the compliance time for the required action is shorter than the time necessary for the public to comment and for the FAA to publish the final rule. Comment dispositions are only published when a comment warrants a change to the FRC, or when a significant issue is raised that might have wide or continuing interest among members of the affected public.

   c. Emergency ADs. These ADs are of an urgent nature (e.g., immediate safety of flight) and cannot wait for publication in the FR. When an Emergency AD is issued, the AD applies only to the people who receive "actual notice" by First-Class mail and/or fax to the registered owners of those aircraft. Therefore, a followup AD is published in the FR normally as an FRC. The FR version contains the "good cause" findings required by §§ 553(b)(3)(B) and 553(d) of the APA and makes the AD effective to all persons. Other than very minor corrections (such as obvious typographical errors) and the addition of certifications and analyses required by statute, standard formatting required for FR publication, and material required for incorporation by reference, the version published in the FR is identical to the Emergency AD.

8. ELECTRONIC DISTRIBUTION OF ADS.

   a. AD Copies. Official copies of any AD are available in the FR at the Web site, http://www.gpoaccess.gov/fr/index.html. The FAA only distributes Emergency ADs by

First-Class Mail and/or fax. All other final rule ADs are available by signing up for electronic delivery via the FAA RGL Web site, http://rgl.faa.gov. On this Web site, you will find a link entitled "Subscribe for email delivery of ADs and SAIBs." Subscribers must enter their e-mail address and pick the aircraft/engine/propeller makes and models they want to receive information for. Subscribers will automatically receive all applicable ADs and Special Airworthiness Information Bulletins (SAIB) by e-mail.

   b. Appliance AD. A final rule AD related to an appliance is distributed using the electronic delivery described above for the aircraft model(s) selected.

   c. NPRMs. The FAA does not electronically distribute NPRMs. To find NPRMs, you must visit the FAA's RGL at the Web site, http://rgl.faa.gov, or the FR Web site listed above.

9. APPLICABILITY OF ADs. Each AD contains an applicability statement specifying the product (aircraft, aircraft engine, propeller, or appliance) to which it applies. Unless stated otherwise (see subparagraph 9b of this AC), ADs only apply to type-certificated (TC) aircraft, including ADs issued for an engine, propeller, and appliance.

   a. TC'd Aircraft, Engines, and Propellers. For ADs issued against aircraft, engines, and propellers certified under 14 CFR part 21, the Type Certificate Data Sheet (TCDS) is used to identify the affected product. Limitations may be placed on applicability by specifying the serial number or number series to which the AD is applicable. When there is no reference to serial numbers, all serial numbers are affected. The following are examples of AD applicability statements for TC'd products:

   (1) "This AD applies to Hawker Beechcraft Corporation (Type Certificate previously held by Raytheon Aircraft Company) Model 1900, 1900C, and 1900D airplanes, certificated in any category." This statement makes the AD applicable to all airplanes of the model listed, regardless of the type of airworthiness certificate issued to the TC'd aircraft.

   (2) "This AD applies to Hawker Beechcraft Corporation (Type Certificate previously held by Raytheon Aircraft Company) Model 1900D airplane, Serial Numbers UE-1 through UE-439, certificated in any category." This statement specifies certain aircraft by serial number within a specific model, regardless of the type of airworthiness certificate issued to the TC'd aircraft.

   (3) "This AD applies to Aerotek II, Inc. Models B-1 and B-1A airplanes, certificated in any category except restricted." This statement makes the AD applicable to all TC'd airplanes except those issued a special airworthiness certificate in the restricted category.

   (4) "This AD applies to Learjet Inc. (Type Certificate Previously Held by Gates Learjet Corporation) Model 23, 24, 24A, 24B, 24B-A, 24D, 24D-A, 24E, 24F, 25, 25A, 25C, 25D, and 25F airplanes, certificated in any category, modified by Supplemental Type Certificate SA1731SW, SA1669SW, or SA1670SW." This statement makes the AD applicable to all TC'd airplanes listed when altered by the Supplemental Type Certificate (STC) listed, regardless of the type of airworthiness certificate issued to the TC'd aircraft.

(5) "This AD applies to Lycoming Engines Models AEIO-360-A1A and IO-360-A1A."
This statement makes the AD applicable to the engine models listed that are installed on TC'd aircraft.

   b. **Non-TC'd Aircraft and Products Installed Thereon.** Non-TC'd aircraft
(e.g., amateur-built aircraft, experimental exhibition) are aircraft for which the FAA has not issued a TC under part 21. The AD applicability statement will identify if the AD applies to non-TC'd aircraft or engines, propellers, and appliances installed thereon. The following are examples of applicability statements for ADs related to non-TC'd aircraft:

   (1) "This AD applies to Honeywell International Inc. Auxiliary Power Unit (APU) models GTCP36-150(R) and GTCP36-150(RR). These APUs are installed on, but not limited to, Fokker Services B.V. Model F.28 Mark 0100 and F.28 Mark 0070 airplanes, and Mustang Aeronautics, Inc. Model Mustang II experimental airplanes. This AD applies to any aircraft with the listed APU models installed." This statement makes the AD applicable to the listed auxiliary power unit (APU) models installed on TC'd aircraft, as well as non-TC'd aircraft.

   (2) "This AD applies to Lycoming Engines Models AEIO-360-A1A and IO-360-A1A.
This AD applies to any aircraft with the listed engine models installed." This statement makes the AD applicable to the listed engine models installed on TC'd and non-TC'd aircraft.

   c. **Changed Products.** An AD applies to each product identified in the applicability statement, regardless of whether it has been modified, altered, or repaired in the area subject to the requirements of the AD. For products that have been modified, altered, or repaired so that performance of the requirements of the AD is affected, the owner/operator must use the alternative methods of compliance (AMOC) provision of the AD (see paragraph 12) to request approval from the FAA. This approval may address either no action if the current configuration eliminates the unsafe condition, or different actions necessary to address the unsafe condition described in the AD. In no case does the presence of any alteration, modification, or repair remove any product from the applicability of this AD.

10. AD COMPLIANCE. ADs are regulations issued under part 39. Therefore, no person may operate a product to which an AD applies, except in accordance with the requirements of that AD. Owners and operators should understand that to "operate" not only means piloting the aircraft, but also causing or authorizing the product to be used for the purpose of air navigation, with or without the right of legal control as owner, lessee, or otherwise. Compliance with Emergency ADs can be a problem for operators of leased aircraft because they may not be aware of the AD and safety may be jeopardized.

11. COMPLIANCE TIME OR DATE.

   a. **Specified Compliance Time.** The belief that AD compliance is only required at the time of a required inspection (e.g., at a 100-hour or annual inspection) is not correct. The required compliance time is specified in each AD, and no person may operate the affected product after expiration of that stated compliance time without an AMOC approval for a change in compliance time.

b. **Requirements.** Compliance requirements specified in ADs are established for safety reasons and may be stated in various ways. Some ADs are of such a serious, time-critical nature that they require compliance before further flight (e.g., to prevent uncommanded engine shutdown with the inability to restart the engine; the compliance statement may be written as "Prior to further flight, inspect…."). Other ADs express compliance time in terms of a specific number of hours in operation (e.g., "Within the next 50 hours time-in-service after the effective date of this AD, visually inspect…."). Compliance times may also be expressed in operational terms (e.g., "Within the next 10 landings after the effective date of this AD…."). For turbine engines, compliance times are often expressed in terms of cycles. A cycle normally consists of an engine start, takeoff, operation, landing, and engine shutdown.

c. **Expression of Time.** When a direct relationship between airworthiness and calendar-time is identified, compliance time may be expressed as a calendar date. For example, if the compliance time is specified as "Within 12 months after the effective date of this AD…" with an effective date of July 15, 1995, the deadline for compliance is July 15, 1996.

d. **Special Flight Permits.** In some instances, you may need to fly an aircraft to a repair facility to do the work required by an AD. Unless the AD states otherwise, you may apply to the FAA for a special flight permit following the procedures in part 21, § 21.199.

12. AMOCs.

a. **AMOC Definition.** An AD contains the required method for resolving an unsafe condition. An AMOC is a different way, other than the one specified in an AD, to address the unsafe condition on an aircraft, aircraft engine, propeller, or appliance. The term AMOC is used to define a FAA-approved AMOC to the specific requirements of an AD, including a change in the required time to accomplish the AD. An AMOC must ensure the unsafe condition is resolved by providing an acceptable level of safety.

b. **Submitting an AMOC Request.** In accordance with part 39, § 39.19, AMOC requesters should send their AMOC proposal to their principal inspector (PI). The PI may add comments and must forward a copy of the AMOC proposal to the manager of the FAA office identified in the AD. The requester may, at the same time they send it to their PI, send a copy of the proposal to the manager of the office identified in the AD. If the requester doesn't have a PI (such as a design approval holder (DAH)), we advise them to send the proposal directly to the manager of the FAA office identified in the AD.

c. **FAA Approval.** Any AMOC must provide an acceptable level of safety and be substantiated and approved by the Aircraft Certification Office (ACO) before it may be used.

13. RESPONSIBILITY FOR AD COMPLIANCE AND RECORDATION. The owner or operator of an aircraft is primarily responsible for maintaining that aircraft in an Airworthy condition, including compliance with ADs.

a. **Means of Accomplishment.** This responsibility may be met by ensuring that properly certificated and appropriately rated maintenance person(s) accomplish the requirements of the AD and properly record this action in the appropriate maintenance records. This action must be accomplished within the compliance time specified in the AD or the aircraft may not be operated.

   b. **Other Inspections.** Maintenance persons may also have direct responsibility for AD compliance, aside from the times when AD compliance is the specific work contracted by the owner or operator. When a 100-hour, annual, progressive, or any other inspection required under 14 CFR part 91, 121, 125, or 135 is accomplished, § 43.15(a) requires the person performing the inspection to determine that all applicable airworthiness requirements are met, including compliance with ADs.

   c. **Progressive Inspections.** Maintenance persons should note that even though an inspection of the complete aircraft is not made, if the inspection conducted is a progressive inspection, determination of AD compliance is required for those portions of the aircraft inspected.

   d. **Continuous Inspection Programs.** For aircraft being inspected in accordance with a continuous inspection program (§ 91.409), the person performing the inspection must ensure that an AD is complied with only when the portion of the inspection program being handled by that person involves an area covered by a particular AD. The program may require a determination of AD compliance for the entire aircraft by a general statement, compliance with ADs applicable only to portions of the aircraft being inspected, or it may not require compliance at all. This does not mean AD compliance is not required at the compliance time or date specified in the AD. It only means that the owner or operator has elected to handle AD compliance apart from the inspection program. The owner or operator remains fully responsible for AD compliance.

   e. **Required Entries into Records.** The person accomplishing the AD is required by § 43.9 to record AD compliance. The entry must include those items specified in § 43.9(a)(1) through (a)(4). The owner or operator is required by § 91.405 to ensure that maintenance personnel make appropriate entries and, by § 91.417, to maintain those records. Owners and operators should note that there is a difference between the records required to be kept by the owner under § 91.417 and those that § 43.9 requires maintenance personnel to make. In either case, the owner or operator is responsible for maintaining proper records.

14. RECURRING/PERIODIC ADs. Some ADs require repetitive or periodic inspection. In order to provide for flexibility in administering such ADs, an AD may provide for adjustment of the inspection interval to coincide with inspections required by part 91, or other regulations. The conditions and approval requirements under which adjustments may be allowed are stated in the AD. Any other modification or adjustment of the compliance time of the AD must be requested through the AMOC process as described in paragraph 13.

15. DETERMINING REVISION DATES.

   a. **Revision Date.** The revision date required by § 91.417(a)(2)(v) is the effective date of the latest amendment to the AD and may be found in paragraph (a) of the body of each AD. For example, "This airworthiness directive (AD) is effective April 12, 2005."

   b. **Emergency ADs.** Similarly, the revision date for an Emergency AD is the date it was issued. For example, "Emergency airworthiness directive (AD) 2006-17-51, issued

August 15, 2006, is effective immediately upon receipt." Each emergency AD is followed by an FRC version published in the FR that will reflect the amendment number of the regulation, including effective date. For example, "This AD is effective September 18, 2006, to all persons except those persons to whom it was made immediately effective by Emergency AD 2006-17-51, issued on August 15, 2006, which contained the requirements of this amendment."

16. SUMMARY.

a. **Owner/Operator Responsibility.** The registered owner or operator of an aircraft is responsible for compliance with ADs for the airframe, engine, propeller, and appliance as stated in the applicability statement of the AD for all aircraft it owns or operates.

b. **Maintenance Personnel Responsibility.** Maintenance personnel are responsible for determining that all applicable airworthiness requirements are met when they accomplish an inspection in accordance with part 43.

ORIGNAL SIGNED by
/s/ Raymond Towles for

John M. Allen
Director, Flight Standards Service

590

**U.S. Department
of Transportation**
Federal Aviation
Administration

Advisory
Circular

Subject: Maintenance Records	Date: 5/8/18	AC No: 43-9C
	Initiated by: AFS-300	Change: 2

1. PURPOSE. This advisory circular (AC) describes methods, procedures, and practices that have been determined to be acceptable means of showing compliance with the General Aviation (GA) maintenance record-making and recordkeeping requirements of Title 14 of the Code of Federal Regulations (14 CFR) parts 43 and 91. This material is not mandatory, nor is it regulatory, and it acknowledges that the Federal Aviation Administration (FAA) will consider other methods that may be presented. It is issued for guidance purposes and outlines several methods of compliance with the regulations.

2. PRINCIPAL CHANGES. This change to AC 43-9C updates paragraph 15 by adding maintenance manuals to the list of documents containing aircraft/powerplant part life limits and reorganizes the table in Appendix 1, Airworthiness Directive Compliance Record (Suggested Format).

PAGE CONTROL CHART

Remove Pages	Dated	Insert Pages	Dated
Page 8	6/8/98	Page 8	5/8/18
Appendix 1, Page 1 (and 2)	6/8/98	Appendix 1, Page 1 (and 2)	5/8/18

John S. Duncan
Executive Director, Flight Standards Service

**U.S. Department
of Transportation**
Federal Aviation
Administration

Advisory
Circular

Subject: Maintenance Records

Date: 6/8/98   **AC No:** 43-9C

Initiated by: AFS-340   **Change:**

---

1. **PURPOSE.** This advisory circular (AC) describes methods, procedures, and practices that have been determined to be acceptable means of showing compliance with the General Aviation (GA) maintenance record-making and recordkeeping requirements of Title 14 of the Code of Federal Regulations (14 CFR) parts 43 and 91. This material is not mandatory, nor is it regulatory, and it acknowledges that the Federal Aviation Administration (FAA) will consider other methods that may be presented. It is issued for guidance purposes and outlines several methods of compliance with the regulations.

> **NOTE: The information in this AC does not apply to air carrier maintenance records made and retained in accordance with 14 CFR part 121.**

2. **CANCELLATION.** AC 43-9B, Maintenance Records, dated January 9, 1984, is canceled.

3. **RELATED REGULATIONS.** Title 14 CFR parts 1, 43, 91, and 145.

4. **DISCUSSION.** The CFR states that a U.S. Standard Airworthiness Certificate is effective until it is surrendered, suspended, revoked, or a termination date is otherwise established by the Administrator. In addition to those terms, a U.S. Standard Airworthiness Certificate is effective only as long as the maintenance, preventive maintenance, and alterations are performed in accordance with parts 43 and 91, and the aircraft is registered in the United States. These terms and conditions are further restated in block 6 on the front of FAA Form 8100-2, Standard Airworthiness Certificate. Qualified persons who perform the maintenance, preventive maintenance, and alterations shall make a record entry of this accomplishment, thus maintaining the validity of the Certificate of Airworthiness. Adequate aircraft records provide tangible evidence that the aircraft complies with the appropriate airworthiness requirements. In accordance with the terms and conditions listed in block 6 of FAA Form 8100-2, insufficient or nonexistent aircraft records may render that Standard Airworthiness Certificate invalid.

5. **MAINTENANCE RECORD REQUIREMENTS.**

   a. **Responsibilities.** Part 91, § 91.417 states that an aircraft owner/operator shall keep and maintain aircraft maintenance records. However, part 43, § 43.9 states that each person who maintains, performs preventive maintenance, rebuilds, or alters an aircraft, airframe, aircraft engine, propeller, appliance, or component part shall make an entry in the maintenance record of that equipment. Section 43.11 states that the person approving or disapproving for return to service an aircraft, airframe, aircraft engine, propeller, appliance, or component part after any inspection performed in accordance with part 91, <u>125</u>, <u>135</u>, § <u>135.411(a)(1)</u>, or § <u>135.419</u> shall make an entry in the maintenance record of that equipment. The persons that are authorized to perform maintenance can be found in §§ <u>43.3</u> and <u>43.7</u>.

b.   Maintenance Records that Are to Be Retained. Section <u>91.405</u> requires each owner or operator to ensure that maintenance personnel make appropriate entries in the maintenance records to indicate that the aircraft has been approved for return to service. Section 91.417(a) sets forth the content requirements and retention requirements for maintenance records. Maintenance records may be kept in any format that provides record continuity, includes required contents, lends itself to the addition of new entries, provides for signature entry, and is intelligible. Section 91.417(b) requires records of maintenance, alterations, and required or approved inspections to be retained until the work is repeated, superseded by other work, or for one year. It also requires the records, specified in § 91.417(a)(2), to be retained and transferred with the aircraft at the time of sale.

> **NOTE: Section 91.417(a) contains an exception regarding work accomplished in accordance with § <u>91.411</u>. This *does not* exclude the making of entries for this work, but applies to the retention period of the records for work done in accordance with this section. The exclusion is necessary since the retention period of one year is inconsistent with the 24-month interval of test and inspection specified in § 91.411. Entries for work done per this section are to be retained for 24 months or until the work is repeated or superseded.**

c.   Section 91.417(a)(1). Requires a record of maintenance for each aircraft (including the airframe) and each engine, propeller, rotor, and appliance of an aircraft. This *does not* require separate or individual records for each of these items. It *does* require the information specified in § 91.417(a)(1) through 91.417(a)(2)(vi) to be kept for each item as appropriate. As a practical matter, many owners and operators find it advantageous to keep separate or individual records since it facilitates transfer of the record with the item when ownership changes. Section 91.417(a)(1) has no counterpart in § 43.9 or § 43.11.

d.   Section 91.417(a)(1)(i). Is identical to § 43.9(a)(1) and requires the maintenance record entry to include "a description of the work performed." The description should be in sufficient detail to permit a person unfamiliar with the work to understand what was done and the methods and procedures used in doing it. When the work is extensive, this results in a voluminous record. To provide for this contingency, the rule permits reference to technical data acceptable to the Administrator in lieu of making the detailed entry. Manufacturer's manuals, Service Letters (SL), bulletins, work orders, FAA ACs, and others, which accurately describe what was done or how it was done, may be referenced. Except for the documents mentioned that are in common usage, referenced documents are to be made a part of the maintenance records and retained in accordance with § 91.417(b).

> **NOTE: Certificated Repair Stations (CRS) frequently work on components shipped to them without the maintenance records. To provide for this situation, repair stations should supply owners and operators with copies of work orders written for the work, in lieu of maintenance record entries. The**

work order copy must include the information required by § 91.417(a)(1) through 91.417(a)(1)(iii) be made a part of the maintenance record and retained per § 91.417(b). **This procedure is not the same as that for maintenance releases discussed in paragraph 16, and it may not be used when maintenance records are available. Section 91.417(a)(1)(i) is identical to its counterpart, § 43.9(a)(1), which imposes the same requirements on maintenance personnel.**

e. **Section 91.417(a)(1)(ii).** Is identical to § 43.9(a)(2) and requires entries to contain the date the work was completed. This is normally the date upon which the work is approved for return to service. However, when work is accomplished by one person and approved for return to service by another, the dates may differ. Two signatures may also appear under this circumstance; however, a single entry in accordance with § 43.9(a)(3) is acceptable.

f. **Section 91.417(a)(1)(iii).** Differs slightly from § 43.9(a)(4) in that it requires the entry to indicate only the signature and certificate number of the person approving the work for return to service, and does not require the type of certificate being exercised to be indicated as does § 43.9(a)(4). This is a new requirement of § 43.9(a)(4), which assists owners and operators in meeting their responsibilities. Maintenance personnel may indicate the type of certificate exercised by using airframe (A), powerplant (P), Airframe and Powerplant (A&P), Inspection Authorization (IA), or CRS.

g. **Section 91.417(a)(2).** Requires six items to be made a part of the maintenance record and maintained as such. Section 43.9 does not require maintenance personnel to enter these items. Section 43.11 requires some of them to be part of entries made for inspections, but it is ultimately the responsibility of the owner or operator to verify and validate all maintenance record entries. The six items are discussed as follows:

(1) **Section 91.417(a)(2)(i).** Requires a record of total time in service to be kept for the airframe, each engine, and each propeller. Part 1, § 1.1, Definitions, defines time in service, with respect to maintenance time records, as that time from the moment an aircraft leaves the surface of the earth until it touches down at the next point of landing. Section 43.9 does not require this to be part of the entries for maintenance, preventive maintenance, rebuilding, or alterations. However, § 43.11 requires maintenance personnel to make it a part of the entries for inspections made under parts 91, 125, and time in service in all entries.

(a) Some circumstances impact the owner's or operator's ability to comply with § 91.417(a)(2)(i). For example, in the case of rebuilt engines, the owner or operator would not have a way of knowing the total time in service, since § 91.421 permits the maintenance record to be discontinued and the engine time to be started at *zero*. In this case, the maintenance record and time in service subsequent to the rebuild comprise a satisfactory record.

(b) Many components presently in service were put into service before the requirements to keep maintenance records on them. Propellers are probably foremost in this group. In these instances, practicable procedures for compliance with the record requirements must be used. For example, total time in service may be derived using the procedures described in paragraph 12; or if records prior to the regulatory requirements are just not available from any source, time in service may be kept since last complete overhaul. Neither of these procedures is acceptable when life-limited parts status is involved or when Airworthiness Directive (AD) compliance is a factor. Only the actual record since new may be used in these instances.

    (c) Sometimes engines are assembled from modules (turbojet and some turbopropeller engines) and a true total time in service for the total engine is not kept. If owners and operators wish to take advantage of this modular design, then total time in service and a maintenance record for each module is to be maintained. The maintenance records specified in § 91.417(a)(2) are to be kept with the module.

    (2) Section 91.417(a)(2)(ii). Requires the current status of life-limited parts to be part of the maintenance record. If total time in service of the aircraft, engine, propeller, etc., is entered in the record when a life-limited part is installed and the time in service of the life-limited part is included, the normal record of time in service automatically meets this requirement.

    (3) Section 91.417(a)(2)(iii). Requires the maintenance record to indicate the time since last overhaul of all items installed on the aircraft that are required to be overhauled on a specified time basis. The explanation in paragraph 5g(2) also applies to this requirement.

    (4) Section 91.417(a)(2)(iv). Deals with the current inspection status and requires it to be reflected in the maintenance record. Again, the explanation in paragraph 5g(2) is appropriate even though § 43.11(a)(2) requires maintenance persons to determine time in service of the item being inspected and to include it as part of the inspection entry.

    (5) Section 91.417(a)(2)(v). Requires the current status of applicable ADs to be a part of the maintenance record. The record is to include, at minimum, the method used to comply with the AD, the AD number, and revision date; and if the AD has requirements for recurring action, the time in service and the date when that action is required. When ADs are accomplished, maintenance persons are required to include the items specified in § 43.9(a)(2), (3), and (4) in addition to those required by § 91.417(a)(2)(v). An example of a maintenance record format for AD compliance is contained in Appendix 1, Airworthiness Directive Compliance Record (Suggested Format).

    (6) Section 91.417(a)(2)(vi). In the past, the owner or operator has been permitted to maintain a list of current major alterations to the airframe, engine(s), propeller(s), rotor(s), or appliances. This procedure did not produce a record of value to the owner/operator or to maintenance persons in determining the continued airworthiness of the alteration since such a record was not sufficient detail. This section of the rule has now been *changed*. It now prescribes that copies of FAA Form 337, Major Repair and Alteration (Airframe, Powerplant, Propeller, or Appliance), issued for the alteration, be made a part of the maintenance record.

6. PREVENTIVE MAINTENANCE.

    a. Preventive maintenance is defined in § 1.1. Part 43 appendix A paragraph (c) lists those items which a pilot may accomplish under § 43.3(g). Section 43.7 authorizes appropriately rated repair stations and mechanics and persons holding at least a private pilot (PP) certificate to approve an aircraft for return to service after they have performed preventive maintenance. All of these persons must record preventive maintenance accomplished in accordance with the requirements of § 43.9. AC 43-12, Preventive Maintenance, contains further information on this subject.

b. The type of certificate exercised when maintenance or preventive maintenance is accomplished must be indicated in the maintenance record. Pilots may use PP, commercial pilot (CP), or air transport pilot (ATP) to indicate private, commercial, or Airline Transport Pilot Certificate (ATPC), respectively, in approving preventive maintenance for return to service. Pilots are not authorized by § 43.3(g) to perform preventive maintenance on aircraft when they are operated under 14 CFR part 121, 125, 129, or 135. Pilots may only approve for return to service preventive maintenance that they themselves have accomplished.

7. REBUILT ENGINE MAINTENANCE RECORDS.

a. Section 91.421 provides that *zero time* may be granted to an engine that has been rebuilt by a manufacturer or an agency approved by the manufacturer. When this is done, the owner/operator may use a new maintenance record without regard to previous operating history.

b. The manufacturer or an agency approved by the manufacturer that rebuilds and grants zero time to an engine is required by § 91.421 to provide a signed statement containing:

(1) The date the engine was rebuilt;

(2) Each change made, as required by an AD; and

(3) Each change made in compliance with Service Bulletins (SB), when the SB specifically requests an entry to be made.

c. Section 43.2(b) prohibits the use of the term "rebuilt" in describing work accomplished in required maintenance records or forms unless the component worked on has had specific work functions accomplished. These functions are listed in § 43.2(b) and, except for testing requirements, are the same as those set forth in § 91.421(c). When terms such as "remanufactured," "reconditioned," or other terms coined by various aviation enterprises are used in maintenance records, owners and operators cannot assume that the functions outlined in § 43.2(b) have been done.

8. RECORDING TACHOMETERS.

a. Time in service recording devices sense such things as electrical power on, oil pressure, wheels on the ground, etc., and from these conditions provide an indication of time in service. With the exception of those that sense aircraft lift-off and touchdown, the indications are approximate.

b. Some owners and operators mistakenly believe these devices may be used in lieu of keeping time in service in the maintenance record. While they are of great assistance in arriving at the time in service, such instruments alone do not meet the requirements of § 91.417. For example, when the device fails and requires change, it is necessary to enter time in service and the instrument reading at the change. Otherwise, record continuity is lost.

9. MAINTENANCE RECORDS FOR AD COMPLIANCE. This subject is covered in AC 39-7, Airworthiness Directives. A separate AD record may be kept for the airframe and each engine, propeller, rotor, and appliance, but is not required. This would facilitate record searches when inspection is needed, and when an engine, propeller, rotor, or appliance is removed, the record may be transferred with it. Such records may also be used as a schedule for recurring inspections. The format, shown in Appendix 1, is a suggested one, and adherence is not mandatory. *Owners* should be aware that they *may be responsible for non-compliance with ADs* when their aircraft are leased to foreign operators. They should, therefore, ensure that leases should be drafted to deal with this subject.

10. MAINTENANCE RECORDS FOR REQUIRED INSPECTIONS.

    a. Section 43.11 contains the requirements for inspection entries. While these requirements are imposed on maintenance personnel, owners and operators should become familiar with them in order to meet their responsibilities under § 91.405.

    b. The maintenance record requirements of § 43.11 apply to the 100-hour, annual, and progressive inspections under part 91; inspection programs under parts 91 and 125; approved airplane inspection programs under part 135; and the 100-hour and annual inspections under § 135.411(a)(1).

    c. Appropriately rated mechanics are authorized to conduct these inspections and make the required entries. Particular attention should be given to § 43.11(a)(7) in that it now requires a more specific statement than previously required under § 43.9. The entry, in addition to other items, must identify the inspection program used, identify the portion or segment of the inspection program accomplished, and contain a statement that the inspection was performed in accordance with the instructions and procedures for that program.

    d. Questions continue regarding multiple entries for 100-hour/annual inspections. As discussed in paragraph 5c, neither part 43 nor part 91 requires separate records to be kept. Section 43.11, however, requires persons approving or disapproving equipment for return to service, after any required inspection, to make an entry in the record of that equipment. Therefore, when an owner maintains a single record, the entry of the 100-hour or annual inspection is made in that record. If the owner maintains separate records for the airframe, powerplants, and propellers, the entry for the 100-hour inspection is entered in each, while the annual inspection is only required to be entered into the airframe record.

11. DISCREPANCY LISTS.

    a. Before October 15, 1982, issuance of discrepancy lists (or lists of defects) to owners or operators was appropriate only in connection with annual inspections under part 91, inspections under § 135.411(a)(1), inspection programs under part 125, and inspections under § 91.217. Now, § 43.11 requires that a discrepancy list be prepared by a person performing any inspection required by parts 91, 125, or § 135.411(a)(1).

    b. When a discrepancy list is provided to an owner or operator, it says in effect, *except for these discrepancies, the item inspected is airworthy.* It is imperative, therefore, that inspections be complete and that all discrepancies appear in the list. When circumstances dictate that an inspection be terminated before it is completed, the maintenance record should clearly indicate that the inspection was discontinued. The entry should meet all the other requirements of § 43.11.

c. It is no longer a requirement that copies of discrepancy lists be forwarded to the local Flight Standards District Office (FSDO).

d. Discrepancy lists (or lists of defects) are part of the maintenance record and the owner/operator is responsible to maintain that record in accordance with § 91.417(b)(3). The entry made by maintenance personnel in the maintenance record should reference the discrepancy list when a list is issued.

12. LOST OR DESTROYED RECORDS. Occasionally, the records for an aircraft are lost or destroyed. In order to reconstruct them, it is necessary to establish the total time in service of the airframe. This can be done by reference to other records that reflect the time in service; research of records maintained by repair facilities; and reference to records maintained by individual mechanics, etc. When these things have been done and the record is still incomplete, the owner/operator may make a notarized statement in the new record describing the loss and establishing the time in service based on the research and the best estimate of time in service.

a. The current status of applicable ADs may present a more formidable problem. This may require a detailed inspection by maintenance personnel to establish that the applicable ADs have been complied with. It can readily be seen that this could entail considerable time, expense, and in some instances, might require the AD being performed again to establish compliance.

b. Other items required by § 91.417(a)(2), such as the current status of life-limited parts, time since last overhaul, current inspection status, and current list of major alterations, may present difficult problems. Some items may be easier to reestablish than others, but all are problems. Losing maintenance records can be troublesome, costly, and time consuming. Safekeeping of the records is an integral part of a good recordkeeping system.

13. COMPUTERIZED RECORDS. There is a growing trend toward computerized maintenance records. Many of these systems are offered to owners/operators on a commercial basis. While these are excellent scheduling systems, alone they normally do not meet the requirements of § 43.9 or § 91.417. The owner/operator who uses such a system is required to ensure that it provides the information required by § 91.417, including signatures. If not, modification to make them complete is the owner's/operator's responsibility and that responsibility may not be delegated.

14. PUBLIC AIRCRAFT. Prospective purchasers of aircraft that have been used as public aircraft should be aware that public aircraft may not be subject to the certification and maintenance requirements in 14 CFR and may not have records that meet the requirements of § 91.417. Considerable research may be involved in establishing the required records when these aircraft are purchased and brought into civil aviation. The aircraft may not be certificated or used without such records.

15. LIFE-LIMITED PARTS.

a.   Present day aircraft and powerplants commonly have life-limited parts installed. These life limits may be referred to as retirement times, service life limitations, parts retirement limitations, retirement life limits, life limitations, or other such terminology, and may be expressed in hours, cycles of operation, or calendar-time. They are set forth in Type Certificate Data Sheets (TCDS), ADs, maintenance manuals, or the limitations section of FAA-approved airplane or rotorcraft flight manuals (RFM). Additionally, instructions for continued airworthiness (ICA), which require life-limits be specified, may apply (Refer to 14 CFR part 23 appendix G and 14 CFR part 27 appendix A).

b.   Section 91.417(a)(2)(ii) requires the owner or operator of an aircraft with such parts installed to have records containing the current status of these parts. Many owners/operators have found it advantageous to have a separate record for such parts showing the name of the part, part number, serial number, date of installation, total time in service, date removed, and signature and certificate number of the person installing or removing the part. A separate record, as described, facilitates transferring the record with the part in the event the part is removed and later reinstalled or installed on another aircraft or engine. If a separate record is not kept, the aircraft record must contain sufficient information to clearly establish the status of the life-limited parts installed.

16. MAINTENANCE RELEASE.

a.   In addition to those requirements discussed previously, § 43.9 requires that major repairs and alterations be recorded as indicated in part 43 appendix B, (i.e., on FAA Form 337). An exception is provided in paragraph (b) of that appendix, which allows repair stations certificated under part 145 to use a maintenance release in lieu of the form for major repairs (and only major repairs).

b.   The maintenance release must contain the information specified in paragraph (b)(1), (2), and (3) of part 43 appendix B; be made a part of the aircraft maintenance record; and be retained by the owner/operator as specified in § 91.417. The maintenance release is usually a special document (normally a tag) and is attached to the product when it is approved for return to service. The maintenance release may, however, be on a copy of the work order written for the product. When this is done (for major repairs only) the entry on the work order must meet paragraph (b)(1), (2), and (3) of the appendix. That is to say that the repair station is required to give the owner: (1) the customer's work order upon which the repair is recorded, (2) a signed copy of the work order, and (3) a maintenance release which has been signed by an authorized representative of the company. In some cases, a work order and a maintenance release may be a different document. Both must be supplied to the customer.

c.   Some repair stations use what they call a maintenance release for other than major repairs. This is sometimes a tag and sometimes information on a work order. When this is done, all of the requirements of § 43.9 must be met (paragraph (b)(3) of appendix B not applicable) and the document is to be made and retained as part of the maintenance records under § 91.417 per discussion in paragraph 5c.

17. FAA FORM 337.

    a. Major repairs and alterations are to be recorded on FAA Form 337, as stated in paragraph 16. This form is executed by the person making the repair or alteration. Provisions are made on the form for a person other than that person performing the work to approve the repair or alteration for return to service.

    b. These forms are now required to be made part of the maintenance record of the product repaired or altered and retained in accordance with § 91.417.

    c. Detailed instructions for use of this form are contained in AC 43.9-1, Instructions for Completion of FAA Form 337.

    d. Some manufacturers have initiated a policy of indicating, on their SL and bulletins, and other documents dealing with changes to their aircraft, whether or not the changes constitute major repairs or alterations. Some manufacturers also indicate that the responsibility for completing FAA Form 337 lies with the person accomplishing the repairs or alterations and cannot be delegated. When there is a question, it is advisable to contact the local FSDO for guidance.

18. TESTS AND INSPECTIONS FOR ALTIMETER SYSTEMS, ALTITUDE REPORTING EQUIPMENT, AND AIR TRAFFIC CONTROL (ATC) TRANSPONDERS. The recordation requirements for these tests and inspections are the same as for other maintenance. There are essentially three tests and inspections (the altimeter system, the transponder system, and the data correspondence test), each of which may be subdivided relative to who may perform specific portions of the test. The basic authorization for performing these tests and inspections, found in § 43.3, is supplemented by §§ 91.411 and 91.413. When multiple persons are involved in the performance of tests and inspections, care must be exercised to ensure proper authorization under these three sections and compliance with § 43.9 and 43.9(a)(3) in particular.

19. BEFORE YOU BUY. This is the proper time to take a close look at the maintenance records of any used aircraft you expect to purchase. A well-kept set of maintenance records, which properly identifies all previously performed maintenance, alterations, and AD compliance, is generally a good indicator of the aircraft condition. This is not always the case, but in any event, before you buy, require the owner to produce the maintenance records for your examination, and require correction of any discrepancies found on the aircraft or in the records. Many prospective owners have found it advantageous to have a reliable unbiased maintenance person examine the maintenance records, as well as the aircraft, before negotiations have progressed too far. If the aircraft is purchased, take the time to review and learn the system of the previous owner to ensure compliance and continuity when you modify or continue that system.

20. AC FEEDBACK FORM. For your convenience, the AC Feedback Form is the last page of this AC. Note any deficiencies found, clarifications needed, or suggested improvements regarding the contents of this AC on the Feedback Form.

APPENDIX 1. AIRWORTHINESS DIRECTIVE COMPLIANCE RECORD (SUGGESTED FORMAT)

AD Number and Amendment Number	Date Received	Subject	Compliance Due Date Hours/Other	Date of Compliance	Airframe Total Time in Service at Compliance	Method Used to Comply with the AD	One Time or Recurring	Next Compliance Due Date Hours/Other	Authorized Signature, Certificate, Type and Number	Remarks

• Aircraft, Engine, Propeller, Rotor, or Appliance: Make _____ Model _____ S.N. _____ N_____

Advisory Circular Feedback Form

If you find an error in this AC, have recommendations for improving it, or have suggestions for new items/subjects to be added, you may let us know by contacting the Flight Standards Directives Management Officer at 9-AWA-AFS-140-Directives@faa.gov.

Subject: AC 43-9C CHG 2, Maintenance Records

Date: _____

Please check all appropriate line items:

☐ An error (procedural or typographical) has been noted in paragraph _____ on page _____.

☐ Recommend paragraph _____ on page _____ be changed as follows:

_____

_____

☐ In a future change to this AC, please cover the following subject:
(Briefly describe what you want added.)

_____

_____

☐ Other comments:

_____

_____

☐ I would like to discuss the above. Please contact me.

Submitted by: _____ Date: _____

**U.S. Department
of Transportation**
Federal Aviation
Administration

Advisory Circular

Subject: Instructions for Completion of FAA Form 337	**Date:** 11/1/19	**AC No:** 43.9-1G
	Initiated by: AFS-300	**Change:**

1   **PURPOSE OF THIS ADVISORY CIRCULAR (AC).** This AC provides instructions for completing Federal Aviation Administration (FAA) Form 337, Major Repair and Alteration (Airframe, Powerplant, Propeller, or Appliance).

2   **AUDIENCE.** This AC applies to all aircraft owners.

3   **WHERE YOU CAN FIND THIS AC.** You can find this AC on the FAA's website at http://www.faa.gov/regulations_policies/advisory_circulars.

4   **WHAT THIS AC CANCELS.** AC 43.9-1F, Instructions for Completion of FAA Form 337, dated January 25, 2007, is canceled.

5   **RELATED REGULATIONS.** Title 14 of the Code of Federal Regulations (14 CFR) part 43, §§ 43.5, 43.7, 43.9, and appendix B.

6   **RELATED INFORMATION.** FAA Form 337 is free and available at all FAA Manufacturing Inspection District Offices (MIDO), Responsible Flight Standards Offices (RFSO), International Field Offices (IFO), certificate management offices (CMO), and online at https://www.faa.gov/forms/index.cfm/go/document.information/documentID/185675.

6.1   **Purpose of FAA Form 337.** The form serves three main purposes:

1. To provide aircraft owners and operators with a record of major repairs and major alterations indicating the details and approvals;

2. To provide the FAA with a copy of the form for inclusion in the aircraft records at the FAA Aircraft Registration Branch; and

3. To document and record compatibility assessment conducted by the installer in accordance with the Form 337 NOTICE header block located above Item 8 – Description of Work Accomplished.

6.2   **Completion of FAA Form 337.** This form can be completed on paper or by using the electronic FAA Form 337. Information can be found online at http://eformservice.faa.gov/eForm337.aspx or by contacting your RFSO.

7 ELECTRONIC FORMAT.

7.1 Electronic Tracking Number. In the upper right corner of the form's header, there is a block titled "Electronic Tracking Number." This block is used only in the electronic version to automatically apply a number that identifies and retrieves forms electronically. Further information on the use of this number is supplied in training material at the website provided in paragraph 6.2 of this document.

7.2 Watermark. Under current policy, the header block titled "For FAA Use Only" has no official use except as a watermark applied automatically to indicate submittal when using electronic media.

8 FORM INSTRUCTIONS.

The person who performs or supervises a major repair or major alteration must prepare FAA Form 337. The form is executed at least in duplicate and is used to record major repairs and major alterations made to an aircraft, airframe, powerplant, propeller, appliance, or a component part thereof. The following instructions apply to Items 1 through 8 of the form as illustrated in Appendix A, FAA Form 337. The terms "Item" and "Block" are used synonymously in FAA documents relating to data collection on FAA Form 337.

8.1 Item 1 – Aircraft. The "Nationality and Registration Mark" is the same as shown on Aircraft Certification (AC) Form 8050-3, Certificate of Aircraft Registration. An "N" prefix denotes the nationality for U.S.-registered aircraft. Information to complete the "Make," "Model," and "Serial Number" blocks is found on the aircraft manufacturer's identification plate. A "Series" block has been provided to further identify the series of a specific model. Proper segregation of the model and series will be useful in collecting data for safety related issues.

Note: When the aircraft registry receives a completed FAA Form 337 for the official aircraft file, it is validated by matching the registration "N" number with the serial number. If an application for a change to the "N" number has been made, it is important for the submitter to receive verification of the change from the FAA registry with a new AC Form 8050-3. If the FAA Form 337 must be submitted before receipt of the new registration, then the old "N" number must be used.

8.2 Item 2 – Owner. Enter the aircraft owner's complete name and address as shown on AC Form 8050-3. When work is performed during a change in ownership, it is permissible to use the name and address shown on AC Form 8050-1, Aircraft Registration Application.

Note: When a major repair or major alteration is made to a component part, Items 1, 2, and in some cases 5 will be left blank and the original and duplicate copies of the form will remain with the part until it is installed on an aircraft. After entering the required information in Items 1, 2, and if appropriate, 5, the person who installed the part will give one form to the owner/operator and forward the duplicate copy to the FAA registry within 48 hours after the aircraft is approved for return to service. If a component part of an airframe, powerplant, propeller, or appliance is repaired or altered and the unit identification information is not known, it is appropriate to apply the preceding procedure and leave Item 5 blank until the airframe, powerplant, propeller or appliance is installed on the aircraft.

8.3   **Item 3 – For FAA Use Only.** Indicate approval in Item 3 when the FAA determines that data used to perform a major repair or major alteration conforms to accepted industry practices and is in compliance with current guidance and regulatory requirements. Approval is indicated by one of the following methods. (See paragraph 9 for further details.)

8.3.1   **Approval of Data by Examination Only.** Enter the following statement on FAA Form 337 when the data package is reviewed and a data approval is completed:

> "The data identified herein complies with the applicable airworthiness requirements and is approved for the above described aircraft, subject to conformity inspection by a person authorized in section 43.7."

8.3.2   **Approval of Data by Physical Inspection.** Enter the following statement on FAA Form 337 when a physical inspection, demonstration, or other type of test of an aircraft is satisfactorily performed and an installation approval is completed:

> "Approval by Physical Inspection, Demonstration, Testing, etc.—One Aircraft: The alteration or repair identified herein complies with the applicable airworthiness requirements and is approved for the above described aircraft, subject to conformity inspection by a person authorized in section 43.7." (Refer to FAA Order 8300.16, Major Repair and Alteration Data Approval.)

8.3.3   **Designated Airworthiness Representative Statement of Completeness.** Authorized designee certification of data indicates that the data in Item 8, Description of Work Accomplished, comes from FAA-approved sources and addresses all the original certification requirements for the aircraft described in Item 1. It does not constitute a field approval or approval of the data. Enter the following statement when an authorized designee has reviewed and certified the alteration data package by signing, dating, and entering its designee authorization number in Item 3:

> "The alteration identified herein has been reviewed and found to be complete with appropriate Designated Engineering Representative approvals. All aspects of the alteration(s) are compatible and eligible for use on the above described aircraft, subject to conformity inspection by a person authorized in § 43.7." (Refer to FAA Order 8100.8, Designee Management Handbook, Function Code 50.)

Note: Advisory material for making compatibility determination can be found in AC 20-188, Compatibility of Changes to Type Design Installed on Aircraft.

8.3.4   Overweight Aircraft Operating Under a Special Flight Permit. Enter the following statement as part of the recordkeeping requirements for overweight flight permits contained in FAA Order <u>8130.2</u>, Airworthiness Certification of Aircraft:

> "No person may operate this aircraft, as altered herein, unless it has within it an appropriate and current special flight permit issued under part <u>21</u>."
> (Refer to Order 8130.2.)

8.4   Item 4 – Type. Enter a checkmark in the appropriate column to indicate whether the unit was repaired or altered. Use only one "Type" line per form.

8.5   Item 5 – Unit Identification. Use the information blocks under Item 5 to identify the airframe, powerplant, propeller, or appliance that has been repaired or altered. It is only necessary to complete the blocks for the unit repaired or altered. The procedure for repair or alteration of a component part when the unit identification is unknown is detailed in paragraph <u>8.2,</u> above. Use only one "Unit Identification" line per form.

Note: A component of an airframe, powerplant, propeller, or appliance repaired or altered must be clearly identified in Item 8 listing the part number, serial number, and any other descriptive information, as applicable.

8.6   Item 6 – Conformity Statement.

8.6.1   "A" – Agency's Name and Address. Enter the name of the certificated person or entity accomplishing the repair or alteration. Mechanics should enter their name and permanent mailing address. Manufacturers, repair stations, and certificated maintenance organizations should enter the name and address under which they are certificated.

8.6.2   "B" – Kind of Agency. Check the appropriate box to indicate the type of person or organization that performed the work.

Note: For the purposes of this form, a Canadian Approved Maintenance Organization is considered a foreign mechanic.

8.6.3   "C" – Certificate Number. Enter the appropriate certificate number for the "Kind of Agency" entered in Item 6B of the form. Mechanics should enter their Mechanic Certificate number. Certificated maintenance organizations and repair stations should enter the number referenced on the Air Carrier, Air Operator, or Air Agency Certificate issued by the FAA, as appropriate. Manufacturers should enter their Production Certificate (PC) or Supplemental Type Certificate (STC) number, as appropriate. When repairing or altering articles, manufacturers holding Technical Standard Order (TSO) approvals should enter the TSO number of the affected article.

8.6.4   "D" – Conformity Statement. Use this space to certify that the repair or alteration complies with part 43. When work was performed or supervised by certificated mechanics, they should enter the completion date of the repair or alteration and sign their full name. Repair stations and maintenance organizations are permitted to authorize their employees to date and sign this conformity statement to comply with their FAA-approved program.

8.6.5   Fuel Tank Modification. For modifications involving installation of extended range fuel tanks in the passenger or baggage compartment as described in part 43, appendix B, check the box provided to indicate the modification.

Note: In this instance, one copy of FAA Form 337 must be placed onboard the aircraft as specified in 14 CFR part 91, § 91.417, when the aircraft is approved for return to service.

8.7   Item 7 – Approval for Return to Service. Part 43 establishes the conditions under which major repairs or major alterations to airframes, powerplants, propellers, and appliances may be approved for return to service. This portion of the form is used to indicate approval or rejection of the repair or alteration and to identify the person or agency making the airworthiness determination.

8.7.1   Check the "Approved" or "Rejected" box to indicate the finding. Rejected forms will be returned to the person who made the modification, as identified in Item 6, for correction. Approved forms will be completed, signed, and submitted to the aircraft registry.

8.7.2   Check the appropriate box to indicate who made the finding. Use the box labeled "Other" to indicate a finding by a person other than those listed. This box is reserved for any entity, not otherwise identified, that the FAA may authorize to perform that function. The person who made the finding should sign and date the form. The person's name should also be typed or printed below their signature and the appropriate certificate or designation number should be entered. If an aviation safety inspector (ASI) signs Item 7, the ASI's office identifier is placed in the "Certificate or Designation No." block.

8.7.3   Before approving FAA Form 337, it is the responsibility of the person approving the product for return to service to ensure that all the work described in Item 8 matches approved data and that the information presented on the form is complete.

8.7.4   If the form is not accepted by the aircraft registry for any reason, it will be routed through the responsible FAA office back to the approval for return to service agent identified in Item 7.

8.8   Item 8 – Description of Work Accomplished.

8.8.1   Enter a clear, concise, and legible statement describing the work accomplished in Item 8 on the reverse side of FAA Form 337. It is important to describe the location of the repair or alteration relative to the aircraft or component. If making a repair to a buckled spar, the description entered in Item 8 might begin by stating, "Removed wing from aircraft and removed skin from outer 6 feet. Repaired buckled spar 49 inches from the tip in accordance with…" and continue with a description of the repair. If the repair or alteration can be concealed by skin or another structure, then an authorized individual should make a pre-closure certification statement. This statement includes a signature and certificate number and says that a pre-closure inspection was made and that covered areas were found satisfactory.

8.8.2   The description should refer to all applicable 14 CFR sections and to the FAA-approved data used to substantiate the airworthiness of the repair or alteration. Forms of FAA-approved data are contained in Order 8300.16 and AC 43-210, Standardized Procedures for Obtaining Approval of Data Used in the Performance of Major Repairs and Major Alterations.

Note: Supplemental data such as stress analyses, test reports, sketches, or photographs are often proprietary and not intended as part of the Item 8 description. Supplemental data submitted as part of the Item 8 description should be identified as an attachment to the form using the following procedure.

8.8.3   If additional space is needed to describe the repair or alteration for Item 8, check the "Additional Sheets Are Attached" box at the bottom of the page. Attach sheets showing the aircraft nationality, registration mark, and the date the work was completed. All attachments to Item 8 must be submitted on 8½ by 11-inch paper to allow for proper processing into the aircraft historical record at the aircraft registry. If attachments to FAA Form 337 are received by the FAA in a format larger than an 8½ by 11-inch page, then the submission will be returned to the person identified in Item 7 for correction and resubmission.

8.8.4   Showing Weight and Balance (W&B) computations under Item 8 is not required but it may be done. If W&B of the aircraft are affected by the work described on FAA Form 337, the changes should be entered in the aircraft W&B records with the date, signature, and reference to the form.

8.8.5   AC 20-188, paragraph 4, provides examples of potentially hazardous additions of new modification to existing aircraft.

8.8.6   AC 20-188, paragraph 5, provides the aircraft owner/operator guidance on how to assess the STC compatibility and other considerations as part of the evaluation.

8.8.7   AC 20-188, paragraph 6, advises installers of their responsibilities in the compatibility assessment.

8.8.8   AC 20-188, paragraph 7, provides guidance on how to address the non-compatible modifications.

9   **ADMINISTRATIVE PROCESSING.** FAA Form 337 will be executed in duplicate with one signed copy given to the aircraft owner and one copy forwarded to the FAA within 48 hours after the airframe, aircraft engine, propeller, or appliance is installed on an aircraft and approved for return to service. FAA processing of the forms and their supporting data will depend on whether approved or unapproved data is used.

9.1   **Approved Data.** Complete the form as instructed in this AC, excluding Item 3, and ensure that Items 6 and 7 have been properly executed. Give a copy of the form to the aircraft owner/operator and send a duplicate copy to the Aircraft Registration Branch within 48 hours after the airframe, aircraft engine, propeller, or appliance is installed on an aircraft and approved for return to service.

9.2   Unapproved Data. Complete the form as instructed in this AC, leaving Items 6 and 7 blank. Both copies of the form and any supplemental data will be sent to the FAA office. When the FAA determines that the major repair or major alteration data complies with regulations and conforms to accepted industry practices, data approval will be recorded by entering an appropriate statement in Item 3. Both forms and any supplemental data will be returned to the applicant who will then complete Items 6 and 7. The applicant will give one of the completed forms to the aircraft owner/operator and ubmit the other completed form to the Aircraft Registration Branch for inclusion in the aircraft records.

Note: The electronic FAA Form 337 allows for electronic approvals and processing of FAA Form 337 from the time it is used to describe the alteration or repair until it is forwarded to the Aircraft Registration Branch. At this time, the FAA does not allow for the mixing of the two processes. If FAA Form 337 is started in the electronic format, it must be completed that way and cannot be completed using the paper process. Further information is supplied at the website shown in paragraph 6.2.

9.3   Signatures of FAA Form 337.

9.3.1   An FAA inspector's signature in Item 3 indicates approval of the data described in that section for use in accomplishing the work described in Item 8 of the form. The statement of completeness in Item 3 by an appropriately rated designee is a "certification of completeness" of required data. It is not a field approval or approval of data.

Note: Signatures in Item 3 count as data approval or completeness of approved data only and do not indicate the approval for return to service for the work in Item 8.

9.3.2   A signature in Item 6 is a certification by the person performing the work that the work complies with all applicable airworthiness requirements and FAA-approved data. The certification is applicable only to the work described in Item 8 or attached sheets.

9.3.3   A signature in Item 7 by a Flight Standards inspector or designee constitutes an authorized approval for return to service. A signature is not an approval of data. Data approval procedures are performed in Item 3 by an authorized individual and further defined in Order 8300.16 and AC 43-210. Other persons listed in Item 7 are authorized to "approve for return to service" if the major repair or major alteration uses and conforms to FAA-approved data and is performed in compliance with part 43.

9.3.4   If engineering assistance was requested, written Aircraft Certification Office (ACO) concurrence (e.g., memo or email) becomes an attachment to FAA Form 337.

9.4   U.S. Military and Foreign Use. FAA Form 337 is not authorized for use with aircraft not registered in the United States. The form may be provided to the U.S. Military or a foreign civil air authority if it is requested as a record of work performed and should be completed following part 43 and this AC. A note on the form should inform the U.S. Military or foreign authority that the form is not an official record and that the FAA aircraft registry will not record it.

9.5 **Completed Forms.** Completed forms should be submitted to the Aircraft Registration Branch, P.O. Box 25504, Oklahoma City, OK 73125. Electronic forms are submitted automatically through the website at http://eformservice.faa.gov/eForm337.aspx.

10 **AC FEEDBACK FORM.** For your convenience, the AC Feedback Form is the last page of this AC. Note any deficiencies found, clarifications needed, or suggested improvements regarding the contents of this AC on the Feedback Form.

Robert C. Carty
Deputy Executive Director, Flight Standards Service

APPENDIX A. FAA FORM 337

Form Approved OMB No. 2120-0020	Electronic Tracking Number
	For FAA Use Only

**US Department of Transportation
Federal Aviation Administration**

MAJOR REPAIR AND ALTERATION
(Airframe, Powerplant, Propeller, or Appliance)

INSTRUCTIONS: Print or type all entries. See Title 14 CFR §43.9, Part 43 Appendix B, and AC 43.9-1 (or subsequent revision thereof) for instructions and disposition of this form. This report is required by law (49 U.S.C. §44701). Failure to report can result in a civil penalty for each such violation. (49 U.S.C. §46301(a))

1. Aircraft

Nationality and Registration Mark	Serial No.	
Make	Model	Series

2. Owner

Name (As shown on registration certificate)	Address (As shown on registration certificate)
	Address
	City _____ State _____
	Zip _____ Country _____

3. For FAA Use Only

4. Type		5. Unit Identification			
Repair	Alteration	Unit	Make	Model	Serial No.
☐	☐	AIRFRAME	————	(As described in Item 1 above)	————
☐	☐	POWERPLANT			
☐	☐	PROPELLER			
☐	☐	APPLIANCE	Type		
			Manufacturer		

6. Conformity Statement

A. Agency's Name and Address	B. Kind of Agency	
Name _____	U. S. Certificated Mechanic	Manufacturer
Address _____	Foreign Certificated Mechanic	C. Certificate No.
City _____ State _____	Certificated Repair Station	
Zip _____ Country _____	Certificated Maintenance Organization	

D. I certify that the repair and/or alteration made to the unit(s) identified in item 5 above and described on the reverse or attachments hereto have been made in accordance with the requirements of Part 43 of the U.S. Federal Aviation Regulations and that the information furnished herein is true and correct to the best of my knowledge.

Extended range fuel per 14 CFR Part 43 App. B ☐	Signature/Date of Authorized Individual

7. Approval for Return to Service

Pursuant to the authority given persons specified below, the unit identified in item 5 was inspected in the manner prescribed by the Administrator of the Federal Aviation Administration and is ☐ Approved ☐ Rejected

BY	FAA Flt. Standards Inspector	Manufacturer	Maintenance Organization	Persons Approved by Canadian Department of Transport
	FAA Designee	Repair Station	Inspection Authorization	Other (Specify)

Certificate or Designation No.	Signature/Date of Authorized Individual

FAA Form 337 (10-06)

NOTICE
Weight and balance or operating limitation changes shall be entered in the appropriate aircraft record. An alteration must be compatible with all previous alterations to assure continued conformity with the applicable airworthiness requirements.

8. Description of Work Accomplished
(If more space is required, attach additional sheets. Identify with aircraft nationality and registration mark and date work completed.)

Nationality and Registration Mark	Date

☐ Additional Sheets Are Attached

FAA Form 337 (10-06)

Advisory Circular Feedback Form

If you find an error in this AC, have recommendations for improving it, or have suggestions for new items/subjects to be added, you may let us know by contacting the Flight Standards Directives Management Officer at 9-AWA-AFB-120-Directives@faa.gov.

Subject: AC 43.9-1G, Instructions for Completion of FAA Form 337

Date: _____

Please check all appropriate line items:

An error (procedural or typographical) has been noted in paragraph _____
on page _____.

Recommend paragraph _____ on page _____ be changed as follows:

_____

_____

In a future change to this AC, please cover the following subject:
(Briefly describe what you want added.)

_____

_____

Other comments:

_____

_____

I would like to discuss the above. Please contact me.

Submitted by: _____   Date: _____

THE AVIATION SAFETY REPORTING SYSTEM (ASRS)

The ASRS is an important facet of the continuing effort by government, industry, and individuals to maintain and improve aviation safety. The ASRS collects voluntarily submitted aviation safety incident/situation reports from pilots, controllers, and others.

The ASRS acts on the information these reports contain. It identifies system deficiencies, and issues alerting messages to persons in a position to correct them. It educates through its newsletter CALLBACK, its journal ASRS Directline and through its research studies. Its database is a public repository which serves the FAA and NASA's needs and those of other organizations world-wide which are engaged in research and the promotion of safe flight.

Purpose

The ASRS collects, analyzes, and responds to voluntarily submitted aviation safety incident reports in order to lessen the likelihood of aviation accidents.

ASRS data are used to:

- Identify deficiencies and discrepancies in the National Aviation System (NAS) so that these can be remedied by appropriate authorities.
- Support policy formulation and planning for, and improvements to, the NAS.
- Strengthen the foundation of aviation human factors safety research. This is particularly important since it is generally conceded that over two-thirds of all aviation accidents and incidents have their roots in human performance errors.

Confidentiality and Incentives to Report

Pilots, air traffic controllers, flight attendants, mechanics, ground personnel, and others involved in aviation operations submit reports to the ASRS when they are involved in, or observe, an incident or situation in which aviation safety may have been compromised. All submissions are voluntary.

Reports sent to the ASRS are held in strict confidence. More than one million reports have been submitted to date and no reporter's identity has ever been breached by the ASRS. ASRS de-identifies reports before entering them into the incident database. All personal and organizational names are removed. Dates, times, and related information, which could be used to infer an identity, are either generalized or eliminated.

The FAA offers ASRS reporters further guarantees and incentives to report. It has committed itself not to use ASRS information against reporters in enforcement actions. It has also chosen to waive fines and penalties, subject to certain limitations, for unintentional violations of federal aviation statutes and regulations which are reported to ASRS. The FAA's initiation, and continued support of the ASRS program and its willingness to waive penalties in qualifying cases is a measure of the value it places on the safety information gathered, and the products made possible, through incident reporting to the ASRS.

Report Processing

Incident reports are read and analyzed by ASRS's corps of aviation safety analysts. The analyst staff is composed entirely of experienced pilots, air traffic controllers, and mechanics. Their years of experience are uniformly measured in decades, and cover the full spectrum of aviation activity: air carrier, military, and general aviation; Air Traffic Control in Towers, TRACONs, Centers, and Military Facilities.

Each report received by the ASRS is read by a minimum of two analysts. Their first mission is to identify any aviation hazards which are discussed in reports and flag that information for immediate action. When such hazards are identified, an alerting message is issued to the appropriate FAA office or aviation authority. Analysts' second mission is to classify reports and diagnose the causes underlying each reported event. Their observations, and the original de-identified report, are then incorporated into the ASRS's database.

Database

The database provides a foundation for specific products and subsequent research addressing a variety of aviation safety issues. ASRS's database includes the narratives submitted by reporters (after they have been sanitized for identifying details). These narratives provide an exceptionally rich source of information for policy development and human factors research. The database also contains coded information from the original report which is used for data retrieval and statistical analyses.

Program Outputs

ASRS uses the information it receives to promote aviation safety in a number of ways:

Alerting Messages When ASRS receives a report describing a hazardous situation -- for example, a defective navigation aid, mischarting, a confusing procedure, or any other circumstance which might compromise safe flight -- it issues an alerting message. Alerting messages take a variety of forms but they have a single purpose: to relay safety information to individuals in a position of authority so that they can investigate the allegation and take needed corrective actions. ASRS has no direct operational authority of its own. It acts through, and with the cooperation of, others.

CALLBACK ASRS distributes CALLBACK, a monthly safety newsletter, to pilots, air traffic controllers, and others. Each issue of CALLBACK includes excerpts from ASRS incident reports with supporting commentary. In addition, CALLBACK may contain summaries of ASRS research studies and related aviation safety information. CALLBACK is one of the ASRS's most effective tools for improving the quality of human performance in the National Aviation System (NAS) at the grass roots level. Editorial use and reproduction of CALLBACK articles, with appropriate attribution, is encouraged.

ASRS Directline Started in 1991, ASRS Directline was published periodically to meet the needs of operators and flight crews of complex aircraft, such as commercial carriers and corporate fleets. Articles contained in ASRS Directline are based on ASRS reports that have been identified as significant by ASRS analysts. Distribution is directed to operational managers, safety officers, training organizations, and publications departments. Editorial use and reproduction of ASRS Directline articles, with appropriate attribution, is encouraged.

Database Search Requests Information in the ASRS database is available to interested parties. Individuals and organizations wishing to access ASRS data on a particular aviation safety subject may contact the ASRS with a statement of need. The ASRS will then search its database for pertinent reports and will print, bind, and mail any information applicable to the request. To date more than 6,800 searches have been accomplished in support of government, industry, and academe.

Operational Support Through frequent communications between the two organizations, the ASRS contributes to the FAA's ongoing safety efforts. The ASRS also supports the FAA and the NTSB during rule-makings, procedure/airspace design efforts, accident investigations, and like circumstances by assembling and digesting relevant information from its database. This is a growing role for the ASRS.

Topical Research ASRS has conducted and published over 60 research studies. ASRS research has always been designed and conducted with an orientation toward real-life operational applications; most have examined human performance in the NAS. Ways are sought to effect incremental improvements in aviation safety through improved procedures, training, design, etc. Recent subjects of ASRS research include: wake turbulence analysis, digital avionics software and hardware problems, TCAS II incidents, cockpit interactions incidents analysis, airport ramp safety incidents, crew performance during aircraft malfunctions, air carrier return-to-land incidents, use of digital flight data to measure safety and crew performance (APMS), and use of ASRS data in the FAA's AQP program.

Caveats

1. The ASRS assurance of confidentiality and the availability of waivers of disciplinary action do NOT extend to reports of accidents or criminal activity (e.g., hijacking, bomb threats, and drug

running). Such reports should not be submitted to ASRS. If such reports are received, they are forwarded identified to cognizant agencies.

2.   FAA policies regarding the ASRS are covered by Advisory Circular 00-46F and FAR 91.25. The waiver of penalties is subject to the following limitations: (A) the alleged violation must be inadvertent and not deliberate, (B) it must not reveal an event subject to Section 609 of the Federal Aviation Act, (C) the reporter must not have been found guilty of a violation of the FARs or the Federal Aviation Act during the preceding five years, and (D) the ASRS report must be submitted within 10 days of the event.

3.   The ASRS professional staff is composed of retired controllers, mechanics, as well as both active and retired pilots. To avoid conflicts of interest, ASRS analysts, researchers, and management personnel are not permitted to have ongoing employment relationships with the FAA, air carriers, or similar organizations.

4.   ASRS's mailing address is P.O. Box 189, Moffett Field, California, 94035-0189.

FAR-AMT Index

FAR INDEX

FAR
INDEX